Guide to the
National Archives of the United States

RICHARD NIXON
President of the United States

ARTHUR F. SAMPSON
Administrator of General Services

JAMES B. RHOADS
Archivist of the United States

Guide to the
National Archives of the
United States

U. S. National Archives and Records Service
General Services Administration
Washington : 1974

Library of Congress Cataloging in Publication Data

United States. National Archives and Records Service.
    Guide to the National Archives of the United States.

    Supt. of Docs. no.: GS 4.6/2: N21.
    Issued in 1948 by the body under its earlier name: National Archives,
under title: Guide to the records in the National Archives.
    1. United States.   National Archives.   2. United States – History –
Sources – Bibliography.   I. United States. National Archives. Guide to the
records in the National Archives.   II. Title. CD3023.U54 1974   027.573
74-600038

For sale by the Superintendent of Documents, U.S. Government Printing Office
Washington, D.C. 20402 - Price $12.30
Stock Number 022-003-00908-6
Catalog Number 4.6/2:N 21

FOREWORD

The General Services Administration, through the National Archives and Records Service, is responsible for preserving the noncurrent records of the U.S. Government that have continuing value and for making these records available to Government officials, scholars, and other persons with an interest in the information contained in them. As of June 30, 1970, these records totaled nearly one million cubic feet.

To establish control over these record holdings, acquaint potential users with them, and facilitate their use, our archivists prepare various kinds of finding aids. This general guide is one such publication. We believe it will be of interest and value to anyone desiring to use the incomparable body of documentary material it describes.

ARTHUR F. SAMPSON
Administrator of General Services

PREFACE

The National Archives of the United States, which document our history from the First Continental Congress and include the basic records of the three branches of our Federal Government, are preserved and made available because of their continuing practical utility for the necessary processes of Government, the protection of both public and private rights, and the uses that can be made of the information contained in them by scholars, students, and the general public.

The present publication supersedes the *Guide to the Records in the National Archives* published in 1948 and provides a general description of these records within the context of those Government agencies that created or received them in the course of conducting official business. It describes official records of the U.S. Government—now legally designated "the National Archives of the United States"— accessioned as of June 30, 1970, regardless of where they are located. It does not include, however, descriptions of Presidential and other personal papers and historical manuscripts in the custody of Presidential libraries.

The guide has been prepared under the immediate direction of E. G. Campbell, Assistant Archivist for the National Archives, with the assistance of Frank B. Evans, Deputy Assistant Archivist for the National Archives. Many other members of the staff of the Office of the National Archives assisted in preparing the copy and completing the work. Shelby G. Bale, Jr., provided editorial supervision and was responsible for seeing the publication through the press.

JAMES B. RHOADS
Archivist of the United States

CONTENTS

	Page
INTRODUCTION	1
DATE SPAN OF ACCESSIONED RECORDS BY RECORD GROUP	19

Part I. UNITED STATES GOVERNMENT – GENERAL

GOVERNMENT UNDER THE ARTICLES OF CONFEDERATION
Records of the Continental and Confederation Congresses and the Constitution Convention (Record Group 360) 29
War Department Collection of Revolutionary War Records (Record Group 93) 37

FEDERAL GOVERNMENT
General Records of the United States Government (Record Group 11) 41

Part II. RECORDS OF THE LEGISLATIVE BRANCH

CONGRESS
Records of the United States Senate (Record Group 46) 49
Records of the United States House of Representatives (Record Group 233) 51
Records of Joint Committees of Congress (Record Group 128) 54

LEGISLATIVE AGENCIES
Records of the Government Printing Office (Record Group 149) 57
Records of the United States General Accounting Office (Record Group 217) 57

Discontinued Agencies

Records of Minor Congressional Commissions (Record Group 148) 61
Records of the Temporary National Economic Committee (Record Group 144) 62
Records of the National Commission on Law Observance and Enforcement (Record Group 10) 63
Records of the Commissions on Organization of the Executive Branch of the Government (Record Group 264) 64
Records of the Public Land Law Review Commission (Record Group 409) 65

Part III. RECORDS OF THE JUDICIAL BRANCH

RECORDS OF FEDERAL COURTS

Records of the Supreme Court of the United States (Record Group 267)......   Page   69

Records of the United States Courts of Appeals (Record Group 276)...... 71

Records of District Courts of the United States (Record Group 21)...... 72

Records of the United States Court of Claims (Record Group 123)...... 90

Discontinued Agencies

Records of the United States Commerce Court (Record Group 172)...... 92

Part IV. RECORDS OF THE EXECUTIVE BRANCH

RECORDS OF PRESIDENTIAL AGENCIES

Records of the White House Office (Record Group 130)...... 95

Records of the Bureau of the Budget (Record Group 51)...... 96

Records of the Office of the Special Representative for Trade Negotiations (Record Group 364)...... 100

Records of the Central Intelligence Agency (Record Group 263)...... 101

Records of the Office of Science and Technology (Record Group 359)...... 101

Discontinued Agencies

Records of Presidential Committees, Commissions, and Boards (Record Group 220)...... 102

Records of the Committee on Public Information (Record Group 63)...... 119

Records of the President's Organization on Unemployment Relief (Record Group 73)...... 120

Records of the National Resources Planning Board (Record Group 187)...... 122

Records of the Office of Government Reports (Record Group 44)... 124

Records of the Office of the Special Adviser to the President on Foreign Trade (Record Group 20)...... 126

Records of the National Commission on the Causes and Prevention of Violence (Record Group 283)...... 127

Records of the President's Commission on the Assassination of President Kennedy (Record Group 272)...... 128

Records of the National Advisory Commission on Civil Disorders (Record Group 282)...... 129

RECORDS OF EXECUTIVE DEPARTMENTS

DEPARTMENT OF STATE

General Records of the Department of State (Record Group   Page

  59).. 131

Records of the Foreign Service Posts of the Department of

  State (Record Group 84).. 140

Records of the Agency for International Development (Rec-

  ord Group 286).. 142

Discontinued Agencies

Records of Boundary and Claims Commissions and Arbitra-

  tions (Record Group 76).. 143

Records of International Conferences, Commissions, and

  Expositions (Record Group 43)...................................... 146

Records of the American Commission To Negotiate Peace

  (Record Group 256).. 148

Records of Interdepartmental and Intradepartmental Com-

  mittees (State Department) (Record Group 353)................ 149

DEPARTMENT OF THE TREASURY

General Records of the Department of the Treasury (Record

  Group 56).. 152

Records of the Treasurer of the United States (Record Group

  50).. 157

Records of the Office of the Comptroller of the Currency

  (Record Group 101).. 159

Records of the Bureau of the Public Debt (Record Group 53).. 162

Records of the Bureau of Accounts (Treasury) (Record Group

  39).. 165

Records of the Bureau of Customs (Record Group 36)........... 168

Records of the Bureau of the Mint (Record Group 104)......... 172

Records of the Bureau of Engraving and Printing (Record

  Group 318).. 175

Records of the United States Secret Service (Record Group

  87).. 176

Records of the Internal Revenue Service (Record Group 58)... 177

Discontinued Agencies

Records of Civil War Special Agencies of the Treasury De-

  partment (Record Group 366).. 179

Records of the Office of Foreign Assets Control (Record Group

  265).. 180

DEPARTMENT OF DEFENSE

GENERAL

Records of the Office of the Secretary of Defense (Record

  Group 330).. 182

RECORDS OF EXECUTIVE DEPARTMENTS—Continued
  DEPARTMENT OF DEFENSE—Continued
    GENERAL—Continued

Records of the United States Joint Chiefs of Staff (Record Group 218)...... 188

Records of the Defense Atomic Support Agency (Record Group 374)...... 189

JOINT AND COMBINED MILITARY AGENCIES

Records of Allied Operational and Occupation Headquarters, World War II (Record Group 331)...... 191

Records of International Military Agencies (Record Group 333)...... 195

Records of United States Theaters of War, World War II (Record Group 332)...... 196

Records of United States Occupation Headquarters, World War II (Record Group 260)...... 197

Records of Joint Commands (Record Group 349)...... 199

Records of Joint Army and Navy Boards and Committees (Record Group 225)...... 200

Records of Interservice Agencies (Record Group 334)...... 201

Records of the Office of Strategic Services (Record Group 226)...... 204

Records of the United States Strategic Bombing Survey (Record Group 243)...... 206

DEPARTMENT OF THE ARMY

Headquarters and Staff

Records of the Office of the Secretary of War (Record Group 107)...... 207

Records of the Office of the Secretary of the Army (Record Group 335)...... 212

Records of the Headquarters of the Army (Record Group 108)...... 214

Records of the War Department General and Special Staffs (Record Group 165)...... 216

Records of the Army Staff (Record Group 319)...... 220

Records of the War Department Claims Board (Record Group 191)...... 223

Records of the Foreign Claims Section (War) (Record Group 213)...... 224

Records of the Chiefs of Arms (Record Group 177)...... 225

Records of Headquarters Army Ground Forces (Record Group 337)...... 227

Records of Headquarters Army Service Forces (Record Group 160)...... 228

RECORDS OF EXECUTIVE DEPARTMENTS—Continued
DEPARTMENT OF DEFENSE—Continued
DEPARTMENT OF THE ARMY—Continued
Offices and Bureaus

Records of the Adjutant General's Office, 1780's–1917 (Record Group 94).. Page 230

Records of the Adjutant General's Office, 1917– (Record Group 407).. 234

Records of the Office of the Chief of Engineers (Record Group 77).. 236

Records of the Office of the Inspector General (Record Group 159).. 241

Records of the Office of the Chief of Ordnance (Record Group 156).. 242

Records of the Office of the Quartermaster General (Record Group 92).. 245

Records of the Office of the Paymaster General (Record Group 99).. 250

Records of the Office of the Surgeon General (Army) (Record Group 112).. 250

Records of the Office of the Commissary General of Subsistence (Record Group 192).. 252

Records of the Office of the Chief of Finance (Army) (Record Group 203).. 252

Records of the Commissary General of Prisoners (Record Group 249).. 253

Records of the Office of the Chief Signal Officer (Record Group 111).. 254

Records of the Provost Marshal General's Bureau (Civil War) (Record Group 110).. 256

Records of the Office of the Judge Advocate General (Army) (Record Group 153).. 258

Records of the Bureau of Refugees, Freedmen, and Abandoned Lands (Record Group 105).. 263

Records of the National Guard Bureau (Record Group 168).. 264

Records of the Selective Service System (World War I) (Record Group 163).. 265

Records of the Chemical Warfare Service (Record Group 175).. 266

Records of the Office of the Chief of Chaplains (Record Group 247).. 266

Records of the Office of the Provost Marshal General, 1941– (Record Group 389).. 267

Records of the Office of Civil and Defense Mobilization (Record Group 304).. 269

RECORDS OF EXECUTIVE DEPARTMENTS—Continued
DEPARTMENT OF DEFENSE—Continued
DEPARTMENT OF THE ARMY—Continued

Field Commands and Installations

Records of United States Army Commands, 1784–1821
(Record Group 98).. Page 271

Records of United States Regular Army Mobile Units,
1821–1942 (Record Group 391)..................................... 271

Records of United States Army Continental Commands,
1821–1920 (Record Group 393)..................................... 273

Records of United States Army Continental Commands,
1920–42 (Record Group 394).. 274

Records of United States Army Coast Artillery Districts
and Defenses, 1901–42 (Record Group 392)................... 275

Records of United States Army Overseas Operations and
Commands, 1898–1942 (Record Group 395)................... 276

Records of United States Army Commands, 1942–   (Record Group 338).. 278

Records of the Military Government of Cuba (Record
Group 140)... 280

Records of the Provisional Government of Cuba (Record
Group 199)... 281

Records of the Dominican Customs Receivership (Record
Group 139)... 282

Records of the Military Government of Veracruz (Record
Group 141)... 283

Records of the American Expeditionary Forces (World
War I), 1917–23 (Record Group 120)........................... 283

Records of the United States Military Academy (Record
Group 404)... 288

Records of the United States Soldiers' Home (Record
Group 231)... 289

DEPARTMENT OF THE NAVY

General

General Records of the Department of the Navy (Record
Group 80)... 291

Naval Records Collection of the Office of Naval Records
and Library (Record Group 45)..................................... 293

Records of the Office of the Chief of Naval Operations
(Record Group 38).. 296

Records of the United States Marine Corps (Record
Group 127)... 300

RECORDS OF EXECUTIVE DEPARTMENTS – Continued
 DEPARTMENT OF DEFENSE – Continued
  DEPARTMENT OF THE NAVY – Continued

Offices and Bureaus

Records of the Bureau of Medicine and Surgery (Record
 Group 52)...   Page   301
Records of the Bureau of Ordnance (Record Group 74)...   302
Records of the Bureau of Ships (Record Group 19)..........   305
Records of the Bureau of Supplies and Accounts (Navy)
 (Record Group 143)..   308
Records of the Bureau of Yards and Docks (Record
 Group 71)...   309
Records of the Bureau of Naval Personnel (Record
 Group 24)...   310
Records of the Hydrographic Office (Record Group 37)......   313
Records of the Naval Observatory (Record Group 78)......   315
Records of the Office of the Judge Advocate General
 (Navy) (Record Group 125)..   317
Records of the Bureau of Aeronautics (Record Group
 72)..   318

Commands and Installations

Records of Naval Districts and Shore Establishments
 (Record Group 181)...   320
Records of the United States Naval Academy (Record
 Group 405)...   321
Records of Naval Operating Forces (Record Group 313)...   323

DEPARTMENT OF THE AIR FORCE
Records of the Army Air Forces (Record Group 18)..........   324
Records of the Office of the Secretary of the Air Force
 (Record Group 340)...   329
Records of Headquarters United States Air Force (Rec-
 ord Group 341)   331
Records of United States Air Force Commands, Ac-
 tivities, and Organizations (Record Group 342)   333

DEPARTMENT OF JUSTICE
General Records of the Department of Justice (Record Group
 60)   336
Records of United States Attorneys and Marshals (Record
 Group 118)...   343
Records of the Office of the Pardon Attorney (Record Group
 204)..   344
Records of the Immigration and Naturalization Service
 (Record Group 85)...   345

RECORDS OF EXECUTIVE DEPARTMENTS—Continued

DEPARTMENT OF JUSTICE—Continued

Page

Records of the Federal Bureau of Investigation (Record Group 65).. 348

Records of the Bureau of Prisons (Record Group 129)........... 349

Records of the Bureau of Narcotics and Dangerous Drugs (Record Group 170)... 350

Records of the Court of Claims Section (Justice) (Record Group 205)... 351

Discontinued Agencies

Records of the Solicitor of the Treasury (Record Group 206)... 352

Records of the Office of Alien Property (Record Group 131)... 354

Records of the Bureau of War Risk Litigation (Record Group 190).. 356

POST OFFICE DEPARTMENT

Records of the Post Office Department (Record Group 28)...... 358

DEPARTMENT OF THE INTERIOR

Records of the Office of the Secretary of the Interior (Record Group 48)... 364

Records of the Bureau of Land Management (Record Group 49)... 371

Records of the Bureau of Indian Affairs (Record Group 75)... 377

Records of the Geological Survey (Record Group 57)............. 389

Records of the Fish and Wildlife Service (Record Group 22)... 394

Records of the National Park Service (Record Group 79)...... 397

Records of the Office of Territories (Record Group 126)......... 403

Records of the Bureau of Reclamation (Record Group 115)... 406

Records of the Bureau of Mines (Record Group 70)............... 407

Records of the Government of American Samoa (Record Group 284)... 409

Records of the Southwestern Power Administration (Record Group 387)... 411

Discontinued Agencies

Records of the Commissioner of Railroads (Record Group 193).. 411

Records of the Alaskan Territorial Government (Record Group 348)... 412

Records of the Bureau of Insular Affairs (Record Group 350)... 413

Records of the War Minerals Relief Commission (Record Group 194)... 414

Records of the Petroleum Administrative Board (Record Group 232)... 415

RECORDS OF EXECUTIVE DEPARTMENTS – Continued

DEPARTMENT OF THE INTERIOR – Continued

Records of the Puerto Rico Reconstruction Administration   Page
(Record Group 323) 416

Records of the National Bituminous Coal Commission, 1935–
36 (Record Group 150)... 417

Records of the Bituminous Coal Division (Record Group 222)... 418

Records of the Solid Fuels Administration for War (Record
Group 245)... 419

Records of the Federal Interagency River Basin Committee
(Record Group 315) 420

Records of the Office of Geography (Record Group 324)......... 421

Records of the Defense Electric Power Administration (Rec-
ord Group 327).. 422

DEPARTMENT OF AGRICULTURE

Records of the Office of the Secretary of Agriculture (Record
Group 16)... 423

Records of the Forest Service (Record Group 95) 426

Records of the Foreign Agricultural Service (Record Group
166).. 430

Records of the Commodity Exchange Authority (Record
Group 180)... 432

Records of the Federal Extension Service (Record Group 33)... 432

Records of the Commodity Credit Corporation (Record Group
161).. 434

Records of the Agricultural Stabilization and Conservation
Service (Record Group 145)... 435

Records of the Soil Conservation Service (Record Group 114)... 437

Records of the Rural Electrification Administration (Record
Group 221)... 440

Records of the Federal Crop Insurance Corporation (Record
Group 258)... 441

Records of the Farmers Home Administration (Record Group
96).. 442

Records of the Agricultural Research Service (Record Group
310) 443

Records of the Farmer Cooperative Service (Record Group
314) 444

Records of the Economic Research Service (Record Group
354) 444

Discontinued Agencies

Records of the Bureau of Animal Industry (Record Group
17)... 445

RECORDS OF EXECUTIVE DEPARTMENTS — Continued

DEPARTMENT OF AGRICULTURE — Continued

Records of the Office of Experiment Stations (Record Group   Page
164).. 446

Records of the Bureau of Dairy Industry (Record Group
152).. 447

Records of the Bureau of Agricultural Engineering (Record
Group 8).. 447

Records of the Bureau of Agricultural and Industrial Chemistry (Record Group 97).. 449

Records of the Bureau of Plant Industry, Soils, and Agricultural Engineering (Record Group 54)........................ 450

Records of the Bureau of Entomology and Plant Quarantine
(Record Group 7).. 453

Records of the Bureau of Agricultural Economics (Record
Group 83).. 455

Records of the Bureau of Human Nutrition and Home Economics (Record Group 176).. 458

Records of the Surplus Marketing Administration (Record
Group 124).. 458

Records of the Office of Labor (War Food Administration)
(Record Group 224).. 459

Records of the Agricultural Marketing Service (Record
Group 136).. 460

DEPARTMENT OF COMMERCE

General Records of the Department of Commerce (Record
Group 40).. 464

Records of the Bureau of the Census (Record Group 29)....... 465

Records of the Patent Office (Record Group 241).................. 469

Records of the Coast and Geodetic Survey (Record Group 23)... 470

Records of the National Bureau of Standards (Record Group
167).. 474

Records of the Weather Bureau (Record Group 27).............. 476

Records of the Maritime Administration (Record Group 357)... 478

Records of the Environmental Science Services Administration (Record Group 370).. 479

Discontinued Agencies

Records of the Bureau of Marine Inspection and Navigation
(Record Group 41).. 480

Records of the Bureau of Foreign and Domestic Commerce
(Record Group 151).. 486

Records of the Inland Waterways Corporation (Record Group
91).. 488

Records of the National Production Authority (Record
Group 277).. 489

RECORDS OF EXECUTIVE DEPARTMENTS – Continued

DEPARTMENT OF LABOR

General Records of the Department of Labor (Record Group
174) 491

Records of the Bureau of Labor Statistics (Record Group
257) 493

Records of the Women's Bureau (Record Group 86) 494

Records of the Bureau of Labor Standards (Record Group
100) 495

Records of the Wage and Hour and Public Contracts Divisions
(Record Group 155) 496

Discontinued Agencies

Records of the Wage Adjustment Board (Record Group 236)... 497

Records of the Bureau of Employment Security (Record
Group 183) 498

DEPARTMENT OF HEALTH, EDUCATION, AND WELFARE

General Records of the Department of Health, Education,
and Welfare (Record Group 235) 501

Records of the Public Health Service (Record Group 90) 502

Records of the Office of Education (Record Group 12) 505

Records of the Food and Drug Administration (Record
Group 88) 507

Records of the Children's Bureau (Record Group 102) 510

Records of the Social Security Administration (Record
Group 47) 510

DEPARTMENT OF HOUSING AND URBAN DEVELOPMENT

General Records of the Department of Housing and Urban
Development (Record Group 207) 513

Records of the Federal Housing Administration (Record
Group 31) 515

Discontinued Agencies

Records of the Federal National Mortgage Association
(Record Group 294) 516

Records of the Office of the Housing Expediter (Record
Group 252) 517

Records of the Public Housing Administration (Record Group
196) 519

DEPARTMENT OF TRANSPORTATION

Records of the United States Coast Guard (Record Group
26) 522

Records of the Bureau of Public Roads (Record Group 30) 525

Records of the Federal Aviation Administration (Record
Group 237) 527

RECORDS OF INDEPENDENT AGENCIES

CURRENT AGENCIES

Records of the American Battle Monuments Commission (Record Group 117) .... **Page** 529

Records of the Civil Aeronautics Board (Record Group 197)... 530

Records of the Commission of Fine Arts (Record Group 66)... 531

Records of the Export-Import Bank of the United States (Record Group 275) 532

Records of the Farm Credit Administration (Record Group 103).. 533

Records of the Federal Communications Commission (Record Group 173).. 535

Records of the Federal Deposit Insurance Corporation (Record Group 34).. 537

Records of the Federal Home Loan Bank System (Record Group 195).. 538

Records of the Federal Maritime Commission (Record Group 358).. 539

Records of the Federal Mediation and Conciliation Service (Record Group 280) 540

Records of the Federal Power Commission (Record Group 138).. 541

Records of the Federal Reserve System (Record Group 82)... 542

Records of the Federal Trade Commission (Record Group 122).. 542

General Records of the General Services Administration (Record Group 269) 544

Records of the Public Buildings Service (Record Group 121).. 545

Records of the Federal Supply Service (Record Group 137).. 548

Records of the National Archives and Records Service (Record Group 64).. 549

Records of the Property Management and Disposal Service (General Services Administration) (Record Group 291).. 551

Records of the Indian Claims Commission (Record Group 279).. 552

Records of the Interstate Commerce Commission (Record Group 134).. 553

Records of the National Aeronautics and Space Administration (Record Group 255).. 553

Records of the National Academy of Sciences (Record Group 189).. 554

RECORDS OF INDEPENDENT AGENCIES – Continued

CURRENT AGENCIES – Continued

Page

Records of the National Labor Relations Board (Record Group 25)... 555

Records of the National Mediation Board (Record Group 13)... 558

Records of the National Science Foundation (Record Group 307)... 561

Records of the Panama Canal (Record Group 185)................. 562

Records of the Securities and Exchange Commission (Record Group 266)... 563

Records of the Selective Service System, 1940–   (Record Group 147)... 563

Records of the Small Business Administration (Record Group 309)... 565

Records of the Smithsonian Institution (Record Group 106)... 565

Records of the Tennessee Valley Authority (Record Group 142)... 567

Records of the United States Civil Service Commission (Record Group 146)... 568

Records of the United States Information Agency (Record Group 306)... 569

Records of the United States Tariff Commission (Record Group 81)... 570

Records of the Veterans Administration (Record Group 15)... 571

DISCONTINUED INDEPENDENT AGENCIES

FROM WORLD WAR I TO 1933

Records of the Allied Purchasing Commission (Record Group 113)... 577

Records of the Capital Issues Committee (Record Group 158)... 577

Records of the Council of National Defense (Record Group 62)... 578

Records of the Federal Fuel Distributor (Record Group 89)... 579

Records of the National War Labor Board (World War I) (Record Group 2)... 580

Records of the Reconstruction Finance Corporation (Record Group 234)... 580

Records of the United States Coal Commission (Record Group 68)... 590

Records of the United States Food Administration (Record Group 4)... 591

Records of the United States Fuel Administration (Record Group 67)... 593

RECORDS OF INDEPENDENT AGENCIES—Continued
DISCONTINUED INDEPENDENT AGENCIES—Continued
FROM WORLD WAR I TO 1933—Continued

Page

Records of the United States Grain Corporation (Record
Group 5).. 595
Records of the United States Housing Corporation
(Record Group 3)... 596
Records of the United States Railroad Administration
(Record Group 14)... 599
Records of the United States Shipping Board (Record
Group 32)... 601
Records of the United States Sugar Equalization Board,
Inc. (Record Group 6).. 607
Records of the War Finance Corporation (Record Group
154).. 608
Records of the War Industries Board (Record Group 61)... 608
Records of the War Labor Policies Board (Record Group
1).. 609
Records of the War Trade Board (Record Group 182)...... 610

FROM 1933 TO 1950

Records of the American Commission for the Protection
and Salvage of Artistic and Historic Monuments in War
Areas (Record Group 239).. 611
Records of the Board of Investigation and Research—
Transportation (Record Group 198)................................. 612
Records of the Board of War Communications (Record
Group 259).. 613
Records of the Civilian Conservation Corps (Record
Group 35).. 614
Records of the Committee for Congested Production
Areas (Record Group 212).. 615
Records of the Committee on Fair Employment Practice
(Record Group 228).. 616
Records of the Federal Coordinator of Transportation
(Record Group 133).. 618
Records of the Foreign Broadcast Intelligence Service
(Record Group 262).. 622
Records of the Foreign Economic Administration (Record
Group 169).. 623
Records of the Maritime Labor Board (Record Group
157).. 626
Records of the National Recovery Administration (Record
Group 9).. 626

RECORDS OF INDEPENDENT AGENCIES—Continued
DISCONTINUED INDEPENDENT AGENCIES—Continued
FROM 1933 TO 1950—Continued

Page

Records of the National War Labor Board (World War II)
(Record Group 202)...   631
Records of the National Youth Administration (Record
Group 119)...   634
Records of the Office of the Bituminous Coal Consumers'
Counsel (Record Group 223)....................................   637
Records of the Office of Censorship (Record Group 216)...   637
Records of the Office of Civilian Defense (Record Group
171)..   639
Records of the Office of Community War Services (Record
Group 215)...   640
Records of the Office of Contract Settlement (Record
Group 246)...   641
Records of the Office of Defense Transportation (Record
Group 219)...   642
Records of the Office for Emergency Management (Record
Group 214)...   644
Records of the Office of Inter-American Affairs (Record
Group 229)...   646
Records of the Office of Price Administration (Record
Group 188)...   647
Records of the Office of Scientific Research and Develop-
ment (Record Group 227)..   657
Records of the Office of War Information (Record Group
208)..   660
Records of the Office of War Mobilization and Reconver-
sion (Record Group 250)..   664
Records of the Petroleum Administration for War (Record
Group 253)...   666
Records of the Philippine War Damage Commission
(Record Group 268)..   667
Records of the Price Decontrol Board (Record Group
251)..   668
Records of the Prison Industries Reorganization Ad-
ministration (Record Group 209)..............................   668
Records of the Public Works Administration (Record
Group 135)...   669
Records of the Retraining and Reemployment Adminis-
tration (Record Group 244)......................................   671
Records of the Shipbuilding Stabilization Committee
(Record Group 254)..   672

RECORDS OF INDEPENDENT AGENCIES – Continued

DISCONTINUED INDEPENDENT AGENCIES – Continued

FROM 1933 TO 1950 – Continued

Records of the Smaller War Plants Corporation (Record
Group 240).. 673

Records of the United States Maritime Commission
(Record Group 178)... 675

Records of the United States War Ballot Commission
(Record Group 230)... 678

Records of the War Assets Administration (Record Group
270).. 678

Records of the War Manpower Commission (Record
Group 211).. 679

Records of the War Production Board (Record Group
179).. 687

Records of the War Relocation Authority (Record Group
210).. 689

Records of the War Shipping Administration (Record
Group 248).. 692

Records of the Work Projects Administration (Record
Group 69).. 693

National Archives Collection of World War II War Crimes
Records (Record Group 238).. 699

SINCE 1950

Records of the Committee on Government Contract
Compliance (Record Group 325)................................. 702

General Records of the Economic Stabilization Agency
(Record Group 296)... 703

General Records of the Federal Works Agency (Record
Group 162).. 704

Records of the Office of Price Stabilization (Record Group
295).. 705

Records of the Wage and Salary Stabilization Boards of
the Economic Stabilization Agency (Record Group
293).. 706

Part V. RECORDS OF OR RELATING TO OTHER GOVERNMENTS

DISTRICT OF COLUMBIA

Records of the Government of the District of Columbia (Record
Group 351).. 711

Records of the National Capital Housing Authority (Record
Group 302).. 712

DISTRICT OF COLUMBIA—Continued

Records of the National Capital Planning Commission (Record   Page

Group 328).. 713

Records of the Office of Public Buildings and Grounds (Record

Group 42)... 714

Records of the Rent Commission of the District of Columbia

(Record Group 132)... 718

OTHER GOVERNMENTS

War Department Collection of Confederate Records (Record

Group 109)... 719

Treasury Department Collection of Confederate Records (Record

Group 365)... 721

Records of Former Russian Agencies (Record Group 261)........... 722

Records of the Government of the Virgin Islands (Record Group

55).. 723

Records of the Spanish Governors of Puerto Rico (Record Group

186).. 725

National Archives Collection of Foreign Records Seized, 1941–

(Record Group 242)... 727

Part VI. OTHER HOLDINGS

GIFT COLLECTIONS

National Archives Collection of Records of Inaugural Committees

(Record Group 274)... 741

National Archives Gift Collection (Record Group 200)................. 742

National Archives Gift Collection of Materials Relating to Polar

Regions (Record Group 401).. 749

Appendix A. Public use of records, donated historical materials, . . .

in the National Archives and Records Service.............................. 753

Appendix B. Suggestions for citing records in the National Archives

of the United States... 761

Appendix C. List of record groups arranged by record group number... 765

Index 775

INTRODUCTION

Origin of the National Archives

The establishment of the National Archives in 1934 marked the successful culmination of a movement that had begun more than a century earlier. Originating within the Federal Government, this movement had as its immediate objective the physical protection and preservation of those records no longer needed by agencies in the conduct of their current business. The ultimate success of the movement and the nature of the new institution that was created, however, were due largely to the efforts of historians and other scholars. It was the scholarly community that helped to create an understanding and appreciation of public archives as a cultural resource, and that succeeded in gaining acceptance by the Government of its responsibility for not only preserving that resource but also for making it accessible to the people. To the initial objective of safekeeping records, the historians added the objectives of centralization of the Government's permanently valuable records and the application to them of professional archival principles and techniques to facilitate their use. The new institution was intended to be preeminently a service agency; its mission, according to one of its earlier statements, was "to make the experience of the Government and people of the United States as it is embodied in records of the Federal Government and related materials available to guide and assist the Government and the people in planning and conducting their activities."

The National Archives, 1934–49

The National Archives began operations late in 1935, and during the next decade and a half it laid the foundations for its future programs and activities. It began with a comprehensive survey of Federal records in Washington—approximately three million cubic feet—and followed with a survey of other Federal records throughout the country, which totaled about four million cubic feet. Guidelines and techniques were developed for the appraisal of this material in terms of its continuing values—administrative, legal, fiscal, historical or other research values—and policies and procedures were established for the systematic disposition of non-current records of the Government. In these initial activities the National Archives was able to profit but little from the experience of older archival institutions. No other institution had ever been faced with such a quantity and variety of government records of relatively modern origin, and traditional archival principles and techniques had to be modified radically

1

to deal effectively with this unique situation.

Adaptation and innovation were also required in handling those bodies of records selected for preservation by the National Archives. New techniques for cleaning and fumigating were developed, and the new method of thermoplastic lamination replaced older and less effective preservation and repair techniques. Experiments with traditional classification and cataloging practices soon revealed their inadequacies for establishing effective control over masses of modern public records, and new techniques of collective arrangement and description were developed. Traditional concepts of reference service were critically examined and liberalized, and the launching of a microfilm publication program marked a radical departure from the proprietary attitude toward their holdings that had long characterized archival institutions.

It should be noted that all of these activities were conducted during a period of rapid governmental expansion and reorganization under the successive impacts of depression and global war, and that the war period in particular diverted necessary resources and deprived the institution of experienced professional personnel. On the positive side, the demand for offices and space generated by the war effort and its resulting records enabled the National Archives to achieve by 1949 the highest degree of centralization of national archives in one institution and building of any major country in the world.

Paralleling these developments, and of equal importance for the future history of the National Archives, were its efforts to better serve the needs of Government agencies. With regard to every basic archival function involving modern records – appraisal, disposition, accessioning, preservation, arrangement, description, and reference service – it had early become evident that major improvements in recordkeeping by Government agencies would not only greatly facilitate the task of the archivist, but would also effect economies and increase efficiency in the conduct of current business. Thus the National Archives early in 1941 formally established a "records administration program" intended "to assist in developing throughout the Government principles and practices in the filing, selection, and segregation of records" that would facilitate their disposal or transfer as they became noncurrent. This program continued to develop rapidly during World War II, particularly in the military departments and through the activities of former staff members of the National Archives. By the end of the war it had evolved into the broader concept of "records management," which included responsibility for records creation as well as for records maintenance and disposition.

The National Archives and Records Service Since 1949

The obvious necessity for this program and its early successes prompted the First Hoover Commission—the President's Commission on Organization of the Executive Branch of the Government—to recommend in 1948 that Congress take whatever action was necessary to coordinate the management of the great and rapidly growing volume of Federal records and to develop Government-wide programs that would improve and reduce the cost of managing records. The form congressional action took, when this recommendation was combined with those of other task forces of the Commission, was passage in 1949 of the Federal Property and Administrative Services Act, which created the General Services Administration. To this agency was assigned the National Archives, which was then given new records management responsibilities as the National Archives and Records Service.

These records management responsibilities were strengthened by the Federal Records Act of 1950, which also authorized the establishment of Federal records centers in several regions of the country. Within 2 years nine such centers had been established. The need for such centers is perhaps best illustrated by noting that the seven million cubic feet of Federal records the National Archives had surveyed in 1935–37 had increased by 1954 to more than 25 million cubic feet. By 1956, however, the Archivist was able to report that this long-established trend toward ever larger accumulations of Federal records had at least temporarily been arrested. The nationwide

system now consists of 13 Federal records centers, whose total holdings in 1970 were more than 10.5 million cubic feet of records, and the National Personnel Records Center in St. Louis, which has about 2.4 million cubic feet of records. In this system the Washington National Records Center at Suitland, Md., occupies a unique position; its General Archives Division serves essentially as an extension of the National Archives Building to contain the overflow of archival material the National Archives Building cannot accommodate.

Although most of the records in Federal records centers are not of archival value and are scheduled for eventual destruction, some of their holdings merit preservation. For such records that relate primarily to the States or region in which they were created and accumulated, the National Archives and Records Service has developed regional archives branches in 11 Federal records centers. After adequate physical facilities were provided for archival storage, these records were accessioned; to them have been added records formerly maintained in Washington but more appropriately located, in terms of interest and use, in the regional archives branches. This program of selective relocation of "field-type" Federal archives is being supplemented by depositing in regional archives branches copies of National Archives microfilm publications of official records.

Another dimension to the responsibilities of the National Archives and Records Service has been added by the emergence of Presidential libraries. The Franklin D. Roosevelt Library at Hyde Park, N.Y., accepted by Congress in 1939 by joint resolution and placed under the Archivist of the United States for its administration, was a unique institution, but the effectiveness of the solution it offered to the many problems relating to modern Presidential papers ensured that it would serve as a model for future Presidents. In 1955 Congress amended the Federal Property and Administrative Services Act of 1949 to provide for acceptance and maintenance of other Presidential libraries, and to the Roosevelt Library have since been added the Herbert Hoover Library at West Branch, Iowa; the Harry S. Truman Library at Independence, Mo.; the Dwight D. Eisenhower Library at Abilene, Kans.; the John F. Kennedy Library temporarily located at Waltham, Mass.; and the Lyndon B. Johnson Library at Austin, Tex. The Presidential libraries contribute significantly to the nationwide system of research centers administered by the National Archives and Records Service and to the variety and value of the research resources it makes available to meet the needs and interests of the Government, the scholarly community, and the general public.

General Guides to the National Archives

The basic tool in meeting these needs and interests is the guide to accessioned holdings. An earlier listing of Federal records, Claude H. Van Tyne and Waldo G. Leland, comps., *Guide to the Archives of the Government of the United States in Washington* (2d ed., Washington, 1907),[1] preceded the establishment of the National Archives by nearly 3 decades. By calling attention to both the research value and the neglect and losses of Government records, it contributed substantially to the success of the movement for a national archives. The new institution had been in operation less than 2 years when it published the first guide to its holdings—"Guide to the Materials in the National Archives, June 30, 1937"—in the *Third Annual Report of the Archivist of the United States, 1936-1937* (1937),[2] app. VI, pp. 111-168. This preliminary listing, which covered about 250,000 linear feet of records accessioned since December 1935, was replaced 3 years later by the more comprehensive *Guide to the Material in the National Archives* (1940). The 1940 guide described in considerable detail the 320,000 linear feet of records accessioned by December 31, 1939.

---

[1] Hereafter, unless otherwise indicated, the place of publication of all works cited both in the introduction and throughout the guide is Washington, D.C.

[2] Unless otherwise indicated, all guides, preliminary inventories, other finding aids, and microfilm publications are publications of the National Archives before 1949 and of the National Archives and Records Service thereafter. The names of compilers and other staff members responsible for publications are given in this guide if they appear on the title pages of the publications.

During World War II the record holdings of the National Archives more than doubled, and in 1946 the National Archives published a summary guide intended primarily for the general public, *Your Government's Records in the National Archives* (1946), which provided an overall view of the more than 700,000 cubic feet of records in its custody. More directly intended for the use of the scholarly researcher was the expanded guide that appeared 2 years later, *Guide to the Records in the National Archives* (1948), which included in its descriptions the 813,000 cubic feet of records accessioned by June 30, 1947. Two years later total accessions had grown to more than 900,000 cubic feet, and descriptions of the new material were included in *Your Government's Records in the National Archives* (revised, 1950).

Of the general guides cited above, those published in 1940 and 1948 were the most comprehensive in their coverage of accessioned records and the most detailed in their descriptions. The 1948 guide was intended to supersede rather than to supplement that of 1940. Records accessioned since the cutoff date used for the 1948 guide, June 30, 1947, have been described both in professional journals and in *National Archives Accessions*, whose 25 numbers appeared intermittently between 1948 and 1968. In January 1969 *National Archives Accessions* was replaced by *Prologue: The Journal of the National Archives*, which describes the most important records accessioned since the previous issue.

Guide to the National Archives of the United States

This publication is intended to supersede the 1948 guide and includes all official records of the U.S. Government—now legally designated as "The National Archives of the United States"—accessioned as of June 30, 1970, regardless of where such records are located. It does not include, however, Presidential and other personal papers and historical manuscripts in the custody of Presidential libraries. All records described in this guide are located in the National Archives Building unless otherwise indicated. Those located in the General Archives Division of the Washington National Records Center (designated as WNRC), the relatively small quantity accessioned as of the cutoff date of the guide in the various regional archives branches (each designated by the symbol FRC and the city in which it is located; e.g., FRC Atlanta), and the relatively few official records in Presidential libraries (each designated by the President's initials and the letter "L"; e.g., FDRL) are noted and their specific locations given in the form indicated above.

The nearly one million cubic feet of records described in this guide include more than 1.5 million maps, about 201,000 rolls of microfilm, more than 43,000 reels of motion pictures, approximately 4,523,000 still pictures, about 2.4 million aerial photographs, and approximately 66,500 sound recordings. Most of this material was originally created or received by legislative, judicial, or executive agencies of the Government in pursuance of their legal obligations or in the transaction of their official business. This material was maintained by these agencies as an official record of their activities or because of the value of the information it contained. A very small percentage consists of records of other governments or of unofficial documentary materials that from time to time and for various reasons has come into the Government's possession.

Collectively, these records document the history of the Government from its establishment through the mid-20th century. In addition they contain information of importance for understanding many aspects of American life, both past and present. Although they do not include the records of States or lesser jurisdictions, they contain much valuable information on particular localities and, in some cases, on individuals. The National Archives of the United States embrace the greater part by far of the Government's records for the period before 1950 that is of sufficient value to merit continued preservation.

The Record Group Concept

The unit of entry in this guide is the record group; i.e., a body of organizationally and functionally related records established with particular regard for the administrative history, complexity, and volume of the records and archives of an agency. A typical record group consists of the records of a bureau or some other comparable unit of an executive department at the bureau level, or the records of an independent agency of somewhat comparable importance in the Government's administrative hierarchy. Record groups with titles beginning "General Records" have been established for most of the executive departments and several of the independent agencies as a practical modification of the record group concept. Such record groups include the records of the office of the head of the department or agency and the records of other units concerned with matters, such as fiscal and personnel, that affect the department or agency as a whole. Several of the record groups of this type include records that were produced by bureaus or comparable units but that were incorporated into central files maintained for the entire department or agency.

Collective record groups constitute a second modification of this "records control" concept. For purposes of convenience, collective record groups generally bring together the records of a number of relatively small and short-lived agencies that have an administrative or functional relationship, the records of each such agency constituting a separate subgroup. Examples include Records of Boundaries and Claims Commissions and Arbitrations (Record Group 76) and Records of Presidential Committees, Commissions, and Boards (Record Group 220). The latter collective record group consists of the records of the relatively smaller and less well-known committees and commissions; the larger and more important ones have been accorded separate record group status.

A third modification of the record group concept is its application to one or more bodies of collected records, such as the Naval Records Collection of the Office of Naval Records and Library (Record Group 45) and the National Archives Collection of Foreign Records Seized, 1941– (Record Group 242).

When the name of a particular agency is part of a record group title, it should be understood that the records of predecessor agencies are frequently included in the record group. For example, Records of the United States Coast Guard (Record Group 26) include the records of the Bureau of Lighthouses, the Life-Saving Service, the Revenue-Cutter Service, and other predecessors of the present-day Coast Guard. When a successor agency has been concerned chiefly with liquidation of the affairs of its predecessor, however, the name of the predecessor appears in the title of the record group. For example, the War Trade Board Section of the Department of State succeeded in 1919 to functions of the War Trade Board, one of the major emergency agencies of World War I, and continued some of its activities for a short time; nevertheless, the records of both predecessor and successor agencies together constitute the Records of the War Trade Board (Record Group 182). In Records of the War Production Board (Record Group 179) are records not only of the Board itself,

but also records of its predecessors, the Supply Priorities and Allocations Board and the Office of Production Management, and of its successor, the Civilian Production Administration. The index to this guide provides the most convenient method of locating the descriptions of records of such predecessor and successor agencies.

At the time the record group system was developed in 1944, the 190 record groups first established were numbered consecutively in the order in which the first records in each group had been accessioned. Record groups subsequently established generally have been numbered in the order in which they were established. When all of the known records of archival value that should be allocated to a particular record group are in the National Archives, that record group is considered "closed." Record groups to which further accessions are expected are regarded as "open." Generally, the latter record groups are for continuing agencies, while closed record groups contain the records of discontinued agencies. Record group numbers canceled for any reason are not used again until at least 10 years have elapsed in order to minimize confusion in reference service and in citations. For the convenience of persons who may have use for it, a list of record groups arranged by record group number is provided in appendix C.

General Organization of the Guide

This guide to the National

Archives of the United States is organized in general to reflect the current organization of the Government, with the table of contents of the *United States Government Organization Manual* serving as a model.

The initial part, "General United States Government," includes the central government records of the pre-Federal period and the general records of the Federal Government.

The second part, "Records of the Legislative Branch," describes the accessioned records of Congress and, in succession, the records of current and discontinued legislative agencies, generally in the order of the date of their creation.

The third part, "Records of the Judicial Branch," continues this pattern of grouping current agencies followed by discontinued agencies.

The fourth part, "Records of the Executive Branch," constitutes much of the volume and is subdivided into "Records of Presidential Agencies," "Records of Executive Departments" (listed in the order of their creation), and "Records of Independent Agencies." The grouping of current agencies followed by discontinued agencies is continued for Presidential agencies and the executive departments, except for the Department of Defense and its component departments of Army, Navy, and Air Force. Because of the volume, complexity, and organizational and functional relationships that characterize military records, the organization of entries under these four departments utilizes additional headings to group adminis-

trative units as headquarters and staff or general, offices and bureaus, and commands and installations. Under these subheadings, entries are generally in the order of the date of creation of the administrative unit involved. Because of the number of independent agencies, past and present, entries in this section of the fourth part of the guide are divided first between current and discontinued agencies, and the discontinued agencies are further grouped in terms of three periods—"From World War I to 1933," "From 1933 to 1950," and "Since 1950." Entries under the "Current Agencies" heading and under each of the subgroupings of discontinued agencies are generally alphabetical by official name of the agency.

The fifth part consists of "Records of or Relating to Other Governments," with entries listed under "District of Columbia" and "Other Governments."

The sixth and concluding part describes other holdings of documentary materials in the National Archives Building.

Scope of Guide Entries

In making records available for use, the National Archives and Records Service has found that the most useful guide to the subject content of official records is a knowledge of the organization and functions of the Government agencies in which they originated. For this reason the description of accessioned records for each record group is generally preceded in this guide by a brief administrative history and a concise statement of the major functions of the agency or agencies that created the records. The descriptions of records usually provide general information as to their type, purpose, content, chronological span, and quantity. At times they provide information as to the completeness and the arrangement of the records and the existence of indexes, registers, and other devices for facilitating their use, but such information has been provided on a selective basis only, with no attempt at completeness. Dates given are generally those between which a particular body of records was accumulated and organized, rather than the dates of the oldest and most recent documents included in the records, although in many instances these two sets of dates are identical. When a body of records is known to include documents dated earlier or later than the inclusive dates given, this fact is mentioned in the description. The total volume of records in each record group is given in cubic feet. For the convenience of researchers the quantity of specific bodies of records is given in linear feet, with the linear footage representing the approximate number of feet of shelving or filing equipment that would be occupied by the records if they were all shelved or filed vertically. Cartographic and audiovisual records are described in separate paragraphs following the description of textual records for each record group if warranted by

either their volume or significance; otherwise no separate description is provided for such records.

This guide can present only the most general view of the records that constitute the National Archives of the United States. Some conception of the degree to which the entries are necessarily generalized may be gained from noting that 1,500 cubic feet of records – about 3,000,000 individual sheets of paper – are covered, on the average, by about one page of description. It should also be noted that the amount of information given about any record group or subgroup is not necessarily in proportion to the quantity of the records or their value for research or other purposes. The degree of completeness with which the records are described has frequently been determined by such considerations as the relative administrative complexity of the agency, its history, and its records.

The task of analyzing, arranging, describing, and otherwise establishing completely adequate control over all the records described in this volume is still far from finished. The description of records should be understood, therefore, to be necessarily provisional in character; there are, no doubt, errors and deficiencies that will need to be corrected in later and more detailed finding aids and guides.

At the end of many statements in this guide pertaining to record groups and subgroups are indicated those published finding aids—generally inventories and special lists—that had appeared before copy for this volume went to press. Also listed, if not too numerous, are the microfilm publications reproducing records from a particular record group or subgroup. Most microfilm publications include a descriptive pamphlet that informs potential users of the nature and scope of the publication and assists them in determining the relevance of the records to their interests. These pamphlets also include information intended to facilitate use of the microfilm copy of the records. In some instances records have been published on microfilm in advance of the publication of a descriptive pamphlet. As resources permit these T-numbered, or temporary, publications are converted to permanent, or M-numbered, publications, each with a descriptive pamphlet. In instances where more than five microfilm publications are based on records in a particular record group or subgroup, and for more detailed information about specific microfilm publications, the reader should consult the current edition of the *List of National Archives Microfilm Publications*.

Also included in many of the record group entries are citations of references. These citations, from which bibliographical data have been omitted when the department or agency responsible for the publication is obvious from the context, are not exhaustive and are only intended to call attention to some of the more generally useful published materials that provide additional information on particular Government agencies and their records. No attempt has been made to cite the appropriate sections of the following guides, which should be consulted regarding records for particular periods or relating to certain areas or subjects:

Guide to Federal Archives Relating to the Civil War, comp. by Kenneth W. Munden and Henry P. Beers (1962).

Guide to the Archives of the Government of the Confederate States of America, comp. by Henry P. Beers (1968).

Civil War Maps in the National Archives (1964).

Introduction to the American Official Sources for the Economic and Social History of the World War, comp. by Waldo G. Leland and Newton D. Mereness (New Haven, 1926).

Handbook of Federal World War Agencies and Their Records, 1917–1921 (1943).

Federal Records of World War II, Vol. 1: *Civilian Agencies* (1950); Vol. 2: *Military Agencies* (1951).

Guide to Materials on Latin America in the National Archives, Vol. 1, comp. by John P. Harrison (1961).

Guide to Genealogical Records in the National Archives, comp. by Meredith B. Colket, Jr., and Frank E. Bridgers (1964).

The text of this guide contains only a limited number of cross-references, but a comparatively full index has been provided. It should be noted that the index is limited to organizational units, names, and functions or broad subjects mentioned in the text. Since the guide describes records basically within the context of organizational units and in relation to the functions they document, the index is not intended and cannot serve as a general subject guide to the specific content of records. Generally, the subjects and names mentioned in the records descriptions are intended to be exemplary or illustrative, rather than a comprehensive analysis of informational content.

Access to and Use of Records

The specific regulations applicable to the public use of records described in this guide are reprinted in appendix A. Since the records are arranged and maintained by agency of origin, a researcher should first determine, to the extent possible, which Federal agencies were concerned with the subject of his research and where their records are currently located. Although a researcher is welcome to come directly to the particular depository where the records are held, he will usually save time by writing in advance of his visit. If he writes early enough to permit a reply and indicates the subject of his study as specifically as possible and the approximate date of his arrival, the depository will send him any necessary information and instructions. Most of the records in the National Archives have no restrictions on access, and they are normally made available promptly to the researcher for his use.

Research in restricted records (see General Restrictions on Access, below) may require a security clearance in advance, which must be obtained from the agency or agencies whose records are involved. This also may entail subsequent review by the agency of notes taken from such records and ultimate review of the completed manuscript. The processing of a request for security clearance usually requires 6 to 12 weeks, and the review of notes and manuscript also requires considerable time. Persons wishing to conduct extensive research in security-classified records should, therefore, write to the National Archives and Records Service as far as possible in advance of the time they plan to begin work, explaining the nature and scope of their prospective research in order to obtain the necessary application forms and instructions for their completion and submission. The National Archives and Records Service has limited authority to review certain types of security-classified records for declassification. Because of the time required for such review, however, only a small quantity of records can be made available in this manner. Most agencies, it should also be noted, limit access to security-classified records to United States citizens.

In addition to security-classified records, there are other types of records or categories of information to which access has been restricted. The researcher should review these general restrictions and any additional restrictions specifically applicable to the records in which he is interested in preparation for his visit to a depository.

When a researcher first comes to a depository, he is asked to identify himself and complete a short application form before being issued a researcher identification card. This procedure is intended both to facilitate service and to safeguard the records. A research consultant will then confer with him regarding his project and will inform him of the detailed procedures to be followed at the depository. In the National Archives Building, because of the volume and variety of its holdings, a general research consultant will talk to him briefly and in general about his research subject and tell him which of the custodial units is most likely to have relevant material. The consultant will arrange for him to discuss his project with reference specialists in those units and provide him with information about published and unpublished finding aids and indexes that may be of value.

The identification card that the researcher receives during the application procedure is valid for 1 year for the use of records at the depository where issued and is renewable upon request. It permits access to the research rooms of the depository, where the researcher will be asked to sign a register daily. Records will be brought to a research room by a staff member for use by the researcher. If the records have been microfilmed, a microfilm copy will be made available for his use.

At the National Archives Building most records may be examined in the central research room or the microfilm research room, but some records must be consulted in research rooms near where they are stored. These include security-classified records, some series of indexes, and audiovisual and cartographic records. Records may be examined, as a rule, only within the depository in which they are housed, but under appropriate circumstances loans of records are made to Federal agencies for official use.

Research room hours during the workday vary among depositories; in the National Archives Building the central research room and the microfilm research room are open evenings Monday through Friday and on Saturday in addition to the regular workday. Records must be requested early in the afternoon to be used that same evening, and on Friday afternoon to be used on Saturday. It should be noted, however, that research rooms in which security-classified records can be made available are open only from 9 a.m. to 5 p.m., Monday through Friday. During the researcher's visit to a depository he will find the research consultants available to answer any questions, discuss problems, and further advise him on sources of information.

The National Archives Building has facilities for making electrostatic copies, photostats, microfilms, and photographic and diazo prints of documents and duplicates of motion pictures and sound recordings. The National Archives is empowered by law to provide copies—certified or uncertified—of records in its custody that are not exempt from public examination or protected by copyright. It may provide copies of records protected by copyright if so authorized by the copyright owner, but it will not undertake to obtain such authorization. Under the law no charge is made for providing limited numbers of copies of records to Government agencies required for official use; in all other cases a fee for this service sufficient to cover costs is charged. Inexpensive facsimile copies of certain documents are available for purchase, and photocopies of National Archives publications currently out of print may also be purchased. For a listing of such items see the current *Select List of Publications of the National Archives and Records Service*, National Archives General Information Leaflet 3.

General Restrictions on Access

The use of some records in the National Archives of the United States, especially those of recent date, is subject to restrictions imposed by the Congress, the President, the Archivist of the United States, the transferring Government agencies, and donors of personal papers and historical manuscripts. In this guide restrictions currently in effect on access to records that have been specified by the transferring agency or donor—"specific restrictions"—are indicated at the end of the entry for the record group (or subgroup in the case of collective record groups) to which they apply. Such specific restrictions are subject to modification or removal, and researchers are advised to inquire in advance concerning the current status of specific restrictions. Restrictions on access that may apply to more than one record group are termed "general restrictions." They are applicable to the kinds of information or classes of accessioned records designated, regardless of the record group to which such records have been allocated. The following is a summary listing of general restrictions intended only to indicate their general scope and content. It is not intended to be an authoritative statement of the law or other legal authorization for such restrictions.

1. Records marked as containing "atomic energy restricted data."

Restrictions: Information contained in records so marked will be made available only (a) as authorized by the head or a specially designated official of the *transferring* agency or its successor agency or (b) when the restrictive marking has been canceled by proper authority.

Specified by: Congress of the United States.

2. Records marked in accordance with the provisions of any Federal law, Executive order, or regulation explicitly intended to safeguard official information in the interest of the national security (security-classified records).

Restrictions: Information contained in records so marked

will be made available only (a) as authorized by the head or a specially designated official of the *originating* agency or its successor agency or (b) when the security marking has been canceled by proper authority.

Specified by: Congress of the United States and the President.

3. Records containing personal, business, or industrial information obtained by any Federal agency under the provisions of the Federal Reports Act of 1942 (56 Stat. 1078), or other subsequent statutory authority, that were deemed confidential by the agency or with reference to which a request for confidential treatment was made by the person (individual, partnership, association or any organized group of persons, or their legal successor or representative) furnishing such information. In general, the types of information so restricted are data about the technical and financial operations of individual firms or persons including the "operations, style of work, or apparatus of any manufacturer or producer"; and "the amount or source of income, profits, losses, expenditures," or "methods of doing business" of any individual or concern (59 Stat. 415).

Restrictions: Such information may not be published or disclosed in any way to the public or to another Federal agency with the following statutory exceptions: (1) information may be released in statistical totals or summaries in such manner that the source thereof is not disclosed

or identified directly or indirectly, and "studies, graphs, charts, or other documents of like general character" containing statistical data of this type may be published; (2) information may be released if the persons who supplied the information agree to its release; (3) certain defense and related agencies specified in the legislation, or their successors, may be furnished in confidence "such data and information [obtained by the Office of Price Administration] as may be requested by them for use in the performance of their official duties"; (4) information may be released "to any other Federal agency" that has authority supported by provisions of legal penalties to collect the same information itself; and (5) information obtained under the Defense Production Act of 1950, as amended, and not made public before April 30, 1953, may be furnished to the Congress or any duly authorized committee thereof, the Department of Justice in the performance of its functions, and the successors to the Economic Stabilization Agency (56 Stat. 1078, 59 Stat. 412, and 67 Stat. 131).

Specified by: Congress of the United States.

4. Records less than 75 years old containing information about the physical or mental health or the medical or psychiatric care or treatment of individuals.

Restrictions: Access to information in such records is subject to current regulations of the agency that created the records or that succeeded to that agency's functions. If there are no such current regulations or if existing regulations do not provide adequate guidance in a specific instance, access to information in the records will be subject to current regulations of the Public Health Service (42 C.F.R. 1.102, 1.104, and 1.108).

Imposed by: Archivist of the United States.

5. Records less than 75 years old of the following types: (1) intercepted private letters or other intercepted private communications, including facsimile or other copies of such communications, and (2) records resulting from censorship or interception of private communications that identify the sender or recipient and that quote, paraphrase, or describe the content of such communications.

Restrictions: Such records may be used only by the intercepting or recipient agencies or their successor agencies and by investigative agencies of the Federal Government.

Specified by: Office of Emergency Preparedness.

6. Records less than 75 years old of the investigation of persons or groups of persons by investigative authorities of the executive branch, except for such record series of the Department of Defense and all components and predecessors thereof specified in general restriction 12 (below).

Restrictions: Information in these records will be made available only as authorized by an appropriate official of the *originating* agency or its successor agency.

Imposed by: Archivist of the United States.

7. Documents less than 75 years old among the records of an agency of the Government that (1) are identifiable as having originated in the Federal Bureau of Investigation or its predecessor, the Bureau of Investigation (established July 26, 1908); (2) include quotations from or paraphrase statements identifiable as originating in Federal Bureau of Investigation documents; (3) identify by name personnel of the Bureau; or (4) reveal sources of information identifiable as Federal Bureau of Investigation sources.

Restrictions: Information in these documents will be made available only as authorized by an appropriate official of the Federal Bureau of Investigation.

Specified by: Federal Bureau of Investigation.

8. Certificates of arrival, declarations of intention, certificates of naturalization, and certificates of citizenship.

Restrictions: These records shall not be reproduced (62 Stat. 683, sec. 1426(h); 66 Stat. 163, secs. 335(i)(2), 339(a), 343(b), and 343(e); and 64 Stat. 583, sec. 507(b)).

Specified by: Congress of the United States and Department of Justice.

9. Naturalization records dated after September 26, 1906.

Restrictions: Information from these records shall not be furnished in writing.

Specified by: Department of Justice.

10. Copyrighted record material.

Restrictions: Record material protected by subsisting copyright shall not be reproduced without the written permission of the copyright owner.

Specified by: Congress of the United States.

11. Records of the Department of Defense and of all components and predecessors thereof that relate to events less than 75 years old and that contain information about the military service of members of the Armed Forces of the United States, including not only separately maintained personnel records but also similar personnel-oriented files.

Restrictions: Such records may be examined only by authorized representatives of the Government. No information based on such records will be furnished without the written consent of the person concerned, his legal representative, or (after his death) his next of kin, except a summary statement of service and latest known address, which may be furnished without restriction.

Specified by: Department of Defense.

12. Records less than 50 years old of the following kinds that originated in any of the components of the Department of Defense: inspector general reports of investigation or of inquiry; aircraft accident reports; and records of boards of investigation, courts of inquiry, military commissions, and provost courts.

Restrictions: Information in these records will be made available only as authorized by an appropriate official of the *originating* agency or its successor agency.

Specified by: Department of Defense.

13. All records that originated in the Joint (and Combined) Chiefs of Staff, except those that bear no security classification marking and declassified records over 20 years old that do not carry such restrictive markings as "For Official Use Only" and "Not for Public Use."

Restrictions: Requests for access to or information from such records interfiled with records of any department or agency of the Government shall be referred to the appropriate records administration officer of such department or agency.

Specified by: Department of Defense.

14. Records of the Department of the Army and of all components and predecessors thereof.

Restrictions: Access to such records or information contained therein will be in accordance with the provisions of Army Regulations 345–20 and 340–16. These regulations exempt from public access records relating to the matters that may be exempted from access under the Public Information Act of 1966 (see below) and cite several specific examples for each category. In all cases of denial based on Army Regulations 345–20 and 340–16 the requester will be advised of his rights to appeal to the Secretary of the Army through the Adjutant General.

Specified by: Adjutant General, Department of the Army.

15. Records of the Department of the Navy and of all components and predecessors thereof.

Restrictions: Access to such records or information contained therein will be in accordance with the provisions of SECNAV Instruction 5720.42. This instruction exempts from public access records relating to the matters that may be exempted from access under the Public Information Act of 1966 (see below) and cites several specific examples for each category. In all cases of denial based on SECNAV 5720.42 the requester will be advised of his rights to appeal to the Secretary of the Navy.

Specified by: Assistant Vice Chief of Naval Operations/ Director of Naval Administration.

16. Records of the Department of the Air Force and of all components and predecessors thereof.

Restrictions: Access to such records or information contained therein will be in accordance with the provisions of Air Force Regulation 12–30. This regulation exempts from public access records relating to the matters that may be exempted from access under the Public Information Act of 1966 (see below) except categories (8) and (9) that are not mentioned in the regulation. Several specific examples are cited for each category. In all cases of denial based on Air Force Regulation 12–30 the requester will be advised

of his right to appeal to the Secretary of the Air Force.

Specified by: Director of Administration, Department of the Air Force.

17. Documents originated in the International Prosecution Section, Supreme Commander for the Allied Powers, and documents originated in the prosecuting groups for classes B and C Japanese war crime trials comparable to those originating in the International Prosecution Section.

Restrictions: These documents may be used by official and non-official researchers only with the permission of the Department of State.

Specified by: Department of State.

Public Information Act of 1966

All restrictions on access to records, insofar as they relate to records of the executive branch, must be consistent with the provisions of the Public Information Act of 1966 (P.L. 89–487, now codified as 5 U.S.C. 552), also known as the Freedom of Information Act. This act, which became effective on July 4, 1967, provides for making information in executive branch records available to the public unless it comes within specific categories of matters that may be exempted from public disclosure. Subject to exemption from public disclosure are:

(1) all matters specifically required by Executive order to be kept secret in the interest of national defense or foreign policy;

(2) all matters related solely to the internal personnel rules and

practices of an agency;

(3) all matters specifically exempted from disclosure by statute;

(4) trade secrets and commercial or financial information obtained from a person as privileged or confidential;

(5) inter-agency or intra-agency memorandums or letters that would not be available by law to a party other than an agency in litigation with the agency;

(6) personnel and medical files and similar files whose disclosure would constitute a clearly unwarranted invasion of personal privacy;

(7) investigatory files compiled for law enforcement purposes except to the extent available by law to a party other than an agency;

(8) information contained in or related to examination, operating, or condition reports prepared by, on behalf of, or for the use of an agency responsible for the regulation or supervision of financial institutions; and

(9) geological and geophysical information and data, including maps, concerning wells.

The act also prescribes the procedure for obtaining access to agency records, and, in the event access is denied, for appeal.

Other Informational Services

In addition to making records or copies of records available for direct use, the National Archives and Records Service also provides information about particular records and, to a limited extent, information derived from the records both to agencies of the Government and private persons. Inquiries may be made in person, by telephone, or by mail. In furnishing information it is the practice of the National Archives and Records Service not to make any evaluation of a particular record or any interpretation of the information it contains.

For the convenience of researchers as well as staff members, the National Archives and Records Service maintains a special non-circulation library comprising a working collection of about 150,000 books and pamphlets. Its special subject fields are archives administration in the United States and abroad, Federal administrative history, and U.S. history in the national period. Approximately two-thirds of the collection consists of Federal Government documents carefully selected for their contribution to understanding the organization, functions, or records of an agency of the Federal Government and including a collection of hearings of congressional committees. These materials are available for reference purposes to researchers when their use of records will be facilitated thereby, but researchers are normally expected to have conducted their research in published materials before consulting archival holdings.

DATE SPAN OF ACCESSIONED RECORDS BY RECORD GROUP

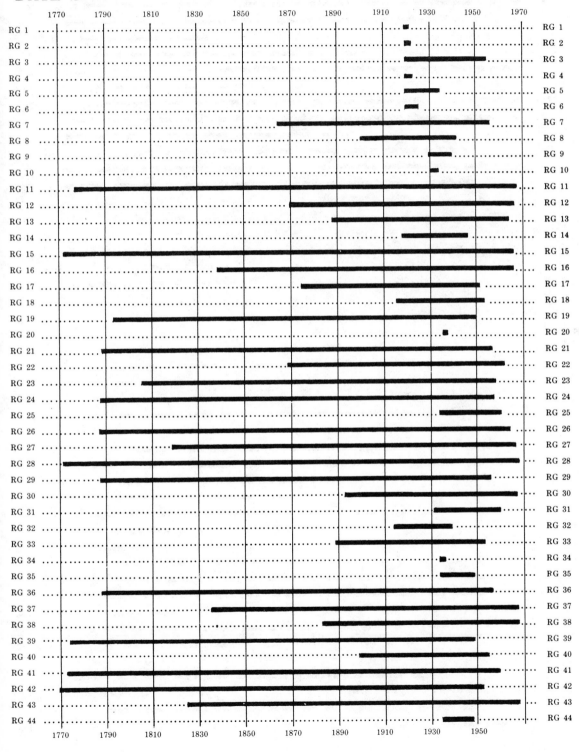

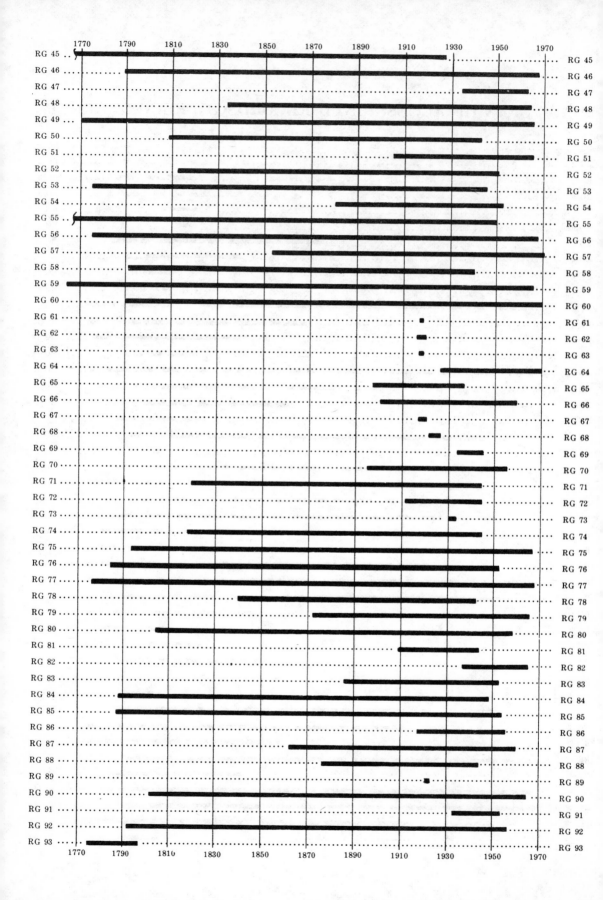

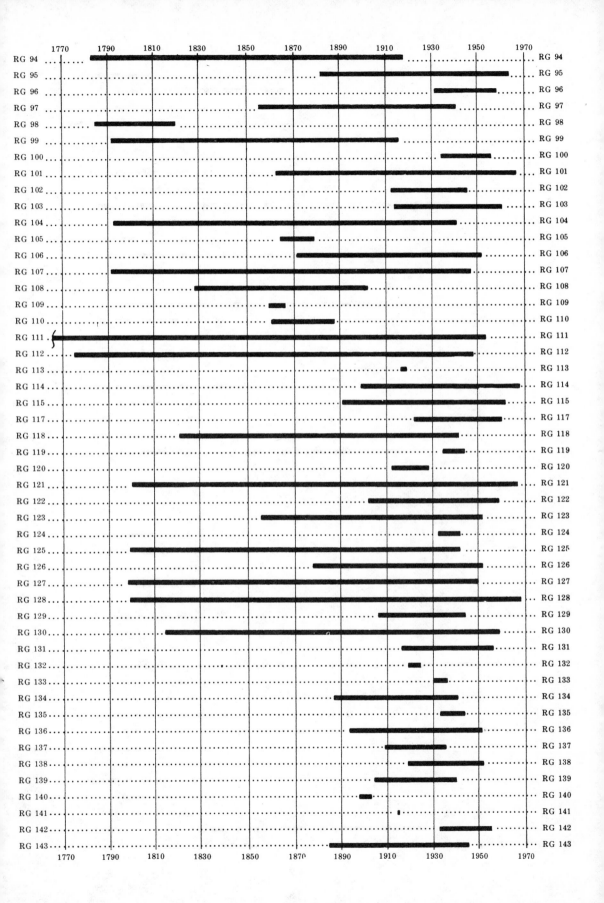

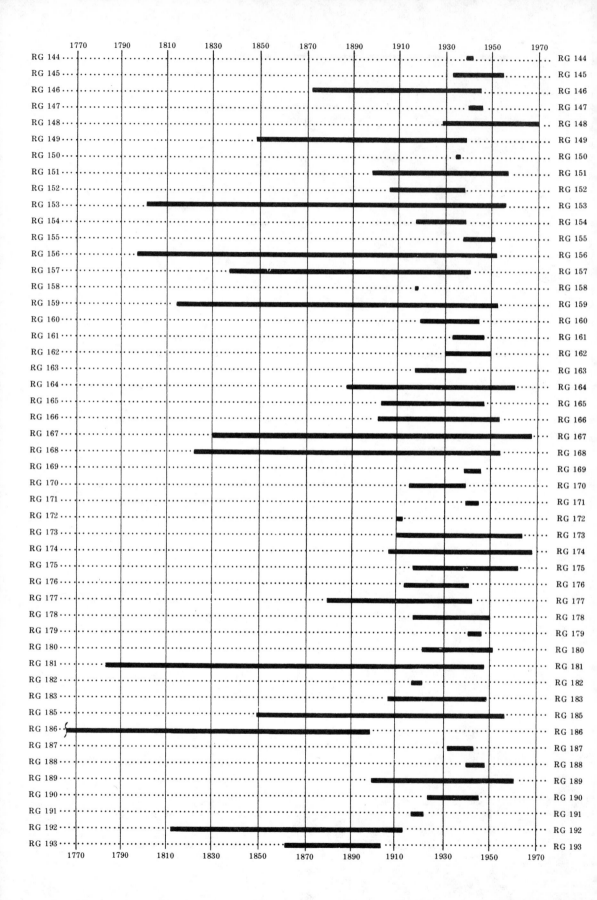

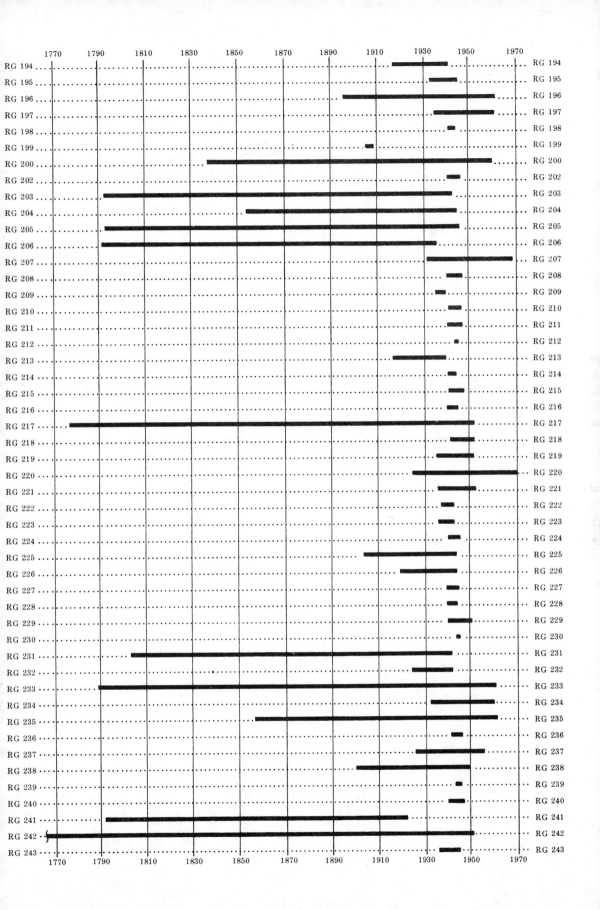

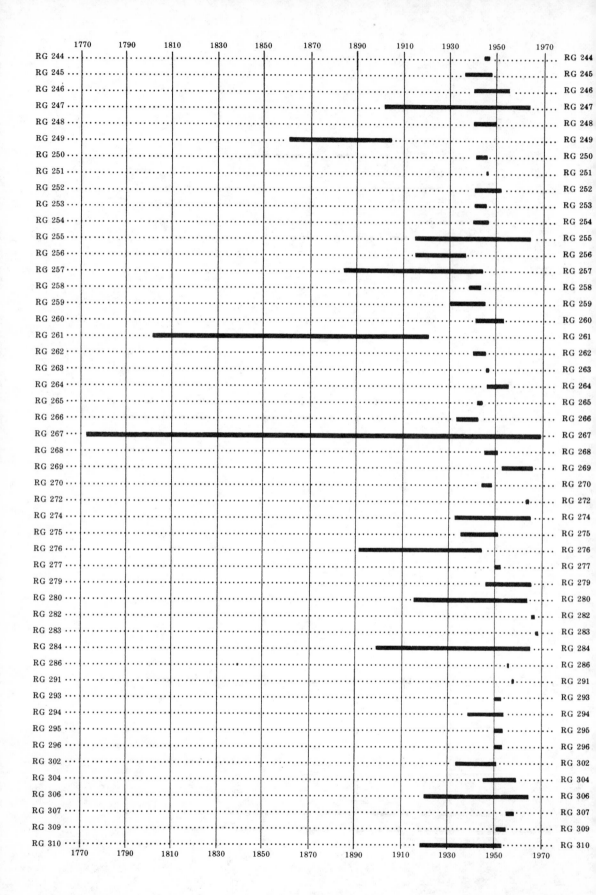

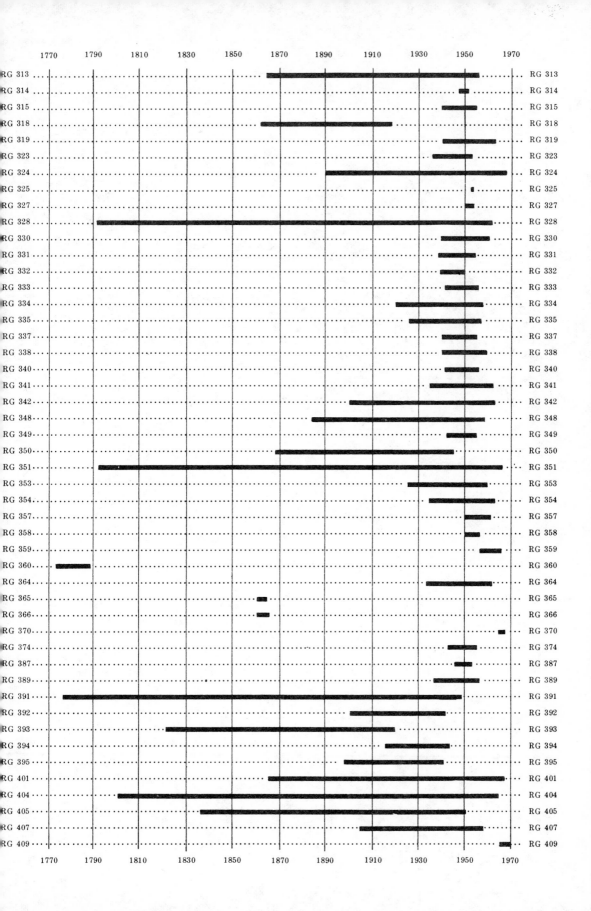

PART I

UNITED STATES GOVERNMENT—
GENERAL

GOVERNMENT UNDER THE ARTICLES OF CONFEDERATION

RECORDS OF THE CONTINENTAL AND CONFEDERATION CONGRESSES
AND THE CONSTITUTIONAL CONVENTION
(RECORD GROUP 360)

The First Continental Congress, which met in Philadelphia on September 5, 1774, included representatives from all of the 13 Colonies except Georgia. Convened to discuss and address grievances to the British Crown and Parliament, the Congress elected Peyton Randolph as President and, as Secretary, Charles Thomson, who served in that capacity until the Federal Government was established in 1789. In contrast to the First Continental Congress, which adjourned October 26, 1774, after having been assembled less than 2 months, the Second Continental Congress met over a period of almost 6 years. Meeting for the first time on May 10, 1775, at Philadelphia, it convened successively at Baltimore, Philadelphia, Lancaster (1 day only), York, and Philadelphia.

With the final ratification of the Articles of Confederation on March 2, 1781, a new central government was created by a series of Confederation Congresses. The final business of the last Congress under the Articles was transacted October 11, 1788, and on March 4, 1789, the First Congress of the United States met in New York City.

It should be noted that the records allocated to this record group are not, for the most part, organized in a manner that reflects the identity, structure, or function of each of the Continental and Confederation Congresses. They were arranged and bound by previous custodians, chiefly by type, such as journals, committee reports, correspondence, memorials, and petitions, and thereunder chronologically or alphabetically. In many instances the date span of individual series encompasses the Continental and Confederation Congresses. In addition, groups of closely related records and even parts of essentially the same body of documents are widely separated in the numbered series, while collections of unrelated records constitute a single volume of a series. It should not be assumed that all records of a given type are to be found in a particular series, nor that the title of a series always accurately reveals either its principal or its total contents.

Most of the records of the Continental and Confederation Congresses, 1774–89, are arranged in a numerical sequence of 196 series referred to as item numbers. The numbers 1–194 were assigned by William A. Weaver, a clerk in the Department of State, and listed in his *Catalogue of Manuscript Books* in 1835. The numbers 195 and 196 were added after the records came into the custody of the Library of Congress in 1903. There are miscellaneous records that are not among the numbered series. In 1952, as official records of the Federal Government, the records were transferred to the National Archives and Records Service.

The 518 bindings in the 196 numbered series, with the indexes, the unnumbered miscellaneous records of the Continental and Confederation Congresses, and the records of the Federal Constitutional Convention, comprise this record group. The engrossed copies of the Constitution of the United States, the Bill of Rights, their instruments of ratification, and the resolution of the Constitutional Convention accompanying the Constitution are among general records of the U. S. Government (see RG 11).

There are 312 cubic feet of records dated between 1774 and 178⁹, with some dated as late as 1796, in this record group.

The Congresses and Evolution of the Executive Departments, 1775–89

The First Continental Congress conducted its affairs either through the body as a whole or through committees that were appointed as needed. When it became apparent that this system was too unwieldy, the Congress established standing committees and boards to which Delegates were permanently assigned. This arrangement, too, proved unsuccessful, and with the ratification of the Articles of Confederation in March of 1781, the Second Congress established executive offices under the direction of persons who were not Members of the Congress, including a Secretary for Foreign Affairs, a Superintendent of Finance and Agent of Marine, and a Secretary at War.

Documentation of the conduct of affairs in each of these major areas is found in the journals of the Congresses and among related records, including let-

ters and reports to the President of the Congress by the committees and the executive departments that succeeded them. The old standing Committee of Secret Correspondence, which later came to be called the Committee for Foreign Affairs, led the way for the establishment on January 10, 1781, of the Department of Foreign Affairs. Robert Livingston's term as the first Secretary ended in June 1783, and there was no Secretary for Foreign Affairs until John Jay took office in December 1784. During the interim the President of the Confederation Congress and special committees conducted foreign affairs.

Fiscal affairs were managed by the Congress or by special committees until some time after the Second Continental Congress convened. On July 29, 1775, two Delegates to the Congress were appointed Joint Treasurers of the United Colonies, and in September a Committee of Accounts or Claims was established. The Committee on the Treasury, established February 17, 1776, became known as the Board of Treasury and was composed of five Members of the Congress whose duties were to superintend the Treasury and report to the Congress on the state of funds, the liquidation and settlement of accounts, and other Treasury business.

Under the Articles of Confederation Robert Morris served as Superintendent of Finance and Agent of Marine until November 1, 1784; at that time a plan for reestablishing the Board of Treasury, which had been approved by the Confederation Congress May 28, 1784, was put into effect. The Board continued until the new Federal Government was formed in 1789.

The evolution of the Department of War was somewhat similar to that of the Treasury Department. The Congress or special committees managed national defense until a Board of War and Ordnance was established June 12, 1776;

but its authority was limited and the special committees continued to function. Responsibility for military affairs was shifted by a resolution of July 18, 1777, to a Board of War. Four years later, on February 7, 1781, in accordance with the plans for establishing executive departments, a resolution was passed providing for a Secretary at War. Because many records of the Board of War and its predecessors were transferred to the Department of War established under the Constitution, the records relating to the conduct of the war that remain among the records of the Continental and Confederation Congresses consist chiefly of documents submitted to the Presidents of the Congresses.

Early naval affairs were similarly administered by special committees and later by a standing Naval Committee. A second committee was formed December 14, 1775, and since the membership of the two groups was nearly identical, the old committee was absorbed by the new one, which later became known as the Marine Committee. The Marine Committee continued to manage naval affairs until October 28, 1779, when it was replaced by a Board of Admiralty. The Second Continental Congress provided for a Secretary of Marine in 1781, but none was elected. The Board of Admiralty and the two naval boards continued to function until the duties of the Office of the Marine were delegated on September 7, 1781, to Robert Morris as Superintendent of Finance and Agent of Marine.

The plan for the post office approved by the Second Continental Congress on July 26, 1775, provided for a postal system to be supervised by a Postmaster General with offices at Philadelphia. Benjamin Franklin was appointed the first Postmaster General and was succeeded by Richard Bache in 1776 and Ebenezer Hazard in 1782.

The Federal Convention, 1787

Because of apparent weaknesses in the Confederation Government, efforts of the States to solve mutual problems resulted in the Mt. Vernon Conference in 1785 and a convention at Annapolis in 1786. The Mt. Vernon Conference was called to discuss navigation problems on the Potomac River; under Madison's suggestion the Virginia Legislature extended invitations to the States to send delegates to a convention the following year at Annapolis, where broader implications of commerce could be considered. Delegates from only five States attended the Annapolis Convention in 1786 and adopted a report inviting all States to attend a convention at Philadelphia the following year to contemplate amending the Articles of Confederation. The Confederation Congress sanctioned the invitation in February 1787.

The first official gathering of State delegates to the Federal Convention was in the State House (later known as Independence Hall) at Philadelphia on May 14, 1787. With only the delegations from Virginia and Pennsylvania initially present, the members adjourned from day to day until May 25 when a quorum of seven States was obtained. As the sessions progressed, 26 additional delegates were seated, with all States being represented except Rhode Island. The intended purpose of the Convention as resolved by the Confederation Congress on February 21, 1787, was to revise the Articles of Confederation and report to "Congress and the several legislatures such alterations and provisions therein as shall when agreed to in Congress and confirmed by the states render the federal constitution adequate to the exigencies of the Government & the preservation of the Union."

With George Washington elected as its presiding officer, the Convention, after 16 weeks of deliberation, framed a new Federal Constitution, the engrossed copy of which was signed by most of the delegates on September 17, 1787. The new Constitution was reported to the Congress of the Confederation for subsequent transmittal to the States for ratification. It was adopted in June 1788 when New Hampshire became the ninth State to ratify, followed a few days later by Virginia and then by New York. North Carolina and Rhode Island joined after the establishment of the new Federal Government in March 1789.

RECORDS OF THE CONTINENTAL AND CONFEDERATION CONGRESSES (NUMBERED SERIES). 1774-89. 415 lin. ft.

Congressional Activities

Included are rough journals, 1774-89, transcript journals, 1775-79, and secret journals, 1775-88; letter books of the Presidents of the Congresses, 1775-87, including those of John Hancock, Henry Laurens, John Jay, Samuel Huntington, Thomas McKean, John Hanson, Elias Boudinot, Thomas Mifflin, Richard Henry Lee, and Arthur St. Clair, and letters, 1775-89, addressed to the Congresses, chiefly to the Presidents of the Congresses; letter books of Charles Thomson, Secretary of the Congresses, including letters sent, 1779-89, a general index to the records of the Confederation Congress, and other letters and records, 1781-89; reports, 1785-88, of the Secretary of the Confederation Congress, which are part of the records of the proceedings of the Congress and are similar to those kept by the Committee of the Week, 1781-85; credentials of Delegates from the States to the Confederation Congress, 1781-89; and registers and indexes kept by the Secretary, which are supplemented by eight bound manuscript indexes compiled between 1835 and 1855 in the Department of State and three card indexes prepared

by the Manuscript Division of the Library of Congress.

There are books of motions made in the Congress, 1777-88; sundry motions and resolves of the Congress, 1785-86 and 1788; abridged resolves; memorials, petitions, and remonstrances, 1775-89, addressed to the Congress; ordinances of the Confederation Congress, 1781-88; a letter book of the Second Congress Executive Committee, 1776-77; Office of the Congress records, 1781-89; and intercepted letters, 1775-81.

Among the many reports of the committees of the Congresses are those of the Committee of the States, 1784, appointed to transact the business of the United States during the adjournment of the Confederation Congress, June 4-October 31, 1784; reports on the administrative affairs of the Congress, establishment of a residence for its President, and the qualifications of its Members, 1775-88; and the proceedings of the Convention of Committees at New Haven, 1778, and Hartford, 1779-80. There are also drafts of the Articles of Confederation and a record of the proceedings of the Second Continental Congress, relating to the adoption and ratification of the Articles; and proposals on locating the seat of government and printing the journals, 1777-89.

Foreign Affairs

A few of the records relating to foreign affairs are dated after 1789. Included are letters and reports of the Committee for Foreign Affairs, of Robert R. Livingston, Secretary for Foreign Affairs, 1776-83, and of John Jay, Secretary for Foreign Affairs, 1785-88; foreign letters of the Department of Foreign Affairs and of the Department of State, 1785-90; daily journal or despatch book, 1781-83 and 1784-90, and resolve book, 1785-89, of the Department; treaties and contracts, 1778-88; commissions and letters of credence of foreign ministers and consuls, 1778-1821; commissions of foreign consuls, 1778–87; letters from the Joint Commissioners for Negotiating Treaties with France and Great Britain, 1777–84; letters from the Joint Commissioners for the Formation of Treaties of Amity and Commerce, with plans of treaties in French and Italian, 1784–86; letters with enclosures from diplomatic and consular representatives of France in the United States, 1778–90; letters from ministers of France in the United States, 1779–84, and ministers representing the United Provinces of the Netherlands, 1783–96; records relating to the Barbary Powers, 1779–92 and 1795; letters and records relating to Spain, 1780–89; letters and a memorial relating to American trade in the French West Indies, 1788–89; and applications for passports or sea letters, 1788–93.

There are also records and accounts of Silas Deane, Beaumarchais, and Arthur Lee, 1776–84; letters from Arthur Lee, 1776–80, Benjamin Franklin, 1776–88, William Carmichael, 1776–91, Charles W. F. Dumas, 1776–96, William Bingham and others, 1777–82, Ralph Izard and others, 1777–84, John Adams, 1777–88, William S. Smith and others, 1779–89, Thomas Barclay and John Lamb, 1782–88, and Thomas Jefferson, 1785–89; and transcripts of many of the letters and reports mentioned above, 1776–89. Also included are records relating to the claims for captured vessels, 1777–84, and reports of the committees of the Congresses, relating to Canada, treaties and foreign loans, 1776–86, and foreign affairs, 1776–88.

Fiscal Affairs

The records include committee reports on the operation of the Board of Treasury and the national finances, 1776–88; reports of the Committee of Commerce; reports on the public debt in 1781, and estimates of expenses with related papers, 1779–86; letters and reports from the Comptroller of the Treasury and claims of Canadian refu-

gees, 1783–86; reports on domestic loans and loan offices and on foreign loans, 1776–86; and committee reports and records on claims of New York and Vermont to the New Hampshire Grants, 1776–84.

There are also Board of Treasury reports, 1776–81 and 1784–88; Board of Treasury reports on applications from the States and on other subjects, including a plan for selling the public lands, 1785–89; letters and reports from Robert Morris, Superintendent of Finance and Agent of Marine, 1781–85, with an appendix volume, 1776–78 and 1781–86; Board of Treasury letters, 1785–88; bonds required by commissioners appointed to the Board of Treasury, 1785 and 1787; estimates and statements of receipts and expenditures, 1780–88; estimates and other records relating to the Treasury, including records on the Grand Committee of Congress to consider the national debt, 1780–88; letters and records of bankers in Holland and contracts for loans, 1779–90; records relating to investigations of Treasury offices, 1780–81; accounts of the Register's Office, 1781–83; records respecting unsettled accounts, 1788, and returns of stores, 1783–84; and Charles Thomson's incidental accounts (office expenses), 1785–89.

Military Affairs

Included are oaths of allegiance of military and public officers, 1776–89; reports on the Army and its various units, 1775–85; reports of the Commissioners of Accounts for the Clothing and Hospital Departments; reports on the War Office and the Department of War, 1776–88; reports on the Prisoners' Department; reports of the Committees of Conference with the Commander in Chief at Cambridge, 1775, and at Valley Forge, 1778–79; reports of committees on the Philadelphia mutiny and the peacetime establishment, 1783–86; letters and records of the Committee to

Headquarters appointed to confer with the Commander in Chief, 1780; reports on the Commissary Department and on the loss of certain Army posts, 1776–86; records relating to the British evacuation of New York, 1783; and records and affidavits relating to the "plunderings, burnings, and ravages committed by the British," 1775–84.

There are reports, 1776–81, and letters, 1780–81, of the Board of War and Ordnance; letters from the Secretary and Paymaster of the Board of War and Ordnance; letters and records concerning the "convention troops," 1777–80; letters and reports from Maj. Gen. Benjamin Lincoln, Secretary at War, 1781–83; letters and reports from Maj. Gen. Henry Knox, Secretary at War, 1785–88; letters from Gen. George Washington, Commander in Chief of the Army, 1775–84; letters and records relating to the Quartermaster's Department, 1778–80; letters of Maj. Gen. Nathanael Greene, 1780–83, with various records relating to the Quartermaster's Department, 1778–80; letters from generals and other officers, 1775–89; transcripts of many letters from military officers, 1775–83; letters from Comte d'Estaing, 1777–86; letters and records relating to the exchange of officers, 1778 and 1780; letters and reports from the Paymaster General and Commissioner for Army Accounts, 1781–88; letters and records relating to charges against Gen. John Sullivan and Dr. John Morgan and to British advances in the Mohawk Valley, 1776–79; and letters and other records relating to the trial of Capt. Richard Lippincott, 1782.

Naval Affairs

These consist chiefly of reports on the Board of Admiralty and Agent of Marine, 1776–86; Marine Committee and Board of Admiralty reports, 1776–81; ship bonds required for letters of marque and reprisal granted by the States, 1776–83; letters and records of John Paul Jones, 1777–91; transcripts of his letters, 1778–80; and correspondence of Captain Jones, and letters and records relating to the trials of Capt. Peter Landais and Lt. James Degge, 1778–81.

Territorial and State Affairs

Included are an undated narration of a journey to the western country by an Indian; petitions about the Indiana region, 1779–83; and ordinances of the Confederation Congress and other records relating to the Western Territory of the United States, 1787–88. Also memorials of the inhabitants of Illinois, Kaskaskia, and Kentucky, 1780–89; reports relating to communications received from Governors and other State officials, 1777–88; committee reports on relations between the Congress and the States: reports on lands in the Western Territory, 1776–88; committee reports and records on claims of New York and Vermont to the New Hampshire Grants, 1776–84; letters received by Congresses (State Papers), 1775–91, from Governors and other State officials, committees of safety, and State assemblies, relating to the coordination of the Congress and the State Governments and including records relating to claims of territory by Pennsylvania and Connecticut, 1780–85; letters from Thomas Hutchins, relating to his duties as Geographer of the United States in surveying State boundaries; and statistics on population of certain States and calculations of the land area of the United States and the Western Territory, 1774–86.

Indian Affairs

In addition to a variety of records relating to Indian affairs, 1765–89, there are proceedings of commissioners appointed by the Second Continental Congress to negotiate a treaty with the Six Nations of Indians, 1775, letters and records relating to negotiations with the northern Indians, 1776–79, copies of

Indian treaties, 1784-86, and committee reports on Indian affairs, 1776-88.

Other Records

There are also committee reports on applications from individuals, 1776-89; reports on hospitals and on applications of invalids, 1776-88; reports on the executive departments, 1776-86; miscellaneous reports, with lists of postponed reports; and letters and records of Postmasters General, and reports of committees of the Congress on the post office, 1776-88.

CARTOGRAPHIC RECORDS. 1781. 1 item.

A manuscript map of the Revolutionary War battlefield of Yorktown, Va., compiled by Lt. Col. Jean-Baptiste Gouvion.

MISCELLANEOUS RECORDS OF THE CONTINENTAL AND CONFEDERATION CONGRESSES (UNNUMBERED SERIES). 1774-89. 17 lin. ft.

The miscellaneous records of the Continental and Confederation Congresses consist of those records not a part of the numbered series of volumes comprising the main body of records and include the engrossed copies of the Declaration of Independence and the Articles of Confederation. Those relating primarily to foreign affairs include the ordinance, 1781, establishing the Department of Foreign Affairs; reports, 1782, and drafts of letters, 1782-83, of the Secretary for Foreign Affairs; diplomatic despatches received from Charles W. F. Dumas, 1777-82, Benjamin Franklin, 1777 and 1779-84, John Adams, 1779-83 and 1785, Francis W. Dana, 1780-83, and William Carmichael, 1780-83 and 1785; diplomatic despatches and letters received from Ralph Izard, 1777 and 1779, Arthur Lee, 1777-79, John Laurens, 1781, Henry Laurens, 1781-84, and John Jay, 1781 and 1785-86; and despatches received from agents and con-

suls, 1779-90. Many of the despatches duplicate those in the numbered series.

There are also letters, memorials, and notes, 1778-79 and 1782, from the Ministers of France in the United States; originals and copies of letters, 1778-87, of Louis XVI of France received by the Congress; letters from the Marquis de Lafayette, 1782-83; edict, June 1, 1786, of Louis XVI providing for the payment at Amsterdam of interest and capital of certain royal loans due in the United Provinces of the Netherlands; correspondence of the Amsterdam firm of John de Neufville and Son, 1778-85, with William Lee, Le Ray de Chaumont, Benjamin Franklin, John Paul Jones, and Charles W. F. Dumas; letters from the Amsterdam firms of Jacob van Staphorst, Wilhelm and Jan Willink, and De la Lande and Fynje, 1782-89, to John Jay, Secretary for Foreign Affairs; bills, 1782-83, drawn on Ferdinand le Grand, Parisian banker; letters relating to Spain and the Barbary States, 1779-86; draft of the proclamation, April 10, 1783, by the Confederation Congress, declaring the cessation of hostilities between United States and Great Britain; draft of a commission, May 12, 1784, for John Adams, Benjamin Franklin, and Thomas Jefferson to negotiate a commercial treaty with Denmark; and a copy of the treaty signed by the United States and Prussia and ratified by the Confederation Congress, 1786.

Records relating to naval affairs include reports of the Marine Committee, 1776-79; the Committee's letter book, 1776-80; an account of commissions for private armed vessels, received and forwarded to the several States, 1779-83; and records relating to fiscal affairs, 1783, 1785, and 1787. Records relating to specific States, 1779-1802, include those for Virginia, Massachusetts, and New York, and the Pennsylvania and Connecticut boundary dispute; and deeds of cession of western lands, with related documents, for Connecticut,

Georgia, Massachusetts, New York, North Carolina, South Carolina, and Virginia.

Among the records relating to the Congresses themselves are credentials of Delegates from each State to Congress, 1774-89, and broadsides and other imprints, 1775-88, issued by the Second Continental and Confederation Congresses.

Several of the numbered series of the records of the Continental and Confederation Congresses have been included in various publications. The journals of the Congresses have been published by the Library of Congress in *Journals of the Continental Congress, 1774-1789* (34 vols., 1904-37). These volumes print selected documents but contain numerous references to many others among the numbered series. The published *Journals*, which reproduce a significant but small fraction of the manuscripts in this record group, are readily available in printed form to the public. Diplomatic correspondence from 1776 to 1783 was compiled by Jared Sparks and published as *The Diplomatic Correspondence of the American Revolution* (12 vols.; Boston, 1829-39); in 1857 it was reprinted in six volumes. A revised and expanded edition of Sparks' compilation was published as *The Revolutionary Diplomatic Correspondence of the United States*, edited by Francis Wharton (6 vols., 1889). Diplomatic correspondence from 1783 to the formation of the Federal Government was compiled by William A. Weaver of the State Department and published as *The Diplomatic Correspondence of the United States of America, From the Signing of the Definitive Treaty of Peace, 10th September, 1783, to the Adoption of the Constitution, March 4, 1789* (7 vols., 1833-34). In addition to records in State archives, another important source on the naval history of the Revolution is the one-volume calendar *Naval Records of the American Revolution, 1775-1788*, compiled by Charles Henry Lincoln of the Library of Congress, 1906.

Other publications relating to the Continental and Confederation Congresses include Carl L. Lokke, "The Continental Congress Papers; Their History, 1789-1952," *National Archives Accessions*, No. 51 (June 1954), pp. 1-19; Jennings B. Sanders, *Evolution of Executive Departments of the Continental Congress, 1774-1789* (Magnolia, Mass.: Peter Smith, 1971); Jennings B. Sanders, *The Presidency of the Continental Congress, 1774-89: A Study in American Institutional History* (Magnolia, Mass.: Peter Smith, 1971); Herbert Friedenwald, "The Journals and Papers of the Continental Congress," American Historical Association, *Annual Report* (1896), pp. 85-135; Herbert Friedenwald, "The Continental Congress," American Historical Association, *Annual Report* (1894),

pp. 227-236; and Edmund C. Burnett, *Letters of Members of the Continental Congress* (8 vols.; Carnegie Institution, 1921-36).

RECORDS OF THE CONSTITUTIONAL CONVENTION. 1787. 1 lin. ft.

The official records of the Convention include documents turned over to Timothy Pickering, Secretary of State, by George Washington on March 19, 1796: Journal of the Convention, May 14-September 15, 1787; Journal of the Proceedings of the Committee of the Whole House, May 30-June 19, 1787; a volume containing a detail of the yeas and nays given on questions in the Convention; loose sheets of yeas and nays (now bound into one volume); two copies of the Virginia Plan as amended in the Philadelphia Convention, June 13, 1787; Washington's annotated printed draft of the Constitution, as reported by the Committee of Detail, August 6, 1787; an undated draft of the letter from the Convention to the Confederation Congress, to accompany the Constitution; and a few letters received by the Convention from various sources.

Documents in the possession of David Brearley, a New Jersey Delegate, were transmitted May 22, 1818, to John Q. Adams, Secretary of State, by Gen. Joseph Bloomfield, executor of Brearley. Not official records of the Constitutional Convention, these include a copy of the propositions offered to the Convention by William Paterson, June 15, 1787; a copy of a plan for a constitution—"Plan of Government"—presented in a speech to the Convention by Alexander Hamilton, June 18, 1787; two copies of the population returns of the several States; a copy of the resolutions submitted to the Convention by Edmund Randolph of Virginia on May 29, 1787; a copy of the report of the Grand Committee on the eighth resolution reported from the Committee of the Whole House, and as much of the seventh as had not been decided upon, July 5, 1787; an annotated printed draft of the Constitution brought into the Convention on August 6, 1787, and reported by the Committee of Detail; an annotated printed draft of the Constitution brought into the Convention by the Committee on Revision of Style and Arrangement on September 12, 1787; and an original motion (not part of the Brearley material or the official records) in the hand of Elbridge Gerry [July 24, 1787].

The proceedings of the Constitutional Convention are available in Max Farrand, ed., *The Records of the Federal Convention of 1787* (4 vols., revised; New Haven: Yale University Press, 1966); and in the Department of State *Documentary History of the Constitution of the United States of America, 1786-1870* (5 vols., 1894-1905).

Microfilm Publications: *Papers of the Continental Congress, 1774-1789*, M247, 204 rolls, DP; *Miscellaneous Papers of the Continental Congress, 1774-1789*, M332, 9 rolls, DP; and *Madison Items From the Continental Congress Papers*, T270, 1 roll.

WAR DEPARTMENT COLLECTION OF REVOLUTIONARY WAR RECORDS
(RECORD GROUP 93)

The act of August 7, 1789, that established the War Department provided that the Secretary of War should have custody of all books and papers in the office of the Secretary at War, who had headed the Department of War created in 1781 by the Continental Congress. These books and papers included the records of the Board of War, which had administered military affairs from 1776 to 1781. Most of these records were destroyed by fire on November 8, 1800. When Government buildings in Washington were burned in August 1814 by British soldiers, the War Department's remaining records for the Revolutionary War period were in a fireproof room and were not damaged by the flames. It was subsequently reported, however, that many of them had been destroyed or carried away by persons who entered the room after the fire. As a result there were, until 1873, few records for the period before 1789 in War Department custody.

In 1873 Secretary of War William Belknap purchased the Pickering Papers for the War Department. This private collection consisted of papers of Timothy Pickering, who between 1777 and 1785 had been a member of the Board of War, Adjutant General of the Continental

Army, and Quartermaster General; the papers of Samuel Hodgdon, Commissary General of Military Stores for several years during the war; and miscellaneous contemporary papers. Belknap also obtained some minor groups of records and single record items for the Department during his tenure. In 1888, however, the War Department collection of Revolutionary War records was transferred to the State Department, which was considering the possibility of publishing the Government archives for the Revolutionary War period.

The War Department established in 1889 a Record and Pension Division— called the Record and Pension Office after 1892—to take charge of the records of past U.S. volunteer armies. The purpose of this Office was to increase the efficiency with which military service statements were being provided to the Commissioner of Pensions of the Interior Department. To achieve this purpose Col. Fred C. Ainsworth, Chief of the Record and Pension Office, attempted to have transferred to the War Department all Revolutionary War records from other Government departments. Although he did not succeed in having all such records transferred, the Congress in 1892 and 1894 did authorize transfer to the War Department of all military records for the Revolutionary War period then in the custody of other executive departments. These military records were transferred between 1894 and 1913 from Interior Department pension files, Treasury Department auditors' records, and State Department records including the Pickering Papers and some Continental Army returns that had once belonged to George Washington.

In 1909 Henry G. Pickering, great-grandson of Timothy Pickering, gave to the War Department through the Quartermaster General a number of record books, mostly relating to supply and pay accounts. In 1914 and 1915, under authority of an act of March 2, 1913, the Department made photographic copies of Revolutionary War records in the custody of public and private institutions in Virginia, North Carolina, and Massachusetts to supplement its original record holdings.

There are 820 cubic feet of records dated mainly between 1775 and 1798 in this record group.

BOUND RECORDS. 1775-98.
20 lin. ft.

About three-quarters of the bound records are volumes numbered 1-197 and arranged according to subject matter or the creating office or officer. Derived largely from the Pickering Papers or those donated by Henry G. Pickering, they include account and receipt books; orderly books; letter books of officers, such as 13 volumes of outgoing letters of Timothy Pickering and four volumes of outgoing letters of Samuel Hodgdon; rosters of State and Continental troops; returns of personnel and supplies; and pay accounts and related correspondence. Also included are four volumes of oaths of allegiance and fidelity and of oaths of office, and one volume of officers commissions. There are about 50 unnumbered volumes, con-

sisting mainly of returns, registers of muster rolls, account books, lists of officers and enlisted men, and reference aids compiled by employees of the War Department after the Revolution for use in providing reference service on the original records. Among the unnumbered aids is a "Catalogue and Subject Index" that lists and indexes the numbered record books.

UNBOUND RECORDS. 1775-84.
94 lin. ft.

Almost all of the unbound records are organized into two large series created mainly from records transferred to the War Department by the Interior, Treasury, and State Departments. The first series consists of records of military organizations arranged by State and thereunder by organization. These include muster rolls, returns, pay abstracts, guard reports, and other lists relating to the composition of the organizations. The second series contains letters, diaries, receipts for pay and land, reports, memorandums, supply and provision returns, oaths of allegiance, commissions, orders, and other records relating to supplies and to individual officers and enlisted men. There is also a small series of miscellaneous papers relating to supplies, personnel, pensions, and other subjects. Not all of these miscellaneous papers relate to the Revolutionary War.

PHOTOGRAPHIC COPIES OF RECORDS AND RELATED INDEXES. 1775-83. 52 lin. ft.

Included are minutes of boards, including boards of war; reports and letters sent and received by State boards of war, Governors, and military officers; court records; prize vessel accounts; rolls and returns; and receipts for money and stores. There are also a few indexes to Connecticut records. Arranged by State and partially indexed by name and subject.

COMPILED MILITARY SERVICE RECORDS AND RELATED INDEXES. 1775-84. 2,710 lin. ft.

Compiled military service records form a single file of thousands of paper jackets, each bearing the name of a Revolutionary War officer or enlisted man and containing one or more record cards with information about him abstracted from that series of unbound records consisting of muster rolls, returns, pay abstracts, guard reports, and other organizational lists. Certain numbered record books were also abstracted. The compilation of these carded records took place mainly between 1894 and 1912. The jackets are arranged by State and organization and are indexed by a number of card indexes, the most comprehensive of which is a "general index" arranged alphabetically by name of officer or enlisted man. A "special index," also on cards but arranged alphabetically by name of civilians as well as military personnel, indexes that series of unbound records not used in creating the compiled record cards—letters, diaries, receipts, and other records relating to supplies and to individual officers and men. Some numbered record books and some photographic copies of Virginia records (including 5,050 glass plate negatives) are also indexed by the "special index."

Microfilm Publications: Nearly all of these records have been published on microfilm or are scheduled for such publication. For a complete listing see the current *List of National Archives Microfilm Publications.*

FEDERAL GOVERNMENT

GENERAL RECORDS OF THE UNITED STATES GOVERNMENT
(RECORD GROUP 11)

This record group consists of the Constitution of the United States, the Bill of Rights and other amendments, and related records; laws of the United States and related records; international treaties and agreements; Indian treaties; Presidential proclamations, Executive orders, and other Presidential documents; rules and regulations of Federal agencies; electoral records; and the Great Seal of the United States.

There are 1,694 cubic feet of records dated between 1778 and 1969 in this record group.

THE CONSTITUTION AND AMENDMENTS. 1787-1967. 7 lin. ft.

These records, originally deposited with the Department of State, consist of the engrossed copy of the Constitution and the accompanying resolution of the Constitutional Convention directing that the Constitution be laid before Congress; the formal documents from the States ratifying the Constitution; the enrolled original joint resolution of Congress of September 25, 1789, proposing 12 amendments (including the 10 adopted, known as the Bill of Rights); "Bankson's Journal," 1786-90 (1 vol.), prepared for the Secretary of the Congress of the Confederation Charles Thomson and containing copies of various reports, res-

olutions, credentials, and acts of the period in which the Constitution was proposed, written, and ratified; other ratified amendments with related records from the States, 1795-1967; and unratified amendments concerning titles of nobility, 1810, and child labor, 1924, as well as a few documents from State legislatures proposing other constitutional amendments. The original congressional resolutions proposing constitutional amendments are among the enrolled resolutions described below. From 1789 to 1950 correspondence with States concerning the ratification of amendments was the responsibility of the Secretary of State, who also issued a certificate whenever the required number of States had ratified an amendment; in 1950 this function was transferred to the Administrator of General Services.

See Department of State, *Documentary History of the Constitution of the United States, 1786-1870*, Andrew H. Allen, ed. (5 vols., 1894-1905); and the Library of Congress, *Documents Illustrative of the Formation of the Union of the American States*, Charles C. Tansill, comp. (1927). See also *The Constitution of the United States of America*, S. Doc. 49, 87th Cong., 1st sess., Serial 12349.

LAWS OF THE UNITED STATES AND RELATED RECORDS. 1789-1968. 186 lin. ft.

The act establishing the Department of State required the Secretary to receive and preserve original congressional acts and resolutions and to have them recorded in books and published in newspapers. The Secretary was later made responsible for the publication of "session laws," containing all laws passed and all treaties ratified and proclaimed during a session of Congress, and of various collected editions of the laws as directed by Congress, particularly the *United States Statutes at Large*. Recording the laws in books was terminated by an act passed in 1838, and publication of the laws in newspapers was discontinued in 1874; records relating to these functions are among records of the Department of State (see RG 59). In 1950 responsibility for publishing the laws was transferred from the Secretary of State to the Administrator of General Services, who delegated the function to the Office of the Federal Register of the National Archives and Records Service (NARS).

In this record group are the following records received from the Department of State and the Office of the Federal Register: original engrossed copies of laws of the United States and of joint resolutions, signed by the Speaker of the House, the President of the Senate, and the President of the United States; original and printed copies of a few miscellaneous House and Senate resolutions, 1926 and 1933; and enrolled bills kept from becoming law by the pocket veto, 1815–96 (1 vol.).

INTERNATIONAL TREATIES AND RELATED RECORDS. 1778–1969.
229 lin. ft.

Before the adoption of the Constitution, the treatymaking power was exercised by the Continental Congress and the Congress of the Confederation, which appointed commissioners to carry on negotiations on the basis of terms approved by the Congress. Since the adoption of the Constitution, which authorizes the President to make treaties with approval of the Senate, treaty negotiations have usually been conducted through the Secretary of State, who has preserved not only the treaties and related records originating since 1789 but also those of the Continental Congress and of the Confederation period that were turned over to him when the Department of State was established.

The files of perfected treaties and executive agreements include perfected treaties, 1778–1945; executive agreements, 1922–45, with lists by number, date, and country, 1922–40; and treaties and other international acts, 1942–69, which include both executive agreements and perfected treaties ratified and proclaimed after January 1, 1946.

A treaty file usually consists of an original signed treaty; the attested Senate resolution of advice and consent to ratification; a copy of the U.S. instrument of ratification (since about 1835); the original of the certificate, protocol, or process-verbal of the exchange of ratifications; the exchanged instrument of ratifications of the other contracting party; and the original proclamation of the treaty by the President. Files of bilateral treaties also usually include a copy of the treaty as ratified by the other country. For multilateral treaties there is ordinarily one signed original deposited with a specified government or international body; the file, therefore, may contain a certified copy of the original treaty or the original treaty together with instruments of ratification or adherence deposited by various governments. Executive agreements are not ratified or proclaimed; the files, therefore, usually consist only of the signed original agreement.

Many of the early treaty files lack one or more of the types of records enumerated above, but some contain other relevant documents, such as documents granting full powers to negotiate the treaty and to exchange ratifications, and correspondence. Most of the records relating to negotiations are filed with the diplomatic correspondence among records of the Department of State (see RG 59).

The unperfected treaties, 1803-1949, are those that have not gone into effect. Some signed treaties never reached the stage of ratification and the exchange of instruments of ratification; some have been rejected by the legislative body of another country; some have been approved by the Senate with stipulations to which the President could not assent; and some were never submitted to the Senate. Documents in the unperfected treaty files are similar to those in the perfected treaty files.

As early as 1792 the Postmaster General was authorized to conclude agreements with foreign postal officials regarding the transportation of the mails, and in 1872 he was empowered by the President to negotiate postal treaties or conventions. These do not require Senate approval. There are some postal agreements among the treaty files and others among the records of the Post Office Department (see RG 28). Filed separately are postal conventions, 1853-97, including draft conventions with France in 1853, with Italy in 1877 and 1880, and ratifications by the signatory countries of the Universal Postal Convention of 1897.

See David Hunter Miller, ed., *Treaties and Other International Acts of the United States of America* (8 vols., 1931-48). The first volume contains tables and lists, a bibliography, and other important data regarding treaties; the other volumes contain the texts in the original languages of those treaties that went into force from 1776 to July 1863, together with extensive editorial notes on the background of negotiations and procedural history. The Senate Committee on Foreign Relations directed the compilation by William M. Malloy of *Treaties, Conventions, International Acts, Protocols and Agreements Between the United States of America and Other Powers, 1776-1909* (2 vols., 1910); a third volume, dealing with the period 1910-23, was compiled by C. F. Redmond and published in 1923; a fourth volume, for the 1923-37 period, was compiled by Edward J. Trenwith and

published in 1938. These will be superseded by a new 15-volume compilation by Charles I. Bevans of the Department of State, *Treaties and Other International Agreements of the United States of America, 1776-1949*. Texts of treaties and other international agreements that took effect before 1950 were printed contemporaneously in the *United States Statutes at Large*; a complete list is in volume 64, part 3. Those that took effect after January 1, 1950, are printed in *United States Treaties and Other International Agreements*, a continuing publication prepared by the Department of State.

TREATIES WITH INDIAN TRIBES AND RELATED PAPERS.
1778-1868. 8 lin. ft.

Indian treaties were negotiated on behalf of the colonies and the British Crown during the colonial period and on behalf of the Continental Congress and the Congress of the Confederation during and after the Revolutionary War. This treatymaking power continued as a prerogative of the Federal Government under the Constitution. From 1789 to 1849 Indian treaties were negotiated by special commissioners acting for the President under supervision of the War Department. In 1849 responsibility for negotiating the treaties was transferred to the Office of Indian Affairs and the Department of the Interior, created in that same year. An act passed in 1871 prohibited further negotiation of treaties with Indian tribes but provided that existing treaties would stand. The Department of State continued to preserve the treaties.

Although most Indian treaties in this record group were ratified, there are some that were not. Most of the unratified treaties are among the records of the Senate (see RG 46) or of the Bureau of Indian Affairs (see RG 75). Although the first original treaty is the one concluded with the Delawares at Pittsburgh on September 17, 1778, the records also include a few contemporaneous handwritten and printed copies of treaties concluded as early as 1722 that were used as precedents for later treaties.

The last treaty is with the Nez Perces, signed August 13, 1868. The treaties are usually accompanied by Senate resolutions of advice and consent to ratification and Presidential ratifications and proclamations. In some cases copies of messages from the President to the Congress regarding treaties, copies of letters of instructions to Indian commissioners, and journals and correspondence of the commissioners have been preserved. There are also card indexes to and lists of the treaties.

Indian treaties have been published in Charles J. Kappler, *Indian Affairs, Laws, and Treaties*, Vol. 2 (1904); in the *United States Statutes at Large*, Vol. VII (Boston, 1846); and in *American State Papers: Indian Affairs* (2 vols., 1832–34).

PRESIDENTIAL PROCLAMATIONS, EXECUTIVE ORDERS, AND OTHER PRESIDENTIAL DOCUMENTS.
1789–1968. 101 lin. ft.

Proclamations, many having the effect of law, have been issued by the Presidents for several purposes since the beginning of the Government. They were sealed with the Great Seal of the United States and countersigned by the Secretary of State (until July 1, 1967) and remained in his possession until 1936. Proclamations generally concern matters of widespread public interest. Executive orders are similar in effect to proclamations but are generally concerned with the organization of the executive departments or with the conduct of Government business. They are rarely sealed or countersigned, and until 1905 they were usually sent to the agencies involved and not to the Department of State.

In 1907 the Department of State began to number the Executive orders and proclamations previously issued, and later it assigned numbers as the orders and proclamations were received and printed. The Executive orders in this record group form part of the "numbered series"; most of the Executive orders issued before 1929 are in the "unnumbered series" distributed among the records of other Government agencies. In 1936 the Office of the Federal Register was assigned the duties of numbering and supervising the promulgation of all Executive orders and proclamations, and those in the custody of the Department of State were transferred to the National Archives.

Other Presidential documents are those that are not numbered Executive orders or proclamations and include Presidential reorganization plans, military orders, regulations, administrative orders, designations of officials, interpretive letters, and other executive documents.

The records consist of Presidential proclamations, 1791–1968, with card indexes and lists, 1789–1947, and drafts and worksheets of proclamations, 1930–42; Executive orders, 1862–1968, with card indexes and lists, 1862–1947, and drafts of Executive orders, 1929–42; and other Presidential documents, 1945–68. Other card indexes and lists are in the Office of the Federal Register of NARS.

Many proclamations and orders are printed in James D. Richardson, *A Compilation of the Messages and Papers of the Presidents* (1896–99 and later editions). Most proclamations are printed in the *United States Statutes at Large*. Numbered Executive orders are both listed and indexed in *Presidential Executive Orders Numbered 1–8030; 1862–1938*, compiled by the New York Historical Records Survey (2 vols.; New York, 1944); some of the unnumbered Executive orders are noted in the *List and Index of Presidential Executive Orders (Unnumbered Series), 1789–1941*, compiled by the New Jersey Historical Records Survey (Newark, 1943). Proclamations having general applicability and legal effect that were in force as of March 19, 1936, and orders as of March 13, 1936, are printed or cited in the *Code of Federal Regulations*, while those issued after that date appear in the *Supplements* and annual volumes of the *Code*. Beginning March 14, 1936, all proclamations and orders having general applicability and legal effect have also been printed in the *Federal Register*. See also U.S. House of Representatives, Committee on Government Operations, *Executive Orders and Proclamations: A Study of a Use of Presidential Powers* (Dec. 1957), 85th Cong., 1st sess.

RULES AND REGULATIONS OF FEDERAL AGENCIES. 1936–68.
1,117 lin. ft. (in WNRC).

Before the passage of the Federal Register Act of July 26, 1935, no provision existed for the central filing and publication of administrative rules, regulations, notices, and similar documents that have general applicability and the force of law. This act created the Division of the Federal Register of the National Archives to receive, file, and register such documents; make them available for public inspection; publish them in the *Federal Register;* and codify and publish at regular intervals those documents remaining in effect. The Office of the Federal Register has also received documents for filing only.

The records consist of originals of administrative rules, regulations, orders, notices, and other documents, 1936–68, arranged by chronological groups and thereunder alphabetically by Government departments and independent agencies; and a photostatic copy of the register of documents filed with the Division of the Federal Register, 1936–41 (2 vols. and unbound sheets).

ELECTORAL RECORDS. 1888–1968.
16 lin. ft.

Article II of the Constitution stipulates that "Electors shall meet in their respective States . . . make a List of all the Persons voted for, and of the Number of Votes for each," sign and certify the lists, and transmit them to the President of the Senate. For the elections before 1888, these lists are among the records of the Senate (see RG 46). By an act of February 3, 1887, the Secretary of State became part of the electoral system. He was required to receive from each State Governor a certified list, known as a final ascertainment of electors, showing the names and total votes of all persons receiving votes for electors and indicating the persons chosen. The Secretary was required to transmit a copy of each ascertainment to each House of Congress and to have the ascertainments published in a newspaper of his choice. This procedure was modified in 1928 by an act that provided that in addition to receiving the ascertainment from each Governor, the Secretary was to receive two copies of the ascertainment for each State directly from the electors of that State, each copy to be accompanied by a certified statement of the votes of the electors for President and Vice President. He was required to hold one copy of each document subject to the call of the President of the Senate and to keep the other copy for 1 year. The same act discontinued the requirement for the newspaper publication of the ascertainments. In 1950 functions concerning the ascertainments of electors were transferred from the Secretary of State to the Administrator of General Services.

Records consist chiefly of certified copies of ascertainments of electors, 1888–1968, correspondence and memorandums concerning selection of electors, newspaper clippings of the ascertainments as published through 1924, statements of electoral votes, 1928 and 1932, and some miscellaneous correspondence and records, 1904–42. Many of these records are duplicates of electoral records among the records of the Senate (see RG 46) and the House (see RG 233).

THE GREAT SEAL OF THE UNITED STATES. 1782–1909.
1 lin. ft.

A design for the Great Seal of the United States, submitted by Secretary of the Continental Congress Charles Thomson, was adopted in 1782. On September 15, 1789, the Secretary of State became custodian of the seal. Several dies of the obverse of the seal have been cut for authentication of documents, but the reverse of the seal has never been cut for use.

Early in its history the United States followed procedures of European countries by attaching large wax seals to treaties. In 1825 the Department of State made and used an oversize Great Seal for this purpose, but since 1871 the regular die of the Great Seal has been used on treaties as well as other documents. A die of the 1825 oversize seal was cut in 1854 for embossing the skippets (metal boxes containing the wax seals that were attached to treaties). After 1871 the skippet also went out of use. Today the Great Seal is affixed to the following kinds of documents after they are signed by the President and countersigned by the Secretary of State: ratifications of treaties; papers granting power to negotiate treaties; exequaturs; Presidential warrants for extradition of fugitives from justice; commissions of Cabinet officers, ambassadors, ministers, and other Foreign Service officials; commissions of other high ranking civil officers appointed by the President; and envelopes containing letters of recall and credences. There are six dies of the Great Seal in this record group.

See Gaillard Hunt, *The History of the Seal of the United States* (1909); and *The Seal of the United States*, Department of State Publication 6455 (Apr. 1957).

CARTOGRAPHIC AND AUDIOVISUAL RECORDS. 1818–67 and 1909. 9 items.

A published copy of the 1818 edition of the John Melish map of the United States, referred to in the 1819 treaty with Spain; a published copy of the 1847 edition of J. Disturnell's map of Mexico used in preparing the Treaty of Guadalupe Hidalgo, 1848; a manuscript map of the harbor of Simoda (Shimoda), Japan, compiled in 1854 by surveyors with Commodore Perry's fleet, to accompany the American treaty with Japan; and a manuscript plan of Sitka, Alaska, compiled in 1867 and later published in H. Ex. Doc. 125, 40th Cong., 2d sess., Serial 1337. There are also photographs (5 items) of the naturalization convention of July 22, 1909, between the United States and Paraguay.

See Ralph E. Huss, comp., *Preliminary Inventory of United States Government Documents Having General Legal Effect*, PI 159 (1964). This is the former title of Record Group 11.

Microfilm Publications: *Ratified Indian Treaties, 1722–1869*, M668, 16 rolls, DP; *Certificates of Ratification of the Constitution and the Bill of Rights, Including Related Correspondence and Rejections of Proposed Amendments, 1787–1792*, M338, 1 roll; and *Enrolled Original Acts and Resolutions of the Congress of the United States, 1789–1823*, M337, 17 rolls.

PART II

RECORDS OF THE LEGISLATIVE BRANCH

CONGRESS

RECORDS OF THE UNITED STATES SENATE
(RECORD GROUP 46)

The U.S. Senate and House of Representatives were established by article I, section 1, of the Constitution as the legislative branch of government. The Senate was empowered to try all impeachments and to judge the elections, returns, and qualifications of its Members. The Constitution also provides that the Senate share executive responsibility with the President by requiring its advice and consent in the negotiation of treaties and the appointment of certain Federal officials.

There are 12,141 cubic feet of records dated between 1789 and 1968 in this record group.

JOURNALS OF LEGISLATIVE PROCEEDINGS AND MINUTE BOOKS. 1789-1966. 196 lin. ft.

Under article I, section 5, of the Constitution the Senate is required to keep and publish journals of its proceedings. These records consist of rough and smooth journals of Senate legislative proceedings and of Senate executive business. Also included are minute books consisting of memorandums made contemporaneously with Senate actions to which they relate and used in preparing the journals.

BILLS AND RESOLUTIONS. 1789-1968. 1,770 lin. ft.

Included are bills and joint, concurrent, and simple resolutions originating in the Senate, with amended versions resulting from the actions of the Senate and its committees; engrossed Senate bills and resolutions (the versions passed by the Senate and sent to the House), with House amendments and conference committee reports; and copies of bills and joint and concurrent resolutions originating in the House and submitted for Senate action, with amendments and conference committee reports.

COMMITTEE RECORDS AND REPORTS. 1789-1968. 3,134 lin. ft.

These comprise records created and received by standing and select Senate committees and consist of minutes, dockets, correspondence, memorandums, transcripts or prints of hearings, and prints of committee reports, bills, and resolutions; and committee reports to the Senate on bills or resolutions and other committee activities.

BILLS AND RESOLUTIONS FILES. 1901-66. 2,541 lin. ft.

Earlier records relating to particular bills and resolutions are included with committee records. From the 57th Congress (Dec. 2, 1901-Mar. 3, 1903) to the present, standing and select Senate committees have generally created a separate file for each bill or resolution referred to or originated by them and have placed in these files all related records. These bills and resolutions files concern private relief claims and public matters.

SENATE DOCUMENTS. 1789-1968. 1,806 lin. ft.

Included are Presidential messages to the Senate other than those concerning executive business, messages and reports to the Senate from executive departments and agencies, and miscellaneous Senate documents.

PETITIONS AND MEMORIALS. 1789-1968. 2,587 lin. ft.

Petitions and memorials, with supporting documents, from individuals and organizations dealing with private and public matters.

ELECTION RECORDS. 1789-1968. 131 lin. ft.

These consist of Senators' credentials, senatorial candidates' campaign expense reports, electors' votes for President and Vice President, tabulations of electoral votes, and certificates of messengers appointed to bring electoral votes to the Capitol.

OTHER LEGISLATIVE RECORDS. 1789-1966. 108 lin. ft.

Included are tabulations of Senators' votes, Senators' resignations, messages from the House, and motions and orders.

RECORDS OF IMPEACHMENT PROCEEDINGS. 1797-1936. 6 lin. ft.

Included are articles of impeachment, answers to the articles, motions and orders, yeas and nays on the motions and orders, certificates of subpenas served, testimony, documentary evidence, and journals of Senate activities during the periods it sat as a Court of Impeachment.

RECORDS OF EXECUTIVE PROCEEDINGS. 1789-1966. 400 lin. ft.

Included are Presidential messages concerning treaties and relations with Indian tribes and foreign nations, treaties and conventions, Presidential messages transmitting nominations, records concerning nominees, fitness for office, and journals and minute books of executive proceedings.

RECORDS OF THE OFFICE OF THE SECRETARY OF THE SENATE. 1789-1966. 80 lin. ft.

These consist chiefly of correspondence, billbooks giving legislative actions on bills and resolutions, other registers, accounts for printing and binding, records concerning stationery supply, and lobbyists' quarterly reports.

CARTOGRAPHIC AND AUDIOVISUAL RECORDS. 1800-1955. 1,432 items.

Cartographic records, 1800-1955 (1,432 items), were compiled principally by Government executive agencies and forwarded to the Senate. They include land surveys, maps pertaining to exploration and military operations, State and national boundary maps, maps showing road and railroad rights-of-way, maps of Indian land cessions, and maps and plans pertaining to dams and to river and harbor improvements.

Motion pictures, 1936-38 (4 reels), consist of films received from the Subcommittee of the Senate Committee on Education and Labor, relating to a San Francisco dock strike, the Republic Steel strike in Chicago, and a Stockton, Calif., cannery strike.

Sound recordings, 1946 (5 items), are of hearings on the investigation of the national defense program at the Philadelphia Signal Depot and were created by the Senate Special Committee To Investigate the National Defense Program.

See *American State Papers* (38 vols., 1832-61) for many published records of the first 25 Congresses, 1789-1838; the congressional or serial set for many published records of the 15th Congress to the present Congress (printed hearings of Senate committees are generally issued as separate documents, not as part of the set); *Public Papers of the Presidents of the United States* (1957-) and James D. Richardson, *A Compilation of Messages and Papers of the Presidents* (1896-99 and later editions), for most Presidential messages other than those submitting nominations; Theodore J. Cassady and Harold E. Hufford, comps., *Preliminary Inventory of the Records of the Senate Committee on Appropriations: Subcommittee on Inquiry in re Transfer of Employees, 1942* , PI 12 (1948); Harold E. Hufford and Watson G. Caudill, comps., *Preliminary Inventory of the Records of the United States Senate*, PI 23 (1950); George P. Perros, comp., *Preliminary Inventory of the Records of the Senate Committee on Education and Labor: Subcommittee on Wartime Health and Education, 1943-46*, PI 42 (1952); Harold E. Hufford, comp., assisted by Toussaint L. Prince, *Preliminary Inventory of the Records of the Special Committee of the Senate To Investigate the National Defense Program, 1941-48*, PI 48 (1952); George P. Perros and Toussaint L. Prince, comps., *Preliminary Inventory of the Records of Certain Committees of the Senate Investigating the Disposal of Surplus Property, 1945-48*, PI 59 (1953); George P. Perros, comp., *Preliminary Inventory of the Records of the Special Committee of the Senate To Investigate Petroleum Resources, 1944-46*, PI 61 (1953), and *Preliminary Inventory of the Records of the Special Committee of the Senate on Atomic Energy, 1945-46*, PI 62 (1953); Watson G. Caudill, Toussaint L. Prince, and Albert U. Blair, comps., *Preliminary Inventory of the Records of the Special Committee of the Senate To Investigate Air-Mail and Ocean-Mail Contracts, 1933-35*, PI 63 (1953); Albert U. Blair and John W. Porter, comps., *Preliminary Inventory of the Records of the Senate Committee on Interstate Commerce: Subcommittee To Investigate Interstate Railroads, 1935-43*, PI 75 (1954); George P. Perros,

James C. Brown, and Jacqueline A. Wood, comps., *Papers of the United States Senate Relating to Presidential Nominations, 1789-1901*, SL 20 (1964); and Laura E. Kelsay and Charlotte M. Ashby, comps., *Cartographic Records Relating to the Territory of Wisconsin, 1836-1848*, SL 23 (1970).

Microfilm Publications: *Territorial Papers of the United States Senate, 1789-1873*, M200, 20 rolls, DP; and *The Territorial Papers of the United States: The Territory of Wisconsin, 1836-1848*, M236, 122 rolls.

SPECIFIC RESTRICTIONS

I. *Records*: Records of certain committees dated after December 31, 1921.

Restrictions: Some of these records may not be used except by permission of the committee, its chairman, staff director, or other designated official.

Specified by: Committee officials or the Chief Clerk of the Senate.

II. *Records*: Documents created in executive or closed session.

Restrictions: These records may not be used except by permission of the chairman or the chief counsel of the committee (or its successor) that created the documents.

Specified by: Chairman of each committee concerned.

RECORDS OF THE UNITED STATES HOUSE OF REPRESENTATIVES
(RECORD GROUP 233)

The U.S. House of Representatives was created by article I, section 1, of the Constitution. Although it shares legislative power with the Senate, the House originates all bills for raising revenue and, by custom, general appropriation bills. The House has the sole power to impeach U.S. civil officers, and judges elections, returns, and qualifications of its Members.

There are 13,662 cubic feet of records dated between 1789 and 1962 in this record group.

JOURNALS AND MINUTE BOOKS. 1789-1962. 241 lin. ft.

These consist of manuscript journals (official reports of House proceedings) kept in compliance with article I, section 5, of the Constitution; and minute books containing memorandums prepared contemporaneously with the transactions to which they relate and used in preparing the journals.

BILLS AND RESOLUTIONS.
1789–1962. 1,376 lin. ft.

These consist of original House bills and joint, concurrent, and simple resolutions; amended versions of bills and resolutions; engrossed bills and resolutions; Senate amendments to bills and resolutions; bills and resolutions that originated in the Senate, including bills passed and joint and concurrent resolutions adopted by the Senate; House amendments to Senate bills and resolutions; and conference committee reports on bills and resolutions.

COMMITTEE RECORDS. 1789–1962.
11,415 lin. ft.

The records consist of minutes, dockets, general correspondence, memorandums, stenographic transcripts and prints of hearings, prints of committee reports and bills and resolutions, documents concerning bills and resolutions referred to or originated by committees, and committee reports.

PETITIONS AND MEMORIALS.
1789–1962. 1,993 lin. ft.

Unpublished petitions and memorials sent to the House, sometimes with supporting documents, that relate to a wide range of private and public matters.

HOUSE DOCUMENTS. 1789–1962.
1,580 lin. ft.

Consisting primarily of messages and reports sent to the House by Presidents, 1793–1962, and by executive departments and agencies, 1789–1962, this series includes records originally referred to as House miscellaneous documents.

ELECTION RECORDS. 1805–1962.
88 lin. ft.

These consist of Members' credentials, Representatives' and Delegates' oaths of office, and certificates of electors' votes for President and Vice President.

RECORDS OF IMPEACHMENTS.
1816–1944. 22 lin. ft.

Included are reports, correspondence, memorandums, depositions, exhibits, testimonies, and articles of impeachment.

OTHER HOUSE RECORDS.
1791–1962. 64 lin. ft.

These include rolls of yea and nay votes, telegrams received and sent over telegraph lines connecting the House with executive departments and the Government Printing Office, and notices of constitutional amendment ratifications.

RECORDS OF THE OFFICE OF THE CLERK OF THE HOUSE.
1789–1962. 233 lin. ft.

These include correspondence; transcribed reports of standing and select committees; transcribed reports and communications from executive departments; registers of bills, resolutions, executive and miscellaneous documents, committee reports, petitions and memorials, and documents received from or sent to the Senate; records of claims referred to the U.S. Court of Claims under the Bowman Act; receipts for documents withdrawn from House files; the Clerk's contingent accounts; applications of House Members for leaves of absence; communications to the Speaker, chiefly from House Members; and records relating to bills and resolutions presented to the President for approval, the purchase of books and newspapers for House Members, and the provision of coal, wood, stationery, and other supplies for the House.

CARTOGRAPHIC AND AUDIOVISUAL RECORDS.
1828–1930. 621 items.

Cartographic records, 1828–1930 (395 items), were compiled principally by executive agencies of the Government and include land surveys, maps pertaining to exploration and military operations, State and national boundary maps, maps showing road and railroad rights-of-way, maps of Indian reservations, and maps and plans pertaining to dams and to river and harbor improvements.

Audiovisual records consist of photographs (226 items) relating to rivers and harbors, including the banks of the Mississippi River and wharves at New Orleans, the wharves and harbor at Bridgeport, Conn., the destruction of Flood Rock in the East River at New York City, and the sinking of the *Susan E. Peck* in the St. Mary's River, 1880–91; of Round Pond, Wharton, and Enid, Okla., 1893–94, made in connection with the "Oklahoma Railroad Bill" (H.R. 3606, 53d Cong., 1st sess.); of exhibits at the World's Columbian Exposition, 1893; and of members of the Board of Lady Managers of the Exposition, 1893–96. There is also a lithograph of Congressman John E. Russell of Massachusetts, 1893.

See *American State Papers* (38 vols., 1832–61) for many published records of the first 25 Congresses, 1789–1838; the congressional or serial set for many published records of the 15th Congress to the present Congress (printed hearings of House committees are generally issued as separate documents, not as part of the set); *Public Papers of the Presidents* (1957–) and James D. Richardson, *A Compilation of Messages and Papers of the Presidents* (1896–99 and later editions) for most Presidential messages other than those submitting nominations; George P. Perros, comp., *Preliminary Inventory of the Records of Certain Committees of the House of Representatives Investigating the Disposal of Surplus Property, 1946–48*, PI 65 (1954); Perros, comp., *Preliminary Inventory of the Records of the Select Committee of the House of Representatives To Investigate Air Accidents, 1941–43*, PI 67 (1954); Perros, comp., *Preliminary Inventory of the Records of the House Committee on the Civil Service Pertaining to the Investigation of Civilian Employment in the Federal Government, 1942–46*, PI 69 (1954); Perros, comp., *Preliminary Inventory of the Records of the Select Committee of the House of Representatives on Post-War Military Policy, 1944–46*, PI 70 (1954); Perros, comp., *Preliminary Inventory of the Records of the Select Committee of the House of Representatives Investigating National Defense Migration, 1940–43*, PI 71 (1954); Perros, comp., *Preliminary Inventory of the Records of the Military Affairs Committee of the House of Representatives Relating to an Investigation of the War Department, 1934–36*, PI 80 (1955); Perros, comp., *Preliminary Inventory of the Records of the Select Committee of the House of Representatives To Investigate Acts of Executive Agencies Beyond the Scope of Their Authority, 1943–46*, PI 84 (1955); Jose D. Lizardo, comp., *Preliminary Inventory of the Records of the House of Representatives Select Committee To Investigate Real Estate Bondholders' Reorganizations, 1934–38*, PI 96 (1956); Perros, comp., *Preliminary Inventory of the Records of the Appropriations Committee of the House of Representatives: Subcommittee on the Works Progress Administration, 1939–41*, PI 107 (1958); Perros, comp., *Preliminary Inventory of the Records of the House of Representatives Select Committee of Inquiry Into Operations of the United States Air Services, 1924–25*, PI 108 (1958); Perros, comp., *Preliminary Inventory of the Records of the Select Committee of the House of Representatives on Foreign Aid, 1947–48*, PI 111 (1958); and Buford Rowland, Handy B. Fant, and Harold E. Hufford, comps., *Preliminary Inventory of the Records of the United States House of Representatives, 1789–1946*, PI 113 (2 vols., 1959).

SPECIFIC RESTRICTIONS

Records: All records of the House of Representatives that have not heretofore been made public.

Restrictions: No one may examine these records and no information from them or copies of them may be furnished to anyone except upon order of the Clerk of the House of Representatives.

Specified by: House of Representatives.

RECORDS OF JOINT COMMITTEES OF CONGRESS
(RECORD GROUP 128)

Joint standing committees are created infrequently by the two Houses of Congress; select joint committees are created more frequently, sometimes for investigative or ceremonial purposes. The records of joint committees are similar to those of standing and select committees of the Senate and of the House of Representatives and consist, in general, of correspondence of chairmen, correspondence and memorandums of staff members, hearings, exhibits, committee reports, and petitions and memorials.

This collective record group includes the records of four standing joint committees: the Joint Committee on the Library, provided for by the acts of 1800 and 1802 establishing the Library of Congress; the Joint Committee on Printing, established by an act of 1846; the Joint Committee on Internal Revenue Taxation, established by the Revenue Act of 1926; and the Joint Committee on Atomic Energy, established by the Atomic Energy Act of 1946. It also includes the records of 45 select joint committees.

There are 442 cubic feet of records dated between 1799 and 1969 in this record group.

RECORDS. 1799-1969. 589 lin. ft.

These consist primarily of records of the Joint Committee To Investigate the Pearl Harbor Attack, 79th Congress (1945-46); and of the Joint Committee on Atomic Energy, 79th-90th Congresses (1945-68). Other records are of the Joint Committees: on Property in the Hands of the President, 6th Congress (1799-1801); on the Library, 10th (1807-9), 13th-73d (1813-1934), 82d-85th (1951-58), and 87th (1961-62) Congresses; on Disposal of Paintings by Trumbull, 17th Congress (1821-23); To Arrange for the Funeral of Major General Brown,

20th Congress (1827-29); on Celebration of the Birthday of General George Washington, 22d Congress (1831-33); To Prepare a Code of Laws for the District of Columbia, 22d Congress (1831-33); on the Occasion of the Death of General Lafayette, 23d Congress (1833-35); on the Death of James Madison, 24th Congress (1835-37); on the Documentary History of the American Revolution, 26th Congress (1839-41); To Devise a Mode of Examining and Counting the Electoral Votes, 26th (1839-41) and 28th (1843-45) Congresses; on Printing, 30th (1847-49), 36th (1859-61), 45th (1877-79), 46th (1879-81), and 56th-91st (1899-1969) Congresses; on the Conduct of the War, 38th (1863-65) and 39th (1865-67) Congresses; To Inquire Into the Condition of the States That Formed the Confederate States of America, 39th Congress (1865-67); on Reconstruction, 39th-41st Congresses (1865-71); on Retrenchment, 40th Congress (1867-69); To Inquire Into the Condition of Affairs in the Late Insurrectionary States, 42d Congress (1871-73); To Inquire Into the Affairs of the District of Columbia, 43d Congress (1873-75); To Frame a Government for the District of Columbia, 44th Congress (1875-77); on Epidemic Diseases, 45th Congress (1877-79); on the Census, 46th (1879-81) and 47th (1881-83) Congresses; on American Shipbuilding, 47th Congress (1881-83); on the Geological Survey, 48th Congress (1883-85); To Investigate the Work on the Washington Aqueduct, 50th Congress (1887-89); and on the Disposition of Useless Papers, 51st (1889-91), 53d (1893-95), 55th (1897-99), 56th (1899-1901), 58th (1903-5), 60th (1907-9), and 63d-78th (1913-44) Congresses.

Also records of the Joint Committees: on the Ford's Theater Disaster, 53d and 54th Congresses (1893-97); on Additional Accommodations for the Library of Congress, 54th Congress (1895-97); To Investigate the Interior Department and the Forestry Service, 61st Congress (1909-11); on the Revision of the Laws of the United States, 61st Congress (1909-11); on Rural Credit, 64th Congress (1915-17); on the Fiscal Relations of the District of Columbia and the United States, 64th Congress (1915-17); on the High Cost of Living, 66th Congress (1919-21); on the Civil Service Retirement Act, 69th Congress (1925-27); on Muscle Shoals, 69th Congress (1925-27); on Postal Rates, 69th Congress (1925-27); on Veterans' Affairs, 72d Congress (1931-33); To Investigate Dirigible Disasters, 73d Congress (1933-34); on Tax Evasion and Avoidance, 75th Congress (1937-38); on Internal Revenue Taxation, 75th-77th Congresses (1937-42); To Investigate the Tennessee Valley Authority, 76th Congress (1939-41); on Reduction of Nonessential Federal Expenditures, 77th Congress (1941-42); on the Centennial of the Telegraph, 78th Congress (1943-44); on the Organization of Congress, 79th Congress (1945-46); on the Disposition of Executive Papers, 79th-87th Congresses (1945-62); on the Economic Report, 80th Congress (1947-48); on Labor-Management Relations, 80th Congress (1947-48); on Aviation Policy, 80th Congress (1947-48); and on Housing, 80th Congress (1947-48).

AUDIOVISUAL RECORDS. 1965 and 1969. 2 reels.

Motion pictures of the inauguration ceremonies of Presidents Johnson and Nixon, made under the direction and authority of the Joint Committee on Inaugural Ceremonies.

SPECIFIC RESTRICTIONS

I. *Records*: Records of the Congressional Aviation Policy Board, 1947–48.

Restrictions: Unclassified records may be used by representatives of Government agencies for official purposes, and such records may be used by non-Government searchers only by permission of the Secretary of the Senate. No classified records may be examined by any searcher without permission of the Secretary of the Senate.

Specified by: Secretary of the Senate.

II. *Records*: Records of the Joint Committee on Atomic Energy, 1947- .

Restrictions: These records may not be used except by persons authorized by the Joint Committee on Atomic Energy or its Chairman.

Specified by: Joint Committee on Atomic Energy.

III. *Records*: Records of the Joint Committee on the Library, 1951- .

Restrictions: These records may not be used except by persons authorized by the Chairman of the Joint Committee or by its Chief Clerk.

Specified by: Chief Clerk of the Joint Committee.

LEGISLATIVE AGENCIES

RECORDS OF THE GOVERNMENT PRINTING OFFICE
(RECORD GROUP 149)

The Government Printing Office (GPO) was established by Congressional Joint Resolution 25 of June 23, 1860. Printing for the Federal Government was previously done by private firms under provisions of congressional acts. Although management of the GPO is vested in a Public Printer, an act of January 12, 1895, delegated certain supervisory powers to the Joint Committee on Printing, composed of three members each from the Senate and House. The GPO executes orders for printing and binding placed by Congress and Federal departments, independent establishments, and agencies; furnishes, on order, blank paper, ink, and similar supplies for Government activities; distributes Government publications as required by law and maintains a library of them and the necessary catalogs; and prints unclassified documents for sale to the public.

See Government Printing Office, *100 GPO Years, 1861-1961: A History of United States Public Printing* (1961); and Robert E. Kling, Jr., *The Government Printing Office* (New York, 1970).

There are 347 cubic feet of records dated between 1847 and 1939 in this record group.

RECORDS. 1847-1939. 416 lin. ft.

Included are correspondence, 1852-1936; ledgers, 1863-1930; personnel, payroll, and time records, 1861-1933; and accounting and related books and records, 1847-1939.

Microfilm Publication: *Superintendent of Documents: Card List of Publications of the 1st Through 17th Congresses, 1789-1823*, T304, 2 rolls.

RECORDS OF THE
UNITED STATES GENERAL ACCOUNTING OFFICE
(RECORD GROUP 217)

The U.S. General Accounting Office (GAO) was established under the Budget and Accounting Act of June 10, 1921. It is headed by the Comptroller General of the United States, who is appointed for a 15-year term by the President. The GAO was assigned the duties of the auditors and Comptroller of the Treasury Department, together with those functions relating to personal ledger accounts of disbursing and collection officials that had been acquired by the Division of Bookkeeping and Warrants in 1894 from the Office of the Register of the Treasury. Records maintained in the offices of these officials and of their predecessors were transferred to the GAO and are described below by office of origin.

The chief duties of the GAO are to

perform an independent Government-wide audit of receipts, expenditures, and use of public funds; settle fiscal accounts of officers accountable to the Federal Government; settle certain claims by or against the United States; make investigations relating to the receipt, disbursement, and application of public funds; prescribe principles, standards, and related requirements for accounting by executive agencies; cooperate with the Bureau of the Budget and Treasury Department in the joint program to improve Federal accounting; render legal decisions on fiscal matters; and report the results of its activities to Congress.

See Darrell H. Smith, *The General Accounting Office* (Baltimore, 1927).

There are 18,905 cubic feet of records dated between 1776 and 1952 in this record group.

GENERAL RECORDS OF THE GAO. 1921–26. 33 lin. ft. (in WNRC).

These include chiefly selected contracts, leases, and agreements made by or on behalf of civilian agencies, 1921–26, and military agencies, 1922–26, with related indexes. Civilian contracts comprise mainly those for construction and equipping of lighthouse tenders and Coast Guard vessels, naval air stations, helium production plants, public buildings and monuments, and repairs to waterways; rental or purchase of special machinery and scientific equipment; and granting grazing and water rights on public lands by the Department of the Interior. Military contracts consist chiefly of those for design and construction of lighter- and heavier-than-air craft and roads and railroads, development of a coastal defense system, leases of land on military reservations, and research on explosives. These contracts and indexes are part of a larger series of contracts dating from 1894.

RECORDS OF THE FIRST COMPTROLLER. 1791–1921. 970 lin. ft.

The Office of the First Comptroller was created in 1789 by the act establishing the Treasury Department. His responsibilities included final approval of all settled accounts, keeping records relating to receipts and disbursements of public funds, and keeping copies of contracts. In 1817 the Comptroller's functions relating to military accounts were turned over to the newly created office of the Second Comptroller, and in 1849 some of his functions relating to customs accounts were turned over to the Office of the Commissioner of Customs, established that year. In 1894 all functions of the Second Comptroller and the Commissioner of Customs were restored to the First Comptroller, who then became known as the Comptroller of the Treasury. He was succeeded in 1921 by the Comptroller General of the United States.

The records include correspondence, 1791–1912; registers of correspondence, 1802–1915; appointment records, 1804–1913; appropriation ledgers and registers and copies of appropriation warrants, 1822–1918; registers and copies of pay, repay, counter, and covering warrants, 1808–1912; abstracts and registers of accounts and claims submitted for final approval, 1797–1921; contracts and proposals, 1799–1921, including those for construction of public buildings (contracts and indexes dated after 1894 are in WNRC); and registers of contracts, 1870–98.

RECORDS OF THE SECOND COMPTROLLER. 1790–1895. 408 lin. ft.

The Office of the Second Comptroller was established in 1817 to perform functions relating to military matters, including final approval of all accounts and claims, approval of some accounts relating to Indian affairs, keeping pertinent accounting records, and filing contracts entered into by military agencies. These functions were formerly performed by the First Comptroller and were returned to his jurisdiction in 1894. The records include correspondence, 1817-95, registers of correspondence, 1847-94, registers of accounts and claims submitted for final approval, 1817-94, contracts, 1790-1894, registers of contracts, 1817-95, and records relating to the payment of pensions, 1812-82.

RECORDS OF THE COMMISSIONER OF CUSTOMS. 1789-1894. 122 lin. ft.

The Office of the Commissioner of Customs was established in 1849 to perform functions relating to settlement of customs, revenue-cutter, lighthouse, and marine hospital accounts. These functions were formerly performed by the First Comptroller and were returned to his jurisdiction in 1894. The records include letters received (including those transferred from the Office of the First Comptroller), 1789-1894, letters sent, 1849-94, registers of correspondence, 1877-87, records relating to the settlement of accounts, 1789-1894, oaths of office of customs and other officials, 1849-94, and registers of oaths of office, 1865-94.

RECORDS OF THE FIRST AUDITOR. 1789-1916. 5,163 lin. ft.

The Office of the First Auditor was created in 1789 to settle all accounts and claims and certify their balances to the First Comptroller for approval. Additional auditors were appointed in 1817 and assigned some duties of the First Auditor. In 1894 this Office was renamed the Office of the Auditor for the Treasury Department. The records include correspondence, 1801-1908; registers of correspondence, 1842-1912; accounts, 1790-1906, including "miscellaneous" Treasury accounts, 1790-1894; customs accounts, 1837-94; accounts re-

lating to noncustoms functions of collectors of customs, 1878-94, and several fragmentary series of accounts dating to 1906; reports, registers, and abstracts relating to the settlement of accounts, 1789-1914; and records relating to the seizure of merchandise illegally imported, 1889-1916.

RECORDS OF THE SECOND AUDITOR. 1776-1916. 3,716 lin. ft.

In 1817 the Office of the Second Auditor succeeded that of the Accountant for the War Department. His functions included settlement of Army and some Indian accounts, of pay and bounty claims, and of claims for expenses of raising volunteer troops for service during the Spanish-American War. The settlement of Army accounts was shared with the Third Auditor until 1894 when all such accounts became the responsibility of the Second Auditor and his office was renamed the Auditor for the War Department. The records include correspondence, 1795-1899; registers of correspondence, 1839-99; warrants, ledgers, and journals, 1776-1908, including journals relating to furnishing supplies at New York and Philadelphia during the Revolutionary War; accounts, 1817-50; and records relating to pay of troops, payment of pensions, and awards of bounty land, 1803-1916.

RECORDS OF THE THIRD AUDITOR. 1794-1919. 7,134 lin. ft.

The duties of the Third Auditor, whose office was established in 1817, included settlement of subsistence accounts, Quartermaster Department accounts, and all Army accounts not assigned to the Second Auditor. He settled pension accounts, claims for horses and other property destroyed in war, Civil War-related claims of several loyal States, and Signal Service and Signal Corps accounts. In 1894 he was made responsible for settlement of all pension accounts and Interior Department accounts. All other functions formerly exercised by the Third Auditor, who became known as the Auditor for the Interior Department, were transferred to the Second Auditor. The records include correspondence, 1812–1912, and related registers, 1817–1909; warrants, ledgers, and journals, 1815–99; accounts, 1817–50 and 1878–94; pension accounts and claims, 1817–1907; and records relating to the settlement of accounts and claims, 1794–1919, including those arising from Indian wars and the following special claims commissions: R. B. Lee Commission, 1816–18, Davis-Holt-Campbell Commission, 1861–79, Southern Claims Commission, 1871–90, and Steadman Board of Claims, 1863–64.

RECORDS OF THE FOURTH AUDITOR. 1789–1922. 3,707 lin. ft.

The Office of the Fourth Auditor was created in 1817 to settle all Navy Department accounts and claims. No significant change occurred in its functions through the years, and in 1894 it was renamed the Office of the Auditor for the Navy Department. The records include correspondence, 1795–1897, and related registers, 1836–1910; ledgers, journals, and warrants, 1789–1903; accounts of naval personnel, 1789–1922; pension accounts and claims, 1818–96; and records relating to the settlement of accounts and claims, 1800–1907.

RECORDS OF THE FIFTH AUDITOR. 1814–1925. 610 lin. ft.

The duties of the Fifth Auditor, whose office was established in 1817, included the settlement of State and Post Office Department accounts, some relating to Indian affairs, and those relating to lighthouses and internal revenue. In 1894 this office was renamed the Office of the Auditor for the State and Other Departments, with responsibility for settlement of accounts for the Departments of State and Justice and accounts not assigned to other auditors. The

records include correspondence, 1817–1900, and related registers, 1863–1920; accounts, 1817–50 and 1894–1907; and records relating to settlement of accounts and claims, 1814–1925, including land taxes assessed by the Federal Government in Southern States during the Civil War.

RECORDS OF THE SIXTH AUDITOR. 1844–1910. 3 lin. ft.

Functions of the Sixth Auditor, whose office was established in 1836, related chiefly to settlement of Post Office Department accounts. Although he was nominally an official of the Treasury Department, the Sixth Auditor reported directly to the Postmaster General. The records consist chiefly of letters sent, 1844–69, with gaps; registers of letters received, 1909–10; and registers of accounts received from postmasters, 1844–45 and 1850–51. Most of the remaining records are among records of the Post Office Department (see RG 28).

RECORDS OF THE REGISTER OF THE TREASURY DEPARTMENT. 1776–1924. 3,383 lin. ft.

The Office of the Register was created when the Treasury Department was established, and his main functions were to maintain the central fiscal records for the Government, including ledgers and journals; keep records of all receipts and expenditures; record warrants for the receipt or payment of moneys at the Treasury; and certify the balances of adjusted accounts to the Secretary of the Treasury. The Register was also responsible for maintaining records documenting U.S. merchant vessels, keeping statistics on foreign and domestic commerce, and recording the issue and redemption of bonds and other evidences of the public debt. His responsibilities in connection with the documentation of vessels were transferred to the Commissioner of Navigation in 1884, and after 1894 the Register retained only his duties related to the public debt. The records consist of ledgers, 1776-1924, journals, 1776-99 and 1869-97, warrants, 1818-1922, registers of warrants, 1805-1913, waste books, 1779-85, daybooks, 1789-1852, and records relating to accounts, 1809-1910.

CARTOGRAPHIC RECORDS. 1922-37 and 1952. 27 items.

These consist of two published maps of the United States, showing administrative regions of the GAO and locations of GAO records depositories, 1952, with one of the sheets annotated to show changes in the Alaska office; and 25 published maps of areas in the Central and Western States, annotated in the Indian Tribal Section of the Claims Division, 1922-37.

Microfilm Publications: Included on microfilm are waste books, 1776-86, daybooks, 1789-91, and journals, 1776-99, from records of the Office of the Register of the Treasury; ledgers of pension payments, 1818-72, from records of the Office of the Third Auditor of the Treasury; miscellaneous Treasury accounts, 1790-1840, from records of the Office of the First Auditor of the Treasury; and records of the Board of Commissioners for the Emancipation of Slaves in the District of Columbia, 1862-63. For a complete listing see the current *List of National Archives Microfilm Publications.*

Discontinued Agencies

RECORDS OF MINOR CONGRESSIONAL COMMISSIONS (RECORD GROUP 148)

Congress has created various temporary commissions composed of Government officials, private individuals, and Members of the Senate and the House of Representatives to represent the U.S. Government at world's fairs and expositions, plan and conduct anniversary celebrations, design and construct memorials, and conduct investigations or other business of concern to the Congress.

There are 266 cubic feet of records dated between 1928 and 1967 in this record group.

RECORDS. 1928-67. 319 lin. ft.

Included are records of the following commissions:

The George Rogers Clark Sesquicentennial Commission, consisting of reports, proceedings, correspondence, contracts, and accounting papers, 1928-40.

The Northwest Territory Celebration Commission, consisting of reports, correspondence, and miscellaneous records of the Executive Director; correspondence and other records of the publicity director; and correspondence, payrolls, vouchers, ledgers, and other records relating to disbursement of funds, 1935-39.

The U.S. New York World's Fair Commission, consisting of minutes, agreements, correspondence, memorandums, accounting records, press releases, newspaper clippings, drawings, posters, and related printed and processed material, 1937-41.

The U.S. Golden Gate International Exposition, consisting of correspondence, contracts, reference material, and fiscal and personnel records, 1937-41.

The Thomas Jefferson Bicentennial Commission, consisting of reports, correspondence, and financial records, 1940-44.

The National Capital Sesquicentennial Commission, consisting of reports, correspondence, and workpapers, 1947-52.

The George Washington Bicentennial Commission, 1928-33, and the U.S. Constitution Sesquicentennial Commission,

1937-40, consisting of the file of Albert Bushnell Hart (Historian of the Bicentennial Commission), workpapers, documents obtained from individuals and other sources (including historical societies and organizations), photographs, correspondence, and comments on the validity and interpretation of the data relating to the life of George Washington; research material relating to the history of Washington, D.C., and environs, gathered by Special Researcher of the Bicentennial Commission Verda Woods; photographs of artworks portraying Washington and other leaders in the movement for American independence and the establishment of the Federal Union; and reproductions of maps relating to or used by Washington, showing the States at the time of the ratification of the Constitution.

The Commission on Government Security, consisting of minutes, reports, correspondence, investigators' questionnaires, and reports of interviews and related records, 1955-57.

The Alexander Hamilton Bicentennial Commission, consisting of correspondence, historical data files, publications, and fiscal records, 1954-58.

The Lincoln Sesquicentennial Commission, consisting of minutes, correspondence, press releases, charts, and fiscal records, 1957-60.

The United States-Puerto Rico Commission on the Status of Puerto Rico, consisting of transcripts of hearings, correspondence, reference material and workpapers on economic and legal-constitutional issues, publications, and fiscal records, 1964-67.

CARTOGRAPHIC AND AUDIOVISUAL RECORDS. 1931-40. 2,473 items.

Cartographic records (23 items) consist of an atlas published in 1932 by the George Washington Bicentennial Commission, containing 85 maps relating to the career of George Washington; and a set of facsimiles published during the period 1937-40 by the U. S. Constitution Sesquicentennial Commission of maps of the United States and the Thirteen Original Colonies dating from the time of the ratification of the Constitution.

Audiovisual records (2,450 items) consist of photographs of artworks of George Washington from the George Washington Bicentennial Commission, 1931-33; and photographs of artworks of the signers and the signing of the Declaration of Independence and the Constitution, of the deputies to the Constitutional Convention and their families, and of memorabilia relating to the Constitution, from the U.S. Constitution Sesquicentennial Commission, 1937-39.

Microfilm Publication: *Card Index to Pictures Collected by the George Washington Bicentennial Commission*, T271, 1 roll.

RECORDS OF THE
TEMPORARY NATIONAL ECONOMIC COMMITTEE
(RECORD GROUP 144)

The Temporary National Economic Committee (TNEC) was created by a joint resolution of the Congress, June 16, 1938, to study monopoly and concentration of economic power and to make recommendations for legislation. The TNEC was composed of Members of both Houses of Congress and representatives of several executive departments and commissions. Information was obtained largely from hearings and special studies that were conducted by participating agencies or by the TNEC staff. Extensive investigations of insurance, investment banking, and corporate practices were conducted by the Securities and Exchange Commission, one of the participating agencies. The TNEC, which held its first meeting on July 1, 1938, was abolished as of April 3, 1941.

There are 645 cubic feet of records dated between 1938 and 1941 in this record group.

RECORDS. 1938-41. 774 lin. ft.

Records of the TNEC include reports, copies of hearings, correspondence, remedial social and economic plans, an "industry file" of information about industrial problems, questionnaires, records relating to unpublished special studies and to the 43 published monographs of the TNEC, reference material, and personnel and accounting records; questionnaires, exhibits, correspondence, memorandums, and other records of investigations and special studies by the Securities and Exchange Commission; and records of hearings and special studies by the Departments of the Treasury, Justice, and Labor.

SPECIFIC RESTRICTIONS

Records: Records created and filed by the Securities and Exchange Commission on behalf of the TNEC except certain records relating to the insurance study, consisting of replies to formal questionnaires, not including replies to questionnaires sent to State supervisory officials and the questionnaire dated February 9, 1940, sent to life insurance agents; all exhibits including ratebooks and form insurance policies; and all conventional-form annual statements.

Restrictions: No one may have access to these records or to information in them except Government officials for official purposes.

Specified by: Securities and Exchange Commission.

RECORDS OF THE NATIONAL COMMISSION ON LAW OBSERVANCE AND ENFORCEMENT (RECORD GROUP 10)

The National Commission on Law Observance and Enforcement, popularly known as the Wickersham Commission, was appointed by President Hoover under provisions of an act of March 4, 1929, to inquire "into the problem of the enforcement of prohibition under the provisions of the eighteenth amendment of the Constitution and laws enacted in pursuance thereof, together with the enforcement of other laws." Each of the 11 commissioners headed a committee that investigated and reported on one general aspect of criminal law enforcement—including prohibition; official lawlessness; the courts; the police; criminal justice and the foreign born; prosecution; the causes, cost, and statistics of

crime; juvenile delinquency; and penal institutions, probation, and parole. Disbursements of the Commission's funds were made by the Office of Public Buildings and Public Parks of the National Capital, the functions and records of which were inherited in 1933 by the National Park Service. Appropriations for the Commission extended only to June 30, 1931, but its administrative office was not closed until August 1931.

There are 154 cubic feet of records (in WNRC) dated between 1929 and 1931 in this record group.

RECORDS. 1929-31. 185 lin. ft.

These consist of records of the Office of the Chairman, the research staff and library, and the Committees on Prohibition and Official Lawlessness (including records of staff members Walter H. Pollak and Carl S. Stern, concerning the Mooney-Billings case), and include Commission minutes, administrative records, circulars, correspondence, workpapers and research data, reports of committees, speeches, press releases, newspaper clippings, and proofs and copies of Commission publications.

RECORDS OF THE COMMISSIONS ON ORGANIZATION OF THE EXECUTIVE BRANCH OF THE GOVERNMENT (RECORD GROUP 264)

The two Commissions on Organization of the Executive Branch of the Government were known as the Hoover Commissions after their chairman, former President Herbert Hoover. The first Commission, established by an act of July 7, 1947, to promote economy, efficiency, and improved service in public business transactions of Federal executive agencies, investigated the organization and operating methods of the entire Federal executive branch. It established task forces, each of which studied a specific area or function of government and recommended necessary changes. The Commission evaluated the task force reports and made its own recommendations, mainly concerning reorganization of and relations among Government agencies, to the Congress. It presented a concluding report to the Congress in May 1949 and ceased to exist June 12, 1949.

The second Commission was established by an act of July 10, 1953, to investigate organization methods of all Government agencies except the Congress and the judiciary. That Commission, which also organized task forces and determined changes needed to promote economy, efficiency, and improved service, was scheduled to terminate June 30, 1955, but was given an additional 90 days to complete its liquidation activities. Fiscal records of the second Hoover Commission are in the custody of the Civil Service Commission. Papers (53 lin. ft.) relating to both Commissions are in HHL.

There are 229 cubic feet of records dated between 1947 and 1955 in this record group.

RECORDS. 1947–55. 275 lin. ft.

Records of the first Commission on Organization of the Executive Branch of the Government include minutes and transcripts, and an official project file of the Secretary's Office; correspondence, drafts of reports, and a task force operations file of the Executive Director; a general subject and a task force file of the Library and Research Section; staff studies, correspondence, administrative files, and reference material of the task forces, concerning agricultural activities, medical services, Federal supply, Federal personnel management, foreign affairs, independent regulatory commissions, Federal field services, accounting, and the national security organization; and fiscal records.

Records of the second Commission include correspondence and related records of the Office of the Executive Director; minutes, correspondence, and budgetary and legislative data of the Office of the Executive Secretary; correspondence and memorandums of the Office of the Editorial Director; bills of the Office of Legislative Drafting that were introduced in the Congress to implement Commission recommendations; and minutes, transcripts, reports, correspondence, reference material, and questionnaires of the Department of Defense Committee on Business Organization and its subcommittees, of the Staff on Independent Agencies, and of task forces concerned with budgetary and accounting matters, Federal medical services, intelligence activities, legal services and procedures, lending agencies, overseas economic operations, paperwork management, personnel and civil service, procurement, real property management, subsistence services, the use and disposal of Federal surplus property, and water resources and power.

Also included are sound recordings (3 items) of interviews of Chairman Hoover, 1949.

RECORDS OF THE
PUBLIC LAND LAW REVIEW COMMISSION
(RECORD GROUP 409)

The Public Land Law Review Commission was established by an act of September 19, 1964, as amended by an act of December 18, 1967, to review the public land laws and rules and regulations promulgated under them and to recommend a future public land policy designed to provide maximum benefit for the general public. Public lands were defined as the public domain, including lands withdrawn and reserved from disposition; outstanding U.S. interests in patented lands; national forests, wildlife refuges, and ranges; and surface and subsurface resources of all such lands, including mineral deposits in the Outer Continental Shelf. The Commission submitted its report and recommendations to Congress and the President on June 30, 1970.

There are 78 cubic feet of records dated between 1965 and 1970, with a few dated as early as 1960, in this record group.

GENERAL RECORDS. 1965-70.
81 lin. ft.

These consist of central files, 1965-70, including a few records as early as 1960; minutes, 1965-70; memorandums, 1965-69; office files of the Director and Assistant Director, 1965-70; and magnetic-taped data on revenue sharing and payments in lieu of taxes on public land.

REPORTS PREPARED BY AND FOR THE COMMISSION. 1968-70.
7 lin. ft.

These consist of reports prepared by Commission staff members, Government departments, universities, and private organizations and individuals. The reports, which relate to all aspects of public land law requirements, contain information relating to legal and administrative practices and data on resources, economics, and fiscal matters. They include *Digest of Public Land Laws* (June 1968), *History of Public Land Law Development* (November 1968), *Revenue Sharing and Payments in Lieu of Taxes on the Public Land* (July 1968), *Fish and Wildlife Resources on the Public Lands* (January 1969), *Study of Outer Continental Shelf Lands of the United States* (October 1968), *Administrative Procedures and the Public Lands* (1969), *Federal Legislative Jurisdiction* (May 1969), *Land Grants to States* (April 1969), *Public Land Timber Policy* (April 1969), *Legal Study of Nonfuel Mineral Resources* (May 1969), *Regional and Local Land Use Planning*

(June 1969), *Outdoor Recreation Use of the Public Lands* (September 1969), *State Land Resources and Policies* (January 1970), and the Commission's final report *One Third of the Nation's Land, a Report to the President and to the Congress by the Public Land Law Review Commission* (June 1970).

PART III

RECORDS OF THE JUDICIAL BRANCH

RECORDS OF FEDERAL COURTS

RECORDS OF THE
SUPREME COURT OF THE UNITED STATES
(RECORD GROUP 267)

The Supreme Court of the United States, provided for in article III, section 1, of the Constitution, was established by the Judiciary Act of September 24, 1789. The Court's jurisdiction extends to all cases in law or equity arising under the Constitution, the laws of the United States, and treaties made under their authority; all cases affecting ambassadors, other public ministers, and consuls; all cases of admiralty and maritime law; and controversies in which the United States is a party, between two or more States, between a State and citizens of another State, between citizens of different States, between citizens of the same State claiming lands under grants of different States, and between a State or its citizens and foreign states, citizens, or subjects. In all cases involving ambassadors, ministers, and consuls, and those in which a State is a party, the Supreme Court has original jurisdiction. Its appellate jurisdiction is defined in various statutes.

The Supreme Court consists of the Chief Justice of the United States and the number of Associate Justices determined by Congress. This number has ranged from five to nine, but since 1869 has been fixed by law at eight. Officers appointed by the Court to assist in the performance of its functions are the Clerk, the Deputy Clerk, the Reporter of Decisions, the Marshal, and the Librarian.

Until 1869, except for a brief interval in 1801-2, members of the Supreme Court served also as members of the Federal circuit courts of which the Federal district judges also were members. In 1869 Congress provided for the appointment of a circuit judge within each circuit, but still required some service on circuit courts by members of the Supreme Court. By an act of March 3, 1891, which established the present Circuit Courts of Appeals, Congress provided that Supreme Court members may sit on these appellate courts within their circuits.

By statute the Supreme Court has power to prescribe rules of procedure for lower U.S. courts. Accordingly, the Court has promulgated rules governing proceedings in bankruptcy, admiralty, and copyright cases; appellate proceedings in criminal cases; and criminal petty offense proceedings before U.S. commissioners.

See *United States Reports;* and Charles Warren, *The Supreme Court in United States History* (Boston, 1935).

There are 3,742 cubic feet of records dated between 1772 and 1969 in this record group.

THE "REVOLUTIONARY WAR PRIZE CASES": RECORDS OF THE COURT OF APPEALS IN CASES OF CAPTURE. 1772–89. 6 lin. ft.

Records of prize cases heard on appeal from Colonial and State courts by committees of the Continental Congress, 1776–80, and by the Court of Appeals in Cases of Capture, 1780–87. The cases arose from libeling as prizes British commercial ships captured by armed vessels of individual Colonies and ships outfitted by the Continental Congress to intercept vessels bringing provisions to the besieged British garrison at Boston. Included are minutes, correspondence, and other records of the Court, 1777–89; case files containing petitions to Congress, copies of proceedings in lower courts, and depositions and briefs, 1776–86; and records of cases referred to but not tried by the Court, 1772–84.

MINUTES, DOCKETS, AND OTHER GENERAL RECORDS OF THE SUPREME COURT. 1790–1934. 144 lin. ft.

These include the Supreme Court's engrossed minutes, 1790–1934; rough minutes (minutes recorded daily), 1790–1894 and 1929–33; journals, 1890–1934, consisting chiefly of a printed record of the minutes; engrossed dockets, 1791–1934; rough dockets, 1810–1904; engrossed opinions, 1835–1915; a volume of manuscript opinions delivered by Chief Justice John Marshall and several Justices at the Court's 1832 term; notes taken by Marshall during oral arguments on several cases and by Justice John McLean on one case, 1831–34; and notes and briefs of Justice Henry Baldwin, 1830–44.

TRANSCRIPTS OF ORAL ARGUMENTS. 1968–69. 2 lin. ft.

These consist of verbatim typed transcripts of oral arguments before the Supreme Court during the October term, 1968.

APPELLATE JURISDICTION RECORDS. 1792–1944. 4,769 lin. ft.

These consist chiefly of case files, 1792–1934, containing writs of error or certiorari and petitions, exhibits, transcripts from lower courts, and correspondence and other records on the handling of cases in the Supreme Court; an alphabetical card index to appellate case files, 1792–1909; manuscript and revised printed opinions, 1808–1913; and case exhibits, 1917–44.

ORIGINAL JURISDICTION RECORDS. 1792–1934. 175 lin. ft.

Included are case files, 1792–1934, containing bills of complaint and other records in cases between States, between the United States and a State, cases involving diplomatic officials, and suits for writs of habeas corpus, mandamus, and prohibition; manuscript and revised printed opinions, 1815–1909; and records of habeas corpus cases heard in chambers, 1861, 1869, 1881, and 1882.

GENERAL RECORDS OF THE CLERK'S OFFICE. 1791–1941. 32 lin. ft.

These consist chiefly of the Clerk's general correspondence, 1791–1941; letters to and from Supreme Court Justices, 1791–1935; a subject file, 1800–1910, including records relating to officers, quarters, and records of the Court, organization of the Federal judiciary, and personal dockets of Chief Justice Marshall for the 1815 and 1820 terms of the Court; oaths of office of Justices, 1823–1910; oaths and bonds of Court officers, 1827–1907; orders concerning Court rules, 1792–1910; allotment of circuits to Justices, 1796–1910; and scrapbooks containing newspaper and other contemporary accounts of the Court and its members and officers, 1880–1935.

RECORDS OF ADMISSIONS TO THE BAR OF THE SUPREME COURT. 1790–1955. 72 lin. ft.

These consist chiefly of signatures of attorneys admitted to practice before the Court, 1790–1934, and a card index to names of such attorneys, 1790–1955.

FISCAL RECORDS OF THE CLERK'S OFFICE. 1818–1957. 20 lin. ft.

Included are fee books, fee bonds, bills, receipts for disbursements, and other records relating to the Clerk's accounts.

RECORDS OF THE OFFICE OF THE MARSHAL. 1864–1913. 40 lin. ft.

Until 1867 the marshal of the district in which the Supreme Court sat acted as Marshal of the Supreme Court, for which he received fees and compensation for expenses incurred in executing Supreme Court orders. In 1867 the Supreme Court was given the power to appoint its own Marshal with an annual salary. The records include a subject file, 1864–1913, relating to the Supreme Court Building and containing photographs of Court members; applications and endorsements for positions as Court officers or registers in bankruptcy, 1867–1909; and records relating to the Marshal's accounts, 1867–1911.

AUDIOVISUAL RECORDS. 1955–67. 747 items.

These consist of tape recordings of oral arguments before the Supreme Court during the 1955–67 terms.

See James R. Browning and Bess Glenn, "The Supreme Court Collection at the National Archives," *American Journal of Legal History*, Vol. 4 (July 1960); Marion M. Johnson, comp., *Preliminary Inventory of the Records of the Supreme Court of the United States*, PI 139 (1962); and Marion M. Johnson, Elaine C. Everly, and Toussaint L. Prince, comps., *Index to the Manuscript and Revised Printed Opinions of the Supreme Court of the United States in the National Archives, 1808–73*, SL 21 (1965).

Microfilm Publications: *Records of the Court of Appeals in Cases of Capture (Revolutionary War Prize Cases), 1776–1787*, M162, 15 rolls, DP; *Minutes of the Supreme Court, 1790–1950*, M215, 41 rolls, DP; *Attorney Rolls of the Supreme Court, 1790–1951*, M217, 4 rolls, DP; *Dockets of the Supreme Court, 1791–1950*, M216, 27 rolls, DP; *Index to Appellate Case Files of the Supreme Court, 1792–1909*, M408, 20 rolls, DP; and *Appellate Case Files of the Supreme Court, 1792–1831*, M214, 96 rolls, DP.

SPECIFIC RESTRICTIONS

Records: Transcripts of oral arguments, 1968–69.

Restrictions: Duplicating or copying these transcripts by photographic, electrostatic, or other facsimile means is prohibited.

Specified by: Supreme Court of the United States.

RECORDS OF THE UNITED STATES COURTS OF APPEALS (RECORD GROUP 276)

The courts of appeals are intermediate courts created by an act of March 3, 1891, to relieve the Supreme Court of considering appeals in cases originally decided by Federal trial courts. They are empowered to review final and certain interlocutory decisions of district courts except where the law provides for direct review by the Supreme Court. The courts of appeals also review and enforce orders of Federal administrative bodies, such as the Securities and Exchange Commission and the National Labor Relations Board. Decisions of the courts are final except when subject to discretionary review or appeal to the Supreme Court. The United States is divided into 11 judicial circuits, with the

District of Columbia constituting a separate circuit. There is one U.S. court of appeals with a Supreme Court Justice assigned to it in each circuit. The judges of U.S. courts of appeals constitute the judicial council of each circuit and meet at least twice a year to consider Federal judicial business in the circuit and to give necessary orders for its effective administration. The chief circuit judge calls an annual conference of all circuit and district judges in his circuit, sometimes including members of the bar, to discuss Federal business.

There are 4,142 cubic feet of records (in Federal records centers) dated between 1891 and 1945 in this record group.

RECORDS OF THE U.S. COURT OF APPEALS, SECOND CIRCUIT, NEW YORK, N.Y. 1891–1944.
1,305 lin. ft. (in FRC New York).

These are appellate court case files consisting of copies of records submitted to the court of original jurisdiction, including briefs, petitions, affidavits, notices of appeals, motions, and orders.

RECORDS OF THE U.S. COURT OF APPEALS, FIFTH CIRCUIT, NEW ORLEANS, LA. 1891–1941.
2,669 lin. ft. (in FRC Fort Worth).

These are appellate court case files consisting of copies of records similar to those noted above.

RECORDS OF THE U.S. COURT OF APPEALS, EIGHTH CIRCUIT, ST. LOUIS, MO. 1891–1945. 168 lin. ft. (in FRC Kansas City).

These are copies of records, including decrees, motions, memorandums, notices, and orders accumulated by the court of original jurisdiction, 1891–1941; appellate court case files consisting of documents as noted above, 1891–1945; and copies of proceedings in receivership cases, 1893–1942.

RECORDS OF DISTRICT COURTS OF THE UNITED STATES (RECORD GROUP 21)

U.S. district and circuit courts were created by the Judiciary Act of 1789 under the authority of the constitutional provision that the judicial power of the United States be vested in a Supreme Court and in such inferior courts as the Congress may establish. The Judiciary Act provided that these courts were to have original jurisdiction in cases involving crimes, remedies of common law, and aliens suing for a tort. The district courts were to have exclusive original cognizance of civil cases of admiralty and maritime jurisdiction, of seizures and all suits for penalties and forfeitures incurred, and of all suits against consuls or vice consuls. The circuit courts were to have jurisdiction over actions involving aliens or citizens of different States and, concurrent with the courts of the several States, equity suits where the matter in dispute exceeded $500. Provision was also made for appeals from the district to the circuit court.

Subsequent legislation and other factors caused the amount and type of work performed by the circuit and district courts to vary. The national bankruptcy acts, the first of which was passed in 1800, added a heavy burden to the district courts. In 1891 the appellate jurisdiction of the circuit courts was transferred to the newly created circuit courts of appeals, and the Judiciary Act of 1911 abolished the circuit courts and provided for the transfer of their records and remaining jurisdiction to the district courts.

Most States have had one district and one circuit court, with the State constituting a Federal judicial district. As the business of the courts increased the Congress authorized two or more district and circuit courts in some States. Some district and circuit courts were organized into two or more divisions, and court sessions were held at two or more locations. In 1838 the Northern District of New York became the first district to be divided into two divisions. Today at least 23 district courts are organized into divisions, and several courts have as many as six, seven, or eight divisions.

The administration of Federal district and circuit courts has been aided, especially in criminal procedures, by the U.S. commissioners. Authority to appoint them was first given to the circuit courts in 1812 to provide for more convenient taking of bail and affidavits. Subsequent acts and court rules increased the commissioners' functions. Their powers include authority to issue arrest warrants, examine persons charged with offenses against Federal law, and imprison or bail the accused for trial in U.S. courts; initiate action in admiralty matters; entertain complaints under extradition treaties; and institute proceedings for violation of civil rights legislation. In 1896 authority to appoint commissioners was transferred to the U.S. district courts.

This record group includes records of district and circuit courts and their predecessors. Many of them, such as those in equity and law jurisdiction case files, are common to most district and circuit courts and are not identified at length in this guide. Descriptions of records of courts of the Southern District of New York (and to some degree those of the District of Columbia and the Eastern District of Pennsylvania) generally apply to the same types of records for all courts. The records descriptions are arranged alphabetically by Federal judicial district.

Court records of the district courts of the Confederacy, which were vested with the combined jurisdictions of the U.S. district and circuit courts, of U.S. territories that eventually became States, and of Colonies that became States, are also included in this record group and described under headings for the judicial districts of the corresponding U.S. courts.

In instances where record dates cited for territorial courts extend beyond the term of existence of the courts or where those for the U.S. circuit courts continue after 1911, it may be assumed that a particular record series relating to certain functions was intentionally kept intact even though not all the records were created by the courts under whose headings they are described.

There are 89,929 cubic feet of records dated between 1789 and 1955, with a few dated as early as 1685, in this record group.

ALABAMA, MIDDLE DISTRICT.
1839-1943. 988 lin. ft. (in FRC Atlanta).

U.S. District Court. Montgomery division records include records of civil actions, 1938-43; bankruptcy, 1867-1943, criminal, 1865-1943, equity, 1865-1938, and law, 1866-1938, cases; and book records in bankruptcy, criminal, equity, and law matters, 1839-1943. There are similar records for divisions at Dothan, 1906-43, and Opelika, 1913-43.

U.S. Circuit Court. The records consist of book records of civil and criminal matters created by the Montgomery division, 1839-1911.

ALABAMA, NORTHERN DISTRICT.
1866-1943. 1,637 lin. ft. (in FRC Atlanta).

U.S. District Court. Included are records of the Birmingham division relating to bankruptcy, 1868-1943, civil action, 1938-43, criminal, 1885-1943, equity, 1885-1938, and law, 1885-1938, cases; naturalization papers, 1883-1929; and book records in bankruptcy, criminal, equity, and law matters, 1885-1942. There are similar records for divisions at Anniston, 1900-1943, Gadsden, 1909-43, Huntsville (northeastern, 1874-1943, and northwestern, 1893-1943, divisions), Jasper, 1912-43, and Tuscaloosa, 1909-43.

U.S. Circuit Court. Records consist of case records of the Birmingham division, 1866-99.

ALABAMA, SOUTHERN DISTRICT. 1820-1943. 629 lin. ft. (in FRC Atlanta).

U.S. District Court. The records consist of admiralty, 1866-1943, bankruptcy, 1842-1943, civil action, 1938-43, criminal, 1869-1943, equity, 1912-38, and law, 1866-1938, case records; book records, including minutes, in admiralty, bankruptcy, chancery, civil, equity, law, and naturalization matters, 1820-1943; and records of U.S. commissioners, 1928-31.

U.S. Circuit Court. Records consist of criminal, 1869-1911, and law, 1887-1911, case files; and book records in civil, criminal, and other matters, 1824-1911.

Confederate States District Court for the Southern Division of Alabama. The records consist of a minute book (entered in the minute book of the U.S. circuit court), 1861-65, dockets, 1861-65, and case files, 1861-65, chiefly in sequestration and garnishment proceedings.

ARIZONA. 1864-1912. 300 lin. ft. (in FRC Los Angeles).

Territorial Courts of Arizona for the First, Second, Third, Fourth, and Fifth Districts. Records consist of case files and book records, 1864-1912.

CALIFORNIA, NORTHERN DISTRICT. 1851-1950. 4,294 lin. ft. (in FRC San Francisco) and 123 rolls of microfilm (in WNRC).

U.S. District Court for the Northern District and all U.S. Circuit Courts of

California. The records consist of admiralty, 1851-1945, bankruptcy, 1867-78 and 1898-1945, civil action, 1938-43, common law, 1855-1942, criminal, 1851-1945, and equity, 1913-38, case records; common law and equity cases, 1851-55, 1868-1907, and 1920-38; book records in bankruptcy, civil action, criminal, equity, and law matters, 1851-1945; clerks' records, 1851-1945, including naturalization records, 1871-1945; and case files and dockets of U.S. commissioners, 1868-1929. There are microfilm copies (123 rolls) of minutes, decree registers, journals, rulebooks, and other records of the district court and its predecessors, 1851-1950, including certain records of the district and circuit courts for the Southern District of California, 1861-66, and the circuit courts for the Northern District and the District of California, 1855-1911.

CONNECTICUT. 1789-1948. 1,262 lin. ft. (in FRC Boston).

U.S. District Court. Included are final records, 1789-1917; general, 1789-1912, criminal, 1923-48, equity, 1913-29, civil, 1913-28, and bankruptcy, 1867-1939, dockets; criminal, 1913-46, equity, 1912-38, law, 1912-38, admiralty, 1914-45, civil, 1938-47, and bankruptcy, 1801-1940, case files; marshals' bonds, 1806-9; rulebooks, 1809-41; minutes, 1853-1927; records of U.S. commissioners, 1905-18; cashbooks, 1919-34; copies of grand jury reports, 1936-45; and naturalization records, including declarations, 1898-1939, petitions, 1875-1929, related index, 1906-24, and judges' memorandums on petitions, 1903-6. Also included are district and circuit court records filed together, consisting of general, 1789-1915, and equity, 1884-1915, case files; dockets, 1871-73; records of U.S. commissioners, 1900-1948; cashbooks, 1896-1934; and naturalization records, 1906-48.

U.S. Circuit Court. Included are final records, 1790-1912, dockets, 1791-1877, records of naturalization, 1896-1906,

Revolutionary War claims of invalid pensioners, 1792–95, and minutes, 1853–1911.

DELAWARE. 1847–1921. 66 lin. ft. (in FRC Philadelphia).

U.S. Circuit Court. Records consist of equity case files, 1847–1921.

DISTRICT OF COLUMBIA. 1801–1934. 2,370 lin. ft. (in WNRC).

This court and its predecessors, because of their location in the Federal district, have had jurisdiction in both Federal and non-Federal matters.

U.S. Circuit Court. This court was established in 1801 under the first Organic Act for the government of the Federal District, and in it were vested all the powers of the U.S. circuit courts. It had jurisdiction in civil and criminal law, in equity, over seizures on land and water, and over all penalties and forfeitures under Federal law. It also exercised the functions previously possessed by the Virginia county courts and the levy and county courts of Maryland, and it had appellate jurisdiction over the orphans' courts in the District counties of Washington and Alexandria. Records of this court created in Alexandria County are in the custody of the clerk of Arlington County, Va. Other records that may have been created by this court are among the naturalization and probate records described below.

The law, appellate, and criminal records (grouped together here because civil suits at law, appeals, and criminal cases were docketed together until 1838) chiefly include docket books, 1801–63, minute books, 1801–63, case papers, 1802–63, bonds to secure release of debtors, 1834–44, and grand jury lists and related records, 1809–63. Chancery (equity) jurisdiction records include a divorce and other dockets, 1801–63, case files, 1804–63, and divorce records, 1860–63. Bankruptcy records consist of insolvency minutes, 1836–50, a bankruptcy docket, 1842–43, insolvents' case papers, 1814–50, and bankruptcy case papers, 1842–43. Slavery records include a manumission and emancipation record, 1821–62, fugitive slave case records, 1851–63, and manumission and emancipation papers, 1862–63. Other court records include habeas corpus papers, 1820–63, lien law papers (for dockets, see below under U.S. Supreme Court of the District of Columbia), 1833–62, and marriage licenses, 1837–62.

U.S. District Court of the District of Potomac and the District of Columbia. Records consist chiefly of minutes, 1801–63; a docket of admiralty cases, 1857–63, admiralty case files, 1839–63, including those that resulted from captures made during the Civil War by the Potomac Flotilla and the South Atlantic Squadron; and title pages of works for copyright, 1854–63, including titles and legends for Civil War photographs taken by Matthew B. Brady.

U.S. Criminal Court for the District of Columbia. This court was established in 1838 to try criminal cases in the District, which until then had been handled in the U.S. Circuit Court for the District of Columbia. Records consist chiefly of dockets, 1838–63, minutes, 1838–63, a record of proceedings, 1844–59, and case papers, 1838–63.

U.S. Supreme Court of the District of Columbia. This court was established in 1863 to replace the circuit, district, and criminal courts of the District. In 1936 its name was changed to the District Court of the United States for the District of Columbia. Its records consist chiefly of minutes, dockets, and case papers in equity cases (including adoptions), 1863–1900; law, 1863–1934, criminal, 1863–1934, habeas corpus, 1863–1933, condemnation and admiralty, 1863–1929, bankruptcy, 1867–78, and appellate jurisdiction, 1870–1924, cases; and general term minutes, 1863–1903. The case papers include documentation of the trials of persons charged in the assassinations of Presidents Lincoln and Garfield.

Records of Naturalizations in Courts for the District of Columbia. These include indexes, 1802-1926, naturalization records, 1824-1906, copies of declarations of intention, 1802-1926, and military naturalization records, 1918-24.

Probate Records of the Courts for the District of Columbia. These consist chiefly of proceedings, 1801-1934; indexes to wills, 1801-1920, and to administration of estates case files, 1801-78; transcripts of wills probated, 1801-88; administration case dockets, 1801-37 and 1853-89; accounts submitted by administrators of estates, guardians, and others, 1802-79; inventories and sales of estates, 1801-85; guardianship records, 1801-1905; and indentures of apprenticeship, 1801-93.

FLORIDA, MIDDLE DISTRICT.
1888-1945. 1,469 lin. ft. (in FRC Atlanta).

U.S. District Court. The records of the Jacksonville division, which also sat at Fernandino and Ocala, include admiralty, criminal, and equity minutes, 1888-1945, and admiralty, 1898-1945, bankruptcy, 1898-1945, civil, 1938-45, criminal, 1892-1945, equity, 1892-1938, and law, 1913-45, case files. The records of the Orlando division include dockets of U.S. commissioners, 1932-45, and bankruptcy, 1933-45, civil, 1937-45, criminal, 1933-45, equity, 1928-38, and law, 1927-38, case files. The records of the Tampa division include dockets of U.S. commissioners, 1894-1945, and admiralty, 1938-45, bankruptcy, 1908-45, civil, 1921-45, criminal, 1900-1945, equity, 1913-38, and law, 1907-38, case files.

FLORIDA, NORTHERN DISTRICT.
1842-1943. 429 lin. ft. (in FRC Atlanta).

U.S. District Court. The records of the Pensacola division, with which records of the former circuit court for this district are interfiled, include records of admiralty, 1935-43, bankruptcy, 1912-43, civil action, 1938-43, criminal, 1860-1943, equity, 1934-38, law, 1935-38, and mixed civil and admiralty, 1899-1934, cases; naturalization records, 1884-1922; and book records relating to chancery, civil, criminal, equity, and law matters, 1847-1943. There are similar records for divisions at Gainesville, 1904-43, Marianna, 1928-43, and Tallahassee, 1842-1943, including U.S. circuit court book records of the Tallahassee division, ca. 1867-1911.

Confederate States District Court for the Northern District of Florida. The records are of the court's middle division (Tallahassee), 1861-65.

FLORIDA, SOUTHERN DISTRICT.
1828-1943. 717 lin. ft. (in FRC Atlanta).

Superior Court for the Southern District of the Territory of Florida. The records consist of minutes, chiefly relating to admiralty matters, 1828-ca. 1845.

U.S. District Court. The records of the Miami division include naturalization files, 1907-43; and book and other records of admiralty, 1938-43, bankruptcy, 1922-43, civil action, 1938-43, criminal, 1916-43, equity, 1926-38, and law, 1929-38, cases. There are similar records for divisions at Key West, ca. 1847-1943, and Fort Pierce, 1912-43.

U.S. Circuit Court. The records consist chiefly of dockets of the Key West division, ca. 1865-1911.

GEORGIA, MIDDLE DISTRICT.
1879-1946. 1,798 lin. ft. (in FRC Atlanta).

U.S. District Court. These consist of records of the Macon division, including records of bankruptcy, 1879-1943, civil action, 1938-43, criminal, 1882-1943, equity, 1880-1926, law, 1880-1926, and mixed admiralty and law, 1880-1911, cases; and book records in bankruptcy, criminal, equity, and law matters, 1880–1943. There are similar records for the divisions at Albany, 1902–43, Americus, 1927–43, Athens, 1901–43, Columbus, 1891–1943, and Valdosta, 1907–46.

U.S. Circuit Court. Records consist of criminal dockets of the Macon division, 1882–1902, and minutes and dockets of the Valdosta division, 1903–11.

GEORGIA, NORTHERN DISTRICT.
1847–1942. 1,881 lin. ft. (in FRC Atlanta).

U.S. District Court. The records of the Atlanta division include records of bankruptcy, 1867–1942, civil, 1847–1942, criminal, 1849–1942, equity, 1852–1942, and law, 1849–1942, cases; naturalization records, 1878–1905; and book records in bankruptcy, civil, criminal, equity, law, and naturalization matters, 1849–1942. There are similar records for divisions of the court at Rome, 1900–1942, and Gainesville, 1923–42.

U.S. Circuit Court. Included are records of the Atlanta division, relating to appellate and original jurisdiction cases, 1859–61 and 1866–1911, "final records," 1869–1907, and book records, 1867–1911; and a jury book, 1900–1910, of the Rome division.

Confederate States District Court for the Northern Division of Georgia. The records consist of sequestration and garnishment case records, 1861–64, and book records, 1861–64.

GEORGIA, SOUTHERN DISTRICT.
1789–1943. 1,021 lin. ft. (in FRC Atlanta).

U.S. District Court. The records of the Savannah division include records of admiralty, 1789–1943, bankruptcy, 1867–1943, civil, 1790–1860, civil action, 1938–43, and criminal, 1920–43, cases; mixed admiralty, civil, and criminal cases, 1790–1938; book records in admiralty, bankruptcy, criminal, equity, and law matters, 1790–1943; and book and case

records of the Savannah division of the U.S. circuit court for this district, 1789–1911. There are similar records for divisions of the court at Augusta, 1890–1943, including U.S. circuit court book records of the Augusta division, ca. 1890–1911, Brunswick, 1938–43, Dublin, 1926–43, and Waycross, 1926–43.

Confederate States District Court for the Southern Division of Georgia. Included are records of sequestration and garnishment cases, 1861–64; and admiralty, criminal, and habeas corpus cases and book records, 1861–65.

IDAHO. 1889–1944. 400 lin. ft. (in FRC Seattle).

U.S. District Court. Records consist of case and book records of bankruptcy matters.

INDIANA, NORTHERN DISTRICT.
1879–1947. 671 lin. ft. (in FRC Chicago).

U.S. District Court. The records of the Fort Wayne division include records of U.S. commissioners, 1927–42, and bankruptcy, 1898–1945, civil, 1939–46, equity, 1901–38, law, 1914–38, criminal, 1925–44, and admiralty, 1939–46, case files. The records of the Hammond division include naturalization declarations, 1906–21, and bankruptcy, 1904–46, criminal, 1927–46, equity, 1917–38, civil, 1938–46, and admiralty, 1938–47, case files. The records of the South Bend division include bankruptcy, 1925–46, civil, 1925–46, criminal, 1925–46, law, 1925–38, and equity, 1925–38, case files.

INDIANA, SOUTHERN DISTRICT.
1837–1948. 2,173 lin. ft. (in FRC Chicago).

U.S. District Court. The records of the Indianapolis division consist of naturalization petitions, 1903–45; dockets, 1858–1938; and bankruptcy, 1867–1948, equity, 1913–38, law, 1843–1928, criminal, 1867–1946, and civil, 1939–47, case files. The Evansville division records consist of bankruptcy proceedings, 1899-1923, and law, 1928-44, bankruptcy, 1874-1944, equity, 1926-44, criminal, 1928-33, and civil, 1934-44, case files. The New Albany division records consist of law, 1926-38, civil, 1938-45, bankruptcy, 1898-1945, criminal, 1926-45, and equity, 1928-38, case files. The Terre Haute division records consist of dockets, 1925-43, and bankruptcy, 1926-46, criminal, 1925-46, equity, 1925-39, law, 1925-39, and civil, 1939-46, case files.

U.S. Circuit Court. The records consist of dockets, 1840-1912, and case files, 1837-1912.

ILLINOIS, EASTERN DISTRICT.
1905-46. 1,154 lin. ft. (in FRC Chicago).

U.S. District Court. The records of the East St. Louis division include final records, 1907-20; civil, 1913-45, law, 1923-38, equity, 1922-32, bankruptcy, 1905-43, and criminal, 1907-45, dockets; bankruptcy, 1905-44, criminal, 1905-45, equity, 1928-37, and civil, 1938-45, case files; law and chancery records, 1905-35; civil orders, 1938-40; and bankruptcy minute books, 1905-6. There are also similar records for the court when it sat in Danville, 1923-46.

U.S. Circuit Court. Included are final records, 1905-12, civil dockets, 1907-12, and chancery records, 1905-11.

ILLINOIS, NORTHERN DISTRICT.
1819-1943. 3,390 lin. ft. (in FRC Chicago).

U.S. District Court. Included are dockets, 1819-41; and criminal, 1873-1942, equity, 1916-39, civil, 1874-1943, and admiralty, 1938-42, case files.

ILLINOIS, SOUTHERN DISTRICT.
1855-1946. 853 lin. ft. (in FRC Chicago).

U.S. District Court. Included among the records of the northern division are dockets, 1887-1939; and criminal, 1887-1946, civil, 1906-46, law, 1931-46, admi-

ralty, 1931-36, and equity, 1903-38, case files. There are also similar records for the court's southern division, 1855-1946.

IOWA, NORTHERN DISTRICT.
1863-1945. 1,402 lin. ft. (in FRC Kansas City except as noted).

U.S. District Court. The records of the eastern division (Dubuque) include records of bankruptcy, 1867-83 (in WNRC) and 1898-1945, civil, 1938-45, criminal, 1863-1945, equity, 1908-38, and law, 1907-38, cases; and book records of U.S. commissioners, 1874-1943. There are similar records for the divisions at Cedar Rapids, 1890-1945, Fort Dodge (central division), 1882-1945, and Sioux City (western division), 1880-1945.

U.S. Circuit Court. The records of the eastern division (Dubuque) consist of records of equity, 1880-1911, and law, 1880-1911, cases. There are similar records for the divisions at Cedar Rapids, 1891-1911, Fort Dodge, 1882-1911, and Sioux City, 1882-1911.

IOWA, SOUTHERN DISTRICT.
1842-1945. 1,468 lin. ft. (in FRC Kansas City).

U.S. District Court. The records of the Des Moines division include records of bankruptcy, 1867-1945, civil, 1938-45, criminal, 1871-1933, equity, 1900-1938, and law, 1911-38, cases; and of combined civil, criminal, and law matters, 1842-69. Also, book records of U.S. commissioners and book records of bankruptcy, criminal, equity, and law matters, 1859-1945. There are similar records for the divisions of the court at Council Bluffs (western division), 1871-1945, Creston (southern division), 1900-1945, Keokuk (eastern division), 1865-1945, and Ottumwa, 1907-45.

U.S. Circuit Court. The records of the Des Moines division consist of records of equity, 1860-1909, and law, 1862-1911, cases; and book records in equity, 1859-1920. There are similar records for the divisions at Council Bluffs, 1880-1911,

Creston, 1907-11, Davenport, 1904-13, Keokuk, 1876-1916, and Ottumwa, 1907-11.

KANSAS. 1855-1945. 2,231 lin. ft. (in FRC Kansas City).

Territorial Courts of Kansas. Records of these courts, which sat at Leavenworth, Tecumseh, and Lecompton, are of civil, 1855-60, and criminal, 1855-60, cases, and consist of book records of civil and criminal matters, 1855-61.

U.S. District Court. The records of the Topeka division include records of bankruptcy, 1867-1945, civil, 1940-45, criminal, 1861-1945, equity, 1913-38, law, 1861-1940, habeas corpus, 1925-45, and criminal, 1883-94, cases of the second division; and book records of bankruptcy, civil, criminal, equity, law, and habeas corpus matters, 1861-1945. There are similar records for divisions at Fort Scott, 1880-1945, and Wichita, 1883-1945.

U.S. Circuit Court. The records of the Topeka division consist of civil cases (including some Territorial cases), 1861-1912, and book records of civil and criminal matters, 1861-1912. There are similar records for the Fort Scott, 1892-1912, and Wichita, 1890-1912, divisions.

LOUISIANA, EASTERN DISTRICT. 1842-50 and 1867-82. 110 lin. ft. (in WNRC).

U.S. District Court. These consist of case files and dockets created under the Second and Third National Bankruptcy Acts, 1842-50 and 1867-82.

MAINE. 1789-1950. 1,010 lin. ft. (in FRC Boston except as noted).

U.S. District Court. The records of the southern division (Portland)—including some interfiled records of the former U.S. circuit court and of the U.S. district court before it was divided into southern and northern divisions (in 1916)—include records of bankruptcy cases, 1796-1803, 1842-52 (in WNRC), 1867-81 (in WNRC), and 1898-1945, "old term" cases (criminal, law, equity, and admiralty), 1790-1911; equity, 1870-1939, civil, 1938-46, law and admiralty, 1899-1940, criminal, 1903-50, seamen's, 1873-1937, and appealed, 1852-1938, cases; naturalization matters, 1790-1911; final records, 1789-1932; U.S. cases, 1860's-1880's and 1925-38; minutes, dockets, and other book records of criminal, equity, civil, bankruptcy, law, admiralty, pension, and prize matters, 1789-1946; and records of clerks and U.S. attorneys, 1800-1932. Records of the northern division (Bangor) consist of criminal, equity, and law case files, 1916-50.

U.S. Circuit Court. Included are law and equity case files, 1880-1913, final records, 1820-54 and 1860-1912, and book records, 1820-1911.

MASSACHUSETTS. 1789-1948. 5,807 lin. ft.

U.S. District Court. The records (5,550 lin. ft., in FRC Boston) consist of final records, 1789-1918, and related index, 1806-1918; general, 1789-1906, criminal, 1882-1944, equity, 1912-38, admiralty, 1927-48, law, 1912-38, civil, 1938-45, bankruptcy, 1898-1946, naturalization, 1935-47, and opinion, 1917-21, dockets; general, 1789-1917, criminal, 1917-46, equity, 1912-38, admiralty, 1926-46, law, 1912-38, civil, 1938-45, seamen's, 1909-47, and bankruptcy, 1898-1946, case files; records relating to prize case proceedings, 1812-16; a journal and list of Revolutionary War pension applicants, 1806-32; a rulebook, 1836-42; copies of search warrants, 1840-50; records of U.S. commissioners, 1858-65, and clerks, 1817-43 and 1930-47; records relating to naturalization, including declarations, 1789-1945, petitions, 1846-1945, lists, 1927-45, and depositions, 1927-45; and various other series of records, including grand jury reports, 1934-45, minutes, 1930-31, cashbooks, 1907-45, letters and papers seized during the Civil War, 1861-65, an order book, 1913-

21, and transcripts of proceedings, 1807–1937. Also included are some district and circuit court records filed together, such as an index to attorneys and counselors, 1790–1932; jurors' lists, orders, and accounts, 1831–56; certificates of naturalization, 1907–25; a rulebook, 1894–1920; and a record of trademarks and label certificates approved, 1874–78.

Other records (in WNRC) include case papers, dockets, and minutes created under the first three national bankruptcy acts, 1801–30, 1841–57, and 1867–82.

U.S. Circuit Court. The records (in FRC Boston) include final records, 1790–99 and 1806–1911, and related index, 1790–1847; general, 1800–1906, decision, 1882–1903, criminal, 1886–1911, law, 1907–11, and equity, 1874–1911, dockets; case files, 1790–1911; a rulebook, 1846–64; docket of Judge John Davis, 1833–34; registry of orders and receipts, 1832–1911; correspondence of the clerk, 1874–86; and naturalization records, including declarations, 1845–1911, petitions, 1845–47 and 1906–11, and related indexes, 1845–1906.

MICHIGAN, NORTHERN
DISTRICT. 1863–1946. 981 lin. ft. (in FRC Chicago).

U.S. District Court. Included are bankruptcy, 1868–1945, equity, 1864–1938, law, 1864–1938, admiralty, 1878–1945, civil, 1878–1946, and criminal, 1864–1946, case files; and records of U.S. commissioners, 1863–1942.

MINNESOTA. 1858–1945. 3,404 lin. ft. (in FRC Kansas City).

U.S. District Court. The records of the fourth division (Minneapolis) include bankruptcy, 1898–1945, civil, 1938–45, criminal, 1907–45, equity, 1912–38, habeas corpus, 1914–36, and law, 1892–1938, case records; records relating to naturalization matters, 1907–45; and book records of U.S. commissioners and of bankruptcy, civil, criminal, equity, law, and naturalization matters, 1890–

1945. There are similar records for the first (Winona), 1891–1945, second (Mankato), 1890–1945, third (St. Paul), 1858–1945, fifth (Duluth), 1894–1945, and sixth (Fergus Falls), 1890–1945, divisions.

U.S. Circuit Court. The records of the third division (St. Paul) consist of admiralty, 1864–80, chancery, 1862–1913, and criminal, 1862–1900, cases; and book records of U.S. commissioners and of admiralty, chancery, criminal, and naturalization matters, 1860–1911. There are similar records for divisions at Winona, Mankato, Minneapolis, Duluth, and Fergus Falls.

MISSISSIPPI, NORTHERN
DISTRICT. 1838–1943. 741 lin. ft. (in FRC Atlanta).

U.S. District Court. The records of the Oxford division of this court and interfiled records, ca. 1865–1911, of the former circuit court for this district include bankruptcy, 1867–1943, civil, 1858–1910, civil action, 1938–43, criminal, 1899–1943, equity, 1881–1938, and law, 1894–1938, case records; and book records relating to bankruptcy, criminal, equity, and law matters, 1838–1943. There are similar records for divisions at Aberdeen, 1877–1943, and Clarksdale, 1912–43.

Confederate States District Court for the Northern Division of Mississippi. Included are an issue and appearance docket, August 1861–April 1862 and 1864 (in a volume for 1857–68), an execution docket, February 1862 term (in a volume for 1858–98), and a bar docket, August 1861 term (in a volume for 1858–82).

MISSISSIPPI, SOUTHERN
DISTRICT. 1819–1943. 1,442 lin. ft. (in FRC Atlanta).

U.S. District Court. The records of the Jackson division and interfiled records, ca. 1823–1911, of the former circuit court for this district include records of admiralty, 1875–85, bankruptcy, 1898–1943, civil action, 1938–43, criminal, 1903–43, equity, 1879–1943, and law, 1882–1940, cases; of mixed cases in bankruptcy, civil, and criminal matters, 1848-1925; and book records of bankruptcy, criminal, law, and equity matters, 1819-43. There are similar records for divisions at Biloxi, 1888-1943, Hattiesburg, 1936-43, Meridian, 1894-1943, and Vicksburg, 1887-1943.

MISSOURI, EASTERN DISTRICT.
1824-1945. 3,328 lin. ft. (in FRC Kansas City).

U.S. District Court. Included are eastern division (St. Louis) records of admiralty, equity, and law cases, 1839-1938; of bankruptcy, 1867-78 and 1898-1945, civil, 1938-45, criminal, 1864-1945, habeas corpus, 1865-1915, and internal revenue, 1865-1922, cases; and book records of U.S. commissioners and of admiralty, bankruptcy, civil, criminal, equity, law, and naturalization matters, 1824-1945. There are similar records for the southeastern (Cape Girardeau), 1905-45, and northern (Hannibal), 1887-1945, divisions.

U.S. Circuit Court. Records of the eastern division consist of law and equity cases, 1824-1912, and book records of equity and law matters, 1839-1913. There are similar records for the southeastern, 1905-21, and northern, 1887-1911, divisions.

MISSOURI, WESTERN DISTRICT.
1822-1945. 3,057 lin. ft. (in FRC Kansas City).

U.S. District Court. The records of the Kansas City division include records of bankruptcy, 1898-1945, civil, 1938-45, criminal, 1879-1945, and equity, 1912-38, cases; and book records of bankruptcy, civil, criminal, equity, law, and naturalization matters, 1879-1945. There are similar records for divisions at Chillicothe, 1924-45, Jefferson City, 1822-1945, Joplin, 1901-45, St. Joseph, 1883-1945, and Springfield, 1883-1945.

U.S. Circuit Court. There are records of the Kansas City division, consisting of law and equity cases, 1879-1911, and book records of equity and law matters, 1879-1911; and similar records for the Jefferson City, 1870-1911, and St. Joseph, 1887-1906, divisions.

NEBRASKA. 1855-1955. 2,374 lin. ft.
(in FRC Kansas City).

Supreme Court of the Territory of Nebraska. Records consist of civil and criminal case files, 1855-63.

District Courts of the Territory of Nebraska. Records consist of civil and criminal case files, 1855-66, and book records in civil and criminal matters, 1855-67.

U.S. District Court. The records of the Omaha division include records of admiralty, criminal, equity, and law cases, 1867-1911; bankruptcy, 1867-1955, civil, 1938-55, criminal, 1912-55, equity and law, 1907-13, equity, 1913-38, and law, 1913-38, cases; and book records of U.S. commissioners and of admiralty, bankruptcy, civil, criminal, equity, and law matters, 1867-1954. There are similar records for divisions at Chadron, Grand Island, Hastings, Lincoln, McCook, Norfolk, and North Platte, 1907-55.

U.S. Circuit Court. The records of the Omaha division consist of case and book records of admiralty, criminal, equity, and law cases, 1867-1911. There are similar records for divisions of the court at Chadron, 1907-11, Grand Island, 1908-11, Hastings, 1907-11, Lincoln, 1907-12, McCook, 1907-11, Norfolk, 1907-11, and North Platte, 1907-11.

NEW HAMPSHIRE. 1789-1952.
404 lin. ft. (in FRC Boston).

U.S. District Court. The records of this court, with which are interfiled some records of the former U.S. circuit court, consist chiefly of "D.C." series case files, 1804-24 and 1831-59; "new" series case files, 1866-1902; bankruptcy case files, 1842-53, 1867-78, and 1898-1942; criminal, 1904-45, law, 1910-38, equity, 1907-38, admiralty, 1907-45, and civil, 1938-42, case files; and book records of bankruptcy, copyright, naturalization, and other matters, 1789-1948.

U.S. Circuit Court. The records consist of series "A" case files, 1790-1874; equity, 1867-1912, criminal, 1877-1912, and law, 1881-1912, case files; and book records in equity, law, and other matters, 1790-1912.

NEW JERSEY. 1789-1950. 97 lin. ft. and 186 rolls of microfilm (in WNRC).

U.S. District Court. The records consist of bankruptcy records (including 92 rolls of microfilm), 1842-43 and 1867-81; microfilm copies (58 rolls) of minutes, 1789-1950; and microfilm copies of admiralty (10 rolls), 1876-1944, civil (7 rolls), 1863-1923, and criminal (11 rolls), 1870-1928, dockets.

U.S. Circuit Court. The records consist of microfilm copies of minutes (4 rolls), 1790-1911, and dockets (4 rolls), 1862-1911.

NEW MEXICO. 1843-1952. 452 lin. ft. (in FRC Denver).

District Courts of the Territory of New Mexico. The records of the District Court for the First Judicial District (Santa Fe) of the Territory of New Mexico include bankruptcy, 1899-1911, civil, 1881-96, and civil and criminal, 1843-1911, case files; naturalization records, 1882-1917; and book records, 1852-1912. There are similar records for the second (Fernandez de Taos and Albuquerque), 1861-1917, third (Albuquerque and Las Cruces), 1851-1912, fourth (Las Vegas), 1887-1912, fifth (Roswell), 1888-1912, sixth (Alamogordo), 1900-1911, and seventh (Socorro), 1902-12, judicial districts.

U.S. District Court. The records consist of bankruptcy, 1911-43, civil, 1938-43, criminal, 1918-43, and law and equity, 1912-38, case files; book records of bankruptcy, civil, criminal, and equity matters, 1912-52; and dockets of U.S. commissioners, 1896-1943.

NEW YORK, EASTERN DISTRICT. 1867-80. 85 lin. ft. (in WNRC).

U.S. District Court. The records are those created under the National Bankruptcy Act of 1867, consisting of case files, 1867-78, and dockets, 1867-80.

NEW YORK, NORTHERN DISTRICT. 1837-1944. 909 lin. ft. (in FRC New York).

U.S. District Court. Included are minutes and dockets, 1895-1944; and civil, 1938-44, admiralty, 1899-1944, equity, 1905-38, law, 1899-1938, bankruptcy, 1898-1944, and criminal, 1900-1944, case files.

U.S. Circuit Court. Included are minutes and dockets, 1837-1919, and equity, 1838-1917, law, 1838-1921, and criminal, 1867-1910, case files.

NEW YORK, SOUTHERN DISTRICT. 1789-1911, with a few dated as early as 1685 and as late as 1920. 3,710 lin. ft. (in WNRC except as noted).

Early Admiralty Courts of New York. The records consist chiefly of case papers in prize cases, 1757-62; seamen's wage suits, 1761-72; salvage cases, 1768-70; customs regulations cases, 1760-75; cases relating to seamen, 1758-63; minutes of the vice admiralty court, 1701-74 (with gaps); and papers, 1685-1834, including four depositions (in the National Archives Building) taken in proceedings before Gov. Thomas Dongan in 1685 and extracted from the files in 1916 by Judge Charles M. Hough, chiefly to illustrate practices in admiralty.

U.S. District Court. The records consist of daily minutes of the court, including naturalization proceedings, 1789-1913; rolls of attorneys, 1789-1834; opinions of judges, 1846-1917; admiralty case files relating to all aspects of admiralty and maritime jurisdiction, including seizure for violation of customs laws and embargoes, operating a steamboat without an annual inspection certificate, carrying an excess of passengers, and engaging in the slave trade, as well as suits resulting from collisions, salvage, pilotage and towage, breach of charter party, debts for supplies and materials, seamen's wages, bills of bottomry, and marine insurance; ship logs, 1839-1920; dockets, 1828-1907, containing a record of papers filed and proceedings held in each admiralty case; and prize and related records for the War of 1812, 1812-17, and the Civil War, 1857-67.

Also included are bankruptcy case files and other records created under the Bankruptcy Acts of 1800, 1841, 1867, and 1898, and dated, respectively, 1801-9, 1842-1902, 1867-1917, and 1898-1912; records created under the court's common law jurisdiction, primarily concerning seizures made and suits brought for penalties and forfeitures under Federal laws and consisting chiefly of law case files, 1795-1906, judgment records in law cases, 1795-1911, rulebooks, 1800-1878, dockets, 1844-1906, and internal revenue case files and dockets, 1867-1906; records created under the court's limited equity jurisdiction, chiefly case files and dockets, 1869-1911, minutes, 1870-1912, and case files on naturalization suits in equity, 1909-17; criminal, 1845-68, and habeas corpus, 1852-83, case files; copyright records deposited with the court, 1809-53; and records of U.S. commissioners, including transcripts of testimony taken before them, 1855-1914, documents filed with them by owners of runaway slaves, 1837-60, dockets, 1845-1910, and a record of proceedings in criminal cases, 1897-1911.

U.S. Circuit Court. The records consist of daily minutes of the court, including naturalization proceedings, 1790-1808 and 1813-75; minutes of motions, 1887-1911, and minutes relating to the appointment of supervisors of election, 1871-94; and rolls of attorneys, 1790-1834.

Appellate jurisdiction records, relating chiefly to the circuit court's review of final decrees and judgments of the district court, consist of case files, 1793-1911; bonds, 1879-1912; dockets, 1842-1912, one of which relates only to bankruptcy cases, 1842-43; and minutes, 1875-83, relating chiefly to admiralty cases appealed from the district court.

Law jurisdiction records include case files, 1790-1912, that document, for the most part, suits for recovery of sums due, personal injuries, damages resulting from forcible ejectment from lands and tenements, publication of false and defamatory matter, infringement of patent rights and copyrights, and recovery of penalties imposed by the Congress upon persons and corporations encouraging the migration of aliens to perform contract labor; dockets, 1846-1912; minutes, 1875-1911; judgment records, 1799-1911, relating to cases in which judgments or final decrees were rendered for the recovery of debts, damages, or costs; judgment registers, 1794-1817, 1829-59, and 1864-77; judgment dockets, 1795-1911; and writs of capias, 1792-1877.

Records relating to customs and internal revenue matters include case files of suits brought by the United States, 1845-75, and against collectors of customs, 1833-1903; dockets in customs and internal revenue cases, 1843-1903; minutes of cases against collectors of customs, 1887-1903; case files, dockets, and minutes in suits appealing decisions of the U.S. Board of General Appraisers, 1890-1910; and transcripts of testimony, 1891-1907.

Records of equity cases, which were the major activity of this court, include case files, 1792-1911, resulting from cases of alleged infringements of patents and copyrights, threatened violations of contracts, conveyance of property to delay or deter payment of debt, trademark matters, actions by labor unions to restrain persons from working on certain projects, and conspiracies in restraint of trade and commerce; dockets, 1827-1911; minutes, 1874-1908;

bonds, 1907–15; and extracts of testimony, ca. 1855–1911.

Other records include criminal case files, 1790–1912, dockets, 1853–1906, and minutes, 1873–1913; habeas corpus case files, 1828–1914, and a docket, 1891–1906; and case files relating to alleged seamen deserters and wages of deceased seamen, 1872–1915.

U.S. Circuit Court for the District of New York in the Second Circuit. This court, presided over by one of the "midnight judges" appointed by President John Adams, existed from 1801 to 1802. A record of its proceedings, June 5, 1801, through June 7, 1802, appears in the minutes of the circuit court for the Southern District (then the U.S. Circuit Court for the District of New York). Other records of this court may also be among the records of the U.S. Circuit Court for the Southern District.

NEW YORK, WESTERN DISTRICT. 1842–1944. 1,837 lin. ft. (in FRC New York).

U.S. District Court. Included are bankruptcy case files, 1842–1900, transferred to the western district from the northern district of the court; other bankruptcy case files, 1900–1939; civil, 1939–44, and equity, 1913–39, order books; and copies of equity decrees and orders, 1913–38.

NORTH CAROLINA, EASTERN DISTRICT. 1789–1942. 1,212 lin. ft. (in FRC Atlanta).

U.S. District Court. The records of the Raleigh division of this court and interfiled records of the former circuit court, 1791–1911, and of the Confederate States district court for North Carolina, 1861–65, include records in admiralty, 1809–1936, bankruptcy, 1867–1942, civil, 1871–1942, criminal, 1789–1942, equity, 1789–1942, and law, 1789–1942, cases; and book records in admiralty, bankruptcy, civil, criminal, equity, and law matters, 1791–1942, There are similar

records for divisions at Elizabeth City, 1801–1942, Fayetteville, 1917–42, New Bern, 1832–1942, Washington, 1895–1942, Wilmington, 1825–1942, and Wilson, 1906–42.

NORTH CAROLINA, MIDDLE DISTRICT. 1872–1943. 558 lin. ft. (in FRC Atlanta).

U.S. District Court. The records of the Greensboro division and interfiled records, ca. 1872–1911, of the former circuit court include records in bankruptcy (for all divisions), 1903–43, civil action, 1938–43, criminal, 1873–1943, equity, 1875–1938, and law, 1872–1938, cases; and book records in bankruptcy, civil action, criminal, equity, and law matters, 1872–1943. There are similar records for divisions at Durham, 1936–43, Rockingham, 1927–43, Salisbury, 1927–43, Wilkesboro, 1903–43, and Winston-Salem, 1926–43.

NORTH CAROLINA, WESTERN DISTRICT. 1871–1943. 927 lin. ft. (in FRC Atlanta).

U.S. District Court. The records of the Asheville division include records of bankruptcy, 1873–1942, "old" civil, 1874–1925, criminal, 1871–1942, criminal (Bryson City division), 1924–43, equity, 1925–37, law, 1924–37, and libel (for all divisions), 1925–43, cases; and book records of bankruptcy, criminal, equity, and law matters, 1871–1932. There are similar records for the Charlotte division, 1878–1943, including interspersed dockets (and possibly other records), ca. 1878–ca. 1902, of the former U.S. circuit court for this district; and the Statesville division, 1872–1943.

NORTH DAKOTA. 1861–1945. 727 lin. ft. (in FRC Kansas City).

U.S. Courts of the Territory of Dakota. The records of these courts, which sat at Bismarck, Fargo, and Grand Forks, consist of admiralty, 1875–84, criminal and civil, 1879–89, equity, 1875–77, and law, 1877–86, cases; and book records in admiralty, civil, criminal, equity, and law matters, 1861–89.

U.S. District Court. There are records of bankruptcy, 1898–1945, civil, 1938–45, criminal, 1890–1945, equity, 1891–1938, and law, 1889–1939, cases; and book records of U.S. commissioners and of bankruptcy, civil, criminal, equity, and law matters, 1890–1945.

U.S. Circuit Court. Records consist of criminal, 1890–1911, equity, 1891–1911, and law, 1890–1913, case records; and book records of criminal, equity, and law matters, 1890–1913.

OHIO, NORTHERN DISTRICT. 1855–1946. 3,980 lin. ft.

U.S. District Court. The records (in FRC Chicago) created by this court at Cleveland consist of naturalization records, including petitions, 1855–1903, and declarations, 1906–43; bankruptcy, equity, law, and criminal dockets, 1855–1940; law, equity, and civil journals, 1855–1946; and law, 1913–35, bankruptcy, 1898–1946, civil, 1855–1946, equity, 1855–1913, admiralty, 1855–1946, criminal, 1855–1946, and forfeiture, 1868–1915 and 1926–36, case files. The records (in FRC Chicago) created by the court at Toledo consist of bankruptcy, law, admiralty, and naturalization dockets, 1867–1946; and equity, 1898–1938, forfeiture, 1910–38, criminal, 1922–37, and bankruptcy, 1873–1946, case files. Also included are some circuit court records, 1878–1937. The records (in WNRC) created under the National Bankruptcy Act of 1867 consist of minutes, 1867–97, dockets, 1867–78, and case files, 1867–78.

U.S. Circuit Court. Records (in WNRC) consist of minutes, 1868–81, and a docket, 1868–88, of cases resulting from the 1867 bankruptcy act and appealed from the district court.

OHIO, SOUTHERN DISTRICT. 1805–1949. 2,603 lin. ft. (in FRC Chicago).

U.S. District Court. The records of the Cincinnati division of the court include final records, 1814–42; civil, 1844–1911, bankruptcy, 1867–1936, and criminal, 1888–1931, dockets; bankruptcy, 1841–1949, equity, 1912–38, law, 1921–38, and general, 1849–1921, journals; civil, 1849–1945, equity, 1910–39, law, 1925–38, criminal, 1935–42, and admiralty, 1853–68, case files; records relating to bankruptcy cases, 1841–1946; chancery records, 1869–1915; miscellaneous records of the clerks, 1920–40; an order book, 1883–1931; jury lists, 1900–1949; records of U.S. commissioners, 1888–1945; and a few miscellaneous records, 1808–1940. There are also similar records for the court when it sat at Columbus, 1880–1943, and Dayton, 1901–45.

U.S. Circuit Court. Included are records, 1805–8, relating to the proposed trials of Aaron Burr and Harman Blennerhasset; criminal, 1850–98, appearance, 1862–1915, and civil, 1904–14, dockets; journals, 1808–1911; a rulebook, 1808–37; chancery records, 1828–1919, and orders, 1843–57; and records relating to criminal, 1872–1909, and law, 1863–1919, cases.

OKLAHOMA, EASTERN DIVISION. 1893–1946. 702 lin. ft. (in FRC Fort Worth).

U.S. District Court. The records include criminal, 1893–1945, civil, 1894–1907, and equity, 1907–38, case files; records of clerks, 1908–41, and of U.S. commissioners, 1908–46; and a few bankruptcy records, 1907–35.

OKLAHOMA, WESTERN DISTRICT. 1900–1945. 1,585 lin. ft. (in FRC Fort Worth).

U.S. District Court. Included are bankruptcy, 1900–1945, equity, 1913–39, law, 1907–12, civil, 1935–45, and criminal, 1907–45, cases; and bankruptcy, civil, criminal, equity, and law dockets, final records, and rulebooks, 1906–45.

U.S. Circuit Court. Included are law, 1910–41, civil, 1908–11, and criminal, 1906–11, cases.

OKLAHOMA, NORTHERN
DISTRICT. 1925-45. 458 lin. ft. (in
FRC Fort Worth).

U.S. District Court. Included are
bankruptcy, 1925-45, criminal, 1925-45,
civil, 1938-45, equity, 1925-38, and law,
1925-38, cases; and bankruptcy dockets,
1925-45.

PENNSYLVANIA, EASTERN
DISTRICT. 1789-1915, with a few
dated as early as 1740. 986 lin. ft.
(textual records in WNRC except as
noted).

U.S. District Court. Until the judicial
reorganization of 1911 the court's activities concerned the adjudication of admiralty and bankruptcy matters, actions
brought by the United States, and minor
criminal violations.

The records consist chiefly of minutes,
1789-1911; case files and other records
in admiralty matters, 1789-1911; prize
and related records for the War of 1812,
1812-15, and the Civil War, 1861-66;
bankruptcy case files and other records
created under the bankruptcy acts of
1800, 1841, and 1867, dated, respectively,
1800-1806, 1842-57, and 1867-78; case
files and dockets of common law cases,
1789-1911; records relating to forfeitures in customs, internal revenue, prize,
and other cases, 1843-1911; habeas corpus case files, 1791-1915; case files and
other records created under the limited
criminal jurisdiction of the district court,
1789-1914; and criminal dockets of U.S.
commissioners, 1864-1915.

U.S. Circuit Court. The records consist of minutes, 1792-1911; bonds made
by bondsmen and parties in cases, 1841-
1905; law and appellate jurisdiction
records, including dockets, 1790-1911,
case files, 1790-1911, and writs, 1790-
1907; equity dockets and case files, 1790-
1911; originals of certain Presidential
pardons, 1835-66; habeas corpus, 1848-
62, criminal, 1791-1883, and fugitive
slave, 1850-60, case files; copies of
reports made by the clerk of the court,

1874-1910; and naturalization records
(60 lin. ft.), 1796-1911 (in FRC Philadelphia). Included also are three reels
of motion picture film filed as plaintiff's
exhibits in American Mutoscope and Biograph Co. *v.* Sigmund Lubin, Equity
Case 27 in the October 1903 session.

*U.S. Circuit Court for the Western
District of Pennsylvania (1801-2).* This
court, presided over by one of the "midnight judges," created a few records during its brief existence from 1801 to 1802.
These consist chiefly of law and equity
case files and a docket, 1801-2. The
records were first transferred to the
reestablished circuit court for Pennsylvania and later to the U.S. District Court
for the Eastern District of Pennsylvania.

PENNSYLVANIA, MIDDLE
DISTRICT. 1887-1911. 26 lin. ft. (in
FRC Philadelphia).

U.S. Circuit Court. Records consist of
equity case files, 1887-1911.

PENNSYLVANIA, WESTERN
DISTRICT. 1806-1926. 385 lin. ft. (in
FRC Philadelphia).

U.S. Circuit Court. The records for
terms held at Pittsburgh include records
in equity, 1806-1912, law, 1877-1917, and
civil cases; naturalization records; and
book records in law, civil, civil appearance, partition, and execution and equity
matters, 1825-1926. There are also book
records for terms held at Erie, 1868-
1911.

PUERTO RICO. 1898-1944. 66 lin. ft.
(in FRC New York).

U.S. District Court. The records
include civil, equity, and law dockets and
journals and bankruptcy and criminal
dockets, 1898-1944; and civil, 1940-44,
equity, 1938-40, admiralty, 1940-44, and
bankruptcy, 1930-42, case files.

RHODE ISLAND. 1790-1945.
821 lin. ft. (in FRC Boston except as
noted).

U.S. District Court. The records consist of bankruptcy case records, 1801-

12 (in WNRC), 1841-58 (in WNRC), 1867-81 (in WNRC), and 1898-1943; criminal, 1893-1945, admiralty, 1885-1945, law, 1887-1938, equity, 1906-38, civil, 1938-45, civil action, 1938-42, and claims, 1791-1888, case records; final records, 1791-1920; naturalization proceedings, 1842-1945; and minutes, dockets, and other book records, 1790-1939.

U.S. Circuit Court. The records consist of final records in equity and law cases, 1790-1912, all types of case files, 1791-1913, naturalization proceedings, 1846-1906, and minutes, dockets, and other book records, 1790-1911.

SOUTH CAROLINA, EASTERN AND WESTERN DISTRICTS. 1716-63 and 1789-1942. 1,265 lin. ft. (in FRC Atlanta).

Court of Vice Admiralty of the Province of South Carolina. The records consist of journals, 1716-30, 1736-49, and 1752-63.

U.S. District Court for the Eastern District. The records of the Charleston division of this court, including interfiled records, ca. 1790-1911, of the former U.S. Circuit Court for the District of South Carolina, consist of records of admiralty, 1867-1942, bankruptcy, 1867-1942, civil, 1875-1942, criminal, 1867-1942, equity, 1867-1938, and law, 1867-1938, cases; and book records of admiralty, bankruptcy, civil, criminal, equity, law, and naturalization matters, 1789-1942. There are similar records for the Columbia division, 1930-42.

U.S. District Court for the Western District. Records are those of the Greenville division, relating to bankruptcy, 1915-42, civil action, 1938-42, criminal, 1915-42, and equity and law, 1915-38, cases; and book records of bankruptcy, criminal, equity, and law matters, 1869-1942.

SOUTH DAKOTA. 1861-1945. 795 lin. ft. (in FRC Kansas City).

Courts of the Territory of Dakota. The records of these courts, which sat at Vermillion, Yankton, and Huron, consist of admiralty, 1868-80, bankruptcy, 1868-78, and criminal and law, 1863-89, case records; and book records in admiralty, bankruptcy, criminal, equity, and law matters, 1861-95.

U.S. District Court. The records of the southern division (Sioux Falls) include records of bankruptcy, 1899-1945, civil, 1938-45, criminal, 1887-1945, equity, 1913-38, and law, 1911-38, cases; correspondence, 1927-45; and book records of U.S. commissioners and of bankruptcy, civil, criminal, equity, and law matters, 1887-1945. There are similar records for the northern (Aberdeen), 1894-1945, western (Deadwood), 1890-1945, and central (Pierre), 1891-1945, divisions.

U.S. Circuit Court. The records of the southern division (Sioux Falls) consist of records of admiralty, equity, and law cases, 1890-1911; and book records in equity and law matters, 1889-1913. There are similar records for the divisions at Aberdeen, 1902-12, Deadwood, 1890-1908, and Pierre, 1890-1911.

TENNESSEE, EASTERN DISTRICT. 1863-1943. 1,575 lin. ft. (in FRC Atlanta).

U.S. District Court. The records of the Knoxville division include records of bankruptcy, 1901-43, civil action, 1938-43, criminal, 1894-1943, equity, 1913-38, law, 1914-42, and mixed law and equity, 1863-1938, cases; and book records of bankruptcy, criminal, equity, and law matters, 1909-43. There are similar records of the Chattanooga division, 1880-1943, and criminal case records of the Winchester division, 1941-43.

U.S. Circuit Court. Records of this court, chiefly book records of divisions at Knoxville, ca. 1880-1911, and Chattanooga, 1880-1911, are included in the records described above for the district court.

TENNESSEE, MIDDLE DISTRICT.
1797-1943. 1,654 lin. ft. (in FRC
Atlanta).

U.S. District Court. The records of the
Nashville division, with which are interfiled records of the former circuit court
for this district and of the former U.S.
district courts for the districts of Tennessee and western Tennessee, include
records in criminal and civil, 1799-1861,
mixed civil, 1842-97, bankruptcy, 1898-
1943, civil action, 1938-43, criminal,
1873-1943, equity, 1913-38, and law,
1907-38, cases; and book records in
bankruptcy, civil action, criminal, equity,
and law matters, 1797-1943, including
book records of the U.S. circuit court
for this district, ca. 1865-99 and 1909-
11. There are similar records for divisions at Columbia, 1925-43, Cookeville,
1909-43, and Winchester, 1925-41.

*Confederate States District Court for
the Middle District of Tennessee.* The
records consist of case papers, 1862-65.

TENNESSEE, WESTERN
DISTRICT. 1864-1944. 1,649 lin. ft.
(in FRC Atlanta).

U.S. District Court. The records of
this court, with which are interfiled
records, 1864-1911, of the former circuit
court for this district, were created by
divisions at Memphis and Jackson. Those
of the Memphis division include records
of bankruptcy, 1868-1944, civil action,
1938-44, criminal, 1865-1944, and equity
and law, 1864-1938, cases; and book
records of bankruptcy, criminal, equity,
and law matters, 1864-1940. There are
similar records for the division at Jackson, 1879-1944.

TEXAS, WESTERN DISTRICT.
1879-1945. 619 lin. ft. (in FRC Fort
Worth).

U.S. District Court. The records are
those of the San Antonio division relating to bankruptcy, 1898-1945, criminal,
1879-1944, equity, 1879-1938, and law,

1886-1938, cases; and book records of
bankruptcy and other matters, 1879-
1944.

U.S. Circuit Court. The records consist of the San Antonio division's law
cases, 1879-1912.

VERMONT. 1792-1945. 306 lin. ft.

U.S. District Court. The records (in
FRC Boston) include dockets, 1801-
1906; general, 1792-1841, criminal, 1906-
45, and civil, 1906-45, case files; copyright books, 1793-1830; title pages submitted for copyright, 1821-42; bankruptcy records, including dockets, 1842-1906,
assignments, 1867-78, and case files,
1867-1945; cashbooks, 1834-52; declarations of intentions for naturalization,
1859-1917; dockets of Judge Hoyt H.
Wheeler, 1877-1900; minutes, 1841-1902;
and records of U.S. commissioners,
1872-1945. Also included are records
(2 lin. ft., in WNRC) consisting of population census schedules for the 1830 and
1840 censuses in Vermont.

U.S. Circuit Court. The records (in
FRC Boston) include dockets, 1792-
1906; criminal, 1859-1912, civil, 1870-
1912, and equity, 1871-1911, case files;
and an order book, 1882-1911.

VIRGINIA, EASTERN DISTRICT.
1795-1913. 337 lin. ft. (in WNRC).

The National Archives holds only a
portion of the records of this court and
its predecessors. Many of their records,
notably the pre-Civil War records of the
circuit court, are in the Virginia State
Library.

U.S. District Court. The records consist of minutes of proceedings held at
Richmond, Alexandria, and Norfolk,
1865-90; dockets of confiscation, admiralty, and chancery cases, 1864-65 and
1873-99; confiscation records, 1863-65;
admiralty case files and related records,
1866-98; records created under the Second and Third National Bankruptcy
Acts, 1842-43 and 1867-85; criminal case
files, 1878-92, and a criminal docket,

1913; equity (chancery) case files in cases that arose from bankruptcy proceedings, 1868-84; an election supervision docket, 1868-94; habeas corpus case files, 1870-98; law case files, 1867-98; and law cases relating to internal revenue matters, 1867-96. Other records include declarations, petitions, and certificates of naturalization, 1855 and 1867-96; correspondence of the clerk, 1855-89 and 1898-1901; lists of jurors, 1866-74 and 1889-90; and case files and dockets of U.S. commissioners, 1867-73 and 1896-97.

U.S. Circuit Court. The records consist of minutes of proceedings held at Norfolk and Richmond, 1866-68; a law, bankruptcy, and equity docket, 1876-97; case files in bankruptcy cases appealed from the district court, 1868-77; error and appeal case files, 1867-78; photostatic copies of records of the Aaron Burr treason trial, 1807; criminal, 1867-93, equity, 1866-78 and 1893-1910, habeas corpus, 1868-82, and law, 1866-1911, case files; a law docket, 1866-99; an equity docket, 1866-1901; debtors writs, 1795-1840; and records concerning supervision of elections, 1870-94.

VIRGINIA, WESTERN DISTRICT. 1819-1942. 80 lin. ft. (in WNRC).

U.S. District Court. Records of the "old" court, which sat at Wytheville from 1819 to 1861, consist of criminal, 1819-61, equity, 1819-56, and law, 1820-59, case files; and appointment papers and other records of the office of the clerk, 1819-61.

Records of the "new" court, created by an act of February 3, 1871, consist of a grand jury docket, 1889-90, and other dockets, 1880-88 and 1900-1906; miscellaneous case papers, 1871-1930; civil case files, 1872-91 and 1913-29; criminal case files, 1871-1922; records created under the Third National Bankruptcy Act, 1868-85; naturalization records, 1907-17; and records of the U.S. commissioner, consisting of case files,

1889-1927, and other records, 1875-1928.

Records of the office of the clerk consist chiefly of correspondence, 1871-1936, records relating to executions, 1871-1909, writs of capias and venire facias, 1875-1934, rules of court, 1819-1942, accounting records, 1874-1927, and appointment papers, 1859-1919.

U.S. Circuit Court. Records of this court, which sat at Abingdon, consist of dockets, 1880-94 and 1907; and equity, 1871-88, law, 1871-1903, and civil (in which equity, law, and habeas corpus cases were combined), 1879-1911, case files.

Confederate States District Court for the Western District of Virginia. Records of this court, which held sessions at Staunton, Lexington, and Wytheville, include sequestration case papers, 1861-64, and a common law and chancery docket, 1861-63 (entered in an "Issue Docket" of the U.S. district court).

WASHINGTON, EASTERN DISTRICT. 1889-1944. 300 lin. ft. (in FRC Seattle).

U.S. District Court. Records consist of case and book records in bankruptcy matters, 1889-1944.

WASHINGTON, WESTERN DISTRICT. 1927. 5 reels.

U.S. District Court. The records consist of motion pictures of the Dempsey-Tunney and Dempsey-Sharkey heavyweight boxing matches, 1927.

WISCONSIN, EASTERN DISTRICT. 1849-1946. 1,257 lin. ft. (in FRC Chicago).

U.S. District Court. The records include appearance, 1849-62, and civil, 1900-1938, dockets; and bankruptcy, 1842-1944, civil, 1907-46, criminal, 1849-1946, law, 1862-1908, chancery, 1849-1908, and admiralty, 1853-1907, case files.

WISCONSIN, WESTERN DISTRICT. 1862-1947. 1,018 lin. ft. (in FRC Chicago).

U.S. District Court. Records of this court, which sat at Madison, Milwaukee, La Crosse, Superior, and Wausau, include chancery, 1873-89, bankruptcy, 1870-1929, law, 1870-77, criminal, 1870-1916, and admiralty, 1871-1925, dockets; minute books, 1870-1913; naturalization declarations, 1870-1900; equity journals, 1914-23; miscellaneous indexes, n.d., and bankruptcy, 1870-1946, law, 1870-1938, equity, 1900-1938, admiralty, 1913-46, and civil, 1938-47, case files; and records of U.S. commissioners, 1934-46.

U.S. Circuit Court. Records of this court, which sat at Madison and La Crosse, include calendars, 1870-78, of clerks, attorneys, and judges; chancery, 1870-1916, law, 1870-1910, and civil, 1870-1910, dockets; and chancery, 1865-1904, and equity, 1862-73, final records.

WYOMING. 1888-1949. 322 lin. ft. (in FRC Denver).

U.S. District Court. The records of the Cheyenne division include records in bankruptcy, 1899-1943, civil, 1888-1943, and criminal, 1890-1943, cases; book records, 1895-1949; and records of U.S. commissioners, 1894-1943. There are similar records for divisions at Evanston, 1892-1923, Lander, 1911-23, and Sheridan, 1910-20.

U.S. Circuit Court. The records include civil files, 1888-1911, final records, 1890-1908, and book records, 1895-1911, of the Cheyenne division; and civil case files, 1892-1911, of the Evanston division.

See Charles M. Hough, *Reports of Cases in the Vice Admiralty of the Province of New York and in the Court of Admiralty of the State of New York, 1715-88* (New York, 1925); Henry T. Ulasek and Marion M. Johnson, comps., *Preliminary Inventory of the Records of the United States District Court for the Southern District of New York,* PI 116 (1959); and Johnson, Mary Jo Grotenrath, and Ulasek, comps., *Preliminary Inventory of the Records of the United States District Court for the Eastern District of Pennsylvania,* PI 124 (1960).

Microfilm Publications: For a complete listing see the current *List of National Archives Microfilm Publications.*

SPECIFIC RESTRICTIONS

I. *Records*: Declarations of intention, certificates of naturalization, and certificates of arrival, regardless of the length of time they have been in existence.

Restrictions: Records of the kinds enumerated above shall not be reproduced by the National Archives (62 Stat. 683, sec. 1426 (h); 66 Stat. 163, secs. 335 (i) (2), 339 (a), and 343 (b) and (e); and 64 Stat. 583, sec. 507 (b)).

Specified by: Congress of the United States.

II. *Records*: Sealed adoption records of the U.S. District Court for the District of Columbia.

Restrictions: These records are not to be opened except on order of the court.

Specified by: U.S. District Court for the District of Columbia.

RECORDS OF THE UNITED STATES COURT OF CLAIMS (RECORD GROUP 123)

The U. S. Court of Claims was established by an act of February 24, 1855, to hear claims against the United States based on any law of the Congress, regulation of an executive department, or contract with the Government, express or implied, including all claims referred to the court by the Congress. Under this act the court was only a factfinding agency, and its conclusions were submitted to the Congress for approval and the granting of awards. In 1863 the Congress enlarged the court's jurisdiction and gave it authority to render judgments against the Government, with the right of appeal to the Supreme Court. An act of 1925 abolished appeals from the Court of Claims to the Supreme Court and substituted writs of certiorari.

Litigation before the court arises under legislation that confers either permanent or temporary jurisdiction. The court has permanent jurisdiction in general jurisdiction cases, which concern claims brought directly by claimants under general provisions of law, and in congressional and departmental cases, which concern claims referred by the Congress or by executive departments. It has had temporary jurisdiction in District of Columbia cases, French spoliation cases, and Indian depredation cases.

See *Court of Claims Reports* (1857-1968).

There are 2,840 cubic feet of records dated between 1855 and 1952, with some dated as early as 1783, in this record group.

RECORDS OF DEPARTMENTAL CASES. 1883-1949. 24 lin. ft.

These are case files referred to the court by executive agencies of the Government in accordance with the Bowman and Tucker Acts, including general cases, 1883-1949, and naval bounty cases, 1899-1903. Case records usually consist of petitions or references, motions and pleadings and replies thereto, briefs, affidavits, depositions, testimony, documents, papers in evidence, and the findings or opinion of the court.

RECORDS OF FRENCH SPOLIATION CASES. 1885-1908. 174 lin. ft.

These are claims files that arose from depredations committed by French warships and privateers upon American commerce, chiefly 1793-1801, and include ship records and other documents dated as early as 1783.

RECORDS OF DISTRICT OF COLUMBIA CASES. 1880-87. 31 lin. ft.

These are claims files based on contracts entered into by officials of the District of Columbia in the 1870's.

RECORDS OF INDIAN DEPREDATION CASES. 1891-1918. 279 lin. ft.

These concern claims for property taken or destroyed by Indians in amity with the United States, and include documents dated as early as 1812.

RECORDS OF THE GUION MILLER ENROLLMENT OF EASTERN CHEROKEES. 1906-11. 175 lin. ft.

Case files concerning enrollment to share in an award made to Eastern Cherokees by the Court of Claims (in general jurisdiction cases 23199, 23212, and 23214), including copies of some Cherokee enrollment records dated as early as 1835.

CASE FILES FOR GENERAL JURISDICTION CASES. 1855-1939. 2,060 lin. ft. (in WNRC).

Case files for suits brought directly by claimants under general provisions of law, chiefly involving Government contracts, war service, war property damage, losses incurred by disbursing officers, and the use and infringement of patent rights.

CASE FILES FOR CONGRESSIONAL CASES. 1884-1952. 722 lin. ft. (in WNRC).

Case files for claims referred by the Congress under the Bowman and Tucker Acts of March 3, 1883, and March 3, 1887, and under authority of section 151 of the Judicial Code of March 3, 1911, consist in large part of claims that arose out of the Civil War and other wars.

CARTOGRAPHIC RECORDS. ca. 1940–47. 194 items.

These consist of annotated aerial mosaics (photomaps), topographic maps of quadrangles, and large- and small-scale maps concerning Ute tribal lands and contiguous areas; annotated base maps prepared by the Department of the Interior, showing types of grazing and similar activities; negative photo-stats of "Range Survey Computation Summaries"; and related materials used by both claimant and defendant as exhibits in case No. 45585, *Confederated Bands of the Ute Indians* v. *The United States.* They are arranged in two groups, claimant's exhibits and defendant's exhibits. The case file itself is in WNRC.

See Gaiselle Kerner, comp., *Preliminary Inventory of the Records of the United States Court of Claims,* PI 58 (1953).

Discontinued Agencies

RECORDS OF THE UNITED STATES COMMERCE COURT (RECORD GROUP 172)

The U. S. Commerce Court was created by the Mann-Elkins Act of June 18, 1910, as a specialized tribunal whose jurisdiction included the enforcement, suspension, or repeal, in whole or in part, of orders of the Interstate Commerce Commission and the trial of cases arising under the Interstate Commerce Act of 1887 and amendatory acts. The jurisdiction of the court had previously been invested in the Central States circuit courts; judgments of the Commerce Court were now made reviewable by the Supreme Court. The Attorney General represented the United States in all proceedings before the court. An act of October 22, 1913, abolished the court and transferred its jurisdiction and pending cases to U. S. district courts. The court's administrative books, dockets, files, and case papers not transferred to district courts were placed in the custody of the Department of Justice.

Records of cases pending at the time the court was abolished are among records of U. S. district courts (see RG 21).

There are 22 cubic feet of records dated between 1910 and 1913 in this record group.

RECORDS. 1910–13. 26 lin. ft.

These consist of a docket, a court journal, a roll of attorneys, case files, a calendar of cases, stenographic minutes and reporters' transcripts of testimony for some cases, letters sent by the marshal, and records concerning accounts and disbursements.

PART IV

RECORDS OF THE EXECUTIVE
BRANCH

RECORDS OF PRESIDENTIAL AGENCIES

RECORDS OF THE WHITE HOUSE OFFICE
(RECORD GROUP 130)

The White House Office was established by an Executive order of September 8, 1939, as one of the five divisions of the Executive Office of the President. In addition to serving the President by performing many detailed activities, it maintains communication with the Congress, individual Members of the Congress, heads of executive agencies, the press, and the general public. In addition to records of the White House Office, this record group includes records maintained by various White House offices and officials before 1939 that were not regarded as personal papers of the Presidents.

Records of the military aide to the President that relate to arrangements for dinners, receptions, and other official and semiofficial functions at the White House, 1897-1929, are among records of the Office of Public Buildings and Grounds (see RG 42). Films relating to administrations of various Presidents and sound recordings of speeches and addresses made by various Presidents are in the National Archives Gift Collection, Record Group 200. Papers and collections of former Presidents beginning with President Hoover are in the appropriate Presidential library. Papers of many earlier former Presidents are in the Manuscript Division of the Library of Congress. The White House Office has retained many of its records.

There are 56 cubic feet of records dated between 1814 and 1959 in this record group.

RECORDS. 1814-1959. 67 lin. ft.

These records, which are closely related to those of other Government agencies, consist chiefly of copies of Executive orders and proclamations; congressional resolutions of inquiry and other resolutions, 1861-1913; Presidential messages to the Congress, 1869-1913; letters sent by President Hayes and his secretary, 1877-81; White House news releases, 1909-12; registers of Presidential nominations and appointments, 1857-1912 (with an index, ca. 1814-20), of Presidential actions taken on acts and resolutions of the Congress, 1861-1912, of court-martial cases, 1863-65 and 1870-83, of criminal pardons, 1869-85 and 1907-13, and of the disposition of requests for Executive action from Government departments, 1885-1913; and records relating to pocket vetoes, 1886-1941.

There are records concerning the "German-Bolshevik conspiracy," procured by Edgar Sisson, Associate Chairman of the Committee on Public Information, in Russia under personal orders from President Wilson and submitted by him to President Wilson in 1918, including the report of a committee of the National Board for Historical Service regarding their authenticity and a deposition by Sisson as to their custody.

Records of the World War II Medal for Merit boards (on which a Presidential assistant served as secretary) consist of case files of approved awards for the Medal for Merit, 1942-48, and the

Certificate of Merit, 1946–48; of awards withdrawn or refused, 1945–48; a name index to persons given awards, 1942–48; and correspondence and related records concerning the awards and the boards, 1942–48.

There are also motion pictures (5 reels) relating to the administrations of

Calvin Coolidge and Herbert Hoover, 1924–32, and sound and tape recordings (164 items) of speeches of and ceremonies participated in by Presidents Harry S. Truman, 1950–53, and Dwight D. Eisenhower, 1959.

RECORDS OF THE BUREAU OF THE BUDGET
(RECORD GROUP 51)

The Bureau of the Budget, under the immediate direction of the President, was established in the Department of the Treasury by an act of June 10, 1921. Reorganization Plan No. I of 1939 transferred the Bureau to the Executive Office of the President. The Bureau assists the President in formulating Government fiscal programs, clearing legislative proposals from Federal agencies, and preparing the U.S. annual budget, Executive orders, and Presidential proclamations. It develops plans to improve the efficiency and administrative management of the Government; improves, develops, and coordinates Federal and other statistical services; and informs the President about the progress of activities in Government agencies. It has inherited some functions of the President's Commission on Economy and Efficiency, the Bureau of Efficiency, and the Central Bureau of Planning and Statistics, and has assumed functions of the Central Statistical Board, the Central Statistical Committee, the Federal Board of Surveys and Maps, and the Federal Hospitalization Board. Records of some temporary executive agencies have been transferred to the Bureau.

See Gustavus A. Weber, *Organized Efforts for the Improvement of Methods of Administration in the United States* (New York, 1919); and Bureau of Efficiency, *Annual Reports*, 1916–32.

There are 1,684 cubic feet of records dated between 1905 and 1964 in this record group.

RECORDS OF THE BUREAU OF THE BUDGET. 1921–64. 1,750 lin. ft.

Included are reports, correspondence, memorandums, exhibits, statistical tables, press clippings, records of congressional hearings, copies of other congressional records, and finding aids relating to general administrative and budgetary matters in the Government, the history of general legislation, and legislation for individual cases, 1921–40. Also records of the same types relating to the functions of the Division of Administrative Management, 1937–47; Division of Estimates, 1939–52; Division of Fiscal Analysis, 1940–52; Division of Legislative Reference, 1923–64; Division of Statistical Standards, 1940–48; War Projects Unit and its predecessor, the Defense Projects Unit, concerning investigations on the progress of defense and war construction projects and production, 1940–45; Office of the Foreign Observer, 1941; Committee on Records of War Administration, 1941–47; and the Field Service, concerning the organization and administration of Federal, State, and local government field offices, 1943–53.

RECORDS OF THE PRESIDENT'S COMMISSION ON ECONOMY AND EFFICIENCY. 1905–13. 127 lin. ft.

Authorized by an act of June 25, 1910, and appointed by President William H. Taft, this Commission made a comprehensive investigation of the executive branch. It acquired some records of the Committee on Department Methods (the Keep Commission), appointed by President Theodore Roosevelt in 1905 to investigate and report ways to improve business methods and practices of Federal executive departments and discontinued in 1909. Records of the Keep Commission in this record group are interfiled with those of this Commission; some Keep Commission records are among records of the Forest Service (see RG 95). On June 30, 1913, the President's Commission on Economy and Efficiency expired.

These records consist of minutes, correspondence, and personnel and fiscal records reflecting Commission organization and activities; records relating to the history, organization, and operation of Government agencies; and records concerning Government personnel, budget-making, and business procedure problems.

RECORDS OF THE BUREAU OF EFFICIENCY. 1913-33. 232 lin. ft.

An act of February 28, 1916, gave the Division of Efficiency, created in 1913 in the Civil Service Commission, independent agency status as the Bureau of Efficiency. The Bureau served the President and administrative agencies by studying and recommending solutions for problems in organization and business methods and made special surveys at the request of heads of agencies, congressional committees, and Members of Congress. It established a system of efficiency ratings for and investigated the classes, numbers, and work of Federal employees; collected material about employee retirement; studied duplication of work by and introduced new accounting, statistical, and filing methods to Government agencies; and assisted Federal agencies in organizing large-scale operations and other activities during World War I. In 1928 the investigations of the Bureau were extended to

the District of Columbia government. An act of March 3, 1933, abolished the Bureau.

These records consist of general files that contain most Bureau records, including studies, reports, and other records relating to Government organization, personnel, equipment, financial and statistical work, and filing methods. There are also accounting records; an index, 1913-33, to subjects in Government publications and in other published material concerning Government activities; and cards describing projects or continuing functions of Government agencies, with references to cooperating agencies and agencies doing similar work.

RECORDS OF THE CENTRAL BUREAU OF PLANNING AND STATISTICS. 1918-19. 49 lin. ft.

This Bureau, headed by Edwin F. Gay, was organized in June 1918 to make a survey of Government war activities against which actual operations and results could periodically be checked. It operated as an independent agency under the President but reported through Chairman of the War Industries Board Bernard Baruch. The Bureau worked with other agencies that dealt with economic informational and statistical matters, and it operated the Central Statistical Clearing House. It prepared a *Conspectus of Special War Activities*, special reports, and periodic surveys of commodity, shipping, labor, and railroad statistics. In December 1918 the President designated the Bureau as the official source through which economic data required by the U.S. delegation to the Paris Peace Conference would be obtained. On July 1, 1919, the Bureau was dissolved, and some of its functions were transferred to the Bureau of Efficiency.

These records include minutes, weekly and special reports to the President, correspondence, memorandums, general subject files, the *Conspectus*, data accumulated for and material sent to the Paris Peace Conference, and reports and charts received or prepared by the Bureau that concern U.S. shipping, labor, prices, railroads, food, fuel, and mineral resources and production.

RECORDS OF THE FEDERAL BOARD OF SURVEYS AND MAPS. 1920-42. 8 lin. ft.

The Board of Surveys and Maps, created by Executive order in 1919, was renamed in 1936 the Federal Board of Surveys and Maps. It advised member Federal agencies on surveying and mapping matters and was abolished in 1942. The records include minutes, correspondence of the Board secretary and committees, reports concerning mapping activities, and maps (2,000 items) of the United States that show the status of topographic mapping and aerial photography, 1933-39, and areas recommended for further mapping.

RECORDS OF THE FEDERAL BOARD OF HOSPITALIZATION. 1921-48. 32 lin. ft.

This Board, established November 1, 1921, by Budget Bureau Circular 44 to coordinate Federal hospitalization activities, was abolished by Budget Bureau Circular A-27 of May 28, 1948. The records consist of minutes; resolutions; annual reports; correspondence about Board organization, policies, and operations; budgetary and other fiscal records; data concerning hospital standards and construction; surveys of hospital facilities, patient loads, and requirements; newspaper clippings, press releases, and organization charts; and site files, including records of Board hearings concerning proposed hospital sites, and Board correspondence and resolutions concerning site selection.

RECORDS OF CENTRAL STATISTICAL BOARDS. 1931-40. 41 lin. ft.

The first Central Statistical Board, created in 1933, and the second Board, created in 1935, were established to improve, develop, coordinate, and eliminate duplication in Federal and other U.S. statistical services. The Central Statistical Committee, created in 1935, supervised Board activities until Reorganization Plan No. I of 1939 transferred the Board to the Bureau of the Budget. The Board ceased to exist July 25, 1940, and the Bureau's Division of Statistical Standards assumed its functions. These records include reports, correspondence, memorandums, and statistical and other records of the Boards. There are also records of predecessor and cooperating agencies, including the Federal Statistics Board, 1931-33; Office of Economic Adviser to the National Emergency Council, 1933-35; Central Statistical Board-Works Progress Administration Coordinating Committee, and its predecessors—the Special Advisory Committee on Statistical Projects of the Civil Works Administration, the Coordinator of Civil Works Administration, and the Central Statistical Board, 1933-37; Special Committee on Returns Made by the Public to the Federal Government, 1938-39; and Committee on Government Statistics and Information Service, 1933-36, and Advisory Committee to the Secretary of Labor, 1933-35, both of the American Statistical Association.

RECORDS OF THE ADVISORY COMMITTEE ON FISCAL RELATIONS BETWEEN THE UNITED STATES AND THE DISTRICT OF COLUMBIA. 1936-37. 3 lin. ft.

On July 1, 1936, under authority of the District of Columbia appropriation act for 1937, the President directed the Bureau of the Budget to make a study of fiscal relations between the United States and the District and to determine the annual amount to be paid by the United States for the District's expenses. This Committee, appointed to make the study, submitted its final report to the President on December 19, 1936. The records consist chiefly of correspondence and memorandums concerning the creation and membership of the Committee; minutes; progress reports; reports concerning the study; maps, reports, correspondence, statistical tabulations, and other records relating to general and public school population, employment conditions, public relief, tax assessments and rates, and other social and economic conditions in the District; records about fiscal relations between foreign governments and their capital cities; and the final Committee report.

RECORDS OF THE FISCAL AND MONETARY ADVISORY BOARD. 1938-40. 5 lin. in.

This Board, appointed by President Franklin D. Roosevelt on November 18, 1938, to advise him on fiscal and monetary matters, apparently ceased to function in 1940. These records were accumulated by Acting Director of the Bureau of the Budget Daniel W. Bell as a Board member and include lists of public relief projects and Board recommendations to the President concerning those projects; memorandums from the Board, Treasury Department, and National Resources Planning Board, concerning Secretary of Agriculture Henry A. Wallace's farmers income certificate plan; summary studies of such subjects as the impact of public spending on the national economy, national production and unemployment, State and local relief legislation, and the establishment of a Federal railroad equipment authority; and letters and memorandums suggesting plans for maintaining a sound economy.

RECORDS OF THE DIRECTOR OF LIQUIDATION AND THE LIQUIDATION ADVISORY COMMITTEE. Jan.-June 1946. 1 lin. ft.

These units were created in the Office for Emergency Management by Executive order in January 1946 to assist in liquidating temporary World War II agencies. They were terminated by Executive order in June 1946. The records consist chiefly of minutes of the January 28, 1946, Committee meeting; the Director's final report; reports on the state of liquidation of emergency agencies; memorandums suggesting plans for liquidation; correspondence, memorandums, and statistical tabulations concerning such problems as release of personnel, records disposal, and release and reassignment of office space; George E. Allen's "A Study of the Liquidation of War Agencies"; reports, correspondence, and memorandums from emergency agencies concerning liquidation plans; and Executive orders and correspondence concerning creation, functions, membership, and termination of the Committee.

CARTOGRAPHIC AND AUDIOVISUAL RECORDS. 1917-61. 2,223 items.

Cartographic records, 1917-51 (2,200 items), consist of the minutes of the general meetings of the Federal Board of Surveys and Maps; correspondence files of the Secretary of the Board; maps of the United States, showing the status of aerial photography and of topographic mapping; and a published chart showing standard mapping symbols. Audiovisual records consist of photographs, 1921-61 (23 items), of Directors and other Bureau of the Budget officials.

See Gaiselle Kerner, comp., *Preliminary Inventory of the Records of the Central Bureau of Planning and Statistics*, PI 98 (1957).

SPECIFIC RESTRICTIONS

Records: All records of the Bureau of the Budget less than 15 years old.

Restrictions: No one may examine these records or be given information from them or copies of them except by permission of the Record Officer of the Bureau of the Budget.

Specified by: Bureau of the Budget.

RECORDS OF THE OFFICE OF THE SPECIAL REPRESENTATIVE FOR TRADE NEGOTIATIONS (RECORD GROUP 364)

The Office of the Special Representative for Trade Negotiations was established by Executive Order 11075 of January 15, 1963, as amended, in the Executive Office of the President, concurrently with the termination of the Committee for Reciprocity Information, whose pending business was to be completed or transferred as the Special Representative should direct. The Committee had been first established by Executive order in 1934 and was succeeded in 1948 by a new Committee for Reciprocity Information.

The Office operates under authority of the Trade Expansion Act of 1962 and Executive Order 11075, as amended. The Special Representative, who holds ambassadorial rank and is directly responsible to the President, directs the interagency Trade Executive, Trade Staff, and Trade Information Committees, the last of which performs functions of the former Committee for Reciprocity Information. He also advises and assists the President in administering the trade agreements program and advises him concerning nontariff barriers to international trade, international commodity agreements, and other matters related to the trade agreements program; and serves as Chairman of the Trade Expansion Act Advisory Committee.

There are 131 cubic feet of records dated between 1934 and 1963 in this record group.

RECORDS. 1934-63. 168 lin. ft.

Records consist of reports, correspondence and a related card index, briefs, transcripts, digests of correspondence and briefs, notices, publications, and press releases.

SPECIFIC RESTRICTIONS

Records: Records marked "Business Confidential" in the general files of the Office of the Special Representative for Trade Negotiations.

Restrictions: No one may examine these records or be given information from or copies of them except by permission of the Chairman, Trade Information Committee, Office of the Special Representative for Trade Negotiations.

Specified by: Office of the Special Representative for Trade Negotiations.

RECORDS OF THE CENTRAL INTELLIGENCE AGENCY
(RECORD GROUP 263)

The Central Intelligence Agency (CIA) was established under the National Security Council by the National Security Act of 1947. It inherited the personnel, property, and records of the Central Intelligence Group, set up under a Presidential directive of January 22, 1946, to assist the National Intelligence Authority, both of which ceased to exist when the 1947 act took effect. Headed by a director appointed by the President, the CIA coordinates intelligence activities of Government departments and agencies, correlates and evaluates intelligence relating to national security and disseminates it within the Government, advises and makes recommendations to the National Security Council concerning intelligence matters, and performs for the benefit of existing intelligence agencies such additional services of common concern as the National Security Council decides can be more efficiently carried out by a central organization. The Foreign Broadcast Information Branch of the Central Intelligence Group (see RG 262) became part of the CIA on July 26, 1947. The CIA has retained its records except those described below.

There are 133 cubic feet of records dated between 1947 and 1948 in this record group.

RECORDS OF THE FOREIGN BROADCAST INFORMATION BRANCH (LATER DIVISION). 1947-48. 133 lin. ft.

These consist of daily transcripts and summaries in English of monitored foreign radio broadcasts, 1947-48, daily teletypes of material selected for transmission to Government agencies, 1947, and daily reports of such broadcasts, 1947, with a few miscellaneous reports and notes.

RECORDS OF THE OFFICE OF SCIENCE AND TECHNOLOGY
(RECORD GROUP 359)

The Office of Science and Technology was established in the Executive Office of the President by Reorganization Plan No. 2 of 1962, and certain functions of the National Science Foundation were transferred to it. The Special Assistant to the President for Science and Technology was made Director of the Office, and the records of his former office, established on November 7, 1957, were also transferred to the new Office. The Director advises and assists the President in coordinating Federal policies for promoting basic research and education in the sciences, evaluates scientific research programs of Federal agencies, and otherwise assists the President in coordinating Federal scientific and technological functions and agencies.

Some materials relating to the Office of the Special Assistant to the President for Science and Technology are in the Dwight D. Eisenhower Library, Abilene, Kans. Other records concerning governmental scientific activity are among records of the Office of Scientific Research and Development (see RG 227) and records of the National Science Foundation (see RG 307).

There are 258 cubic feet of records dated between 1957 and 1967 in this record group.

RECORDS. 1957-67. 304 lin. ft.

Records of the Office of the Special Assistant to the President for Science and Technology consist chiefly of reports, correspondence, memorandums, and publications relating to national defense, atomic energy, space technology, and other scientific fields; records of the Office of Science and Technology consist chiefly of reports, correspondence, memorandums, studies, and scientific publications.

SPECIFIC RESTRICTIONS

Records: All records.

Restrictions: These records may not be examined by or copies of or information from them furnished to any person except by permission of the Director of the Office of Science and Technology, Executive Office of the President.

Specified by: Office of Science and Technology, Executive Office of the President.

Discontinued Agencies

RECORDS OF PRESIDENTIAL COMMITTEES, COMMISSIONS, AND BOARDS
(RECORD GROUP 220)

Temporary committees, commissions, boards, and other bodies have been appointed from time to time by the President to serve in factfinding or advisory capacities or to perform policymaking or coordinating functions with regard to the work of other executive agencies. This collective record group includes the records of a number of such bodies that have not been established as separate record groups. Excluded from this record group are records of Presidential committees, commissions, and boards that gained permanent status or whose functions and records were transferred to other agencies, those whose records have been interfiled with or otherwise have become part of the records of an agency that had them in its custody or of the White House files (now in Presidential libraries), and those bodies established to serve the heads of other agencies rather than the President.

There are 1,001 cubic feet of records dated between 1924 and 1970 in this record group.

RECORDS OF THE NATIONAL CONFERENCE ON OUTDOOR RECREATION. 1924-29. 21 lin. ft.

This Conference, composed of representatives of private and Government organizations, met in Washington in May 1924 at the President's request. Until its termination on July 1, 1929, it attempted to work out a national policy for the coordination of the outdoor recreational activities of Federal, State, municipal, and unofficial agencies, chiefly through privately financed committees.

The records include the general files of the Executive Secretary, 1924-29; records of the Joint Committee on Recreational Survey of Federal Lands, 1924-26, consisting of minutes, drafts of interim and final reports, correspondence, financial records, and copies of publications resulting from the Conference; records of the 1924 and 1926 Conference meetings; and records relating to a projected third meeting, to the work of the committees, and to subjects of interest to the Conference, such as State parks and forests, highways, wildlife, and education.

RECORDS OF THE PRESIDENT'S COMMISSION FOR THE STUDY AND REVIEW OF CONDITIONS IN THE REPUBLIC OF HAITI. 1930. 2 lin. ft. (in HHL).

A joint congressional resolution of February 6, 1930, authorized the President to make an investigation of conditions in and a study of policies relating to Haiti. The President appointed a commission under the chairmanship of W. Cameron Forbes that held hearings and made investigations in Haiti during February and March concerning political aspects of American intervention, effectiveness of American administration, and social and economic conditions. Its report was submitted on March 26, 1930. The records consist principally of minutes, reports, petitions, correspondence, and materials assembled, primarily in Haiti, concerning public health and economic conditions.

See *Report of the President's Commission for the Study and Review of Conditions in the Republic of Haiti* (1930).

RECORDS OF THE COMMITTEE ON THE CONSERVATION AND ADMINISTRATION OF THE PUBLIC DOMAIN. 1930-31. 7 lin. ft. (in HHL).

This Committee, popularly known as the Public Lands Commission, was appointed by the President under authority of an act of April 10, 1930, and submitted its report to him on February 11, 1931. Legislation resulting from its findings continued as late as 1932, and the records include correspondence dated as late as 1937.

There are drafts of the Committee's report, general records relating to administration and supplies, correspondence with the House and Senate, reports of concerned departments and bureaus,

maps showing Forest Service proposals for administering the public domain, and State maps showing the extent of unsurveyed and vacant public lands and of grazing lands in Nevada.

See the *Report* of the Committee, (1931); Senate Public Lands and Surveys Committee, *Hearings . . . on Bills to Grant Vacant, Unreserved, Unappropriated Lands to Accepting States* (1931); and House Public Lands Committee, *Hearings on H. Res. 5840, Proposing to Grant Vacant, Unreserved, Unappropriated Non-Mineral Lands to Accepting States* (1931).

RECORDS OF THE INTERDEPARTMENTAL COMMITTEE TO COORDINATE HEALTH AND WELFARE ACTIVITIES. 1935-41. 20 lin. ft. (in FDRL).

This Committee, established by the President on August 15, 1935, originally consisted of representatives of the Treasury, Interior, Agriculture, and Labor Departments, but was later augmented by representatives of the Social Security Board, Public Health Service, and National Youth Administration. The Committee sponsored cooperative working agreements among Government agencies in the fields of health and welfare, continued the work under agreements already in effect, and studied and made recommendations concerning specific aspects of Government health and welfare activities to achieve a more nearly complete coordination of them. The Committee ceased to function in 1939, but its chairman's correspondence was continued until 1941. Its files include minutes, special reports, correspondence, memorandums, and publications.

THE GOETHALS MEMORIAL COMMISSION. 1935-57. 2 lin. ft.

This Commission was established by an act of August 24, 1935, to choose a site for and a suitable memorial to George W. Goethals in commemoration of the operation of the Panama Canal. Gen. John J. Pershing was appointed

Chairman, and the memorial project was assigned to the War Department by an Executive order of July 5, 1939. Plans were suspended during World War II, and the Commission was not reactivated until May 28, 1947. The memorial was dedicated on March 31, 1954.

The records of the Commission include correspondence relating to its establishment and reactivation; minutes; general correspondence; a correspondence file of the Secretary of the Commission; and reports of the architect, P. P. Cret, with blueprints.

RECORDS OF THE INQUIRY ON COOPERATIVE ENTERPRISE IN EUROPE. June 1936–Feb. 1937. 4 lin. ft. (in FDRL).

This Inquiry, also known as the President's Commission on Cooperatives, was initiated by President Roosevelt in June 1936 "to study cooperative enterprise in Europe and to report to [the President] upon the nature, ways of operation, and place in the economic structure of consumers' cooperation, cooperative housing, and cooperative power distribution in a number of countries abroad." Six persons were appointed to conduct the study, four by the President and two by the Secretary of Agriculture at the President's direction. Investigations were conducted in various European countries, and the final report was published in February 1937. The records include a copy of the final report, material concerning interviews with people abroad, correspondence and memorandums, and press releases concerning the Inquiry's purpose and personnel.

RECORDS OF THE ADVISORY COMMITTEE ON EDUCATION. 1936–39. 12 lin. ft. (in FDRL).

The President's Committee on Vocational Education was appointed on September 19, 1936. Its scope and membership were enlarged on April 19, 1937,

and it was renamed the Advisory Committee on Education. The Committee studied the existing program of Federal aid for vocational education and prepared a report embodying its recommendations on Federal relationships to State and local conduct of education. It submitted its report in 1938 and ceased operations in 1939.

The records consist of minutes, correspondence, studies and reports, records of Committee conferences, statements submitted to or issued by the Committee, personnel files, and other material. Included are transcripts of Committee conferences held at Nashville, New Orleans, Chicago, Washington, and New York in February and March 1937; statements on vocational education submitted by other Federal agencies, by organizations and individuals outside the Government, and by the Commissioner of Education; a statement approved by the Committee when its name was changed to the Advisory Committee on Education; 17 studies by Committee staff members on various phases of education and the Government's relation to it; and a two-volume summary of the Committee's findings.

RECORDS OF THE PRESIDENT'S COMMITTEE ON CIVIL SERVICE IMPROVEMENT. 1939–41. 28 lin. ft. (in FDRL).

This Committee was established by an Executive order of January 31, 1939, to make a comprehensive study of methods of recruiting, testing, selecting, and promoting personnel for Civil Service positions. The Committee's report to Congress was issued in February 1941 (H. Doc. 118, 77th Cong., 1st sess.). The records include reports of proceedings and minutes of executive sessions, hearings, statistical and special studies, press releases, and reports from advisory committees, such as the Advisory Committees on Lawyers, Architects, Natural Scientists, Specialized Engineering

Fields, Administrators, and Social Scientists and Economists, and the Committee on Retirement.

RECORDS OF THE NATIONAL DEFENSE ADVISORY COMMISSION. 1940-42. 8 lin. ft. (in FDRL).

The Advisory Commission to the Council of National Defense, also known as the National Defense Advisory Commission, was nominated by the Council of National Defense and formally appointed by the President on May 29, 1940. It was composed of seven members (later designated commissioners): the advisers on Industrial Production, Industrial Materials, Employment, Farm Products, Price Stabilization, Transportation, and Consumer Protection. Though formally constituted as an advisory body to the Council of National Defense, the Commission in fact advised the President and at times met under his chairmanship. It had no regular chairman, but the Administrative Assistant to the President in charge of the Office for Emergency Management (the liaison officer of that Office) was the Advisory Commission's Secretary and presided at meetings not attended by the President. The Commission acted as a body on matters of general policy, but for the most part each member was separately responsible for conducting investigations, making recommendations, and organizing defense activities in his designated field.

On January 7, 1941, an administrative order of the President (6 F.R. 192) provided that the activities and agencies of the Advisory Commission should henceforth be coordinated through the Office for Emergency Management. Gradually the functions and personnel of the Commission were transferred to other agencies. On October 22, 1941, it was announced that since the Commission had been relieved of its last function, that of acting on applications for Certificates of Necessity, its meetings would be suspended indefinitely.

The records are those of the Office of the Secretary, including minutes, orders and regulations of the Council of National Defense, correspondence, press releases, and publications.

RECORDS OF THE PRESIDENT'S SOVIET PROTOCOL COMMITTEE. 1941-45. 12 lin. ft. (in FDRL).

The President's Soviet Protocol Committee was appointed by the President on October 30, 1942, to be responsible for overall coordination of lend-lease assistance to Russia. The Committee's Chairman was Harry Hopkins, and its other members were representatives of the War, Navy, State, Treasury, and Agriculture Departments; the Office of Lend-Lease Administration; the War Shipping Administration; the War Production Board; and other interested agencies. The Committee was abolished by the President on August 20, 1945. Its records include minutes of the Committee and its subcommittees, minutes of the Joint War Aid Committee, reports, cables, interoffice memorandums, correspondence with Government agencies, and related records.

RECORDS OF THE RUBBER SURVEY COMMITTEE. 1942. 8 lin. ft. (in FDRL).

This Committee, consisting of Bernard M. Baruch, James B. Conant, and Karl T. Compton, was appointed by the President on August 6, 1942, to make a "quick but adequate survey of the entire rubber question" and to recommend such action as would "best produce the synthetic rubber necessary for our total war effort including essential civilian use." The Committee conferred with representatives of the rubber industry and the Government and held formal hearings on the rubber problem. It examined military requirements, priorities, the chemical reliability of synthetic rubber processes, the effect of synthetic rubber production on other aspects of the economy, the requirements of critical materials for the rubber industry, the construction schedules needed for new rubber-manufacturing plants, and the general subject of rubber compounding and rubber substitutes. The Committee completed its investigation in about a month, and on September 10, 1942, it submitted its report to the President and was terminated. The records include transcripts of Committee hearings, reports, technical studies, correspondence, and related records concerning the rubber situation.

See Philip P. Brower, comp., *Inventory of the Records of the Rubber Survey Committee* (1947).

RECORDS OF THE PRESIDENT'S COMMITTEE ON PORTAL TO PORTAL TRAVELTIME. 1943–44. 5 lin. ft. (in FDRL).

This Committee was appointed by the President on November 8, 1943, to obtain "more exact information as to the actual travel time" in bituminous coal mining and to investigate the "possibility of reducing travel time." Chairman Morris L. Cooke represented the public, R. L. Ireland, Jr., represented the mine operators, and Thomas Kennedy represented the United Mine Workers of America. Information on which the Committee's report was based was collected by questionnaires distributed to the mines and returned to Washington for tabulation and analysis by the Solid Fuels Administration for War. Preliminary reports were submitted in February and April 1944, and the final report was made in May 1944. Records of the Committee consist of schedules, correspondence, and related material.

RECORDS OF THE AMERICAN WAR PRODUCTION MISSION IN CHINA. 1944–45. 21 lin. ft. (in FDRL).

This Mission, headed by Donald M. Nelson, personal representative of the President, was sent to China in November 1944 by President Roosevelt. Mission personnel attended meetings of the Chinese War Production Board, its staff and technical committees, and appropriate industry advisory committees and subcommittees. The Mission also coordinated its activities with those of representatives from the American Embassy, the Foreign Economic Administration, the Office of Strategic Services, the Office of War Information, and the U. S. China Theater Command. The industry programs that were carried on began with iron and steel and industrial alcohol, and grew to include all the important war production industries of Free China. Through the technical programs the Mission came into close contact with Free China's industrial structure and built up a body of information on the Chinese economy. By means of these programs the Mission provided assistance to Chinese industry both for war purposes and the postwar economy. Nelson resigned on May 15, 1945, and was replaced by Edwin A. Locke, Jr. The Mission became known as the American Production Mission in China on August 14, 1945, and was terminated in November 1945. Locke submitted his report to the President on December 18, 1945. The records of the Mission consist of the final report, other reports, memorandums, and related records.

See John E. Maddox, comp., *Preliminary Inventory of the Records of the American War Production Mission in China*, PI 88 (1955).

SPECIFIC RESTRICTIONS

Records: All records.

Restrictions: These records may be used by official and unofficial researchers only with the permission of the Department of State.

Specified by: Department of State.

RECORDS OF THE WAR REFUGEE BOARD. 1944-45. 48 lin. ft. (in FDRL).

This Board was established in the Executive Office of the President by an Executive order of January 22, 1944. It consisted of the Secretaries of State, the Treasury, and War. Its administrative functions were carried on by an Executive Director and by special attaches having diplomatic status. Its functions were, in cooperation with other Federal agencies and with foreign governments, to effect the rescue and relief of victims of Axis oppression and provide temporary refuge for them. The Board was terminated by an Executive order of September 14, 1945. The records consist of reports, memorandums, correspondence, and related records.

See Henry T. Ulasek and Ira N. Kellogg, Jr., comps., *Preliminary Inventory of the Records of the War Refugee Board*, PI 43 (1952).

SPECIFIC RESTRICTIONS

Records: All records.

Restrictions: These records may be used by official and unofficial researchers only with the permission of the Department of State.

Specified by: Department of State.

RECORDS OF THE PRESIDENT'S SCIENTIFIC RESEARCH BOARD. 1946-47. 9 lin. ft. (in HSTL).

The President's Scientific Research Board was established by Executive Order 9791 of October 17, 1946. The order provided that the Director of War Mobilization and Reconversion, John R. Steelman, should investigate and report upon the entire scientific program of the Federal Government, make recommendations concerning its content, report upon its administration and recommend administrative improvements, survey the national scientific resources of the United States, and examine the training of scientific personnel. To assist the Director the order set up an interdepartmental body known as the President's Scientific Research Board with Steelman as Chairman. The studies and investigations that formed the basis of the Chairman's report were conducted by a special staff under the direction of Executive Secretary J. Donald Kingsley. The staff obtained data from Federal agencies through questionnaires, interviews, and correspondence. Hundreds of private scientists, heads of foundations, scientific departments of universities, and industrial research laboratories contributed suggestions and advice. The activities of the Board terminated upon presentation of the Chairman's report to the President in August 1947.

The records consist of minutes of the first meeting of the Board, correspondence and memorandums relating to the survey of Federal scientific research activities and the administration of the Board's affairs, statements and supporting documents on the legal basis for research and development activities in Federal agencies, correspondence and statistical data on expenditures for research in universities, comments by certain Federal agencies on drafts of the Chairman's report, and related material.

RECORDS OF THE PRESIDENT'S ADVISORY COMMISSION ON UNIVERSAL TRAINING. 1946-47. 13 lin. ft. (in HSTL).

This Commission was appointed by President Truman on December 19, 1946, to investigate the feasibility and desirability of military training programs, including universal military training. The Commission was dissolved in May 1947 after making its final report to the President.

The records include copies of the Commission's report, minutes, correspondence of members and of the Executive Secretary, correspondence with prospective witnesses relating to testimony before the Commission, reports and other reference material accumulated by the Commission, reference files and correspondence of the director of research, and staff studies requested by the Commission.

RECORDS OF THE PRESIDENT'S AIR POLICY COMMISSION. 1947-48. 15 lin. ft. (in HSTL).

President Truman on July 18, 1947, appointed a temporary Air Policy Commission composed of private citizens to make an objective inquiry into national aviation policies and problems and to assist him in formulating an integrated national aviation policy. Thomas K. Finletter was appointed Chairman. The Commission presented its report, *Survival in the Air Age,* on January 19, 1948. Its records consist of drafts and a record copy of the report to the President; general administrative files; minutes or other records of press conferences, public hearings, executive sessions, and informal meetings; correspondence and statements filed with the Commission; background data prepared by the consultant staff; and related material.

See Henry T. Ulasek, comp., *Preliminary Inventory of the Records of the President's Air Policy Commission,* PI 49 (1952).

SPECIFIC RESTRICTIONS

Records: All records.
Restrictions: These records may not be examined by or information from or copies of them provided to any person other than a Government official for official purposes except as approved in each instance by the Archivist of the United States.
Specified by: The Commission.

RECORDS OF THE PRESIDENT'S COMMITTEE ON FOREIGN AID. 1947-48. 13 lin. ft. (in HSTL).

This Committee was created by the President on June 22, 1947, to advise him on economic assistance to foreign countries. Its membership consisted of 18 men prominent in business, finance, labor, agriculture, and education, with the Secretary of Commerce as Chairman. Administrative services were handled by the Office of International Trade, Department of Commerce. The Committee was terminated when its report was submitted to the President on November 7, 1947.

The records consist of general subject files relating to the resources, productive capacity, commodity requirements, and foreign exchange problems of foreign countries; plans for the rehabilitation of the Western European economy; the economic impact on the United States of foreign aid; and U. S. exports and imports of various goods.

RECORDS OF THE PRESIDENT'S COMMITTEE ON EQUALITY OF TREATMENT AND OPPORTUNITY IN THE ARMED SERVICES. 1949-50. 5 lin. ft. (in HSTL).

This Committee, popularly known as the Fahy Committee, was established by Executive Order 9981 of July 26, 1948, to determine in what ways operations of the armed services might be altered or improved to ensure equality of treatment and opportunity for all members without regard to color, religion, or national origin. The Committee's final report was submitted to the President on May 22, 1950. The records include transcripts of Committee meetings, correspondence, drafts of reports, and newspaper clippings and records relating to rules and procedures followed by the Army, Navy, Air Force, and Coast Guard in utilizing personnel from minority groups.

RECORDS OF THE COMMISSION ON THE RENOVATION OF THE EXECUTIVE MANSION. 1945-52. 26 lin. ft.

This Commission was established by an act of April 14, 1949, to plan and supervise the renovation of the White House. Maj. Gen. Glen E. Edgerton was Executive Director. Its final report was submitted on September 30, 1952, and the Commission was terminated 30 days later.

The records of the Commission include minutes, with an index; general correspondence and memorandums; letters sent; an inventory of public property in and belonging to the White House on June 30, 1949; photographs, 1945-52 (1,002 items), of the White House before renovation and during its progress; blueprints and architectural drawings of the renovation; legislative reference material; and orders and other records concerning the sale of souvenirs.

See Bess Glenn, comp., *Preliminary Inventory of the Records of the Commission on the Renovation of the Executive Mansion, PI 117 (1959).*

SPECIFIC RESTRICTIONS

Records: Blueprints, drawings, and photographs of the White House.

Restrictions: No access may be had to these records without the express approval of the U. S. Secret Service.

Specified by: The U. S. Secret Service.

RECORDS OF THE PRESIDENT'S ADVISORY COMMITTEE ON MANAGEMENT IMPROVEMENT. 1949-53. 1 lin. ft. (in HSTL).

This Committee was initiated by Executive Order 10072 of July 29, 1949, in response to a recommendation of the Commission on Organization of the Executive Branch of the Government (the first Hoover Commission) for the establishment of a Presidential program designed to improve Federal administration throughout the Government. The records include the Committee's final report to the President made on December 18, 1952; interim reports dated November 3, 1950, and August 7, 1951; agenda and related documents pertaining to each of the 17 meetings held by the Committee between October 1949 and December 1952; and files on organization and membership of the Committee, program planning records, and correspondence.

RECORDS OF THE PRESIDENT'S COMMISSION ON MIGRATORY LABOR. 1950-51. 6 lin. ft. (in HSTL).

This Commission was created by Executive Order 10129 on June 3, 1950, to inquire into and report on the social, economic, health, and educational conditions among domestic and alien migratory workers; the problems created by their migration to the United States; the responsibilities being assumed by Federal, State, county, and municipal authorities concerning them; the need for foreign workers to supplement the domestic labor supply; and the extent of and problems created by illegal migration of foreign workers to the United States and how enforcement measures might be strengthened and improved to eliminate such migration. Maurice T. Van Hecke was appointed Chairman. The Commission published its report on April 6, 1951, and was terminated on May 31, 1951.

The records consist of record copies of the Commission's two-volume printed report, originals of charts used in the report, transcripts of hearings, statements submitted in connection with hearings, staff studies and related background material, and administrative files.

See President's Commission on Migratory Labor, *Migratory Labor in American Agriculture* (1951); and Hardee Allen, comp., *Preliminary Inventory of the Records of the President's Commission on Migratory Labor*, PI 86 (1955).

RECORDS OF THE PRESIDENT'S WATER RESOURCES POLICY COMMISSION. 1950-51. 25 lin. ft. (in HSTL).

This Commission was created by Executive Order 10095 of January 3, 1950, to study the problem of Federal responsibility for and participation in the development, utilization, and conservation of water resources, including related land uses and other public purposes to the extent they were directly concerned with water resources. Morris L. Cooke was appointed Chairman. Organized into a number of committees, the Commission consulted with experts, gathered data and opinions from private institutions and persons and from Federal agencies, and held regional conferences. It issued a three-volume report and prepared a proposed "Water Resources Act of 1951." In March 1951 the Commission terminated its activities.

The records consist of preliminary and final drafts of the report; minutes, memorandums, reports, and correspondence of the various committees relating to the Commission's deliberations; correspondence and other records concerning the establishment, organization, relations, and meetings of the Commission; correspondence with and reports and statements from Federal agencies, State and local governments, and private institutions, associations, and individuals; proceedings of regional conferences; data concerning national and State laws; staff memorandums and the Chairman's correspondence with the Commissioners, concerning the preparation and release of the Commission's report; and recommendations concerning national water resources legislation.

RECORDS OF THE PRESIDENT'S COMMISSION ON INTERNAL SECURITY AND INDIVIDUAL RIGHTS. 1951-52. 4 lin. ft. (in HSTL).

This Commission was established by Executive Order 10207 on January 23, 1951, with Fleet Adm. Chester W. Nimitz as Chairman, to consider the problem of providing for the internal security of the United States and at the same time protecting the rights of individuals. The areas considered by the Commission were to include the Government's employee-loyalty and employee-security programs. Its members resigned when Congress failed to pass legislation exempting them from the operation of conflict-of-interest laws. In the absence of such legislation, the President declared it was virtually impossible to appoint new satisfactory members and issued Executive Order 10305 on November 15, 1971, revoking the order that established the Commission.

The records consist of interim reports, minutes, a subject file containing correspondence, memorandums, press releases, and related materials documenting the organization, administration, and planning of the Commission, including offers of cooperation and suggestions on internal security problems from interested individuals and organizations, and requests from persons dismissed from Government employment as security risks or for questionable loyalty for consideration of their cases; an alphabetical file of miscellaneous correspondence; an alphabetical card index to the files; mounted press clippings; and a scrapbook of official actions of and regarding the Commission.

RECORDS OF THE PRESIDENT'S COMMISSION ON THE HEALTH NEEDS OF THE NATION. 1951-52. 27 lin. ft. (in HSTL).

This Commission was established by Executive Order 10317 on December 29, 1951, to make a critical study of the requirements, both immediate and long term, for safeguarding and improving the health of the Nation, and to recommend appropriate governmental action. The Commission organized panels of inquiry on various subjects, at which experts clarified and suggested solutions for existing problems, and conducted public hearings in various cities to obtain information on health needs at the local level. The Commission, headed by Paul Magnuson, was composed of eminent doctors and representatives of universities and farm, labor, and consumer organizations. The Commission ceased to exist 1 year after the date of the order creating it.

The records consist of transcripts of Commission meetings, of meetings of panels of inquiry, and of public hearings; official correspondence of the Chairman; correspondence, statistical data, and research materials of the office of the director of studies; and correspondence, memorandums, press releases, newspaper clippings, and a file of statements and addresses made at public hearings, arranged by subject matter, and maintained by the publicity director.

RECORDS OF THE PRESIDENT'S MATERIALS POLICY COMMISSION. 1951–52. 55 lin. ft. (in HSTL).

This Commission was created by a Presidential letter of January 22, 1951, which also appointed William S. Paley as Chairman. The Commission, as part of the Executive Office of the President, was directed to inquire into the major aspects of the problem of assuring an adequate supply of production materials for the Nation's long-range needs and to make recommendations for formulation of a comprehensive policy on such materials. It was to study matters such as the outlook for the country's long-range requirements and supply, the prospect of shortages, and the adequacy of existing Government policies and programs and of practices of private industry. The Commission was assisted by other Government agencies, particularly the National Security Resources Board, and individuals and organizations out-

side the Government. The Commission was terminated June 2, 1952, when its final report was issued.

The records consist of a report file that includes unpublished reports prepared chiefly by the Battelle Memorial Institute and a copy of the Commission's report; drafts of the Commission's report; correspondence, administrative, and general subject files; questionnaires on minerals and metals production and forest resources and production, summaries, and correspondence with companies about the questionnaires; files relating to such subjects as taxation and incentives, statistics, energy resources, commodities, security and market policy, construction materials, and stockpiling of strategical and critical materials; and editorial files concerning the Commission's report.

See President's Materials Policy Commission, *Resources for Freedom* (5 vols., 1952).

RECORDS OF THE PRESIDENT'S COMMISSION ON IMMIGRATION AND NATURALIZATION. 1952–53. 6 lin. ft. (in HSTL).

This Commission was established by Executive Order 10392 on September 4, 1952, to study U.S. immigration and naturalization policies and to make recommendations for such legislative, administrative, or other action that would best serve the interests, needs, and security of the Nation. It was composed of seven members with Philip B. Perlman, former Solicitor General of the United States, as Chairman. It held public hearings in various cities at which any interested person could appear. To assure attendance of qualified persons, the Commission invited certain individuals and organizations with experience and knowledge of immigration problems to express their views. It also held a number of executive conferences with Federal officials in charge of immigration programs. The Commission submitted its final report to the President on January 1, 1953, and, in accordance with the directive creating it, ceased to exist on January 30, 1953.

The records consist of statements of witnesses who testified at hearings and statements submitted to the Commission for consideration; special studies submitted by certain Government agencies on immigration matters peculiar to each agency; galleys, printer's copy, and drafts of the Commission's report, and galleys of transcripts of hearings and special studies; and a file of correspondence relating to the conduct of public hearings and the preparation of the Commission's report.

RECORDS OF THE MISSOURI BASIN SURVEY COMMISSION.
1952-53. 13 lin. ft. (in HSTL).

This Commission was established by an Executive order of January 3, 1952, to study the land and water resources of the Missouri River Basin and make recommendations for their better protection, development, and use. During May and June 1952 the Commission held public hearings at Denver, Colo.; Sioux City, Iowa; Manhattan and Topeka, Kans.; St. Paul, Minn.; Herman, St. Charles, Jefferson City, and Kansas City, Mo.; Billings and Great Falls, Mont.; Lincoln, Nebr.; Bismarck, N. Dak.; Aberdeen and Pierre, S. Dak.; and Worland, Wyo. A final report, dated December 29, 1952, was submitted to the President on January 12, 1953. The Commission's records include transcripts of hearings, an administrative file, maps, charts, photographs, newspaper clippings regarding the Commission's activities, and a reference file.

RECORDS OF THE COMMISSION ON INTERGOVERNMENTAL RELATIONS. 1953-55. 45 lin. ft. (in DDEL).

This Commission was established by an act of July 10, 1953 (67 Stat. 145), that provided for a study and investiga-

tion of the activities through which Federal aid was extended to State and local governments, the interrelationships of the financing of this aid, and the sources of financing governmental programs. The Commission was also to determine whether there was justification for existing Federal-aid programs, for their limitation, and for their extension to additional fields. Clarence Manion was appointed Chairman in September 1953 and served until February 1954. Following his resignation Meyer Kestnbaum was appointed Chairman in April 1954 and served until the Commission submitted its report and was terminated on June 30, 1955.

The records consist of central files, comprising all the Commission's records, arranged by a subject-numeric filing system, and consisting of minutes, preliminary and final drafts of reports, background studies, survey studies, correspondence, and memorandums relating to the organization and membership of the Commission and its studies and recommendations concerning education, unemployment compensation and employment services payments in lieu of taxes and shared revenues, local government, national disaster relief, vocational rehabilitation, civil defense, and Federal grants-in-aid to the States. There is an alphabetical index to the central files, consisting of copies of outgoing correspondence and cross-reference forms showing names of writers of selected letters received and subjects of correspondence and of other material in the files.

RECORDS OF THE PRESIDENT'S ADVISORY COMMITTEE ON GOVERNMENT ORGANIZATION.
1953-61. 10 lin. ft. (in DDEL).

This Committee was established by Executive Order 10432 of January 24, 1953, to advise the President, his assistant, and the Director of the Bureau of the Budget concerning changes in the organization and activities of the executive branch that would promote economy and efficiency in its operations. The Committee was abolished by Executive Order 10917 on February 10, 1961.

The records include minutes, reports, memorandums, correspondence, and other materials relating to the organization, administration, operation, and liquidation of the Committee. Included are correspondence with the White House, budget reports, biographical sketches of personnel, and records concerning plans for establishing or reorganizing agencies.

SPECIFIC RESTRICTIONS

Records: All records of the Committee.

Restrictions: These records may not be made available to any person without the written permission of the Director of the Office of Management and Budget or his authorized representative.

Specified by: Office of Management and Budget.

RECORDS OF THE PRESIDENT'S ADVISORY COMMISSION ON PRESIDENTIAL OFFICE SPACE. 1956-57. 1 lin. ft.

This Commission was appointed by the President under authority of an act of August 3, 1956, with Robert V. Fleming as Chairman. It studied the problem of office space for the Executive Office of the President and made its report on May 31, 1957. The records include a general file, which contains minutes, reports, proposed plans for Presidential office space, correspondence, and press releases; floor plans; and a chart of personnel and space requirements.

RECORDS OF THE PRESIDENT'S COMMITTEE FOR HUNGARIAN REFUGEE RELIEF. 1956-57. 19 lin. ft. (in DDEL).

As a result of the suppression of the Hungarian revolution of 1956, thousands of refugees fled from Hungary, chiefly to Austria. To coordinate all efforts for aiding the refugees, President Eisenhower appointed Tracy S. Voorhees Coordinator for Hungarian Relief on November 29, 1956, and on December 12, 1956, announced creation of the President's Committee for Hungarian Refugee Relief, with Voorhees as Chairman. The Committee's chief function was to coordinate the work of voluntary agencies with related activities of Government agencies, such as the State Department, the International Cooperation Administration, the Immigration and Naturalization Service, the Air Force, and the Navy, which were primarily responsible for the transfer of the refugees to the United States. The Committee received offers of homes and jobs for refugees and made these offers available for use by the voluntary agencies. Refugees coming to the United States were taken to the Joyce Kilmer Reception Center at Camp Kilmer, N.J., where the Army housed and fed them and provided other necessary care pending their resettlement. The Committee released its final report and completed its activities on May 14, 1957.

The records of the Committee consist of a general subject file of its Washington office, which concerns all activities of the Committee and includes its report, minutes, and correspondence with Congressmen; a general subject file of the Kilmer Reception Center, consisting chiefly of congressional and other correspondence concerning subjects such as housing, employment, and education for the refugees; subject files of the Administrative Services Office and of the chief of the Public Information Office at the Kilmer Reception Center; forms and letters received concerning offers to adopt refugee orphans and offers of employment and housing; and mimeographed copies of reports of the Intergovernmental Committee for European Migration from the Operations Office at Salzburg, Austria, in regard to the movement of Hungarian refugees, consisting chiefly of lists of refugees transported to the United States.

RECORDS OF THE PRESIDENT'S SCIENCE ADVISORY COMMITTEE. 1957-61. 2 lin. ft. (in DDEL).

The Science Advisory Committee was first established by the President on April 20, 1951, within the Office of Defense Mobilization. The Committee was reconstituted and enlarged on November 22, 1957, and transferred to the White House as the President's Science Advisory Committee on December 1, 1957. The Committee's purpose was to advise the President on matters relating to a national policy on science and technology. The records consist of minutes and agenda for committee meetings, briefing papers, memorandums, correspondence, and printed materials relating to the Committee's work.

RECORDS OF THE PRESIDENT'S COMMITTEE ON EMPLOYMENT OF THE HANDICAPPED. 1957-66. 1 lin. ft.

This Committee was established by Executive Order 10994 of February 14, 1962, as amended, to continue the work of the President's Committee on Employment of the Physically Handicapped provided for under Executive Order 10640 of October 10, 1955. The Committee was to facilitate the development of maximum employment opportunities for the handicapped.

The records consist of five documentary films produced for the Committee: a film concerning the 1957 annual meeting of the Committee (6 reels); "The Boy Who Couldn't Walk," the Glen Cunningham story (1 reel); "The Fire Within," concerning the training of the handicapped (1 reel); and two 1-minute television spots featuring President Eisenhower and Roy Campanella (2 reels).

RECORDS OF THE PRESIDENT'S COMMITTEE TO STUDY THE U.S. MILITARY ASSISTANCE PROGRAM. 1958-59. 11 lin. ft. (in DDEL).

This Committee was appointed by President Eisenhower on November 24, 1958, to make a "completely independent, objective, and non-partisan analysis of the military assistance aspects of our Mutual Security Program," as the President stated in a letter to the Chairman, William H. Draper. The Committee submitted interim reports on March 17, June 3, and July 13, 1959, and a final report on July 13, 1959.

The records of the Committee include the composit Committee report, minutes, correspondence, central files, staff studies, indexes, and newsclippings.

RECORDS OF THE COMMISSION ON INTERNATIONAL RULES OF JUDICIAL PROCEDURE. 1959-66. 42 lin. ft.

This Commission was created by Public Law 85-906 of September 2, 1958, to study existing procedures of judicial assistance and cooperation between the United States and foreign countries, and to recommend improvements. The members of the Commission chose their chairman, a director (who was to serve as a reporter and administrator of the Commission staff), and an advisory committee. The Commission was extended by Public Laws 86-287, 87-324, and 88-522 until December 31, 1966.

The records are those of the Director and his staff, which consist of general records relating to the advisory committee as well as office and administrative records. Included are minutes, reports, correspondence, legal documents, press releases, speeches, lectures, publications, reference materials, draft legislation, memorandums, and working papers. These records do not include the records of the Chairman, the advisory committee chairman, working papers of the Columbia Law School project on international procedure, and working papers of the six project subcommittees of the advisory committee. The Director retained certain records for use in writing the final Commission report and for completing its work through other organizations.

SPECIFIC RESTRICTIONS

I. *Records*: Any records originating with the Department of Justice that are less than 25 years old.
   Restrictions: Only authorized employees of the Department of Justice and other persons specifically authorized by the Attorney General or his alternate may have access to these records.
   Specified by: Department of Justice.
II. *Records*: All records originating with the Department of State.
   Restrictions: These records may be used by official and nonofficial researchers only with the permission of the Department of State.
   Specified by: Department of State.

RECORDS OF THE PRESIDENTIAL RAILROAD COMMISSION. 1961-62. 99 lin. ft. (in JFKL).

This Commission was established by Executive Order 10891 of November 1, 1960, to study a dispute between the major rail carriers and the five brotherhoods of operating employees involving the manning of engines and trains, the structure of the pay system, rules governing the assignment of employees and other work rules, and maintenance of employee security. Secretary of Labor Mitchell and later Simon H. Rifkind served as Chairman. The Commission held extensive public hearings on railroad labor-management relations and made its report on February 28, 1962.

The records include the Commission's report, transcripts of proceedings, exhibits presented by employers and workers, studies and contracts for studies, and press releases; general files of the Chairman and the Executive Director; and administrative and studies files, reference material, and other records of the Executive Director.

SPECIFIC RESTRICTIONS

Records: Records in the general files of the Commission's Chairman, Executive Director, and Deputy Executive Director that were not circulated to the full Commission.
Restrictions: These records are closed to unofficial inquires until March 1, 1982, except as authorized by the Secretary of Labor, the Administrative Assistant Secretary, or a representative of either.
Specified by: Department of Labor.

RECORDS OF THE PRESIDENT'S COMMISSION ON THE STATUS OF WOMEN. 1961-63. 7 lin. ft. (in JFKL).

This Commission was established by Executive Order 10980 of December 14, 1961, and was headed by Eleanor Roosevelt. Its main functions were to study discriminations against women in governmental and private employment, recommend constructive action to eliminate it, and provide services that would enable women to continue their roles as mothers and homemakers while at the same time making a maximum contribution to national life. The Commission submitted its report to the President on October 11, 1963.

The records of the Commission include minutes, reports, transcripts, correspondence, press releases, and drafts and a copy of the final report.

RECORDS OF THE PRESIDENT'S COMMITTEE ON EQUAL OPPORTUNITY IN THE ARMED FORCES. 1961–65. 10 lin. ft. (in LBJL).

The establishment of this Committee was set forth in a letter from President Kennedy to the Chairman, Gerhard A. Gesell, dated June 22, 1962. The Commission considered means of improving equality of opportunity in the Armed Forces.

The records consist of drafts of the report, correspondence, research studies, and questionnaires with replies.

SPECIFIC RESTRICTIONS

Records: All records of the Committee.
Restrictions: These records will be made available only upon the written authorization of an appropriate White House officer.
Specified by: The Committee.

RECORDS OF THE PRESIDENT'S COMMITTEE ON JUVENILE DELINQUENCY AND YOUTH CRIME. 1961–67. 17 lin. ft.

The 1960 White House Conference on Children and Youth called for expansion of the Federal role in stimulating action to cope with the national problem of juvenile delinquency, asking that a Federal commission be appointed "to advise the President and Congress on matters relating to delinquency, including general coordination of Federal activities in this field . . . ." In anticipation of the passage of the Juvenile Delinquency and Youth Offenses Control Act of 1961, President Kennedy established this Committee by Executive Order 10940 of May 11, 1961. It was composed of the Attorney General as Chairman, the Sec-

retary of Labor, and the Secretary of Health, Education, and Welfare, and was to coordinate Federal activities relating to juvenile delinquency and youth crime and to promote cooperation and sharing of information between Federal agencies and concerned State, local, and private organizations.

The records include a publications file, project and program files, correspondence, speeches, memorandums, and a file of publications issued by or with the help of the Committee.

SPECIFIC RESTRICTIONS

Records: All records of the Committee.
Restrictions: Requests for access to these records are to be referred to the Assistant Attorney General for Administration, Department of Justice.
Specified by: Department of Justice.

RECORDS OF THE PRESIDENT'S COMMITTEE ON EQUAL OPPORTUNITY IN HOUSING. 1962–68. 40 lin. ft. (in LBJL).

This Committee was established November 20, 1962, by Executive Order 11063 to recommend general policies and procedures relating to the prevention of discrimination in housing in which the Government had a primary interest, to check on the progress made by the departments and agencies subject to this order and promote coordination of their activities, and to encourage educational programs for eliminating the causes of housing discrimination. It was terminated June 30, 1968.

The records consist of reports prepared for the President and the heads of various Government agencies; correspondence of the Chairman, the General Counsel, and other Committee members; transcripts of meetings and conferences; copies of speeches; and material relating to housing activities in the United States.

RECORDS OF THE PRESIDENT'S COMMISSION ON REGISTRATION AND VOTING PARTICIPATION.
1963-64. 11 lin. ft. (in JFKL).

This Commission was created by Executive Order 11100 on March 30, 1963, to study and report by November 30, 1963, on the causes of the generally low rate of participation in the electoral processes of the Nation. Twenty-one recommendations ("Standards"), directed to the States, were presented to the President in the final report on December 20, 1963. On the same day the Commission was extended to March 30, 1964, by Executive Order 11134 to allow the States time to consider the proposals and to provide information and services to those States that desired this assistance. The records consist of correspondence, published material relating to the election laws of all the States, staff studies and reference material, and administrative support files.

RECORDS OF THE PRESIDENT'S COMMITTEE ON EQUAL EMPLOYMENT OPPORTUNITY.
1963-65. 2 lin. ft.

This Committee was established by Executive Order 10925 of March 6, 1961, as amended by Executive Order 11114 of June 22, 1963. It studied employment practices of the Federal Government and large employers and recommended steps to completely eliminate discrimination in employment within the executive branch and by Government contractors. The Committee's functions were transferred to the Department of Labor by Executive Order 11126 of September 24, 1965.

The records include memorandums showing committee deliberations; correspondence, chiefly of the White House Press Secretary with civil rights leaders; and case files concerning discrimination in large firms.

RECORDS OF THE TEMPORARY ALASKA CLAIMS COMMISSION.
1964-65. Negligible (in LBJL).

By Executive Order 11144 of March 5, 1964, a Commission was appointed to settle disputes with regard to the transfer of Federal property to the State of Alaska. The Commission concluded its business on March 5, 1965. Its records consist chiefly of the Commission's report, copies of oaths and commissions, correspondence, financial statements, vouchers, and two aerial photographs showing the area around Anchorage and approximate settlement boundaries.

RECORDS OF THE NATIONAL ADVISORY COMMISSION ON SELECTIVE SERVICE. 1966-67.
48 lin. ft.

This Commission was established by Executive Order 11289 of July 2, 1966, to consider and report on the functioning of selective service and other systems of national service in the light of various relevant factors, and to make recommendations concerning selective service matters. Its records include first and second drafts of the final report, copies of verbatim transcripts of Commission meetings, Commission staff papers, studies, interviews and records of tests or surveys filed by subject or name of person involved, selected reference and research material, correspondence, proposals and plans submitted for the Commission's consideration, drafts and working papers concerning various phases of studies and investigations, and index cards to correspondence and material in subject files.

See National Advisory Commission on Selective Service, *In Pursuit of Equity: Who Serves When Not All Serve?* (1967).

RECORDS OF THE PRESIDENT'S COMMISSION ON POSTAL ORGANIZATION. 1967-68. 33 lin. ft.

This Commission was established April 8, 1967, by Executive Order 11341 to recommend better ways of organizing and operating the postal service. It concluded its business in July 1968. The records consist of drafts of the Commission's reports; minutes; alphabetical subject files relating to the Commission's functions, activities, and administration; rejected proposals for studies; "chronological files" of the Commission's correspondence, memorandums, reports, and speeches; staff studies; papers of consultants; contract files; administrative and personnel records; and press releases and clippings.

SPECIFIC RESTRICTIONS

Records: "Commission Hearings" and "Commission Interviews: Prominent Individuals" among the records.

Restrictions: Access to these records is subject to the approval of the Postmaster General or his authorized representative.

Specified by: Post Office Department.

RECORDS OF THE PRESIDENT'S COMMITTEE ON URBAN HOUSING. 1967-68. 29 lin. ft. (in LBJL).

This Committee was appointed by the President on June 3, 1967, to prepare a report on ways to stimulate rebuilding depressed areas of American cities. The study focused on the role of the private sector of the economy in rebuilding urban housing and methods enlarging the size and skills of the labor force available for rehabilitative work. The Committee was terminated when its report was submitted to the President on August 31, 1968. Its records include minutes, reports, correspondence, and other records relating to legislative research, housing goals, research and technology, manpower, and land.

SPECIFIC RESTRICTIONS

Records: Minutes of the Committee's meetings and the Executive Director's files; correspondence of Committee members; correspondence with the White House; and the Committee's interim report to the President (not released or intended for release).

Restrictions: Access to these records is limited to persons having the written permission of an authorized member of the White House Staff.

Specified by: The Committee.

RECORDS OF THE PRESIDENT'S COMMISSION FOR THE OBSERVANCE OF HUMAN RIGHTS YEAR 1968. 1968-69. 1 lin. ft.

This Commission was appointed by Executive Order 11394 of January 30, 1968, to "promote the effective observance in the United States of 1968 as the 20th Anniversary of the United Nations Universal Declaration of Human Rights." The order stipulated that the Commission provide a focus for the interest of official bodies sharing its purpose and enlist the cooperation of organizations planning to participate in the observance. The Commission could engage in other activities it deemed appropriate, such as conducting studies, issuing reports and other publications, and holding public or private meetings at times to be determined by the Chairman.

The records include copies of documents relating to the Commission's establishment, minutes, agendas, working papers, reports of committees, speeches, articles, correspondence, press clippings, programs of the Commission's three conferences, papers pertaining to related conferences (the Montreal Assembly and the Tehran Conference), a list of publications, proclamations of Governors, photographs (62 items), a set of the Commission's publications, and sound recordings (25 items) of conferences and radio broadcasts.

RECORDS OF THE PRESIDENT'S COMMISSION ON INCOME MAINTENANCE PROGRAMS. 1968–70. 18 lin. ft.

This Commission was appointed by the President on January 2, 1968, to investigate existing welfare and related programs and to make recommendations for constructive improvements. Its records consist of transcripts of hearings, reports of studies prepared by or for the Commission, correspondence, clippings from journals and newspapers, and data printouts.

SPECIFIC RESTRICTIONS

Records: Transcripts of closed meetings (executive sessions) of the commissioners.

Restrictions: No one may have access to these records until February 26, 1980.

Specified by: The Commission.

RECORDS OF THE PRESIDENT'S COMMISSION ON AN ALL-VOLUNTEER ARMED FORCE. 1969–70. 8 lin. ft.

In January 1969 the President asked the Secretary of Defense to initiate a study within the Department of Defense on ending the draft, and, after consultation with his staff, appointed this Commission on March 27, 1969. Its records include reports, minutes, basic source documents, and correspondence documenting its activities until its termination on March 26, 1970.

RECORDS OF THE PRESIDENT'S TASK FORCE ON INTERNATIONAL DEVELOPMENT. 1969–70. 7 lin. ft.

On September 2, 1969, the President announced the establishment of this Task Force that was to make comprehensive recommendations on the U.S. role in assisting less-developed countries in the 1970's. Its records include reports, minutes, Government and private studies, background reference material, and correspondence.

CARTOGRAPHIC RECORDS. 1918–31. 35 items.

Maps prepared by the Committee on the Conservation and Administration of the Public Domain, relating to national forests, public lands, minerals, Indian reservations, and agriculture in the Western States; and a map of Alaska, compiled by the Alaska Railroad, Department of the Interior, showing routes of the Alaska Railroad and River Service, steamship routes, and commercial river lines.

RECORDS OF THE COMMITTEE ON PUBLIC INFORMATION
(RECORD GROUP 63)

The committee on Public Information was created by an Executive order of April 13, 1917, with George Creel as Chairman and the Secretaries of State, War, and the Navy as ex officio members. Its functions were to release Government news during World War I, sustain morale, and administer voluntary press censorship. Authors, artists, professors, and volunteer speakers (the "four minute men") contributed their services. Commissioners were stationed at major foreign capitals to represent the Committee. After July 1, 1918, the work of the Committee was curtailed, and after the signing of the Armistice its domestic activities were discontinued. Some of the foreign work was continued until June 30, 1919, when the Committee ceased to function. By an Executive order of August 21, 1919, the Committee was abolished and the liquidation of its affairs assigned to the Council of National Defense.

Some of the Committee's records were distributed among other agencies and never reassembled. In 1928, 1930, and 1962 many of the remaining routine records were disposed of under congressional authority. Documents relating to the "German-Bolshevik conspiracy," procured by Edgar Sisson in Russia in 1918, are among records of the White House Office (see RG 130).

See Committee on Public Information, *Complete Report of the Chairman* (1920); George Creel, *How We Advertised America* (New York, 1920); Waldo G. Leland and Newton D. Mereness, comps., *Introduction to the American Official Sources for the Economic and Social History of the Great War* (New Haven, 1926); and James R. Mock and Cedric Larson, *Words That Won the War* (Princeton, 1939).

There are 92 cubic feet of records dated between 1917 and 1919 in this record group.

RECORDS. 1917–19. 110 lin. ft.

These consist of general correspondence and other records of the Chairman and Associate Chairman; records of nearly all divisions concerned with domestic activities, including reports and correspondence relating to the preparation and distribution of information, the use of motion picture film and photographs, the work of the "four minute men," the war work of women, copy prepared for publication, bulletins, copies of speeches, photographs, news releases, and card lists of speakers; records of the Director of the Foreign Information Section and of the divisions concerned with foreign activities, including correspondence with representatives abroad, telegrams, press releases, posters, and reports relating to the gathering of data abroad and the dissemination of information about the United States in foreign countries; and some records of officials in the Soviet Union and commissioners at Paris, Rome, Madrid, The Hague, London, Santiago, Buenos Aires, and Lima.

RECORDS OF THE PRESIDENT'S ORGANIZATION ON UNEMPLOYMENT RELIEF
(RECORD GROUP 73)

The President's Organization on Unemployment Relief and its predecessor, the President's Emergency Committee for Employment, were established to stimulate and coordinate employment and relief activities during the economic depression that began in 1930. The Emergency Committee had been preceded by a committee organized on October 17, 1930, of six Cabinet members and the Governor of the Federal Reserve Board. On October 21, 1930, the President appointed Col. Arthur Woods to organize and chair a special committee of industrialists, economists, and Government officials. The Emergency Committee (the Woods Committee) was to work in an advisory and facilitative capacity with State and local governments and quasi-public and private organizations. On August 19, 1931, the Emergency Committee was reorganized as the President's Organization on Unemployment Relief, with Walter S. Gifford as Director. The President appointed a nationwide Advisory Committee to assist Gifford. Through committees created from the membership of the Advisory Committee, the Organization worked with relief and employment agencies in sponsoring programs, encouraged public works construction, and served as a clearinghouse for ideas and information. It was terminated June 30, 1932, when Congress failed to appropriate funds to continue its work.

See Erving P. Hayes, *Activities of the President's Emergency Committee for Employment, 1930-31* (Concord, 1936).

There are 107 cubic feet of records dated between 1930 and 1933, with a few dated as early as 1928, in this record group.

RECORDS. 1928-33. 226 lin. ft.

These include records of the Office of the Secretary, consisting of files of Edward Eyre Hunt, chiefly as Secretary of the Committee on Recent Economic Changes and as Executive Secretary of the President's Research Committee on Social Trends, 1928-31; a card index of names of members and staff of the President's Organization and Emergency Committee, 1930-32, central files of the Emergency Committee, 1930-31, and central files of the Organization, 1931-32, comprising minutes, reports, issuances, correspondence, memorandums, and publications arranged by decimal classification schemes; records of the Office of the Director, consisting of files of Walter S. Gifford, 1931-32; records of the Office of the Assistant Director, consisting of files, 1930-33, of Fred C. Croxton (who served as a regional adviser, Acting Chairman of the Emergency Committee, Assistant Director of the Organization, and Chairman of its Committee on Administration of Relief), and correspondence, 1930-33; completed questionnaires from manufacturers on their employment practices and financial situations, 1932; correspondence with officials of State and city relief organizations and local public and private organizations, 1930-32; files of Executive Assistant Erving P. Hayes, 1930-33; and housekeeping records of the Office of the Chief Clerk, 1930-32.

There are also records of the Public Works Section, consisting of questionnaires and project summaries relating to construction of public works, 1930-32, and correspondence, memorandums, reports, statistical data, publicity material, publications, and mailing lists relating to construction projects, 1930-32; office files of the Chief of the Relief Division, 1930-31, and issuances concerning programs for community action, 1931-32; records of the Industrial Division, consisting of reports, correspondence, memorandums, speechs, newsclippings, questionnaires, and publications relating to business, employment, relief conditions, and activities of local organizations, 1930-32; records of the Women's Division, consisting of files relating to activities of Division officials, 1930-31, and correspondence, reports, issuances, publicity material, mailing lists, and publications relating to women's work in providing relief and employment, and to the effect of unemployment on women's health and morale, 1930-31; records of the Statistical Division, consisting of correspondence, statistical data, work materials, reports, bibliographies, and issuances relating to economic conditions, employment, relief, and public works, 1930-32; and records of the Publicity Section, consisting of press releases, issuances, and other publications of the Emergency Committee and the Organization, with a related index, 1930-32, and correspondence, memorandums, minutes, reports, statistical data, and publicity material, 1930-32.

In addition, there are records of committees of the Organization, consisting of correspondence of Chairman Eliot Wadsworth, minutes, and reports relating to the Committee on Cooperation with National Groups and Associations, 1931-32; files of Chairman Harry A. Wheeler and publications accumulated by the Committee on Employment Plans and Suggestions, 1930-32; and office files of the Washington representative of the Committee on Mobilization of Relief Resources, 1913. There are also office files of field representatives, 1930-32.

See Leo Pascal, comp., *Preliminary Inventory of the Records of the President's Organization on Unemployment Relief,* PI 137 (1962).

RECORDS OF THE
NATIONAL RESOURCES PLANNING BOARD
(RECORD GROUP 187)

The National Resources Planning Board (NRPB) was established in the Executive Office of the President by Reorganization Plan No. I of 1939. The NRPB inherited the functions of the National Resources Committee, which had been established June 7, 1935, to succeed the National Resources Board, established June 30, 1934, and its predecessor, the National Planning Board (NPB) of the Federal Emergency Administration of Public Works, created July 20, 1933. Other predecessor agencies of the NRPB were the Federal Employment Stabilization Office and, in turn, its predecessor, the Federal Employment Stabilization Board. The NRPB was abolished by an act of June 26, 1943, and its liquidation was completed by January 1, 1944.

The NRPB and its predecessors served as national planning agencies concerned with development and use of the Nation's resources. Their major functions were to plan public works, coordinate Federal planning related to conservation and efficient use of national resources, conduct a research program of long-range studies as requested by the Congress or as directed by the President, and stimulate local, State, and regional planning. After 1939 the NRPB also performed special duties related to the war effort.

There are 1,400 cubic feet of records dated between 1931 and 1943 in this record group.

RECORDS OF THE FEDERAL EMPLOYMENT STABILIZATION BOARD. 1931-34. 40 lin. ft.

This Board, established by the Employment Stabilization Act of February 10, 1931, collected information and prepared reports on employment and business trends and provided assistance to Federal, State, and local agencies in planning public works. In 1934 the Board was abolished, and the Federal Employment Stabilization Office was established in the Department of Commerce as its successor. The functions of that Office, which was inactive after June 1935, were transferred to the NRPB by Reorganization Plan No. I of 1939. Records of the Stabilization Board and its successor include reports, correspondence, memorandums, general subject and employment data files, charts, and graphs.

RECORDS OF THE NRPB CENTRAL OFFICE. 1933-43. 1,200 lin. ft.

Central office classified files include minutes, reports, administrative and fiscal correspondence, records of special committees, records relating to NRPB publications and studies, and statistical data. Also records of three administrative divisions established to assist functional sections and committees engaged in particular studies, including general and technical reports and correspondence, records of the Full Employment Stabilization Unit of the Trends and Stabilization Section, and records of the Youth and Education Unit of Division A. This Division reported current business and employment trends; prepared studies about economics, finance, and fiscal policies and special trend studies on relief, technology, unemployment, population, and youth; and administered Science Committee activities relating to business and industrial research, including the compilation of the National Roster of Scientific and Specialized Personnel, which the NRPB established in July 1940 in cooperation with the U.S. Civil Service Commission. (The War Manpower Commission of the Office for

Emergency Management assumed responsibility for the roster in April 1942, but the NRPB continued to act in an advisory capacity with respect to it.) Reports, general correspondence, and records of the Industrial Location and the Land Sections of Division B, which made technical studies on transportation, the location of industry, and land, water, and energy resources. Reports, general and technical correspondence, and records of the State and Local Program Section and the Water Resources Section of Division C, which conducted a Federal public works program, studied Federal financial relief programs, kept informed of and encouraged State and local public works programs, conducted water resource planning activities, and assisted in planning the large-scale and long-range development of capital budget expenditures of railroads, public utilities, and industry.

Also records of Frederic A. Delano, Chairman of the NPB and the NRPB. Records of the Office of the Director, including office files of the Executive Officer, and records of the Post-War Agenda, Urban, and Field Service Sections. Records documenting the NRPB's participation in joint investigations and on such joint committees as the Committee for Congested Production Areas and the Committee on Conservation of Cultural Resources, the latter of which was established by the NRPB on March 6, 1941, to study wartime protection of cultural resources, survey cultural materials possessed by the Federal Government, and sponsor establishment of State committees for conservation of cultural resources. Office files of Thomas C. Blaisdell, a member of the Industrial Committee and an assistant director in charge of Division A, and of Lewis Lorwin, a member of the NRPB panel of consultants and economic adviser for Division A, that consist primarily of personal files accumulated by them while they were employed by other agencies.

RECORDS OF NRPB REGIONAL OFFICES. 1934-43. 410 lin. ft.

In 1934 the National Resources Board set up regional field offices, each with a nontechnical staff to which consultants from a panel on special studies were occasionally assigned. These offices operated throughout the continental United States and, for a time, in Alaska and the Caribbean region.

The subject content of the records, which are closely related to central office records, often depends on the social, economic, and geographic conditions in the region under consideration. The records, many of which are from the New England, Northern Lakes-Ohio Valley, and Pacific Northwest regions, are those of the 11 regional offices and include minutes, procedural issuances, correspondence, personnel records, legislative and publicity files, accounting records, technical planning files, and files for special investigations, projects, and studies, chiefly for the 1937-43 period.

RECORDS INHERITED BY THE BUREAU OF THE BUDGET. 1934-43. 107 lin. ft.

Executive Order 9834 of October 4, 1943, assigned the Bureau of the Budget responsibility for long-range planning and coordination of public works, a function carried out jointly by the Bureau and the NRPB or its predecessors under the Federal Employment Stabilization Act of 1931, as implemented by Executive Order 8455 of June 26, 1940. The records inherited by the Bureau of the Budget consist of legislation, minutes, reports, correspondence, and project records (including some material on the Federal Employment Stabilization Office and the Federal Works Agency) of the NRPB and its predecessors, relating to coordinating and planning Federal public works programs.

CARTOGRAPHIC RECORDS. 1933–43. 3,326 items.

These consist of general and regional maps of the United States, prepared by the NRPB and its predecessors and showing major drainage basins, population, mineral and water resources, land use, transportation routes and facilities, recreation areas, national defense, war industries, crop production, and military, industrial, and resource locations; maps illustrating progress reports and status of mapping and aerial photography; and maps showing urban areas and transportation routes from 1800 to 1930.

See Virgil E. Baugh, comp., *Preliminary Inventory of the Central Office Records of the National Resources Planning Board*, PI 50 (1953); and Baugh, comp., *Preliminary Inventory of the Records of the Regional Offices of the National Resources Planning Board*, PI 64 (1954).

RECORDS OF THE OFFICE OF GOVERNMENT REPORTS (RECORD GROUP 44)

The Office of Government Reports was created in 1939 as an administrative unit in the Executive Office of the President to succeed the Executive Council, 1933–34, and the National Emergency Council, 1934–39. The general functions of these agencies were to coordinate Federal relief and recovery programs and later the homefront aspects of the defense and war effort, to provide a clearinghouse for Government information, and to serve as a liaison between Federal and State Governments, including assistance in the preparation of State legislation. In 1942 the Office of Government Reports was consolidated with other agencies to form the Office of War Information (OWI). The Office of Government Reports was reestablished in 1946, but reduced appropriations in 1947 restricted its activities to advertising and motion picture liaison and operation of a library. Liquidation of the Office was completed June 30, 1948.

There are 698 cubic feet of records (in WNRC except for nontextual records) dated between 1933 and 1947 in this record group.

RECORDS OF THE EXECUTIVE COUNCIL. 1933–34. 2 lin. ft.

The Executive Council was established by an Executive order of July 11, 1933, to provide for the orderly presentation of business to the President and coordinate interagency problems of organization and work of new Government agencies. The Council, which consisted of members of the Cabinet and heads of certain agencies, held weekly or biweekly meetings until it was consolidated with the National Emergency Council on October 29, 1934. Its records consist of agenda prepared by the Executive Secretary, minutes, and related correspondence.

RECORDS OF THE NATIONAL EMERGENCY COUNCIL. 1933–40. 337 lin. ft.

The National Emergency Council was established by an Executive order of November 17, 1933, to coordinate and make more efficient the work of Government field agencies. On October 29, 1934, the Executive Council and the Industrial Emergency Committee were merged with it, and on July 1, 1939, it was replaced by the Office of Government Reports. There were an Executive Director for the Council and a number of divisions and other administrative units, some short lived. State directors were appointed to maintain coordinating, reporting, and information services.

General correspondence and other records of the Council are interfiled with the records of the Office of Government Reports. Segregated records of the

Council include proceedings and minutes, reports, correspondence, and other records of the Office of the Executive Director, the Administrative Division, and the Division of Field Operations, which supervised the work of field offices in the States and Alaska. There are also some press clippings of the Division of Press Intelligence, 1938, records of the Better Housing Division, 1934, correspondence of the Consumers' Division, 1934-35, and a U.S. Government Manual Service collection of organizational charts of Federal agencies, 1934. Some records of the Assistant Director of the Film Service, 1937-40, are with the records of the Council.

Included also are records of the Council's Division of Applications and Information, established in 1935 to process applications for funds for projects to be undertaken by the Federal Emergency Administration of Public Works (later Public Works Administration, PWA) and the Works Progress Administration (later Work Projects Administration, WPA), and to furnish information concerning the projects. The Division was abolished in 1935, but later records were incorporated into the files during 1936. The records of the Division include detailed reports on the status of work relief applications, other reports, summaries of WPA and PWA projects, resolutions and digests of proceedings of the Advisory Committee on Allotments, correspondence, tables, charts, graphs, and press releases.

RECORDS OF THE OFFICE OF GOVERNMENT REPORTS. 1933-47. 466 lin. ft.

These include general correspondence of the Office and of the National Emergency Council; correspondence and other records of the Executive Division of the Office, including radio scripts of the radio consultant; records of the Administrative Division, concerning the history of the Office; records of the Divi-

sion of Press Intelligence, including summaries and digests of press and radio comments and press clippings; records of the Division of Field Operations, including special reports by State directors, reports on surveys of public opinion and on Federal expenditures in the States, correspondence, directories of Federal agencies in the States, and records concerning State legislation; and records, 1941-42, of the Office of the Coordinator of Government Films.

Records of the U.S. Information Service to 1942 include reports on relief operations and contracts and expenditures under the national defense program, correspondence, and records concerning participation in the New York World's Fair. In 1942 the Service became the Division of Public Inquiries of the Bureau of Special Services, Domestic Operations Branch, OWI. It was reconstituted in the Office of Government Reports following the termination of the OWI. There are reports, correspondence, memorandums, processed materials for distribution, background material, and other records of the Bureau of Special Services; of its Divisions of Public Inquiries, Educational Services, Research, and Surveys; and of the OWI Bureau of Intelligence.

AUDIOVISUAL RECORDS. 1939-45. 14,198 items.

Still pictures, 1942-45 (14,150 items), include photographs of posters and posters assembled and distributed by the Division of Public Inquiries, OWI, relating to all campaigns and programs; photographs of newsmaps indicating the progress of the war; and posters produced for distribution in this country by foreign information offices and U.S. war relief associations.

Sound recordings, 1939-40 (48 items), consist of recordings of weekly broadcasts known as the Cabinet Series, the Agency Series, and the National Defense Series, sponsored by the Office of Government Reports, containing the voices of the President, Cabinet members, and other Federal officials.

See H. Stephen Helton, comp., *Preliminary Inventory of the Records of the Office of Government Reports*, PI 35 (1951).

Microfilm Publications: *Records of the Office of Government Reports: Minutes of the Executive Council, July 11, 1933-November 13, 1934*, T37, 1 roll; and *Records of the Office of Government Reports: Proceedings of the National Emergency Council, December 19, 1933-April 28, 1936*, T38, 1 roll.

RECORDS OF THE OFFICE OF THE SPECIAL ADVISER TO THE PRESIDENT ON FOREIGN TRADE (RECORD GROUP 20)

The Office of the Special Adviser to the President on Foreign Trade was created by an Executive order of March 23, 1934, under authority of the National Industrial Recovery Act. The functions of this Office were to coordinate information concerning U.S. foreign trade and to negotiate specific trade transactions with any individual or group desiring Federal assistance in financing or bartering. The Office also studied trade resources of foreign countries and the amount of blocked American funds abroad. It was represented on several interdepartmental committees, including the Committee for Reciprocity Information (which conducted hearings on proposed executive trade agreements), and cooperated with other agencies interested in foreign trade. George N. Peek, the only person appointed Special Adviser, was also president and trustee of the Export-Import Bank of Washington; the Office's personnel performed many functions of that bank (see RG 275). The legislation under which the Office was created provided that the agency should cease to exist on June 16, 1935. An Executive order of June 15, 1935, continued the Office until April 1, 1936, but a ruling of the Comptroller General limited appropriated funds to June 30, 1935. On that date employees of the Office were transferred to the Export-Import Bank. The Special Adviser did not resign, however, until November 26, 1935, and the records of the Office were not closed until the following year.

See Laurence F. Schmeckebier, *New Federal Organizations* (1934).

There are 57 cubic feet of records dated between 1934 and 1936 in this record group.

RECORDS. 1934-36. 330 lin. ft.

Because the Office of the Special Adviser was primarily a coordinating agency, much of the material in its files was assembled from or based on records and compilations of other agencies concerned with foreign trade. These include files arranged by country, commodity, or other subject, consisting of studies, reports, and statistical data and containing consular reports and cablegrams received from the Department of State on foreign trade and economic conditions abroad; analyses of U.S. foreign trade prepared by the U.S. Tariff Commission; returned questionnaires and other records obtained by the Bureau of Foreign and Domestic Commerce and the Export-Import Bank in 1935 while determining for the Office of the Special Adviser the amount of foreign currency owned by Americans and kept abroad as a result of exchange controls and other devices; reports and other records concerning executive trade agreements prepared by the Committee for Reciprocity Information; and integrated economic reports prepared by the Office. There are also records of administrative units and officials of the Office, consisting of correspondence, procedural issuances, publicity material, and facilitative records relating to the work of the administrative officer, the Division of Research and Statistics, and the special representative on the Committee for Reciprocity Information; tabulations, worksheets, and accounting records and drafts relating to an international accounts monograph; and copies of statements and speeches of George N. Peek, including some dated as early as 1933 when he was serving as a special assistant to the President on American trade policy.

RECORDS OF THE NATIONAL COMMISSION ON THE CAUSES AND PREVENTION OF VIOLENCE (RECORD GROUP 283)

The National Commission on the Causes and Prevention of Violence was established by Executive Order 11412 of June 10, 1968, to investigate and make recommendations concerning the causes and prevention of lawless acts of violence in the United States, including assassination, murder, and assault; of disrespect for law and order and public officials; of violent disruptions of public order by individuals and groups; and any other matters the President might place before it. Milton Eisenhower was appointed Chairman. The Commission was terminated after its report, *To Establish Justice, To Insure Domestic Tranquility*, was submitted to the President on December 10, 1969.

There are 131 cubic feet of records dated between 1968 and 1969 in this record group.

RECORDS. 1968–69. 157 lin. ft. and 10 rolls of microfilm.

Included are records relating to functions of the Executive Director and other staff officers and background information and records relating to the Commission's eight task forces and their publications, including data submitted to the Commission by interested parties and opinions and comments relating to the study of violence. Also included are the final report, transcripts of executive session proceedings and Commission hearings, correspondence, interview reports, witness statements, microfilm (10 rolls) of doctoral dissertations relating to violence, newsclippings, and published and private source material; the Chicago study team's report, *Rights in Conflict*, on violence in Chicago during the 1968 Democratic National Convention and records used in its compilation, including interview reports, witness statements, injury and arrest records, Chicago Police Department and Illinois National Guard material, research material relating to the convention, and newsclippings; and the Miami study team's "Miami Report," concerning violence in Miami during the 1968 Republican National Convention, and records used in its compilation, including police reports, interview transcripts, and newsclippings.

AUDIOVISUAL RECORDS. 1968–69. 1,663 items.

Audiovisual materials include photographs relating to disorders at the Chicago and Miami conventions, disturbances in Cleveland, and disorders in Washington during the 1969 presidential inauguration; of persons outside the Post Office Building in Richmond, Va., during the trial of H. "Rap" Brown in 1968; and of miscellaneous subjects. There are sound recordings (18 items) of a talk by Tom Anderson, publisher of agricultural periodicals, called Bi-Partisan Treason; of the songs "Wallace for President" and "Ride With Wallace"; and of speeches, songs, interviews, and radio programs concerning the Ku Klux Klan and related activities. Included are tapes relating to the San Francisco State College disturbances.

SPECIFIC RESTRICTIONS

I. *Records*: Proceedings of the Mass Media Conference, December 1968; and executive session proceedings, October 1968.

Restrictions: For periods of 10 years and 5 years, respectively, beginning May 13, 1970, access to both of these files is limited to persons having the written permission of an authorized member of the White House staff.

Specified by: The Commission.

II. *Records*: The following files among the records of the Chicago and Miami Study Teams: Chicago, A-201 (arrest records); Miami, No. 4 (homicide details) and Nos. 8, 9, and 20 (arrest records).

Restrictions: For a period of 15 years beginning June 10, 1969, access to these records is limited to persons having the written permission of an authorized member of the White House staff.

Specified by: The Commission.

RECORDS OF THE PRESIDENT'S COMMISSION ON THE ASSASSINATION OF PRESIDENT KENNEDY (RECORD GROUP 272)

The President's Commission on the Assassination of President Kennedy, commonly called the Warren Commission, was appointed November 29, 1963, by Executive Order 11130. Chief Justice Earl Warren was appointed Chairman. The President directed the Commission to evaluate all facts and circumstances surrounding the assassination and the subsequent killing of the alleged assassin, Lee Harvey Oswald, by Jack Ruby, and to report its findings and conclusions to him. The Commission submitted its report September 24, 1964.

See *Report of the President's Commission on the Assassination of President Kennedy* (1 vol., 1964), and *Investigation of the Assassination of President John F. Kennedy: Hearings Before the President's Commission on the Assassination of President Kennedy* (26 vols., 1964).

There are 363 cubic feet of records dated between 1963 and 1964, with some records of earlier dates, in this record group.

RECORDS. 1963–64. 434 lin. ft.

These include minutes of Commission and staff meetings; agenda, proceedings, transcripts of testimony, depositions, and affidavits; correspondence and memorandums; summary reports relating to the assassination and to Oswald, prepared by the Federal Bureau of Investigation, the Secret Service, and the Department of State; investigative reports and other basic source materials submitted by the Federal Bureau of Investigation, the Secret Service, the Central Intelligence Agency, other Federal agencies, State authorities, and private citizens; exhibits (1 roll of microfilm) and evidence; and newspapers and press clippings. Also photographs (9,800 items) used in publishing the report of the Commission, photographs (1,000 items, including 170 color transparencies), motion pictures (15 reels), and sound recordings (400 items). There are also records of the interrogation and trial of Jack Ruby.

SPECIFIC RESTRICTIONS

Records: Certain records of the following types: records withheld from disclosure by specific statutes, such as income tax returns; records related to national security; records withheld as part of investigatory files compiled for law enforcement purposes, the public disclosure of which would be detrimental to law enforcement, might reveal confidential sources of information, or would be a source of embarrassment to innocent persons; and personnel and medical records, the disclosure of which would constitute a clearly unwarranted invasion of personal privacy.

Restrictions: These records are withheld from research except as authorized by the originating agency.

Specified by: Department of Justice and other agencies that furnished records to the Commission.

RECORDS OF THE NATIONAL ADVISORY COMMISSION ON CIVIL DISORDERS (RECORD GROUP 282)

The National Advisory Commission on Civil Disorders, commonly called the Kerner Commission from the name of its Chairman, Gov. Otto Kerner of Illinois, was appointed by President Johnson under Executive Order 11365 on July 29, 1967. The Commission was instructed to investigate and make recommendations concerning the origins of civil disorders; the development of means to avert or control such disorders and the appropriate role of local, State, and Federal authorities in dealing with them; and any other matters the President might place before it. The Commission's report to the President was published March 1, 1968.

See *Report of the National Advisory Commission on Civil Disorders* (1968), *Supplemental Studies for the National Advisory Commission on Civil Disorders* (1968), and *Meeting the Insurance Crisis of Our Cities: A Report by the President's National Advisory Panel on Insurance in Riot-Affected Areas* (1968).

There are 219 cubic feet of records dated between 1967 and 1968 in this record group.

RECORDS. 1967-68. 263 lin. ft.

The Commission's records consist of reading and subject files, correspondence, transcripts and exhibits of hearings, depositions, questionnaires, studies prepared for the Commission, other studies related in any way to the subject matter of the Commission's investigation, reports and other published works of Federal and non-Federal agencies, congressional resolutions, press releases and clippings, bibliographies, broadcast tapes, and investigative reports prepared by the Commission's Office of Investigation and other Federal agencies. Also included are the records of the Commission's National Advisory Panel on Insurance in Riot-Affected Areas, which consist of program planning records, minutes, correspondence, staff memorandums, proposed legislation, press clippings, completed questionnaires, transcripts of interviews, and material relating to field surveys and research studies of insurance problems.

SPECIFIC RESTRICTIONS

I. *Records*: Reports of confidential interviews conducted under an explicit representation of confidentiality, 1967-68.

Secondary materials derived from the reports described in the preceding paragraph that either identify or provide a basis for identifying the Commission's confidential informants, 1967-68.

Portions of the transcript of Commission hearings containing the testimony of witnesses who requested and received assurance that their testimony would be treated as confidential, 1967-68.

Restrictions: These records may not be used by Government or private researchers for a period of 15 years beginning October 29, 1968.

Specified by: National Advisory Commission on Civil Disorders.

II. *Records*: Materials restricted by originating agencies and received by the Commission.

Restrictions: These records may not be made available for examination without approval of the originating agency, if extant, or the agency from which they were received.

Specified by: National Advisory Commission on Civil Disorders.

RECORDS OF EXECUTIVE DEPARTMENTS

DEPARTMENT OF STATE

GENERAL RECORDS OF THE DEPARTMENT OF STATE (RECORD GROUP 59)

A Department of Foreign Affairs, whose Secretary was empowered to commission and direct the activities of U.S. ministers and consuls, negotiate with ministers of foreign states, and conduct any other matters relating to foreign affairs assigned by the President, was established by an act of July 27, 1789. By an act of September 15, 1789, it was designated the Department of State, and its Secretary was given such additional functions as preserving and publishing laws and treaties, keeping the seal of the United States and affixing it to certain documents signed by the President, and serving as custodian of the records of the United States previously held by the Secretary of Congress. Other domestic functions were eventually assigned to the Department, but with the expansion of the Government most of these were passed to other agencies, and the Department has again become concerned almost exclusively with foreign affairs.

See Gaillard Hunt, *The Department of State of the United States* (New Haven, 1914); and Graham H. Stuart, *The Department of State* (New York, 1949).

There are 17,239 cubic feet of records dated between 1764 and 1967 in this record group.

GENERAL ADMINISTRATIVE RECORDS. 1790-1946. 42 lin. ft.

These include circulars, regulations, and orders issued by the Secretary and the Diplomatic and Consular Bureaus, 1797-1946, reports of bureau officers, 1790-1911, and miscellaneous records, 1834-1943.

DIPLOMATIC CORRESPONDENCE. 1785-1906. 991 lin. ft.

These records are for the most part arranged in four main series of letters, generally bound separately for each country. Diplomatic instructions bound in 214 volumes, 1785-1906, are copies of communications to American diplomatic representatives and, for the early years, to consular representatives. They relate to all phases of U.S. foreign relations and the administration of diplomatic posts. Instructions dated between 1785 and 1791 are in a separate volume of "foreign letters" begun during the Confederation period. For the 1791-1833 period there are 13 volumes arranged chronologically without regard to country. These are continued by series of volumes for individual countries or groups of countries, begun at different times, with the earliest in 1829. Before 1870 most volumes of instructions contain a register of contents; thereafter instructions may be found through an eight-volume register that also lists notes to foreign missions.

Diplomatic despatches bound into 2,202 volumes, 1789–1906, are communications from American diplomatic representatives, together with enclosures, such as copies of notes received from ministers of foreign states or printed or manuscript material bearing on foreign conditions. They are arranged alphabetically by country and thereunder chronologically. Despatches sent before 1870 are listed in 58 volumes of registers arranged by country or area and thereunder chronologically; thereafter despatches may be found through a 10-volume register that also lists notes from foreign missions.

Notes to foreign missions bound into 137 volumes, 1793–1906, are copies of communications to foreign legations and embassies in the United States. For the 1793–1810 period there is one volume, including notes to foreign consuls, arranged by country and thereunder chronologically, that contains copies of some notes assembled to replace the original missing volume. The notes for 1810–34 are arranged chronologically for all countries in four volumes, each containing an alphabetical index to names of foreign diplomats. The notes after 1834 are arranged alphabetically by country and thereunder chronologically. Various registers list some of the notes dated before 1870; thereafter notes are entered in the eight-volume register that also lists diplomatic instructions.

Notes from foreign missions bound into 871 volumes, 1789–1906, are communications and enclosures received from foreign legations and embassies in the United States. They are arranged alphabetically by country and thereunder chronologically. Various indexes and registers list the notes before 1870; thereafter notes are entered in the 10-volume register that also lists diplomatic despatches. There are also four volumes

of notes from miscellaneous states, territories, or regimes that had no recognized diplomatic representatives in the United States.

Other series of diplomatic correspondence consist of ceremonial letters, including four volumes of communications to foreign sovereigns and heads of state, 1829–77, 24 volumes and unbound papers from heads of state, 1778–1903, and nine volumes of credences, 1789–1906. Records relating to special agents, missions, and commissions employed by the President and the Secretary of State for such functions as the negotiation and ratification of treaties, the collection of information on political conditions and public opinion, and investigations of various kinds are sometimes among the diplomatic instructions and despatches, sometimes filed separately, or are among four volumes of instructions to special missions, 1823–1906, and 56 volumes and unbound papers of despatches from special agents, 1794–1906.

CONSULAR CORRESPONDENCE.
1789–1906. 971 lin. ft.

These records are primarily arranged in four main series of bound letters. Consular instructions bound into 201 volumes, 1800–1906, are copies of communications to American consular officers and relate to the protection of U.S. citizens, relief of U.S. seamen, commercial matters, and consular administration. They are arranged chronologically without regard to post, except that for the years 1835–74 they are arranged geographically and thereunder chronologically. Each volume of instructions dated before 1833 contains an index of names of addressees, and there are registers for the 1833–1906 period. Consular despatches bound into 3,528 volumes, 1789–1906, are communications with enclosures from American consular representatives that report on foreign conditions and consular administration. Despatches from each post are arranged chronologically and bound separately. There are registers for the 1828–1906 period.

Notes to foreign consuls bound into four volumes, 1853–1906, are copies of communications to foreign consular officers in the United States and are arranged chronologically. Each volume dated before 1870 contains a register; notes after 1870 were entered in separate register volumes. Notes from foreign consuls bound into 17 volumes, 1789–1906, are communications and enclosures received from foreign consular officers in the United States and are arranged chronologically. There are registers for the 1870–1906 period.

MISCELLANEOUS CORRESPONDENCE. 1784–1906.
594 lin. ft.

Most of the correspondence is with individuals, firms, and Federal and State officials, but there is also correspondence with people in foreign countries and U.S. territories. Domestic letters bound into 292 volumes, 1784–1906, are copies of letters sent to other Cabinet officers, State and territorial officials, and other persons, relating not only to foreign policy but also to domestic duties of the Department, such as printing of the laws, registration of copyrights, census taking, and other matters. The volumes for the 1799–1802 period are missing. Each volume of letters dated before June 1870 contains a name index, and there are registers for those of the 1870–1906 period.

Miscellaneous letters, 1,533 volumes and loose papers, 1789–1906, are letters and enclosures received covering both domestic and international affairs not filed with diplomatic or consular correspondence. The Department's *Calendar of the Miscellaneous Letters Received by the Department of State From the Organization of the Government to 1820* (1897) is the finding aid for that period;

there are registers for the 1817–1906 period.

There are a number of special series of domestic and miscellaneous letters filed separately, including correspondence with the President and the Congress; letters and reports on seamen; correspondence regarding publishers of the laws; reports of district courts; miscellaneous petitions, memorials, and messages of condolence; and correspondence on official ceremonies and visits.

NUMERICAL FILE. 1906–10.
639 lin. ft.

In August 1906 the separate series of letters among the diplomatic, consular, and miscellaneous correspondence were discontinued; thereafter all correspondence, reports, and internal memorandums were filed by subject in a single series—the numerical file. As new subjects arose they were designated by case numbers, and subsequent documents filed on the same subject were given subordinate enclosure numbers. The enclosure number is set off from the numerical file number by a slash mark. There are 25,892 separate case files bound in 1,172 volumes. Routine communications were filed separately in a minor file bound in 62 volumes and arranged alphabetically by subject, correspondent, Foreign Service post, or country. A few offices, such as the Passport Office and the Bureau of Accounts, continued to maintain their own files apart from the central files.

The records for both the numerical and minor files are indexed on cards arranged alphabetically (by subject, name, Foreign Service post or country, and Government department), thereunder as "to" or "from," and thereunder chronologically. There also are purport lists for each numerical case file arranged by subject according to the decimal filing system adopted in 1910.

DECIMAL FILE. 1910-44.
17,727 lin. ft.

Beginning in August 1910 the central file records of the Department were arranged by subject according to a decimal classification system comprising nine major classes of subjects: (0) general and miscellaneous; (1) the administration of the U.S. Government, including the Department of State and the Foreign Service; (2) the negotiation, application, and interpretation of extradition treaties and individual extradition cases; (3) the protection of private and national interests; (4) the negotiation, application, and interpretation of treaties on claims and individual claims cases; (5) international congresses and conferences, multilateral treaties, and international organizations; (6) commerce, customs administration, and trade agreements; (7) political relations of states, including diplomatic and consular representation and bilateral treaties, conventions, and agreements; and (8) the internal affairs of states. Subjects are further defined within each class and identified by a decimal file number, and as documents were filed under a specific subject they were given subordinate enclosure numbers. The enclosure number is set off from the decimal file number by a slash mark. The decimal file is divided into three time periods, 1910-29, 1930-39, and 1940-44. Most of the decimal file records were filed loose, but for certain time periods some files, such as World War I and its termination (763.72), internal political affairs in Russia (861.00), and the Italo-Ethiopian War (765.84), were bound in volumes.

Finding aids for decimal file records are purport books and cards that list all documents in each subject file; a limited card index of subjects and names; and a card index arranged by place or office originating communications and memorandums and thereunder by date.

RECORDS RELATING TO
VARIOUS FUNCTIONS. 1764-1967.
836 lin. ft.

The Department supervised affairs in U.S. territories from 1789 to 1873. The 70 volumes of "territorial papers" include correspondence, reports, copies of journals of proceedings of legislative assemblies, and other records relating to the administration of Alabama, 1818-19; Arizona, 1864-72; California, 1846-47; Colorado, 1859-74; Dakota, 1861-73; the District of Columbia, 1871; Florida, 1777-1828; Idaho, 1863-72; Illinois, 1809-18; Indiana, 1804-16; Kansas, 1854-61; Louisiana, 1796-1812; Michigan, 1802-36; Minnesota, 1858; Mississippi, 1797-1817; Missouri, 1812-20; Montana, 1864-72; Nebraska, 1854-67; Nevada, 1861-64; New Mexico, 1851-72; Oregon, 1792-1858; Utah, 1853-73; Washington, 1854-72; Wyoming, 1868-73; and the Indian, 1869, Northwest, 1787-1801, Orleans, 1764-1813, and Southwest, 1775-96, Territories. Other territorial records relate to West Florida, 1813-18, and Puerto Rico, 1900-1908.

Miscellaneous records relating to treaties include drafts of treaties negotiated in Washington, 1852-82, and other records relating to the revision of the Treaty of Yedo with Japan, 1872; reciprocity negotiations, 1848-54, 1884-85, and 1891-92; a convention with Denmark for the purchase of the Danish West Indies, 1899-1902; and correspondence regarding the Canadian-Alaskan boundary, 1899-1903.

Records relating to the appointment and commissioning of departmental and Foreign Service personnel and other Federal officials include letters of application and recommendation for public office, 1797-1901, and for appointment to the Foreign Service, 1901-24, and related finding aids; letters of resignation and declination of Federal office, 1789-1895 and 1904; copies of Presidential nominations for Federal offices sent to the Senate, 1928-66, and copies of Senate resolutions of confirmation or rejection of nominations, 1794-1967; letters from Presidential appointees accepting commissions and copies of orders issued by the Secretary for the preparation of their commissions, 1789-1893; letters from the President directing the Secretary to issue exequaturs and commissions to those foreign consuls and Foreign Service officers named on lists, 1929-66; copies of commissions, 1789-1958; various lists and record cards that serve as finding aids, 1776-1952; oaths of office, 1799-1959; consular bonds, 1796-1826 and 1853-56; orders of suspension of various officers, 1869-87; and miscellaneous appointment records.

Other program records are transcripts of laws, 1789-1837, and records relating to their printing and distribution, 1829-33 and 1841-49; general pardon records, including petitions for pardon, 1789-1869, and copies of Presidential pardons and remissions, 1793-1893 (petitions and pardons of a later date are among Department of Justice records—see RG 204); commissions of foreign consuls and exequaturs issued to them, 1790-1953; records relating to the publication of the *Biennial Register* of Federal employees, 1819-53; miscellaneous census records, 1830-70; extradition case files, warrants of arrest and extradition, and other extradition records, 1836-1910; letters requesting authentication of documents, 1843-50 and 1903, and copies of the seals of States, territories, and foreign governments; records relating to the deaths of U.S. citizens in foreign countries, including 34 bound volumes of form notices sent to newspaper publishers in the United States, 1857-1922; records relating to the Great Seal of the United States, including Presidential warrants directing the Secretary of State to affix the seal to certain documents, 1878-1952; Foreign Service inspection records, including inspection reports on diplomatic posts, 1925-37, and consular

posts, 1896-1939; reports of consular courts in extraterritorial jurisdictions, 1907-29; and a record set consisting of 135 bound volumes of original final drafts of press releases showing corrections and changes made by drafting and clearing offices, 1922-63.

RECORDS OF ORGANIZATIONAL UNITS. 1793-1961. 3,346 lin. ft. and 702 rolls of microfilm.

Some Secretaries kept certain office records separate from the central file. These include James Monroe's drafts of letters and memorandums, 1818-24, William Jennings Bryan's correspondence with President Woodrow Wilson, 1913-15, Robert Lansing's letters to Wilson, 1915-18, and appointment books of Frank B. Kellogg and Henry L. Stimson, 1925-32. The following offices also maintained separate files, sometimes duplicating material in the central file, for the periods indicated: Office of the Commissioner of Immigration, 1864-67, Office of the Chief Clerk, 1877-1941, Bureau of Indexes and Archives, 1894-1916, Foreign Service Buildings Office, 1900-1948, Division of Latin American Affairs, 1905-44, Office of News, 1906-60, Foreign Service Personnel Board, 1914-18 and 1924-46, War History Branch, 1939-45, Division of Defense Materials, 1941-45, and Office of Foreign Liquidation Commissioner, 1945-49.

Other records of organizational units are passport applications and other records of the Passport Office, 1784-1910; records of the Board of Examiners for positions in the Department and Foreign Service, 1853-1925; letters and telegrams received by the U.S. Despatch Agency at New York, including papers of Agent Isaac P. Roosa, 1864-1928; correspondence of Reciprocity Commissioner John A. Kasson and other records relating to reciprocity treaties, 1892-1908; printed and processed reports and other records of the Division of Current Information, 1895-1944; receipts and inventories of gifts and decorations, 1900-1930, and memorandums relating to social functions, 1942-61, maintained by the Office of Protocol; records of the Division of Commercial Affairs, 1904-50, including copies of consular trade reports, 1925-50 (including 681 rolls of microfilm), and political reports, 1925-35 (in WNRC); lectures and reports used by the Foreign Service School, 1909 and 1925-26; records of the Visa Office, including correspondence regarding immigration, visas, and visa case files, 1910-40 (in WNRC); reports by the Office of the Economic Adviser, 1911-29, and records concerning the Economic Liaison Committee, 1919-26; investigative records and index (on 21 rolls of microfilm) to general records, 1916-28, of the Office of the Counselor and Chief Special Agent, 1915-28; policy books, staff studies, memorandums, correspondence, and other records relating to the U.S.S.R., 1917-41, kept by the Division of Eastern European Affairs; records of the Foreign Permits Office, 1918-20, relating to departure permits for aliens; files of Geographers Lawrence Martin, 1921-24, and S. W. Boggs, 1924-54, consisting of correspondence, diaries, and work reports; files of the Department's representative on the Federal Traffic Board, 1921-26; reports of the Board of Review of Foreign Service Personnel, 1921 and 1925-27; files of Francis White, 1921-23, Assistant Secretary of State for Latin American Affairs; memorandums regarding United States-Spanish claims, 1927-31, among records of the Office of the Solicitor; files of Leo Pasvolsky, 1938-45, Special Assistant to the Secretary of State; and intelligence reports, studies, and surveys prepared or filed by the Research and Analysis Branch of the Office of Strategic Services and the Department of State, 1941-61.

The records of the Bureau of Accounts, 633 bound volumes and loose papers dated 1785-1925, include correspondence, requisitions, daybooks, cashbooks, journals, record books, ledgers, account books, contracts and leases, receipts, salary records, index books, and accounting forms.

Among the records of the Bureau of Rolls and Library are correspondence, memorandums, indexes and other records, 1825-1930, and hundreds of miscellaneous manuscript and printed items, engravings, printing plates, medals, and miscellaneous museum objects. These include a history of the French in Louisiana for the period 1700-1724; the journal of Charles Mason and Jeremiah Dixon, 1763-68, relating to the boundary between Pennsylvania and Maryland; miscellaneous Revolutionary War account books and journals; papers of Robert Fulton, 1804-6, relating to his invention of the steamboat; the journal of Lewis Seeger, 1817-24; papers of Estanislao Reyes, an officer in the Philippine Insurgent Army, 1898-1903; the diary of Joseph C. Grew, Ambassador to Turkey, 1927-32; transcripts from the Annamese archives regarding the special missions of Edmund Roberts, 1832-36; copies of letters of the Popes for the period 1206-1532; William J. Stone's copperplate engraving of the Declaration of Independence, 1823; and a ceremonial sword sent to the President by the King of Siam, 1861.

RECORDS RELATING TO
SPECIAL SUBJECTS OR EVENTS.
1794-1962. 316 lin. ft.

Records relating to impressed seamen, 1794-1815; miscellaneous War of 1812 papers, including intercepted correspondence and records relating to letters of marque, enemy aliens, passports, passenger lists, and prisoners of war, 1812-15; miscellaneous records relating to activities of pirates and privateers, 1813-35; correspondence relating to guano islands, and bonds of guano companies, 1852-1912; miscellaneous Civil

War papers, including "secret correspondence," and records relating to treason, prisoners of war, passes to visit the South, drafted aliens, intercepted correspondence, and other records, 1861-66; and Civil War amnesty and pardon records, 1863-67.

Orders for engraving and receipts for awards to foreign seamen for efforts to save the lives of U.S. seamen and to rescue vessels in distress, 1875-1940; reports of the Presidential commissions to study surveys of routes and determine the best route for a canal across the Central American isthmus, 1875, and across Nicaragua, 1897-99; records of the Presidential commission to investigate the Philippine Islands, 1898-1901; correspondence and minutes of the Thomas Jefferson Statue Commission, 1904-8; copies of the "Sisson Documents" on German-Bolshevik cooperation and records relating to the investigation of their authenticity, 1917-21; correspondence and case files of the National Alien Enemy Relief Committee, organized to provide relief to German and Austro-Hungarian internees and prisoners of war, 1918-19; correspondence on the licensing of arms and munitions for export to Mexico, 1919-23 and 1927; and records of the Department's mission in South Russia, headed by Adm. R. P. McCully, 1920.

Records of the Department's representative on the Advisory Committee on the National Archives Building, 1929-30; memorandums relating to Japanese activities in Manchuria, 1930-33; copies of notes to the International Sanitary Commission regarding epidemic diseases, 1931-41; circular notes to foreign missions in Washington, 1933-42; memorandums on international law compiled by Green H. Hackworth for his *Digest of International Law*, 1934-42; correspondence, minutes, and memorandums of the Joint Preparatory Committee on Philippine Affairs, relating to United States-Philippine trade relations, 1934-

40; and miscellaneous petitions to the President, 1938-40.

A background file of correspondence, press releases, and newspaper clippings relating to the establishment of the United Nations, 1941-45; intelligence reports of the Psychological Warfare Branch, Allied Force Headquarters, based on the files of Italy's Fascist Ministry of Popular Culture, the Italian Armistice Commission in France, and the Italian Social Republic, 1944-45; reports of the Special Interrogation Mission to Germany, 1945-46; the "Argentine Blue Book," a memorandum on Argentina's relations with Germany and Italy during World War II, and records relating to its compilation, 1945-46; and records of the U.S. Citizens Commission on NATO, 1960-62.

There are also records relating to foreign gift items, 1937-45 (40 lin. ft. in FDRL); files consisting chiefly of congratulatory letters following the 1948 elections, 1948-49 (2 lin. ft. in HSTL); condolence messages and books from U. S. embassies and consulates and from foreign heads of state on the death of President Eisenhower, 1969 (11 lin. ft. in DDEL); and condolence messages and books from U.S. embassies and memorials and resolutions of foreign governments on the death of President Kennedy, 1963 (55 lin. ft. in JFKL).

CARTOGRAPHIC RECORDS. 1844-1967. 1,627 items.

These consist of miscellaneous maps of areas throughout the world, some showing the locations of U.S. diplomatic and consular posts, 1844-1951; a map of Mexico, 1900; economic and political maps of areas in central and western Europe, published to accompany a report presented at the London Conference of the Council of Foreign Ministers of France, the United Kingdom, the United States, and the Soviet Union, 1947; maps of cities in foreign countries, annotated by U.S. consular representatives to show the locations of American and foreign consulates and embassies and significant commercial and industrial establishments, 1906-39; a political map of Central America, 1923; maps and graphs from U.S. consular reports, showing natural resources and economic activities in various foreign countries, 1943-49; a map of Germany, showing Allied occupation zones, 1947; and miscellaneous maps, chiefly relating to mapping activities in certain foreign countries, 1946-47.

Maps and other documents published by the Office of the Geographer of the State Department, including the *Geographic Bulletin*, 1963-67, the *Geographic Notes*, 1965-67, the *Geographic Reports*, 1961-67, and the *International Boundary Studies*, 1961-67.

AUDIOVISUAL RECORDS. 1776-1965. 45,776 items.

Still pictures, 1776-1955 (14,046 items), consist of engravings, paintings, charcoal drawings, lithographs, photographs of artworks, and photographs of Department officials, 1898-1914; American statesmen, including consuls at Gibraltar, 1776-1955; Revolutionary legislators and the signers of the Declaration of Independence, the Articles of Confederation, and the Constitution, 1774-89; signers of the Franco-American alliance, 1778, peace treaty with Great Britain, 1782, Oregon Territory boundary settlement, 1846, treaty ending the Spanish-American War, 1898, and United States-Venezuela Arbitration Protocol, 1909; U.S. Presidents and their wives, 1789-1923; Vice Presidents and Presiding Officers of the Senate, 1801-1901; Vice President Richard Nixon's tour of the Far East, 1953; antislavery legislators in the 38th Congress, 1865; and foreign diplomats, 1898-1918. There are also photographs, some of artworks, of Secretaries of State and other Department officials at staff confer-

ences, 1906-30; Department officials and visiting diplomats at ceremonies and conferences, 1789-1955; UNESCO officials, conferences, seminars, and meetings, 1945-51; the Congress of Peking, 1901; the International Court of Justice at The Hague, 1903; and the signing of the Russo-Japanese peace treaty, 1905. Included are photographs and drawings of the design for a uniform for U.S. ministers, 1817; of the Department's and other Federal buildings in Washington, 1867-75; of American consulates and embassies, 1869-1938; relating to American commercial enterprises in Ecuador, Panama, and Cuba, 1915-43; concerning liquidations of overseas war assets, 1945-49; and of excavations for the remains of John Paul Jones in Paris, 1905. There are overseas propaganda releases concerning American housing projects and posters depicting life in America, 1945-49. There are also photographs, drawings, and posters of the Swedish Red Cross ship *Gripsholm* with American and Canadian repatriates arriving in New York, Red Cross supplies and mail being loaded aboard, and Japanese repatriates embarking, 1943-44; German and Japanese internees at Camp Kenedy, Tex., 1943-44; promoting the third Liberty Loan, 1918; the floor plan and assembly room of the Hall of Nobility, Petrograd, Russia, 1915; German and Allied military units on visits to the Balkan States, 1916; and war damage in French cities, 1917.

Motion pictures, 1911-65 (203 reels), include films depicting activities of U.S. Presidents, Secretaries of State and other Department officials, other Cabinet members, military leaders, and foreign visitors to the United States; relating to the training and duties of new Foreign Service officers and to the functions of several Department bureaus, 1938; buildings and grounds of the U.S. Legation at San Salvador, El Salvador, 1926; La Paz, Bolivia, and activities of the U.S. minister there, 1929; a July 4 celebration in Shanghai, 1924; the signing of the Japanese peace treaty following World War II; American participation in the United Nations, including the Korean action; UNESCO activities in Mexico, Europe, and Asia; Marshall plan activities in Greece and Great Britain; and propaganda produced during and following World War II and consisting of overseas releases with sound tracks in English, Swedish, Spanish, Arabic, Hungarian, Afrikaans, Bulgarian, Greek, and Italian about life in America and world and home news. There are also films of Japanese repatriates embarking on the Swedish Red Cross ship *Gripsholm* and the loading of American and Canadian Red Cross supplies, 1943, World War II damage and reconstruction in Italy, Arab refugees in the Gaza Strip, and a U.S. cemetery in the Netherlands. Films relating to the Brussels World's Fair of 1957 include a travelog of the United States and shorts on science, industry, education, religion, occupations, sports, and other aspects of life in America, and show the construction of the American Pavilion.

Sound recordings, 1938-42 and 1946-55 (31,527 items), consist of recordings of radio broadcasts by Secretaries of State Cordell Hull (chiefly on the subject of reciprocal trade programs), John Foster Dulles, and Christian Herter; recordings in the "Good Neighbor" series about Brazilian economic, cultural, and political history; and a dramatization of world history for the period 1918-39, entitled "And Then Came War." There are 31,509 memovox recordings (in WNRC) of broadcasts of the International Broadcasting Division of the Office of Information and Educational Exchange, formerly the Office of War Information, to foreign countries, 1946-49, with gaps.

See Daniel T. Goggin and H. Stephen Helton, comps., *Preliminary Inventory of the General Records of the Department of State*, PI 157 (1963); and Natalia Summers, comp., *List of Documents Relating to Special Agents of the Department of State, 1789-1906*, SL 7 (1951). Many documents for the years 1789-1828 are printed in *American State Papers: Foreign Relations* (6 vols., 1832-59). Adelaide R. Hasse, comp., *Index to United States Documents Relating to Foreign Affairs, 1828-1861* (3 vols., 1914-21), provides references to documents in scattered congressional and departmental publications. Documents relating to United States-Latin American relations for the period 1809-60 and United States-Canadian relations for the period 1784-1860 are published in three works edited by William R. Manning: *Diplomatic Correspondence of the United States Concerning the Independence of the Latin-American Nations* (3 vols.; New York, 1925); *Diplomatic Correspondence of the United States: Inter-American Affairs, 1831-1860* (12 vols., 1932-39); and *Diplomatic Correspondence of the United States: Canadian Relations, 1784-1860* (4 vols., 1940-45). Since 1861 many documents have been published in the Department's annual volumes of *Foreign Relations of the United States*. There are excerpts from and citations to other documents in John Bassett Moore, *Digest of International Law* (8 vols., 1906); Green H. Hackworth, *Digest of International Law* (8 vols., 1940-44); and Marjorie M. Whiteman, *Digest of International Law* (15 vols., 1963-   ).

Microfilm Publications: There are separate microfilm publications for almost all of the main series of diplomatic, consular, and miscellaneous correspondence through 1906. Records in classes 7 and 8 of the decimal file for the 1910-29 period relating to most countries have been filmed on more than 130 separate microfilm publications. There are also microfilm publications for several other small series of records and finding aids. For a complete listing see the current *List of National Archives Microfilm Publications*.

SPECIFIC RESTRICTIONS

Records: All records dated later than December 31, 1941, except Presidential nominations, copies of commissions, oaths of office, and related records concerning appointment to the Federal service; and Senate confirmations and rejections of appointments.

Records of the following classes that are less than 50 years old; records that relate to unsettled claims in which the United States or its citizens have a financial interest; Foreign Service inspection reports; applications and recommendations for appointment to public office or for transfer from one post or position to another; records that relate to the efficiency, security, financial affairs, medical history, personal property, or private affairs of employees, former employees, or prospective employees of the U.S. Government; trade secrets and commercial or financial information received by the U.S. Government as privileged or confidential; and classified records originated by other Federal agencies, foreign governments, or international organizations, except insofar as such records are open under the regulations or practice of the originating agency, government, or organization.

Records of the following classes that are less than 75 years old; records concerning passports and related citizenship matters; intelligence and counterintelligence documents and reports; records of the investigation of persons or groups of persons by investigative authorities of the United States or foreign governments; name files relating to the issuance or refusal of visas; and other records the disclosure of which would constitute a clearly unwarranted invasion of privacy or a breach of confidence placed in the U.S. Government.

Restrictions: These records may be used by official and nonofficial researchers only with the permission of the Department of State.

Specified by: Department of State.

RECORDS OF THE FOREIGN SERVICE POSTS OF THE DEPARTMENT OF STATE (RECORD GROUP 84)

The Continental Congress sent diplomatic agents on missions to European courts early in the Revolutionary War. The first permanent diplomatic representative was appointed in 1778 and the first consul in 1780. Diplomats frequently served also in a consular capacity until the Congress established an independent consular service in 1792. Both the diplomatic and consular services were reorganized on several occasions by legislation and Executive order, and in 1924 they were combined into a single Foreign Service. Diplomatic and consular posts have been established or discontinued as the interests of the Nation have dictated. As of January 1, 1970, the United States maintained 268 diplomatic and consular posts, but the total number of posts that existed during earlier periods is considerably larger.

Duties of a diplomatic officer, a minister or ambassador, have included sending to the Department of State reports on the policies of the government to which he was accredited and other information relating to the government, finances, commerce, arts, sciences, and condition of the host nation that might be considered useful to the United States. Duties of a consular officer have included receiving marine protests and declarations involving an American interest, settling the estates of Americans who died within the consular district, taking measures for the conservation of wrecked American vessels and their cargoes, ensuring that masters of American vessels comply with legal requirements respecting the custody of ship papers and the discharge of American seamen, providing for the relief and repatriation of destitute American seamen, issuing passports to American citizens, and certifying invoices of goods shipped to the United States.

The records of many posts, especially for the early years, are incomplete. Some officers, upon leaving their post, took the correspondence, regarding it as personal property; other records were destroyed by fires, earthquakes, insects, and adverse climatic conditions. Among post records the instructions received from the Department of State and the copies of despatches to the Department are largely duplicated by records maintained by the Department (see RG 59). The Department's records are more complete, and the finding aids for them are more comprehensive. Records received earlier from posts by the Department were transferred to the National Archives in 1938. That same year the posts began to send all records created before 1913 directly to the National Archives. In 1948 posts began to transfer all records dated through 1935. The National Archives has also received a considerable quantity of records from closed posts, several in politically unstable areas, dated later than 1935, and now has records of more than 60 diplomatic and 850 consular posts.

There are 25,307 cubic feet of records dated between 1788 and 1949 in this record group.

RECORDS OF DIPLOMATIC POSTS. 1788-1945. 5,447 lin. ft.

These consist of embassy and legation records of the following types that have been bound into volumes: original signed instructions and copies of despatches; notes from the government of the country in which the post was located and copies of notes to it; copies of instructions and communications to subordinate consulates and despatches and reports from them; miscellaneous correspondence; passport records; records of births, marriages, and deaths of American citizens; listings of important events; notes of administrative changes; and inventories of consular property. There

are also registers and some card indexes. The records dated before 1912 are generally bound by series and thereunder chronologically; after 1912 they are arranged by year and thereunder by subject according to the decimal classification scheme of the Foreign Service.

RECORDS OF CONSULAR POSTS. 1790-1949. 28,274 lin. ft.

Chiefly bound volumes of consulate general, consulate, and commercial and consular agency records of the following types: original signed instructions and copies of despatches and reports; correspondence between supervising consulates and subordinate consular offices; miscellaneous correspondence; records of notarial, shipping, and other fees; passport records; records of births, marriages, and deaths of American citizens; records regarding disposal of property, settlement of estates, and protection of American citizens; certifications of merchandise shipped from or received in the consular district; listings of important events; notes on administrative changes; inventories of consular property; and court records of posts where ministers and consuls exercised judicial authority over American citizens. In addition, from seaport consulates there are records of the arrival and departure of American vessels and descriptions of their cargoes; records of services performed for American ships and seamen; lists of seamen shipped, discharged, or deceased; records of marine protests; and other maritime documents. There are also registers and some card indexes. Records dated before 1912 are generally bound by series and thereunder chronologically; records dated later than 1912 are arranged by year and thereunder by subject according to the decimal classification scheme of the Foreign Service.

See Mark G. Eckhoff et al., comps., *List of Foreign Service Post Records in the National Archives*, SL 9 (1967); and John P. Harrison, "The

Archives of United States Diplomatic and Consular Posts in Latin America," *Hispanic American Historical Review*, 33 (February 1953). The records of five representative posts—the embassies in Great Britain, 1826-1935, and Russia and the U.S.S.R., 1807-1919 and 1934-38, and the consulates general in Amsterdam, 1833-1935, Hong Kong, 1843-1935, and Winnipeg, 1869-1935—are described in some detail in Alexander P. Marvo, comp., *Preliminary Inventory of the Records of Selected Foreign Service Posts*, PI 60 (1953).

Microfilm Publications: Selected series of records of U.S. legations and embassies in Chile, France, Japan, Paraguay, and Peru, and of U.S. consular posts at Bangkok, Boma (Belgian Congo), Bombay, Callao (Lima), Kunming, Madras, and St. John's (Newfoundland) are available in microfilm publications. For a complete listing see the current *List of National Archives Microfilm Publications*.

SPECIFIC RESTRICTIONS

Records: All records dated later than December 31, 1941. Records of the following classes that are less than 50 years old: records that relate to unsettled claims in which the United States or its citizens have a financial interest; Foreign Service inspection reports; records that relate to the efficiency, security, financial affairs, medical history, personal property, or private affairs of employees, former employees, or prospective employees of the U.S. Government; trade secrets and commercial or financial information received by the U.S. Government as privileged or confidential; and classified records originated by other Federal agencies, foreign governments, or international organizations and conferences that were furnished to the Department of State for its information.

Records of the following classes that are less than 75 years old: records concerning passports and related citizenship matters; intelligence and counterintelligence documents and reports; records of investigation of persons or groups of persons by investigative authorities of the United States or foreign governments; name files relating to the issuance or refusal of visas; and other records the disclosure of which would constitute a clearly unwarranted invasion of privacy or a breach of confidence placed in the U. S. Government.

Restrictions: These records may be used only with the permission of the Department of State.

Specified by: Department of State.

RECORDS OF THE
AGENCY FOR INTERNATIONAL DEVELOPMENT
(RECORD GROUP 286)

The Agency for International Development (AID) was established on November 3, 1961, by State Department Delegation of Authority 104 as an agency within the Department of State. AID carries out nonmilitary U.S. foreign assistance programs and exercises continuous supervision over all assistance programs under the Foreign Assistance Act of 1961, the 1960 act providing for Latin American development and Chilean reconstruction, and the Agricultural Trade Development and Assistance Act of 1954. It provides assistance through development loans, grants, and research; investment guaranties and surveys; contributions to international organizations; and other activities. Under the Alliance for Progress, AID promotes technical and financial cooperation among the American Republics to strengthen democratic institutions through comprehensive national programs for economic and social development. Under Public Law

480 of 1954, AID administers certain local currency and Food for Peace programs.

Certain programs of AID and its predecessor agencies had their origin in the Economic Cooperation Act of 1948, which established the Economic Cooperation Administration (ECA) to administer the European recovery program (the Marshall plan). The functions of the ECA were transferred in 1951 to the Mutual Security Agency (MSA), established to maintain security and provide for the general welfare of the United States by furnishing military, economic, and technical assistance to friendly nations in the interest of international peace and security. Reorganization Plan No. 7 of August 1, 1953, established the Foreign Operations Administration (FOA) to centralize operations, control, and direction of all foreign economic and technical assistance programs and to coordinate mutual security activities. The FOA took over the functions of the MSA, the Office of the Director of Mutu-

al Security in the Executive Office of the President, the Technical Cooperation Administration, the Institute of Inter-American Affairs, and several other foreign assistance activities. The FOA was abolished in 1955 and succeeded by the International Cooperation Administration (ICA), which coordinated foreign assistance operations and conducted all but military mutual security programs. AID replaced ICA in 1961.

There is less than 1 cubic foot of records dated 1955 in this record group.

AUDIOVISUAL RECORDS. 1955. 2 items.

These are films of the ICA, showing U.S. assistance to India, Libya, Ecuador, Indochina, Sudan, Ethiopia, Paraguay, Thailand, Indonesia, and Afghanistan in improving educational, agricultural, medical, and other techniques; and concerning U.S. military assistance programs and cooperation in the RIO, NATO, and SEATO countries.

Discontinued Agencies

RECORDS OF BOUNDARY AND CLAIMS COMMISSIONS AND ARBITRATIONS
(RECORD GROUP 76)

This collective record group was established for segregated files relating to international boundaries, claims, and arbitrations received from the Department of State and international commissions.

The boundaries of the United States have been defined and described by treaties and conventions with Great Britain, France, Russia, Spain, Mexico, and the Republic of Texas. Disputed points concerning the boundaries have been resolved by joint international commissions, arbitration before a neutral

party, and, in at least one case, direct diplomatic negotiation.

Claims of American citizens against foreign governments and claims of foreign nationals against the Government of the United States have usually been settled according to terms of treaties, conventions, or other international acts by claims commissions, arbitration, or outright award. Most of the claims commissions have been international commissions created by two or more countries, but domestic claims commissions have also been established to distribute to claimant citizens lump-sum indemnities received from foreign countries following diplomatic negotiations.

U.S. participation in arbitrations has been of two types: those in which the United States has acted as an arbitrator and those in which the United States has been a party in the dispute.

Other records relating to boundaries, claims, and international arbitrations are among general records of the Department of State (see RG 59) and the records of the Foreign Service posts of the Department of State (see RG 84).

See John Bassett Moore, *History and Digest of the International Arbitrations to Which the United States Has Been a Party* (6 vols., 1898), and *Digest of International Law* (8 vols., 1906); Green H. Hackworth, *Digest of International Law* (8 vols., 1940-44); and Marjorie M. Whiteman, *Digest of International Law* (15 vols., 1963-   ).

There are 3,018 cubic feet of records dated between 1783 and 1952 in this record group.

RECORDS RELATING TO INTERNATIONAL BOUNDARIES. 1783-1952. 449 lin. ft.

Records of commissions and arbitrations authorized between 1794 and 1925 to locate, survey, define, describe, settle, or mark boundaries of the United States. The records, which include some documents dated as early as 1719, are organized geographically and thereunder by commission. Included are records relating to the appointment of commissioners and other personnel; journals and records covering the organization and daily procedure and progress of the commissions; manuscript and printed documentary and cartographic materials assembled for background information or evidence; orders and instructions for field surveys and exploratory work; fieldbooks, sketches, and other material of field parties; reports, statements, and arguments of the commissioners; final reports and declarations of the commissioners relating to boundary lines; maps prepared under the direction of the commissioners and based on surveys of the territory contiguous to the boundary line; and sketches and photographs of boundary monuments and areas along the boundary line. Records pertaining to boundary arbitrations include the arguments of each party in the form of a case and a countercase, to which supporting documentary and cartographic data are appended, and the award or decision of the arbitrator.

See Daniel T. Goggin, comp., *Preliminary Inventory of the Records Relating to International Boundaries*, PI 170 (1968).

RECORDS RELATING TO CLAIMS. 1794-1941. 3,439 lin. ft.

These records, arranged by country, relate to both international and domestic claims commissions and consist of records relating to the appointment of commissioners; rules of procedure for prosecuting and adjudging the claims; determinations of the president, umpire, or arbitrator; correspondence, record books, and working papers of the commissioners; and memorials, pleadings, depositions, evidence, and arguments—manuscript or printed—comprising the cases of the individual claimants.

The records pertain to Civil War claims of the United States and Great Britain, 1860-85, settled according to terms of the Treaty of Washington, May 8, 1871; United States and Mexican claims commissions, 1825-1938; the Mixed Claims Commission (United States and Germany), 1914-41; and the Tripartite Claims Commission (United States, Austria, and Hungary), 1925-34 (in WNRC). There are other claims records relating to Great Britain, to 39 other governments, miscellaneous claims, and Yazoo Land Claims, 1790-1815, involving territory south of the Tennessee River.

See George S. Ulibarri and Daniel T. Goggin, comps., *Preliminary Inventory of Records Relating to Civil War Claims, United States and Great Britain*, PI 135 (1962); Ulibarri, comp., *Preliminary Inventory of the Records of United States* and Mexican Claims Commissions, PI 136 (1962); and Ulibarri and Francis J. Heppner, comps., *Preliminary Inventory of Records Relating to United States Claims Against the Central Powers*, PI 143 (1962).

RECORDS RELATING TO INTERNATIONAL ARBITRATIONS. 1866-1945. 133 lin. ft.

These records generally include documentary and cartographic evidence, statements and arguments submitted by the disputants, minutes of proceedings, and reports, decisions, and awards of the arbitrators. Records relating to arbitrations in which the President or a representative of the United States acted as an arbitrator between foreign governments include the Bulama arbitration between Portugal and Great Britain, 1870; the armistice agreement between Spain and the Republics of Peru, Bolivia, Chile, and Ecuador, 1871; the claims arbitration between Colombia and Italy, 1897; the Tacna-Arica arbitration and resulting plebiscite, 1925-26; and the commission of inquiry and conciliation between Bolivia and Paraguay, 1929. There are also records relating to boundary arbitrations between the following states: Argentina and Paraguay, 1878; Costa Rica and Nicaragua, 1888; Argentina and Brazil, 1895; Chile and Argentina, 1898; Venezuela and British Guiana, 1899; Panama and Costa Rica, 1914; Honduras and Nicaragua, 1918; and Honduras and Guatemala, 1918.

Records of arbitrations in which the United States was a party in the dispute include the Fisheries Commission under the Reciprocity Treaty of 1854, the Halifax Fisheries Commission of 1877 under the Treaty of Washington of 1871, the Fur Seal Arbitration of 1895, and the Bering Sea Claims Commission of 1896-97—all with Great Britain; the North Atlantic Fisheries Arbitration at The Hague, 1910; and the International Fur Seal Convention of 1911.

CARTOGRAPHIC AND AUDIOVISUAL RECORDS. 1794-1952. 21,070 items.

The maps, 1794-1952 (19,534 items), constitute an original cartographic record of the settlement of boundary questions. They range from field sketches through field sheets and fair drawings to the signed copies of the final printed versions. Frequently they represent the first detailed mapping of the areas concerned; in some cases they remain the best representation of those areas. Some reference maps assembled by boundary commissions and some maps submitted as evidence in arbitrations date from the 18th century, and there are other outstanding contemporary maps. Other maps are historically significant, such as those bearing indications of use by Benjamin Franklin, Daniel Webster, Alexander Baring (Lord Ashburton), and other negotiators, or by arbitrators such as the King of the Netherlands.

Audiovisual records (1,536 items) include photographs taken on and near the United States-Canadian border of Alaskan rivers, forts, settlements, scenery, and mountains, 1898 and 1926; Canadian mountains along the border, 1903; and northwest boundary sites and markers, 1860-61. There are also photographs of United States-Mexican border monuments west of the Rio Grande, 1892-94, and of the Costa Rica-Panama boundary, 1910-12.

Microfilm Publications: *Records Relating to the Northwest Boundary, 1853-1901; Records Relating to the First Northwest Boundary Survey Commission, 1853-69,* T606, 4 rolls; and *Records of and Relating to the C.S.S.* Florida, *1862-64,* T716, 4 rolls.

RECORDS OF INTERNATIONAL CONFERENCES, COMMISSIONS, AND EXPOSITIONS (RECORD GROUP 43)

Since 1826 the United States has participated in numerous international congresses, conferences, committees, commissions, and international exhibitions and expositions. This participation has been, for the most part, under the auspices of the Department of State as authorized by the Congress, and the resulting records have usually been preserved by the Department.

Records of Boundary and Claims Commissions and Arbitrations, Record Group 76, Records of the American Commission To Negotiate Peace, Record Group 256, and Records of Minor Congressional Commissions, Record Group 148, constitute separate record groups. Related records are among the general records of the Department of State (see RG 59) and the records of Foreign Service posts of the Department of State (see RG 84). Other departments have participated in some conferences, commissions, and expositions; the resulting records are usually among the general records of these departments or among the records of their subordinate agencies.

There are 1,056 cubic feet of records dated between 1825 and 1968 in this record group.

RECORDS OF PARTICIPATION IN INTERNATIONAL CONFERENCES. 1825-1941. 362 lin. ft.

Included are records of the U.S. delegation to each conference and of the secretariat for conferences held in the United States. Documentation for conferences varies greatly in quantity and character but usually includes minutes, acts, resolutions, conventions, declarations, reports, and correspondence.

Many of the records relate to inter-American conferences, including the Panama Congress of 1826; the first eight International Conferences of American States, 1889-90, 1901-2, 1906, 1910, 1923, 1928, 1933, and 1938; conferences on Central American affairs, 1922-23, conciliation and arbitration, 1928-29, and maintenance of peace, 1936; the Fifth Pan American Commercial Conference, 1935; and the first and second meetings of foreign ministers, 1939 and 1940.

Records relating to disarmament conferences include those held at Washington, 1921-22, Geneva, 1927 and 1932, and London, 1930 and 1935. Topics of other conferences include alcohol, architecture, communications, dams, emigration and immigration, opium, peace, the Red Cross, safety at sea, sanitary conditions, science, trademarks, and world economic and monetary matters.

RECORDS RELATING TO MEMBERSHIP ON INTERNATIONAL COMMISSIONS AND COMMITTEES. 1871 and 1890-1952. 647 lin. ft.

These include minutes, reports, correspondence, and newspaper clippings, with a wide variety of type and quantity for each commission or committee. U.S. relations with Canada (Great Britain) is the subject of two Joint High Commissions, 1871 and 1898, and Joint Economic Committees, 1941-44. Records concerning U.S. relations with Latin America include the Intercontinental Railway Commission, 1890-99, International American Monetary Commission, 1891, International High Commission, 1916-33, American and Mexican Joint Commission, 1916, and U.S. Electoral Missions to Nicaragua, 1928-32.

Records of the Paris Peace Commission, 1898, relate to the Spanish-American War. Records concerning Russian railways, 1917-22, and the Reparation Commission, 1919-30, relate to World War I. Relations with Japan are reflected in records relating to the Sino-Japanese dispute, 1930-32, the Far Eastern Commission, 1945-51, and the Allied Council for Japan, 1946-52. Other records of commissions relate to the Samoan High Commission, 1898-99, International Institute of Agriculture, 1908, Third Meeting of the International Technical Consulting Committee on Radio Communications, 1934, and British-American Joint Patent Interchange Committee, 1941-46.

RECORDS OF PARTICIPATION IN INTERNATIONAL EXPOSITIONS AND EXHIBITIONS. 1856-1963. 250 lin. ft.

U.S. participation in foreign and domestic expositions and exhibitions is usually authorized by the Congress, which provides for the appointment of a commission and funds for its activities. Records, which vary widely in quantity and type, range from a program for the Universal Agricultural Prize Exhibition at Paris, 1856-57, to audiovisual records (in FRC Seattle, described below) of the U.S. science exhibit at the Seattle World's Fair, 1956-63.

CARTOGRAPHIC AND AUDIOVISUAL RECORDS. 1890-1968. 3,807 items.

Cartographic records consist of maps and related graphs, topographic profiles, and panoramic sketches (1,045 items) prepared for use in published reports relating to the survey for a railroad to connect the American nations, 1890-98. Included are maps showing existing and proposed routes, topography, and cities and towns in Central America and Colombia, Ecuador, and Peru.

Audiovisual records consist of photographs (896 items) of Intercontinental Railway Commission surveys of Central and South America, 1890-99, and triangulation stations in the upper Niagara River area, ca. 1910; photographs (815 items in FRC Seattle) used at the Seattle World's Fair, 1956-63; a motion picture (2 reels) illustrating power resources in the United States, 1936; the Film "US," shown at the U.S. Federal Pavilion at the 1968 Hemisfair at San Antonio, Tex., with film made for but not used in the finished production, showing all aspects of life in America, 1968 (1,000 reels); and motion pictures (36 reels in FRC Seattle) and sound tapes (13 items in FRC Seattle) used at the exhibit at the Seattle World's Fair, 1956-63.

See H. Stephen Helton, comp., *Preliminary Inventory of the Records of United States Participation in International Conferences, Commissions, and Expositions,* PI 76 (1955).

Microfilm Publications: *Records of the Department of State Relating to the First Panama Congress, 1825-1827,* M662, 1 roll, DP; and *Records of the Department of State Relating to the Paris Peace Commission, 1898,* T954, 3 rolls.

SPECIFIC RESTRICTIONS

Records: Records relating to participation on international commissions and committees dated later than 1941.

Restrictions: These records may be used only with the permission of the Department of State.

Specified by: Department of State.

RECORDS OF THE
AMERICAN COMMISSION TO NEGOTIATE PEACE
(RECORD GROUP 256)

The American Commission To Negotiate Peace, organized in November 1918, consisted of five commissioners plenipotentiary of the United States headed by the President, a secretariat, administrative officers, and technical advisers. In December 1918 its Division of Territorial, Economic, and Political Intelligence absorbed most of the specialists of The Inquiry, a group assembled in the fall of 1917 by Col. Edward M. House at the request of President Wilson to prepare for the peace conference after World War I. The Commission ceased to exist in December 1919, and the Department of State arranged and bound its records.

There are many related records among the general records of the Department of State (see RG 59) and the records of the Foreign Service posts of the Department of State (see RG 84). Duplicate copies of many documents are also available at the Library of Congress and the Hoover Institution on War, Revolution, and Peace at Stanford University.

See Lawrence E. Gelfand, *The Inquiry: American Preparations for Peace, 1917-1919* (New Haven, 1963); and the Department of State, *Foreign Relations, 1919: The Paris Peace Conference* (13 vols., 1942-47).

There are 262 cubic feet of records dated between 1914 and 1937 in this record group.

RECORDS OF THE INQUIRY. 1914-19. 68 lin. ft.

These records consist of administrative records; correspondence; special reports and studies; digests of statements by Allied and Entente spokesmen; statistical files; newspaper clippings; 1,178 maps portraying such subjects as ethnology, linguistics, religion, economics, terrain, boundaries, and transportation facilities for parts of Europe, Africa, and the Middle East; and related indexes.

GENERAL RECORDS OF THE AMERICAN COMMISSION TO NEGOTIATE PEACE. 1918-31. 277 lin. ft.

Arranged according to a decimal classification scheme in 537 volumes, the records include minutes of various councils, plenary sessions, committees, and commissions of the peace conference; minutes of the Conference of Ambassadors, 1920-31, which considered certain political questions following the termination of the peace conference; reports of committees and commissions; telegrams and letters sent and received by the American Commission; instructions to and reports from field missions of the Commission; and memorandums, publications, and pamphlets. Finding aids include a "Key to the Records," which shows how to locate, use, and record the materials and briefly describes them; lists of documents by decimal file number; and a topical card index.

RECORDS OF THE DEPARTMENT OF STATE. 1919 and 1930-37. 4 lin. ft.

Included are materials relating to the indexing, binding, and arrangement of the records made by the Division of Communication and Records of the Department, and a record of requests for information from the records.

See H. Stephen Helton, comp., *Preliminary Inventory of the Records of the American Commission To Negotiate Peace*, PI 89 (1955); and James Berton Rhoads, comp., *Preliminary Inventory of the Cartographic Records of the American Commission To Negotiate Peace*, PI 68 (1954).

Microfilm Publication: *General Records of the American Commission To Negotiate Peace, 1918-1931*, M820, 563 rolls, DP.

RECORDS OF INTERDEPARTMENTAL AND INTRADEPARTMENTAL COMMITTEES (STATE DEPARTMENT) (RECORD GROUP 353)

Interdepartmental committees, for which the Department of State provided chairmen or secretarial services, and intradepartmental committees and task forces under the Department performed administrative, policy, advisory, or informational functions within the Department or in liaison with other departments of the executive branch. From 1945 to 1953 a Committee Secretariat in the State Department provided secretarial and recordkeeping services for both interdepartmental and intradepartmental committees.

There are 108 cubic feet of records dated between 1926 and 1960 in this record group.

RECORDS OF THE FOREIGN SERVICE BUILDINGS COMMISSION. 1926-45. 2 lin. ft.

This Commission, established by an act of May 7, 1926, formulated and approved plans for acquiring and using sites and buildings for diplomatic and consular establishments. Its records consist of minutes, authorizations and progress reports on building projects, and correspondence.

RECORDS OF THE CLAIMS BOARD. 1931-39. 2 lin. in.

Established in 1931 to examine Foreign Service personnel claims for personal losses suffered in the line of duty, the Claims Board was discontinued in 1939. Its records consist of minutes and claims lists.

RECORDS OF THE COMMITTEE ON ARCHIVES. 1928-37. 4 lin. in.

This Committee was established in 1935 to consider relations between the State Department and the National Archives. The records consist of reports, legal opinions, congressional bills, correspondence, memorandums, and records surveys, 1928-37, but chiefly 1935.

RECORDS OF THE STANDING LIAISON COMMITTEE. 1938-43. 1 lin. in.

The Committee was established in 1938 to treat matters relating to the defense of the Latin American countries. Its records consist only of summaries of staff conferences with representatives of Latin American countries.

RECORDS OF THE INTERDEPARTMENTAL PATENT INTERCHANGE COMMITTEE. 1946-60. 3 lin. ft.

This Committee was established in 1946 to evaluate the exchange of patents recorded in the records of the British-American Joint Patent Interchange Committee (see RG 43). The International Patent Interchange Committee was discontinued in 1960. Its records include minutes, personnel reports, congressional correspondence, legal opinions, and documents relating to American and British claims.

RECORDS OF THE INTERDEPARTMENTAL ADVISORY BOARD ON RECIPROCITY TREATIES. 1933-40. 4 lin. in.

This Board was established in the Department of State to study and provide information about trade reciprocity, especially about the economic and political aspects of reciprocity treaty negotiations from 1933 to 1934 and bilateral arrangements with American Republics for mutual defense in 1940. Its records, 1933–34 and 1940, include minutes of the Board subcommittee, records relating to the negotiations of reciprocity treaties with Brazil and Colombia, summaries of 1940 staff conversations with representatives of all the American Republics except Panama to establish a bilateral basis for cooperation among their armed forces, and excerpts from the Democratic platform of 1932 and from the campaign speeches of Franklin D. Roosevelt regarding reciprocity.

RECORDS OF THE INTERDEPARTMENTAL ADVISORY COUNCIL ON TECHNOLOGICAL COOPERATION. 1938–53. 22 lin. ft.

The Committee of Executive Departments and Independent Agencies To Consider the Question of Cooperation With the American Republics, established in 1938, was successively renamed the Committee on Cooperation With the American Republics, the Interdepartmental Committee on Cooperation With the American Republics, the Interdepartmental Committee on Scientific and Cultural Cooperation, the Interdepartmental Advisory Committee on Technical Assistance, and, in 1950, the Interdepartmental Advisory Council on Technological Cooperation. Its records include minutes of meetings, memorandums, correspondence, and other records relating to budgets and appropriations, international conferences, scientific and technological investigations, and agency projects and scientific and cultural exchange programs with the American Republics, the Philippines, and other countries.

RECORDS OF THE INTERDEPARTMENTAL COMMITTEE ON THE PROCLAIMED LIST. 1941–46. 29 lin. ft.

This Committee, established in 1941,

compiled and published the Proclaimed List of Certain Blocked Nationals (containing names of persons suspected of aiding hostile countries or nationals). The Division of World Trade Intelligence, established in the Department of State in 1941, kept the records of the Committee; collected, evaluated, and organized biographic data; and applied restrictions on the trade and financial activities of persons on the Proclaimed List. The Division later became part of the Board of Economic Operations and successor economic offices in the Department of State. It was renamed the Division of Economic Security Controls on March 1, 1945, was transferred to the Office of Economic Security Policy on October 20, 1945, and was discontinued in 1946. The records include a printed set of the "Proclaimed List of Certain Blocked Nationals," with 10 revisions and a record set of changes in the list; case files; memorandums and working drafts; procedural notes; and an index to the list of blocked nationals.

RECORDS OF THE STATE-WAR-NAVY COORDINATING COMMITTEE. 1944–49. 65 lin. ft.

Established in December 1944 to reconcile views of officials of the three Departments and to formulate their politico-military policies, this Committee prepared such policies for occupying and controlling Japan, Germany, and Austria, and also prepared position papers for use by the United States at international conferences; made studies and recommendations for the postwar downgrading and declassifying of security-classified records; and reviewed directives and procedures for seizing enemy records. It was renamed the State-War-Navy-Air Force Coordinating Committee in 1947 and was terminated in June 1949. Its records consist of minutes, agenda, decisions, rosters, reports, memorandums, letters of sub-committees that include histories of dealings with each enemy country, and indexes to the records.

SPECIFIC RESTRICTIONS

Records: All records less than 30 years old.

Restrictions: They may be used for official use by officers and employees of the U. S. Government only with the permission of the Department of State.

Specified by: Department of State.

DEPARTMENT OF THE TREASURY

GENERAL RECORDS OF THE
DEPARTMENT OF THE TREASURY
(RECORD GROUP 56)

The Department of the Treasury was established by an act of September 2, 1789, which directed the Secretary of the Treasury to prepare plans for improving and managing revenues and supporting public credit, prepare and report revenue and expenditure estimates, superintend the collection of revenues, decide on forms for keeping and stating accounts and making returns, and grant all warrants for money issued from the Treasury. The functions of settling accounts and countersigning warrants for the War and Navy Departments were performed in those Departments from 1792 and 1798, respectively, until the responsibilities were returned in 1817 to the Treasury Department. An auditor who functioned as a Post Office official audited and settled accounts for the Post Office Department from 1836 to 1921. Functions relating to the settlement and adjustment of accounts were transferred to the General Accounting Office by the Budget and Accounting Act of 1921; those relating to the preparation of expenditure estimates were transferred to the Executive Office of the President in 1939.

This record group includes records of the Office of the Secretary and its subdivisions and those of units performing service functions for the entire Department.

There are 4,027 cubic feet of records dated between 1775 and 1968 in this record group.

GENERAL RECORDS OF THE OFFICE OF THE SECRETARY. 1789-1968, with a few dated as early as 1775.

Correspondence, with indexes and registers. 1789-1935. 2,342 lin. ft. Consists primarily of many separate series of letters received, 1833-1912, and letters sent, 1833-1909. The series dated from 1789 to 1833 are copies of letters received and sent solicited by the Department from its field offices to fill gaps in the Department's records after a fire in 1833. The letters dated to 1935 are copies of letters sent by the Bookkeeping and Warrants Division, chiefly concerning claims. The main series are arranged according to office—the President, heads of executive departments and bureaus, the Congress, the judiciary, and private individuals—and/or by function—customs, internal revenue, banks and banking, public lands, claims, and personnel appointments. When a function attained bureau status the related correspondence accumulated in the Secretary's Office was generally transferred to the newly created bureau. When a function or bureau was transferred to another department, the accumulated records were transferred to that department.

Central Files. 1917-56. 235 lin. ft. A subject-classified correspondence file that includes records of the Secretary, Under Secretaries, Assistant Secretaries, Assistant to the Secretary, and the former Section of Financial and Economic Research, and comprises reports, correspondence, memorandums, newspaper clippings, drafts of proposed legislation, and other records concerning national, international, economic, monetary, and fiscal policies; relations with Government agencies and officials and the public; and departmental administrative policies. Also included are separate case files containing correspondence with and memorandums about private individuals, and records about tax cases.

Records of the Secretary, Under Secretaries, and Assistant Secretaries. 1931-68. 143 lin. ft. Included are reports, correspondence, memorandums, and other records of Secretaries of the Treasury George M. Humphrey, 1953-57, Robert Anderson, 1957-61, and Douglas Dillon, 1961-65; Under Secretaries of the Treasury A. A. Ballentine, 1931-32, T. J. Coolidge, 1934-35, A. L. M. Wiggins, 1947-48, Edward H. Foley, 1948-53, Marion B. Folsom, 1953-55, Fred C. Scribner, Jr., 1955-61, and Henry Fowler, 1965-68; Under Secretary for Monetary Affairs Julian B. Baird, 1957-61; and Assistant Secretaries Wayne C. Taylor, 1936-39, John W. Hanes, 1938-39, John L. Sullivan 1942-44, John W. Pehle, 1936-46, John S. Graham, 1949-52, and David W. Kendall, 1955-57. Also included are records of Edward F. Bartelt, U.S. Representative to the Fiscal Commission of the United Nations Economic and Social Council, and Fiscal Assistant Secretary of the Treasury, 1947-54. These records, maintained in the offices of the officials named, include many informational copies documenting the development of Department policy, particularly in the area of responsibility of the respective Secretary.

Records relating to appointments. 1791-1945. 1,565 lin. ft. Included are records of Presidential appointees, 1833-1945; nominations and applications for appointments in the Customs Service, Internal Revenue Service, and other departmental units, 1833-1910; letters sent by the Division of Appointments, 1878-1902; correspondence with the Civil Service Commission, 1882-1910; and lists, registers, and related records of Department employees, 1791-1916.

RECORDS OF THE OFFICE OF THE CHIEF CLERK. 1862-1937. 300 lin. ft.

The Office of the Chief Clerk, authorized by an act of April 20, 1818, was designated the Office of the Chief Clerk and Superintendent from 1871 until 1937. Its duties included supervising expenditures for furnishing, maintaining, and guarding public buildings outside the District of Columbia but under the Department's control until about 1910 when that function was assumed by the Office of the Supervising Architect; superintending Department-occupied buildings in the District until 1937 when that duty was transferred to the Office of the Superintendent of Treasury Buildings; controlling expenditures incurred by Government participation in expositions; and coordinating within the Department the work of boards, committees, and commissions, including the Committee on Personnel, 1911-19, the President's Commission on Economy and Efficiency, 1909-16, and the Treasury Improvement Committee, 1915-16.

Records relating to public buildings include correspondence concerning expenditures for their maintenance, repair, and equipment, 1862-1934; drawings and blueprints of buildings in Washington owned or rented by the Government and occupied by the Department; and tabulations, estimates, analyses, and regulations relating to space requirements and the operation and maintenance of public buildings in and out of the District, 1890-1935.

Records of Government participation in expositions include correspondence, awards records, ledgers, cashbooks, and photographs for the Paris Universal Exposition, 1867; Philadelphia International Centennial Exposition, 1876; World's Industrial and Cotton Centennial Exposition (New Orleans), 1884-85; World's Columbian Exposition (Chicago), 1893; Cotton States and International Exposition (Atlanta), 1895; Tennessee Centennial Exposition (Nashville), 1897; Trans-Mississippi and International Exposition (Omaha), 1898; Pan American Exposition (Buffalo), 1901; South Carolina Interstate West Indian Exposition (Charleston), 1901-2; Louisiana Purchase Exposition (St. Louis), 1904; Lewis and Clark Exposition (Portland), 1905; Jamestown Tercentennial Exposition (Hampton Roads), 1907; Alaska-Yukon-Pacific Exposition (Seattle), 1909; Panama Pacific International Exposition (San Francisco), 1915; Brazilian International Exposition (Rio de Janeiro), 1922-23; Philadelphia Sesquicentennial International Exposition, 1926; Chicago World's Fair Centennial Celebration, 1933-34; California Pacific International Exposition (San Diego), 1935-36; and Texas Centennial Exposition and Greater Texas and Pan American Exposition (Dallas), 1936-37.

Records relating to boards and committees include records pertaining to the Taft (1906-16) and Keep (1905-8) Commissions; correspondence, reports, and related records, 1902-10, of the Chief Clerk and Superintendent as Secretary of the Board of Awards, an interdepartmental unit established in 1894 to purchase equipment and supplies commonly used by more than one Government agency; correspondence, 1908-33, of the Chief Clerk and Superintendent as Chairman of the General Supply Committee, which assumed the duties of the Board of Awards in 1910 and functioned until 1933; and correspondence relating to awarding contracts, 1918-24.

Miscellaneous items maintained among the files of the Chief Clerk include a manuscript volume of George Washington's expenses as Commander in Chief of the Continental Army, 1775-83. There are also records relating to the purchase of Louisiana and the Government issue of stock in payment for the territory, 1803-4, to canal construction, 1830-67, to the public debt of the Republic of Texas, 1837-40 and 1856, and newspaper clippings concerning the Department, 1913-21.

RECORDS OF THE SOUTHERN CLAIMS COMMISSION. 1871-80. 18 lin. ft.

Commissioners of claims (the Southern Claims Commission) were appointed by an act of March 3, 1871, to receive, examine, and consider claims of citizens in rebellious States who remained loyal to the Union during the Civil War for supplies confiscated for the use of the U.S. Army. An act of May 11, 1872, authorized commissioners to appoint special agents to investigate pending claims, procure evidence, and examine witnesses. In March 1880 the last claim was reported to the Congress; the Commission was discontinued by an act of June 16, 1880. These records include journals of the commissioners, general letters received, letters received from and about special agents, summary reports on claims submitted by the commissioners to the House of Representatives, and registers, indexes, and lists used to compile a printed geographical list of claimants and a consolidated index to claims. Case files of allowed claims are among records of the U.S. General Accounting Office (see RG 217), and disallowed claims records are among records of the U.S. House of Representatives (see RG 233). Other Commission records are in the Library of Congress.

RECORDS RELATING TO CAPTURED AND ABANDONED PROPERTY. 1863-1906. 276 lin. ft.

During the Civil War the Division of Restricted Commercial Intercourse and

Captured and Abandoned Property was established under the Commissioner of Customs to supervise work of the Special Agencies (see RG 366) of the Department. After the war, duties concerning captured and abandoned property were administered successively by the Division of Captured and Abandoned Property; the Division of Captured Property, Claims, and Land; and the Miscellaneous Division, which was abolished in 1906. These records principally concern claims brought against the Government for illegal seizures of property during the Civil War and include correspondence and other records about the work of the Special Agencies, 1864-68; correspondence of the Division of Captured and Abandoned Property and its successors, 1864-1906; miscellaneous records relating to all types of captured and abandoned property, 1863-75; and records relating to cotton claims based on an act of May 18, 1872, which authorized the Secretary of the Treasury to pay owners or their legal represenatives for all cotton unlawfully seized after June 30, 1865, by Government agents.

RECORDS OF THE BUREAU OF WAR RISK INSURANCE. 1917-20. 12 lin. ft.

The Trading With the Enemy Act of October 6, 1917, provided for controlling and liquidating enemy insurance companies and licensing all other foreign insurance companies operating in the United States. Those responsibilities were assigned to the Secretary of the Treasury, who delegated them to the Bureau of War Risk Insurance. The Bureau issued liquidating licenses to affected companies until those licenses were revoked November 7, 1918, and January 15, 1919; the Alien Property Custodian (see RG 131) took over the assets and affairs of the companies on November 18, 1918. The licensing of insurance companies other than those owned by

enemies or allies of enemies was continued by the Bureau until 1920.

Bureau records consist of administrative records relating to the organization and operation of the Trading With the Enemy Section of the Bureau; correspondence with applicants for licenses; reports (including exhibits) made by the Bureau, the War Trade Board, the Alien Property Custodian, and American consuls abroad, concerning applicants; correspondence with Federal agencies and State governments, concerning licensing, operating, and liquidating foreign insurance companies; applications for licenses; records of licenses granted; and copies of laws, proposed legislation, regulations, decisions, Executive orders, and proclamations relating to control of foreign insurance companies.

RECORDS CONCERNING THE RECONSTRUCTION FINANCE CORPORATION. 1933-45. 33 lin. ft.

The Reconstruction Finance Corporation Act of January 22, 1932, and the Emergency Relief and Construction Act of July 21, 1932, authorized the Treasury Department to cooperate with the Reconstruction Finance Corporation in negotiating and granting loans to banks in need of financial aid. The Division of Research and Statistics and later the Office of the Technical Staff informed the Secretary on the financial status of individual banks and made recommendations concerning loans to the Corporation. The records include reports and correspondence, with related indexes and statistical compilations, documenting actions of the Secretary (as authorized in 1933) in requesting the Reconstruction Finance Corporation to subscribe for preferred stock in national banking institutions and State banks and trust companies in need of funds for capital purposes, or to make loans secured by such stock as collateral, 1933-37. Also included are miscellaneous reports and tabulations, 1938-45.

CARTOGRAPHIC AND AUDIOVISUAL RECORDS. 1804-1961. 530 items.

Cartographic records (18 items) comprise a published geological map of Wisconsin, Iowa, and Minnesota by David Dale Owen, the principal geologist of the U.S. Geological Corps, and others, 1851; published maps of the Eastern United States and adjacent areas in Canada and Mexico, prepared to accompany Israel Andrew's report on trade and commerce of the British North American Colonies, 1852-53; a published map of the United States, showing customs collection districts and ports of entry and delivery, 1883; and maps prepared or used by special agents, including miscellaneous maps of the parts of Louisiana along the Mississippi River, published General Land Office maps of Louisiana and Florida, manuscript maps showing locations of Government farms for freedmen in the First and Second Districts of Negro Affairs of the Department of Virginia and North Carolina, and maps of land districts along the Mississippi River in Arkansas, Louisiana, and Mississippi, showing abandoned, leased and abandoned, and other plantations, 1860-74.

There are photographs (372 items) that illustrate departmental activities, 1804-1918, and of Indian delegates to Washington, D.C., 1875. Included are motion pictures (54 reels) used in defense and Victory bond promotional drives, relating to activities on the homefront and in the theaters of operations during World War II, and postwar activities in the United States and abroad, 1941-48. There are also sound recordings (86 items) of dramatic and musical radio broadcasts promoting purchase of defense and Victory bonds and featuring many prominent entertainers, including samples of "Treasury Salute," "Treasury Star Parade," "I Pledge America," "Any Bonds Today?" and "Guest Star," the recorded radio programs sponsored by the Treasury Department, 1941-48; the

voices of Members of the U.S. Senate, Cabinet members, and other distinguished persons; a rendition of the last message from Corregidor before its surrender, May 5, 1942; and the celebration of the 20th anniversary of the U.S. savings bonds program, 1961.

Microfilm Publications: *Letters Received by the Secretary of the Treasury From Collectors of Customs, 1833-1869*, M174, 226 rolls, DP; *Letters Sent by the Secretary of the Treasury to Collectors of Customs at All Ports (1789-1847) and at Small Ports (1847-1878)*, M175, 43 rolls, DP; *Letters Sent by the Secretary of the Treasury to Collectors of Customs at Pacific Ports, 1850-1878*, M176, 10 rolls, DP; *Correspondence of the Secretary of the Treasury With Collectors of Customs, 1789-1833*, M178, 39 rolls, DP; *Letters Sent to the President by the Secretary of the Treasury, 1833-1878*, M415, 1 roll; *Letters Relating to Claims Received in the Office of the Secretary of the Treasury, 1864-1887*, M503, 91 rolls, DP; *Letters Received by the Secretary of the Treasury Relating to Public Lands ("N" Series), 1831-49*, M726, 23 rolls; *Letters Sent by the Secretary of the Treasury Relating to Public Lands ("N" Series), 1801-1878*, M733, 4 rolls; *Circular Letters of the Secretary of the Treasury ("T" Series), 1789-1878*, M735, 5 rolls, DP; *Letters Received by the Secretary of the Treasury Relating to the Subtreasury System ("U" Series), 1846-1860*, M736, 23 rolls; and *Letters Sent by the Secretary of the Treasury Relating to the Subtreasury System ("U" Series), 1840-1878*, M737, 7 rolls. For a complete listing of microfilm publications relating to this record group see the current *List of National Archives Microfilm Publications.*

SPECIFIC RESTRICTIONS

I. *Records*: Office files of the Secretary, Under Secretary, and Assistant Secretaries, 1931-68; and records concerning the Reconstruction Finance Corporation, 1933-37.

Restrictions: No one may examine these records or obtain information from them or copies of them except by written permission of the Secretary of the Treasury or his duly authorized representative.

Specified by: Department of the Treasury.

II. *Records*: Samples of series of recorded radio programs sponsored by the Treasury Department during 1941-48.

Restrictions: There are copyright or contractual restrictions applicable to most of these recordings, and no recording may be reproduced without the consent of the Treasury Department.

Specified by: Department of the Treasury.

III. *Records*: Correspondence and reports, with related indexes and statistical compilations, that document actions of the Secretary of the Treasury (as authorized by section 304 of an act of March 9, 1933, to provide relief to banks and for other purposes) in requesting the Reconstruction Finance Corporation to subscribe for preferred stock in national banking associations and State banks and trust companies that were in need of funds for capital purposes, or to make loans thereto secured by such stock as collateral, 1933-37.

Restrictions: No one may examine these records or obtain information from them or copies of them except as authorized by the Secretary of the Treasury or his duly authorized representative.

Specified by: Department of the Treasury.

RECORDS OF THE TREASURER OF THE UNITED STATES (RECORD GROUP 50)

The Office of Treasurer of the United States was created by the act of September 2, 1789, that established the Department of the Treasury. The Office has since been essentially the banking facility for the Federal Government. It is charged with the receipt, disbursement, and accounting of public funds; the procurement, custody, issue, and redemption of U.S. paper currency and coin; the issue of checking account facilities to all Government agencies; and the payment of principal and interest on the public debt and on bonds of the Puerto Rican and Philippine Governments and of Government corporations and agencies. It prepares and issues the *Daily Statement of the United States Treasury* and other fiscal reports and maintains the Treasury general ledger accounts of the trust, reserve, and general funds. It also directs the activities of Federal Reserve banks when they act as fiscal agents of the United States.

The basic banking functions enumerated above were performed under the Treasurer's supervision by assistant treasurers during the existence of the subtreasuries from 1846 to 1921. For a time the Treasurer functioned as ex officio commissioner of the sinking fund of the District of Columbia and as fiscal agent for the payment of principal and interest on District bonds. The Treasurer also had custody of the reserve fund of the former Postal Savings System, of bonds and other securities purchased by the System for investment purposes, and of collateral pledged by depository banks as security for the Postal Savings Fund. Under the President's Reorganization Plan No. III of June 30, 1940, the Office of Treasurer of the United States became part of the Fiscal Service of the Treasury Department.

Many records of the Treasurer's Office dated before June 1, 1829, were lost in the fire that destroyed the Treasury Building in 1833.

There are 3,488 cubic feet of records dated between 1808 and 1943 in this record group.

RECORDS OF THE CHIEF CLERK. 1831-1930. 1,059 lin. ft.

These include letters received, 1869-1906 (520 lin. ft.), and a letters received register, 1861-1911; domestic letters sent, 1831-97 (with some as early as 1814); a subject index to letters sent, 1861-1908; and general letters sent, 1869-1927 (444 lin. ft.). Also letters sent to national banks, 1862-76, and to assistant treasurers and designated depositories, 1863-76; letters sent concerning Indian trust funds, 1876-91, and the railroad sinking fund, 1879-1907; and registers of employees, 1861-1905.

RECORDS OF THE CASH DIVISION. 1833-1937. 400 lin. ft.

The Division is responsible for the actual receipt and disbursement of funds from the Treasury. Included are general ledgers, 1865-1914; ledgers on specialized functions, including Philippine and Puerto Rican loans, 1833-1932; journals, 1853-1914; registers of drafts, 1837-66 and 1915-30; and Treasury asset and liability statements, 1876-1931. Also included are statements of cash on hand, 1862-63; records relating to the issue and redemption of notes and currency, 1837-58 and 1870-80; Mexican Indemnity records, 1837-50, and *Alabama* claims payment records, 1888-95; records of interest paid on Pacific Railroad loans, 1896-83; and monthly statements of accounts of public officers, including the Treasurer, with the Second Bank of the United States and its branches, 1833.

RECORDS OF THE DIVISION OF ACCOUNTS. 1813-1943. 2,000 lin. ft.

The Division of Accounts (also known as the Division of General Accounts) kept overall accounting records for the Treasurer's Office while other divisions kept accounting records for specialized functions. The records include general ledgers, 1863-1931; several series of special ledgers, 1829-1931, including some for accounts with banks, 1829-69, with quartermasters, 1862-65, with national banks, 1863-1914, and with national bank depositories and Federal Reserve banks, 1914-31; journals of receipts and disbursements, 1863-1915; journal vouchers, 1916-30; and registers of drafts, warrants, and copies of warrants, 1822-1943 (registers of drafts after 1913 and copies of warrants after 1928 are in WNRC). Also included are copies of the Treasurer's quarterly accounts, 1813-1932, the Treasurer's daily cash statements, 1847-1912, and Treasury asset and liability statements, 1879-1931.

RECORDS OF THE DIVISION OF NATIONAL BANKS. 1855-1936. 62 lin. ft.

This Division handled accounts chiefly for national banks designated as depositories for public funds and for securities held as backing for national bank note circulation. Records include ledgers, 1855-1904; journals, 1864-1901; a ledger and a journal relating to sinking fund accounts of the Central Pacific and Union Pacific Railroads, 1879-88; registers of bonds held as securities for public deposits, 1863-1911, and as backing for national bank note circulation, 1863-1920; and duty collected on national bank note circulation, 1864-1936.

RECORDS OF THE REDEMPTION DIVISION. 1873-1933. 3 lin. ft.

Schedules of currency and securities delivered for destruction, 1875-1933, a currency redemption ledger, 1876-80, and a record of notes redeemed by affidavit, 1873-81.

RECORDS OF THE DIVISION OF SECURITIES. 1862-1935. 400 lin. ft.

Records include ledgers for the issue and redemption of gold certificates, 1865-1933; registers relating to the issue, redemption, conversion, and interest payments on loans, 1862-1931; and registers of certificates of indebtedness, 1862-66, with a related journal, 1862-64. Also included are a daybook on the issue of notes and fractional currency, 1862-67, records of bond purchases, 1862-72, registers of the issue and redemption of certificates of deposit, 1876-1913, and registers of redemption of Pacific Railroad bonds, 1895-1903.

RECORDS RELATING TO THE POSTAL SAVINGS SYSTEM. 1910-30. 282 lin. ft.

Included are records relating to the establishment of the System, 1910-13, correspondence with members of the Board of Trustees, 1911-13, correspondence with depository banks relating to the Postal Savings System, 1911-30 (241 lin. ft.), and registers of securities held as backing for the System, 1911-22.

RECORDS RELATING TO THE DISTRICT OF COLUMBIA. 1871-1925. 70 lin. ft.

Included are correspondence, 1873-1913, and a register of letters received, 1878-1915; ledgers, 1874-1925; journals, 1871-1922; miscellaneous fiscal records, 1872-82; records relating to bond redemption, 1874-1924; reports to the First Auditor, 1878-1902; and certificates issued by the Board of Audit, with related records, 1874-95.

RECORDS OF THE ASSISTANT TREASURER OF THE UNITED STATES. 1870-1914. 4 lin. ft.

Daily issue and redemption reports, 1881-1914, ledgers of accounts with other assistant treasurers, 1903-12, and statements of transactions with depositories and independent treasurers, 1870-76.

OTHER RECORDS. 1808-1935. 112 lin. ft.

These include general fiscal records of the Treasurer's Office, 1808-1931; receipt books, 1830-1930; records of issue, redemption, and interest payments on securities, 1861-1926; records relating to the Indian and Smithsonian Trust Funds, 1836-81; and miscellaneous published material, 1883-1935.

RECORDS OF THE OFFICE OF THE COMPTROLLER OF THE CURRENCY (RECORD GROUP 101)

The Office of the Comptroller of the Currency was created in the Department of the Treasury by an act of February 25, 1863, to administer the National Banking System. The Comptroller executes laws relating to the supervision of national banks in the United States, its territories, and possessions, and banks and trust companies in the District of Columbia. He also redeems national bank notes and supervises the issue of Federal Reserve notes. His approval is needed for organizing new national banks, consolidating national banks, converting State-chartered banks to national banks, and establishing branches, including foreign branches, of national banks. His functions have included administering receiverships of insolvent national banks (until 1950); liquidating the Freedman's Savings and Trust Company (from 1881 to 1920) and Japanese-owned banks in Honolulu and Seattle (from 1941 to 1943); carrying out 1933 emergency banking legislation; supervising national agricultural credit corporations created under the Agricultural Credits Act of March 4, 1923 (until about 1938), building and loan associations in the District of Columbia (until 1951), and credit unions chartered under the District of Columbia Credit Unions Act of 1932 (until 1954); issuing national bank currency (until 1935); and redeeming Federal Reserve notes (until 1966).

There are 12,892 cubic feet of records dated between 1863 and 1967 in this record group.

RECORDS OF THE ORGANIZATION DIVISION. 1863-1967. 675 lin. ft.

These consist of case files (638 lin. ft.) relating to organization and voluntary liquidation of closed national banks, 1863-1967; closed District of Columbia nonnational banks, savings institutions, and building and loan associations, 1909-67; and National Agricultural Credit Corporations, 1925-38. There are also records relating to the banking emergency of 1933 and the issue of licenses to national banks, non-Federal credit unions in the District, and other banking institutions to reopen after the "bank holiday," 1933-47. Also included are incomplete applications for authority to organize national banks, 1872-1903; correspondence with and about State and private banks seeking national bank status, 1904-10, banks in foreign countries, 1903-10, and in U.S. insular possessions, 1902-8; and correspondence with national banks concerning establishment of branch banks, 1923-24.

RECORDS OF THE DIVISION OF ISSUE. 1863-1935. 375 lin. ft.

Annual summaries of national banknote circulation were included in the Comptroller's annual reports, but the status of banknote circulation for individual banks can be determined only from these records, which include ledgers of national banknote circulation (currency and bond ledgers), 1863-1935 (240 lin. ft.); ledgers of national banknotes received from the Bureau of Engraving and Printing issued to national banks, 1863-87; registers of Treasury numbers on national bank currency also received from the Bureau, 1864-1912; and a journal of gold note circulation, 1871-84.

RECORDS OF THE EXAMINING DIVISION. 1863-1935. 2,575 lin. ft.

Included are bank examiners' reports and correspondence, 1863-1917 (those for the period 1914-17 are in WNRC), relating to national banks and other banking institutions. The reports include itemized statements of resources and liabilities of such institutions and information relating to the amount and character of their loans, deposits, real estate holdings, bonds, and securities; to their histories and the conditions of their records, safes, and physical plants; and to their directors, other officers and employees, affiliates, and holding companies. The correspondence includes letters received from banks and fragmentary correspondence with the Comptroller about organization of banks, bad loans, low reserves, examiner fees, and redemption of banknotes. Also included are correspondence with Government and other officials, 1863-1926; reports and correspondence concerning examination of nonnational banks, trust companies, and building and loan associations in the District of Columbia, 1874-1914; and reports of examining committees, 1912-13.

Fragmentary miscellaneous correspondence of the Comptroller, 1864-1909 and 1913-22 (originally part of the main body of early Office correspondence that is no longer extant), includes letters concerning specifications for banknote paper, 1864-75; from bankers requesting information about banking legislation; from the Secretary of the Treasury and other Treasury officials and bureaus concerning administrative matters, such as amendments to regulations and rulings and requests for decisions, 1867-98; from the Treasurer of the United States concerning bank accounts, bank deposits, and fund transfers, 1882-98; from U.S. attorneys concerning banks and bank officials, 1884-93; and from the Department of Justice concerning charges against bank officials, requests for examiners, and banknote issuances, 1882-1908.

RECORDS OF THE DIVISION OF INSOLVENT NATIONAL BANKS. 1865-1950. 13,389 lin. ft.

Included are the Comptroller's correspondence with national bank receivers and others concerning administration of receiverships, 1865-1950; receivership records sent to the Comptroller, 1865-1927; the Conservator Division correspondence file, 1933-35; records of the Special Liquidator of Securities, 1932-39; Finance Section account books, 1868-1944; and records of the Freedman's Savings and Trust Company, including correspondence, depositor signature books, records of dividends paid by the bank, loan and real estate ledgers and journals, and indexes to deposit ledgers, 1865-1920.

Also included (in WNRC) are general correspondence about receiverships numbering from 577, with an index, 1913-48; receivers' first quarterly and final reports, 1913-50; dividend schedules, 1893-1950; paid dividend checks, 1873-1937; the Comptroller's letters and telegrams to receivers and Government officials regarding the liquidation of insolvent banks, 1872-1934; and records kept while administering the First National Bank of Detroit, 1933-46.

RECORDS OF THE FEDERAL RESERVE ISSUE AND REDEMPTION DIVISION. 1914-44. 175 lin. ft. (in WNRC).

The records consist of correspondence, daily issue reports, vault balances, and destruction schedules documenting issue and redemption of Federal Reserve notes and currency.

Microfilm Publications: *Registers of Signatures of Depositors in Branches of the Freedman's Savings and Trust Company, 1865-1874*, M816, 27 rolls.

SPECIFIC RESTRICTIONS

Records: Records of the Organization Division less than 50 years old; records of the Examining Division less than 50 years old, and examiner reports and correspondence relating to banking institutions still in existence regardless of date; and records of the Division of Insolvent National Banks less than 50 years old.

Restrictions: No one may examine these records or be given information from them or copies of them except as authorized by the Secretary of the Treasury or the Comptroller of the Currency or by their duly authorized representatives.

Specified by: Comptroller of the Currency.

RECORDS OF THE BUREAU OF THE PUBLIC DEBT
(RECORD GROUP 53)

From 1776 to 1817 subscriptions to Government loans were handled by offices of the commissioners of loans established in the States under supervision of the Continental Congress and continued under the Federal Government. An act of March 3, 1817, abolished the loan offices and transferred their duties and records to the Second Bank of the United States. After the bank's charter expired in 1836 the loan office records and related records of the bank were transferred to the Register of the Treasury, an office created in 1781 to keep accounts of the public money and the public debt and continued after 1789 within the Department of the Treasury. A Division of Loans, created in 1868 in the Office of the Secretary of the Treasury, shared with the Register's Office functions relating to public debt obligations. The Division of Loans was combined in 1876 with the Division of Currency, which had also been created in 1868, to form the Division of Loans and Currency. That Division, which was given responsibility for conducting subsequent transactions with creditors, and the Register's Office, which retained only those functions relating to issuing securities, were placed in 1919 under the Commissioner of the Public Debt; in 1921—with the addition of the Division of Public Debt Accounts and Audit, created in 1920—they were designated the Public Debt Service. Reorganization Plan No. III of 1940 converted the Public Debt Service into the Treasury Department Bureau of the Public Debt. In 1956 the Office of the Register became the Division of Retired Securities.

The Bureau of the Public Debt generally conducts or directs transactions related to public debt issues of the United States, the former governments of Puerto Rico and the Philippine Islands, and Government-owned corporations for which the Treasury acts as agent. Similar functions relating to District of Columbia securities were performed by Bureau predecessors from 1874 to 1931. The Bureau supervises manufacturing and issuing distinctive paper used for public debt securities, issuing and calling in securities, examining and filing redeemed bonds and other securities, and moving securities. Federal Reserve banks as fiscal agents of the United States have performed public debt services for the Bureau and its predecessors since World War I.

The records described here relate chiefly to debts contracted by the United States between 1776 and 1900. A few records of the Rhode Island Loan Office are held by the Newport Historical Society at Newport, R.I., and by the Rhode Island Historical Society at Providence, R.I. Some early, related fiscal records are in the Library of Congress.

See Robert Mayo, *The Treasury Department and Its Various Fiscal Bureaus* (2 vols., 1847); Rafael A. Bailey, *The National Loans of the United States . . . to June 30, 1880* (1882); and William F. DeKnight, *History of the Currency of the Country and of the Loans of the United States . . . to June 30, 1900* (1900).

There are 1,995 cubic feet of records dated between 1775 and 1947 in this record group.

CONTINENTAL CONGRESS TREASURY BOOKS. 1775-89.
2 lin. ft.

Although the Register of the Treasury at one time kept the ledgers, journals, and daybooks that were in the Treasury during the Revolutionary War, most of those records were transferred to the Bureau of Accounts (see RG 39), the U.S. General Accounting Office (see RG 217), or the Library of Congress.

These records include waste books, 1776–78 and 1785–86; a ledger and a journal, 1780–81; a journal, 1787–89; an accounts ledger of Ferdinand Grand—the Parisian banker who dealt with Benjamin Franklin, Thomas Barclay, and other U.S. representatives—and a transfer ledger, 1777–85; and Revolutionary War lottery journals listing ticket numbers and prizes. Included also is a 1786 printed edition of *The Register of the Certificates Issued by John Pierce . . ., Paymaster General and Commissioner of Army Accounts for the United States,* which lists certificates of indebtedness issued to members of the Continental Army under a congressional ordinance of July 4, 1783, and contains manuscript annotations showing the cancellation of those certificates; a manuscript volume, which supplements the printed register and lists certificates issued during part of 1787; and the *Seventeenth Annual Report* of the National Society of the Daughters of the American Revolution (1915), which lists alphabetically the names in the printed register.

RECORDS OF LOANS. 1776–1836. 224 lin. ft.

These records, which are of domestic loans of the Revolutionary and Confederation periods, the great loan of 1790, and all loans subsequently floated until the discharge of the U.S. debt in 1836 (the last of which was in 1825), include loan records of commissioners and of the Second Bank of the United States, 1776–1836, that vary from State to State as to period covered and quantity. The commissioners' and bank's records consist principally of journals, ledgers, and registers of subscriptions to loans, interest (dividend) payments, and unclaimed dividends created by loan offices in the Thirteen Original States. Also included are letters sent by Commissioners in Massachusetts, 1785–91, Pennsylvania, 1790–1804, and Georgia, 1810–17. The Register's records, 1790–1836, comprise the centrally maintained records concerning loans from 1790 through 1825,

among which are book records similar to those of the commissioners and the bank, registers of powers of attorney, and accounts with commissioners.

RECORDS OF INDEBTEDNESS. 1836–1935. 1,738 lin. ft.

These records relate to issues of stock and Treasury notes after the United States returned to debtor status following discharge of the debt in 1836. They include accounting books, 1838–1930, consisting of registers of original issue, transmission, redemption, and interest or dividends; and journals and ledgers concerning Spanish and French indemnity certificates of 1836, Mexican and Peruvian indemnity certificates of 1846, Mexican bounty land certificates of 1847, Texas indemnity certificates of 1850, the Oregon war debt of 1861, bond issues for constructing several Pacific railroads in 1862, loans to finance the Civil and Spanish-American Wars, other U.S. loans floated from 1836 to 1900, and District of Columbia loans under an act of June 20, 1874, and later acts. There are registers and other records of Treasury note issues except issues of 1837–39 and 1843.

Also included are records relating to public debt transactions, 1838–1918, consisting of warrants, deposit certificates, and other documents that authorize the original issue, transfer, or exchange of registered or coupon securities for Spanish and Mexican indemnities, bounty land issues, the Oregon war debt, Civil War loans, and other loans floated from 1836 to 1917.

OTHER RECORDS OF PUBLIC DEBT TRANSACTIONS. 1789–1918. 593 lin. ft.

These consist of correspondence, 1840–1918, that comprises letters received and sent by divisions of the Office of the Secretary of the Treasury and the Register's Office, with registers and indexes, including investors' acknowledgments of receipts of securities, notices of securities transfers, redemption statements, bids for and offers of stocks, and miscellaneous letters concerning loans; letters sent by the Register, 1816-28; "Estimates and Statements," 1791-1858, including letters received and sent by the first Register, but consisting chiefly of estimates of governmental expenditures compiled for submission by the Secretary to the Congress; statements of accounts; and Register's reports.

Also included are miscellaneous records—either relating to functions once performed by the Register or collected by his office—including financial accounts, with letters or notes of justification, of American ministers and consuls in France, Holland, Spain, Portugal, and the Barbary States, 1793-1813; a report detailing accounts related to treaty obligations with Algiers and the naval war with Tripoli, 1795-1812; summaries and balance sheets of the Postmaster General's accounts, 1789-1814; ledgers of receipts and expenditures of the commissioners appointed to establish a permanent U.S. capital, 1794-1802; a journal of Department of State accounts with the Bank of the United States, 1795-1800; a ledger for the privateer pension fund, 1813-30; a register of bills of exchange purchased by the United States, 1793-1833; a list of American prisoners held at British depots, 1812-14; documents regarding the Bank of the United States at Norfolk, Va., 1829-30, Portsmouth, Va., 1831-32, and Charleston, S.C., 1833; certified copies from the Department of State of awards made to American citizens under treaties with France in 1831 and with Mexico in 1839; correspondence about claims against Denmark, 1831, France, 1834-38, and Mexico and Spain, 1838; receipts for securities issued by the Treasury to cover awards made under the French treaty, the Neapolitan treaty of 1832,

and the Peruvian treaty of 1841; graphs of railway gradients, including those of the Union Pacific Railroad, 1865-68; correspondence regarding the *Alabama* claims and Geneva awards, 1871-74; reports concerning a counterfeit money detector, 1870-82; correspondence with banknote companies, chiefly the American and the National Banknote Cos., 1858-77; reports concerning the Bureau of Engraving and Printing adoption and use of power presses, 1874-82 and 1912, and of committees to examine Bureau vaults, 1870-89; correspondence with Government papermills at Pittsfield, East Pepperell, and Dalton, Mass., 1880 and 1908-16, and Glen Mills, Pa., 1876; and correspondence with and relating to the National Currency Association, 1867-1914.

RECORDS OF THE COMMISSIONERS OF THE SINKING FUND. 1834-36. 1 lin. in.

An act of August 4, 1790, established a sinking fund from which the national debt was gradually to be retired. An act of May 8, 1792, designated the President of the Senate, the Chief Justice, the Secretaries of State and of the Treasury, and the Attorney General as commissioners to administer the fund and liquidate the U.S. debt. After notification from the commissioners that the fund was adequate to meet the outstanding U.S. debt, the Congress on July 4, 1836, directed that the commissioners' functions be suspended and transferred their records to Treasury custody. These records consist of transcribed minutes, February 7, 1834-February 6, 1836 (vol. 118). (A printed report of the commissioners' activities from November 28, 1800, to December 16, 1801, is also available. Vol. 117.)

RECORDS OF THE WAR LOAN ORGANIZATION AND THE DIVISION OF SAVINGS. 1917-25. 79 lin. ft.

Five campaigns for selling World War I liberty bonds were directed by the Secretary of the Treasury. The War Loan Organization, created in April 1917 to advertise, sell, and distribute the bonds, took charge of selling war savings certificates in October 1918. The records of the Organization, which was disbanded after the war, went to the Public Debt Service, and some of its functions relating to savings were continued by the Division of Savings of the Public Debt Service as part of a thrift program. The records of the Organization and its successor, which functioned until 1924, include correspondence, scrapbooks, leaflets, and press releases.

AUDIOVISUAL RECORDS. 1914-19. 487 items.

Audiovisual records consist of still pictures, 1917-19 (483 items), including charcoal and pen-and-ink drawings, watercolor and oil paintings, photographs of artworks used in liberty loan campaigns and of participating screen stars and other prominent persons, and posters, including those by Howard Chandler Christy, James Montgomery Flagg, and George Luchs.

Also included are motion pictures, 1914-18, of the Salvation Army Congress in London and of dramatizations of heroic acts performed by World War I American infantrymen.

See Philip D. Lagerquist, Archie L. Abney, and Lyle J. Holverstott, comps., *Preliminary Inventory of the "Old Loans" Records of the Bureau of the Public Debt*, PI 52 (1953).

Microfilm Publications: *Card Index to "Old Loan" Ledgers of the Bureau of the Public Debt, 1790-1836*, M521, 15 rolls, DP, which indexes ledger volumes not individually indexed for the New York Loan Office, the Pennsylvania Loan Office, and the Register's Office of the Treasury Department, and provides information for tracing subscriptions to U.S. domestic loans. Other microfilm publications are described in the current *List of National Archives Microfilm Publications*.

RECORDS OF THE BUREAU OF ACCOUNTS (TREASURY) (RECORD GROUP 39)

The Bureau of Accounts was created in the Department of the Treasury under Reorganization Plan No. III of 1940. The Bureau succeeded the Office of the Commissioner of Accounts and Deposits established in January 1920 to coordinate the work of divisions engaged in accounting transactions and the deposit of public funds throughout the country. Foremost among these divisions was the Division of Bookkeeping and Warrants that was formally established by the Dockery Act of 1894 and had evolved in the Secretary's Office from the Division of Warrants (1868) and the Division of Warrants, Estimates, and Appropriations (1875). Under the Dockery Act, the Division took over functions and records relating to the receipt and expenditure of public funds from the Division of Receipts and Expenditures of the Register's Office. In 1920 the Division of Bookkeeping and Warrants was placed under the supervision of the Commissioner of Accounts and Deposits, and in 1921 certain duties of the Division of Public Moneys, established in the Secretary's Office in 1877, were transferred to it. These duties related to covering revenues and repayments into the Treasury, issue of duplicate checks and warrants, certification of outstanding liabilities for payment, and the special accounts of the Secretary of the Treasury, including funds deposited with the Alien Property Custodian.

The Bureau of Accounts, now headed by the Commissioner of Accounts, maintains for the Federal Government a unified system of central accounts, prepares and publishes central financial reports, furnishes technical guidance and assistance to Treasury bureaus, collaborates with the U.S. General Accounting Office and the Bureau of the Budget in developing plans for simplifying and improving Government accounting and other fiscal procedures, and disburses moneys of the executive branch (with the principal exceptions of the Post Office and the military services).

Other functions of the Bureau include payment of claims under international agreements and collection of principal and interest on debts of foreign governments to the United States, investment of certain trust funds, administration of loans made by the Treasury Department to Government corporations and other Federal agencies, administration of the Federal depository systems, supervision of surety companies authorized as sureties on Federal bonds, and liquidation of the Postal Savings System. Some records of the Bureau's predecessor, dating in some instances to the pre-Federal period, and of the predecessors of some of its divisions, are included in this record group.

There are 2,014 cubic feet of records dated between 1775 and 1948 in this record group.

GENERAL RECORDS. 1775-1945.
2,139 lin. ft.

Included are appropriation and transfer warrants, 1794-1945; ledgers, chiefly relating to appropriations, 1790-1945; registers of pay, repay, counter, and covering warrants, 1814-1945; indexes to pay warrants, 1861-1919; journals, 1849-94, with some dated 1789-91 and a few dated as late as 1908; general correspondence, 1807-1920, and correspondence on fiscal relations with other countries, 1918-41; and records and published

material relating to receipts and expenditures of the Government and to the public debt, 1777-1936.

Other records, illustrative of the wide range of subjects documented in this record group, include account ledgers of Robert Morris and Joseph Nourse as Superintendents of Finance, 1779-89, journals of financial transactions of the Treasurer at Philadelphia and at Yorktown, Pa., 1776-81, copies of records relating to the settlement of accounts of Silas Deane, 1775-1835, journals of the Navy and Privateer Pension Funds, 1798-1830, and records relating to the settlement of claims with foreign countries, 1835-86. Also included are registers of claims paid under relief and appropriation acts, including the *Alabama* claims and the French, Neopolitan, Mexican, and Peruvian indemnities and private claims, 1789-1912; records relating to financing of railroads, 1865-1928; a ledger relating to the Panama Canal, 1899-1916; records relating to the direct tax, 1813-21; a scrapbook of Confederate currency; and copies of letters from Col. Thomas Barclay, His Majesty's Agent for British Prisoners in the United States, to Gen. John Mason, American Commissary General of Prisoners, April-June 1813.

RECORDS RELATING TO DISBURSING CLERKS. 1865-1927.
15 lin. ft.

From the beginning of the Federal Government, disbursing agents were designated in Federal agencies. The appointment by department heads of bonded disbursing clerks from among their regular clerical forces was authorized in 1853. In the Treasury Department the work of the disbursing clerks was consolidated in 1910 under a single disbursing clerk, who made disbursements for the entire Department with the exception of the Bureau of Engraving and Printing. An Executive order of June 10, 1933, directed the transfer of disbursement functions for all Government agencies to the Division of Disbursement in the Treasury Department. This Division took over the functions and records of the Office of Disbursing Clerk.

The records include letters received, 1865-1910, with a register of letters answered and referred, 1906-12; letters sent, 1910-12; appropriation ledgers, 1911-27; cashbooks, 1906-10; ledgers of accounts, 1906-18; and registers of payroll and advances, 1897-99 and 1910-16.

RECORDS RELATING TO CAPTURED AND ABANDONED PROPERTY. 1862-1901. 3 lin. ft.

Included are a blotter of cotton purchases and shipping permits from Memphis, 1864-65; accounts of captured and abandoned property, 1862-75; indexes to names of claimants, 1881-83, and to cotton cases, 1863-68; a register of claims of British subjects, 1865-72; an index to the journal of the Southern Claims Commission, 1871-78, and a register of names of property owners, 1876-81; and registers of judgments of the Court of Claims, 1868-73 and 1886-1901.

RECORDS RELATING TO ALIEN PROPERTY. 1898-1939. 115 lin. ft. (in WNRC).

These include reports and correspondence, 1917-37; records relating to suits, 1921-39; registers of enemy alien property seized, 1917-26; case files of settled enemy alien trust fund claims, 1918-34, with card files of closed accounts; and fiscal records of German companies, 1898-1903.

RECORDS RELATING TO DEPOSITORIES OF PUBLIC MONEYS. 1836-1920. 56 lin. ft.

Form letters to depositories relating to settlement of interest accounts, 1836-37; ledgers of moneys received by depositories, 1869-1919; registers of national bank covering warrants, 1874-1920, and deposits made in national banks, 1862-72; registers of miscellaneous accounts of depositories, 1863-68, and regular accounts, 1865-75 and 1904-7; accounts current of the depository at Buffalo, 1870-76; cashbooks, 1870-76, and daily statements of assets and liabilities at the same depository, 1876; letters of the assistant treasurer at Charleston, S.C., 1866-76; fiscal records of the depositories at Charleston, 1865-76, Louisville, 1861-74, Santa Fe, 1862-76, Tucson, 1870-81, Pittsburgh, 1847-76, Mobile, 1866-73, and Olympia, Wash., 1862-72; receipts and accounts current at the Oregon City Depository, 1856-72, and a ledger of receipts and expenditures, 1867-68; and accounts current of the depository at St. Paul, 1863-68.

RECORDS OF SPECIAL ACCOUNTS, SURETY BONDS, AND FEDERAL SAVINGS AND LOAN ASSOCIATIONS. 1789-1948. 375 lin. ft.

Ledgers and receipts in compromise offers, 1879-1940; a ledger of national bank accounts, 1891-1912; surety bonds of officials responsible for the collection and disbursement of public funds, with index, 1789-1925 (those dated after 1915 in WNRC); and closed case files of subscriptions of Federal Savings and Loan shares, 1933-48.

Microfilm Publications: *Foreign Ledgers, Public Agents in Europe, 1776-1787,* T244, 2 rolls; *Account Book of Receipts and Expenditures, Temporary Loans, Estimates of Appropriations, and Interests, 1793-1800,* T292, 1 roll; *Statement of the Accounts of the United States During the Administration of the Superintendent of Finance, 1781-84,* T293, 1 roll; *Blotters of the Office of the Register of the Treasury, 1782-1810,* T723, 10 rolls; and *Journal "A," April 16, 1776-September 20, 1781,* T909, 1 roll.

RECORDS OF THE BUREAU OF CUSTOMS
(RECORD GROUP 36)

The Customs Service, created by an act of July 31, 1789, became part of the Department of the Treasury when it was established in September 1789. The Office of the Secretary of the Treasury and later the Division of Customs, created in the 1860's, administered the Service until the establishment of the Bureau of Customs on March 3, 1927. The Bureau took over the functions of the Special Agency Service, successor to the Division of Special Agents created in the Secretary's Office in 1878 to supervise the activities of the Treasury Department special agents (first authorized in 1846). An executive order of February 28, 1942, transferred to the Bureau from the Bureau of Marine Inspection and Navigation of the Department of Commerce the maritime functions of registering, enrolling, licensing, and admeasuring merchant vessels. Other functions of the Secretary of the Treasury administered by the Bureau relate to import and export of merchandise, collection of tonnage taxes, entrance and clearance of vessels and aircraft, regulation of vessels in the coastwise and fishing trades, and protection of passengers. It also assists other agencies in the export control program, the control of persons entering or leaving the United States, and the enforcement of restrictions on the importation of certain plants, foods, and drugs.

Records of the Customs Service, particularly for the earlier period, also relate to superintendence of aids to navigation (until 1852), revenue cutter activities, collection and accounting of marine hospital moneys, and the administration of civil affairs in Alaska immediately after its purchase. Fragmentary records of a few ports during the colonial, Revolutionary War, and confederation periods are included, as are a few records produced by the Customs Service of the Confederate States of America.

See Laurence F. Schmeckebier, *The Customs Service* (Baltimore, 1924).

There are 8,016 cubic feet of records dated between 1789 and 1956, with a few dated as early as 1745, in this record group.

HEADQUARTERS RECORDS OF THE BUREAU. 1815-1956.
1,559 lin. ft. and 32 rolls of microfilm.

These include case files and correspondence of the Commissioner of Customs and his predecessors, 1880-1936 (case files for the period 1902-36 are in WNRC), records of the Division of Special Agents, 1833-1915, marine documents, 1942-56, records relating to passenger lists, 1820-74, and records relating to the protection of seamen, 1815-70. The case files concern mainly the appraisal of merchandise and the collection of import duties, and comprise reports, correspondence, and Treasury decisions. Case files for 1870-80 are not extant, but indexes to and registers of the letters that comprised them are available.

Records of the Division of Special Agents include letters sent to special agents, 1861-1915, regarding special appraisals, smuggling, illegal entry, and investigations of customs employees and procedures; registers of letters received, 1867-1902; letters sent, 1875-1912; and case files and reports relating to investigations of customs employees, Chinese immigration, administration of customs in Alaska, narcotics peddling and control, smuggling, and appraisal of complex ad valorem and other duties on imports, with registers and indexes, 1854-1915.

Maritime documents comprise surrendered copies of registers, enrollments, and licenses for American merchant vessels and yachts not in active service, March 1, 1942–December 31, 1956. Similar records from 1815 to 1942 are among records of the Bureau of Marine Inspection and Navigation (see RG 41). (Those from 1789 to 1803 are among customhouse records used in the settlement of French spoliation claims described below.)

Records relating to passenger lists consist of abstracts and transcripts of passenger arrivals, 1820–74, submitted by the collectors of customs to the Secretary of State, with an index to arrivals at New York, 1820–46, and arrivals at all other ports, 1820–74, and a microfilm index (32 rolls) of arrivals at New Orleans, 1853-99. These indexes, compiled by the Work Projects Administration during the period 1937-39, show name of passenger, port, vessel, and date of arrival.

Records relating to the protection of seamen consist of abstracts of certificates issued by collectors of customs to American seamen, 1815–70, with an index made by the Work Projects Administration. Earlier abstracts, 1808-16, are among the records of the Department of State (see RG 59). Application for these certificates, first issued under an act of May 28, 1796, and some surrendered certificates are among the records of the collectors of customs (see below). A later series of applications for seamen's protection certificates is with records of the Bureau of Marine Inspection and Navigation (see RG 41).

RECORDS OF COLLECTORS OF CUSTOMS. 1789-1899, with a few dated as early as 1745 and as late as 1954.

Customs collection districts were established in more than 100 coastal, river, Great Lakes, and inland ports by an act of July 31, 1789. The boundaries of the districts changed from time to time until 1913 when a single district was established in each State and territory.

In each district was a headquarters port with a customhouse. The collector was responsible for collecting duties, keeping records of and reporting his financial transactions, admeasuring and documenting American merchant vessels, administering the customhouses and lighthouses (until 1852) in his district or region, collecting hospital moneys from seamen and accounting for their stays in marine hospitals, and administering revenue cutters assigned to his district (until 1871). The enforcement of other acts for the protection of American seamen and American and foreign passengers, and the forwarding of basic data on immigration, imports, and exports (until 1923) became his responsibility. Upon occasion the collector acted as the depository for Federal funds and collected taxes for the Bureau of Internal Revenue.

The naval officer, coordinate in rank with the collector, was required to keep separate accounts and copies of all manifests and entries, and to countersign certain of the collector's accounts. The surveyor, under the collector's supervision, kept a daily record of all vessel arrivals and clearances and was assisted by inspectors, weighers, and gagers in the collection and payment of bounty allowances and fees and the admeasurement of foreign vessels for tonnage duties.

The records of more than 100 collectors or collection districts that are in the National Archives represent many ports and subports, some discontinued, and consist in general of correspondence; records of the entrance and clearance of vessels; cargo manifests; impost books; passenger lists and abstracts; records relating to warehousing, drawbacks, nonintercourse, embargo, and other bonds; crew lists; accounts of hospital moneys paid and other fiscal records; wreck reports; and a few logbooks of privateer vessels. Records for each district vary in date, type, and completeness. Those for the New England ports and New Jersey contain many records of fishing vessels and fishing bounties; those for Southern ports—especially Mobile, Savannah, and New Orleans—include coastwise slave manifests and records relating to the enforcement of prohibitions on slave trade with foreign ports; and those of districts along the Canadian border include records of warehousing and transportation. For ports existing during the Napoleonic wars there are embargo and non-intercourse bonds and bonds against trade with Spanish and French possessions.

For many years the collector and naval officer were the chief representatives of the Federal Government in their districts. They not only interpreted navigation and customs laws and regulations but were usually the political representatives of the party in power. As such, their correspondence frequently contains information on Federal-State relationships and on partisan political matters. For many of the customhouses there are cargo manifests and entrance and clearance papers. There are large series of incoming passenger lists for New York, Baltimore, Boston, Philadelphia, and New Orleans. They are particularly important for Baltimore and New York where fires destroyed records dated before 1891 and June 1897, respectively, of immigration authorities.

From 1884 to 1887 many records relating to the documentation of vessels and their cargoes, 1789-1803, were brought to the Treasury Department for use in settling French spoliation claims. The records requested were for the period 1792-1801. Because many of them were bound with earlier or later records, entire volumes were sent. Two volumes from New Haven show entries dated as early as 1762. These records are maintained as a discrete series but are included in the listing of customs districts

below. Fires, wars, and weather have destroyed many records, and others have been deliberately disposed of, including cargo manifests for New York, 1865-1917. Some are in private depositories; those for Salem and its subports are in the Essex Institute in Salem, Mass. Most of the records of the port of Providence, R.I., are in the Rhode Island Historical Society in Providence.

Records of the collectors at Charleston, Galveston, Savannah, Mobile, and New Orleans include some Confederate customs records.

Listed below are customs districts for which records are available, with approximate dates and quantities shown in linear feet.

Records of the New England Collection Districts or Customhouses. 1762-1942. 999 lin. ft.

Maine: Passamaquoddy, 1807-1930 (12 ft.), Machias, 1810-1913 (13 ft.), Frenchmen's Bay, 1835-1913 (7 ft.), Penobscot (Castine), 1796-1916 (13 ft.), Bangor, 1847-82 (1 in.), Belfast, 1808-1918 (9 ft.), Waldoboro, 1863-1913 (4 ft.), Wiscasset, 1792-1941 (2 ft.), Bath, 1789-1942 (35 ft.), Portland and Falmouth, 1820-1925 (5 ft.), Saco, 1875-1905 (2 in.), Kennebunk, 1800-1842 (1 ft.), and York, 1789-1913 (1 ft.). *New Hampshire*: Portsmouth, 1789-1916 (22 ft.). *Massachusetts*: Newburyport, 1789-1839 (9 in.), Gloucester, 1789-1801 and 1820-1919 (6 ft.), Salem-Beverley, 1784-1918 (11 ft.), Marblehead, 1789-1802 and 1888-1900 (3 ft.), Boston and Charlestown, 1789-1918 (378 ft.), Plymouth, 1789-1803 and 1820-44 (1 ft.), Barnstable, 1798-1912 (44 ft.), Edgartown, 1820-94 (9 in.), Dighton (Fall River), 1789-1806 and 1864-1916 (8 in.), and New Bedford, 1796-1939 (87 ft.). *Rhode Island*: Providence, 1790-1805 and 1820-1914 (10 ft.), Bristol-Warren, 1790-1911 (2 ft.), and Newport, 1768-1912 (42 ft.). *Connecticut*: Stonington, 1865-1910 (4 in.),

New London, 1790-1918 (6 ft.), Middletown (Hartford), 1795-1913 (85 ft.), New Haven, 1762-1916 (155 ft.) and 1763-1802 (1 ft. in FRC Boston), and Fairfield (Bridgeport), 1789-1918 (63 ft.).

Records of Middle Atlantic Collection Districts or Customhouses. 1780-1946. 3,310 lin. ft.

New York: New York, 1784-1919 (1,909 ft.), and Sag Harbor, 1791-1844 (6 in.). *New Jersey*: Newark, 1836 and 1912 (negligible), Perth Amboy, 1789-1897 (17 ft.), Little Egg Harbor, 1790-1897 (4 ft.), Great Egg Harbor, 1789-96 and 1868-1915 (4 ft.), Bridgeton, 1789-1913 (3 ft.), and Burlington, 1866-91 (1 in.). *Pennsylvania*: Philadelphia, 1789-1936 (1,002 ft.). *Delaware*: Wilmington, 1820-48 and 1877-1918 (14 ft.). *Maryland*: Eastern District (Crisfield), 1878-1946 (11 ft.), Baltimore, 1780-1939 (322 ft.), Annapolis, 1789-1912 (7 in., including one volume dated 1745), and Cedar Point, 1857-67 (1 in.). *District of Columbia*: Georgetown (Washington), 1809-1934 (23 ft.).

Records of Southern Atlantic Collection Districts or Customhouses. 1773-1936. 285 lin. ft. and 30 rolls of microfilm.

Virginia: Alexandria, 1789-1932 (21 ft.), Dumfries, 1789-1805 (2 in.), Tappahannock, 1876-98 (2 ft.), Yorktown (Newport News), 1865-1909 (2 ft.), Richmond, 1820-44 and 1875-1910 (3 ft.), Petersburg, 1820-21 and 1866-1907 (6 ft.), Bermuda Hundred or City Point, 1790-95 (1 in.), Norfolk and Portsmouth, 1820-1909 (2 ft.), and Cherrystone, 1888-90 (2 in.). *North Carolina*: Camden, 1824-27 (1 in.), Edenton, 1773-1913 (4 ft.), Plymouth, 1820-40 and 1880-89 (2 in.), Albemarle (Elizabeth City), 1866-1923 (7 ft.), Ocracoke, 1889-97 (3 in.), Washington, 1820-48 and 1867-1901 (1 ft.), New Bern, 1820-64 and 1866-1916

(6 ft.), Pamlico, 1889-1910 (36 ft.), and Wilmington, 1886-1918 (2 in.). *South Carolina*: Charleston, 1818-1930 (94 ft.), Georgetown, 1870-75 (1 in.), and Beaufort, 1825 and 1862-1928 (12 ft.). *Georgia*: Savannah, 1789-1921 (57 ft., and 30 rolls of microfilm in FRC Atlanta), and Brunswick, 1823-25 and 1865-1917 (3 ft.). *Florida*: Fernandina, 1869-1912 (3 ft.), Jacksonville (St. Johns), 1865-1901 (1 ft.), St. Augustine, 1821-70 (1 in.), Key West, 1831-99 (2 ft.), Tampa, 1880-1914 (14 ft.), St. Marks, 1866-1903 (3 ft.), Apalachicola, 1881-1917 (5 ft.), and Pensacola, 1880-1909 (1 ft.).

Records of Gulf Coast and Caribbean Collection Districts or Customhouses. 1803-1934. 756 lin. ft.

Alabama: Mobile, 1806-1934 (174 ft.). *Mississippi*: Pearl River, 1820-1919 (26 ft.). *Louisiana*: Teche, 1867-1903 (2 ft.), and New Orleans, 1803-1919 (538 ft.). *Texas*: Galveston, 1846-1911 (11 in.), Saluria, 1857 and 1879-1904 (9 ft.), Corpus Christi, 1851-1914 (3 ft.), and Brazos de Santiago, 1867-1912 (6 in.). *Puerto Rico*, 1900-1903 (1 in.). *Virgin Islands*, 1917-33 (3 ft.).

Records of the Customhouses or Collection Districts on the Great Lakes and Canadian Border. 1799-1925. 80 lin. ft.

Vermont: Vermont (Burlington), 1863-66 and 1888-99 (8 in.), and Memphremagogg, 1855-1901 (2 ft.). *New York*: Champlain, 1872-1902 (8 in.), Oswegatchie, 1867-1912 (24 ft.), Oswego, 1835-1910 (9 ft.), Genesee (Rochester), 1864-1901 (3 ft.), Niagara, 1867 (1 in.), and Buffalo Creek (Buffalo), 1875-1900 (4 ft.). *Pennsylvania*: Presque Isle (Erie), 1799-1887 (2 ft.). *Ohio*: Cuyagahoga (Cleveland), 1893-99 (3 in.), and Sandusky, 1820 and 1883-99 (5 in.). *Michigan*: Detroit, 1889-1907 (1 ft.),

Port Huron, 1867 (1 in.), and Michilimackinac (Superior), 1886-97 (3 in.). *Illinois*: Chicago, 1861-95 (2 ft.). *Wisconsin*: Milwaukee, 1851-1900 (16 ft.). *Minnesota*: Duluth, 1871-1925 (15 ft.). *North and South Dakota* (Pembina), 1866-67 (1/4 in.). *Montana and Idaho*, 1889-1916 (5 ft.).

Records of the Mississippi, Ohio, and Missouri River Collection Districts or Customhouses. 1848-1930. 2 lin. ft.
  Pennsylvania: Pittsburgh, 1865-90 (2 in.). *Kentucky*: Louisville, 1873-92 (2 in.), and Paducah, 1910-30. *Ohio*: Cincinnati, 1848-53 and 1891-1900 (2 in.). *Indiana*: Indianapolis, 1882-87 (2 in.). *Tennessee*: Memphis, 1863-1905 (5 in.). *Missouri*: St. Louis, 1874-96 (4 in.).

Records of Collection Districts and Customhouses of the Pacific Coast. 1848-1942. 464 lin. ft.
  California: Los Angeles, 1882-1910 (6 in.), and San Francisco, 1850-1942 (258 ft.). *Oregon*: Astoria, 1848-1914 (8 ft.), Southern Oregon, 1873-98 (1 ft.), and Willamette, 1870-96 (2 in.). *Washington*: Puget Sound, 1874-98 and 1907 (1 ft.) and 1851-1913 (194 ft. in FRC Seattle). *Alaska*, 1867-1935 (1 ft.).

CARTOGRAPHIC AND
AUDIOVISUAL RECORDS. 1875-1954. 101 items.
  Cartographic records (24 items) consist of a tract chart of the U.S. North Pacific Surveying Expedition, John Rodgers, U.S. Navy, 1854-58; two copies of a map of Sitka, Alaska, attested by H. H. McIntyre, special agent, as an enclosure to the printed report of Gen. Jefferson C. Davis, dated December 1, 1869, on distribution of property under the purchase agreement; and maps of the United States, 1929-54 (21 items), showing customs districts and other administrative divisions.
  Audiovisual records consist of photographs, 1875-1910 (77 items), of special agents and employees of the Bureau.

See Elmer W. Lindgard, comp., *Preliminary Inventory of the Records of the Collector of Customs, Puget Sound District, in the Federal Records Center, Seattle, Washington*, PI 122 (1960).
Microfilm Publications: On microfilm are passenger lists and related card indexes for Baltimore and Boston, 1820-91, New Orleans, 1820-1902, New York, 1820-97, Philadelphia, 1800-1882, and other Atlantic, Gulf, and Great Lakes ports, 1820-74. For a complete listing see the current *List of National Archives Microfilm Publications.*

SPECIFIC RESTRICTIONS

Records: Records pertaining to countervailing duties comprising customs case files 3947K, 6761h, 24866, 50995, 67746, 67760, and 69424, and customs case files relating to certain countervailing duty orders, 1897-1905, concerning sugar from various countries.

Restrictions: No one other than Bureau of Customs personnel may examine these records or be given information from them except as authorized by the Commissioner of Customs.

Specified by: Commissioner of Customs.

RECORDS OF THE BUREAU OF THE MINT
(RECORD GROUP 104)

The Bureau of the Mint, established in the Department of the Treasury by an act of February 12, 1873, succeeded the Mint of the United States, founded in 1792 at Philadelphia and continued there after the Federal Government moved to Washington, D.C., in 1800. Although the Mint was nominally an independent agency, the Secretary of the Treasury supervised its coinage operations from 1835 to 1873, and after 1857 the Director was required by law to submit his annual report to the Secretary. With the creation of the Bureau, its Director was charged with supervising all mints (including the Mint at Philadelphia) and assay offices previously administered by the Director of the Mint of the United States.

The Bureau manufactures domestic and foreign coins, acquires metals for coinage, produces medals of a national character, assays, refines, and receives, stores, and sells gold and silver bullion. The Director makes annual estimates of the value of foreign coins and reports the proceedings of annual assay commissions, which are required by law to make annual inspections of the coinage. Until October 9, 1961, the Director also administered regulations issued under the Gold Reserve Act of 1934 and those concerning newly mined silver, and collected statistics on U.S. gold and silver production. Those functions are now the responsibility of the Office of Domestic Gold and Silver Operations in the Treasury Department.

There are 528 cubic feet of records dated between 1792 and 1942 in this record group.

RECORDS OF THE U.S. MINT AT PHILADELPHIA. 1792-1923.
285 lin. ft. and 2 rolls of microfilm.

These include correspondence (188 lin. ft. and 1 roll of microfilm) relating to supervision of the Mint Service, 1792-1873; correspondence relating to operations at the Philadelphia Mint, 1873-99; letters sent by the Director of the Mint of the United States and later by the Superintendent of the U.S. Mint at Philadelphia to the Treasury Department, other Government agencies, branch mints, and banks, 1866-1900, and to private persons, 1866-79, relating to operations at the Philadelphia Mint and field institutions; letters sent to private persons requesting information about coins, dies, and the history of the Mint Service, 1879-1904; correspondence with

branch mints and assay offices, 1835-98; and letters from the Treasurer of the Mint relating to fiscal operations, 1816-74.

Operational records consist primarily of assay workbooks, reports, and other records relating to assaying, 1795-1906; and records relating to: manufacturing bars and coins, including recoinage, redemption, and coin exchange, 1794-1914; maintaining the bullion fund and accounting for bullion purchased by the Mint for coinage, 1794-1916; clippings, dies, and medals, 1839-1919; melting and refining, 1866-1923; and weighings, 1815-1903. Also included are statistics on coinage, 1794-1888, reports of weekly settlements of the amount of gold and silver used, 1854-70, and a visitor register, 1836-71.

Administrative records contain ledgers of receipts and expenditures of the Mint of the United States, 1794-1854 (including 1 roll of microfilm); account books from branch mints, 1855-72; ledgers of the Philadelphia Mint, 1883-1907; personnel appointment registers, 1865 and 1876-1910; and property and supply records, including letters sent relating to repairs on the mint building, 1855-57, correspondence about constructing the new Philadelphia Mint, 1897-1901, and specifications for machinery and supplies, 1896-98.

RECORDS OF THE SECRETARY OF THE TREASURY AND THE BUREAU OF THE MINT. 1792-1942.
419 lin. ft.

Correspondence (283 lin. ft.) includes a register of the Secretary of the Treasury's correspondence, 1792-1835; letters sent by the Secretary to the Mint of the United States and branch mints, 1834-71, and letters received from those mints, 1834-73; letters received by the Bureau from the Philadelphia Mint, branch mints, assay offices, other Government agencies, and private persons, 1873-1932; other letters sent by the Secretary of the Treasury, 1834–73; and letters sent by the Director of the Mint, 1873–1938, including those about mining statistics, 1880–97.

Reports and other statistical records include annual, quarterly, and monthly reports relating to assaying, manufacturing coins and medals, melting, recoining, importing and exporting coins, acquiring and disposing of bullion, depositing and purchasing gold and silver, and the assets and liabilities of mints and assay offices, 1874–1929; reports relating to mining gold and silver and producing precious metals, records relating to bullion operations and authority to purchase silver, and schedules of silver offers and purchases, 1875–1919; records relating to operations under the Pittman Silver Act, including records about silver transactions and international silver movements, statements of miners and smelting company officials concerning sources of silver purchases, monthly bulletins and related records concerning silver, and reports of silver deposits and purchases, 1918–27; records relating to foreign coinage, including statistical and other records of gold and silver production in foreign countries and coinage in the Philippine Islands, Puerto Rico, and Hawaii, 1889–1932; reports on gold holdings of nonnational banks in 1899 and 1901, with tables and schedules used by the Bureau; accounts of gold and silver bars used in the industrial arts, 1899–1931; and other reports relating to imports and exports of gold and silver, gold and silver production in the United States, the value of foreign coins, and bullion quotations.

Records of or about annual assay commissions include minutes, 1841–73; letters received concerning Presidential appointments to the commissions, 1879, 1887, 1889–1906, and 1914–18; records of coins received and returned by the commissions, 1885–89; records of annual assays, 1873–1911; and records of coins

reserved for the assays of 1890, 1902–5, 1915–16, and 1920–25.

Administrative records include ledgers and journals of appropriations and expenditures, 1873–75 and 1899–1912, and other fiscal records, such as cashiers' daily statements, 1913–41; correspondence regarding personnel, 1908–30; miscellaneous records concerning supplies, patents, and machinery, 1924–25; and motion picture film (1 reel) depicting coin minting and medal casting at the Philadelphia Mint, 1940.

There are also records, many of them fragmentary, of all closed branch mints and assay offices except the Mint at Dahlonega, Ga., whose records have not been located. There is, however, correspondence relating to the Dahlonega Mint among records of the U.S. Mint at Philadelphia and the Secretary of the Treasury. Records include those of the San Francisco Mint (in FRC San Francisco); the Boise, Idaho, Assay Office—which existed from 1871 to 1933—comprising assay records, 1918–33, and office accounts, reports, and bullion registers, ledgers, and stockbooks, 1923–33; the Carson City, Nev., Branch Mint and Assay Office—which operated as a coinage institution from 1870 to 1893 and as an assay office from 1893 to 1933—including assay records, 1877–1903, registers of deposits and warrants paid, 1877, coinage records, 1889–93, receipts for silver bullion and gold ingots, 1892–94, and payment certificates, 1898–1919; the Charlotte, N.C., Branch Mint and Assay Office—which originated in 1835 as a branch mint, became an assay office in 1873, and ceased to exist in 1913—including correspondence, registers, records relating to melting and refining deposits, journals, ledgers, other accounting records, and administrative records, 1835–1913; the Deadwood, S. Dak., Assay Office—which operated from 1898 to 1927—consisting of correspondence relating to assays and assay records, 1898–1927, a register of deposits, 1901-23, bullion accounts, 1915-16 and 1923-27, and miscellaneous Office accounts, 1907-27; the Helena, Mont., Assay Office, including correspondence, administrative records, and bullion accounts, 1877-1933, records of deposits and purchases, 1890-1900, and assay records, 1917-33; the New Orleans Branch Mint—which existed from 1835 to 1942—including letters received about repairing the mint building, 1840-58, other letters received, 1912-19, letters sent, 1880-97 and 1912-21, bullion accounts, 1890-93 and 1935-42, and a register of warrants, 1879-87; the Salt Lake City Assay Office—which operated from 1909 to 1933—including assay records, 1918-33, bullion accounts and

general Office records, 1909-33, and melting records, 1909-23; and the St. Louis Assay Office—which functioned from 1882 to 1911—consisting of a register of accounts, 1906-9, the only extant record of the Office.

See Lyle J. Holverstott and Jean McNiece, comps., *Preliminary Inventory of the Records of the United States Mint at Philadelphia*, PI 40 (1952).

Microfilm Publications: *Letters Sent by the Director of the United States Mint at Philadelphia, 1795-1817,* M64, 1 roll, DP; *Bullion Ledgers of the U.S. Mint at Philadelphia, 1784-1802,* T587, 1 roll; *Selected Records of the Bureau of the Mint Relating to the Buffalo Nickel,* T620, 1 roll; and *Correspondence of the Mint of the United States at Philadelphia With the Branch Mint at Dahlonega, Georgia, 1835-1861,* T646, 3 rolls.

RECORDS OF THE
BUREAU OF ENGRAVING AND PRINTING
(RECORD GROUP 318)

Acts of February 25 and July 11, 1862, authorized the engraving of signatures on Treasury notes and the imprinting of the Treasury Department seal on notes made for the Department by private firms, and empowered the Secretary of the Treasury to have the notes engraved at the Department, purchase equipment, and employ necessary personnel. As early as 1866 the First Division in the Office of the Comptroller of the Currency, created by an act in 1863, was informally referred to as the Bureau of Engraving and Printing. The "Bureau" designation was officially adopted in 1869 when the unit was administratively separated from the Office. The first legislative recognition of the Bureau as an organizational unit of the Department of the Treasury was made in an appropriation act of June 20, 1874.

The Bureau designs, engraves, and prints for the Federal Government and U.S. insular possessions all paper currency, bonds, notes, bills, and certificates; Federal Reserve notes; obligations of Government-owned

corporations; revenue, customs, postage, and savings stamps; Government checks; and other engraved documents. Bureau operations are financed by reimbursements to a working capital fund authorized by law.

The Bureau has retained most of its records. General correspondence between the Secretary of the Treasury and the Director of the Bureau, correspondence about Bureau appointments, and personnel registers are among general records of the Department of the Treasury (see RG 56).

There are 130 cubic feet of records dated between 1862 and 1913 in this record group.

RECORDS. 1862-1913. 156 lin. ft.

Letters received relating to Bureau activities and including printing orders for currency, stamps, and bonds, 1864-1912; letters received relating to supplies, 1870-75; general and miscellaneous letters sent, 1862-1912; letters sent relating to personnel and supplies, 1871-89; and indexes to letters received and sent, 1885-1913.

RECORDS OF THE UNITED STATES SECRET SERVICE
(RECORD GROUP 87)

The U.S. Secret Service was organized in July 1865 as a division in the Office of the Solicitor of the Treasury. This Office had been given responsibility by the Secretary of the Treasury in 1863 for detecting and bringing to trial persons involved in the counterfeiting of treasury notes, bonds, and other securities of the United States in accordance with an act of June 23, 1860. In 1870 the Solicitor's Office was transferred to the Department of Justice, and although the Secret Service remained in the Treasury Department, it continued under the supervision of the Solicitor until 1879. In 1882 it received statutory recognition as a division in the Office of the Secretary of the Treasury.

The Secret Service has been primarily responsible for combating counterfeiting, forgery, and the alteration of the currency and securities of the United States and foreign governments. Until 1908, when the practice was prohibited by law, Secret Service agents also conducted special investigations for other bureaus of the Treasury Department and for other departments. During World War I the President was authorized to direct the use of the Secret Service wherever necessary, and agents conducted investigations for the War Trade Board, the United States Food Administration, the State Department, and other departments. During World War II the Service again undertook special work, including cooperation with investigators of the Office of Price Administration in detecting and arresting persons who manufactured, used, or distributed counterfeit ration stamps.

Occasionally after 1893 and regularly since the assassination of President McKinley the Service has provided protection to the President. This service has been expanded to include members of the President's immediate family, the President-elect, the Vice President or other official next in succession to the office of President, the Vice President-elect, and candidates for the Offices of President and Vice President. Protection is also provided for former Presidents, the widow of a President during her lifetime, and for their minor children until age 16, unless such protection is declined.

The White House police force, created by an act of September 14, 1922, was placed under the Chief of the Secret Service by an act of May 14, 1930, and renamed the Executive Protective Service by an act of March 19, 1970. The Service protects the White House, Executive offices and grounds, the President and his immediate family, and foreign diplomatic missions in the Washington, D.C., area. A Treasury Department order of April 30, 1937, gave jurisdiction over and responsibility for the guard force of the Treasury Department in Washington to the Service. The Treasury guard force is responsible for the safety of currency, bonds, and other securities in the Treasury Building and its vaults.

There are 650 cubic feet of records (in WNRC except one reel of motion picture film and those records identified as in various Presidential libraries) dated between 1863 and 1961 in this record group.

RECORDS. 1863–1961. 564 lin. ft. and 843 rolls of microfilm.

Included are orders, circulars, bulletins, and other administrative records, 1874–1935; transcripts of agents' monthly reports, 1864–67; abstracts of agents' reports, 1865–71; agents' daily reports, 1875–1936, including those of agents on White House detail, 1902–36 (all on 843 rolls of microfilm); and reports on special investigations, 1871–74 and 1906–20.

Other records include closed case files of investigations and other records relating to apprehended criminals and to suspects, 1863-1938; correspondence and related registers and indexes, 1863-1937; ledgers, journals, and cashbooks, 1865-1921; scrapbooks of newspaper clippings, 1894-1912; and the motion picture "Know Your Money," 1939. There are field office records, including general orders and circulars, reports of agents, and correspondence with headquarters, 1874-1938. There are also records relating to the safety of the President for certain periods as follows: 1933-53 (111 lin. ft. in FDRL), 1945-53 (40 lin. ft. in HSTL), and 1952-61 (20 lin. ft. in DDEL).

See Lyle J. Holverstott, comp., *Preliminary Inventory of the Records of the United States Secret Service*, PI 16 (1949).

Microfilm Publication: *Register of Monthly Reports by United States Secret Service Agents, Dec. 1864-Feb. 1871*, T917, 7 rolls.

SPECIFIC RESTRICTIONS

Records: All records less than 50 years old, except the motion picture "Know Your Money."

Restrictions: No one other than an employee of the United States Secret Service may examine these records or obtain information from them or copies of them, except by permission of the Director of the Service.

Specified by: Director of the United States Secret Service.

RECORDS OF THE INTERNAL REVENUE SERVICE
(RECORD GROUP 58)

The Office of the Commissioner of Internal Revenue was established in the Treasury Department by an act of July 1, 1862, to help finance the Civil War. The agency under the Office was known as the Bureau of Internal Revenue until 1953, and thereafter as the Internal Revenue Service. During the periods 1791-1802 and 1813-17 the Treasury Department collected internal revenue taxes through an office headed by the Commissioner of the Revenue. In 1866 the Commissioner of Internal Revenue was given responsibility for terminating the work of commissions that had been created to collect direct taxes in the States declared to be in insurrection. Wartime taxes were gradually abolished or reduced until only taxes on liquor and tobacco existed in 1883. From that time until 1913 the Bureau was chiefly concerned with the collection of taxes on these two commodities, although other tax and regulatory activities were occasionally assigned to it. It enforced the abortive 1894 income tax and collected corporation income taxes after 1909.

With the adoption of the 16th amendment in 1913, the collection of income taxes became one of the Bureau's principal functions. From 1919 to 1927 it enforced Prohibition laws. During World War II, under the Stabilization Act of October 2, 1942, the Bureau was responsible for stabilizing salaries over $5,000, as well as salaries under $5,000, of certain employees not represented by recognized labor organizations. Today the Service is responsible for the administration, assessment, and collection of all internal revenue taxes and the administration of laws relating to alcohol, alcoholic beverages, tobacco, and firearms.

There are 2,284 cubic feet of records dated between 1791 and 1940 in this record group.

GENERAL RECORDS. 1791-1940. 2,956 lin. ft.

In the pre-Civil War period these include letters sent by the Commissioner of the Revenue and the Revenue Office, 1792-1807, and records received by the

Commissioner and the Secretary of the Treasury, 1791-1862; records, including assessment lists, relating to the collection of U. S. direct taxes in Pennsylvania during hostilities with France, 1798-1803, and the War of 1812; and records of taxes levied on carriages, whiskey, and stills in Pennsylvania, 1793-1802. The early correspondence, much of which is with Federal revenue supervisors in the States, concerns taxes on carriages, window glass, snuff, auction sales, household furniture, watches, distilled spirits, and the Whiskey Rebellion of 1794. Letters dated after 1817 are concerned largely with outstanding taxes and collectors' unsettled accounts. A few relate to public lands, Indians, and the public debt.

For the period since the Civil War these include annual reports of the Commissioner of Internal Revenue, 1874 and 1886-1900; letters and telegrams sent by the Commissioner to assessors, collectors, public officials, banks, and private individuals, with registers, 1862-1915; registers of letters received, with fragmentary series of the letters received, 1862-95 and 1907-10; circular letters, 1893-1929; letters sent by the Miscellaneous Division, 1892-1916, Assessment Division, 1870-1917, Chief Clerk, 1908-17, Division of Accounting and Statistics, 1887-98 and 1911-17, and Customs Division, 1913; general correspondence of the Prohibition unit, 1918-25; and correspondence of the Industrial Alcohol Division, relating to basic permits, 1926-34.

Also included are assessment lists, 1862-73; assessment lists for individual taxpayers, 1874-1910 and 1914-15, and for corporations, 1910-15. There are copies retained from the collection districts of Massachusetts, 1911-17, and Connecticut, 1910-17 (in FRC Boston); Buffalo, 1862-1917, Syracuse, 1883-1917, Albany, 1910-17, Lower Manhattan, 1910-17, and Newark, 1917 (in FRC New York City); Alabama, 1910-17, Florida, 1917, Geor-

gia, 1913-17, and Mississippi, 1915-17; North Carolina, 1914-17, South Carolina 1866-1917, and Tennessee, 1910-17 (in FRC Atlanta); Detroit, 1870-1917 (in FRC Chicago); Nebraska, 1906-17, Iowa, 1873-1917, Minnesota, 1866-1917, and South Dakota, 1915-17 (in FRC Kansas City); Colorado, 1873-1917, Wyoming, 1874-79, and New Mexico, 1885-1917 (in FRC Denver); San Francisco, 1909-12 and 1914-17, and Honolulu, 1910-17 (in FRC San Francisco); and Montana, 1897-1917, Oregon, 1910-16, and Washington, 1909-17 (in FRC Seattle).

There are lists of special returns and penalties, 1862-70; records of taxes on bank dividends, 1863-66, and bonds and dividends of railroad and canal companies, 1863-73; abstracts of tax collections by taxes and States, 1869-1940; a record of abatement claims rejected and allowed, 1864-1911; lists of unassessed penalties, 1866-67; reports of U.S. attorneys on actions concerning taxes, 1871-92; a record of tax suits, 1871-92 and 1900-1911; compromise dockets, 1866-1912, with an index to deposits of offers of compromise, 1882-95 and 1907-10; a record of taxes collected and refunded, 1862-1915, and of depreciation allowances for mining companies, 1917-29; appointment registers of collectors and assessors, 1862-73; copies of assignments of storekeepers, 1898-1910; lists of Bureau employees, 1872-92; identification cards, with photographs, of Prohibition agents, 1921-25; and a record set of the publication *Internal Revenue Record and Journal*, 1866-97.

RECORDS OF DIRECT TAX COMMISSIONS OR RELATING TO DIRECT TAXES. 1863-98. 47 lin. ft.

These comprise chiefly minutes and correspondence of commissioners; tax sale certificates, including certificates for land sold in South Carolina to heads of black families; claims for surplus proceeds from land sales; applications to redeem land; receipts for direct taxes;

and records of land surveys, with related maps. There are records for the Colorado Territory, District of Columbia, Alabama, Arkansas, Florida, Louisiana, Mississippi, North and South Carolina, Tennessee, Texas, and Virginia. Some letters sent by the Commissioner relating to collection of direct taxes in rebellious States were interfiled with these records.

RECORDS OF THE COLLECTOR AND ASSESSOR OF INTERNAL REVENUE FOR THE 4TH DISTRICT [MARSHALL], TEX. 1866-89. 4 lin. ft.

These comprise assessment lists for the 5th division, 1866-67, tax returns, 1866-70, and correspondence of the collector, 1885-89.

CARTOGRAPHIC RECORDS. 1862-1912. 85 items.

Records of the Collector of Internal Revenue, Charleston, S.C., comprising chiefly land survey maps and field notebooks of areas in St. Helena's and St. Luke's Parishes, S.C., and in the cities of Port Royal and Beaufort, 1862-89. Also included is an annotated photostat of a 1912 Corps of Engineers topographic quadrangle.

Microfilm Publications: *Letters Sent by the Commissioners of the Revenue and the Revenue Office, 1792-1807*, M414, 3 rolls, DP; *U.S. Direct Tax of 1798: Tax Lists for the State of Pennsylvania*, M372, 24 rolls, DP; *Corporation Assessment Lists, 1909-1915*, M667, 82 rolls, DP; and *Internal Revenue Assessment Lists, 1862-66*, for the following States: Alabama, M754, 6 rolls, DP; Arkansas, M755, 2 rolls, DP; California, M756, 33 rolls, DP; Colorado, M757, 3 rolls, DP; Connecticut, M758, 23 rolls, DP; Delaware, M759, 8 rolls, DP; District of Columbia, M760, 3 rolls, DP; Florida, M761, 1 roll, DP; Georgia, M762, 8 rolls, DP; Idaho, M763, 1 roll, DP; Illinois, M764, 63 rolls, DP; and Indiana, M766, 42 rolls.

Discontinued Agencies

RECORDS OF CIVIL WAR SPECIAL AGENCIES OF THE TREASURY DEPARTMENT (RECORD GROUP 366)

The Civil War Special Agencies of the Treasury Department were established under an act of July 13, 1861, to regulate trade in the insurgent areas of the South controlled by the U.S. military and in adjacent areas of loyal States. Special agents were first appointed by the Secretary of the Treasury to enforce this law at places where there were no customs officers, but between 1863 and 1864 a system of Special Agencies having geographical jurisdictions was established. Until the Supervising Special Agent of the First Special Agency was designated as General Agent on July 30, 1864, the Commissioner of Customs exercised some supervision over the Agencies,

kept accounts of captured and abandoned property and of commercial intercourse in rebellious States, and audited and settled agents' accounts. An act of July 2, 1864, authorized the Secretary also to appoint purchasing agents.

Special agents issued "authorities" for merchandise transported to or from restricted areas; collected and received captured, abandoned, and confiscable property within their agencies and from military and naval personnel; and were responsible for the employment and welfare of freedmen until the creation of the Bureau of Refugees, Freedmen, and Abandoned Lands (see RG 105). Purchasing agents bought for the United

States products of insurgent States. Special Agencies ceased to function soon after June 1865 when the Secretary—acting on a Presidential order that ended restrictions on commerce in the South—rescinded Treasury regulations governing captured and abandoned property. Duties of the purchasing agents were terminated at about the same time.

Closely related records are those relating to restricted commercial intercourse and to captured and abandoned property, and the Southern Claims Commission—all among general records of the Department of the Treasury (see RG 56); correspondence relating to captured and abandoned property, special agents' accounts, and allowed southern claims among records of the U.S. General Accounting Office (see RG 217); and disallowed southern claims among records of the U.S. House of Representatives (see RG 233).

There are 180 cubic feet of records dated between 1861 and 1866 in this record group.

RECORDS. 1861-66. 216 lin. ft.

Included are records of the Agencies; the General Agent, who eventually supervised the nine Special Agencies; and the purchasing agents, including general correspondence; letter books; daybooks; cashbooks; ledgers; registers of "authorities" for establishing supply and trade stores; applications for "authorities" to engage in commerce and transportation, with bonds and oaths of loyalty; manifests of river steamers; abstracts of customhouse transactions and internal and coastwise commerce; records relating to captured, abandoned, and confiscable property that include monthly returns of property received and collected, libels concerning land seizures, leases for dwellings and lands, and statements of auctioned property; records relating to the purchase, sale, and shipment of cotton; and records concerning the administration of regulations relating to the employment and general welfare of freedmen.

RECORDS OF THE OFFICE OF FOREIGN ASSETS CONTROL (RECORD GROUP 265)

The Foreign Funds Control, a predecessor of the Office of Foreign Assets Control, was established in the Office of the Secretary of the Treasury in April 1940 to administer functions assigned to the Secretary by Executive Order 8389 under authority of the Trading With the Enemy Act, as amended. Through a system of licenses, rulings, and other "freezing" regulations, the Control, which had bureau status after September 1942, functioned as part of the Government's financial warfare program to prevent enemy-dominated countries or their nationals from using frozen assets. It administered import controls over enemy assets and wartime restrictions on trade with the enemy, participated in administering the "Proclaimed List of Certain Blocked Nationals," and

took censuses of foreign-owned assets in the United States and American-owned assets abroad. Control activities were transferred in 1947 to the Treasury Department Office of International Finance. In 1948 activities relating to blocked foreign funds were transferred to the Office of Alien Property, Department of Justice.

A Treasury Department order of December 1950 established a new foreign funds control unit, the Division of Foreign Assets Control of the Office of International Finance, to administer controls over the assets of China and North Korea frozen after Chinese intervention in Korea and certain regulations and orders issued under the amended Trading With the Enemy Act. The Office of Foreign Assets Control was established as a separate office under the Assistant Secretary for International Affairs by a Treasury Department order of October 15, 1962. The Office administers the foreign assets control program and Cuban assets control regulations, which block Communist Chinese, North Korean, North Vietnamese, and Cuban assets in the United States and prohibit unlicensed trade and financial transactions on behalf of those countries.

There are 461 cubic feet of records (in WNRC) dated between 1943 and 1945 in this record group.

RECORDS. 1943–45. 532 lin. ft.

These consist chiefly of Form TFR 500 census schedules of property in foreign countries owned on May 31, 1943, by persons and organizations subject to the jurisdiction of the United States or its territories and possessions, including summary reports, detailed property reports, and reports of interests in primary allied organizations submitted by individuals; by corporations or other organizations; by executors, administrators, or trustees; and by custodians or nominees who held property for persons not subject to U.S. jurisdictions. Also included are indexes to the names of U.S. corporations filing such schedules that had subsidiaries in foreign countries.

See Treasury Department bulletin *Census of American-Owned Assets in Foreign Countries* (1947) for an analysis of data in Forms TFR 500.

SPECIFIC RESTRICTIONS

Records: Form TFR 500 census schedules of property in foreign countries owned on May 31, 1943, by persons and organizations subject to the jurisdiction of the United States or its territories and possessions, and indexes to names of U. S. corporations filing such schedules that had subsidiaries in foreign countries.

Restrictions: These records may not be examined by or copies of or information from them provided to any person except upon the written authorization of the Secretary of the Treasury or his delegate.

Specified by: Secretary of the Treasury.

DEPARTMENT OF DEFENSE

General

RECORDS OF THE
OFFICE OF THE SECRETARY OF DEFENSE
(RECORD GROUP 330)

The Office of the Secretary of Defense, created in 1947 to head the National Military Establishment, later renamed the Department of Defense (DOD), is responsible for providing for the security of the United States by integrating policies and procedures for Government departments, agencies, and functions relating to national security. Subordinate offices were created to carry out activities relating to engineering, international security affairs, legal and legislative matters, manpower and personnel, health and medical activities, public information, real estate and construction, and atomic energy. In 1949 three Assistant Secretaries of Defense were authorized, and in 1952 the Joint Secretaries Group was established to advise the Secretary on matters of broad policy covering DOD administration and operation. Reorganization Plan No. 6 of 1953 abolished various offices, including the Munitions Board and the Research and Development Board, and provided for six additional Assistant Secretaries and the General Counsel. This record group includes records of some boards and committees that existed before the Office was established. The records of some offices under the direction of the Secretary of Defense have been established as separate record groups, including the U.S. Joint Chiefs of Staff (see RG 218) and the Defense Atomic Support Agency (see RG 374).

There are 2,914 cubic feet of records dated between 1940 and 1961 in this record group.

GENERAL RECORDS. 1941–55.
459 lin. ft. and 6 rolls of microfilm.

These consist primarily of central files, 1947–53, with indexes, maintained by the Correspondence Control Section, Assistant Secretary of Defense, Administration. They include reports, directives and other issuances, and correspondence relating to organization and administration, DOD general policies and programs, and the exercise of authority and control over its departments and agencies, including the supervision of budgetary programs. Other records of the Office include transcripts of hearings of the House Armed Services Committee, August–October 1949, Executive Office correspondence, 1946–50, messages, 1950–51, microfilm copies (6 rolls) of speeches and testimonies of Secretaries of the Army and Defense, 1945–53, aircraft procurement reports, 1948–51, naval combat narratives, 1941–45, Service Academy Board records, 1949, Air Coordinating Committee minutes, 1949–50, Armed Forces Medical Advisory Committee minutes, 1948–50, and records of special assistants to the Secretary of Defense, relating to topics such as budget, plans and organization, applications engineering, aircraft production, guided missiles, military assistance programs, research, and public affairs, 1947–53. Also included are some records of the Chairman of the Military Liaison Committee on the Development of the Atomic Energy Program, 1947–54, a personnel security policy file, 1951–54, and records of the Office of the General Counsel, including the Loyalty Security Board file, 1947–55.

RECORDS OF THE DEFENSE MANAGEMENT COUNCIL. 1949–53. 93 lin. ft.

The Defense Management Committee was established as an agency of the Office of the Secretary of Defense on August 10, 1949, to improve organizational structure, interdepartmental working relationships, and management in the Department. It was redesignated the Defense Management Council Staff on June 21, 1952, and abolished in August, with continuing projects reassigned among staff agencies of the Office of the Secretary of Defense and military departments. Records consist of minutes and agenda of meetings, charts, directives, reports, studies, and correspondence; and studies of interdepartmental working relationships, policies, procedures, programs, and facilities of the Office of the Secretary of Defense and military departments. Included are records of the Office of the Director of Administration, the Munitions Board Committee on Facilities and Services, and the Advisory Committee on Service Pay.

RECORDS OF THE ASSISTANT SECRETARY OF DEFENSE (COMPTROLLER). 1947–57. 49 lin. ft.

The Assistant Secretary of Defense (Comptroller) assists the Secretary in his programing, budgetary, and fiscal functions; provides for resources management systems throughout DOD; and collects, analyzes, and reports resources information for the Secretary, the Bureau of the Budget, the Congress, the General Accounting Office, and other agencies. The records consist of general correspondence, 1947–55, and Fiscal Management Staff reports and correspondence relating to procedures and operations and to surveys of facilities at installations, 1950–53.

Records of the Progress Reports and Statistics Division consist of facility expansion studies, 1952–54, supply operations reports, 1952–53, public works commitment reports, 1951–53, inventories of military real property, 1954–57, and cost reports of training foreign nationals, 1952–53.

RECORDS OF THE ASSISTANT SECRETARY OF DEFENSE (MANPOWER AND RESERVE AFFAIRS). 1941–56. 340 lin. ft.

The Assistant Secretary of Defense (Manpower and Reserve Affairs) is the principal staff assistant to the Secretary in manpower, personnel, and reserve affairs, including health and medical matters, Armed Forces information and education, health and sanitation, medical care and treatment of patients, hospitals and related health facilities, industrial relations, and Federal voting assistance.

Records of the Executive Office include general correspondence, 1949–54, with indexes; correspondence maintained by Anna Rosenberg, Assistant Secretary of Defense (Manpower and Personnel), 1951; weekly activity reports, 1951–53; and records of the Public Relations Advisory Council, 1948–49, the Citizens Advisory Committee on Medical Care of Dependents of Military Personnel (Moulton Commission), 1953, and the Advisory Commission on Service Pay (Hook Commission), 1947–50.

Records of the Office of Administrative Services include correspondence, 1947–55, military defense assistance program reports, 1942–54, a Budget and

Finance Division U.S. regional organization file, 1951–54, Personnel Division personal name files, 1949–54, and Administrative Facilities and Service Division space reports, 1948–55.

Records of the Office of Armed Forces Information and Education and its predecessors consist of correspondence, 1943–52; Research Division records relating to universal military training surveys, 1942–54; a historical file, 1941–55; surveys of troop attitudes and opinions, 1942–55, with indexes; and attitude reports of overseas personnel, 1942–43, with indexes.

Records of the Office of Domestic Programs consist of Civil Defense Division general records, 1941–56. Records of the Office of Manpower Utilization consist of correspondence, 1950–53; strength, personnel, and workload reports, 1951–52; military occupational classification project reports, 1948–51; training cost studies and reports, 1949–53; Army strength reports, 1951–52; tables of organization and equipment special projects file, 1953–54; and reports of meetings of the National Security Training Commission, 1951.

Records of the Office of Personnel Policy include a Civilian Personnel Policy Division general file, 1948–52; Separation Committee reports and correspondence, including special and final reports of the Committee on Retirement Policy for Federal Personnel, 1952–54; and Military Personnel Policy Division records, 1949–52. Records of the Personnel Policy Board consist of directives, minutes and agenda, and a historical file, 1949–51; correspondence, 1948–51; joint agreements, 1942–49; military occupational classification project contracts and subcommittee studies, 1948–51; and decoration and award studies, 1945–51.

Other records consist of Armed Services Personnel Board agenda, minutes, and correspondence, 1947–50; Joint Army and Navy Personnel Board correspondence, 1942–47; and Office of Personnel Security Policy correspondence, 1951–54.

RECORDS OF THE ASSISTANT SECRETARY OF DEFENSE (INTERNATIONAL SECURITY AFFAIRS). 1944–55. 125 lin. ft.

The Assistant Secretary of Defense (International Security Affairs) is the principal staff assistant to the Secretary for international security and issues instructions for carrying out security policies approved by the Secretary of Defense. Records of the Executive Office consist of conference notes, 1950–52, correspondence, 1952–53, monthly activity reports, 1950–55, export control security lists, 1951–54, U.S. European Command effectiveness reports, 1953–54, State Department documents relating to the participation of U.S. delegates in the development of plans and policies for defense of the United Nations, 1952–54, and transcripts of proceedings of congressional committees relating to the allotment of appropriated funds to foreign nations under the mutual security program, 1952–53.

Records of the Office of Military Assistance consist of correspondence relating to the military defense assistance program, 1949–53, Military Assistance Advisory Group activity reports, 1952–53, Foreign Assistance Correlation Committee records, 1949–50, and Military Information Control Committee records, 1949–51. Other records include a Statistical Section subject file, 1950–52, case files of the Reimbursable Aid Branch, 1949–55, and minutes, reports, studies, and other documents relating to the Geneva Conference ("Summit Conference"), the Geneva meeting of foreign ministers, and a report of the Tripartite Working Group in Paris, 1953–55.

Records of the Office of Special International Affairs consist of minutes, agenda, reports, and correspondence relating to military and economic development of nations belonging to the North

Atlantic Treaty Organization, 1951-52, and correspondence of the Office of North Atlantic Treaty Affairs, 1949-53.

There are general records of the Office of Programming and Control, 1950-51, Office of Military Aid Programs, 1950-53, and Office of Foreign Military Affairs, 1948-54. Records of the Office of Foreign Economic Defense Affairs include general records, 1952-53, and records of commissions, committees, and conferences in which the Assistant Secretary of Defense (International Security Affairs) participated. They consist of reports, agenda, minutes, charters, correspondence, and other records, 1944-52, relating to trade agreements, international trade and tariff negotiations, economic potentialities of certain countries and territories, allocation of quotas of essential commodities supplied to foreign industries by U.S. export firms, and reciprocity information.

RECORDS OF THE ASSISTANT SECRETARY OF DEFENSE (LEGISLATIVE AND PUBLIC AFFAIRS). 1940-55. 287 lin. ft.

The Assistant Secretary of Defense (Legislative and Public Affairs) assisted the Secretary of Defense in departmental legislative programs, legislative liaison, and public information and other public affairs activities. In 1958 the office was reorganized and the functions divided between the Assistant Secretary of Defense (Legislative Affairs) for DOD relations with the Congress and an Assistant Secretary of Defense (Public Affairs) for public information activities and community relations.

Records of the Office of Legislative Programs consist of correspondence, 1949-52. Records of the Office of Public Information consist of correspondence, 1940-52; activity reports, 1950-55; columnists' digests and feature articles, 1948-52; articles on George C. Marshall and James Forrestal, 1949-52; press items on the first Armed Forces Day, 1950, on investigation of B-36 aircraft, 1948-49, and on blacks' newspapers, 1944-46; news items, feature articles, and editorials concerning public opinion on national defense matters, 1948-51; and clippings, digests, and studies on universal military training and other subjects of interest to DOD, 1948-52. Records of the News Division consist of correspondence relating to the review and release of films and scripts, 1949; records relating to the production of motion pictures for the Armed Forces, 1943-52; general correspondence of the Pictorial Branch, 1951-53; correspondence relating to daily activities of the Still Pictures Section, 1951-52; minutes, 1949-53, and journals, 1951-53, of the National Organizations Branch; and news pamphlets of the Industrial Services Branch, 1951-52.

Records of the Office of Security Review consist of correspondence relating to review and release of military information for public dissemination, 1945-54; records relating to review of speeches of important persons, 1951, release of military security information on manufacture of aircraft and other Government-contracted items, 1948-50, and evaluation of foreign military intelligence after its release for public dissemination, 1953; and stenotype notes of speeches made by important persons at the Secretaries conference held at the Marine Corps Schools, Quantico, Va., July 23-26, 1953.

Records of the Office of Special Services include correspondence and reference cards relating to military and civilian celebrations and special events in which the Armed Forces participated, 1948-52, with indexes, 1950-51; and records relating to air demonstrations and exhibits, 1948-52.

RECORDS OF THE ASSISTANT SECRETARY OF DEFENSE (SUPPLY AND LOGISTICS). 1941–55. 108 lin. ft.

The Assistant Secretary of Defense (Supply and Logistics) assisted the Secretary in planning procurement, production, distribution, transportation, communications, storage, cataloging, requirements, and mobilization. The functions of this office were combined with those of the Assistant Secretary of Defense (Properties and Installations) and redesignated Office of Assistant Secretary of Defense (Installations and Logistics). The records include correspondence of the Office of the Assistant Secretary of Defense (Supply and Logistics), 1953-55, and policy directives for control of activities and instructions supplementing policies, plans, and directives, 1951-55.

Correspondence of the Office of Transportation and Communications relates to establishing plans, policies, and procedures for military transportation and traffic, 1949-55. Records of the Office of Procurement and Production Policies include a general subject file, 1951-53, production schedules for meeting Army, Navy, and Air Force needs, 1951-53, records relating to programing materials for the Department of Defense, 1954-55, tabulations of World War II and Korean war reports on the dollar value of industrial shipments, 1941-52, and reports of the "Air Force Elgin Jewel Bearing Project," July 1954. General records of the Petroleum Logistics Division relate to various aspects of petroleum programs in the Zone of Interior and overseas, 1948-55.

RECORDS OF THE ASSISTANT SECRETARY OF DEFENSE (PROPERTIES AND INSTALLATIONS). 1949-53. 30 lin. ft.

The functions of this office included real estate acquisition, use, and disposal; construction; real property maintenance and management; reserve facilities; and family housing. The duties of this office were combined with those of the Assistant Secretary of Defense (Supply and Logistics) and the office renamed Assistant Secretary of Defense (Installations and Logistics). Included are general records of the Storage and Distribution Division, relating to storage, distribution, mobilization planning, and material requirements, 1949-53; and surveys of the Office of the Director of Real Property Management, relating to Federal rent control, and correspondence of the Real Estate Division, 1951-53.

RECORDS OF THE OFFICE OF THE DIRECTOR OF DEFENSE RESEARCH AND ENGINEERING. 1946-54. 179 lin. ft.

The Office was established in 1947 as the Research and Development Board; in 1953 the name was changed to Assistant Secretary of Defense (Research and Development); later it was renamed the Assistant Secretary of Defense (Research-Development and Engineering), and still later, the Director of Defense Research and Engineering. The Director supervises all DOD research and engineering activities. The Advanced Research Projects Agency and the Weapons Systems Evaluation Group operate as separate agencies but are under the direction and supervision of the Director of Defense Research and Engineering. Almost all of the records were created by the Research and Development Board and its committees and panels. They relate to organizational plans and policies, the allocation of research and development responsibilities to military departments, and recommendations on fiscal and budgetary aspects of programs, 1946-53; the status of research and development projects of the Army, Navy, and Air Force, 1946-54; and meetings of the committees and panels, 1946-51. Records of the Weapons Systems Evaluation Group consist of correspondence, 1948-53, and reports and staff studies relating to analysis and evaluation of weapons and weapons systems, 1951-55.

RECORDS RELATING TO HEALTH AND MEDICAL POLICIES AND PROGRAMS. 1948-54. 43 lin. ft.

Included are general records of the Armed Forces Medical Policy Council, relating to plans and policies for health and medical programs, 1949-52, standardization of medical services, 1949-53, and implementation of the whole blood and blood derivatives programs, 1950-52. There are some reports, studies, directives, and agenda of medical committee meetings, 1949-52; and transcripts of meetings of the Military Medical Advisory Council, 1950.

Records of the Hawley Board/Committee consist of a study of military medical services, 1948-49, subcommittee reports and studies, 1948-49, and reports of the Hoover Commission Task Force on Government medical services, 1948.

Records of the Armed Forces Medical Advisory Committee, known also as the Cooper Committee, include minutes, reports, and publications relating to the reorganization of medical services and to cooperation between civilian and military medical groups, 1946-51.

Records of the Assistant Secretary of Defense (Health and Medical) consist of studies relating to joint use of medical services in the Zone of Interior and overseas, 1954, and minutes, reports, and press releases relating to the blood program, 1950-54.

RECORDS OF THE MUNITIONS BOARD. 1940-53. 1,029 lin. ft. (in WNRC).

The Munitions Board, established in 1947, coordinated DOD activities in industrial matters, planned military aspects of industrial mobilization, assigned interservice procurement responsibility, prepared potential production and personnel estimates for evaluating logistic feasibility of strategic operation, determined priorities within military procurement programs, supervised subordinate agencies, established interservice logistic organization, developed policy for military vs. civilian requirements, and reconciled Joint Chiefs of Staff logistic requirements with those of supply agencies and recommended action to the Secretary of Defense. The Board was dissolved June 30, 1953, and most of its functions were transferred to the Assistant Secretary of Defense (Supply and Logistics).

Records of the Office of the Chairman include correspondence of Gen. Leroy Lutes, Chairman, 1948, and correspondence relating to surveys dealing with aircraft procurement and appropriations for the Armed Forces, 1948; records of the historian and special assistant to the Chairman, 1948-53; records maintained by Chairmen Donald F. Carpenter, Hubert E. Howard, and Thomas J. Hargrave; and records of the Acting Chairman and Deputy Chairman, 1947-50.

General records, 1942-53, consist of minutes and agenda, issuances, reports, correspondence, and historical files. There are indexes to the minutes and some cross-reference sheets filed with the decimal correspondence. The records relate to organization and functions of the Board, policies affecting production and distribution of supplies and equipment, material requirements, procurement coordination between the Air Force and the Navy Bureau of Aeronautics in connection with industrial mobilization, and procurement, distribution, and stockpiling of critical materials.

Other records include those of the Office of the Vice Chairman for Production and Requirements, 1951-52; and minutes, issuances, reports, surveys, studies, correspondence, and related records, with some indexes, of the Offices of Programming, 1942-53, Production Equipment, 1949-53, Support Materiel Programs, 1941-52, Priorities and Controls, 1950-53, Clothing, Equipage, and Subsistence Program, 1949-52, Petroleum Programs, 1946-53, Guided Missiles Programs, 1945-46, Industrial Security, 1942-52, Aircraft Programs, 1948-52, and Material Resources, 1944-53.

There are some records of the Office of the Vice Chairman for International Programs, 1951-52, and the Office of the Vice Chairman for Supply Management, 1949-53, including the Offices of Small Business, 1952-53, and Supply, 1950-53. Also records of the Industrial Advisory Committee, 1949-53; the Armed Services Petroleum Board, 1943-51; the Joint Aircraft Committee, 1942-53, including

the Subcommittee on Supply and Maintenance Requirements, 1940-51; and the Joint Logistics Committee, 1947-49.

AUDIOVISUAL RECORDS. 1949-61. 968 items.

These consist of motion pictures (19 reels) of the inaugural parade and ceremonies for President Kennedy, 1961. Also sound recordings (949 items), including recordings of the Secretaries conference held at the Marine Corps Schools, Quantico, Va., July 23-26, 1953; of press conferences, briefings, speeches, and statements of DOD and other Government officials, political and military leaders, and others on defense policy, foreign affairs, military aid, and the Korean war; and of radio and TV programs, 1949-60.

RECORDS OF THE UNITED STATES JOINT CHIEFS OF STAFF (RECORD GROUP 218)

The Joint Chiefs of Staff were originally the U.S. members of the Combined Chiefs of Staff, an agency established February 6, 1942, to ensure coordination of the war effort of Great Britain and the United States. The National Security Act of 1947 established the Joint Chiefs of Staff as a permanent agency within the National Military Establishment, now the Department of Defense. Principal military advisers of the President, National Security Council, and Secretary of Defense, the Joint Chiefs of Staff consist of the Chairman, the Army Chief of Staff, the Chief of Naval Operations, and the Air Force Chief of Staff. Their major duties include preparation of strategic plans and joint review of major material, personnel, and logistic requirements of the Armed Forces, and formulation of policies for joint training of the Armed

Forces. The Chairman serves as presiding officer of the Joint Chiefs of Staff, provides agenda for their meetings, and informs the Secretary of Defense of issues upon which no agreement has been reached.

There are 31 cubic feet of records dated between 1942 and 1953 in this record group.

INSTRUMENTS OF SURRENDER AND ARMISTICE. 1942-53. 1 roll of microfilm.

These documents consist of microfilm copies of instruments of surrender of the German forces signed at Luneburg, May 4, 1945, at Reims, May 7, 1945, and at Berlin, May 8, 1945, including authorizations to the German representatives to sign on the behalf of the German Government and orders of the Supreme

Allied Commander, Allied Expeditionary Forces, to the German High Command; instruments of surrender of the Japanese forces signed in Tokyo Bay, September 2, 1945; instruments of surrender of Japanese forces in southern Korea, Southeast Asia, and the Ryukyus, Philippines, and Ocean, Nauru, and Saishu Islands, September 1945; and the Korean Armistice Agreement of June 8, 1953, and the Temporary Agreement Supplementary to the Armistice Agreement of July 27, 1953.

GENERAL RECORDS OF THE JOINT NEW WEAPONS COMMITTEE. 1942-46. 31 lin. ft.

This research and development committee of the Joint Chiefs of Staff functioned from February 1942 to June 1946, when its functions and personnel were transferred to the Joint Research and Development Board (later the Research and Development Board/Committee). Records consist mainly of reports and general correspondence on evaluation of new weapons and equipment and use of guided missiles and other strategic weapons.

AUDIOVISUAL RECORDS. 1942-46. 9 reels.

These consist of motion pictures of the Joint New Weapons Committee, relating to development of radar, guided missiles, and other equipment and weapons.

Microfilm Publication: *German, Japanese, and Korean Surrender Documents for World War II*, T826, 1 roll.

RECORDS OF THE DEFENSE ATOMIC SUPPORT AGENCY (RECORD GROUP 374)

The Defense Atomic Support Agency (DASA) succeeded on May 6, 1959, the Armed Forces Special Weapons Project (AFSWP) that, in turn, had replaced the Manhattan Engineer District in 1947. DASA is an interservice agency whose director is responsible to the Secretary of Defense through the Joint Chiefs of Staff. DASA administers Defense Department nuclear weapons policy and programs and the nuclear stockpile, coordinates policy with the Atomic Energy Commission and advises the Joint Chiefs of Staff on nuclear weapons matters, performs research and testing, inspects installations associated with nuclear activities, and conducts training and educational programs. DASA also maintains and operates the Joint Nuclear Accident Coordinating Center and provides support for the Joint Atomic Information Exchange Group. The agency maintains a headquarters in Washington, a joint task force, a test command, a field command in Albuquerque, N. Mex., an Armed Forces Radiobiology Research Institute in Bethesda, Md., and military units at certain storage locations.

There are 450 cubic feet of records dated between 1943 and 1955 in this record group.

GENERAL RECORDS. 1947-55. 181 lin. ft.

Almost all general records are in classified decimal correspondence files, 1947-55, and relate to policy and programs for organization, administration, and operation of nuclear weapons programs. The files consist of issuances, intraoffice communications, reports of investigations and inspections, correspondence, and reference material.

RECORDS OF OFFICES, DIVISIONS, AND BRANCHES. 1943-55. 45 lin. ft.

These include a subject correspondence file, 1945-54, of the Office of the

Deputy Chief; records of the Office of the Technical Director, including minutes, reports, and correspondence of the Armed Forces-Atomic Energy Commission Panel on Radiological Warfare and the Ad Hoc Committee on underwater atomic weapons testing, 1947-54; reports concerning the evaluation and analysis of research and development projects, 1943-48, of the Office of the Historian; the special projects file of the Analysis Branch, Weapons Effects Division, consisting of correspondence and other records relating to the collection of atomic weapon effects and the development of radiological defense procedures, 1950-53; logs and journals of the Radiation Branch, 1947-54; technical publications of the Technical Library Branch, 1946-50; records of the Security Division, consisting of the counterintelligence investigative file, 1947-52, and material relating to security clearances and the exchange of information with foreign countries, 1952-54; a Budget and Fiscal Division subject file of correspondence relating to budget estimates and justifications, 1947-55, and the subject file of reports, contracts, correspondence, and other records relating to construction of facilities at test sites, 1948-51; records of the Plans Division, consisting of the organizational planning records of the Manpower and Organization Branch, 1952-55; records of the Special Field Projects Division, consisting of reports, budgetary records, correspondence, and records relating to Operation Wigwam, 1953-55; records of the Test Division, consisting of the special operations file of orders, reports, and correspondence relating to special atomic weapons test operations, 1948-53; and records of the Weapons Development Division, relating to development, production, and administrative practices concerning nuclear and thermonuclear weapons, 1948-53.

RECORDS OF SPECIAL DETACHMENTS. 1943-52. 4 lin. ft.

AFSWP personnel served on occasion in facilities of the Atomic Energy Commission to collaborate on matters relating to military application of Commission work. Records of special detachments consist of the file of general and special orders relating to military personnel assigned to the detachment at Oak Ridge, Tenn., 1943-52, and the administrative subject decimal file of the 8453d Antiaircraft Unit, Special Weapons Detachment, 1946-52.

RECORDS OF JOINT TASK FORCES. 1946-55. 230 lin. ft.

For each AFSWP nuclear test operation a specific joint task force was established, composed of a task group from each service. The groups were identified by a decimal added to the number designating the task force. Special technical groups associated with a specific operation were also identified in this manner.

Records of Joint Task Force 1 relate chiefly to Operation Crossroads and subsequent followup activities. The records include a numeric-subject correspondence file, 1946-47, the numeric file of the Bikini Scientific Resurvey Group, 1947-48, and records of the Office of the Director of Ship Material relating to the planning, preparation, and execution of all nonscientific matters in the operation. Other records include incoming and outgoing messages, 1946, civilian and military orders, 1946, personal history data, 1946, a commendation file, 1945-46, and letters, formal petitions, and other records relating to protests against the testing, 1946. Records of the Army Ground Group at Bikini consist of Operation Plan 1-46 with attached organization charts, annexes, appendixes, and photographs, 1946; a reading file relating to quartermaster activities during the operation, 1946; and test crew reports on the effects of radioactivity, heat, pressure, and blast on certain equipment, 1946.

Records of Joint Task Force 3 relate to Operation Greenhouse and include general correspondence relating to organization and administration, 1949-51; a personal name file of orders and other records relating to the assignment, travel, and relief of personnel, 1950-51; cost control reports relating to expenditures, 1949-51; a general topic file of orders, memorandums, reports, and journals; and a supply administrative file, 1950-52. Records of Task Group 3.2 (Army) consist of incoming messages, 1950-51. Records of Task Group 3.3 (Navy) consist of correspondence logs and copies of outgoing messages, 1950-51, and a numeric file of correspondence relating to the Navy's role in the operation, 1950-52. Records of Task Group 3.4 (Air Force) consist of a decimal correspondence file, 1950-51; a general file of orders, plans, and diaries, 1950-51; transcripts of teleconferences, 1950-51; and reports, summaries, and procedural instructions.

Joint Task Force 7 participated in both Operation Sandstone and Operation Castle. Records of this joint task force consist of the general records, with index, of Operation Sandstone, 1947-48; the decimal correspondence file of the Intelligence and Security Section of the Intelligence Division, 1947-48; and correspondence and other records relating to participation of the joint task force in Operation Castle, 1952-54. Records of Task Group 7.2 (Army) consist of the decimal administrative correspondence file, 1953-55, and memorandums, letters, and court-martial orders, 1953-55. Records of Task Group 7.3 (Navy) consist of messages, 1952, a numeric-subject file relating to Operation Ivy, 1952-53, and histories, 1948-53. Records of Task Group 7.6 (Joint Radiological Safety Group) consist of a subject file relating to conduct of radiological safety operations performed as part of Operation Sandstone, 1947-48.

Joint Task Force 132 participated in Operation Ivy and in Operation Windstorm. The records include general decimal correspondence relating to Operation Windstorm, 1950-52, and histories and other papers of previous operations, 1949-52, of Task Group 132.2 (Army); and the decimal file, 1952, and general file, 1951-52, relating to the participation of Task Group 132.4 (Air Force) in Operation Ivy.

Joint and Combined Military Agencies

RECORDS OF ALLIED OPERATIONAL AND OCCUPATION HEADQUARTERS, WORLD WAR II
(RECORD GROUP 331)

Through the Combined Chiefs of Staff (CCS), established at Washington in January 1942, Great Britain and the United States controlled Allied efforts in World War II. The CCS was responsible for all overseas operations and for occupation headquarters that were essentially inter-Allied, and collaborated in formulating and executing plans for strategic conduct of the war, determining requirements, and allocating munitions, transportation, and other resources. Inter-Allied operational headquarters were created locally to administer those functions. The complete records of World War II inter-Allied headquarters are kept at both London and Washington, either in their original form or on microfilm.

There are 17,948 cubic feet of records dated between 1938 and 1954 in this record group.

RECORDS OF SUPREME HEADQUARTERS ALLIED EXPEDITIONARY FORCES

(SHAEF). 1942-45. 834 lin. ft. and 120 rolls of microfilm.

SHAEF, established in February 1944 to direct Allied military operations in Western Europe, absorbed the planning group known as Chief of Staff Supreme Allied Command (COSSAC). Records of a combined nature were microfilmed in duplicate, with both Governments receiving a set and one receiving the originals as well. Most SHAEF records are in the National Archives. They consist of general records (700 lin. ft. and 100 rolls of microfilm) of the secretary of the General Staff, the European Allied Contact Section, the Office of the Headquarters Commandant, the Headquarters of the Berlin District (all Historical Section records on microfilm), General Staff Divisions G-1 to G-5 (partly on microfilm), and the Adjutant General's, Engineer, Medical, Signal (on microfilm), Public Relations, Psychological Warfare, and Air Defense Divisions, including partially indexed general correspondence and issuances, 1942-45, staff conference notes, 1942-44, message logs and daily summaries of war teams, 1944-45, and operational plans and war diaries, 1943-45.

There are also plans, fortnightly reports, messages, conference notes, war diaries, and general correspondence of SHAEF missions, 1944-45, established in liberated Belgium (on microfilm), Denmark, France, the Netherlands (on microfilm), Luxembourg, and Norway to represent the Supreme Allied Commander in and maintain contact with those countries without interfering with military operations.

The Allied Expeditionary Air Force, organized in November 1943 to furnish air support for ground operations in Europe, was renamed Air Staff, SHAEF, in October 1944. In July 1945 it was discontinued. The records (most are in the Historical Division Archives, Air University, Maxwell Air Force Base, Ala.), 1943-45, include general correspondence, radio messages, directives, operational plans, minutes, and photographs relating to the combined bomber offensive over Europe.

RECORDS OF SUBORDINATE SHAEF COMMANDS. 1943-45.

233 lin. ft. and 20 rolls of microfilm.

These consist of general correspondence and other records of the 1st Allied Airborne Army and the 6th and 21st Army Groups (21st on microfilm), 1944-45, and the 12th Army Group, 1943-45; and records of the Allied Naval Commander, Expeditionary Force, 1944-45 (partly on microfilm).

RECORDS OF COMBINED LIQUIDATING AGENCIES. 1945-47.

11 lin. ft.

After the inactivation of SHAEF in July 1945, the Combined Administrative Liquidating Agency and its successor, the Combined Civil Affairs Liquidating Agency, dissolved the joint or combined organizational elements of SHAEF. The records consist of general correspondence, 1945-46; and vouchers, bills, receipts, ledgers, and commodity lists relating to the disposal of property and supplies and to microfilming, processing, and shipping records of SHAEF and its subordinate headquarters, 1945-47.

RECORDS OF ALLIED FORCE HEADQUARTERS (AFHQ). 1942-47. 361 lin. ft. and 4,544 rolls of microfilm (in WNRC).

The AFHQ was established on September 12, 1942, as an Allied command to plan and direct ground, air, and naval operations and military government activities in the North African Theater of Operations (renamed the Mediterranean Theater of Operations in November 1944). Its records, most of which are microfilm copies (in WNRC) of records in the British Cabinet Office, London, include general records (282 lin. ft. and 3,608 rolls of microfilm) consisting of correspondence and other records of the Command Group and of General Staff Sections G-2 to G-5 (G-5 partly on microfilm), 1942-47, and of Special Staff sections, boards, committees, commissions, and other organizations, 1942-46 (partly on microfilm). Also included are records of subordinate commands, comprising correspondence and other records (partly on microfilm) of the 15th Army Group, 5th Army, Mediterranean Allied Air Forces Headquarters, Mediterranean Allied Photographic Reconnaissance Wing, Mediterranean Allied Strategic Air Force Headquarters, Mediterranean Allied Tactical Air Force Headquarters, Mediterranean Air Transport Service Headquarters, and Flag Office Command, Navy, Northwest African Waters, 1943-45; general correspondence of the Commander in Chief, Mediterranean Station, 1942-45; and records of the Military Headquarters (Balkans) and Military Liaison Headquarters in Greece, Albania, and Yugoslavia, 1941-46.

RECORDS OF THE ALLIED COMMISSION/ALLIED MILITARY GOVERNMENT (ITALY). 1943-47. 4,104 lin. ft. (in WNRC).

In Italy the Commission represented the CCS and the United Nations in forming foreign policy, operated military government courts, advanced public health, and supervised civil courts, the reconstruction of the armed forces, local governments, and educational, financial, and economic operations; the control, rehabilitation, and repatriation of displaced persons, refugees, and Italian war prisoners in Allied hands; and the preservation of monuments, artworks, and archives. On December 31, 1945, all territory in Italy except Venezia Giulia and the Province of Udine was returned to Italian administration. The Commission was abolished January 31, 1947, and its residual functions were assigned to the G-5 Section, AFHQ. These records include general correspondence, with indexes, of the Commission, the military government, and their subordinate regional headquarters.

RECORDS OF THE ALLIED SCREENING COMMISSION (ITALY). 1944-47. 327 lin. ft. (in WNRC).

This Commission handled claims for compensating and recognizing Italians and Austrians who assisted Allied personnel behind enemy lines after September 8, 1943. The records consist chiefly of war prisoner claims but include some death claims, Austrian registered claims, and correspondence, with indexes.

RECORDS OF THE ALLIED MILITARY GOVERNMENT, BRITISH-UNITED STATES ZONE, FREE TERRITORY OF TRIESTE. 1945-54. 943 lin. ft. (in WNRC).

Under the 1947 peace treaty with Italy, the territory administered by the Allied Military Government for Venezia Giulia was divided between Italy and Yugoslavia, except for the Free Territory of Trieste. That Territory, established on September 15, 1947, was occupied by British and American forces as the Allied Military Government, British-United States Zone, Free Territory of

Trieste. In October 1954 military government was abolished and the Territory was turned over to the Italian Government. These records consist of reports, correspondence, memorandums, and other records relating to organization, administration, military personnel, internal security, legal affairs, finances and economics, labor, transportation, internal and external trade, displaced persons, patriots' compensatory claims, personal injury and property damage claims, the postal and communications systems, real estate, and public information, safety, health, works, and utilities.

RECORDS OF GENERAL HEADQUARTERS, SUPREME COMMANDER FOR THE ALLIED POWERS (SCAP). 1945-52, with a few dated as early as 1938. 10,214 lin. ft. and 162 rolls of microfilm.

This headquarters was organized in October 1945 to carry out the occupation of Japan and the terms of the Japanese surrender. The occupation of Japan was terminated by the United States-Japanese peace treaty of March 20, 1952, and General Headquarters was inactivated on April 28, 1952. Included are general records (in WNRC), consisting of correspondence and other records of such administrative units as the Offices of the Chief of Staff, 1949-51, and the Deputy Chief of Staff, 1945-51; the Allied Council for Japan and the Public Information Section, 1946-50; and the Soviet Liaison Office, Office of the Comptroller, and the Adjutant General Section, 1945-52.

The records (in WNRC) of General Staff sections, 1945-52, consist of reports, general correspondence, and other records relating to the organization and operation of General Staff Sections G-1 to G-4.

Records of Special Staff sections include records of the International Prosecution Section (partly on 162 rolls of microfilm), 1945-48, and the Judge Advocate Section (in WNRC), 1945-49, from war crimes trials. Correspondence and other records of the Legal Section (in WNRC), chiefly 1945-52, with some records from 1938; the Civil Affairs Section, chiefly 1945-52, with some records from 1942; the Civil Communications Section, 1945-51; the Government Section, Civil Historical Section, Office of the Civil Property Custodian, Civil Information and Education Section, Civil Transportation Section, Natural Resources Section, Public Health and Welfare Section, and Provost Marshal's Section, 1945-52; the Economic and Scientific Section, 1946-52; and the Civil Intelligence Section, 1945-49.

RECORDS OF GENERAL HEADQUARTERS, SOUTHWEST PACIFIC AREA (SWPA). 1941-49. 116 lin. ft.

General Headquarters, SWPA, established at Melbourne, Australia, on April 18, 1942, had operational control over all Allied ground, air, and sea forces in the area, including the U.S. Army units that had been in Australia since 1941. It was an integrated, combined headquarters, with staff officers drawn from the air, ground, and naval services of the United States, Australia, the United Kingdom, and the Netherlands. In February 1943 a subordinate element, later designated the Far East Command, was established under General Headquarters, SWPA, to supervise Army training and administrative activities not closely related to the tactical and strategic direction of the war in the Southwest Pacific. The records consist of directives, plans, intelligence summaries, correspondence, and propaganda pamphlets of the Psychological Warfare Branch, General Headquarters, SWPA, relating to operations in the Southwest Pacific, 1941-45. Also historical monographs, indexes, intelligence summaries, operation reports, staff studies, directives, SCAP summations, and related documents (100 lin. ft.) collected for a history of operations in the SWPA and the Far East Command (known as the MacArthur Histories), 1942-49 (in WNRC).

RECORDS OF THE SOUTHEAST ASIA COMMAND (SEAC). 1943-45. 38 lin. ft. (in WNRC).

Headquarters, SEAC, established by Prime Minister Churchill on June 18, 1943, and discontinued in November 1945, was the combined command directing the campaigns from India to Burma. It was composed of British, Chinese, Indian, and American naval, air, and ground forces under Adm. Lord Louis Mountbatten, Supreme Allied Commander, and Lt. Gen. Joseph W. Stilwell, Deputy Supreme Allied Commander. Most of these records consist of war diaries, but there are also minutes, messages, conference notes, intelligence reports, and publications relating to SEAC activities.

CARTOGRAPHIC AND AUDIOVISUAL RECORDS. 1940-45. 4,421 items.

Cartographic records (1,401 items) consist of war room situation maps (photographs and negatives) from SHAEF, 1944-45.

Audiovisual records (3,020 items) consist of photographs of personnel that illustrate SHAEF activities during the European invasion, 1944-45, and of charts that illustrate reports relating to Japanese population changes and imports, 1940-45.

RECORDS OF INTERNATIONAL MILITARY AGENCIES (RECORD GROUP 333)

International military agencies were established jointly by the United States and Allied Nations during and after World War II to accomplish objectives of mutual interest. These agencies consisted of representatives of the Departments of the Army, Navy, and Air Force and their counterparts from the nations concerned. This record group includes the records of those agencies not allocated to Records of Allied Operational and Occupation Headquarters, World War II, Record Group 331.

There are 150 cubic feet of records dated between 1941 and 1957 in this record group.

RECORDS OF THE MUNITIONS ASSIGNMENTS BOARDS. 1941-46. 62 lin. ft.

Creation of the Munitions Assignments Board, Washington (MBW), and its counterpart, the London Munitions Assignments Board (LMAB), was announced by the President of the United States and the Prime Minister of Great Britain on January 26, 1942. The U.S. board, in close collaboration with the London organization, maintained full information on the munitions resources of the United States and Great Britain, balanced resources against requirements, and assigned munitions to the two countries and to other members of the United Nations. The MBW was abolished November 8, 1945; the LMAB, November 10, 1945.

The records consist of general correspondence, 1941-46, and messages, 1942-45, of the U.S. Section, Executive Office, LMAB; records of the Office of the Executive, MBW, 1942-45; and records of the Aviation Petroleum Allocations Committee, a subcommittee of the Munitions Assignments Committee (Air), relating to the allocation of aviation petroleum supplies, 1942-45.

RECORDS OF THE U. S. SECTION, JOINT BRAZIL-UNITED STATES MILITARY COMMISSION, RIO DE JANEIRO, BRAZIL. 1943-47.
7 lin. ft.

The Joint Brazil-United States Military Commission (JBUSMC) in Brazil and the Joint Brazil-United States Defense Commission (JBUSDC) in the United States were established in May 1942. The Commissions were concerned with bilateral studies and plans necessary for common defense. In 1947 the U.S. Section, JBUSMC, included a Joint Secretariat and Army and Air Force Sections. The records consist of correspondence, reports, and issuances of these offices, including some records of the Northern Brazil Training Group.

RECORDS OF THE HEADQUARTERS, UNITED NATIONS COMMAND. 1950-57.
121 lin. ft.

The United Nations Command (UNC), with General Headquarters in Tokyo, was established on July 24, 1950. It was organized along the lines of an army field headquarters with general and special staff sections. The Command also included a Headquarters, UNC (Advance), which was established in July 1951 to assist negotiations for an armistice with the Communist forces of North Korea and China. On January 1, 1953, it was reorganized as a joint command. Late in 1953 two organizations were added: the UNC Military Armistice Commission and the Repatriation Group, both with staff sections. The UNC was transferred from Tokyo to Seoul on July 1, 1957.

Records consist of correspondence, 1951-55; daily summaries of unit strength assigned by countries of the United Nations, 1951; an orders file, 1951-54, of the Adjutant General Section; a United Nations-Japan administrative working file, 1952-53, of the J-1 Personnel Division; UNC Liaison Section general administrative and country file, 1950-55; correspondence, memorandums, and orders, January–June 1952, of the Civil Information and Education Section; and correspondence, publications, Korean armistice negotiation records, July 1951-July 1953, and Korean armistice agreement documents, July 1953, of the Headquarters, UNC (Advance). Records of the United Nations Command Military Armistice Commission (UNCMAC) include records relating to the Korean armistice negotiation and implementation, June 1951-57; daily reports of arrival and departure of military personnel, combat aircraft, and other materiel, 1953-57; and reports, correspondence, and other records relating to service, supply, and liaison functions of the UNCMAC, 1953-57. Records of the UNC Repatriation Group consist of correspondence, journals, and publications, 1953-54.

See Paul Taborn and Andrew Putignano, comps., *Preliminary Inventory of the Records of the Headquarters, United Nations Command,* PI 127 (1960).

RECORDS OF UNITED STATES THEATERS OF WAR, WORLD WAR II
(RECORD GROUP 332)

From September 1939 to December 1941 the major overseas tactical commands of the Army consisted of five departments in U.S. territorial possessions. Major Navy overseas commands included several naval districts and, after July 1941, naval coastal frontiers (later sea frontiers) having geographical boundaries comparable to Army departments. In December 1941 Army territorial departments were replaced by theaters of operations. After strategic direction of the war was made a joint Army-Navy and Allied responsibility through establishment of the Joint and Combined Chiefs of Staff, the term "theater of operations" came to embrace a specified geographical area and all commands in it. The Army often used the term to designate its own headquarters in an area. Most records in this record group are of units at the theater level.

There are 479 cubic feet of records (in WNRC) dated between 1939 and 1950 in this record group.

RECORDS. 1939-50. 599 lin. ft.

Most of the records are of the European Theater of Operations, consisting of administrative files of the Historical Division, 1942-46; MIS (Military Intelligence Service) files, 1942-48; BIOS (British Intelligence Objectives Subcommittee) technical and intelligence reports, 1939-48; correspondence of the 92d Infantry Division, 1942-45; and subject files of the Office of the Chief Surgeon, 1942-45, and the Office of the Chief of Transportation, 1942-46. Records of the China-Burma-India Theaters include historical files, correspondence and messages of Gen. Joseph W. Stilwell, and office files of his successor, Gen. Albert C. Wedemeyer, 1941-46. Also an office file of the Command and General Staff School, Chinese Training Center, U.S. Forces, China Theater, 1944-45; a decimal file of U.S. Forces in the Far East (Philippines), 1941-44; historical files of U.S. Armed Forces, Korea, 1945-48; a subject file of U.S. Army Military Government in Korea, 1945-50; and inventories of records from the Mediterranean Theater of Operations.

RECORDS OF UNITED STATES OCCUPATION HEADQUARTERS, WORLD WAR II (RECORD GROUP 260)

After V-E Day, May 8, 1945, Germany and Austria were each divided into British, French, Russian, and American occupation zones. The Office of Military Government for Germany (U.S.), or OMGUS, successor to the U.S. Group Control Council, was established in October to administer the American Zone. The European Theater commander was both military governor of the U.S. Zone and U.S. member of the Control Council of the Allied Control Authority. In January 1947 an economic union of the British and American Zones was formed under the Bipartite Control Office and the Bipartite Board, which consisted of the British and American military governors. An Executive order of June 6, 1949, established the Office of U.S. High Commissioner for Germany within the State Department to exercise all govern-mental functions of the United States in Germany except command of troops. Liquidation of OMGUS was completed by September 21, 1949.

The U.S. Element of the Allied Commission for Austria (USACA), formed in July 1945 as part of Headquarters, U.S. Forces in Austria (USFA), assumed military government responsibilities in the American Zone of Austria. The USFA commanding general served as U.S. High Commissioner for Austria. USACA was discontinued October 15, 1950, and its functions were taken over by the State Department's Office of the U.S. High Commissioner for Austria.

There are 10,401 cubic feet of records (in WNRC except for nontextual records) dated between 1942 and 1954 in this record group.

RECORDS OF THE OFFICE OF MILITARY GOVERNMENT FOR GERMANY (U.S.). 1944-52.
10,535 lin. ft. and 78 rolls of microfilm.

There are records of the Bipartite Control Office; the U.S. Element, Allied Control Authority; OMGUS headquarters in Frankfurt, including the Legal, Intelligence, Finance, Public Affairs, Manpower, Transportation, and other Divisions; offices of the military governors of the States of Bavaria, Hesse, and Baden-Wuerttemberg, the Berlin Sector, and the Bremen Enclave, whose organizations generally reflected that of OMGUS headquarters; and district and local resident offices. The records relate to such subjects as civil administration, political affairs, democratization and denazification (including case files for individuals), public safety, administration of justice, commerce, industry, manpower, European recovery, food and agriculture, land reform, forestry, communications, public opinion, information services, intelligence, transportation, finance, banking, insurance, health, education, cultural affairs, religion, community affairs, welfare, and youth programs. Others relate to reparations and restitution of property seized during the war, particularly monuments, works of art, and archives (partly on 78 rolls of microfilm); decartelization, with special reference to I.G. Farben and I.G. Chemie Industries; war crimes; prisoners of war; displaced persons; and relations between occupation forces and the Germans.

RECORDS OF THE UNITED STATES ELEMENT, ALLIED COMMISSION FOR AUSTRIA. 1942-54. 1,738 lin. ft.

Included are records of the Director's office and most headquarters divisions, such as the Political, Economics, Finance and Social, Legal, Displaced Persons, Education, and Civilian Supply Divisions. In many respects the functions of these Divisions corresponded to those of ministries and departments of the Austrian Government. There are also records, including court case files relating to property claims and restitution, of the Linz and Salzburg field offices, which were the headquarters of the two U.S. Zone military government-military occupation area divisions of Land Upper Austria and Land Salzburg. Although responsible for carrying out local governmental functions, organizationally they were military government detachments whose commanders were Army officers directly responsible to their area military commanders. The records relate to all military government activities and concern generally the same subjects as the OMGUS records.

RECORDS OF THE U.S. CIVIL ADMINISTRATION OF THE RYUKYU ISLANDS. 1952-54.
6 lin. ft.

This Administration was organized August 27, 1951, to further economic, political, and social recovery of the Ryukyu Islands. The records consist of a correspondence file, 1954, and issuances, 1952 and 1954.

AUDIOVISUAL RECORDS. 1944-49.
83,700 items.

Included are photographs of war-damaged institutions, monuments, and historically important buildings in Germany and Italy; damaged monuments in other European battle areas; Polish art evacuated to Canada; Einsatzstab Reichsleiter Rosenberg Headquarters and other German depositories; and artworks and books looted from Belgium, Poland, Russia, Greece, Hungary, and elsewhere. There are also photographs of political and social functions at Obersalzberg, 1919-35; and illustrations used in a book about the Hitler family tree, consisting of Austrian scenes of Hitler's youth.

RECORDS OF JOINT COMMANDS
(RECORD GROUP 349)

In December 1946 the President approved a comprehensive system of joint military commands based on recommendations of the Joint Chiefs of Staff. This system places responsibility for conduct of military operations of all U.S. forces under a single commander in a strategic area when a unified command is deemed to be in the interest of national security. Commanders of joint commands have full operational control over these forces and are responsible to the President and the Secretary of Defense, through the Joint Chiefs of Staff, for accomplishing assigned missions. Orders to such commanders are issued by the President, the Secretary of Defense, or by the Joint Chiefs of Staff under authority and direction of the Secretary of Defense.

There are 251 cubic feet of records dated between 1942 and 1956 in this record group.

RECORDS OF HEADQUARTERS, U.S. EUROPEAN COMMAND (US EUCOM). 1942-55. 120 lin. ft.

Headquarters, US EUCOM, was activated August 1, 1952, to provide a direct line of authority to the Joint Chiefs of Staff for plans, policies, and logistics involving two or more U.S. military services in its jurisdiction. It also administered military aspects of the mutual defense assistance and offshore procurement programs. These records include series begun by predecessor offices and continued by Headquarters, US EUCOM.

General records of the command group and secretariat consist of correspondence, 1942-54; overseas joint command files, and administrative issuances and messages received and sent, 1952-54; tables of distribution, with related documents, 1952; and a message file of the U.S. Military Representative at Supreme Headquarters, Allied Powers, Europe, 1951-53.

Records of detachment "A" (Paris, France) include general correspondence and messages, 1953-54, and the European Defense Community and Interim Committee's foreign documents and work status file, 1952-54.

Records of the Joint Construction Agency, which managed military construction in specified areas, comprise such records of the central office at Paris as administrative publications and progress reports of the Administration and Services Branch, 1953-54; Comptroller Division planning and procedural files, 1953; and reports of investigations of the Office of the Inspector General, 1953-54. Records of the North, Northeast, Eastern, Southern, and Port Districts of the Agency consist of general records, 1950-54, and contracts and purchase orders, 1952-53, of the central files units; Supply Branch records relating to logistics, 1950-54; budget correspondence, organizational data, management surveys, and manning charts of Management Branches, 1953-55; and correspondence of the Northern Area Office, the Special Area Office, and the Port District's Legal Branch, 1953.

Records of the Joint Military Transportation Board consist of reports, general correspondence, and the military historian's correspondence, 1952-54.

RECORDS OF HEADQUARTERS, FAR EAST COMMAND. 1945-55. 106 lin. ft.

Headquarters, Far East Command, was reorganized as a joint headquarters January 1, 1953. It was discontinued July 1, 1957, and its functions were assumed by the Commander in Chief, Pacific. The records consist of minutes, correspondence, and messages of the Secretary of the Joint Staff, 1953-54;

records of the Office of the Adjutant
General, including command reports,
planning files, issuances, and correspondence, 1953–54; Korean armistice
negotiation documents, 1951–53; and
Exercise Jigsaw reports, 1955. Also general records of the J-1, J-2, J-3, J-4,
and J-5 Divisions, relating to personnel,
intelligence, operations, logistics, and
plans and policy, 1953–54; unit histories
and command reports of the Public
Information Office, 1952–54; and minutes and correspondence of the Joint
Welfare Board, 1945–55.

RECORDS OF THE ALASKAN
COMMAND. 1947–54. 2 lin. ft.

The Alaskan Command was established January 1, 1947, by instruction of
the Joint Chiefs of Staff. The records
consist of background material relating
to the issuance of general, special, and
letter orders; staff memorandums; and
circulars.

RECORDS OF THE
CONTINENTAL AIR DEFENSE
COMMAND. 1954–55. 2 lin. ft.

These comprise records relating to
general orders of the 9th, 25th, 27th, and
28th Joint Air Defense Divisions.

RECORDS OF THE HAWAIIAN
DEFENSE COMMAND. 1953–54.
2 lin. ft.

These consist of decimal files relating
to organizational and emergency planning, 1953–54, and general orders and
staff memorandums relating to operations and special Command assignments,
1954.

RECORDS OF THE U.S.
NORTHEAST COMMAND. 1950–56.
6 lin. ft.

These consist of decimal files, 1950–
56, publications, 1951–56, records of Project Rising Star, 1955–56, and planning
files of the 64th Air Division, 1951–56.

RECORDS OF THE COMBINED
COMMAND FOR
RECONNAISSANCE ACTIVITIES,
KOREA (CCRAK). 1952–53. 15 lin. ft.

CCRAK was organized February 15,
1952, to supervise clandestine operations
supporting combat operations of U.S.
Forces in Korea. It was inactivated September 13, 1953, and its functions were
assumed by the Combined Command for
Reconnaissance Activities, Far East
(CCRAFE). The records consist of intelligence reports, combat report files, and
administrative   correspondence   of
CCRAK and CCRAFE.

RECORDS OF JOINT ARMY AND NAVY
BOARDS AND COMMITTEES
(RECORD GROUP 225)

The War and Navy Departments tra-
ditionally established joint boards and
committees in response to the need for
interservice cooperation. Throughout
the 19th century such boards and committees were of a temporary nature, but
the Joint Board, established in 1903, set
the precedent for continuing joint action
on common problems. During World
Wars I and II extensive use was made
of interservice boards and committees.
The U.S. Joint Chiefs of Staff (see RG
218), created in 1942, became the princi-

pal agency for coordination between the
Army and the Navy, but about 75 other
interservice agencies (see RG 334) existed during World War II.

There are 136 cubic feet of records
dated between 1903 and 1946 in this
record group.

RECORDS OF THE JOINT BOARD.
1903–38. 5 lin. ft.

Established by the Secretaries of War
and Navy to advise them on matters of
common   interest,   the   Joint   Board

required, for action on any Board proposal, joint departmental approval and the additional approval of the President in matters of important policy. The Board was placed under the President in 1939 and was terminated by the National Security Act of 1947. The records consist of general correspondence, 1903-38, and letters sent, 1903-11.

RECORDS OF THE JOINT ARMY AND NAVY MUNITIONS BOARD. 1922-46. 108 lin. ft.

Established in 1922 by approval of a Joint Board proposal, this Board was placed under the direction of the President in 1939, the Chairman of the War Production Board in 1942, and the Joint Chiefs of Staff in 1943. The Board revised industrial mobilization plans in 1939 and coordinated munitions procurement, critical materials stockpiling, foreign purchases, and machine tool allocation. It was abolished in 1947 by the National Security Act.

The records include correspondence and other records of the Executive Committee, 1922-46, the Clearance and Joint Optics Committees, 1942-45, the Commodities Division, 1925-44, the Facilities Division, 1941-42, and the Priorities Division, 1940-42.

RECORDS OF THE JOINT ADVISORY BOARD ON AMERICAN REPUBLICS. 1940-46. 1 lin. ft.

Established in 1940 to review requests from Latin American countries for munitions, this Board also handled requests for equipment under lend-lease provisions after March 1941. In 1944 its activities were expanded to include general matters of military cooperation, but in September 1945 the new American Republics Allocations Board assumed responsibility for allocation of war surplus and other supplies. The earlier Board was abolished by the Secretary of Defense in 1949.

The records include correspondence of the Board, mainly 1940-46.

RECORDS OF THE JOINT ARMY AND NAVY COMMITTEE ON WELFARE AND RECREATION. 1941-46. 23 lin. ft.

The Committee was established in February 1941 to plan Army and Navy welfare and recreational activities and to coordinate them with those of civil agencies. As a result of its studies and recommendations the United Service Organizations (USO) was established. The Committee inspected facilities in the United States sponsored by the armed services and the USO, and handled problems of these units and of the American Red Cross.

The records include minutes and correspondence, 1941-46.

RECORDS OF INTERSERVICE AGENCIES (RECORD GROUP 334)

During World War II about 75 major interservice agencies representing two or more military services were created to deal with a particular aspect or phase of the war. Some of these agencies helped determine top-level policy; others engaged in factfinding activities related to strategic policy, coordinated Army and Navy activities, or engaged in procurement operations. All of them functioned in a staff relation to the War and Navy Departments and the Department of Defense and are to be distinguished from joint commands responsible for the conduct of military operations. Most of the interservice agencies were discontinued after the war, but some concerned with peacetime military activity were eventually placed under the Office of the Secretary of Defense. A few of the agencies were established before World War II. Records of interservice agencies that served overseas with a theater command are among records of U.S. Army commands, 1942– (see RG 338).

There are 706 cubic feet of records dated between 1916 and 1958 in this record group.

RECORDS OF AREA JOINT COMMITTEES. 1947-52. 35 lin. ft.

Area subcommittees of the Committee on Facilities and Services were established June 9, 1948, by the Munitions Board to promote joint use of facilities and services in the event of mobilization and to establish uniform policies for procurement, transportation, and research. In December 1949 area joint committees replaced area subcommittees. Records of joint committees and predecessor subcommittees consist of minutes, survey reports, correspondence, and photographs; and other records of the Northeast Area Joint Committee, 1950-52, the Southeast Area Joint Committee, 1947-50, and the Southwest Area Joint Committee, 1948-50.

RECORDS OF THE AERONAUTICAL BOARD. 1916-48. 29 lin. ft.

Created in October 1916, this Board functioned during World War I as the Joint Army and Navy Board on Aeronautic Cognizance. Its name was changed in 1919 first to Joint Army and Navy Board on Aeronautics and then to Aeronautical Board. In July 1939 it was placed under authority of the President. The Board was inactive between December 1943 and October 1945, and was dissolved in August 1948 when its functions, personnel, property, and funds were transferred to the Munitions Board, the Research and Development Committee, and other agencies. The records consist of agenda and minutes of meetings, summary reports, and other documents relating to Army and Navy aviation development, 1916-48; correspondence, 1916-47; case files, 1923-48, with card indexes; and committee and subcommittee files, 1938-48.

RECORDS OF THE STATE-ARMY-NAVY-AIR FORCE COORDINATING COMMITTEE. 1947-49. 5 lin. ft.

Originally known as the State-War-Navy Coordinating Committee, this Committee coordinated plans and policies for domestic security, internal administration, and economic development of various countries and territories. The records, apparently maintained by the Department of Defense representative, consist of numbered reports, memorandums, and related correspondence.

RECORDS OF THE ARMED FORCES COURIER SERVICE (ARFCOS). 1952-54. 1 lin. ft.

Established as a joint departmental agency February 10, 1953, ARFCOS consolidated the Army-Air Forces Security Service and the Naval Officer Messenger Mail System. Alternately directed by the three military departments, ARFCOS is responsible for safe and fast transmission of material requiring protected handling by officer courier. The records consist of reports and directives relating to policies and procedures and inspection of courier transfer stations, correspondence, and historical data on ARFCOS activities.

RECORDS OF THE ARMED FORCES DISCIPLINARY CONTROL BOARD. 1944-49. 1 lin. ft.

The Joint Army-Navy Disciplinary Control Board was organized August 29, 1944, to comply with provisions of an agreement of the Acting Secretaries of War and the Navy. On July 31, 1947, its name was changed to the Armed Services Disciplinary Control Board. The records consist of minutes, reports, correspondence, and other records relating to the reduction and repression of conditions detrimental to the morale and welfare of service personnel.

RECORDS OF THE ARMED FORCES EPIDEMIOLOGICAL BOARD. 1946–54. 5 lin. ft.

Included are correspondence of the Office of the Executive Secretary of the Board, 1946–53, and reports, correspondence, and related records of the Commission on Liver Diseases, 1948–54.

RECORDS OF THE ARMED FORCES MEDICAL LIBRARY. 1948–52. 2 lin. ft.

The Army Medical Library was redesignated as a joint agency of the Army, Navy, and Air Force on December 23, 1952, under the Secretary of Defense and managed by the Secretary of the Army. It served as a central library for medical bibliographical research. The library was discontinued October 5, 1956, and its functions transferred to the National Library of Medicine. The records consist of administrative correspondence and publications.

RECORDS OF THE ARMED SERVICES MEDICAL REGULATING OFFICE (ASMRO). 1950–54. 1 lin. ft.

ASMRO was established October 25, 1950, as a joint agency of the Army, Navy, and Air Force to coordinate movement of patients from military hospitals to Veterans Administration facilities for specialized medical and rehabilitation care. The records consist of minutes of staff meetings, reports, correspondence, messages, and memorandums.

RECORDS OF THE ARMED SERVICES TEXTILE AND APPAREL PROCUREMENT AGENCY (ASTAPA). 1952–53. 8 lin. ft.

ASTAPA was created June 18, 1952, as a joint agency of the three military departments subject to the policy control of the Munitions Board and management by the Department of the Army. It was dissolved October 31, 1953. Its records include correspondence, memorandums, and studies relating to industrial mobilization planning for textile and apparel items and to military procurement functions.

RECORDS OF THE ARMED SERVICES PETROLEUM BOARD. 1942–49. 29 lin. ft.

The Armed Services Petroleum Board was established in 1942 as the Army-Navy Petroleum Board to achieve cooperation between the military services on all matters relating to petroleum, petroleum products, and containers. The Board was reconstituted as the Armed Services Petroleum Board on February 14, 1948, and transferred to the Munitions Board on May 1, 1949 (see RG 330). Records of the Board include minutes, reports, and correspondence.

RECORDS OF THE ARMY SECURITY CENTER (ASC). 1953. 1 lin. in.

The Army Security Center is a joint agency of the Army, the Air Force, the Navy, and the Central Intelligence Agency, with the Department of the Army serving as executive agent. Its records consist of administrative correspondence and publications.

RECORDS OF THE INDUSTRIAL COLLEGE OF THE ARMED FORCES. 1924–55. 40 lin. ft.

The Army Industrial College was opened on February 21, 1924, for training Army officers in supervision of wartime military procurement, mobilization of material, and industrial organization. The college suspended operations December 24, 1941, to permit faculty and students to enter war mobilization and combat duty, and opened December 28, 1943, with special courses in cost and price analysis, property disposal, contract termination, and other war readjustment problems. On April 11, 1946, it was renamed the Industrial College of the Armed Forces, and in September it resumed its regular courses. Simultaneously, the college was raised to the highest level in the military educational system and was placed under joint Army-Navy control. The records consist of correspondence, 1924-55, "contract board" records, 1925-41, course problem directives, 1935-41, and recordings (11 items) of addresses made on Defense Test Day, September 12, 1924.

RECORDS OF MILITARY ASSISTANCE ADVISORY GROUPS (MAAG). 1942-58. 511 lin. ft.

During and immediately following World War II military assistance advisory offices were established in various parts of the world to supervise military defense assistance programs. Most offices are organized with a chief and Army, Air Force, and Navy sections. Direction is alternately vested in the three military departments, with the Department of the Army or the Air Force serving as executive agent.

Records consist of correspondence, messages, publications, organization tables, activity reports, mobilization planning and training files, historical files, and budget and fiscal records.

RECORDS OF THE UNITED STATES MILITARY MISSION TO MOSCOW. 1943-45. 23 lin. ft.

The U.S. Military Mission to Moscow was established October 1, 1943, to promote coordination of U.S. and U.S.S.R. military efforts. The Mission was closed October 31, 1945. The records include reports and messages, 1943-45, correspondence, memorandums, and records of the shuttle-bombing of Axis-controlled Europe (Operation Frantic), October 26, 1943-June 24, 1945.

RECORDS OF THE NATIONAL WAR COLLEGE. 1943-54. 391 lin. ft.

After World War II the Joint Chiefs of Staff proposed establishment of an institution for closer integration of military and diplomatic policies on the national level. On February 1, 1946, after the Secretary of State agreed to State Department participation, the National War College was created. The records consist of correspondence, 1943-50, budget estimates, 1947-54, and published material, 1942-47, with indexes relating to strategic politico-military planning, operations, and intelligence (in WNRC).

RECORDS OF THE OFFICE OF STRATEGIC SERVICES (RECORD GROUP 226)

The Office of Strategic Services (OSS) was established under the Joint Chiefs of Staff on June 13, 1942, as successor to the Office of Coordinator of Information. An executive order of the same date transferred certain foreign propaganda activities of the Coordinator of Information, with related records, to the

Office of War Information (see RG 208). The duties of the Office of Strategic Services were to collect and analyze information required by the Joint Chiefs of Staff and to plan and operate special services at their direction. The Office was terminated October 1, 1945, by an Executive order, and some remaining functions and its records were divided between the Department of State and the War Department.

There are 935 cubic feet of records dated between 1919 and 1946 in this record group.

RECORDS OF THE RESEARCH AND ANALYSIS BRANCH. 1941-46. 1,593 lin. ft.

Included are minutes of the Board of Analysts, 1941-43; minutes and reports of the Projects Committee, 1942-46; records of the Office of the Branch Chief, consisting of orders, bulletins, and other issuances, 1942-45; general correspondence, 1942-46; cablegrams received and sent, 1941-46; studies and reports concerning political, sociological, and economic conditions in various countries, 1941-46; and biographic sketches and photographs of prominent Italians from the Italian newspaper *Popolo d'Italia*, 1929-43. There are also two typed manuscripts prepared by Consultant Walter C. Langer—"A Hitler Source Book," containing excerpts from published articles and books about Adolf Hitler, and "A Psychological Analysis of Adolph Hitler: His Life and Legend," both undated; and interoffice memorandums relating to OSS studies of Hitler, 1942-43.

Records of divisions within the Branch include Central Information Division intelligence reports relating to enemy logistics, 1942-45, with name and subject indexes and descriptive lists, 1941-45; Economics Division reports and correspondence relating to manpower, military supplies, industrial resources, and economic and industrial conditions in Germany and the other Axis powers, 1941-45; Europe-Africa Division correspondence, 1941-45, "Civil Affairs Guides" and correspondence on conditions and institutions in Germany and German-occupied countries, and other records relating to outposts (Algiers, the Balkans, Cairo, France, Germany, Italy,

and London), 1941-45; Far East Division correspondence with OSS outposts, 1942-46, and reports relating to China and Formosa, 1941-46; and reports by the Latin American Division, 1944-45. Also records of the Interdepartmental Committee for the Acquisition of Foreign Publications, including correspondence of the New Delhi outpost, 1944-45; intelligence reports relating to conditions in Southeast Asia, 1944-45; general records of the Stockholm outpost, 1942-45; and Swedish language newspaper clippings and related material, 1943-45.

Field office records include correspondence of the European Theater of Operations, 1944-45, the Mediterranean Theater of Operations, 1943-45, and the China Theater of Operations, 1944-45.

RECORDS OF OTHER BRANCHES. 1941-45. 14 lin. ft.

Case files relating to maps, motion pictures, and other graphics prepared by the Visual Presentation Branch, 1942-45; and a small amount of correspondence of the Foreign Nationalities Branch with "hyphenated nationality groups," 1941-45.

CARTOGRAPHIC AND AUDIOVISUAL RECORDS. 1919-45. 1,953 items.

Included are maps, 1941-45 (1,701 items—most of them security classified), prepared or acquired in the Office of the Coordinator of Information and the Division of Map Intelligence and Cartography of the Research and Analysis Branch by or for Dr. J. A. Morrison.

Still pictures, 1919-40 (228 items), include photographs of industrial development in China, Japan, and the Philippine Islands before World War II.

Motion pictures, 1942-45 (24 reels), relate to the people and industry of Pearl Harbor before World War II; the Japanese attack on December 7, 1941; Japanese geography, natural resources, and social structure and behavior patterns; and the Allied landing in Sicily, 1943.

RECORDS OF THE
UNITED STATES STRATEGIC BOMBING SURVEY
(RECORD GROUP 243)

The U.S. Strategic Bombing Survey (USSBS) was established November 3, 1944, by the Secretary of War to study the direct and indirect effects of the strategic bombing of Germany. The USSBS, composed of civilian and military personnel and headed by a civilian chairman, investigated the extent of bomb devastation and its effects on industry, utilities, transportation, medical care, social life, morale, and the will to fight of the bombed populations. After the defeat of Japan a similar study was undertaken in Japan and other Pacific areas. The USSBS was discontinued in August 1946. In both Europe and the Pacific the USSBS conducted detailed inspections of plants, industries, cities, and areas; interviewed surviving political, military, and industrial leaders; and accumulated a large amount of statistical and documentary material.

See USSBS, *Index to Records of the United States Strategic Bombing Survey* (1947), which contains detailed lists of the contents of nearly all record series of the European and Pacific Survey teams.

There are 567 cubic feet of records dated between 1937 and 1947 in this record group.

GENERAL RECORDS. 1944–47.
79 lin. ft.

Included are records of the office of the Chairman, consisting of final reports of European and Pacific Surveys, messages sent and received, general correspondence, and correspondence relating to distribution of USSBS reports.

RECORDS OF THE EUROPEAN AND PACIFIC SURVEYS. 1937–47.
466 lin. ft. and 411 rolls of microfilm.

These comprise reports, drafts of reports, drawings, and photographs relating to the effects of Allied air attacks on Germany and Japan and areas they occupied, 1937–47, arranged according to a numerical list in the USSBS *Index*; records of the Intelligence Branch Library, comprising Survey intelligence bulletins, memorandums, and studies, 1939–45, with card indexes, and the microfilm collection (411 rolls) of the library; reports relating to bombing targets; and damage assessment reports, 1942–45.

AUDIOVISUAL RECORDS. 1944–45.
12,873 items.

Included are photographs, 1945 (12,500 items), of bombing effects in Belgium, France, Germany, Italy, and Japan, and of atomic bomb effects on Hiroshima and Nagasaki; captured German films, ca. 1944 (7 reels), relating to American incendiary bombs and bombing methods and German war industry; and sound recordings, 1945 (366 items), of interviews with Japanese civilians concerning American bombing effects on several cities, including an eyewitness of the bombing of Hiroshima.

Department of the Army

Headquarters and Staff

RECORDS OF THE OFFICE OF THE SECRETARY OF WAR (RECORD GROUP 107)

The act of August 7, 1789, that created the Department of War entrusted to the Secretary of War the responsibility for recruiting, provisioning, and regulating U.S. military and naval forces; administering pensions and bounty lands granted for military service; and overseeing Indian affairs. Naval matters were removed from the Secretary's jurisdiction when the Department of the Navy was established April 30, 1798. Administration of Indian affairs, pensions, and bounty lands were assigned to various bureaus and staff departments, and finally were transferred in 1849 to the Department of the Interior. Additional bureaus were established in the War Department to assume other functions of the Secretary's Office, which by the middle of the 19th century was almost exclusively concerned with matters of policy and general administration.

By the outbreak of World War II the Secretary had responsibility for supervision of all activities of the War Department, including finances, equipment, training, and operations; protection of seacoast harbors and cities; execution of the National Defense Act of 1920; policy control of the U.S. Military Academy; and certain civil functions, among which were administration of the Panama Canal and civil works projects of the Corps of Engineers, supervision of land controlled by the Department, and handling the Army's interest in the Civilian Conservation Corps before it was disbanded in 1943. On February 28, 1942, an Executive order reorganized the administration of the Department and transferred many operational and administrative duties to Army commands for wartime control. The Secretary's wartime duties included determining policy for the military establishment as a whole, supervising materiel procurement, and serving on major departmental boards. Under the National Security Act of 1947, the War Department became the Department of the Army within the National Military Establishment (after 1949, the Department of Defense) and lost jurisdiction over aviation matters to the newly created Department of the Air Force.

The records reflect the changing scope of the Office of the Secretary. Files of the earlier period contain most of the correspondence for the entire War Department, although most of the records dated before 1800 were destroyed by a fire in the War Department. After 1890 much of the correspondence of the Secretary remained with records of the bureaus to which it had been referred. Shortly after the establishment of central files for the War Department in the Adjutant General's Office, correspondence files of the Office of the Secretary of War were suspended, and from March 1921 to February 1942 almost all correspondence of the Office was interfiled with records of the Department in the Adjutant General's Office (see RG 407). Records relating to Indian affairs before 1849 are among records of the Bureau of Indian Affairs (see RG 75), and records relating to military pension and land bounty matters under the Secretary of War's jurisdiction are among records of the Veterans Administration (see RG 15). Records dated after 1947 are among records of the Office of the Secretary of the Army (see RG 335).

See Benjamin Thomas and Harold Hyman, *Stanton: The Life and Times of Lincoln's Secretary of War* (New York, 1962); Philip C. Jessup, *Elihu Root* (New York, 1938); Daniel R. Beaver, *Newton D. Baker and the American War Effort, 1917-1919* (Lincoln, Nebr., 1966); Henry L. Stimson and McGeorge Bundy, *On Active Service in Peace and War* (New York, 1948); and Paul Hammond, *Organizing for Defense: The American Military Establishment in the Twentieth Century* (Princeton, 1961).

There are 3,147 cubic feet of records dated between 1791 and 1948 in this record group.

LETTERS RECEIVED AND SENT. 1791-1889. 329 lin. ft.

The earliest holdings of the Office consist of a volume of miscellaneous correspondence relating to conduct of departmental business, 1791-97. Largely copied from sources in other offices, this volume is all that survives of the records of the Department before 1800 and of its predecessor, the Board of War. Correspondence for the remainder of the period before 1890 consists of letters sent, with an index, and letters received, with registers and indexes, 1800-1889, including letters sent to the President, 1800-1863; letters to and from Army officers, Cabinet officers, Members of Congress, State or Territorial Governors, and other Government officials, 1818-47; letters relating to the Mexican War, 1847-48; communications concerning the use of volunteer troops in the Civil War, 1862-65; claim letters, 1876-83; and correspondence relating to military affairs and administrative duties of the Secretary.

TELEGRAMS. 1861-82. 82 lin. ft.

Included are telegrams sent by the President, 1865-68; the Secretary of War, 1861-81; the General of the Army, 1866-82; the Provost Marshal General, 1865-68; General Grant, 1864-69; Generals Halleck, Hooker, Burnside, Meade,

McClellan, and Pope, 1862-65; and miscellaneous telegrams, 1869-82. Incoming telegrams include those to the President, 1862-69, the Secretary of War, 1861-75, the Provost Marshal General, 1863-68, General Grant, 1864-69, and field generals, 1862-65. Miscellaneous telegrams include those sent and received by the Executive Mansion, 1874-76, the Secretary's Office and the War Department, 1861-62, the Government Telegraph Offices, 1873-79, and an additional volume of telegrams sent by the Adjutant General's Office, relating to the raising of volunteer troops, 1862-65.

GENERAL ADMINISTRATIVE RECORDS. 1799-1894. 18 lin. ft.

These include orders and endorsements, with digests of related letters, referred by the Secretary to departmental bureaus, 1846-70; orders, 1800-1805; decisions, drafts of orders, orders and regulations, and circulars, 1835-94; records relating to passes and transportation orders, 1863-66; departmental visitor registers, 1863-65; and miscellaneous items.

Records relating to relations with the Congress consist of resolutions of the Congress, 1821-70; letters submitting reports, often with reports attached, 1803-70; reports for use in replying to congressional resolutions, 1827-28; and an index to congressional reports on War Department matters, 1871-93.

Legal and financial records consist of contracts, 1799-1810, bondbooks, 1816-35, miscellaneous papers relating to accounts, 1829-65, and statements of legal actions by the Solicitor of the War Department, 1862-65.

CORRESPONDENCE. 1890-1942. 390 lin. ft.

In 1890 separate files of incoming and outgoing letters were replaced by files combining letters received with related documents and copies of replies. Records for this period consist of general correspondence, with an index, 1890-1913; office memorandums, 1909-15; a decimal correspondence file, with an index, 1913-22; and a correspondence file, 1932-42, indexed after 1937. A system of alphabetically arranged record cards, containing digests of letters received, was begun in 1890, discontinued in 1913, and reestablished in 1919 as "tally cards."

CIVILIAN PERSONNEL RECORDS. 1828-1947. 560 lin. ft.

These include incomplete lists of employees, 1828-1934, registers of applications and appointments, 1863-1934, a general information file on personnel and department employment policies, 1899-1912, list of employee status changes, 1894-1908, outgoing correspondence, 1896-1909, correspondence concerning personnel, 1913-19, and miscellaneous correspondence, work reports, and statistical compilations.

Records of the Civilian Personnel Division, reestablished in 1938, include the correspondence file of the Division and predecessor units, 1913-40; a general decimal file, 1941-45; a subject file, 1943-47; inspection reports, 1940-47; records relating to policies, regulations, and procedures, 1923-47; a subject-numeric file, 1941-46, and a training and development correspondence file, 1946-47; employee relation records, 1941-44; and Placement Branch records, 1941-45.

RECORDS OF THE OFFICE OF THE CHIEF DISBURSING CLERK. 1836-1934. 29 lin. ft.

The Chief Disbursing Clerk paid all salaries of civilian employees and other expenses of Department offices. The records include correspondence, 1849-1923, "abstract books" of Department agents and bureaus, 1836-86, miscellaneous account and expense books, 1836-1901, and appropriation ledgers, 1885-1934, with indexes.

RECORDS RELATING TO PRINTING AND BINDING AND SUPPLIES. 1864-1944. 53 lin. ft.

Records of the Printing and Advertising Division include ledgers, record cards, and correspondence, 1914-44; the decimal file of the Printing and Binding Section of the Procurement and Accounting Division, 1912-44; requisitions for printing and binding, 1864-1912 and 1916-40; account books, 1864-1912, 1874-85, and 1916-40; a card record of printing and binding work, 1911-29; and records relating to the procurement of skilled labor and materials, 1870-1917. Records of the Supply Division include a general correspondence file, 1902-17; document files, 1883-1936; leases, plans, and correspondence concerning leased buildings, 1886-1919; account ledgers, 1884-1938; and press copybooks of orders, correspondence, and invoices, 1880-1912.

RECORDS RELATING TO EXPOSITIONS. 1888-1918. 10 lin ft.

These consist of general correspondence, 1888-1918, statements of expenditures, 1908-17, and correspondence and expenditure statements relating specifically to exhibits at the Louisiana Purchase, the Lewis and Clark Centennial, the Jamestown Ter-Centennial, and the Alaska-Yukon-Pacific and Panama-Pacific International Expositions.

RECORDS OF THE OFFICE OF THE SECRETARY. 1937-45. 312 lin. ft.

With the outbreak of World War II the Office of the Secretary of War resumed maintaining its own files through the Coordination and Records Office, a division of the Office of the Administrative Assistant to the Secretary. The records consist of decimal and project files, 1942-47, with an index; a subject file, 1940-47; special reports of the Joint and Combined Chiefs of Staff, 1940-45; and miscellaneous speeches, statements, and newspaper clippings, 1940–45.

Records of the Bureau of Public Relations consist of minutes of the Director's conversations, 1941–45, a correspondence file, 1944–46, press and radio news analyses, 1940–43, and news maps, 1942–45. Records of the Bureau's Industrial Services Division include a collection of *War Times*, a weekly newspaper for employees, 1943–45; a history of the Army-Navy "E" Awards program, 1942–45; employee publication releases, 1942–45; and industrial incentive program records, 1942–45.

Records of the Office of the Special Assistant to the Secretary consist of a decimal and subject file, 1937–45. Records of the Office of the Special Consultant to the Secretary consist of subject files, 1943–44, and personal files of the officials who successively held the position, 1942–46. Records of the Civilian Aide to the Secretary consist of a general subject file, 1940–47, and a file on the racial situation in the Army, 1940–47. Records of the Coordinator for Soldier Voting consist of a correspondence file, 1943–45, and a final administrative report, 1944. Records of the Army Specialist Corps consist of a decimal file, 1942–43, a subject file, 1942–43, and a final administrative report by the director general, 1942.

RECORDS OF THE PLANNING BRANCH. 1918–42. 190 lin. ft.

The Planning Branch was established in 1921 to develop peacetime and wartime plans for procurement of supplies and real estate and to mobilize materiel. In 1941 its functions were transferred to the Office of the Under Secretary, and in 1942 to Headquarters, Services of Supply. The records consist of administrative and technical files of the Director and subordinate officials, 1921–41, a subject-numeric file, 1934–42, a reading file, 1918–42, and a subject file, 1940–42. Records of subsidiary offices consist of technical files of the Construction Division, 1932–41, and the correspondence file of the Facilities Division, 1922–30. Records of the War Policies Commission, created in 1930 to study equalization of wartime burdens, consist of correspondence, 1930–32. Records of the National Defense Power Committee, created in 1938 to study wartime power needs, consist of a few general records, 1938–39, the rest being among the records of the Federal Power Commission (see RG 138).

RECORDS OF THE OFFICE OF THE UNDER SECRETARY OF WAR. 1924–47. 375 lin. ft.

This Office was created December 16, 1940. It was responsible for all matters relating to procurement of materiel, including policy direction of research, development, and standardization of equipment; acquisition and use of patent rights by the Department; the study of legislation affecting procurement; industrial mobilization and demobilization; supervision of the Department's manufacturing facilities; acquisition and lease of new facilities; and determination of policies and procedures governing the letting of contracts. Certain files of this Office are those of its predecessors.

Records of the Administrative Office consist of general decimal files, with indexes and subject files, 1941–47, and general correspondence of the executive assistants to the Under Secretary, 1940–45.

Records of other officials associated with the Under Secretary include correspondence of special assistants, 1940–45, the special advisor, 1940–41, and the special assistant for construction, 1940–45; records of the special assistant for economic warfare, 1943–45; correspondence of the special labor consultant, 1942–43; and the subject file of the Army Personnel Board, 1940–45.

Records of other offices consist of Contracts and Facilities Division files,

1942-45; Production Branch decimal file, 1924-42, and subject file, 1926-40; Purchases and Contracts Branch subject file, 1939-41, and decimal file, 1941-42; Statistical Branch correspondence and weekly statistical reports, 1939-41; Special Legal and Liaison Divison alphabetical file, 1941-45; and Production Division subject file, 1929-43.

RECORDS OF THE OFFICE OF THE ASSISTANT SECRETARY OF WAR. 1917-47. 60 lin. ft.

Statutory provision was made for an Assistant Secretary in 1861, but the position was abolished in 1867. It was again authorized in 1882 and abolished in 1884. The office was permanently reestablished March 5, 1890, to aid the Secretary in whatever ways he prescribed. The National Defense Act of June 4, 1920, made the Assistant Secretary partially independent of the Secretary with responsibility for the procurement of all military supplies and for the mobilization of materiel and industry for wartime needs. This function was assumed by the new Office of Under Secretary after December 1940. At that time a new position of Assistant Secretary was established with responsibility for general administrative functions and for special tasks assigned by the Secretary so that, in effect, the Assistant Secretary became the top level adviser to the Secretary on matters other than materiel procurement, including civil affairs, war crimes, black troops, and the Japanese exclusion program on the west coast.

Many earlier records of this Office were separated from those of the Secretary's Office and placed with the central files in the Adjutant General's Office (see RG 407). Records of the Assistant Secretary relating to materiel procurement, 1939-40, are among records of the Office of the Under Secretary of War. The earliest records are fragmentary, consisting of the outgoing correspond-

ence of Assistant Secretary William Ingraham, 1917, and files of Assistant Secretary Mayhew Wainwright, 1921-22, during his tenure as a member of the Advisory Committee of the American Delegation to the Washington Conference on the Limitation of Armaments. More recent holdings consist of the Assistant Secretary's general decimal files, with index, 1940-47.

RECORDS OF THE OFFICE OF THE ASSISTANT SECRETARY OF WAR FOR AIR. 1926-47. 100 lin. ft.

The Air Corps Act of July 2, 1926, established the position of Assistant Secretary of War for Air to serve as adviser and assistant to the Secretary on all aspects of military aeronautics. From 1933 until 1941 the post was vacant, its functions assumed by the Army Chief of Staff. Early in 1941 the Office was given direct authority over Army Air Forces activities concerning procurement of materiel and real estate as well as other duties. In September 1947 its functions were transferred to the newly created Office of the Secretary of the Air Force. The records include decimal correspondence files, 1926-33 and 1940-47, administrative correspondence, 1926-33, memorandums on aviation matters, 1926-33, a numerical file, 1942-43, and cablegrams, 1942-47. Also records of plans, policies, and agreements, 1943-47; records regarding the establishment of airfields and bases, 1940-45; a civil aeronautics file, 1947; a file of Army Air Forces publications, 1946-47; and records of the Provisional International Civil Aviation Organization, 1946.

RECORDS OF BOARDS AND COMMITTEES. 1929-48. 1,100 lin. ft.

These records include exhibits, hearings, and investigations of the Army Pearl Harbor Board, 1930-44; Officer-Enlisted Man Relationship Board subject file, 1946; the Civilian Awards Board correspondence file, 1942-46; War Department Procurement Review Board subject file, 1943; a correspondence file and a file of applications for transfers to U.S. Armed Forces of the Inter-Allied Personnel Board, 1942-46; Procurement Assignment Board subject file, 1929-42; minutes, reports, correspondence, memorandums, statistical data, and other records of the Manpower Board, 1943-47; Central Deferment Board and Dependency Board records, 1942-46; Army Retiring Board reports and correspondence, 1942-46; Equipment Board reports and correspondence, 1945-46; Army Price Adjustment Board correspondence, 1942-47; proceedings of the Renegotiation Branch, 1942-48 (in WNRC); settled and unsettled cases of the Army Division of the Armed Service Renegotiation Board, 1942-47 (in WNRC); and an index to renegotiation cases, 1942-47 (in WNRC).

AUDIOVISUAL RECORDS. 1941-45. 346 items.

Included are photographs (118 items) of Under Secretary of War Robert P. Patterson's mission to Australia, 1943. There are motion pictures, 1941-45 (191 reels), documenting American military activities in all theaters of operations during World War II and activities of the Allied Military Governments in Europe and in the Far East. Included are some captured German films. Sound recordings, 1942-43 (37 items), include speeches by war correspondents to officers and men of the armed services concerning the background of the war and German and U.S. war aims, and broadcasts of "The Victory Hour" series.

Microfilm Publications: Among the record series available as microfilm publications are the letters received and related registers and indexes to 1870. Letters sent, to 1889, have also been filmed. In addition, there are two microfilm publications of telegrams: 584 volumes of telegrams sent and received, mainly over the central telegraph in the Office of the Secretary of War, 1861-82; and a series of unbound telegrams sent from one field command or installation to another or between the field and Washington, 1860-70. For a complete listing see the current *List of National Archives Microfilm Publications*.

RECORDS OF THE
OFFICE OF THE SECRETARY OF THE ARMY
(RECORD GROUP 335)

The Office of the Secretary of the Army originated when the National Security Act of July 26, 1947, transformed the Department of War into the Department of the Army after relieving the former of responsibility for military aviation. The Secretary of the Army, who had formerly been Secretary of War, became accountable to the Secretary of Defense, head of the National Military Establishment (the Department of Defense after 1949). The Army Organization Act of 1950, which consolidated and revised existing laws to provide the administrative structure of the Department, gave the Secretary of the Army broad organizational powers.

The Secretary of the Army is responsible for all departmental affairs, including those relating to administration, training, operations, logistics, welfare, preparedness, and effectiveness of the Army. He is also responsible for research and development, management of civil defense, civil administration of certain foreign areas, protection of Army facilities, operation of the Panama Canal, the civil works program of the Corps of Engineers, and the national cemetery program.

There are 767 cubic feet of records dated between 1926 and 1957 in this record group.

RECORDS OF THE OFFICE OF THE SECRETARY OF THE ARMY. 1947-57. 247 lin. ft.

These consist of a central correspondence file, with index, 1947-54; personal correspondence files of Secretaries Kenneth Royall, Gordon Gray, and Frank Pace, 1949-51; and records of the Office of the Department Counselor, consisting of documents accumulated during the Army-McCarthy hearings before the Senate Special Subcommittee on Investigations, 1954, and records of the Defense Supply Service—Washington, 1952.

RECORDS OF THE OFFICE OF THE UNDER SECRETARY OF THE ARMY. 1941-57. 260 lin. ft.

As the chief deputy and principal civilian assistant to the Secretary, the Under Secretary of the Army is responsible for civil administration of certain U.S. possessions, military support of civil defense, and helping civil authorities in natural disasters and civil disturbances. Continental defense, cold war activities, military history, personnel security, and disciplinary matters; operations research; and matters related to departmental boards and committees are also his responsibility. The records consist of a file of the Administrative Office, with an index, 1948-49; a correspondence file, 1947-50; a personal correspondence file of Under Secretary Archibald S. Alexander, 1951-52; reports of inspections of Government-owned plants, 1949-54; records relating to Lay-Away Project 54 (moving equipment from factories to

Army facilities), 1954-57; records of Under Secretary Alexander's tours of Alaska and the Far East Command, 1951; records about Senate subcommittee hearings on Korean ammunition shortages, 1951-54; records of the Army bizone European recovery program, 1948-49; Fraud Branch case files, 1943-54; and contract agreements and a correspondence file concerning canceled contracts of the Contracts and Facilities Branch, 1941-49.

RECORDS OF THE OFFICE OF THE ASSISTANT SECRETARY OF THE ARMY. 1945-50. 76 lin. ft.

During most of the period covered by these records the Assistant Secretary was responsible for logistic and fiscal activities of the Department, including procurement, mobilization, Army supply and service operations, labor relations, property acquisition and disposal, the Army Exchange System, contracts and claims, and custody of military prisoners. He also represented the Department before Congress and other departments or agencies and the public. Records include an administrative file, with an index, 1947-50; a general file of Assistant Secretary Gordon Gray, 1947-48; records relating to the State-War-Navy Coordinating Committee, the State-Army-Navy-Air Force Advisory Committee, and the State-Army-Navy-Air Force Coordinating Committee, 1945-49; and records of the Army member of the Committee on a Uniform Code of Military Justice, 1948-49.

RECORDS RELATING TO PERSONNEL. 1945-54. 50 lin. ft.

Departmental personnel matters were handled by the Assistant Secretary of the Army for Manpower and Reserve Forces through the Office of Civilian Personnel. The records of the Office consist of files of the Salary and Wage Administration Division, 1945-53; an inspection file of the Program Evaluation Division, 1949–53; and Training and Development Division manuals, 1948–54. The records of the Civilian Personnel Division consist of documents relating to personnel management, 1947–54; bulletins, circulars, memorandums, directives, and other records, 1948–52; and a correspondence file relating to development of uniform policies for personnel administration, 1948–50. Also sound recordings (2 items) made for use at Army camps during Armed Forces Day, 1951.

RECORDS RELATING TO POSTWAR OCCUPIED AREAS. 1948–52. 28 lin. ft.

After World War II the United States directed military administration in the American zones of Germany and Austria, Trieste, Japan, southern Korea, and the Ryukyu Islands. An Assistant Secretary of the Army formulated Army occupation policy and supervised these areas. The records include general records of the Office of Occupied Areas, 1951–52; files relating to the government and relief in occupied areas programs, 1949–52; and correspondence of the Office of the Food Administrator for Occupied Areas, 1948–50.

OTHER RECORDS RELATING TO PARTICIPATION ON BOARDS AND COMMITTEES. 1926–55. 108 lin. ft.

These consist of summaries of proceedings, 1942–50, and a correspondence file, 1952, of the Armed Services Board of Contract Appeals; minutes, reports, and correspondence of the Army Advisory Board on Government-Furnished Property, 1946–49; wage survey records, 1948–50, and a correspondence file, 1942–50, of the Army-Air Force Wage Board; personnel records of the Army Civilian Legal Personnel Committee, 1942–50; a decimal, a subject, and a Fort Monroe, Va., file of the Army Installations Board, 1951–52; files of the Army representative on the Munitions Board, 1948–53; reports and correspondence of the Committee on Civilian Components, 1949; reports, correspondence, publications, and memorandums of the Ferguson Committee To Review Decartelization in Germany, 1948–49; an administrative correspondence file, 1926–49, and a budgetary file, 1926–50, of the National Board for the Promotion of Rifle Practice; files of the War Contracts Hardship Claims Board, 1947–51; general court-martial reviews of the Clemency and Parole Board, 1947–52; minutes of the Army Welfare Board, 1947–55; and renegotiation case files, 1942–50, and an administrative subject file of the Renegotiation Affairs Branch, 1942–51, of the Army Price Adjustment Board.

RECORDS OF THE HEADQUARTERS OF THE ARMY (RECORD GROUP 108)

The Headquarters of the Army, consisting of the Commanding General of the Army and his staff, existed from 1798 to 1903 under authorization of an act of May 28, 1798. The Commanding General was responsible for distribution of military forces and discipline of troops. Until an act of March 2, 1867, established the Headquarters of the Army at Washington, it had no fixed location. In 1874 Headquarters of the Army was moved to St. Louis, but in 1876 it was reestablished at Washington. A Headquarters of the Army in the

Field existed with General Grant in 1864-65 and with General Miles in 1898.

At various times the Departments of the Adjutant General and the Inspector General were under the control of the Headquarters of the Army. This command ceased to exist after an act of February 14, 1903, created the General Staff Corps and provided that on August 15, 1903, the duties of the Commanding General of the Army would be taken over by the Chief of Staff.

There are 93 cubic feet of records dated between 1828 and 1903 in this record group.

GENERAL RECORDS. 1828-1903.
189 lin. ft.

These records consist of letters sent, press copies of letters sent, and indexes, 1828-46, 1849-69, and 1873-1903, including letters sent by Lt. Gen. Winfield Scott on an expedition to San Juan Island, Washington Territory, in 1859, and Maj. Gen. H. W. Halleck as Chief of Staff in 1864-65; letters received, registers, and indexes, 1828-46, 1849-69, and 1873-1903; correspondence, 1847-48 and 1863-1901, including letters on special subjects and letters relating to officer appointments and brevets; telegrams sent and received, 1861-69 and 1879-88; endorsements, 1845-46, 1849-65, and 1873-1903; and general and special orders issued and received, 1835-39, 1849-61, and 1873-76.

OTHER RECORDS. 1832-1903.
6 lin. ft.

There are letters sent requesting warrants for payment of expenses, 1839-61; a salary and contingent accounts ledger, 1836-61; general service clerks' service and pay accounts, 1877-86; and letters sent and received and other records of staff officers, including those of Asst. Adjs. Gen. Robert N. Scott, 1864-65, and Thomas Ward, 1900-1902, the Disbursing Officer, 1883-1903, and the Assistant Quartermaster, 1897. Miscellaneous records include proceedings of the Military Board, 1832-35; lists of officers reporting to Headquarters, 1849-50, 1853-61, and 1874-76; discharge, resignation, and leave of absence lists, 1853-65 and 1902-3; station books, 1865-68 and 1875-76; descriptive books of posts in the Division of the Pacific and the District of Texas, 1868; marksmanship register, 1881-1903; and personnel, arms, and ammunition reports, 1895-96.

RECORDS OF HEADQUARTERS OF THE ARMY IN THE FIELD.
1864-65 and 1898. 16 lin. ft.

These consist of letters and endorsements sent, letters received and registers, special orders, and reports received, 1864-65; letters and telegrams sent by Aide-de-Camp C. B. Comstock and records of Asst. Adj. Gen. T. S. Bowers; and letters and telegrams sent and received, general orders, special orders, and circulars of Headquarters of the Army in the Field in Cuba and Puerto Rico, 1898.

RECORDS OF THE CAVALRY BUREAU. 1863-66. 5 lin. ft.

These consist of letters and endorsements sent, letters received and registers, applications for appointments as veterinary surgeons, inspection reports of cavalry, strength returns, and reports relating to the efficiency of carbines and rifles of the Office of the Chief of Cavalry; and letters and endorsements sent, letters received and registers, telegrams sent and received, and inspection reports.

See Aloha South, comp., *Records of the Headquarters of the Army,* Inv. 1 (1970).

RECORDS OF THE
WAR DEPARTMENT GENERAL AND SPECIAL STAFFS
(RECORD GROUP 165)

A War Department General Staff was authorized by the Congress February 14, 1903, to include a Chief of Staff, a General Council, and three divisions, which, after frequent reorganizations, developed into the Personnel Division (G-1), the Military Intelligence Division (G-2), the Organization and Training Division (G-3), the Supply Division (G-4), and the War Plans Division (Operations Division after 1942). The General Staff was a separate and distinct staff organization with supervision over most military branches—both line and staff. Its duties were to prepare plans for national defense and mobilization of military forces in time of war, to investigate and report on questions affecting Army efficiency and preparedness, and to give professional aid to the Secretary of War, general officers, and other superior commanders.

During World War II increased responsibilities necessitated the formation of several special staff divisions: the Bureau of Public Relations, which reported directly to the Secretary of War's Office; the Office of the Inspector General; divisions for Legislative and Liaison, Civil Affairs, Budget, Special Planning, and New Developments; the War Department Manpower Board; and several additional special sections and groups. Under provisions of the National Security Act of 1947 the War Department became the Department of the Army within the newly created National Military Establishment, which was renamed the Department of Defense in 1949.

There are 10,973 cubic feet of records dated between 1903 and 1948, with a few dated as early as 1870 and as late as 1954, in this record group.

RECORDS OF THE OFFICE OF THE CHIEF OF STAFF. 1903-47. 366 lin. ft.

The Chief of Staff, immediate adviser to the Secretary of War on matters relating to the Military Establishment, was a member of the Joint Chiefs of Staff and of the Combined Chiefs of Staff. The records consist of reports of the Provisional General Staff, with indexes, June-August 1903; general correspondence, 1903-47, with indexes, 1921-47; records of conferences of the Joint Chiefs of Staff and the Combined Chiefs of Staff, 1939-47; cables and correspondence with the White House, 1939-46; office files of Gens. J. Lawton Collins, 1942-46, and O. L. Nelson, 1938-46; shorthand notebooks of the secretary of Gen. George C. Marshall, July 1942-September 1945; radiograms, 1942; records relating to the proposed Department of National Defense, 1943-46; reports containing personnel and materiel statistics, 1917-45; and records relating to the return of U.S. prisoners of war (Project EVERSHARP), 1945-46.

RECORDS OF THE OFFICE OF THE DIRECTOR OF PERSONNEL AND ADMINISTRATION (G-1). 1921-50. 523 lin. ft.

These consist of general correspondence, 1921-48, with indexes (in WNRC); statistical studies, reports, and correspondence of the office of the Division executive, 1943-47; Women's Army Corps records, 1942-46 and 1949-50; and correspondence and reports relating to Selective Service, 1942-46, and to mobilization procedures, 1942-46.

RECORDS OF THE OFFICE OF THE DIRECTOR OF INTELLIGENCE (G-2). 1917-49. 5,947 lin. ft.

The records consist of general correspondence, 1917-48; records relating to the transmission of messages between the Prime Minister of England and the President of the United States (PRIME-POTUS), 1942-47; English translations of foreign intelligence documents, 1919-47, with indexes; data cards on German Army, Luftwaffe, and SS officers, 1939-45; military attache reports, 1917-41; correspondence relating to awards and decorations, 1944-48; prisoner of war interrogation reports, 1940-46; language and intelligence school correspondence, rosters, questionnaires, reports, and directives, 1942-49, with indexes; intelligence reports, 1917-27; some interim reports of ALSOS (special mission to determine German progress in nuclear physics), 1944-45; records of the Plant Protection Section, 1917-19, with indexes (in WNRC); records of the Office of the Chief Military Censor, 1917-19, with indexes (in WNRC); the "regional file" of intelligence reports, 1933-44 (in WNRC); and the Intelligence Library ("P" Publication file), 1940-45 (in WNRC).

RECORDS OF THE OFFICE OF THE DIRECTOR OF ORGANIZATION AND TRAINING (G-3). 1902-47. 303 lin. ft.

Originally centralized in one division, after March 9, 1942, the functions of this unit were divided between the Organization and Training Division, G-3, and the Operations Division. The records consist of general correspondence, 1918-47; correspondence relating to War Department mobilization plans, 1942-47; correspondence, with indexes, relating to inventions, 1918-21; State Guard records, 1940-42; War Department Civil Defense Mission to England correspondence and reports, 1941; and General Staff histories, 1902-19 and 1929.

RECORDS OF THE OFFICE OF THE DIRECTOR OF SERVICE, SUPPLY AND PROCUREMENT (G-4). 1914-47. 866 lin. ft.

These consist of general correspondence, 1921-46, with indexes; minutes, 1943-46; conference reports, 1944-46; the office file of Lt. Gen. Leroy Lutes, 1944-47; postwar Army supply program reports and correspondence, 1944-47; records relating to War Department reorganization and armed services unification, 1939-47; correspondence relating to lend-lease materiel, 1944-46; transcripts of bilateral military staff conversations, 1944-45; correspondence relating to harbor and costal defense, 1914-46, with indexes; records relating to post-World War I surplus equipment claims and sales, 1917-20; reports and correspondence relating to construction, utilization, and disposal of Army installations, 1944-47; records relating to Chinese officer training, 1946; reports and correspondence relating to military equipment and supply specifications, 1927-47; and Purchase, Storage, and Traffic Division records, 1918-21.

RECORDS OF THE OFFICE OF THE DIRECTOR OF PLANS AND OPERATIONS. 1923-48. 1,001 lin. ft.

The records consist of Aeronautical Board organizational data and minutes, 1923-48; Pearl Harbor investigation records, 1941-46; transcripts of Pan-American staff conversations, 1945; general correspondence, 1942-45, with an index; correspondence, with indexes, relating to American-British-Canadian organizational planning and general combat operations ("ABC" file), 1940-48; correspondence relating to operations and mobilization planning, 1941-46; incoming and outgoing messages, 1942-46; and special reports.

RECORDS OF THE ARMY WAR COLLEGE AND THE WAR COLLEGE DIVISION. 1900-1945.
687 lin. ft. and 36 rolls of microfilm.

The Army War College (AWC) was established in 1901 by Secretary of War Elihu Root to study General Staff functions and to serve as a general staff until one could be established. The AWC operated under supervision of the War College Board until August 1903 when it was placed under the supervision of the Chief of Staff. In 1911 the AWC was included in the War College Division. In 1918 the duties of the War College Division were divided between the Military Intelligence Division and the War Plans Division, with the AWC under the control of the Director of the War Plans Division. The records consist of reports and correspondence, with indexes, of the War College Board, 1902-3; journals, 1903-10; general correspondence, 1903-11, with indexes (some interfiled with records of G-2, the War College Division, and the War Plans Division); monographs and problem reports, 1906-9; issuances, 1917-45; historical records of the War Department and World War I, 1900-1941, including microfilm copies (36 rolls) of digests of documents selected from World War I records; and record cards to Department of Justice reports ("DJ" reports), July-November 1917.

RECORDS OF THE WAR PLANS DIVISION. 1917-42. 1,140 lin. ft.

These consist of general correspondence (some interfiled with that of its predecessors), 1920-42, with indexes; issuances; records of the Service and Information, 1919-20, Morale, 1917-21, and Education and Recreation, 1917-20, Branches, including records of the Commission on Training Camp Activities, 1917-20, with indexes; and the Committee on Education and Special Training, 1918-19.

RECORDS OF THE BUDGET DIVISION. 1941-49. 197 lin. ft.

The records include general correspondence, 1942-47; budget estimates, justifications, revisions, and adjustments, fiscal years 1942-49; correspondence and reports relating to apportionment of War Department funds, 1942-44; budget legislation records, 1942-45; and correspondence and accounting reports relating to foreign and defense aid, fiscal years 1941-49.

RECORDS OF THE CIVIL AFFAIRS DIVISION. 1942-49. 514 lin. ft.

The records include reports, 1943-47; general correspondence, 1943-49, with indexes; incoming and outgoing messages, 1942-49; transcripts of teletype conversations, 1946-49; records of the Army member of the Combined Civil Affairs Committee, 1942-49; policy and planning correspondence, 1943-47; and messages relating to refugees, 1944-48.

RECORDS OF THE INFORMATION AND EDUCATION DIVISION. 1941-45. 7 lin. ft. and 44 rolls of microfilm.

The records consist of copies of *YANK, The Army Weekly* magazine, 1942-45, and microfilm copies of questionnaires relating to the morale of military personnel, 1941-45.

RECORDS OF THE LEGISLATIVE AND LIAISON DIVISION. 1942-48. 65 lin. ft.

These consist of reports, memorandums, transcripts of testimony, correspondence, and other records relating to universal military training, 1944-48; the national defense program, 1946-47; War Department activities, 1942-48, with indexes; legislation affecting the War Department, 1943-46; and general correspondence, 1944-48.

RECORDS OF THE NEW DEVELOPMENTS DIVISION. 1940-46. 29 lin. ft.

The records consist of general correspondence, 1943-46, with indexes; office files and correspondence of divisional officials, 1942-46; and the office file of the Army representative on the National Inventors Council, 1940-45.

RECORDS OF THE PUBLIC INFORMATION DIVISION. 1921-49. 160 lin. ft.

The records consist of general correspondence, 1939-46; correspondence relating to War Department organization and functions, 1947-48; radio and motion picture scripts, 1942-46; wire service bulletins, 1947-49; press and radio news digests, 1940-48, and releases, 1921-47; and a card register of public opinion recorded in various news media, 1940-49.

RECORDS OF THE SPECIAL PLANNING DIVISION. 1943-46. 43 lin. ft.

The Special Planning Division (SPD) was established in 1943 to plan military and related industrial demobilization and the postwar Military Establishment as affected by demobilization. The records consist of general correspondence, with indexes, relating to SPD functions and activities.

RECORDS OF THE WAR DEPARTMENT MANPOWER BOARD. 1943-47. 69 lin. ft.

The War Department Manpower Board (WDMB or Gasser Board) was established as a special staff division in 1943 to ensure that Army organizations and installations were adequately manned but not overstaffed. In 1944 it also studied the use of civilian personnel in North American and European theaters of operations. The records consist of reports of manpower surveys, 1943-45; reports relating to civilian and military personnel ceilings, 1943-44; general correspondence, 1943-47, with indexes; and personnel allotment vouchers, 1944-47, and inventory and appraisal forms, 1944-46.

RECORDS OF DISCONTINUED BOARDS. 1888-1922. 150 lin. ft.

These records consist of minutes, reports, and correspondence, with indexes, of the Board of Ordnance and Fortifications, 1888-1919; and reports of the Board of General Officers, set up in 1922 to recommend officers to be retrained or retired from active duty after January 1, 1923.

CARTOGRAPHIC RECORDS. 1904-46. 13,973 items.

Included are color photographs (11,300 items) of relief models, annotated to show order of battle in World War II theaters of operations; photoprocessed and annotated maps collected by the National Land Defense Board, relating to the Panama Canal Zone and certain U.S. military reservations, 1907-15; maps collected and compiled by sections of the Intelligence Division (G-2) and its predecessors, relating to the Russo-Japanese War, 1904-5, World Wars I and II, the Russian Civil War, Mexico, ca. 1916-22, and areas of strategic interest throughout the world, 1927-46, and including a set of Japanese Imperial land survey maps overprinted by G-2, 1925-35; and maps collected and compiled for training purposes by the Army War College, the U.S. Military Academy, and the Command and General Staff School and its predecessors, 1910-45.

AUDIOVISUAL RECORDS. 1860-1951. 116,767 items.

Still pictures (115,596 items) consist of photographs, 1860-1947, of military personnel, equipment, installations, and activities in the United States, its territories, and some foreign countries; geological formations and manmade structures in the United States; and American Indians, U.S. civilians, and foreign nationals. There are photographs, watercolor sketches, and magazine clippings about the Civil War and other U.S. military operations, 1898–1917; of scenes in Canada, 1889-90, Mexico, 1904-10, and Cuba and the Virgin Islands, ca. 1900; and of foreign military activities, 1901-23. Included are World War I photographs, lithographs, and newspapers illustrating military personnel, equipment, installations, and activities of the Allies (particularly the American Expeditionary Forces) and the Central Powers; and U.S. homefront activities. World War II photographs are of U.S. bomber activities; Japanese atrocities; and Japanese, German, and Russian military equipment, 1931-45. There are also lithographs compiled in 1889 and 1908 of U.S. Army uniforms from 1774 to 1908, and photographs of people and events in the life of Abraham Lincoln.

Sound recordings (1,171 items) consist mainly of recordings collected by the Public Information Division and its predecessors, 1942-51, relating to combat operations in World War II and occupation activities in both Europe and the Pacific, including the surrender of Manila to the Japanese, Gen. Douglas MacArthur's arrival in Melbourne from the Philippines, the death of Ernie Pyle, the Japanese surrender in the Philippines, and the farewell ceremonies in 1951 for MacArthur in Tokyo. There are also recordings of testimony before the Woodrum Committee on Compulsory Military Training, 1945, and of addresses, press conferences, and interviews concerning the postwar defense program. Included are many foreign language recordings used in Axis propaganda.

Microfilm Publications: *List of the Photographs and Photographic Negatives Relating to the War for the Union (War Department Subject Catalogue No. 5, 1897)*, T251, 1 roll; and *The Mathew B. Brady Collection of Civil War Photographs*, T252, 4 rolls.

RECORDS OF THE ARMY STAFF
(RECORD GROUP 319)

The Army Staff, dating from 1947, is the military staff of the Secretary of the Army. It includes the Chief of Staff and his immediate assistants, the Army General Staff, the Special Staff, and the Administrative and Technical Staffs. The duties of the Army Staff include preparing plans relating to the Army's role in national security, investigating and reporting on Army efficiency and readiness, preparing detailed instructions for and supervising Army operations, and representing the Secretary of the Army and the Chief of Staff in coordinating actions of all Defense Department organizations. The Army Staff is a collective organization, presided over by the Chief of Staff; its records are those of its various components. This record group also includes some records of predecessor offices, the General and Special Staffs of the War Department, and of other staff agencies.

There are 14,163 cubic feet of records dated between 1940 and 1964 in this record group.

RECORDS OF THE OFFICE OF
THE CHIEF OF STAFF. 1942-54.
271 lin. ft.

The Chief of Staff is the principal military adviser to the Secretary of the Army and is responsible for the planning, development, execution, review, and analysis of Army programs. Included are minutes of the General Council,

1942–52; general correspondence, with indexes, 1948–54; and budget estimates and justifications and records relating to forms standardization, 1949–51.

RECORDS OF THE OFFICE OF THE COMPTROLLER OF THE ARMY. 1942–54. 390 lin. ft.

The Comptroller of the Army is not only responsible for accounting, fiscal, statistical, and management engineering activities, but also for supervision of legislative policies and programs relating to appropriation acts and General Staff supervision over the Chief, U.S. Army Audit Agency. The records consist of minutes and reports of the Committee on Accounting Policy and Financial Procedures, 1949–54; correspondence, 1948–54, with indexes; statistical reports, 1942–52; studies, management surveys, and other records relating to financial management and accounting policies and procedures, budget estimates and justifications, funding programs and allocations, and training and utilization of civilian and military personnel, 1942–54; reports on the installation of simplified supply systems at various installations, 1949–54; and general correspondence, issuances, reports, and other records of the U.S. Army Audit Agency, relating to technical supervision of audit operations in regional offices and overseas commands.

RECORDS OF THE OFFICE OF THE CHIEF OF INFORMATION. 1940–54. 177 lin. ft.

These include reports, correspondence, memorandums, messages, weekly news summaries, and studies documenting the release of information used to promote public understanding and support of the Army and the direction of its public information and education policies and programs, 1944–54; records of the Public Information Division, consisting of general administrative correspondence, 1940–49, weekly news summaries and digests of public opinion, 1944–48, the Army publication *The Medal of Honor of the United States Army* (including orders, photographs, citations, manuscripts, and other background material), 1946–48, and general correspondence of the Women's Interest Section, 1941–49; and records of the Troop Information and Education Division, including reports, correspondence (with indexes), and studies, 1942–54.

RECORDS OF THE OFFICE OF THE CHIEF OF LEGISLATIVE LIAISON. 1940–57. 241 lin. ft.

These consist of organizational charts, directives, and general correspondence, 1940–54, and correspondence with congressional committees, 1952–53; minutes of conferences, reports, correspondence, and related records of the Plans and Policy Office, relating to Army legislative programs, preparation of the legislative segment of the Army command and management program, and coordination and arrangement of travel for Members of Congress whose official duties involve Army activities, 1947–54; a policy book and a history of the Office, 1947–54; correspondence and related records of the Legislative Division, 1946–57, and reports of hearings conducted by congressional committees, 1947–51; correspondence, reports, and other records of the Congressional Investigations Division, 1946–54; and records relating to the "Uniform Code of Military Justice," 1943–51.

RECORDS OF THE OFFICE OF THE CHIEF OF CIVIL AFFAIRS AND MILITARY GOVERNMENT. 1948–54. 17 lin. ft.

These records consist of correspondence relating to administration of civil affairs and military government activities in liberated and occupied areas.

RECORDS OF THE OFFICE OF
THE ASSISTANT CHIEF OF
STAFF, G-1, PERSONNEL. 1944-54.
614 lin. ft.

This office is responsible for recruitment, administration, and management of Army personnel, including all servicemen of the Army on active duty, the Reserve Officers' Training Corps, and civilian personnel. Almost all the records consist of general correspondence, with indexes, 1949-51 (in WNRC). There are also records of the Career Management Group, 1946-48; inspection and survey records of the Program Evaluation Division, relating to civilian personnel in the Zone of Interior and overseas, 1944-54; and issuances relating to civilian personnel, 1944-54.

RECORDS OF THE DIRECTOR OF
THE WOMEN'S ARMY CORPS
(WAC). 1942-50. 22 lin. ft.

The Headquarters of the Women's Army Auxiliary Corps (WAAC) was authorized May 14, 1942, to enlist and train women volunteers for military service to release enlisted men performing noncombatant duties for combat service. It was renamed the Women's Army Corps in July 1943. The records consist chiefly of correspondence relating to the recruiting, classification, overall utilization, and separation of personnel.

RECORDS OF THE OFFICE OF
THE ASSISTANT CHIEF OF
STAFF, G-2, INTELLIGENCE. 1939-55. 8,549 lin. ft. and 1,163 rolls of microfilm (in WNRC).

The records consist of general correspondence, with indexes, some on microfilm (822 rolls), 1941-52; incoming and outgoing messages, with indexes, 1939-55; the "intelligence document" ("ID") file, with indexes, some on microfilm (193 rolls), 1942-54; and the "intelligence library" ("P") file, with microfilm index (148 rolls), 1946-51.

RECORDS OF THE OFFICE OF
THE DEPUTY CHIEF OF STAFF
FOR MILITARY OPERATIONS.
1942-64. 372 lin. ft.

The Deputy Chief of Staff for Military Operations took over the functions of the Assistant Chief of Staff, G-3, and is responsible for all Army plans, including Army aspects of joint plans; for advising the Chief of Staff on Joint Chiefs of Staff matters; and for all strategic, tactical, and military organization matters and training activities. He also serves as the Army Operations Deputy for the Joint Chiefs of Staff. These records include correspondence, messages, and reports.

RECORDS OF THE OFFICE OF
THE ASSISTANT CHIEF OF
STAFF, G-3, OPERATIONS. 1943-54.
1,532 lin. ft.

These records consist of general correspondence, with indexes, 1943-54, relating to the organization, demobilization, and training of all Army components, including academic training of foreign nationals, 1943-54; and correspondence, with indexes, and other records of the Organization and Training Division, relating to strategic planning and maneuvers conducted by the Armed Forces of the United States and Canada, 1943-50. Also included are records of the Plans and Operations Division, the successor of the Operations Division, which in 1950 was placed under the jurisdiction of the Assistant Chief of Staff, G-3, consisting of general correspondence, with indexes, 1946-50; memorandums of the Combined Forces Planners, the Combined Chiefs of Staff, the State-War-Navy/State-Army-Navy-Air Force Coordinating Committee, and the Joint Chiefs of Staff Secretariat, 1942-June 1951; and correspondence relating to the China aid program, 1945-49.

RECORDS OF THE RESEARCH AND DEVELOPMENT DIVISION. 1940-54. 346 lin. ft.

These consist of minutes and agenda of research and development boards and committees, 1946-48; general correspondence, with indexes, May 1946-February 1949 and 1951-54; technical reports and studies relating to research and development programs of the Army, 1943-47; and general records of the War Department Liaison Officer for the National Defense Research Committee, 1940-47. General correspondence for the March 1949-December 1950 period is interfiled with general correspondence of the Assistant Chief of Staff, G-4, Logistics.

RECORDS OF THE OFFICE OF THE ASSISTANT CHIEF OF STAFF, G-4, LOGISTICS. 1922-54. 1,417 lin. ft.

This Office plans for and supervises Army research and development activities, procurement and related industrial matters, and supply and logistic services, and directs and controls the technical staffs and services. The records include general correspondence, with indexes, 1947-54; publications, 1943-54; management surveys and studies, 1950-53; minutes of the Supply Management Advisory Council, 1951-53; records relating to procurement, 1946-50; Army and joint Army-Navy and Army-Air Force canceled specifications, 1945-53; and Federal specifications and related correspondence, 1922-53. Also included are records relating to ammunition problems during the Korean conflict, 1953, and statistical reports and other records of the Supply Division, relating to civilian aid in foreign and liberated countries, 1943-53. Records of the Research and Development Division for March 1949-December 1950 are interfiled in the general correspondence of this Office.

GENERAL RECORDS OF THE OFFICE OF THE CHIEF OF PSYCHOLOGICAL WARFARE. 1951-54. 34 lin. ft.

These consist of correspondence relating to psychological warfare and special operational plans and policy recommendations for supervision of programs in these areas.

RECORDS OF THE OFFICE OF THE CHIEF OF MILITARY HISTORY. 1933-53. 136 lin. ft.

These consist of correspondence, 1943-53; a "historical manuscript" file of orders, manuscript drafts, authors' notes, and source material, 1940-48; and background material used in preparation of the history "Motor Transport, U.S. Army, 1769 to Date," 1933-48, with some material of earlier date.

RECORDS OF THE OFFICE OF THE EXECUTIVE FOR RESERVE AND ROTC AFFAIRS. 1923-54. 108 lin. ft.

These consist of reports, memorandums, and correspondence relating to procurement of personnel, allocation of funds, and supervision of the Army Reserve and the Reserve Officers' Training Corps.

RECORDS OF THE WAR DEPARTMENT CLAIMS BOARD (RECORD GROUP 191)

The War Department Claims Board was established under the War Department General Staff on January 20, 1919, to supervise and coordinate the work of War Department agencies settling claims arising from termination of contracts and other World War I procurement obligations of the Department. These agencies were the Boards of Contract Review and the claims boards created by War Department procurement bureaus to supervise the preparation of contracts and hear and settle claims arising from bureau contracts; the Board of Appraisers, established April 1, 1918, to adjudicate cases concerned with Government requisitioning and property commandeering; and the Board of Contract Adjustment, created November 6, 1918, to hear and determine claims and disputes arising under contracts made by the War Department. On July 1, 1920, the Board of Appraisers became the Appraisal Section, the Board of Contract Adjustment became the Appeal Section, and procurement bureau claims boards became the Air Service, Chemical Warfare, Construction, Engineer, Ordnance, Purchase, Signal Corps, and Transportation Sections of the Claims Board. The Board was transferred March 15, 1921, to the Office of the Assistant Secretary of War. On March 1, 1922, the Claims Board was dissolved, and its jurisdiction over pending claims was delegated to the Office of the Assistant Secretary of War.

There are 600 cubic feet of records (in WNRC) dated between 1917 and 1922 in this record group.

GENERAL RECORDS OF THE CLAIMS BOARD. 1919-22. 133 lin. ft.

These include minutes, files for cases presented to congressional committees, and files of Board officers.

RECORDS OF CLAIMS BOARD SECTIONS AND THEIR PREDECESSORS. 1917-22. 510 lin. ft.

Board of Contract Adjustment and Claims Board Appeal Section records include minutes, reports, case files, hearings, and correspondence. Board of Appraisers and Claims Board Appraisal Section records consist chiefly of case files but include minutes, reports of awards and adjustments, and correspondence. There are also records of technical committees and of the sections of the Claims Board that succeeded procurement bureau claim boards, but records of bureau boards are with other records of those bureaus.

RECORDS OF THE FOREIGN CLAIMS SECTION (WAR) (RECORD GROUP 213)

A special representative of the Secretary of War was appointed January 22, 1919, to terminate War Department purchasing and manufacturing orders and contracts made in the United States with Allied Governments and to settle resulting claims. On February 11, 1919, the U.S. Liquidation Commission, with headquarters in France, was established to settle similar claims based on transactions made abroad and to dispose of property acquired outside the territorial United States and its possessions as a result of U.S. participation in World War I. To handle property disposal, the Office of the General Sales Agent, American Expeditionary Forces, that had been established January 1, 1919, was placed under the Commission.

Effective June 1, 1920, functions and records of the special representative and the Commission were transferred to the External Relations Section of the Supply Division, War Department General Staff. At the same time the Section acquired the functions and records of the Renting, Requisitions, and Claims Services in France and Germany, both of which had settled claims arising from the presence in those countries of American forces. On December 18, 1920, the Chief of Staff created the Foreign Claims Section under the War Department Claims Board to continue foreign claims work. The Board was dissolved in 1922, and the Foreign Claims Section was placed under the jurisdiction of the Assistant Secretary of War. In 1926 the Section was transferred to the Office of the Chief of Finance.

There are 40 cubic feet of records (in WNRC) dated between 1917 and 1940 in this record group.

RECORDS. 1917-40. 48 lin. ft.

Included are issuances; correspondence of the Foreign Claims Section, the special representatives of the Secretary of War, and the External Relations Section; cables received and sent; reports and correspondence on the cost of maintaining the Army of Occupation in Germany; claims case files concerning German vessels; and miscellaneous reports.

RECORDS OF THE CHIEFS OF ARMS
(RECORD GROUP 177)

The term "Chiefs of Arms" refers to the Chief of Artillery, the Chief of Field Artillery, the Chief of Coast Artillery, the Chief of Cavalry, and the Chief of Infantry. On February 6, 1901, an Artillery Corps of coast and field artillery was established under a Chief of Artillery. On February 2, 1907, the field artillery was separated from the Corps, which was then redesignated the Coast Artillery Corps under the Chief of Coast Artillery. The Chief of Field Artillery, the Chief of Cavalry, and the Chief of Infantry were established on September 21, 1920. Within their respective arms the Chiefs supervised and controlled schools and boards, developed tactical doctrine, prepared manuals and training literature, and recommended organizational changes and personnel assignments. The positions of Chiefs of Arms were discontinued in a 1942 War Department reorganization; their functions, duties, and powers were transferred to the Commanding General, Army Ground Forces.

There are 617 cubic feet of records dated between 1878 and 1943 in this record group.

RECORDS OF THE CHIEF OF ARTILLERY AND OFFICE OF THE CHIEF OF COAST ARTILLERY. 1878-1942. 890 lin. ft.

The records include issuances and correspondence, with index and record cards, 1901-18; correspondence and security-classified correspondence, 1918-42; Antiaircraft Command records; and artillery officer station books, 1878-1900. There are correspondence, with index and record cards, and returns of the Coast Artillery School, Fort Monroe, Va., 1878-1916; and proceedings, subject and general information files, 1905-19, security-classified correspondence, correspondence relating to fortification plans, and research and development project reports with accompanying record cards of the Coast Artillery Board at Fort Monroe. Records of the School of Submarine Defense, Fort Totten, N.Y., include proceedings of the School Board and the Torpedo Board, issuances, letter books, and correspondence, with related index and record cards. Also included is correspondence of the Coast Artillery War Instruction at Fort Andrews, Mass., with index and record cards; of the Coast Artillery Training Center, Fort Monroe, Va.; and of the Radiodynamic Torpedo Unit, Boston, Mass.

RECORDS OF THE CHIEF OF FIELD ARTILLERY. 1904-43. 273 lin. ft.

These consist of issuances; a subject file of the Field Artillery Board, 1904-39; general correspondence, with index, 1917-43; correspondence with liaison officers, 1924-42; and correspondence relating to the ROTC, 1931-41.

RECORDS OF THE CHIEF OF CAVALRY. 1920-43. 41 lin. ft.

Included are correspondence of the Office of the Chief of Cavalry, 1920-42, and the Cavalry School, Fort Riley, Kans., 1936-43; and case files, 1938-39, and correspondence, 1929-39, of the Mechanized Cavalry Board, Fort Knox, Ky.

RECORDS OF THE CHIEF OF INFANTRY. 1920-42. 53 lin. ft.

Included are lists relating to Army War College training and correspondence.

CARTOGRAPHIC RECORDS. 1880-1926. 45 items.

These include manuscript and annotated published charts and maps prepared by students of the Coast Artillery School, 1908-13, the Infantry School of Arms, n.d., and the Mounted Service School, 1908; and manuscript and annotated published charts relating to joint Army and Navy coast defense exercises, Fort Screven, Ga., 1910, and Fort Terry, N.Y., 1913.

RECORDS OF HEADQUARTERS ARMY GROUND FORCES
(RECORD GROUP 337)

Responsibility for administering and training Army field forces was divided among units of the War Department until July 1940 when General Headquarters, U.S. Army (GHQ) was given centralized control of ground combat activities. In a 1942 War Department reorganization, GHQ was abolished and Army combat arms were placed under the Army Ground Forces (AGF); the Commanding General AGF assumed authority formerly held by chiefs of combat arms. Administrative and technical services were placed under the Commanding General, Services of Supply, later Army Service Forces (see RG 160). The AGF was responsible for organizing, training, and equipping ground force units for combat operations. Redesignated the Office of the Chief of Army Field Forces (AFF) in 1948, the Office supervised, coordinated, and inspected matters relating to training Army individuals and units for the field, including the Organized Reserve Corps, Reserve Officers' Training Corps, Army National Guard, and Army General and Special Service Schools. AFF authority was extended in 1953 to include general direction, supervision, and coordination of the development of tactics, techniques, and material for field force use. In February 1955 the Continental Army Command (CONARC) was established as successor to the AFF.

There are 1,890 cubic feet of records dated between 1940 and 1954 in this record group.

RECORDS OF GHQ, U.S. ARMY.
1940-42. 145 lin. ft.

These consist of correspondence relating to training activities, 1940-42; a journal file, August 6, 1941-March 8, 1942, of the Secretary of the General Staff; and correspondence of the G-1, G-2, G-3, and G-4 Sections and the Aviation, Coast Artillery, Quartermaster, and Signal Sections, 1940-42.

RECORDS OF HEADQUARTERS, ARMY GROUND FORCES (AGF).
1942-48. 1,031 lin. ft.

General records of the Adjutant General's Section consist of general decimal files, 1942-48; unit movement orders, 1942-45, with related correspondence; and personnel movement orders, 1943-45. Also included are Classification and Replacement Division statistical reports, 1942-46, and Machine Records Division statistical tabulations and strength reports and Personnel Division records, 1942-46. There are correspondence and reference files of the Office of the Commanding General and journals of the Office of the Chief of Staff, 1940-45. Records of the General Staff consist of G-1 correspondence, 1945-48; records of the Control, Enlisted, and Officers' Divisions, 1946-48; the Women's Army Corps Division, 1943-48; and the Miscellaneous Division, 1942-48. G-2 records include correspondence, 1942-47, and intelligence reports, 1943-46. G-3 records consist of Training Group directives, 1942-43; Training Publications and Aids Division records and the Troop Training Division project file, 1942-46; Maneuvers, Special Projects, and Ammunition Branch records relating to desert training centers, mountain and winter warfare, and reports of an Army project known as "Sphinx," 1942-45; Replacement Training Branch inspection and training reports, 1942-47; and Operations Group correspondence, 1943-46.

G-4 records include correspondence of the Administrative Division, 1944-47, and Maintenance Division, 1941-46. Records of the Requirements Section consist of correspondence of the Executive Office, 1941-45, the Development Division, 1941-46, and the latter's Airborne, Armored Vehicle, Cavalry, Coast Artillery, Field Artillery, and Infantry Branches, 1942-45.

Records of the Special Staff include Budget and Fiscal Section records, 1942-45; Information Section correspondence and press releases, 1942-45; Historical Section AGF histories, studies, and correspondence, 1941-45; and general records of the Engineer and Medical Sections, 1941-47, Ordnance Section, 1944-47, Quartermaster Section, 1941-45, and Signal and Transportation Sections, 1947.

RECORDS OF THE OFFICE OF THE CHIEF OF ARMY FIELD FORCES. 1948-54. 668 lin. ft.

There are general decimal files, 1948-54, of the Adjutant General's Section, with some records relating to decorations and awards, 1945-48; Army Equipment Policy Panel reports, directives, studies, and authorizations, 1949-50; military occupational specialty (MOS) panel studies, 1952; Ground Statistics Section statistical tabulations, 1942-48; Information Section correspondence, 1942-48; and Historical Section historical reports, 1949-54. Records of the Office of the Chief of Staff include inspection reports of posts and camps, military districts, Army areas, overseas commands, and National Guard units, 1948-54; and reports of exercises and maneuvers, 1954.

Records of the General Staff include G-1, July-December 1948, and G-2, 1948,

correspondence. G-3 records consist of general records of the Administrative Division, 1942-52, Executive Group, 1947-48, Operations Group, 1946-48, Plans Division, 1949-54, and Organization and Equipment Division, 1943-48. Records of the Civilian Components Division include the National Guard Branch decimal file, 1945-48, and Organized Reserve Corps Branch general correspondence and Universal Military Training Branch subject files, 1946-48. Records of the Training Group include correspondence; Schools Division project case files and instruction programs, 1942-50; Training Publications and Aids Division records, 1942-48; Troop Training Division reports of peacetime military exercise "Longhorn," 1951-52; Army Air Support Center records, 1950-51; and records relating to the Joint Airborne Troop Board of the Joint Training Division, 1952-54. G-4 records consist of Administrative Division records, 1948-50.

Records of the Special Staff consist of Development and Testing Section correspondence and Budget and Fiscal Section correspondence and administrative memorandums, 1942-50; and correspondence of the Chemical, 1942-48, Engineer, 1948-50, Medical, 1948, Ordnance, 1945-48, Quartermaster, 1948-50, Signal, 1948-50, and Transportation, 1946-50, Sections.

AUDIOVISUAL RECORDS. 1942-44. 1,302 items.

These include photographs (1,300 items) and motion pictures (2 reels) showing mountain and winter warfare training, universal military training, and other AGF activities, 1942-44.

RECORDS OF HEADQUARTERS ARMY SERVICE FORCES (RECORD GROUP 160)

The Services of Supply was established by a War Department circular of March 2, 1942, that placed under the

Commanding General, Services of Supply, the units of the Office of the Under Secretary of War engaged in procurement and industrial mobilization functions; the Budget Advisory Committee; the Offices of the Surgeon General, Chief of Engineers (except civil functions), Chief Signal Officer, Quartermaster General, Chief of Ordnance, and Chief of Chemical Warfare Service; and the supply functions of the Offices of the Chief of Coast Artillery, Chief of Finance, and Judge Advocate General. The Services of Supply was renamed the Army Service Forces (ASF) in 1943. The ASF, which provided services and supplies to meet military requirements except those unique to the Army Air Forces, functioned through a Headquarters Staff, technical and administrative services, service commands, and the Military District of Washington. Its commanding general acted under the direction of the Under Secretary of War on procurement and related matters but reported to the Chief of Staff on military matters. The ASF was discontinued in 1946, and its functions were divided among War Department General Staff units and the Administrative and Technical Services.

There are 2,021 cubic feet of records dated between 1920 and 1946 in this record group.

RECORDS OF THE OFFICE OF THE COMMANDING GENERAL. 1941–46. 65 lin. ft.

These consist of Lt. Gen. Brehon B. Somervell's security-classified correspondence, strategic plans for conducting the war, and records of the public relations advisor to the commanding general, 1942–45; correspondence between General Somervell and private individuals, Members of Congress, and nonmilitary and private agencies, 1941–46; letters sent by Lt. Gen. W. D. Styer, Chief of Staff, ASF, March–May 1942 and 1944–45; speeches by Generals Somervell and Styer, 1941–45; reports, correspondence, memorandums, and messages of the Office of the Chief of Staff,

1942–46; and general correspondence of the Deputy Chief of Staff for Service Commands, 1943–45.

RECORDS OF DIRECTORS AND DIVISIONS ATTACHED TO THE OFFICE OF THE COMMANDING GENERAL. 1920–46. 560 lin. ft.

These consist of records relating to general matters, mobilization, supply and shipping, status of troops and supplies in theaters of operations, histories of divisions, administrative management, intelligence, and the construction, utilization, and disposition of Army installations.

Included are general records, consisting chiefly of decimal and subject correspondence files that contain correspondence, reports, issuances, messages, intraoffice communications, and reference material relating to administration, planning, management, and other activities of directors and divisions attached to the Office of the Commanding General, 1920–46.

Also included are a history of the Movements Branch, ca. 1945; Strategic Logistics Branch correspondence and studies relating to logistic plans and projected supply operations for overseas theaters, 1941–46; Theater Branch correspondence, reports, studies, and plans relating to supplies and equipment for the theaters of operations, and correspondence and a historical file of the Requirements and Stock Control Division, 1940–46; and Intelligence Division reports and studies on Japanese balloons, 1942–45.

RECORDS OF FUNCTIONAL STAFF DIRECTORS AND DIVISIONS. 1939–46. 1,430 lin. ft.

Included are general records, 1939–46 (1,330 lin. ft.), consisting of decimal files, indexes, directors' reading files, office diaries, historical and policy files, and reports that relate to supervising and coordinating activities of the Office of the Director of Personnel and its subordinate units; coordinating, distributing, and storing supplies and equipment for the Army under the Director of Supply; coordinating ASF military training activities with those of staff divisions, technical services, service commands, and other major commands; correlating and supervising procurement and production activities related to the Army supply program; and maintaining requirement programs through international aid.

Records separately maintained by functional divisions include minutes, reports, and issuances of the U.S. Procurement Committee and the Supply Subcommittee of the Combined Civil Affairs Committee, and Distribution Division correspondence, 1942–46; Production Division correspondence on closing ordnance plants, 1944; miscellaneous records of the Power and Machine Tool Sections, 1939–46; tax amortization certificates, Small War Plants Branch reports, and a policy file of the Facilities Branch, 1942–44; Training Contracts Branch records and Readjustment Division messages, transcripts, and teletype conferences, 1943–46; Research and Development Division reports and School Division records relating to the

Army specialized training program, 1943–45; Training Requirements Division histories, 1939–45; Labor Branch records, including the race relations analyst's correspondence, 1942–46, and progress reports relating to labor recruitment in critical areas, 1944–45; histories, 1939–45, and tabulations, reports, and studies, 1942–46, of the Military Personnel Division; and a history of the Officer Procurement Service, 1942–45.

CARTOGRAPHIC AND AUDIOVISUAL RECORDS. 1942–46. 229 items.

Cartographic records, 1942–46 (98 items), include an incomplete series of published maps, posters, and photographic views issued weekly to illustrate Allied and enemy military situations and civilian activities during World War II, and an *Atlas of World Maps* issued by the Army Specialized Training Division to be used in Army training programs, 1942–46.

Audiovisual records, 1943–44 (131 items), consist of foreign language sound recordings made for training purposes by the Army Specialized Training Division of the Office of the Director of Military Training, 1943–44.

Offices and Bureaus

RECORDS OF THE ADJUTANT GENERAL'S OFFICE, 1780's–1917 (RECORD GROUP 94)

The Continental Congress on June 17, 1775, appointed an Adjutant General of the Continental Army. After 1783 no further provision was made for such an officer until an act of March 5, 1792, provided for an adjutant, who was also to do the work of inspector. An act of March 3, 1813, established an Adjutant General's Department and an Inspector

General's Department under one head, the Adjutant and Inspector General. Separate heads for the two Departments were provided for by an act of March 2, 1821.

Except for the brief period 1904–7, the Adjutant General's Office (AGO) has been in continuous existence since 1821. In April 1904 the AGO and the Record and Pension Office of the War Department were united to form the Military Secretary's Office, but the Adjutant General was not included in this union of the two offices. In March 1907 the Congress restored the AGO.

The AGO functioned under the direction of the Secretary of War until the creation of the General Staff in 1903, when the AGO came under the general supervision of the Chief of Staff. When the War Department was reorganized in 1942, the AGO was placed under the supervision of the Commanding General, Services of Supply (later designated Army Service Forces). With the dissolution of this organization in June 1946, the AGO was placed under the General Staff. After the War Department became the Department of the Army in 1947, the Adjutant General came under the direct supervision and control of the Deputy Chief of Staff for Personnel.

The Adjutant General has been charged with matters relating to command, discipline, and administration of the Military Establishment, and has had the duties of recording, authenticating, and communicating the Secretary's orders, instructions, and regulations to troops and individuals in the Army. He has been responsible for issuing commissions, compiling and issuing the *Army Register* and the *Army List and Directory*, consolidating the general returns of the Army and Militia, and recruiting.

The AGO chiefly handled Army orders, correspondence, and other records, and it received final custody of virtually all records concerned with the Military Establishment, including personnel of the Army and discontinued commands, noncurrent holdings of bureaus of the War Department, and special collections.

The organization and size of the AGO has been changed to meet changing needs. Some divisions and other units organized to handle specific functions existed only briefly while some were redesignated or consolidated with other offices. Some units did not create separate records; their correspondence was carried on in the name of the Adjutant General and is found in the main files of the AGO. Others maintained their own records. The records of the AGO include those of the Record and Pension Office. In order to consolidate in one office all records relating to Volunteers, the Record and Pension Division of the Surgeon General's Office and 13 divisions of the AGO having charge of muster rolls and other military records of Volunteers were consolidated and designated the Record and Pension Division of the War Department in July 1889. This Division was charged with the custody of the military and hospital records of Volunteer Armies and the transaction of War Department business with them.

See Livingston Watrous, *A Brief History of the Adjutant General's Department From June 16, 1775, to December 31, 1925* (Governors Island, N.Y., 1927).

There are 38,107 cubic feet of records dated between ca. 1783 and 1917 in this record group.

GENERAL RECORDS. 1784-1917. 17,890 lin. ft.

Included are letter books; endorsement books; reports to the Secretary of War; registers, with indexes, of letters received; letters received; and other records, 1800-1889. Post-Revolutionary War records relate to pay of Regular and Volunteer Armies, 1784-1815. Also record cards containing digests of communications received, letters sent, and notations of AGO action; telegrams and cablegrams sent and received; and an indexed document file containing letters received, replies, reports, and related documents, 1890-1917.

The Adjutant General's collection of manuscripts and printed orders, 1797-1910, includes general, special, and field orders and circulars, with indexes, of the War Department; of armies, brigades, divisions, and corps; and of military divisions, departments, districts, and posts. Muster rolls include those of Regular Army organizations, 1784-1912, and of Volunteer organizations, 1784-1901, that served in the war with the Northwest Indians; the Creek war; other Indian wars; the Cherokee removal; the War of 1812; the Mexican, Civil, and Spanish-American Wars; and the Philippine Insurrection.

There are returns, 1790-1916, of departments; territorial divisions, departments, and districts; military posts; Army commands in the War of 1812, Mexican War, and Civil War; and military organizations. There are also station books of troops, Regular Army officers and organizations, and Volunteer officers.

Regular Army records, 1798-1914, include personal documents, disability certificates, final statements concerning soldiers' deaths, and enlistment registers and records, including those for Indian scouts. Volunteer organization records include letters and orders sent during the Mexican and Civil Wars, descriptive books and morning reports from the Civil War, and regimental and company books from the Spanish-American War and the Philippine Insurrection, 1846-1902.

There are miscellaneous records relating to the War of 1812, the Philippine Insurrection, and the Mexican, Civil, and Spanish-American Wars, 1812-1901. Records relating to the U.S. Military Academy include reports, correspondence, orders, rolls, registers, and records concerning applications and the Board of Visitors, 1803-1917. Also records relating to Office organization and personnel, 1851-1908, and the Government Hospital for the Insane, 1862-1917; provost fund records, 1864-83; National Land Defense Board reports, 1907-15; and reference aids and other special files, 1790-1917.

RECORDS OF UNITS OF THE ADJUTANT GENERAL'S OFFICE. 1783-1917. 3,836 lin. ft.

The records are chiefly letter books, registers of letters received, letters received, and functional records (some of which were withdrawn from the Adjutant General's files), and include records of the Appointment, Commission, and Personal Branch, 1783-1917; Bounty and Claims, 1862-78, Colored Troops, 1863-89, Deserters, 1815-25 and 1866-69, General Courts-Martial, 1866-72, Military Prison Record, 1865-95, Military Reservation, ca. 1800-1916, Recruiting, 1814-1913, and Volunteer Service, 1861-89, Divisions; Drafted Bureau, 1863-66; Enlisted Branch, 1848-89; and Fund Branch, 1871-83.

RECORDS OF THE RECORD AND PENSION OFFICE. 1784-1917. 26,120 lin. ft.

These include office correspondence consisting of record cards, lists of military organization records "carded" by the office, and a document file, with an index, relating primarily to military service of Volunteer soldiers, 1889-1904.

Compiled military service records, with indexes, 1784-1917, include those for Volunteer organizations that served in the post-Revolutionary War period, 1784-1811; War of 1812, 1812-15; Indian wars, 1817-58; Mexican War, 1846-48; Civil War, 1861-65; and the Spanish-American War and Philippine Insurrection, 1898-1903. These service records consist of a jacket-envelope for each soldier, labeled with his name, rank, and unit, and containing the originals of documents relating solely to the soldier and abstracts of information concerning the soldier from original muster rolls, returns, hospital rolls, descriptive books, and lists of deserters.

Medical records consist chiefly of records of and about medical installations, including medical histories of posts, muster rolls and payrolls of Hospital Corps detachments, and hospital field records, including those from the Spanish-American War and the Philippine Insurrection, 1821-1912; "carded" medical records for the Regular Army, 1821-84 and 1894-1912; medical personnel records, 1839-1914; reports on diseases and individual cases, 1841-93; records relating to the sick and wounded, 1814-1917; and miscellaneous records, 1862-1917.

RECORDS OF THE WAR RECORDS OFFICE. 1861-99. 100 lin. ft.

This Office, which originated in 1874 to publish the official records of the Civil War, was at first known as the Publication Office, War Records. In July 1899 it was consolidated with the Record and Pension Office. Its records include letter books, letters received, registers of letters received, correspondence, and records relating to Office operations, 1875-99. Civil War records retained by the Office consist of reports, letters, telegrams, returns, orders, and circulars of Army corps, departments, and divisions; and Union battle reports that include reports, telegrams, letters, maps, and sketches relating to military operations, 1861-65.

RECORDS OF COMMISSIONS. 1861-74. 32 lin. ft.

There are records of the Hawkins Taylor Commission, consisting of indexes and registers of claims allowed, 1861-62; the Smith-Brady Commission, consisting of testimony received and the final Commission report, 1861-65; the Howard Court of Inquiry, consisting of exhibits, testimony, the Judge Advocate's argument, and congressional acts, 1874; and the U.S. Christian Commission, consisting of reports, correspondence, personnel records, records about accounts and contributions, and miscella-

neous records, such as scrapbooks and memorandum books, 1861-66.

CARTOGRAPHIC AND AUDIOVISUAL RECORDS. 1853-1925. 2,986 items.

Cartographic records consist of maps (39 items) published by the Office of Explorations and Surveys and the Bureau of Topographical Engineers, relating to the Pacific Railroad surveys, 1853-55, and to Florida, 1856; manuscript and annotated maps (1,051 items) used by the War Records Office in compiling the *Atlas To Accompany the Official Records of the Union and Confederate Armies*, and published copies of the atlas; and maps (97 items) relating to military operations in Africa, Greece, Korea, China, Cuba, Puerto Rico, and the Philippines, 1897-1902.

Audiovisual records (1,799 items) consist of photographs of Union and Confederate fortifications in Georgia, South Carolina, Tennessee, and Virginia, 1861-64; U.S. Christian Commission personnel, 1864-65; Lookout Mountain, Tenn., 1866; glaciers and geological formations near the Copper, Tanana, and Koyukuk Rivers in Alaska, 1885; the Spanish-American War and the Philippine Insurrection, 1898-1900, and the Mexican Punitive Expedition, 1916; rifle-firing positions, ca. 1900; and military activities, including aviation at Texas City, Tex., 1913. There are also recruiting posters, 1890-1925.

See Lucille H. Pendell and Elizabeth Bethel, comps., *Preliminary Inventory of the Records of the Adjutant General's Office*, PI 17 (1949).

Microfilm Publications: Included are the main series of letters sent and received, with registers and indexes, ca. 1780-1890; name and subject index to general correspondence, 1890-1917; returns of U.S. military posts and Regular Army organizational units, ca. 1780-1916; registers of Regular Army enlistments, 1798-1884; the Turner-Baker case files, 1861-66; and U.S. Military Academy cadet application papers, 1805-66, and other series of records relating to the Academy, 1812-67. Series of Record and Pension Office records include the name and subject index to general correspondence, 1889-1904; compiled service records of some Volunteer soldiers in the Mexican and Civil Wars; and most of the indexes to the compiled service records of Volunteer soldiers, 1812-1900. For a complete listing see the current *List of National Archives Microfilm Publications*.

RECORDS OF THE ADJUTANT GENERAL'S OFFICE, 1917– (RECORD GROUP 407)

The Adjutant General's Office (the earlier records of which have been allocated to Record Group 94) was given authority to assign, promote, transfer, retire, and discharge all Army officers and enlisted men under the National Defense Act of 1916. In 1942 the Adjutant General's Office was placed under the Commanding General, Services of Supply (later Army Service Forces). The above-mentioned responsibilities were transferred in 1946 to the General Staff and in 1947 assigned to the Department of the Army Deputy Chief of Staff for Personnel.

The AGO, as part of the Army Special Staff, has responsibility for administrative services, the Army personnel statistical and accounting system, records management, publications, postal services, and special and heraldic services of the Army. Its duties include developing data processing systems, maintaining personnel records, and administering the nonunit Ready Reserve, Standby Reserve, and the Retired Reserve.

There are 21,789 cubic feet of records dated between 1905 and 1958 in this record group.

DECIMAL FILES. 1917-54.
6,636 lin. ft. and 5,335 rolls of microfilm.

Beginning July 1, 1917, many records of Department of War and Department of the Army offices—including those of the Adjutant General, the Secretary of War, and the Chief of Staff—were filed together. The records consist of classified and unclassified decimal files, including "cut-offs" and "projects," and indexes, some on microfilm.

ORDERS. 1911-47. 450 lin. ft.

These records comprise general, special, and general court-martial orders, memorandums, and directives of the Department of War, the Department of the Army, and posts, camps, stations, schools, and other installations, 1911-42, but chiefly 1922-39. There are also general, special, and movement orders (in WNRC) issued by Army installations overseas and in the Zone of Interior, 1939-47.

RECORDS RELATING TO PERSONNEL. 1905-52. 171 lin. ft.

The records consist of work permits, memorandums, applications, and correspondence relating to employment, claims, and AGO personnel, 1917-40; reports of field inspections, 1941-47; publicity material used in the World War II recruiting and training program, 1942-50; correspondence, with cross-reference sheets, 1949-52; correspondence and files (in WNRC) relating to general officer promotions, 1914-51; and applications (in WNRC) for service medals and awards, 1905-51. Records of the Committee on the Classification of Personnel consist of correspondence, test papers, memorandums, circulars, charts, and other training material relating to Army personnel classification, 1917-19.

RECORDS RELATING TO U.S. DISCIPLINARY AND INTERNMENT FACILITIES. 1912-52. 151 lin. ft. and 61 rolls of microfilm.

The records of disciplinary facilities are administered by the Adjutant General through commanding officers. These records consist of reports, special court-martial orders, and correspondence on administration of disciplinary barracks and internment camps at Fort McPherson and Fort Oglethorpe, Ga., Fort Douglas, Utah, Governors Island, N.Y., and Alcatraz, Calif., 1916-40; case files ("201 files") of prisoners of war and imprisoned enemy aliens, 1917-19; and status reports (in WNRC) on these men, 1912-52. Records up to 1939 are on 61 rolls of microfilm.

RECORDS RELATING TO NATIONAL GUARD UNITS. 1916-18. 286 lin. ft.

These consist of orders, sick reports, circulars, rosters, payroll vouchers, and correspondence concerning recruits, promotions, and furloughs.

CABLEGRAMS. 1914-36. 416 lin. ft.

These consist of indexed World War I cablegrams and radiograms received and sent, relating to the American Expeditionary Forces, the Air Service, military attaches and other U.S. representatives in foreign countries, and war risk insurance records.

RECORDS RELATING TO RECRUITING STATIONS, DEPOTS, OFFICES, AND COMPANIES. 1916-22. 246 lin. ft.

These comprise orders, reports, rosters, applications, memorandums, pay vouchers, and correspondence concerning recruitments, transfers, furloughs, pay allotments, and discharges.

PUBLICATIONS. 1917-54. 500 lin. ft

These comprise sets of the Department of War and Department of the Army publications, 1917-54 (those dated after 1944 in WNRC); unpublished, undated manuscripts of foreign-language military dictionaries; and minutes of the Army Publication Board, 1945-53.

STRENGTH RETURNS AND STATISTICAL TABULATIONS. 1921-54. 1,576 lin. ft.

These records consist of monthly strength returns showing changes in unit strength and records of events, 1921-39; and statistics relating to casualties, prisoners of war, civilian internees, Reserve status, civilian and military strength, and personnel matters, 1940-54.

RECORDS RELATING TO THE U.S. MILITARY ACADEMY. 1920-52. 8 lin. ft.

Included are birth and death certificates, accident reports, cadet ratings, detachment and court-martial orders, lists of graduates and men nominated for Regular Army appointments, compensation claims, Post Exchange Council minutes, and correspondence.

RECORDS RELATING TO THE MILITARY SUPPORT OF THE CIVILIAN CONSERVATION CORPS (CCC). 1933-43. 450 lin. ft.

The CCC was established in 1933 to provide employment in construction and public works. It also contributed to forest protection and national defense programs. These records consist of correspondence and records relating to the location and strength of camps, personnel assignments, construction, medical facilities, fiscal matters, and disposition of excess property.

REPORT FILES. 1941-54. 10,791 lin. ft.

World War II operations reports (in WNRC), 1940-48 (8,219 lin. ft.), contain summaries of events, journals, and supporting documents, with an index. Korean command reports, 1949-54, consist of after-action reports, war diaries, reports of combat and service units, and journals, with supporting documents and indexes, on Army operations in Korea. Foreign (occupied) area reports, 1941-

54, concern economics, education, intelligence work, and natural resources in the Far East; and civil affairs and military government in occupied areas, with an index.

RECORDS OF THE SPECIAL SERVICES DIVISION. 1946-50.
44 lin. ft.

This Division performs special services outlined by the AGO, supervises operation of service clubs, and plans other entertainment; it also administers funds and distributes special services supplies and equipment. The records consist of minutes, reports, correspondence, and other documents relating to Division activities. Other records of the Division and its predecessors are among the records of the Headquarters Army Service Forces (see RG 160) and the War Department General and Special Staffs (see RG 165).

RECORDS OF THE ARMY-AIR FORCE POSTAL SERVICE HEADQUARTERS. 1942-54.
19 lin. ft. and 29 rolls of microfilm.

This Service, established in 1942 as the Army Postal Service, was renamed the Army-Air Force Postal Service Headquarters in 1949. There are administrative and policy records relating to the postal system for the military and for civilians in occupied areas, the courier service for security-classified documents, and logs on microfilm (29 rolls) of V-mail received and sent, 1942-45. Many of the wartime records are in the AGO central files.

OTHER RECORDS. 1917-58.
97 lin. ft.

These include an office file of Secretary of War Newton D. Baker, 1917-

19; a command list of officers of and other records concerning the American Expeditionary Forces, 1917-23; John A. Hillman's correspondence and records relating to publication of *The Tactical Operations of the 78th Division*, 1923-26; an office file of the Chief, Miscellaneous Division, 1923-27; and records of the Records Administration Branch, 1941-54, and the Departmental Records Branch, 1942-58.

CARTOGRAPHIC AND AUDIOVISUAL RECORDS. 1918-46.
14,476 items.

Cartographic records (4,950 items) comprise a copy of the order-of-battle map maintained in the American Expeditionary Forces General Headquarters, 1918; a list of subdivisions of Belgium, 1926; topographic, tactical, and strategic maps relating to overseas operations of U.S. forces in World War II; and captured German, Italian, and Japanese topographic and military maps, 1941-45.

Still pictures (9,500 items) consist of photographs and watercolors illustrating the history of certain military units, 1940-46; aerial photographs of the Philippine Islands taken during World War II; charts used for teaching chemical warfare defense, 1942; and photographs of members of the American Expeditionary Forces, 1918-19, and military activities in Europe and North Africa, 1925-27. Also included are sound recordings (26 items) of the opening exercises at the Army Administration Officer Training Schools at the North Dakota Agricultural College and at Grinnell, Iowa, 1942, and of accounts of combat experiences by Army and Air Force personnel, 1941-45.

RECORDS OF THE OFFICE OF THE CHIEF OF ENGINEERS
(RECORD GROUP 77)

The Corps of Engineers, U.S. Army, was established by an act of March 16, 1802, to organize a military academy at West Point. Orders of April 3, 1818, which directed the Chief Engineer as the Corps commanding officer to fix his headquarters at Washington, D.C., resulted in the establishment of the Office of the Chief of Engineers (OCE) in the War Department. In 1818 the Army topographical engineers were placed under the Chief's supervision; they were transferred in 1831 to the jurisdiction of the Topographical Bureau when it was established in the War Department. River and harbor improvement work was shared by the Corps of Engineers and the Corps of Topographical Engineers, which had acquired corps status in 1838, until the Topographical Bureau was abolished in 1863 and its personnel and functions were again placed under OCE supervision.

OCE's military responsibilities have included supervising the U.S. Military Academy (removed from its sole jurisdiction in 1866), producing and distributing Army maps, building roads, planning camps, and constructing and repairing fortifications and other installations. Civil duties have included maintaining and improving inland waterways and harbors, formulating and executing plans for flood control, operating dams and locks, constructing and maintaining Alaskan roads, caring for public buildings and grounds in the District of Columbia, and approving plans for the construction of bridges, wharves, piers, and other works over navigable waters.

There are 9,763 cubic feet of records dated between 1776 and 1968 in this record group.

GENERAL RECORDS. 1789-1942.
9,026 lin. ft.

Included are letters received, with registers and indexes, and letters sent, with indexes, by the central office, 1789-1870, and by central office divisions, relating to explorations, surveys, mapping, rivers, harbors, general administration, fortifications, accounts, property returns, and claims, 1870-86. Letters received and sent, with record cards and indexes, relating to civil affairs,

1890-1923; correspondence concerning military affairs, 1918-23 (in WNRC); and correspondence, with record cards and indexes, relating to civil works, rivers, harbors, district and other field offices, bridge construction, boats, and permits, 1923-42 (in WNRC).

Also included are annual reports, 1842-67; corps and battalion monthly returns, compendiums and digests, engineer orders, circulars, and other issuances; Chief of Engineers Col. Joseph G. Totten's letters and reports, 1803-64; letters sent by John C. Wrenshall as the chief engineer and receiver for the Danville and New River Railroad Co., 1887-1907, and documents he collected as a civil engineer and a Confederate engineer officer, 1858-94; field survey records, 1793-1916; field notes from Department of the Interior boundary surveys, 1854-77; a name and subject index to Bureau correspondence, 1789-1889; Herbert L. Buell's collection of historical engineer papers, 1801-19; a historical reference file, 1894-1923; and records of Capt. Oberlin M. Carter, who was in charge of river and harbor improvements and fortifications in Georgia and Florida, 1889-97. Also included (in WNRC) are a history of Camp A. A. Humphreys, Va.; civil works projects pamphlets; and charts showing the origin, authorization, and mobilization of engineer units during World War I.

RECORDS RELATING TO VARIOUS FUNCTIONS. 1790-1945.
636 lin. ft.

There are records relating to lands, 1790-1916, that include letters sent, with indexes; records that concern land for military installations, including deeds of cessions, purchase agreements, and a register of title documents; and other land records, 1794-1916. Also records concerning Government roads, 1806-43, including road superintendents' administrative and technical reports; claim, construction, repair, and fund estimate reports; letter books; letters received and their registers; miscellaneous correspondence; and agreements, contracts, and fiscal records relating to the Cumberland, the Chicago, and the New Orleans Roads. Records that relate to fortifications and other defenses include reports, correspondence, and blueprints, 1810-1920; and mobilization plan files, a security-classified decimal file, a geographic file, and an unclassified decimal file concerning harbor defenses, 1918-45.

Records relating to property and procurement, 1816-1923, consist of quarterly returns, inventories, and procurement studies concerning engineering equipment (in WNRC). Those relating to contracts, 1817-1932, include registers of contracts and contracts for equipment, buildings, timber, and other commodities and services. Records concerning internal improvements, 1818-39, consist of reports, letters, and plans. Records of fiscal matters, 1819-1933, comprise registers of requisitions for funds and disbursements and appropriation ledgers, including civil works appropriation ledgers (in WNRC). Personnel records, 1820-1918, include officers' personal reports, engineer officers' military service registers, and a register of projects assigned to engineer officers. Records relating to public works and buildings in the District of Columbia, 1852-1919, include letters and registers of letters received concerning the Washington aqueduct, Potomac waterworks, and Capitol extension. Records of claims, 1862-92, include registers and related records primarily concerning payrolls. In addition, there is a correspondence file relating to electric power, 1917-20 (in WNRC).

RECORDS OF SUBORDINATE UNITS OF THE CENTRAL OFFICE. 1818-1955. 745 lin. ft.

Records of the Topographical Bureau consist of issuances, letter books and indexes, registers of letters received, letters received, and returns of the Bureau central office and its predecessors, 1818-67, and of Bureau field offices, 1833-61, including the Office of Public Works, Chicago Harbor; Office of Harbor Improvements on Lake Erie; Office of Ohio River Improvement; Office of Improvements on the Western Rivers; Office of Military Roads, Pacific Coast; and Topographical Engineers Office, Oswego, N.Y. Letter books, letters received, and accounting records of the U.S. Lake Survey, 1845-1913; correspondence of the Office of Explorations and Surveys, 1857-61; and letter books, fieldbooks, field reports, topographic atlas sheets, and other records of the Office of U.S. Geographical Surveys West of the One Hundredth Meridian, 1869-83.

Records (in WNRC) of other units include those of the Construction Division, 1890-1945, consisting of historical records of buildings; completion, utility, and annual reports; histories of the Division; drawings; plans; sketches; fieldbooks; and sales correspondence, agreements, certificates, and reports of the Real Estate Branch. General correspondence and other records of the Administrative and Special Service Divisions of the Military Branch, 1917-23; general correspondence, engineer officers' personal files, statistical reports, contracts, and miscellaneous correspondence of the Office of the Director General of Military Railways, 1917-19; general correspondence, 1929-31, and plans, estimates, drawings, and reports, 1939-40, of the Nicaraguan canal surveys; and correspondence relating to military real estate and military construction project maps and drawings of the Planning and Control Division, 1900-1955.

RECORDS OF ENGINEER BOARDS AND COMMISSIONS. 1824-1954. 329 lin. ft.

Included are letters of the Board on

Internal Improvements, 1824-31, the Board of Engineers for Fortifications, 1825-30, the Board on River and Harbor Improvements, 1851-53, and the Board of Engineers for the Pacific Coast, 1851-58; proceedings, reports, letter books, letters received, general correspondence, and disbursement accounts of the Board of Engineers, 1866-1920; proceedings of the Board of Engineers on the Washington City Canal, 1866; miscellaneous records of the "Endicott Board," 1885-87; and proceedings, reports, general correspondence, and correspondence relating to estimates, allotments, and supplies of the New York Harbor Line Board, 1888-1936. Also included is general correspondence of the Missouri River Commission, 1900-1902. Additional records (in WNRC) include minutes, reports, letter books, and other records of the Board of Engineers for Rivers and Harbors, 1902-54; general correspondence of the Board on Engineer Equipment, 1911-41; minutes, reports, correspondence, and claims case files of the Engineer Claims Board, 1918-21; investigation plans and reports of the Board of Flood Control, 1928-29; reports, studies, and correspondence of the Beach Erosion Board, 1930-47; and letters received and sent and a general correspondence file of the Mississippi River Commission, 1871-1928, and its special reports and general correspondence, 1918-42.

RECORDS OF ENGINEER DISTRICTS. 1807-1944. 2,351 lin. ft.

Expansion of the OCE's river and harbor improvement work after the Civil War necessitated the establishment of additional engineer offices throughout the United States. The engineer officer in charge of each reported directly to the Chief of Engineers. In 1888 several engineer divisions were created, each with administrative jurisdiction over several engineer district offices.

Records, 1807-1944, include administrative records, contract and project files, field notebooks, general correspondence, fiscal records (journals, ledgers, account books, and vouchers), and project, time, commerce, traffic, boat, river, and weather reports. District offices for which there are records include those at Charleston, Jacksonville (subordinate offices at Fort Clinch, Fort Taylor, Key West, and Tampa), Memphis, Mobile, Nashville, Vicksburg, and Wilmington, N.C. (in FRC Atlanta); Portland (subordinate offices at Bonneville, Florence, Fort Canby, Fort Columbia, and Fort Stevens) and Seattle (in FRC Seattle); Boston and Providence (subordinate offices at New London and Newport) (in FRC Waltham); Baltimore, Washington, Norfolk, and Huntington (in WNRC); Kansas City, Omaha, St. Louis, and St. Paul (in FRC Kansas City); Philadelphia (in FRC Philadelphia); San Francisco and Honolulu (in FRC San Francisco); New Orleans (in FRC Fort Worth); and Buffalo, Oswego, New York, Cincinnati, Detroit, Louisville, and Rock Island.

RECORDS OF THE MANHATTAN ENGINEER DISTRICT. 1942-48. 50 lin. ft.

The records of this District, associated with the development of the atomic bomb, consist of project and investigation files; directives; general correspondence; biographical records; a fiscal and audit file, with certificate of audit registers; auditors' working papers; schedules of property audits; and general audit, foreign intelligence, and personnel files. Also included is the general correspondence of two special assistants to Secretary of War Stimson—George Harrison and Harvey H. Bundy—which relate to this project.

RECORDS OF ENGINEER DIVISIONS. 1888-1940. 29 lin. ft.

Engineer divisions, each having administrative jurisdiction over several engineer districts, were first created in 1888. The records include minutes, reports, letter books, letters received and their registers, and general correspondence of the Gulf of Mexico (in FRC Atlanta); North Pacific (in FRC Seattle); Pacific (in FRC San Francisco); Western and Upper Mississippi (in FRC Kansas City); Chesapeake (in WNRC); and Northeast, Eastern Ohio River, Lakes, and Central Divisions.

CARTOGRAPHIC RECORDS. 1790–1968. 270,402 items.

These consist of headquarters records, including the "published record set," an incomplete set of maps and atlases published under OCE direction, 1804–1960; the "headquarters map file," composed primarily of manuscript maps prepared by the Corps of Engineers and the Corps of Topographical Engineers, relating to civil works, boundary surveys, explorations and surveying expeditions in the Western United States, harbor and coastal surveys, and military campaigns, including the Seminole wars in Florida, the wars with western Indians, and the Mexican and Civil Wars, 1800–1935; the "fortifications map files," composed of manuscript, annotated, and photoprocessed maps and plans, primarily of permanent coastal forts and camps in the United States and its territories and possessions, 1790–1941; and the "miscellaneous fortification file," composed of maps and plans of inland forts and camps located in the Western United States, many of which were temporary installations, 1840–1900.

Records of field agencies responsible for carrying out OCE military surveys and internal improvement activities and for most of the actual mapping and map reproduction work include published general and topographic maps of many land areas of the world, compiled by the Army Map Service (AMS), 1942–68, and its predecessors, especially the Central Map Reproduction Plant, 1917–19, and

the Engineer Reproduction Plant, 1919–42. Other AMS records include the "War Department map collection," which originated ca. 1895 in the Military Information Division of the Adjutant General's Office as the "General Staff map collection" and is composed of domestic and foreign operations and campaign maps, 1836–1942.

There are manuscript, published, and photoprocessed maps and plans prepared or collected by engineer divisions and districts, relating chiefly to internal improvement and construction activities, 1829–1958; an incomplete set of hydrographic charts published by the U.S. Lake Survey, 1850–1958; and maps and charts of the Mississippi and Missouri River Commissions, 1876–96, the Interoceanic Canal Board, 1929–31, the Board of Engineers for Rivers and Harbors, 1940–49, and the Beach Erosion Board, 1941–42.

AUDIOVISUAL RECORDS. ca. 1776–1948. 70,946 items.

These consist of illustrations of military facilities, equipment, and activities, including U.S. Army barracks and officers quarters, 1776–1927; buildings, fortifications, coastal defenses, and equipment at camps, posts, and stations in the United States, Europe, Cuba, Puerto Rico, the Panama Canal Zone, and the Philippine Islands, 1850–1941; Union and Confederate fortifications and other installations; ships, models of ordnance, the experimental firing of ordnance, and surveying equipment, 1863–89; bridge and road construction, 1879–99 and 1918–41; and Army maneuvers, war games, and engineering and ordnance drills, 1901–19. Included are portraits and portrait photographs of Chiefs of Engineers and other engineer officers, 1789–1884 and 1935–39.

There are also photographs of lighthouses, 1827–79; the drawings and plans for and the construction and completion of civil projects, including the Washington aqueduct, 1857-84; river, harbor, flood control, and navigational improvements and related Works Progress Administration projects, 1867-1946; U.S. public buildings, monuments, and parkways, 1868-1916; the U.S. Observatory at Ogden, Utah Territory, 1875; the International Exhibition at Philadelphia, 1876; the activities of the International Boundary Commission and monuments marking the United States-Mexican boundary, 1892-94; bridges, buildings, and roads in and near St. Thomas and London, Canada, 1896-97; areas in other countries, including Vladivostok and vicinity in Russia, China during the China Relief Expedition, and the Philippine Islands, 1900-1926; effects of the San Francisco earthquake, 1906; water diversion investigations on the Niagara River, 1906 and 1917; the proposed area for a Georgian Bay, Canada, ship canal, 1908-9; and the raising of the battleship *Maine* off Havana, Cuba, 1910-13.

Photographs of the members of and territory explored by War Department expeditions and surveys include those of the Geological Exploration of the Fortieth Parallel, 1867-80, U.S. explorations and surveys west of the 100th meridian, 1871-74, Gen. George A. Custer's Black Hills reconnaissance, 1874, and the Orinoco-Casiquiare-Negro waterway survey in Venezuela, Colombia, and Brazil, 1943; photographs made by the U. S. Geological and Geographical Survey of the Territories, Department of the Interior, 1869-78, and the U.S. Naval Expedition and Survey for an Isthmus of Darien ship canal, 1870-74; photographs used in ordnance and engineering training, 1900-1934; and recruiting posters, 1918-20.

See Laura E. Kelsay and Charlotte M. Ashby, comps., *Cartographic Records Relating to the Territory of Wisconsin, 1836-1848*, SL 23 (1970).

Microfilm Publications: For a complete listing see the current *List of National Archives Microfilm Publications*.

RECORDS OF THE OFFICE OF THE INSPECTOR GENERAL (RECORD GROUP 159)

The Inspector General's Department of the Army was created by an act of March 3, 1813, although an inspector general for the Continental Army was authorized as early as July 1777. In 1863 the Adjutant General directed the Inspector General at Washington to receive monthly reports from all inspectors concerning their stations and activities, and in 1864 the office thus established was given responsibility for the receipt of all inspection reports, which previously had been submitted to the Commanding General or the Adjutant General. The Inspector General inspects, investigates, and reports on all matters affecting the efficiency, discipline, and welfare of the Army. The Office of the Inspector General is now an element of the Department of the Army Special Staff.

Records of the Office of the Inspector General include those of the Inspector General's Department.

There are 2,520 cubic feet of records dated between 1814 and 1954 in this record group.

INSPECTION REPORTS. 1814-1939. 1,040 lin. ft.

Included are reports of the Inspectors General to the Commanding General of the Army, 1814-36 and 1842; and reports on posts, depots, and other installations of the Army, on cemeteries, and on the National Home for Disabled Volunteer Soldiers, 1898-1914. There is a separate series of reports (in WNRC) of annual general inspections of all posts, camps, and stations in the continental United States and territories, 1912-39, which comprises a section, set up in 1917 and separately maintained, of the central decimal files (file classification 333.1) of the Office of the Inspector General. There are also miscellaneous inspection reports, 1863-1917; those for the period 1863-97 are among the Inspector General's letters received, and some for the period 1914-17 are in general correspondence files. Inspection reports for the period 1842-63 are not among the records of the Office of the Inspector General.

GENERAL RECORDS. 1863-June 1954. 1,445 lin. ft.

These consist largely of letters received, 1863-1914, in which are included the 1863-97 inspection reports, general and special orders, and miscellaneous correspondence; and letters sent, 1863-1910. There are reports, general correspondence, and reference files, 1914-17,

on complaints, investigations, inspections, departmental organization, and related matters; and central decimal files (with indexes), both classified and unclassified, of the Office of the Inspector General, 1917-June 1954, which include correspondence, the 1939-54 inspection reports, issuances, and intraoffice memorandums (in WNRC).

OTHER RECORDS. 1863-1915. 21 lin. ft.

Included are miscellaneous precedent and decision files, efficiency reports on officers and enlisted men, records relating to special investigations and inquiries, some financial records of the National Home for Disabled Volunteer Soldiers, 1891-1914, and a list of inspectors before 1864.

Microfilm Publication: *Inspection Reports of the Office of the Inspector General, 1814-1842*, M624, 3 rolls, DP.

RECORDS OF THE OFFICE OF THE CHIEF OF ORDNANCE (RECORD GROUP 156)

The Ordnance Department was established as an independent bureau of the Department of War by an act of May 14, 1812. It lost its independent status in March 1821 when it was merged with the artillery, but regained it under an act of April 5, 1832. It retained its status in the War Department and the Department of the Army until it was abolished and its functions transferred to the U.S. Army Materiel Command during a 1962 Department of the Army reorganization. Throughout the period of its existence, the functions of the Ordnance Department were the procurement and distribution to the Army of ordnance and equipment, the maintenance and repair of equipment, and the development and testing of new types of ordnance.

There are 11,094 cubic feet of records

dated between 1797 and 1953 in this record group.

GENERAL RECORDS. 1797-1915. 3,894 lin. ft.

Included are reports, letters, issuances, and endorsements sent, with accompanying indexes; registers of letters received, with accompanying indexes; letters received; general correspondence, with accompanying index and record cards; and target firing reports.

GENERAL RECORDS. 1915-41. 3,597 lin. ft. (in WNRC).

These consist of reports; issuances; general correspondence, with accompanying indexes; special correspondence series relating to inventions, patents, and operation reports; and drawings, plans, and diagrams of weapons.

RECORDS RELATING TO
VARIOUS SUBJECTS. 1808-1939.
132 lin. ft.

Records relating to ordnance property
consist of contracts, statements, registers, and ledgers concerning requirements, procurement, and production,
1812-1918, and production studies and
analyses, 1917-39 (in WNRC); statements and registers relating to distribution, 1808-1914, and statements of ordnance stock on hand, 1920-29 (in
WNRC); digests of decisions and regulations relating to property accountability,
1875-1916; and journals, registers, and
correspondence relating to the disposition of ordnance property, 1864-1914.

Fiscal records consist of estimates,
statements, and ledgers concerning
appropriations; registers and requisitions of funds; statements and registers
of disbursements, 1812-1913, and ledgers relating to disbursements, 1917-21
(in WNRC); and statements, ledgers,
registers, and journals relating to money
accounts, 1817-1905, 1917-20 (in
WNRC), and 1937-38 (in WNRC). Personnel records consist of strength
returns, registers, and military service
histories of ordnance officers, 1812-1922.

Records relating to inventions consist
of registers of letters received, with an
index, and letters sent, 1812-1929.
Records relating to experiments consist
of registers of correspondence and
reports, with indexes, 1812-1913. Those
relating to mineral lands consist of letters sent, leases, and other records,
1821-60. Those relating to inspections
consist of registers of reports and inspection reports, 1826-1918. Those relating to claims consist of registers, with
an index, 1846-93; and correspondence
concerning a claim of Bethlehem Steel
Corp. employees, and exhibits supporting claims of the Winchester Repeating
Arms Co., 1920-39 (in WNRC).

RECORDS OF ORDNANCE
BOARDS. 1846-1925. 512 lin. ft.

These consist of proceedings, letters
sent, correspondence, and other records
of ordnance boards, 1846-68, boards of
examination, 1863-74, Board on the Proposed New Building for the War Department, 1866-69, Board on Heavy Ordnance, 1872, Army Equipment Board,
1878-79, Board for Testing Rifled Cannon, 1884-1915, Ordnance Board, 1892-
1919, Board on Powders and High
Explosives, 1897-98, Small Arms and
Ammunition Board, 1900, Board for
Testing the Experimental Springfield
Rifle, 1903, and Cavalry Equipment
Board, 1912. Also included are records
(in WNRC) consisting of minutes and
correspondence, reports, case files, and
issuances of the Artillery Ammunition
Board, 1918, Ordnance Department
Claims Board and Ordnance Section of
the War Department Claims Board,
1918-25, Gillespie Explosion Investigation and Claims Boards, 1918-21, Board
of Contract Adjustment, 1919-21, Ordnance Salvage Board, 1919-23, Interdepartmental Board of Contracts and
Adjustments, 1922-25, and Joint Board
of Survey of the War and Justice
Departments, 1923-25.

RECORDS OF ORDNANCE
DEPARTMENT UNITS. 1861-1922.
2,929 lin. ft.

Included are letters sent, registers of
letters received, and correspondence of
the Office of the Inspector of Artillery,
1861-67, and the Inspection, 1861-70,
Construction, 1863-70, Returns, 1865-69,
Correspondence and Examining, 1899-
1905, Small Arms and Equipment, 1899-
1911, and Property, 1901-3, Divisions.
The bulk (2,927 lin. ft., in WNRC) of
the records consist of general correspondence (with indexes), special correspondence series, office files, and technical and historical reports of the
Carriage, 1916-18, Nitrate, 1916-22,
Administration, 1917-22, American Base

Depot in France, 1917-18, Engineering, 1917-19, Equipment, 1917-18, Gun, 1917-18, Inspection, 1917-19, Procurement, 1917-19, Production, 1917-18, Small Arms, 1917-18, Supply, 1917-19, Explosives and Loading, 1918-19, and Motor, 1918-19, Divisions, and the Executive Section, 1917-20.

RECORDS OF ORDNANCE DEPARTMENT UNITS. 1917-53. 5,564 lin. ft. (in WNRC).

These consist of minutes; reports; general correspondence; reference, case, historical, project, and research and development files; and histories of the War Plans Division; staff divisions; Military Plans and Training, Field, Manufacturing, Industrial, and Research and Development Services; Technical Staff; and Office of the Chief of Ordnance at Detroit.

MISCELLANEOUS RECORDS. 1812-1941. 226 lin. ft.

Included are an Ordnance Department "special file," 1812-1912, reference aids, 1817-1933, and other records (in WNRC), 1816-1903 and 1915-41.

RECORDS OF ARSENALS AND ARMORIES. 1794-1944. 3,427 lin. ft.

Included are letters, telegrams, and endorsements sent; registers of letters received; letters received; general correspondence; reports and returns; and issuances of Allegheny Arsenal, Pa., 1813-1902; Augusta Arsenal, Ga., 1825-50, 1865-1917, 1917-20 (in WNRC), and 1925-39 (in WNRC); Bellona Arsenal, Va., 1831-56; Benicia Arsenal, Calif., 1846-23 and 1938-41 (in WNRC); Champlain Arsenal, Vt., 1828-65; Columbia Arsenal, Tenn., 1889-1904; Fort Monroe Arsenal, Va., 1824-1901; Frankford Arsenal, Pa., 1816-1917 and 1917-43 (in WNRC); Indianapolis Arsenal, Ind., 1871 and 1902-3; Kennebec Arsenal, Maine, 1831-1901; Picatinny Arsenal, N.J., 1918 and 1925-41 (in WNRC); Raritan Ar-

senal, N.J., 1918-19 (in WNRC) and 1930-39 (in WNRC); Rock Island Arsenal, Ill., 1865-1916, 1918 (in WNRC), and 1938-39 (in WNRC); San Antonio Arsenal, Tex., 1865-1904; Springfield Armory, Mass., 1794-1915, 1916-20 (in WNRC), and 1925-39 (in WNRC); Watertown Arsenal, Mass., 1820-1916 and 1916-44 (in WNRC); and Watervliet Arsenal, N.Y., 1818-1915 and 1915-39 (in WNRC).

RECORDS OF ORDNANCE PROVING GROUNDS. 1889-1941. 505 lin. ft.

These consist of letter books, registers of letters received, letters received, general correspondence, reports and returns, issuances, and other records of proving grounds at Aberdeen, Md., 1916-41 (in WNRC); Erie, Ohio, 1918-19; Sandy Hook, N.J., 1889-1915 and 1915-19 (in WNRC); Savanna, Ill., 1918-28 (in WNRC); and Scituate, Mass., 1918-21 (in WNRC).

RECORDS OF ORDNANCE DEPOTS. 1861-1939. 18 lin. ft.

Included are letters sent, general correspondence, and issuances of ordnance depots at Curtis Bay, Md., 1918-19 (in WNRC); Delaware, N.J., 1919-39 (in WNRC); Erie Ohio, 1918-46 (in WNRC); Havana, Cuba, 1898-1902; Hawaii, 1923-39 (in WNRC); Louisville, Ky., 1861-63; Middletown, Pa., 1918-19 (in WNRC); Nashville, Tenn., 1862-64 (in WNRC); Paterson, N.J., 1918 (in WNRC); Penniman, Va., 1919-23; Philadelphia, Pa., 1918-19 (in WNRC); Pig Point, Va., 1918-19 (in WNRC); Ponce, P.R., 1898-99; San Juan, P.R., 1898-1904; Sandy Hook, N.J., 1918-19 (in WNRC); Santiago, Cuba, 1898-1902; Savanna, Ill., 1928-39 (in WNRC); Tampa, Fla., 1898; Tobyhanna, Pa., 1918-19 (in WNRC); Tuckahoe, N.J., 1917-18 (in WNRC); and Wingate, N. Mex., 1919-20 (in WNRC).

RECORDS OF ORDNANCE DISTRICTS. 1917-46. 41 lin. ft.

These consist of minutes, reports, correspondence, and other records of ordnance districts with headquarters located in Baltimore, Birmingham, Boston, Bridgeport, Conn., Cincinnati, Cleveland, Detroit, New York, Philadelphia, Pittsburgh, Rochester, N.Y., and San Francisco.

RECORDS OF ORDNANCE INSPECTORS AT PRIVATE PLANTS. 1882-84, 1889-1907, 1912-14, and 1918-19. 8 lin. ft.

Included are records of inspectors stationed at plants, such as the American Ordnance Co., Bridgeport, Conn.; the Builders Iron Foundry, Providence, R.I.; and the Ravig Engineering Co., Columbus, Ohio.

RECORDS OF OTHER ORDNANCE FIELD OFFICES AND INSTALLATIONS. 1874-81 and 1918-19. 14 lin. ft.

These records are those of the Ordnance Camp at the Du Pont Engineering Co., Penniman, Va., 1918-19 (in WNRC); the Ordnance Training Center, Camp Hancock, Ga., 1918-19 (in WNRC); and the U.S. Ordnance Agency, New York, N.Y., 1874-81.

CARTOGRAPHIC AND AUDIOVISUAL RECORDS. 1845-1941. 65,392 items.

Cartographic records include a map of mineral lands adjacent to Lake Superior, 1845, and plans (4 items) of the Edgewood Arsenal Experimental Grounds, Md., and Sandy Hook Proving Grounds, N.J., 1908.

Audiovisual records include photographs (65,387 items) relating to ordnance testing and personnel training activities, made or collected by the Army Ordnance Corps at Aberdeen Proving Ground, Md., of buildings and facilities, motor transport material, armored vehicles, airplanes, technical and experimental equipment, guns and gun carriages, antiaircraft artillery, mechanized weapons, aerial bombs, ammunition, machineguns, armorplate, bomb shelters, and the maintenance and repair of ordnance materiel, 1917-41; small arms and ammunition, ca. 1879; and disappearing gun carriages and heavy artillery, 1897-98. There are also photographs of arsenals, including those at Washington, D.C., 1866; Benecia, Calif., 1899-1906; Rock Island, Ill., 1906-18; and Edgewood, Md., 1918. A collection of World War I photographs is of ordnance depots, schools, plants and equipment, and the 1919 transcontinental convoy. There are also photographs of the facilities and activities at the Muscle Shoals, Ala., nitrate plant, 1917-18; interior and exterior views of plants producing ordnance for the Army, 1917-19; and World War I posters.

RECORDS OF THE OFFICE OF THE QUARTERMASTER GENERAL (RECORD GROUP 92)

Until 1818 when the Congress created a Quartermaster's Department under a single Quartermaster General, quartermaster generals (the first of whom had been appointed by the Second Continental Congress on June 16, 1775) were regarded as field staff officers appointed in time of war to serve with the principal armies. The Quartermaster General ensured efficient systems of supply, movement of the Army, and accountability of officers and agents charged with moneys or supplies. The functions of the Office of the Commissary General of Purchases, established in 1812 at Philadelphia, were gradually transferred after 1818 to the Office of the Quartermaster General and to the Clothing Bureau, established in 1832 under the War Office. With the discontinuance of the Clothing Bureau in 1841 and the Office of the Commissary General of Purchases in 1842, their functions and records were transferred to the Office of the Quartermaster General and its field establishments. An act of August 24, 1912, combined the Subsistence (see RG 192), Pay, and Quartermaster's Departments to form the Quartermaster Corps of the Army headed by the Chief of the Quartermaster Corps, who in 1914 was redesignated Quartermaster General.

Although functions of the Office of the Quartermaster General were transferred during World War I to newly created independent units (including the Construction Division, Motor Transport Corps, Inland Transportation Service, and Embarkation Service) or were absorbed by the Office of the Director of Purchase and Storage, the Quartermaster General retained the supply operations of the supply bureaus as the Director of Purchase and Storage (part of the Purchase, Storage, and Traffic Division, War Department General Staff). The National Defense Act of June 4, 1920, restored to the Quartermaster Corps most of its former functions, including those of transportation and construction. The former pay function of the Office was placed in a separate Finance Department.

The transportation and construction functions were permanently removed from jurisdiction of the Quartermaster General during World War II, and in 1961 the quartermaster function of procuring food and clothing was transferred

to the Defense Supply Agency. Office functions of research and development and supply and distribution were delegated to the Army Materiel Command, and the remaining functions were transferred to the Army Combat Developments Command and the Continental Army Command. Department of the Army General Order 44 of July 23, 1962, abolished the Office of the Quartermaster General.

See Erna Risch, *Quartermaster Support of the Army; a History of the Corps, 1775-1939* (1962).

There are 22,942 cubic feet of records dated between 1792 and 1957 in this record group.

CENTRAL RECORDS. 1792-1926. 16,022 lin. ft.

There are letter books of quartermasters, inspection reports, and receipts, 1792-1814. Correspondence, 1818-90, consists of letter books, with indexes; registers of letters received, with indexes; letters received; and reports and general correspondence. Correspondence, 1890-1914, consists of a general correspondence file, with indexes, record cards, and special finding aids; and subject files that were formerly part of the general correspondence. Also included are issuances and annual reports, decision and precedent files, reference aids, a consolidated correspondence file, reports of persons and articles hired, and correspondence, certifications, applications, and serial lists relating to decorations and awards, 1905-26.

RECORDS OF OFFICERS. 1819-1916. 73 lin. ft.

These records consist of reports, returns, letter books, letters received, and financial and miscellaneous records of Quartermaster Generals and quartermasters.

OTHER GENERAL RECORDS. 1819-1915. 62 lin. ft.

There are letter books, issuances, correspondence, and other records of the quartermasters at Boston, 1819-38; the Headquarters Office Battalion, 1864-65; Headquarters, Relief of Sufferers From Floods in the Mississippi and Ohio Valleys, 1912-13; and boards and commissions, 1864-1915. Also records relating to bounty lands, 1855-63, the Mexican War, 1845-49, sutlers, 1863-65, and Office organization, 1865-1911.

PROGRAM RECORDS. 1818-1929. 5,020 lin. ft.

These include correspondence, expenditure lists and analyses, ledgers, estimates of funds, and other records relating to accounting and finance, 1818-1919.

Records that relate to cemeteries, 1828-1929, include letter books and registers of letters received, with indexes; letters received; reports and correspondence; applications for headstones; lists and registers of superintendents at national cemeteries; registers of burials; reports of inspections and estimates; correspondence and registers of cemeterial commissions, such as the Office of the Commissioner for Marking Graves of Confederate Dead, the Antietam Battlefield Commission, the Gettysburg National Military Park Commission, the Shiloh National Military Park Commission, and the Vicksburg National Military Park Commission; and miscellaneous burial records of the post quartermaster at Chattanooga, Tenn.

Claims records, 1839-1914, include correspondence, claims registers, and claims for regular, transportation, and miscellaneous claims; records of Confederate horse claims; registers and proceedings of claims boards, including the Militia Service in Florida, the California Claims Board, and Civil War claims boards; and claims correspondence of the Quartermaster General Depots at Jeffersonville, Ind., and Washington, D.C.

Records that relate to clothing and equipage, 1821-1914, include reports; correspondence, with indexes and record cards; estimates; registers of orders; and specifications. Records relating to construction and repair, 1819-1912, include reports; correspondence, with indexes and record cards; lists of authorized construction; building specifications; and correspondence of construction quartermasters. Inspection records, 1858-70, include reports; and letter books and registers of letters received, with indexes.

Personnel records, 1823-1916, include letter books, registers of letters and personal reports received, personnel reports and correspondence including personal histories of officers of the Quartermaster's Department, annual and personal narrative reports of quartermasters, registers of assignments, and lists and rosters of civilian and military personnel.

There are property and stores reports and returns, 1818-73; and correspondence, narrative histories, and plans relating to military reservations, 1888-1911. Records that relate to supplies include correspondence concerning contracts, proposals, and agreements; registers of contracts; and contracts, 1819-1914. Also reports; letter books; registers of letters received, with indexes; letters received; returns and specifications; and other records of purchase of public animals and regular supplies, 1836-1914.

Records relating to transportation include letter books; registers of letters received, with indexes; letters received; a "vessel file" containing charters, bills of lading, claims papers, plans, and correspondence; registers and lists of chartered vessels; and other miscellaneous records relating to ocean, lake, rail, and river transportation, 1834-1912. Records of the Office of U.S. Military Railroads consist of reports, letter books, letters received, journals, time rolls, payroll books, inventories, property reports, cashbooks, train orders, lists of employees, and miscellaneous records of central, Virginia, and Tennessee offices, 1860-67. Records of the Office of Indebted Railroads consist of letter books and registers of letters received, with indexes, and letters received, 1865-82. Records of the Army Transport Service consist of correspondence of the general, assistant general, and marine superintendents and other officers, as well as registers of officers and passengers, inward and outward cargo manifests, Army transport logs, registers of Army transport movements, and other records, 1898-1917.

RECORDS FOR THE PERIOD 1909-57. 12,228 lin. ft. (in WNRC).

These records consist of central office general correspondence files and subject, geographic, miscellaneous, commercial, and corps area correspondence files; Gold Star Mothers' and Widows' Pilgrimage to Europe correspondence, 1930-33; historical files and special reports; Cemeterial Division and Graves Registration Service correspondence, burial reports, lists, and registers, 1915-39; Control Service War Plans Division correspondence files, 1920-42; Construction Service completion reports, specifications, and fieldbooks, and its Real Estate Branch correspondence, contracts, agreements, leases, and deeds, 1916-38; and Motor Transport Division correspondence and issuances and Supplies Division registers of contracts and purchase orders, 1914-20.

There are Transportation Service central office correspondence files, an Inland Traffic Service correspondence file, an Embarkation Service correspondence file, and Army Transport Service registers of vessels, passenger lists, logs, and registers of arrivals and departures of vessels, 1909-41. Also selected records of several divisions of the Quartermaster's Department, 1941-

55, including records of the Quartermaster Heraldic Field Office, 1922-57.

FIELD RECORDS. 1795-1939. 4,838 lin. ft.

Although War Department General Order 13, issued in 1859, placed general quartermaster depots under general direction of the Quartermaster's Department, it gave commanders of geographical departments in which general depots were located some authority over them for command purposes. War Department General Order 32, issued in 1869, placed the general depots at New York, Philadelphia and Schuylkill Arsenal, Washington, D.C., and Jeffersonville, Ind., directly under the Quartermaster's Department, with officers in charge of depots reporting directly to the Quartermaster General. Subsequently, general depots were established at San Francisco and St. Louis. By the end of World War I there were 15 general supply depots, five subdepots, and three reserve depots under jurisdiction of the Quartermaster Corps. The records consist of reports, correspondence, bills, accounts current, statements, receipts, vouchers, and contracts of Philadelphia supply agencies (the Offices of the Purveyor of Public Supplies, Superintendent of Military Stores, Commissary General of Purchases, Army Clothing and Equipage, Military Storekeeper, the Military Agent, and the Clothing Establishment) that procured, stored, and distributed public supplies, chiefly for the Army, 1795-1858.

The records consist chiefly of correspondence and orders of quartermaster depots at Atlanta, 1918-22 (in WNRC), Boston, 1918-19 (in WNRC), Chicago (organization charts), 1917-19 (in WNRC), Galveston, Tex., 1917-19, Jeffersonville, Ind., 1878-1906, Los Angeles, 1918-21 (in WNRC), New York, 1863-1900, Omaha, 1917-20 (in WNRC), Philadelphia, 1857-1916 and 1917-22 (in WNRC), Pittsburgh, 1910-14, Red Bank,

N.J., 1918–19 (in WNRC), St. Louis, 1879–83, San Antonio, 1918–19 (in WNRC), San Francisco, 1874–75, Schuylkill Arsenal, 1858–1906, Seattle, 1917–39 (in WNRC), and Washington, 1861–1917.

There are also records (in WNRC) of the following specialized quartermaster depots and areas, consisting chiefly of correspondence and orders: Holabird (Baltimore), 1919–39, Normoyle (San Antonio), 1919–31, Reno (Fort Reno, Okla.), 1920–39, and Robinson (Fort Robinson, Nebr.), 1919–45. There are records for the following temporary depots or installations, also consisting mostly of correspondence and orders: port of embarkation at Hoboken, N.J., 1917–26 (in WNRC), Newark Quartermaster Terminal, 1918–19 (in WNRC), Newport News, Va., 1917–21 (in WNRC), Motor Transport General Supply Depot, Chicago, 1919–20 (in WNRC), Motor Transport Overhaul Park, Philadelphia, 1918–19 (in WNRC), Army Reserve Depot, Columbus, Ohio, 1918–19 (in WNRC), Army Reserve Depot, Schenectady, N.Y., 1918–19 (in WNRC), Quartermaster Supply Officer and General Depots, New York and Norfolk, Va., 1918–28 (in WNRC), and Port Tampa, Fla., and Savannah, Ga., 1898–99.

CARTOGRAPHIC RECORDS. 1820–1952. 10,038 items.

These include general maps of the United States, relating to transportation and supply; processed plans of military reservations and national cemeteries in the United States and its territories and possessions, 1903–17; general military maps and manuscript and annotated maps and plans of military installations, buildings, equipment, and expeditionary routes, 1820–1905; published and photo-processed maps of the United States, showing activities of the Construction Division and its predecessors, 1917–19; maps prepared by or for the Research Development Branch of the Military Planning Division, relating to world clothing zones, 1943–52; and published ground plans of American cemeteries established during World War I in France, England, and Belgium.

AUDIOVISUAL RECORDS. 1776–1938. 20,355 items.

These consist of photographs, drawings, color lithographs, watercolors, posters, and clippings from publications, illustrating activities of the Office of the Quartermaster General. Pictures of construction of Army facilities, including an explosives plant, camps, supply bases, airfields, barracks, storage depots, hospitals, and port terminals in the United States and abroad, 1917–36; installations, repairs, and projected sites for posts in the United States, the Philippine Islands, and Hawaii, 1887–1911; completed camps, fortifications, living quarters, hospitals, remount depots, and schools in the United States, U.S. territories, and Cuba, 1865–1924; national cemeteries in the United States, U.S. territories, Mexico, and Europe, 1881–1907 and 1919–22; national military parks, monuments, and tablets, 1891–1910; equipment, including tents, machinery, packs, packsaddles, wagons, ambulances, carts, and stretchers, 1878–1918; Army transports and ship machinery, 1899–1910; Army uniforms and designs for uniforms, 1779–1908; flags of Civil War military units, 1860–65; and Quartermaster exhibits at the World Columbian Exposition, 1893. There are illustrations of such overseas wartime services as procurement, storage, and distribution of equipment and supplies, and salvage, repair, and cemeterial services, 1917–19; Army and Marine Corps recruiting posters, 1910–16; and commemoration of the 75th anniversary of the Battle of Gettysburg, 1938. There are portraits and photographs of Quartermaster officers, 1776–1905; and photographs of personnel, 1865–1924, the fire after the San Francisco earthquake, 1906, and flooding in the Mississippi and Ohio Valleys, 1912.

RECORDS OF THE OFFICE OF THE PAYMASTER GENERAL (RECORD GROUP 99)

A Pay Department, headed by a Paymaster General, was first established by an act of April 24, 1816. As early as 1775 responsibility for the pay of troops had been placed on one official, but his status and duties varied considerably until an act of May 8, 1792, provided for a paymaster to reside near troop headquarters and receive from the Treasurer all money to be used for paying troops. The general system established in 1816 under the Pay Department continued until an act of August 24, 1912, abolished the Office of the Paymaster General and transferred troop payment to the Office of the Quartermaster General.

Some series of records continued for a time by the Office of the Quartermaster General are included in this record group.

There are 559 cubic feet of records (in WNRC) dated between 1791 and 1917 in this record group.

RECORDS. 1791–1917. 531 lin. ft.

These consist of correspondence and related records, 1799–1912, ledgers and other account books, 1791–1917, and personnel records, 1799–1914.

See Roland C. McConnell, comp., *Preliminary Inventory of the Records of the Office of the Paymaster General,* PI 9 (1948).

RECORDS OF THE OFFICE OF THE SURGEON GENERAL (ARMY) (RECORD GROUP 112)

An act of April 14, 1818, regulating the staff of the Army, provided for the establishment of the Office of the Surgeon General. Surgeons and mates had earlier served at posts or with regiments under the orders of the post or regimental commander, but they lacked a common head or organization. A War Department order of April 21, 1818, directed that thereafter all reports, returns, and communications relating to medical matters should be made to the Office of the Surgeon General. The Office is the headquarters of the Army Medical Department, whose mission is to maintain the health of the Army and to conserve its fighting strength. Components of the Service include the Medical Corps, the Dental Corps, the Veterinary Corps, the Medical Service Corps, the Army Nurse Corps, and the Army Medical Specialist Corps.

There are 4,500 cubic feet of records dated between 1775 and 1949 in this record group.

GENERAL CORRESPONDENCE. 1818–1946. 4,743 lin. ft.

For the period 1818–89 records consist of letters, endorsements, and telegrams sent, with accompanying indexes; registers of letters received and letters received; and correspondence relating to Army medical examining boards. For the period 1890–1917 there is general correspondence, with accompanying index and record cards. Records (in WNRC) for the period 1917–46 consist of unclassified and security-classified general correspondence, and unclassified and security-classified correspondence with military installations and units and with civilian organizations; "geographic files"; and correspondence relating to persons and firms.

REFERENCE AIDS. 1861–1948.
37 lin. ft.

These consist primarily of a "policy and precedent file."

ISSUANCES AND REPORTS. 1818–1949. 170 lin. ft.

Included are orders and circulars, 1818–1905, and orders, circular letters, memorandums, and bulletins, 1917–49 (in WNRC). Also included are sanitary and inspection reports, 1890–99 and 1914–16, and annual and monthly reports of sick and wounded, 1867–1917.

OTHER GENERAL RECORDS.
1775–1947. 544 lin. ft.

Records relating to military personnel include lists, registers, personal histories, case files of candidates, military service cards, and strength returns of both Regular Army personnel and Volunteer and Reserve officers. Records relating to civilian personnel include registers, lists, rosters, monthly returns, and service data cards.

Records relating to fiscal matters include estimates; requisitions for funds; ledgers, registers, and abstracts of disbursements; money accounts; daybooks of claims; registers of approved claims; claims; and contracts. Records relating to medical property and supplies consist of registers of property returns and of sales of medical property. Among records relating to hospitals are registers of hospital staffs, lists of hospitals, and registers of construction and repair of post hospitals.

RECORDS OF SUBORDINATE ADMINISTRATIVE UNITS. 1873–1947. 101 lin. ft.

Included are letters sent, registers, and reports of the Finance, Property, Finance and Supply, Sanitary and Disbursing, Supply, Hospital Corps, and Personnel Divisions, 1873–1915. Also included are unclassified and security-classified general correspondence, issuances, special correspondence series, diaries, reports, and other records of the Organization, Hospital, Nursing, Purchase, Medical Statistics, Military Personnel, International, Legal, Technical Information, Training, Medical Consultants, Mobilization and Overseas Operations, and Office Service Divisions, and of the Professional Administrative and Operations Services, 1917–47 (in WNRC).

RECORDS OF ARMY MEDICAL EXAMINING BOARDS. 1862–96.
3 lin. ft.

These records consist of letters sent, proceedings and minutes of meetings, letters received, and reports of examinations.

RECORDS OF MEDICAL DEPARTMENT FIELD INSTALLATIONS. 1859–1939.
608 lin. ft. (in WNRC).

Included are letters sent; letters received, with registers; general correspondence; issuances; medical case files; returns; and other records of the general hospitals at Hot Springs, Ark., San Francisco, Calif., Fort Bayard, N. Mex., and Washington, D.C.; and of medical supply depots and some miscellaneous installations.

CARTOGRAPHIC AND AUDIOVISUAL RECORDS. 1914–49.
1,116 items.

Cartographic records consist of photoprocessed maps (4 items) of the United States, showing mobilization schemes for sanitary equipment, 1914.

Audiovisual records (1,112 items) consist of photographs of Army Medical Corps activities in Europe, 1943–46, and the celebration of the 48th anniversary of the Army Nurse Corps, 1949.

RECORDS OF THE
OFFICE OF THE COMMISSARY GENERAL OF SUBSISTENCE
(RECORD GROUP 192)

The Subsistence Department was established in the War Department by an act of April 14, 1818, to purchase and issue all subsistence, but no other supplies, for the Army. The same act authorized the appointment of a Commissary General and assistants. The Commissary General of Subsistence and the Subsistence Department continued to perform the same general functions until an act of August 24, 1912, abolished the Office of the Commissary General of Subsistence and made the Office of the Quartermaster General responsible for subsistence. Many of the records of the former units were incorporated with those of the latter (see RG 92).

Records of the Office of the Commissary General of Subsistence relating to removal of Indians during the years 1830–36 are now among the records of the Bureau of Indian Affairs (see RG 75).

There are 842 cubic feet of records (in WNRC) dated between 1812 and 1914 in this record group.

RECORDS. 1812–1914. 1,010 lin. ft.

The records include reports, correspondence and related finding aids, provision books, compilations, records of accounts and returns, contracts, and personnel records.

RECORDS OF THE
OFFICE OF THE CHIEF OF FINANCE (ARMY)
(RECORD GROUP 203)

The Office of the Chief of Finance was a successor to the Finance Department established in October 1918 in the Division of Purchase, Storage, and Traffic of the War Department General Staff to centralize financial activities in the War Department. Before World War I, War Department bureaus had individually submitted to the Congress estimates prepared by their own finance sections and approved by the Secretary of War. The Division of Requisitions and Accounts in the Office of the Secretary of War had kept a current general account of the status of appropriations under the Secretary's control, including compilation of annual estimates and accounts for departmental funds drawn on the Treasury.

In April 1919 the Finance Service, an independent War Department bureau, succeeded the Finance Department. The Finance Service was succeeded by the Finance Department, created by an act of June 4, 1920, under the Chief of Finance, who also served as the War Department Budget Officer from 1921 to March 1942. The Office of the Chief of Finance, as one of the technical services, reported to the Chief of Staff until it was made subordinate to the Chief of Administrative Services, Headquarters, Services of Supply (later the Army Service Forces), in March 1942. In June 1946 the Office of the Chief of Finance was again put under the Office of the Chief of Staff as one of the technical services.

Soon after the Department of the Army replaced the War Department in 1947, the Office of the Chief of Finance became a Special Staff agency supervised by the Office of the Comptroller of the Army (the Army Comptroller before 1949). The Office of the Chief of Finance and Accounting, established under the Comptroller on May 14, 1967, replaced the Office of the Chief of Finance and assumed responsibility for all matters relating to Army finances and accounts.

There are 480 cubic feet of records (in WNRC) dated between 1792 and 1942 in this record group.

RECORDS. 1792-1942. 464 lin. ft.

Included are correspondence, chiefly letters sent, of the Office of the Secretary of War, 1800-1912; correspondence of the Office of the Director of Finance, 1918-20; registers of warrants and requisitions for funds, appropriation warrants, and requisitions for funds maintained by the Requisitions and Accounts Division and the Office of the Chief of Finance, 1792-1940; reports, procedural issuances, ledgers, journals, and docket books, 1809-1940; correspondence, estimates and justifications, statistical reports, and other records of the War Department Budget Officer, 1901-42; and minutes and correspondence of the War Credits Board, established during World War I to make advances to contractors supplying materials for the War Department, 1917-25.

See Richard W. Giroux, comp., and Maizie H. Johnson, rev., *Preliminary Inventory of the Records of the Office of the Chief of Finance (Army)*, PI 142 (1962).

RECORDS OF THE COMMISSARY GENERAL OF PRISONERS (RECORD GROUP 249)

The Office of the Commissary General of Prisoners was not established as an independent agency of the War Department until June 17, 1862, although in October 1861 Lt. Col. William Hoffman was detailed as Commissary General of Prisoners under the Quartermaster General. The Commissary General of Prisoners was responsible for supervising Confederate prisoners of war and political prisoners confined in Federal prisons, for correspondence and other business relating to Federal prisoners of war confined in the South, and for maintaining camps for paroled Federal prisoners of war and supervising parolees. Later his office was assigned duties concerning the settlement of claims of all prisoners of war. The Commissary General of Prisoners had recordkeeping responsibility connected with the exchange of prisoners of war, but the negotiations between representatives of Union and Confederate authorities on prisoners-of-war exchange were handled, on the part of the Union, primarily by the Commissioner for the Exchange of Prisoners. On August 19, 1867, the Office of the Commissary General of Prisoners was abolished, and its records and remaining duties were transferred to the newly created Prisoner of War Division of the Adjutant General's Office.

There are 161 cubic feet of records dated between 1861 and 1905 in this record group.

RECORDS OF THE OFFICE OF THE COMMISSARY GENERAL OF PRISONERS. 1861-67. 242 lin. ft.

Included are orders and circulars, fair and press letter books, letters received and registers, telegrams sent and received, and endorsement books. There are also reports, registers, lists, and rolls of Federal prisoners confined in Confederate prisons, and similar records relating to paroled Federal prisoners of war, to exchanged Federal prisoners of war, and to Confederate prisoners of war held in Federal prisons. Also registers and claims of former Federal prisoners of war for money, lost personal property, and commutation of rations.

RECORDS OF THE PRISONER OF WAR DIVISION OF THE ADJUTANT GENERAL'S OFFICE. 1861–1905. 35 lin. ft.

Included are reports, a letter book, and correspondence of the Prisoner of War Division, 1862–1905; registers, lists, returns, and rolls relating to individual Federal prisoners of war, 1861–69; case files of deserters from the Union Army, 1861–87; and two registers of claims of former Federal prisoners of war, 1867–85.

RECORDS OF THE COMMISSIONER FOR THE EXCHANGE OF PRISONERS. 1862–65. 4 lin. ft.

These consist of a letter book, a regis-ter of letters received, and letters received.

RECORDS OF THE FEDERAL PAROLE CAMPS. 1861–66. 145 lin. ft.

Included are orders and circulars issued, reports, letter books, letters received, and registers and rolls of pris-oners for the Federal parole camps at Benton Barracks, Mo., Camp Chase, Ohio, College Green Barracks, Md., and Camp Parole, Md.

RECORDS OF THE FEDERAL PRISONER-OF-WAR MILITARY PRISONS AND PRISON CAMPS. 1862–65. 7 lin. ft.

Telegrams received and morning reports of Confederate prisoners at Johnson's Island, Ohio; orders, letters, and telegrams relating to Confederate prisoners at Fort Lafayette, N.Y.; and morning reports of Confederate prison-ers at Point Lookout, Md., and at Rock Island Barracks, Ill.

RECORDS OF THE OFFICE OF THE CHIEF SIGNAL OFFICER (RECORD GROUP 111)

War Department General Order 18 of July 9, 1860, added to the Army's staff a Signal Officer in charge of signal duty and related records and equipment. The Signal Corps, administered by the Chief Signal Officer, was provisionally estab-lished by War Department General Order 73 of March 24, 1863, and was reconstituted by War Department Gen-eral Order 56 of August 1, 1866. Its functions were extended in 1870 to include taking meteorological observa-tions, and for the next 20 years the Corps was primarily concerned with meteorological work. In 1890 that func-tion was transferred to the Weather Bureau (see RG 27), and the remaining functions of the Corps related exclusive-ly to military matters.

The Office of the Chief Signal Officer was placed under the jurisdiction of the Commanding General, Services of Sup-ply (later designated Army Service Forces) in 1942, under the General Staff of the War Department in 1946, and un-der the General Staff of the Department of the Army in 1947. During fiscal year 1964 the Office of the Chief Signal Offi-cer became the Office of the Chief of Communications-Electronics, under the General Staff supervision of the Deputy Chief of Staff for Military Operations.

There are 5,465 cubic feet of records dated between 1754 and 1954 in this record group.

RECORDS. 1860-70. 37 lin. ft.

These consist of reports, issuances, letter books, registers of letters received, letters received, endorsements, descriptive books, officers' military histories, recruiting and courts-martial records, and other general records, 1860-70. Also issuances, letter books, endorsements, and miscellaneous records of the Signal Camp of Instruction, Georgetown, D.C., 1863-65.

RECORDS. 1870-90. 53 lin. ft.

These consist of annual reports of the Chief Signal Officer, issuances, and miscellaneous records. Records of the U.S. Military Telegraph Lines, Telegraph Division, consist of letter books, registers of letters received, letters and telegrams received, logs of messages received and sent, logs of line repairs, and cashbooks for line receipts of the Northern, New Mexico, Northwestern, and Texas Divisions, and of the signal operators within them.

RECORDS. 1890-1917. 716 lin. ft.

These consist of annual reports, issuances, manuals, general correspondence and indexes, letter books, correspondence relating to Signal Corps volunteers in the Spanish-American War, personal documents, and muster rolls and monthly returns of signal companies.

RECORDS. 1917-40. 891 lin. ft. (in WNRC).

Included are general correspondence of the Office of the Chief Signal Officer; the Alaska Communication System; the Personnel Division, relating to ROTC unit training; and the Fiscal Division, relating to budget estimates. Also correspondence relating to the maintenance of fixed communication networks and of

the War Plans and Training Division, the Aircraft Warning Service Section, and the Air Communications Division; and cablegrams, manuals, instruction pamphlets, bulletins, records relating to Procurement Division activities during World War I and Signal Corps equipment, research and development case files of the Engineering and Technical Service, and miscellaneous records.

CARTOGRAPHIC AND AUDIOVISUAL RECORDS. 1860-1954. 314,260 items.

Cartographic records, 1879-1945 (31 items), include maps indicating locations of signal stations, communications lines, administrative boundaries, and meteorological reporting stations; and published maps, 1918-24, relating to Signal Corps schools.

Audiovisual records include still pictures, 1860-1945 (295,432 items), made during the Civil War period, often by or under the direction of Mathew B. Brady, of Army activities, historical places, naval scenes, individuals and groups, Army transports, and Union and Confederate fortifications in Georgia; photographs—some of paintings, sketches, drawings, and engravings—of American frontier forts, Army units and events during the Indian wars, individual Indians, and Indian life, 1860-1919; illustrations relating to the French and Indian War, the Revolutionary War, the War of 1812, the Mexican War, the Spanish-American War, the Philippine Insurrection, the China Relief Expedition, the Mexican Punitive Expedition, and other aspects of military history, 1754-1916; photographs of American Expeditionary Forces activities in the United States and Europe, battlefields in France on which the AEF served, AEF cemeteries in Europe, President Wilson's trips to Europe, and the Japanese capture of the German treaty port of Tsingtao, China, 1914-21; photographs of Signal Corps officers, activities in Alaska, equipment, and systems, 1881-1938; photographs depicting the history of aviation, 1903-35; photographs of Quartermaster Corps activities, 1918-30; and newspaper clippings relating to Allied and Axis troops, 1941-45.

Filmstrips (3,200 items) used during World War II, which illustrate all aspects of Army training, 1941-45.

Motion pictures, 1909-54 (15,597 reels), include films concerning pre-World War I flight development; the construction of the Panama Canal, 1910-14; President Taft's inspection tour of the canal, ca. 1912; and the Mexican Punitive Expedition, 1916. Films, chiefly concerning World War I, depict activities of the American Expeditionary Forces in France; homefront activities, such as war mobilization, training, and industrial production; U.S. Navy activities, including submarine warfare and convoying overseas troop transports; British, French, Russian, and Italian war participation; the war in the Near East; peace celebrations at Paris and in America; and President Wilson's two trips to France, including the signing of the Treaty of Versailles. Motion pictures made between World War I and II relate to Army, Army Reserves, ROTC, Civilian Military Training Camps, and West Point training, education, and maneuvers; Army activities in the territories and in other countries; military medicine; ordnance manufacture, testing, and demonstration; installing and maintaining communications systems; the history of flight, including Air Service activities, early parachute jumps, and air races; Army civil projects, including river and harbor improvements and disaster relief; such sports and recreational activities as the Olympic games, national rifle matches, and Army-Navy football games; Army participation in parades, celebrations, funeral ceremonies, and the burial of the Unknown Soldier; Lindbergh's transatlantic flight; President Franklin D. Roosevelt's first and second inaugurations; the *Hindenburg* disaster; and volcanic eruptions. Films, chiefly of World War II activities, that concern the conduct of the war by both Allied and Axis powers; the Italian invasion of Ethiopia, 1935; the Spanish civil war and the Japanese invasion of China, 1937; such U.S. homefront activities as war production, mobilization, and training, and the roles of women, blacks, and Japanese-Americans in the war effort; entertainment for troops; the atom bomb; the end of the war; the Cairo, Teheran, Yalta, Quebec, and San Francisco Conferences; the Allied military governments in Germany and Japan; postwar problems in Europe and Asia; and the war crimes trials in Germany and Japan. Other films relate to all aspects of the Korean conflict, including the peace negotiations, and to the inauguration ceremonies and parades of Presidents Truman, 1949, and Eisenhower, 1953. Motion pictures accumulated by the Office of the Chief Signal Officer include those made by the Navy Department, the Bureau of Mines, the War Relocation Authority, the Red Cross, and newsreel companies; and films made in Germany, Japan, Italy, Finland, Great Britain, France, Russia, and Canada.

See Mabel E. Deutrich, comp., *Preliminary Inventory of the Records of the Office of the Chief Signal Officer*, PI 155 (1963); and K. Jack Bauer, comp., *List of World War I Signal Corps Films*, SL 14 (1957).

RECORDS OF THE
PROVOST MARSHAL GENERAL'S BUREAU (CIVIL WAR)
(RECORD GROUP 110)

The Provost Marshal General's Bureau was created by an act of March 3, 1863, which also provided for a Provost Marshal General to head the Bureau and for a provost marshal and a board of enrollment to be established in each congressional district. The Provost Marshal General was responsible for administering all activities connected with enrolling and drafting men for military service and for detecting and arresting deserters. In May 1863 his duties were expanded to include supervision of the volunteer recruiting service. Under the direction of the Provost Marshal General an acting assistant provost marshal general was appointed for each State or for one or more territories to centralize activities of districts and to act as intermediary between the Provost Marshal General's Office and State or territorial agencies. Activities connected with enrolling, drafting, recruiting, enlisting volunteers, and reporting and arresting deserters were carried out by State and district offices. The functions of supervising central office branches and field offices, creating policy and regulations, standardizing quotas, tabulating credits, keeping accounts, and disbursing funds were centralized in the Provost Marshal General's Office at Washington, D.C. In compliance with General Order 66 of August 20, 1866, the Bureau and Office of the Provost Marshal were discontinued and most records transferred to the Adjutant General's Office, where the Enrollment Division was organized to handle remaining activities of the Bureau.

There are 1,582 cubic feet of records dated between 1861 and 1889 in this record group.

RECORDS OF THE CENTRAL OFFICE. 1862-89. 22 lin. ft.

Included are records of the Enrollment Division of the Adjutant General's Office, consisting of letter books, letters received and their registers, endorsement books, and telegrams sent and received, all of which relate to the Bureau as a whole. There are also

reports, correspondence, and records relating to scouts, guides, spies, and detectives; transfers to the Navy; appointments, resignations, and discharges of provost marshals, commissioners of enrollment, and surgeons; and fraudulent activities of provost marshals, bounty agents, and others. Also historical reports of State acting assistant provost marshal generals and district provost marshals, inspection reports, the record copy of the final report made by the Provost Marshal General, and weekly, trimonthly, and quarterly reports of district offices and draft rendezvous. In addition there are lists and registers of officers and applicants, applications for appointment, and returns of officers of the Provost Marshal's Bureau; accounts and registers of accounts and disbursements; records of and relating to Cols. Lafayette C. Baker and Henry S. Olcott and detective Allan Pinkerton; and registers and certificates of appointment or enlistment. There are also descriptive lists for certain organizations, applications for passes to travel to and from rebel States, and monthly medical reports of examinations of drafted men, recruits, and substitutes.

RECORDS OF OFFICE SUBDIVISIONS. 1862-66. 836 lin. ft.

Records of the branches include those of the Enrollment, Deserters, Disbursing, and Veteran Reserve Corps Branches, and the Branch for Disbursing the Collecting, Drilling, and Organizing Volunteers Fund. They consist of reports, letter books, registers of letters received, and letters received. Also enrollment lists and registers, lists, and tabulated statements relating to draft calls and quotas for the Enrollment Branch; for the Deserters Branch, reports, registers, returns, and lists of deserters; for the Disbursing Branch, financial records relating to general accounts and disbursements, commutation funds, and bounties and premiums;

for the Veteran Reserve Corps Branch, registers, descriptive lists, and applications relating to the assignment and appointment of men and officers to the Corps; and for the Branch for Disbursing the Collecting, Drilling, and Organizing Volunteers Fund, financial records relating to accounts and disbursements, claims, and requisitions.

RECORDS OF THE MUSTERING AND DISBURSING OFFICE. 1862-67. 1 lin. ft.

These consist of three letter books, two registers of letters received, and an index book to one of the registers.

RECORDS OF STATE AND DISTRICT PROVOST MARSHAL OFFICES. 1861-72. 1,350 lin. ft.

Included are letter books; registers of letters received; letters and telegrams received; and descriptive books, registers, and lists of troops arranged by State in more than 10,000 volumes.

Microfilm Publication: *Reports and Decisions of the Provost Marshal General, 1863-1866,* M621, 1 roll, DP.

RECORDS OF THE OFFICE OF THE JUDGE ADVOCATE GENERAL (ARMY) (RECORD GROUP 153)

A judge advocate of the Continental Army was appointed in 1775. Legal provision for a U.S. Army judge advocate was made in 1797, but the number and status of judge advocates varied during the following years. In 1849 provision was made for appointing a Judge Advocate of the Army. That officer was designated Judge Advocate General by an act of July 17, 1862, which also provided that he receive the records and proceedings of courts-martial and military commissions and keep the records of courts of inquiry. In 1864 the Judge Advocate General was designated to head the newly created Bureau of Military Justice, which by an act of July 5, 1884, was consolidated with the Corps of Judge Advocates of the Army to form the Judge Advocate General's Department. In 1942 the Judge Advocate General was placed under the Commanding General, Services of Supply (later the Army Service Forces). Since 1946 his Office has been an Army staff agency.

The Office of the Judge Advocate General (Army) supervises the system of military justice throughout the Army, performs appellate review of records of trials by court-martial as provided by the Uniform Code of Military Justice, and furnishes the Army's legal services. The Judge Advocate General serves as legal adviser to the Secretary of the Army and all Army offices and agencies, reports directly to the Secretary of the Army on court-martial cases, and gives legal advice concerning the administration, control, discipline, and civil relations of Army personnel.

There are 5,691 cubic feet of records dated between ca. 1800 and 1957 in this record group.

GENERAL CORRESPONDENCE. 1821-1942. 520 lin. ft.

Included are letters and reports sent by the Adjutant General, acting judge advocates, the Judge Advocate of the Army, and the Judge Advocate General to the Secretary of War, War Department officials, judge advocates, Members of Congress, and others, concerning military justice, 1842-89; letters sent by the Judge Advocate General, 1882-95; and selected letters sent by the Judge Advocate General as head of the system of military justice and legal adviser to the Secretary of War, 1889-95. There are indexes to the letters sent. Also letters received by the Judge Advocate of the Army and the Judge Advocate General, 1854-94, with registers and indexes. Further correspondence consists of letters sent, endorsements, a few letters received, and related records, 1894-1912; and correspondence relating to the Judge Advocate General's opinions and decisions and to administrative and operational matters, 1912-42 (in WNRC).

Other records include the Attorney General's opinions and decisions concerning administration of military justice and legal actions of the War Department, 1821-70, and records of Brig. Gen. Norman Lieber, 1867-98, Brig. Gen. George B. Davis as Judge Advocate General, 1901-10, Col. Blanton Winship of the Judge Advocate General's Department, 1903-19, and Col. Mark Guerin, Judge Advocate of the 6th Corps Area, 1918-24. Also included are office files relating to maritime affairs, 1918-23, and the Commission for Adjustment of British Claims, 1932-33 (in WNRC).

COURT-MARTIAL RECORDS. 1805-1939. 5,269 lin. ft.

Included are court-martial case files for general courts-martial, courts of inquiry, and military commissions, 1809-1939 (court-martial cases dated after 1891 are in WNRC), with a partial index, 1891-1917 (in WNRC), including documents that describe court organizations and personnel; charges and specifications; pleas and arraignments of defendants; papers and exhibits submitted to courts for consideration; court proceedings, findings, and sentences; reviewing authorities' reports; statements of action by the Secretary of War and the President; and related correspondence. Files dated before 1812 are fragmentary. Also included are copies of records of general courts-martial and courts of inquiry, 1805-15; registers of court-martial cases

listing cases represented in the case files and giving names of court presidents and judge advocates, locations and dates the courts were convened, and defendants' names, ranks, and organizations, 1809-90; and case files lost during the Civil War but later recovered by the Judge Advocate General, 1861-65.

There are also applications for and correspondence regarding clemency for prisoners sentenced by general courts-martial to the U.S. Military Prison at Fort Leavenworth, Kans., and clemency orders issued by the Assistant Secretary of War, 1894-97. Records relating to court-martial procedures and regulations include a card file used in revising the manual on courts-martial that shows changes made in Army regulations, 1904-13; reports, correspondence, and working papers relating to later revisions of the *Manual for Courts-Martial*, 1919-27 (in WNRC); a report (in WNRC) made to the Judge Advocate General, relating to criticisms of the system of military justice, February 13, 1919; and records (in WNRC) from a study of the European administration of military justice, 1918-20.

RECORDS OF INVESTIGATIONS. 1864-1927. 13 lin. ft.

These comprise records relating to the investigation of President Lincoln's assassination, including reports, testimony of persons connected with the assassination trial, and correspondence; a "Military Commission Record Book" containing abstracts of letters, testimony, and reports regarding suspects in the assassination; and abstracts of correspondence received by or referred to Judge Advocate Col. H. L. Burnett, who investigated the assassination. Other records relate to activities of the secret Order of American Knights, investigated by the Provost Marshal of the Department of the Missouri, 1864 (in WNRC), and records of the Paxton Hibben and William Mitchell cases and the

Martin-Mitchell controversy, 1923–27 (in WNRC).

PERSONNEL RECORDS. 1877–98 and 1918–28. 9 lin. ft.

These consist of lists of personnel and letters sent by the Acting Judge Advocate General, concerning civilian personnel, 1877–98; and office orders (in WNRC), biographical questionnaires (in WNRC), and records (in WNRC) relating to war risk insurance, the French and Creary retirement cases, and Department personnel, 1918–28.

INTERNATIONAL CLAIMS RECORDS. 1914–40. 7 lin. ft. (in WNRC).

These consist of case files relating to claims of Mexican citizens as a result of the landing at Veracruz in 1914 and General Pershing's Punitive Expedition in 1916, and to cases before the Netherlands Claims Commission, created in 1932 to hear Dutch claims arising from Army ordnance purchases during World War I, 1932–40.

RECORDS OF THE OFFICE OF THE ASSISTANT JUDGE ADVOCATE GENERAL. 1864–67. 3 lin. ft.

The Assistant Judge Advocate General, with headquarters at Louisville, Ky., was appointed in 1864 to review records of courts-martial and military commissions in the Military Departments of the Ohio, the Tennessee, the Cumberland, the Missouri, the Arkansas, and Kansas before they were forwarded to the Judge Advocate General. These records include registers and indexes of court-martial case files received, 1864–67, and an endorsement book containing writers' names, subjects of correspondence received, and dates of communications written, received, and forwarded, 1864–66.

RECORDS OF THE OFFICE OF THE ACTING JUDGE ADVOCATE GENERAL IN EUROPE. 1918–19. 12 lin. ft. (in WNRC).

This field office of the Office of the Judge Advocate General functioned from March 7, 1918, to October 6, 1919, and reviewed general court-martial cases in which death, dismissal, or dishonorable discharge sentences were imposed, and military commission cases originating in the American Expeditionary Forces. The records consist of orders, reports, and correspondence regarding cases examined and reviewed. Case papers received by this Office were forwarded to the Judge Advocate General and are in the court-martial case files.

RECORDS OF THE LANDS DIVISION. 1800–1950. 246 lin. ft.

Since 1894 the Judge Advocate General has had custody of original deeds and other papers concerning titles for and the lease or sale of military reservations and other lands by the Departments of War and of the Army. The Military Reservation Division was created in 1942 to perform this function. After World War II it was renamed the Lands Division. These records consist of legal instruments, maps, plans, correspondence, and other documents relating to real estate no longer owned by the Department of the Army.

RECORDS OF THE LITIGATION DIVISION. 1923–42. 26 lin. ft. (in WNRC).

This Division was established in 1942 to exercise supervision over litigation in which the War Department was involved and to maintain liaison with the Department of Justice. The records include correspondence of the Civil Affairs Section, a predecessor unit created in 1925, regarding cases tried in the U.S. Court of Claims, 1925–31; correspondence, chiefly with Members of Congress, and other records relating to the payment of claims to individuals authorized by private congressional acts, 1926–37; records of hearings, correspondence, and other material relating to cases tried in the U.S. Court of Claims, 1925–42; and files of cases involving the War Department tried in the Supreme Court of the District of Columbia, 1923–40.

RECORDS OF THE WAR TRANSACTIONS BOARD. 1923–26. 3 lin. ft. (in WNRC).

This Board was created in the War Department in February 1923 to cooperate with the Board of Survey of the Department of Justice. They operated as the Joint Board of Survey on war transactions, and subcommittees reporting to the Joint Board investigated frauds arising out of war contracts. Most work of the Joint Board was completed in 1925. The records consist of minutes of the Joint Board, 1923–25, and reports, correspondence, case records, and related records concerning legal review of contractual transactions by both Boards, 1923–26.

RECORDS OF THE INSULAR AFFAIRS SECTION. 1915–39. 26 lin. ft. (in WNRC).

In 1914 the Judge Advocate General took over the legal work formerly handled by the War Department Bureau of Insular Affairs. That work was later centralized in the Insular Affairs Section of his Office; the Section was discontinued in 1939. Records include the Section Chief's memorandums concerning legal matters related to the administration of insular possessions, 1931–37, cards listing legal cases handled by the Section, 1925–36, the Chief's office files, 1920–34, files concerning cases brought before the U.S. Circuit Court of Appeals and the Supreme Court involving residents of Puerto Rico, 1915–34, and files con-

cerning similar cases involving residents of the Philippine Islands, 1915–33.

RECORDS OF THE CENTRAL PATENT SECTION AND RELATED AGENCIES. 1917–42. 316 lin. ft. (in WNRC).

The Central Patent Section was created in the Office of the Judge Advocate General on July 11, 1921, to succeed the Central Patent Section of the Supply Division, War Department General Staff. Its records (243 lin. ft.) include patent case files, 1921–40, U.S. Court of Claims case files, 1921–42, selected case papers, 1917–40, correspondence concerning Muscle Shoals, 1918–34, and records relating to the settlement of German and Austrian patent claims, 1928–33.

The Patent Section—which was organized in January 1919 in the Supply Branch of the War Department General Staff's Purchase, Storage, and Traffic Division to handle matters concerning departmental use of patented articles and War Department employees' rights to patents on inventions—was succeeded by the Supply Division's Central Patent Section, created in 1920 during a General Staff reorganization. Records of these Sections include correspondence and records of action on specific patent cases, 1919–21, Air Service contract files, 1919, administrative information files on contracts involving the use of patented materials, and notes on conferences and personnel, 1921.

Records, 1918–21, of the Munitions Patent Board, which was established to coordinate War and Navy Department policies in patent matters, consist of patent case files containing minutes, copies of patents, reports of Board decisions on applications for and claims to patents, and miscellaneous correspondence with the Patent Section of the War Department Claims Board.

The Patents Branch under the Procurement Division of the Office of the

Chief of Ordnance performed functions related to ordnance patents and inventions, contracts for patent rights, and royalty and other payments from March 1918 to January 1919 when the Patent Section of the War Department General Staff assumed the functions related to contract matters and the payment of compensation for inventions. Branch records, 1917-19, include the Chief's office files, drawings of ordnance equipment, an index to contracts in the contract file of the Office of the Chief of Ordnance that contains information regarding patent rights in contracts, and correspondence relating to investigations of infringements on ordnance patents.

Records, 1922-23, of the Interdepartmental Patents Board, which studied policies concerning Government employees' patent rights to inventions, consist of minutes, the Chairman's correspondence with Government agencies, and correspondence of the Board secretary.

Records, 1922-24, of the Commission for Adjustment of Foreign Claims, which heard and determined questions arising out of the "Bolling Agreement" of June 1917 and other assigned matters relating to foreign claims, consist of administrative correspondence, claims case files, exhibits, and files of aeronautical patents information.

Records, 1917-34, of the Commission for Adjustment of British Claims— which was established June 7, 1932, and submitted its final report February 11, 1933—consist of the Chairman's correspondence, general administrative records, case files, and correspondence relating to claims made after the establishment of the Commission.

RECORDS OF THE WAR CRIMES DIVISION. 1942-51. 151 lin. ft. (in WNRC).

These records consist of case files for war crimes trials held by military com-

missions in the European and Mediterranean Theaters of Operations; copies of trial records for the International Military Tribunal in the Far East; "Safehaven Reports" that relate to freezing enemy assets in neutral countries and restoring artworks and other treasures to their owners; reports of atrocities in the Philippines, with indexes; and a law library file containing guides, handbooks, and other legal and war crimes records.

RECORDS OF THE INTERNATIONAL AFFAIRS DIVISION. 1943-57. 336 lin. ft. (in WNRC).

Included are dossiers of war crimes trials held by military commissions in China, the Far East Command, and the European and Mediterranean Theaters of Operations; prisoner-of-war investigation reports; and case files of the Clemency and Parole Board for War Criminals. Records concerning the Korean conflict include historical reports of the War Crimes Division of the Judge Advocate Section in the Korean Communications Zone, case files for investigations of war crimes in Korea, and interrogation records of returned American prisoners following the prisoner exchange (Operation Big Switch) after the Korean armistice agreement.

CARTOGRAPHIC RECORDS. 1840-1930. 352 items.

These consist of maps and plans, prepared by the Lands Division, of former military reservations and other Army-held lands in the United States that were relinquished to other Government agencies, 1840-1930; and published maps relating to the G. K. Warren court of inquiry, 1880.

Microfilm Publications: *Proceedings of a Court of Inquiry Concerning the Conduct of Major Marcus A. Reno at the Battle of the Little Big Horn River on June 25 and 26, 1876*, M592, 2 rolls;

Investigation and Trial Papers Relating to the Assassination of President Lincoln, M599, 16 rolls, DP; Records Relating to Army Career of Henry

Ossian Flipper, 1873-1882, T1027, 1 roll; and General Court-Martial of Gen. George Armstrong Custer (1867), T1103, 1 roll.

RECORDS OF THE BUREAU OF REFUGEES, FREEDMEN, AND ABANDONED LANDS
(RECORD GROUP 105)

The Bureau of Refugees, Freedmen, and Abandoned Lands was established in the War Department on March 3, 1865, to supervise all activities relating to refugees and freedmen and to assume custody of all abandoned or confiscated lands or property—functions previously shared by military commanders and Treasury Department special agents (see RG 366). The Bureau, which operated in former Confederate States, Border States, the District of Columbia, Delaware, and parts of Kansas, was headed by a commissioner with headquarters at Washington. He supervised assistant commissioners in the States, who in turn supervised subordinate officials usually responsible for Bureau affairs in one or more counties. The Bureau was abolished by an act of June 10, 1872, and its remaining functions, relating chiefly to the settlement of claims, were continued by the Freedmen's Branch in the Office of the Adjutant General. After 1879 this claims work was assumed by the Colored Troops Division of the Office of the Adjutant General.

Officers of the Bureau issued rations, clothing, and medicine to destitute refugees and freedmen; operated or leased abandoned or confiscated lands; established hospitals; and cooperated with benevolent societies in establishing schools. Beginning in 1866 the Bureau helped black soldiers and sailors collect claims for bounties, arrearages, and pensions.

See Oliver Otis Howard, *Autobiography* (New York, 1907); and George Bentley, *A History of the Freedmen's Bureau* (Philadelphia, 1955).

There are 711 cubic feet of records dated between 1865 and 1879 in this record group.

RECORDS OF THE BUREAU HEADQUARTERS AT WASHINGTON. 1865-72. 228 lin. ft.

These consist of records of Commissioner Oliver Otis Howard and his adjutants, including annual and monthly reports from assistant commissioners, letter books, letters received and registers, endorsement books, and circulars and special orders issued. There are also station books of officers and civilians, appointment registers, and volumes of report synopses.

Also included are records of the chief medical officer, 1865-71, chief disbursing officer, 1865-72, Land Division, 1865-71, Claim Division, 1866-72, Education Division, 1865-71, chief quartermaster, 1866-72, and Archives Division, 1869-72. Most of these consist of reports, letters received and registers, letter books and endorsement books, and volumes of report synopses or registers of claimants compiled in the Bureau. There are also records of Assistant Inspector General Whittlesey, relating to distribution of supplies to the South, 1867-68.

RECORDS OF THE FREEDMEN'S BRANCH. 1872-79. 95 lin. ft.

These include records created or received by the adjutant in charge of the Freedmen's Branch at Washington, D.C., and records of disbursing officers stationed in the Southern and Border States. They consist of letter books, letters received and registers, registers of claimants, and disbursement reports.

RECORDS OF THE DISTRICT OR
FIELD OFFICES. 1865-72.
1,150 lin. ft.

Included for each district are records
of the assistant commissioner, staff officers, and subordinate officers. Most of
the records are dated between 1865 and
1868 except those of superintendents of
education, which are dated between 1865
and 1870, and those of the claims agents,
dated between 1866 and 1872. There are
also some records predating the Bureau
that were created by military officers

in charge of matters relating to blacks.
Most of the records consist of letter
books, letters received and registers,
reports, and registers of marriages, complaints, and claimants.

Microfilm Publications: Headquarters records
that are available as microfilm publications consist
of the general correspondence of Commissioner
Oliver O. Howard and records of the Education
Division. Field records of assistant commissioners
and superintendents of education in some districts
have also been filmed. For a complete listing see
the current *List of National Archives Microfilm
Publications.*

RECORDS OF THE NATIONAL GUARD BUREAU
(RECORD GROUP 168)

The National Guard Bureau serves as
the channel of communication between
the Army Chief of Staff and Air Force
Chief of Staff and the States, Puerto
Rico, and the District of Columbia on
matters concerning the National Guard,
Army National Guard of the United
States, and Air National Guard of the
United States. Under an act of February 28, 1795, the President was empowered to employ State militia to execute
laws of the Union, suppress insurrection,
and repel invasion. Subsequent acts of
March 3, 1807, July 29, 1861, and
April 20, 1871, broadened these powers.
Other acts provided for the supply of
arms and equipment and the inspection
and payment of troops that by 1878 were
usually designated as the National
Guard. Until 1903 there was no central
office in the War Department in charge
of militia affairs. In that year the
National Guard was made the country's
reserve force and a Militia Division was
established in the Adjutant General's
Office to handle matters relating to the
National Guard not in the service of the
United States. In 1908 this Division was
replaced by a Division of Militia Affairs

in the Office of the Secretary of War.
In 1910 the Division was made responsible to the Chief of Staff; it became the
Militia Bureau in 1916, and it was redesignated the National Guard Bureau in
1933. In 1942 the Bureau was assigned
to the Adjutant General as one of the
administrative services of the Services
of Supply (later Army Service Forces).
In 1945 the Bureau was transferred to
the War Department Special Staff as a
division. Since 1948 it has been a joint
bureau of the Department of the Army
and the Department of the Air Force.
It is headed by a chief who is adviser to
the Army and Air Force Chiefs of Staff
and directly responsible to them for
matters concerning Army and Air Force
units of the National Guard.

There are 862 cubic feet of records
(in WNRC except for nontextual
records) dated between 1822 and 1954
in this record group.

RECORDS. 1822-1954. 1,139 lin. ft.

These include an incomplete series of
annual returns of militia and abstracts

of returns submitted by the States, 1822-1902; several series of correspondence and central files of the Bureau and its predecessors, 1885-1954; separate files of the War Department decimal classification system concerning State Guards organized during World War II to replace National Guard units called into Federal service; quarterly reports of Regular Army sergeants assigned to National Guard units, 1908-16; and account books, 1887-1941.

CARTOGRAPHIC AND AUDIOVISUAL RECORDS. 1897-1936. 639 items.

Cartographic records (7 items) consist of maps published by National Guard units in several States, 1897-1936. Audiovisual records (632 items) consist of photographs of U.S. Army personnel and activities in Cuba, 1898-99; the Oklahoma National Guard, 1924; and crests, coats-of-arms, and general Guard activities, 1922-35.

RECORDS OF THE
SELECTIVE SERVICE SYSTEM (WORLD WAR I)
(RECORD GROUP 163)

The Selective Service System under the direction of the Office of the Provost Marshal General was authorized by the Selective Service Act of May 18, 1917, to register and induct men into military service. Much of the management of the draft was left to the States, where local draft boards were established on the basis of one for every 30,000 people. These boards, appointed by the President on the recommendation of the State Governor, registered, classified, inducted, and delivered to mobilization camps men eligible for the draft. Legal and medical advisory boards assisted the local boards and registrants, and district boards were established to pass on occupational exemption claims and to hear appeals. The Provost Marshal General's Office worked with local and district boards through Selective Service State headquarters. Classification ceased shortly after the Armistice, and by May 31, 1919, all Selective Service organizations were closed except the Office of the Provost Marshal General,

which was abolished July 15, 1919. The records of the Selective Service System were transferred to the Selective Service Division of the Adjutant General's Office, which remained in operation until 1939, furnishing information concerning the System and its records.

There are 263 cubic feet of records (in WNRC) dated between 1917 and 1939 in this record group.

RECORDS. 1917-39. 452 lin. ft.

Most of the records are of the Provost Marshal General's Office, 1917-19, and include correspondence and other records designated as general, States, miscellaneous, and historical files. There are also a "local board experience" file, consisting chiefly of questionnaires completed by local boards; records relating to draft quotas; sample forms; newspaper clippings; and a "precedent" file of the Selective Service Division of the Adjutant General's Office, 1919-39, containing reports, correspondence, and related records.

RECORDS OF THE CHEMICAL WARFARE SERVICE
(RECORD GROUP 175)

The Chemical Warfare Service, a technical service under the General Staff, was established as part of the National Army on June 28, 1918, to develop, produce, and test materials and apparatus for gas warfare and to organize and train military personnel in methods of defense against gas. By an act of June 4, 1920, the Service was made responsible for the development, manufacture, and procurement for the Army of smoke and incendiary materials, toxic gases, and gas-defense appliances; research, design, and experimentation connected with chemical warfare and its materials; administration of chemical-projectile filling plants and proving grounds; organization, equipment, training, and operation of special gas troops; and supervision of Army training in chemical warfare, including necessary schools. The Chemical Warfare School was organized at Lakehurst Proving Ground, N.J., early in 1920 and was transferred to Edgewood Arsenal, Md., later that year. As part of a War Department reorganization, effective March 9, 1942, the Chemical Warfare Service became part of the Services of Supply, later designated the Army Service Forces. When the Army Service Forces was abolished in 1946 the Service was again placed under the General Staff, and on September 6, 1946, its name was changed to the Chemical Corps. The Corps was abolished on August 1, 1962, as part of an Army reorganization.

There are 923 cubic feet of records (in WNRC) dated between 1917 and 1963 in this record group.

RECORDS. 1917-63. 1,108 lin. ft.

These consist of records of the Office of the Chief of the Service, including general administrative files, 1918-54; organization charts, 1942-46 and 1949-50; special and progress reports about projects, 1942-53; budget and fiscal records, 1929-55; and record sets of publications, 1950-54. Also records of the Gas Defense Production Division, 1917-19, and the Chemical Corps Patent Agency and predecessor offices, 1940-54; the Technical Division, 1920-46; and the Training Division, 1942-43. Also minutes of the Chemical Corps Technical Committee, 1935-63; physical and personnel security files, 1944-50; investigative files of the Chemical Corps Inspector General, 1952-55; and records of the Edgewood Arsenal and other field offices, 1917-42.

See Raymond P. Flynn, comp., *Preliminary Inventory of the Records of the Chemical Warfare Service*, PI 8 (1948).

RECORDS OF THE OFFICE OF THE CHIEF OF CHAPLAINS
(RECORD GROUP 247)

The Office of the Chief of Chaplains was established in July 1920, under terms of the National Defense Act of 1920, as an administrative unit of the War Department. Previously, Army chaplains had been assigned on a regimental basis and functioned only at that level. At different times the Office of the Chief of Chaplains has been an independent bureau of the War Department; under the Chief of Administrative Services, Services of Supply; under the Director of Personnel, Army Service Forces; and an administrative service under the Chief of Staff. The Office, which in 1950 became an independent administrative service of the Department of the Army, is now an Army Special Staff agency.

The Chief of Chaplains provides and supervises moral training and religious ministration for the Army. His responsibilities include enlisting church cooperation in providing trained clergymen to serve as chaplains, maintaining liaison with religious leaders and groups and chaplains of other armed services, coordinating public information, preparing statistical reports, furnishing information to other Government agencies and representation on several interdepartmental boards and committees, administering personnel, and supervising the publication, procurement, and distribution of religious material.

There are 1,090 cubic feet of records dated between 1902 and 1964 in this record group.

CENTRAL RECORDS. 1920–53.
185 lin. ft.

These consist of classified and unclassified central decimal files of the Administrative Office, including reports, correspondence, memorandums, and messages relating to liaison with church bodies, securing assistance in obtaining qualified clergy for service as chaplains, providing for and supervising training, supervising chaplains' activities, and procuring, distributing, and disposing of supplies and equipment.

CHAPLAINS REPORTS. 1917–55.
903 lin. ft. (in WNRC).

These consist of monthly reports, with related correspondence and papers, reflecting services rendered and duties performed by chaplains in the field, services rendered by civilian clergymen at Army installations, and changes in status, duties, and addresses of Army chaplains, 1917–50, with an index, 1923–55; and reports reflecting morale and religious attitudes of military personnel at Army installations, 1917–19.

OTHER RECORDS. 1902–64. 7 lin. ft. and 134 rolls of microfilm.

These consist of general correspondence, 1920–23, chapel registers, 1902–23 and 1939–51, and microfilm copies (134 rolls) of records documenting services performed by Army chaplains, 1917–64.

RECORDS OF THE
OFFICE OF THE PROVOST MARSHAL GENERAL, 1941–
(RECORD GROUP 389)

The Office of the Provost Marshal General (OPMG), an Army Special Staff agency and one of the major Army service organizations, has staff responsibility for developing and supervising plans, policies, and procedures related to protective services, preservation of law and order, Army-wide crime prevention, criminal investigations and law enforcement, traffic control, and military police and prisoner-of-war activities; maintaining security in privately owned industrial facilities important to national security; and planning and supervising the selection, training, and utilization of military government personnel.

Before World War II a Provost Marshal General was appointed only in times of active military operations; the office and its functions were abandoned at the end of hostilities, and individuals and units were designated by installation commanders to perform military police duties. An OPMG was established in 1941 and made directly responsible to the Chief of Staff. Successively, it became responsible to the Chief of Administrative Services, Services of Supply; the Deputy Chief of Staff for Service Commands, Army Service Forces; the Chief of Staff, Army Service Forces; and the Secretary of the Army after 1946. At that time a Corps of Military Police was created to consolidate personnel exercising military police duties as a principal function, and the Chief of Staff ordered the continuation of the Office of the Provost Marshal General and its Corps of Military Police as a permanent part of the Army Establishment.

There are 684 cubic feet of records dated between 1937 and 1956 in this record group.

GENERAL RECORDS. 1941-54.
214 lin. ft.

Included are general decimal correspondence, 1941-54, with indexes; records of the Office of the Executive Assistant to the Provost Marshal General, 1943-45; correspondence of the Legal Office and records of the Technical Information Office, relating to publicity activities, 1942-45; correspondence of the Administrative Division, 1941-48; budget estimates of the Budget and Fiscal Branch,1944-46; and records relating to the Provost Marshal General's participation in preparations for Geneva conventions, 1946-49.

PERSONNEL ACCREDITATION RECORDS. 1943-54. 46 lin. ft.

These consist of personal history statements, investigation reports, canceled Criminal Investigation Division credentials, memorandums, correspondence, and other records relating to accrediting military civilian personnel as criminal investigators.

RECORDS RELATING TO MILITARY GOVERNMENT. 1942-46. 44 lin. ft. and 24 rolls of microfilm.

General decimal files and correspondence of the School of Military Government, Charlottesville, Va., and of the School for Government of Occupied Areas, Carlisle Barracks, Pa., 1942-46; and microfilm copies (24 rolls) of German-language textbooks for schools in Germany, 1944.

RECORDS RELATING TO PRISONERS OF WAR. 1941-56. 315 lin. ft.

General correspondence, with an index, of the Prisoner of War Operations Division, relating to prisoner-of-war operations, 1942-48; messages, 1942-47; the Information Bureau policy and subject files concerning supervision of prisoner-of-war camps, 1942-45; training records relating to German prisoners of war and a special projects file, with an index, of the Prisoner of War Special Projects Division, 1943-46; Italian Service Unit correspondence, 1944-45; and records of the Legal Branch, detention lists and correspondence of the Labor and Liaison Branch, and general correspondence of the Enemy Prisoner of War Information Bureau, 1942-46. Records of the American Prisoner of War Information Bureau include civilian alien internee case files, 1941-45, general correspondence, 1942-49, credit certificates and records relating to impounded and lost property, 1947-55, United Nations Command prisoner-of-war rosters, 1955-56, and a card file of Americans interned by Germany and Japan during World War II, 1942-46.

RECORDS OF THE MILITARY POLICE DIVISION. 1942-54. 43 lin. ft.

Included are general correspondence relating to military police and Provost Marshal General schools, 1942-50; records of the Organization Branch, relating to the Corps of Military Police, 1942-48; decimal correspondence of the Training Branch, 1942-46; and correspondence and reports of the Doctrine and Equipment Branch, 1942-47, and the Military Police Board, 1942-54.

RECORDS OF THE PROVOST DIVISION. 1942-46. 22 lin. ft.

These include general records relating to criminal investigations in the Military Establishment, reports, repatriation

lists, and rosters of residents in relocation centers.

RECORDS OF THE INTERNAL SECURITY DIVISION. 1937-50. 89 lin. ft.

These include reports of race riots and
strikes and correspondence relating to
auxiliary military police, 1942-45; general correspondence of the Coordination
Branch and a library file, 1937-46; and
correspondence of the Fire Prevention
Branch, 1942-46, the Safety Branch,
1942-45, and the Confinement Branch,
1947-50.

RECORDS OF THE OFFICE OF CIVIL AND DEFENSE MOBILIZATION (RECORD GROUP 304)

Reorganization Plan No. 1 of 1958 consolidated the Office of Defense Mobilization (ODM) with the Federal Civil
Defense Administration to form the
Office of Civil and Defense Mobilization.
The ODM was first established in the
Executive Office of the President by
Executive Order 10193 of December 16,
1950, to direct Government mobilization
efforts, including production, procurement, manpower, stabilization, and
transport facilities. In February 1953
functions of the Defense Production
Administration—established in 1951 to
exercise general direction over the
defense production program—were
transferred to the ODM. Reorganization
Plan No. 3 of 1953 established a new
ODM, which assumed all functions of the
old ODM and of the National Security
Resources Board—established by an act
of July 26, 1947, to advise the President
on coordination of military, industrial,
and civilian mobilization—and the critical materials stockpiling functions of
the Army and Navy Munitions Board
and of the Secretaries of the Army,
Navy, Air Force, and Interior.

There are 744 cubic feet of records
(most of them security classified) dated
between 1947 and 1960, with a few dated
as early as 1939, in this record group.

RECORDS OF THE NATIONAL SECURITY RESOURCES BOARD. 1947-53. 437 lin. ft.

Included are office files of the Chairman, 1949-53; correspondence of the
office of the Vice Chairman and office
files of special assistants and consultants
for labor, public relations, information,
and economic affairs, 1947-53. Records
of the Administrative and Coordinating
Staff comprise records of the Administrative Office, relating to budget matters, business services, and personnel,
1947-53; minutes of boards, committees,
and task groups, 1947-52; orders,
reports, memorandums, and other Board
issuances, 1947-53; general correspondence of the Board, 1948-53; letters sent,
1949-53; office files of the Records Service and Management Division and the
General Counsel, 1947-53; records of the
Office of Progress Evaluation, 1951-53;
correspondence of the Office of Plans
and Programs and files of its Program
Division and Program Adjustment Division, 1948-49; general records of the
Information Office, files of the
Resources and Requirements Office, and
correspondence of the Office of Program
and Requirements, 1948-53; office files
of the Board secretary and correspondence of the General Research and

Reports Division, 1947-51; correspondence of the Secretariat, 1948-50; subject files of the Committee Operations Division, 1948-51; records of the Institutional Resources Survey Division, 1947-49; and files of the economic adviser, 1949-53, and other staff assistants.

Records of the Mobilization Planning Staff include records of the Civilian Mobilization Office, 1949-50; of the Energy and Utilities Office, 1948-50; of the Economic Management Office that relate to production controls and priorities, and correspondence of the Foreign Activities Office relating to economic warfare and industrial mobilization, 1947-51; general records of the Health Resources Office, 1948-51; records of the Housing and Community Facilities Office, 1948-53, including some dated 1939; reports and correspondence of the Manpower Office, 1948-52; subject files of the Forest Products, Light Metals, and Non-Metallic Minerals Divisions of the Materials Office, 1948-53; and records of the Office of Aluminum, 1951.

There are also subject files of the Production Office, its directors, and its Production and Industrial Equipment Division, 1948-51; of the directors of its Agricultural Machinery and Aircraft Divisions; of members of its Automotive and Transportation Division; its Communications and Electronics, and Construction and Mining Machinery Divisions; of a member of its Containers and Packaging Division; its Facilities and Construction Materials Division, 1947-51; a food planning specialist of its Food Division, 1948-50; and of its Industrial and Government Dispersion Division, 1947-50. Also included are an office file of the Director of the Production Office's Scientific and Technical Equipment Division; correspondence of the Production Office's Service Equipment and Consumer Durable Goods, Shipbuilding, Small Business, and Textiles and Leather Divisions, 1948-51; subject files of the Transportation Office, 1948-

50, its director, and a transportation specialist; and correspondence and reports of the Air Coordinating Committee. Records of the Human Resources Office include subject files of its directors, 1949-53, its Housing and Community Facilities Division, 1951-52, and consultants and specialists in its Manpower Division, 1949-52. Records of the Natural Resources Office include the Director's correspondence and reports chiefly relating to the President's Materials Policy Commission, 1952-53; subject files of the secretary of the Scientific Manpower Advisory Committee, 1950-52; the general office file of the Materials Division, 1949-52; and subject files of Division directors, 1949-53, and records of a Division member, 1948-52, and a consultant on technology, 1952. There is also a subject file of the Director of the Production Resources Office, 1952-53, and subject and reading files of the Director of the Special Security Programs Office, 1951-53.

RECORDS OF THE DEFENSE PRODUCTION ADMINISTRATION. 1951-53. 110 lin. ft.

These consist of general records of the Office of Program and Requirements, 1951-53; and minutes, correspondence, and memorandums of the Production Office, relating to activities of the Office of the Deputy Administrator for Production, the Aircraft Production Board, and the Production Executive Committee, 1951-52.

RECORDS OF THE OFFICE OF DEFENSE MOBILIZATION. 1948-56. 138 lin. ft.

These comprise application files concerning defense loans to private enterprises, 1951-54; and general subject files of constituent ODM offices, relating to congressional legislation, price and wage stabilization, and the International Materials and Munitions Stockpile Committees, 1948-56.

AUDIOVISUAL RECORDS. 1952-60. 66 items.

Documentary motion pictures produced by predecessor agencies of the Office of Civil Defense, showing nuclear bomb explosions, flood damage, and all phases of civil defense.

Field Commands and Installations
RECORDS OF UNITED STATES ARMY COMMANDS, 1784-1821 (RECORD GROUP 98)

In 1784 the U.S. Army consisted of one infantry regiment. Between 1784 and 1798 additional units were added of infantry, artillery, and dragoons. In 1800 the Army was reduced to four regiments of infantry and two regiments of artillerists and engineers, but additional units were formed in 1802 and 1808, and during the War of 1812 the size of the Army increased to 48 regiments of infantry, a corps of artillery, and two regiments of light dragoons. By 1821 the Army consisted of seven infantry regiments and a corps of artillery. During most of the period 1784-1813 Army units and posts were under the direct command of the chief of the Army, who was responsible to the Secretary of War. There were, however, several periods when Army field establishments were organized into one or more departments, each responsible to the Secretary of War. Not until 1813 when a War Department general order divided the Nation into nine (later 10) military districts did such a division of command become a permanent concept. In 1815 the United States was divided into Divisions of the North and the South, with five military departments under each. The organization was changed again early in 1821 when the United States was divided into Eastern and Western Departments.

There are 48 cubic feet of records dated between 1784 and 1821 in this record group.

RECORDS OF DEPARTMENTS, DISTRICTS, DIVISIONS, AND POSTS. 1786-1821. 12 lin. ft.

The records consist of letter books, letters received, orderly books, monthly returns, and registers of men furloughed, discharged, and detailed.

RECORDS OF UNITS. 1784-1821. 31 lin. ft.

These consist primarily of orderly and company books, with a few morning reports, monthly returns, inspection returns, clothing books, and some correspondence.

Microfilm Publications: *Records of Fort Hays, Kansas (U.S. Army Post), 1866-1869*, T713, 22 rolls; *Records of the Military Post at San Antonio, Texas, 1866-1911*, T789, 4 rolls; and *Selected Records of Kansas Army Posts*, T837, 14 rolls.

RECORDS OF UNITED STATES REGULAR ARMY MOBILE UNITS, 1821-1942 (RECORD GROUP 391)

U.S. Regular Army mobile units in 1821 comprised seven infantry regiments (increased to eight in 1838) and four artillery regiments. During the Mexican War the infantry was increased to 16 regiments, and three dragoon regiments, one mounted rifle regiment, one voltigeur regiment, and one engineer battalion were created. The infantry and the dragoons were reduced to eight and two regiments, respectively, after the war. In 1855 two cavalry regiments were organized. During the Civil War there were 45 infantry regiments; five artillery regiments; and 10 cavalry regiments, five new and five of which replaced cavalry regiments, dragoon regiments, and the mounted rifle regiment.

Only the infantry was reduced after the Civil War—from 45 to 25 regiments— and two new artillery regiments were created during the Spanish-American War. In 1901 two additional engineer battalions were formed; infantry and cavalry regiments were increased to 30 and 15, respectively; and the artillery was divided into 30 field artillery batteries (redesignated regiments in 1907) and 126 coast artillery companies. There was a great increase in the numbers and kinds of mobile units during World War I, and many reorganizations of the units took place, including the introduction of the division as the tactical unit for cavalry and infantry. Other units introduced included tank battalions, motor transport companies, and clothing units.

There are 6,266 cubic feet of records dated between ca. 1776 and 1949 in this record group.

RECORDS OF REGULAR ARMY MOBILE UNITS. 1821-1916.
1,099 lin. ft.

Records of artillery regiments (443 lin. ft.) comprise records of the seven artillery regiments, 1821-1901, including their detachments and batteries, consisting of letter books and registers of letters received, with indexes; letters received; orders issued and received; descriptive books; monthly returns; and muster rolls. Also included are similar records of artillery battalions and batteries, 1901-7; correspondence and miscellaneous records of artillery regiments, 1907-16; and letter books,

registers of letters received, letters received, registers of correspondence, correspondence, orders, and miscellaneous records of coast artillery companies, 1901-16.

Records of cavalry regiments, 1833-1916, include letter books; registers of letters received, with indexes; letters received; orders issued and received; descriptive books; monthly returns; military histories of officers and regiments; rosters; and other records of the 15 cavalry regiments, the mounted rifle and dragoon regiments, and companies and detachments of the cavalry regiments. Records of the three engineer battalions and their companies, 1846-1916, include letter books and registers of letters received, with indexes; letters received; orders issued; and descriptive books.

Records of 46 infantry regiments and their companies and detachments, 1821-1916, comprise letter books, with indexes; endorsement books; registers of letters received, with indexes; letters received; orders issued and received; descriptive books; monthly returns; military histories of officers and regiments; rosters; and muster rolls.

Also included are letter books, registers of letters received, letters received, orders issued, descriptive lists, and other records of the voltigeur regiment, 1847-48; Signal Corps companies and detachments, 1867-1910; Indian scout companies, 1872-93; and Philippine scout companies and other scout units in the Philippines, 1901-16.

RECORDS OF REGULAR ARMY MOBILE UNITS. 1916-43.
4,749 lin. ft.

These comprise correspondence, registers, issuances, returns, rosters, and other records of Coast Artillery Corps units; mine planters; Field Artillery Corps, cavalry, engineer, and infantry units; signal service, bakery, firetruck and hose, salvage, mobile laundry, guard and fire, motortruck, motor transport, and wagon companies; medical regiments; motor commands; motor repair units; and U.S. guard battalions.

CARTOGRAPHIC AND AUDIOVISUAL RECORDS. ca. 1776-1949. 1,901 items.

Cartographic records, 1905-42 (333 items), comprise published and photoprocessed copies of topographic quadrangles used for training exercises.

Audiovisual records (1,568 items) include watercolors of artillerymen in the Provincial Company of the New York Infantry, ca. 1776, and photographs of units, officers, and activities of the 67th New York, 4th, 10th, 15th, 17th, and 19th Infantry Regiments, 1850-1941; the 1st, 2d, 4th, 5th, 6th, 9th, and 10th Cavalry Regiments, 1850-1949; the fort and Indian dwellings at Fort Wingate, New Mexico Territory, 1866; the Southwest, 1879; the Philippine Islands, 1896-1906; and Battery C, 144th Field Artillery, California National Guard, 1939.

RECORDS OF UNITED STATES ARMY CONTINENTAL COMMANDS, 1821-1920 (RECORD GROUP 393)

A War Department general order of May 17, 1821, divided the United States into two geographical Army commands—the Eastern and Western Departments. The names and jurisdictions of the commands were frequently changed after 1821, and new commands were created as the area of the United States grew. The United States was, at times, divided into departments only. At other times it was divided into military divisions which were subdivided into departments. Occasionally some departments functioned under divisions while others operated independently. They were sometimes subdivided into districts and had jurisdiction over posts, camps, stations, forts, and Regular Army units operating within their commands. During the Civil War, departments that functioned virtually as armies and military divisions had jurisdiction over armies, army corps, and such units as railroad defenses, U.S. forces, detachments, and parts of armies and army corps. The former Confederacy was divided into five military (reconstruction) districts comparable to geographical departments between March 1867 and January 1870. Army organization into divisions and departments was replaced in 1920 by the creation of nine corps areas for the continental United States (see RG 394).

There are 10,464 cubic feet of records dated between 1821 and 1920 in this record group.

RECORDS OF GEOGRAPHICAL DEPARTMENTS, DIVISIONS, AND MILITARY (RECONSTRUCTION) DISTRICTS. 1821-1920. 11,700 lin. ft.

These records are of command headquarters, including letter books and registers of letters received, with indexes; letters received; endorsements and telegrams; issuances; correspondence files, with indexes and record cards; reports; station books; rosters; returns; and registers of deserters, discharges, furloughs, and prisoners. Among them are similar records of staff officers (engineers, inspectors, judge advocates, paymasters, provost marshals, quartermasters, signal officers, surgeons, and commissaries), of such offices as the Office of Civil Affairs and the General Recruiting Service, and of expeditions and U.S. troops, primarily in the West, during and after the Civil War. These records comprise those of most Civil

War armies, some records of army corps functioning as territorial commands, and some districts and military installation records inseparable from department and division records.

RECORDS OF ARMY CORPS. 1861-66. 264 lin. ft.

These are records of the 25 Civil War army corps—except the 7th and 22d, which functioned as territorial commands—and of corps divisions and brigades, including letter books and registers of letters received, indexes, endorsements and telegrams, letters received, issuances, and other registers and lists.

OTHER RECORDS OF GEOGRAPHICAL DISTRICTS. 1862-1920. 416 lin. ft.

These consist primarily of letter books, endorsements, registers of letters received, letters received, and issuances of geographical districts.

OTHER RECORDS OF MILITARY INSTALLATIONS. 1835-1920. 6,052 lin. ft.

These consist of military installations in the United States (including Alaska) that comprise letter books; endorsements and telegrams; registers of letters received; letters received; issuances; rosters; correspondence files, with indexes and record cards; guard and morning reports; personnel papers; descriptive books; and returns.

CARTOGRAPHIC RECORDS. 1837-1920. 4,134 items.

These consist of published and photo-processed strategic and tactical maps and city plans compiled by armies, 1837-66; general, tactical, strategic, and topographic maps and plans compiled by territorial commands, 1858-1920; and maps and plans of National Army posts and reservations, 1917-18.

Microfilm Publications: *Records of the 10th Military Department, 1846-1851*, M210, 7 rolls, DP; *Letters Sent by the Post Commander at Fort Bayard, New Mexico, 1888-1897*, T320, 3 rolls; and *Letters Sent, Fort Mojave, Arizona Territory, 1859-1890*, T838, 2 rolls.

RECORDS OF UNITED STATES ARMY CONTINENTAL COMMANDS, 1920-42 (RECORD GROUP 394)

In August 1920 the continental United States was divided among nine U.S. Army corps, whose functions included performing administrative and training services for the Army. These corps also performed tactical command functions for all major ground troop units and defense forces in the continental United States (including field armies, infantry divisions, and harbor defense commands) until October 1940 when General Headquarters, U.S. Army, assumed those functions. The headquarters of corps areas, which had been responsible to the U.S. Army Chief of Staff, were placed in March 1942 under the Services of Supply (later the Army Service Forces). In July 1942 corps areas were designated service commands.

There are 3,576 cubic feet of records dated between 1916 and 1944 in this record group.

RECORDS OF CORPS AREAS I-IX. 1916-44. 3,924 lin. ft.

These consist chiefly of reports, general and miscellaneous correspondence, and issuances of the headquarters of the nine corps areas, 1916-44. There are administrative, supply, and technical and General Staff records for some corps areas. Included are correspondence, special orders, memorandums, and related records of the 1st Military Reserve Area, I Corps Area, 1937-42; the 1st, 2d, 3d, and 4th Military Reserve Areas, II Corps Area, 1934-42; the Illinois Military Reserve Area, VI Corps Area, 1936-40; the 2d Reserve Area, VII Corps Area, 1938; and the 1st, 2d, and 3d Reserve Areas, IX Corps Area, 1930-39. There are also some records of the 1st, 3d, and 4th Armies, 1932-42. Records of most armies have been incorporated with those of the corps areas whose headquarters served also as army headquarters.

RECORDS OF THE DISTRICT OF WASHINGTON AND THE WASHINGTON PROVISIONAL BRIGADE. 1921-27 and 1932-40.
24 lin. ft.

In 1921 Washington, D.C., and vicinity were removed from the III Corps Area and placed directly under the Chief of Staff as the District of Washington. That District was abolished in 1927 and the area was reincorporated in the III Corps Area. Some files begun by the District of Washington were continued by the 16th Brigade and later by the Washington Provisional Brigade. These records include correspondence, with indexes and issuances, 1921-27; and records of the Washington Provisional Brigade, including reports, correspondence, issuances, and a history of the headquarters company, 1932-40.

RECORDS OF FIELD INSTALLATIONS. 1917-44.
422 lin. ft.

These consist of correspondence, issuances, messages, morning reports, post diaries, court-martial orders, activity reports, and other records of camps, posts, and stations throughout the United States and Alaska.

CARTOGRAPHIC AND AUDIOVISUAL RECORDS. 1917-42.
1,670 items.

Cartographic records, 1920-42 (895 items), include published general, tactical, and topographic maps and photomaps compiled by various armies and corps areas.

Audiovisual records (775 items) consist of photographs of activities at Camp Stephen F. Austin, 1936; at citizen military training camps in Maryland, 1925, and Virginia, 1933; buildings and posts in the III Corps Area, 1917-29; and mobilization tests in the VI Corps Area, 1933-38.

RECORDS OF UNITED STATES ARMY COAST ARTILLERY DISTRICTS AND DEFENSES, 1901-42
(RECORD GROUP 392)

In 1901 the Artillery Corps was divided into field artillery batteries and coast artillery companies. Coast artillery companies were organized under newly created artillery districts, which were immobile tactical units established along the coasts of the continental United States, Puerto Rico, and Hawaii. In 1903 an artillery district along the coast of the Philippine Islands was added. Each district consisted of harbor defense forts, with accompanying minefields and land defenses. A district commander, responsible to division and department commanders, controlled matters relating to coast artillery instruction, drill, practice, and procurement within his district.

In 1913 coast artillery districts were redesignated coast defense commands, and those in the continental United

States were placed under the newly created North Atlantic, South Atlantic, and
Pacific Coast Artillery Districts, but the
extracontinental commands remained
directly under the jurisdictions of the
Hawaiian and Philippine Departments.
Coast artillery companies in Panama
were later placed under coast defense
commands in the Panama Canal Department. In 1917 the three U.S. continental
coast artillery districts were increased
to five; in 1920 these five districts
assumed the numerical designation of
the newly created corps areas to which
they reported (1st, 2d, 3d, 4th, and 9th).
Coast defense commands were designated harbor defense commands in 1925.

There are 240 cubic feet of records
dated between 1901 and 1942 in this
record group.

RECORDS OF ARTILLERY
DISTRICTS. 1913-39. 145 lin. ft.

These consist of general correspondence and accompanying index and record
cards, issuances, special correspondence,
returns, and miscellaneous records of
the Middle Atlantic Coast, North Pacific
Coast, Pacific Coast, and South Atlantic
Coast Artillery Districts and of the 1st,
2d, 4th, and 9th Coast Artillery Districts.

RECORDS OF COAST AND
HARBOR DEFENSES. 1901-42.
331 lin. ft.

Included are reports, letter books, correspondence, issuances, battery
emplacement books, fort record books,
and mine command record books of 35
coast and harbor defenses.

RECORDS OF UNITED STATES ARMY OVERSEAS
OPERATIONS AND COMMANDS, 1898-1942
(RECORD GROUP 395)

To this record group have been allocated the records of Army overseas geographical divisions, departments, districts, and subordinate posts; army corps
and armies; and expeditions and troops
sent to Mexico and overseas, except
records of the American Expeditionary
Forces during World War I and those
of commands overseas during World
War II. The U.S. Army had been in Mexico as early as 1846 and in Alaska in
1867, but its first major involvement outside the continental United States was
the Spanish-American War in 1898. During that year it organized seven army
corps for fighting in Cuba and the 8th
Army Corps for the Philippines. The
Army discontinued the 3d, 5th, and 6th
Corps in 1898; the 1st, 2d, 4th, and 7th
Corps in 1899; and the 8th in 1900. During the Boxer Rebellion in China in 1900
the Army sent the China Relief Expedition. In 1906 the Army of Cuban Pacification was dispatched. In 1914 a force

was sent to Veracruz and in 1916 the
Punitive Expedition to Mexico; in the
1920's U.S. troops were again sent to
China. During World War I the Army,
heavily involved in Europe, also sent an
expeditionary force to Siberia.

After the treaty with Spain and the
acquisition of Hawaii in 1898, the command structure of Army field establishments in the continental United States
was gradually extended to overseas areas. The Division of Cuba, in existence
from December 1898 to October 1900,
became the Department of Cuba until
March 1902. The Division of the Philippines functioned from 1900 to 1913 when
it became the Department of the Philippines. The Department of Hawaii, established in 1911, later became the Hawaiian Department. The Panama Canal
Zone was under the Eastern Department until the Panama Canal Department was established in 1917. Puerto
Rico was under the Department of Puer-

to Rico from 1898 to 1900, and under the Eastern Department and the 2d Corps Area until 1939 when the Puerto Rican Department was established. Like their counterparts in the United States, these commands had jurisdiction over posts, camps, stations, mobile units, and coast and harbor defenses within their areas.

There are 2,450 cubic feet of records dated between 1898 and 1942 in this record group.

RECORDS FOR THE PERIOD 1898-1917. 4,570 lin. ft.

Records of the China Relief Expedition, 1900-1905, include reports, issuances, letters sent, endorsements, telegrams, registers of letters received, letters received, returns, and rosters of headquarters, staff officers, brigades, legation guards, and Liscum Barracks. Records of commands in Cuba, 1898-1904 and 1906-9, include reports, letters sent, telegrams, registers of letters received, letters received, registers of charges, and issuances of the division and department, posts, army corps and their subdivisions, and the Army of Cuban Pacification.

Records of commands in Hawaii, 1907-17, consist of issuances of the Hawaiian Department and Schofield Barracks. Records of commands in Mexico, 1914-17, include reports; general correspondence, with accompanying indexes and record cards, of the judge advocate of the U.S. Expeditionary Forces at Veracruz; and general correspondence, with accompanying indexes and record cards, and issuances of Pershing's Punitive Expedition.

Records of commands in the Philippine Islands, 1898-1914, include reports, letters sent, telegrams, registers of letters received, letters received, registers of general correspondence (with accompanying indexes and record cards), returns, and rosters of the department, geographical districts, 8th Army Corps,

separate brigades, expeditionary forces, military governors of districts, and Army posts. Records of commands in Puerto Rico, 1898-1914, include reports, letters sent, registers of letters received, letters received, issuances, returns, and general correspondence of the department, geographical districts, and Army posts.

RECORDS FOR THE PERIOD 1915-42. 253 lin. ft.

Records of U.S. troops in China, 1917-38, include general correspondence, radiograms, and issuances of headquarters, the quartermaster, and a few posts. Records of commands in Hawaii, 1917-42, include reports, general correspondence, and issuances of the Hawaiian Department and Army posts.

Records of commands in Panama, 1915-40, consist of reports, general correspondence, and issuances of the Panama Canal Department and Army posts. Records of commands in the Philippines, 1917-39, consist of returns of medical officers of the Philippine Department and issuances of Camp John Hay.

Records of commands in Puerto Rico, 1918-40, consist of issuances of the Puerto Rican Department and issuances, with some correspondence, of several Army posts. Records of the American Expeditionary Forces in Siberia, 1918-20, include reports and war diaries, general correspondence, cablegrams, telegrams, and issuances.

CARTOGRAPHIC AND AUDIOVISUAL RECORDS. 1900-1942. 3,039 items.

Cartographic records consist of maps, 1900-1942 (2,239 items), including published and photoprocessed general, tactical, hydrographic, and topographic maps and photomaps compiled by various overseas territorial and troop commands in the Philippines, Hawaii, Puerto Rico, the Canal Zone, and Mexico; blueprints of maps and plans from the China Relief

Expedition, 1900-1901; a manuscript set of 316 large-scale topographic sheets of the Philippines annotated in Spanish; and several maps of northwest Mexico collected during Pershing's Punitive Expedition.

Photographs, ca. 1900-1919 (800 items), consist of a pictorial history of the American expedition in Siberia, and snapshots taken in the Philippines, ca. 1900.

RECORDS OF UNITED STATES ARMY COMMANDS, 1942-
(RECORD GROUP 338)

The present system of U.S. Army commands emerged from a War Department reorganization of February 28, 1942, which restructured the Department for the wartime program of organizing, training, arming, supplying, transporting, and providing strategic control to the enlarged U.S. Army. During World War II all Army activities in the United States were grouped under the Commanding Generals of the Army Air Forces, the Army Ground Forces, and the Army Service Forces. A small group of air, ground, and supply officers assisted the Chief of Staff in strategic planning and direction and in coordinating the action of the three commands to provide theater commanders with means for conducting war operations. There existed in the Zone of Interior a separate air force and a ground force for the development of equipment and for organization and training. The fighting units created by these separate commands were merged into fighting teams or task forces in combat under commanders of the various theaters of operations, defense commands, or task forces. There are currently 13 major Army commands, organized both functionally and geographically.

There are 26,888 cubic feet of records dated between 1940 and 1960, with a few dated as early as 1939, in this record group.

RECORDS OF THE U.S. ARMY EUROPE. 1942-60 (including captured records dated as early as 1939).
788 lin. ft.

The top administrative headquarters of the U.S. Army's combat and service forces in the European Theater of Operations was known as Headquarters U.S. Army Forces in the British Isles from January to June 1942, and as Headquarters U.S. Army European Theater of Operations (ETOUSA) from June 8, 1942, to July 1, 1945, when it was renamed U.S. Forces European Theater. In March 1947 it was renamed the European Command; and on August 1, 1952, the headquarters was redesignated U.S. Army Europe.

General records (631 lin. ft., in WNRC) consist of a historical file, 1943-45, of the chief historian; Intelligence Division interrogation reports on German and Italian prisoners of war and persons in the Soviet Union or Soviet-controlled countries, 1942-49; and Judge Advocate Division war crimes correspondence and case files, 1945-58, with indexes. Also included are records of War Criminal Prison No. 1 (Landsberg Prison), Munich District, Southern Area Command, consisting of personal name dossiers relating to the prosecution, execution, or release of war criminals, 1946-54; and a file of European editions of the newspaper *Stars and Stripes*, 1943-60.

Foreign military studies consist of German-language manuscripts, with some English translations, relating to German ground, air, and naval operations during World War II prepared from 1945 to 1959 by German Army officers as part of the U.S. Army's historical program.

British Air Historical Branch records, 1945-56, consist of copies of British Air Ministry translations of captured Luftwaffe studies and other German records, 1939-45, relating primarily to German air operations, losses, and experiences in World War II. Included is some material concerning German ground and naval operations and Allied operations.

Headquarters U.S. Forces in Austria was redesignated Headquarters Southern European Task Force on October 20, 1955. Its records (in WNRC) consist of war crimes case files of the Office of the Staff Judge Advocate, 1945-55.

RECORDS OF THE U.S. ARMY PACIFIC. 1942-52. 131 lin. ft. (in WNRC).

The U.S. Army Forces in the Central Pacific Area (USAFICPA) was established in September 1943 and renamed the U.S. Army Forces Pacific Ocean Area in August 1944. Its jurisdiction was enlarged to include Army garrisons in the South Pacific that had been controlled by the U.S. Army Forces in the South Pacific. In July 1945 the U.S. Army Forces in the Middle Pacific was established as a subordinate command of the Commander in Chief, U.S. Army Ground Forces Pacific, which was redesignated U.S. Army Pacific on February 1, 1947, and which was made command headquarters for all Army units in the Pacific and Far East under the Commander in Chief, Pacific, on July 1, 1957.

The records include a mail distribution scheme file of the Adjutant General's Postal Division, 1942-46, case files of the

Sugamo Prison Supervisory Detachment, 1945-52, and records relating to the guerrilla resistance movement in the Philippines, 1942-45.

RECORDS OF THE HAWAIIAN DEPARTMENT. 1941-45. 1 lin. ft. (in WNRC).

From 1939 the Hawaiian Department served as the Army's major command in the Central Pacific until USAFICPA was established in 1943. The Department's records and most of its responsibilities were transferred to USAFICPA, but it remained active for such purposes as military government. The records consist of correspondence of the Office of Internal Security and Office of the Military Governor and relate to Hawaiian civilian internees.

RECORDS OF HEADQUARTERS EASTERN DEFENSE COMMAND. 1941-46. 13 lin. ft. (in WNRC).

The Northeast Defense Command, established in March 1941, became the Eastern Theater of Operations in December 1941 and the Eastern Defense Command (EDC) in March 1942. EDC was assigned responsibilities of the discontinued Central Defense Command in January 1944 and those of the Southern Defense Command in December 1944. Both these Commands then became EDC sectors. In January 1946 EDC was discontinued. Records of the Southwestern Sector and its predecessor, the Southern Defense Command, consist of investigative case files, 1942-46, relating to the alien exclusion program for U.S. areas adjacent to the Gulf of Mexico. Records of the Chesapeake Bay Sector include periodic reports, plans, field orders, and historical sketches of units assigned to coast or harbor defense projects in the Chesapeake Bay area, 1941-45; and a history of the Chesapeake Bay Sector by Brig. Gen. R. L. Tilton, n.d.

RECORDS OF THE WESTERN DEFENSE COMMAND. 1941–46.
70 lin. ft. and 620 rolls of microfilm.

The Western Defense Command (WDC) was established March 17, 1941, and placed under the direction of the Commanding General of the 4th Army to provide for defense of the U.S. west coast. On December 11, 1941, the WDC and the Alaska Defense Command were placed under the newly established Western Theater of Operations, which was discontinued October 27, 1943. The WDC continued to function as one of the two major Army continental defense commands from November 1943 until March 1946. The records relate to the exclusion program on the west coast, which provided escorts for enemy-alien evacuees from prohibited military areas, supervised the security measures of assembly centers, helped enforce proclamations and restrictive orders, and conducted removals of Japanese and Japanese-Americans to war relocation centers. The records include policy and procedural files, microfilm copies (620 rolls) of records of assembly centers, exclusion orders, transcripts of hearings, and selected case files for individuals excluded, 1942–46; and copies of reports assembled as the final report of the Commanding General of the WDC and the 4th Army, 1941–43.

RECORDS OF OTHER ARMY FIELD COMMANDS. 1940–52.
25,897 lin. ft. (in WNRC).

These records of U.S. Army continental and overseas commands and subordinate organizations include records of such commands as the 3d Army, the U.S. Army Caribbean, the VII Corps, the U.S. Army Forces Korea, the China-Burma-India Theater, the Adriatic Base Command, and smaller geographical commands such as the Philippine Command. The records relate to maneuvers and combat operations, staff and command conferences, inspections by high-ranking officers, visits by important civilians, relationships with foreign governments, and tables of organization and equipment.

CARTOGRAPHIC RECORDS. 1942–52. 116 items.

Included are general maps prepared by the 1st, 5th, 6th, 8th, and 9th Service Commands; plans of military installations; and topographical maps of the Hawaiian Islands and the Panama Canal Zone.

See Headquarters U.S. Army Europe, *Guide to Foreign Military Studies, 1945–54, Catalog and Index* (1954) and its *Supplement* (1959).

Microfilm Publication: *German Documents Among the War Crimes Records of the Judge Advocate Division, Headquarters, United States Army, Europe,* T1021, 20 rolls.

RECORDS OF THE MILITARY GOVERNMENT OF CUBA
(RECORD GROUP 140)

The treaty that ended the Spanish-American War on December 10, 1898, provided that Spain relinquish sovereignty over Cuba. On December 13, 1898, the Adjutant General, U.S. Army, ordered the establishment of the Division (later Department) of Cuba. Maj. Gen. John R. Brooke, who directed military affairs in Cuba, was also military governor and directed civil affairs through the Military Government of

Cuba. On December 20, 1899, he was succeeded by Maj. Gen. Leonard Wood, who served until May 20, 1902, when the Republic of Cuba was established. The Late Military Government of Cuba was established at Washington, D.C., to complete business and transfer the military government records to the Bureau of Insular Affairs in the War Department (see RG 350). Many of the records of the military government were destroyed in 1913 under congressional authorization.

There are 251 cubic feet of records dated between 1898 and 1903 in this record group.

RECORDS. 1898–1903. 301 lin. ft.

These consist of all extant records of the Military Government of Cuba and the Late Military Government of Cuba, including reports of officials, 1901–2; letters received and sent, 1899–1903, with indexes, and abstracts of those received; coasting permits and oaths of masters, 1899–1902; ledgers of the Treasurer of Cuba, 1900–1902; correspondence and related documents of the auditor, 1898–1902, with records relating to audits of the Customs Service, the Post Office, and the Bureau of Internal Revenue, 1899–1902, and financial records of the Jucaro and San Fernando Railroad, 1899–1900; correspondence, orders, circulars, and news bulletins of the collector of customs, 1899–1902, with personnel records, 1898–1901; correspondence, reports, and personnel records of the chief engineer, 1899–1902; a journal of the director of posts, 1899–1903, and letters, cases referred, and reports of special agents, 1899–1902; correspondence of the Department of Havana, 1899–1900, concerning schools and hospitals; journals of the judge advocate and the Legal Division, 1899–1902; correspondence and reports of the inspector general, 1900–1902; letters concerning the Cuban census, 1899–1900; an index to the correspondence of the Captain of the Port of Havana, 1899–1901; property returns of the commissioner of public schools, 1900–1902; correspondence and documents of the Tariff Revision Commission, 1901; and lists of military government records compiled before they were shipped to the United States, 1902–3.

Cartographic records (50 items) consist of maps and plans from engineers surveys, plans of fortified sites, and topographic maps of strategic areas prepared by the Division, 1898–1900, and Department, 1901–2, of Cuba.

See Margareth Jorgensen, comp., *Preliminary Inventory of the Records of the Military Government of Cuba*, PI 145 (1962).

RECORDS OF THE PROVISIONAL GOVERNMENT OF CUBA (RECORD GROUP 199)

In 1906 T. Estrada Palma, President of the Republic of Cuba, requested that the United States maintain order and protect life and property in Cuba after dissatisfaction with his reelection culminated in insurrection. U.S. Secretary of War William H. Taft, acting as mediator between the insurrectionists and President Palma's government, issued a proclamation on September 29, 1906, establishing the Provisional Government of Cuba to restore order, peace, and public confidence, and to hold free elections. On October 13, 1906, Charles E. Magoon, a former law officer in the Bureau of Insular Affairs, succeeded Taft as Provisional Governor, and on October 23, 1906, the Bureau assumed responsibility for all matters in the United States relating to the temporary administration of the Cuban government. The Provisional Government functioned chiefly through existing Cuban executive departments headed by Cuban acting secretaries who were advised by U.S. Army officers. On legal matters the Advisory Law Commission assisted the Governor. When the newly elected Cuban President was inaugurated on January 28, 1909, the Governor relinquished his post.

There are 17 cubic feet of records dated between 1906 and 1909 in this record group.

RECORDS. 1906-9. 20 lin. ft.

Included are the Provisional Governor's confidential correspondence; the treasurer's reports of funds received, warrants paid, movements of funds, and payments made on internal debt bonds; the controller general's reports of money received, warrants issued, expenditures approved, disbursements made, and bond and stamp movements; the auditor's statements of the apportionment of funds, balances, and collections received from maritime, land, and loan taxes; and National Board of Health reports on yellow fever and contagious diseases.

CARTOGRAPHIC RECORDS. 1906-9. 145 items.

These consist of maps prepared by the Army of Cuban Pacification, including a large-scale manuscript military map of Cuba, plans of cities and towns that show billeting of troops, and thematic maps.

See Roland Rieder and Charlotte M. Ashby, comps., *Preliminary Inventory of the Records of the Provisional Government of Cuba*, PI 146 (1962).

RECORDS OF THE DOMINICAN CUSTOMS RECEIVERSHIP (RECORD GROUP 139)

The Dominican Customs Receivership became operative April 1, 1905, after the United States and the Dominican Republic signed an executive arrangement (modified by conventions of February 8, 1907, and December 27, 1924) to avert intervention by other foreign states in Dominican affairs. The United States was to adjust all obligations of the Dominican Government through the collection and administration of its customs duties. Immediate supervision and control of the Receivership, exercised first by the Bureau of Insular Affairs (see RG 350) of the War Department, and later by its successor, the Division of Territories and Island Possessions of the Interior Department, was transferred to the Department of State by Reorganization Plan No. IV of 1940. The funds and most of the records and other property of the Receivership, which ceased functioning March 31, 1941, pursuant to the Trujillo-Hull Convention, were turned over to the Dominican Republic. Many of the records are in the Archivo General de la Nacion at Santo Domingo. Closely related records in the National Archives of the United States are among records of the Office of the Chief of Naval Operations (see RG 38).

There are 33 cubic feet of records dated between 1905 and 1941 in this record group.

RECORDS. 1905-41. 40 lin. ft.

These consist of circulars, orders, and bulletins in Spanish and English, chiefly on administrative matters, 1905-7; administrative reports, 1905-26; classified correspondence primarily concerning political matters, 1907-16; a chronological file of general correspondence and reports, 1905-41; correspondence of General and Deputy General Receivers, chiefly relating to diplomatic matters but including personal letters, 1905-40; and special Receivership inspectors' reports chiefly concerning customhouse administration and smuggling, 1931-39.

See Kenneth W. Munden, comp., *Preliminary Inventory of the Records of the Dominican Receivership*, PI 148 (1962).

RECORDS OF THE
MILITARY GOVERNMENT OF VERACRUZ
(RECORD GROUP 141)

Following the Tampico Incident of April 9, 1914, U.S. naval forces occupied the Mexican port of Veracruz on April 21, 1914. Formal control over Veracruz was assumed by Brig. Gen. Frederick Funston on April 30, and on May 2 the Military Government of Veracruz was proclaimed. Under the military governor, officials were appointed to control city affairs. The provost marshal general conducted the municipal government through a Legal Department and Departments of Finance, Public Works, Public Safety, and Education. Military government ended with the evacuation of U.S. troops on November 23, 1914. This record group includes only those records relating to the government of the city and port of Veracruz.

There are 40 cubic feet of records dated between April and November 1914 in this record group.

RECORDS. 1914. 47 lin. ft.

These consist of reports and correspondence, with an index, of the officer in charge of civil affairs; and reports received and orders issued by the military governor. Customs Service records include correspondence of the administrator of customs and captain of the port, and the customhouse secretary; fiscal records of the cashier and the fiscal officer of the customhouse; and general files of the Office of the Inspector of Lighthouses. Finance Department records include miscellaneous correspondence, reports on receipts and expenditures, and legal opinions; Legal Department records include provost court and civil claims records; and Public Safety Department records include reports, correspondence, and other records concerning sanitation, food supply, licenses, permits, and the maintenance of order.

See Kenneth W. Munden, comp., *Preliminary Inventory of the Records of the Military Government of Veracruz*, PI 138 (1962).

RECORDS OF THE AMERICAN EXPEDITIONARY FORCES
(WORLD WAR I), 1917-23
(RECORD GROUP 120)

The American Expeditionary Forces (AEF) originated May 26, 1917, when Maj. Gen. John J. Pershing assumed the duties of Commander in Chief under General Order 1, Headquarters AEF. AEF General Headquarters, first located at Paris, was transferred to Chaumont in September 1917. Following the Armistice, AEF occupation troops in Germany were designated the American Forces in Germany. Those in other countries were placed under the American Forces in France, which was returned as rapidly as possible to the United

States. General Headquarters was returned in September 1919 and discontinued in August 1920. The AEF was dissolved in January 1923 when the troops in Germany were returned to the United States. Some cablegrams relating to the AEF are among records of the Adjutant General's Office, 1917- (see RG 407).

See John J. Pershing, *My Experiences in the World War* (New York, 1931); and the Historical Division, Department of the Army, *United States Army in the World War: 1917-1919* (1948).

There are 26,513 cubic feet of records dated between 1912 and 1929 in this record group.

RECORDS OF AEF GENERAL HEADQUARTERS. 1917-21.
4,109 lin. ft.

Records of the Office of the Commander in Chief consist of general correspondence and indexes, correspondence relating to AEF schools (the "Training File"), historical reports and monographs accumulated by the General Staff secretary, and correspondence, memorandums, cablegrams, and miscellaneous records of the Chief of Staff, 1917-19; correspondence of Headquarters, General of the Armies, 1920-21; and reports about General Pershing's inspections of U.S. military installations, 1919-20.

General Staff records consist of reports, memorandums, issuances, cablegrams, correspondence, and other records of Sections G-1 (Administration), G-2 (Intelligence), G-3 (Operations), G-4 (Coordination), and G-5 (Training) under Assistant Chiefs of Staff, and of the Historical Section. These records relate to intelligence operations and include information summaries and records of the Provost Marshal General's Office, the Prisoner of War Division, the American Red Cross, and training schools and programs, 1917-19; the AEF newspaper *Stars and Stripes*, 1918-19, and correspondence of its office, 1917-19; and statistical and other reports concerning personnel and equipment, 1917-20.

Administrative Staff records, 1917-19, include reports, issuances, correspondence and cablegrams (with indexes), telegrams, memorandums, and a reference library of the Adjutant General's Office. There are also general, special, and court-martial orders and correspondence of the Headquarters Commandant, the Inspector General, the Judge Advocate General, and the Chief Chaplain.

Technical Staff records, 1917-19, consist of records of the Chief of the Air Service, the Chief of Artillery, the Railway Artillery Reserve, and the Anti-Aircraft Service. They include headquarters correspondence; telegrams, memorandums, issuances, and statistical and other reports of subordinate installations and training centers; and a manuscript history of the Air Service,compiled by Col. Edgar S. Gorrell, 1917-19.

RECORDS OF THE SERVICES OF SUPPLY. 1917-21, with a few dated as early as 1912 and as late as 1929.
4,907 lin. ft.

Responsibility for the procurement and transportation of supplies was shared by the Line of Communication (LOC) and the Technical Services until that responsibility was consolidated in February 1918 under the Service of the Rear (SOR). The SOR, with headquarters at Tours, France, became the Services of Supply (SOS) on March 13, 1918. After the Armistice the SOS was given responsibility for repatriation of American troops, but in September 1919 its functions were transferred to the American Forces in France.

These records, some of which were created in the United States, include headquarters records consisting of cablegrams, general and special orders, bulletins, memorandums, and circulars of the LOC and SOR, 1917-18. Records of the commanding general include correspondence, with indexes, and historical studies and monographs, 1917-19; and cablegrams, with indexes and registers, telegrams, orders, bulletins, and interoffice memorandums, 1918-19. General Staff records consist of correspondence, telegrams, issuances, and equipment and personnel reports of G-1, 1918-19; and correspondence and miscellaneous records of G-2 and G-4, 1918-19. Administrative Staff records include correspondence and miscellaneous records of the Adjutant General, the Inspector

General, the Judge Advocate, and the Headquarters Commandant at Tours, 1918-19.

Technical Staff records include records of the Army Service Corps, 1918-19, consisting of administrative correspondence, telegrams, and issuances of the Office of the Director; records of special and technical units; and records of the Labor Bureau, concerning civilian labor utilized by the AEF. Records, 1918-19, of the Finance Bureau consist of correspondence, memorandums, reports, and periodic financial statements concerning contracts and disbursements; and of correspondence, telegrams, cablegrams, reports, and miscellaneous records of the General Purchasing Agent and field purchasing agents. Records concerning supply, construction, maintenance, and personnel include the administrative correspondence and telegrams of the Chief Ordnance Officers at Chaumont, 1917-18, and at Tours, 1918-19; and other records, 1917-19, of the Chief Ordnance Officer at Tours, consisting of correspondence (with indexes), cablegrams sent and received, and special orders from AEF General Headquarters and LOC, SOR, and SOS Headquarters. Records of the Office of the Chief Surgeon and its subordinate divisions include reports on American sick and wounded and the facilities available for their care, 1912-29, telegrams and cablegrams, 1918-19, and correspondence, issuances, and personnel and financial registers, 1917-19. There are also records of the Chief Engineer, Motor Transport Corps, and Transportation Corps, 1917-19; the Leave Bureau and the War Risk Insurance Section, 1918-19; the Renting, Requisition, and Claims Service, 1918-20; the Chief Quartermaster, 1915-22; and the Chief Signal Officer, 1912-21.

Also included are records of geographic sections, 1917-19, including correspondence, telegrams, issuances, memorandums, reports, rosters, strength returns, and historical studies of six base sections in France, one in England, and one in Italy (each base section encompassed a coastal region that had at least one major seaport); the intermediate section in central France where troops and supplies were stationed; and the advance section, a narrow area from which men and supplies were distributed to frontline units.

RECORDS OF AEF TACTICAL UNITS. 1917-19. 3,887 lin. ft.

The AEF was composed of three armies, each consisting of corps and other tactical units. Records of the 1st and 2d Armies, 1917-19, consist of records of the general, administrative, and technical staffs, and of the offices of the commanders. Included are historical files of monographs, reports, and miscellaneous records maintained in the offices of the commanders.

Records of corps, divisions, and other tactical units, 1917-19, include records of the nine corps and 43 divisions assigned to the AEF, consisting of correspondence, telegrams, historical files, memorandums, issuances, and miscellaneous records of unit commanders, subordinate units of divisions, and general, administrative, and technical staffs. There are also records of tank corps, a chemical warfare service gas regiment, a cavalry brigade, independent infantry brigades, pioneer infantry regiments, several kinds of quartermaster units, machinegun and field signal battalions, ammunition trains, an ordnance guard company, and trench mortar, field artillery, heavy artillery, and military police units.

RECORDS OF THE AMERICAN FORCES IN FRANCE. 1919-20. 79 lin. ft.

The American Forces in France was established September 1, 1919, and discontinued in December 1920. Headquarters records include correspondence, telegrams, and embarkation orders, 1919–20; and cablegrams, memorandums, and other issuances, 1919. There is also correspondence of the Visitors' Bureau, the Headquarters Commandant, Base Section 1, the District of Paris military police detachment, the Chief Surgeon, and the Advance Section, 1919; and of the Inspector General, the Judge Advocate, the Army Service Corps, the Chief Signal Officer, G-1, the Chief Ordnance Officer, the Ordnance Liaison Officer, and Base Section 5, 1919–20.

RECORDS OF THE AMERICAN FORCES IN GERMANY. 1918–23. 801 lin. ft.

In July 1919 the American Forces in Germany succeeded the 3d Army, which had been established November 15, 1918, as an occupation force, and the Advance General Headquarters at Trier. These records, which concern administration and civil affairs, are of the 3d Army, the Advance General Headquarters, and the American Forces in Germany (including records of its commander and general, administrative, and technical staffs).

There are such Advance General Headquarters records as G-2 correspondence and general information dossiers about the Rhine Valley and the Civil Affairs Officer's correspondence, 1918–19. General Staff records include G-2 bulletins on political and economic conditions in Germany and excerpts from the German press, 1920–22. Administrative Staff records include American liaison officers' correspondence with British, 1919–23, and French, 1920–22, armies; reports to the Secretary of State by the American representative on the Inter-Allied Rhineland High Commission, 1920–23; and the Civil Affairs Officer's reports, correspondence, and statistics, 1919–23. Technical Staff records include the Finance Officer's reports and correspondence, 1919–23, and minutes and other records of Allied conferences and committees, concerning occupation costs, 1920–22.

RECORDS OF THE AMERICAN POLISH RELIEF EXPEDITION. 1919–21. 4 lin. ft.

At the suggestion of Herbert Hoover this Expedition was organized in 1919 from AEF units in France. It operated mobile units that conducted delousing and sanitation activities to combat a typhus epidemic in Poland. The records consist of general correspondence, telegrams, historical files, and the Chief Surgeon's records, 1919–20; and strength returns and general, special, and court-martial orders, 1919–21.

RECORDS OF THE AEF, NORTH RUSSIA. 1917–19. 14 lin. ft.

In July 1918 President Wilson ordered three American battalions to aid Allied forces in guarding war supplies at Murmansk, but the British redirected them to Archangel. These troops were withdrawn in June and July 1919. The records include those of the Chief of the American Military Mission to Russia, 1917–19; and medical unit records, troopship lists, rosters, and the general correspondence, issuances, and other correspondence of the Inspector General, the Judge Advocate, and the Chief Surgeon, 1918–19.

RECORDS OF THE AMERICAN SECTION OF THE SUPREME WAR COUNCIL. 1917–19. 17 lin. ft.

This Council was established at the Rapallo Conference of November 7, 1917, by representatives of Great Britain, France, and Italy; U.S. participation began 10 days later. The Council prepared policy recommendations concerning conduct of the war. The records consist of minutes, records of the American Section, and reports, studies, and monographs relating to Council activities.

RECORDS OF THE AMERICAN SECTION OF THE MILITARY BOARD OF ALLIED SUPPLY

(MBAS). 1918-25, with a few dated as late as 1928. 18 lin. ft.

At the suggestion of General Pershing and General Purchasing Agent Brig. Gen. Charles G. Dawes, the MBAS, which met for the first time on June 28, 1918, was established to ensure Allied logistic cooperation. Unanimous MBAS decisions had the force of orders to the Allied armies supply services. From 1919 to 1922 the MBAS prepared comparative studies concerning Allied and German logistic practices. The records consist of minutes of MBAS and its editorial subcommittee, 1918-22; correspondence, with registers, 1918-28; miscellaneous administrative records, 1918-25; studies and reports on transportation and supply problems, 1918-19; maps, charts, and other records collected in studying German logistic practices, 1919-21; and preliminary and final drafts, 1924-25, of the *Final Report of the MBAS*, the comparative study of Allied logistic practices subsequently used as a text in Army War College logistics courses.

RECORDS OF AMERICAN MILITARY MISSIONS. 1917-19. 14 lin. ft.

Included are records of the American Military Missions at British General Headquarters, consisting of correspondence of American officers attached to British Expeditionary Forces headquarters, 1917-19; at French General Headquarters, including correspondence with AEF General Headquarters, 1917-19, and with French General Headquarters, 1918-19; and to Italy, including correspondence and reports, 1917-19.

RECORDS OF THE AMERICAN SECTION OF THE PERMANENT INTERNATIONAL ARMISTICE COMMISSION (PIAC). 1918-20. 23 lin. ft.

The PIAC, composed of American, British, French, Belgian, and German officers, proposed measures for the execution of Armistice terms that concerned repatriating Allied civilians and war prisoners, protecting civilians and civil and military property in areas evacuated by the Germans, maintaining communications and transportation facilities, and delivering German war materials, locomotives, rolling stock, and trucks. The records consist of daily PIAC minutes, minutes and other records about PIAC subcommittees, and Prisoner of War Subcommittee minutes and bulletins, 1918-19; and records of the American commissioner to the Inter-Allied Commission on the Repatriation of Prisoners of War, 1918-19. Also included are the final PIAC report, 1919; correspondence, 1918-19, and telegrams, 1919, of the American section and representative; correspondence of the Belgian, 1918-20, and British and French, 1918-19, sections; correspondence of U.S. troop detachments at prisoner-of-war camps, concerning Russian war prisoners and war prisoner repatriation, 1919; and records of the U.S. Military Mission to Berlin, including headquarters correspondence, Medical Department records, the Chief's final report, and medical detachment inspection reports, 1919.

RECORDS RELATING TO THE AMERICAN COMMISSION TO NEGOTIATE PEACE. 1918-19. 7 lin. ft.

President Wilson organized this Commission to represent the United States at the Paris Peace Conference (see RG

256). These records consist of reports submitted by consuls and military attaches, concerning European countries and special Commission orders, 1919; and daily reports from General Headquarters, G-2, to Gen. Tasker H. Bliss, correspondence and orders of the Commission's headquarters battalion, and other reports, 1918-19.

CARTOGRAPHIC AND AUDIOVISUAL RECORDS. 1914-23. 50,950 items.

Cartographic records, 1914-23 (41,000 items), include manuscript, annotated, and published maps, chiefly large-scale, that indicate Allied and enemy military operations, troop dispositions, campaigns, and the order of battle and final positions of the armies on the Western Front in 1918; large-scale French, American, and German topographic sheets of the Western, Italian, and Balkan Fronts, 1914-18; communications, transportation, and logistic maps of France and adjacent areas; French and American aerial photographs and reconnaissance maps relating to the Western Front; and records concerning American operations in Germany, Italy, and Russia. Many of these records are of British, French, German, Italian, Belgian, and Austro-Hungarian origin.

Audiovisual records, 1915-20 (9,950 items), include photographs of battle damage and American cemeteries in France, inter-Allied marksmanship competitions, the awarding of the Croix de Guerre, and Camouflage, Mining, and Bridging Sections of the Army Engineer School. Also included are liberty bond, Red Cross, Jewish Welfare Board, YWCA, and French and other military posters relating to World War I.

See Franklin W. Burch, comp., *Preliminary Inventory of the Cartographic Records of the American Expeditionary Forces, 1917-21*, PI 165 (1966).

Microfilm Publications: *Records of the 27th Division of the American Expeditionary Forces (World War I), 1917-1919*, M819, 60 rolls, DP; and *Index to Correspondence of the Adjutant General, AEF Headquarters, 1917-1920*, T900, 132 rolls.

RECORDS OF THE UNITED STATES MILITARY ACADEMY (RECORD GROUP 404)

The U.S. Military Academy was established by an act of March 16, 1802, which directed the establishment of the Corps of Engineers at West Point to constitute a military academy and designated the principal engineer as Superintendent under direction of the President. An act of April 29, 1812, provided that the Academy consist of the Corps of Engineers and certain professors and that for military instruction the cadets be arranged into companies officered from the Corps. The Chief Engineer was ordered in 1818 to establish his headquarters at Washington, D.C., but the Academy remained under his jurisdiction until July 1866 when supervisory responsibility was transferred to the Secretary of War. From 1877 until 1882 the Academy and the post at West Point constituted a separate military department, with the Superintendent reporting to the General in Chief of the Army. Since 1947 the Secretary of the Army has supervised the Academy, whose mission is to train Regular Army officers.

There are 1,900 cubic feet of records (at West Point) dated between 1801 and 1966 in this record group.

RECORDS OF THE SUPERINTENDENT. 1818-1964. 27 lin. ft.

These consist of annual reports, correspondence, post returns, consolidated morning reports, rosters, registers of merit, and proceedings of the Council of Administration.

RECORDS OF THE OFFICE OF THE ADJUTANT. 1817–1965. 332 lin. ft.

These consist of general administrative records, letters sent and received, endorsements, memorandums, a general correspondence file and accompanying index, post orders issued, orders received, and reports of officers' absences.

RECORDS OF THE COMMANDANT OF CADETS. 1817–1966. 62 lin. ft.

Included are orders issued, memorandums, bulletins, muster rolls, semiannual and annual rolls of cadets, registers of delinquencies and punishments, and sick returns.

RECORDS OF THE OFFICES OF INSTRUCTION. 1929–65. 18 lin. ft.

These consist of organization and functional charts, rosters, pamphlets, texts, and other records of instruction offices.

RECORDS OF THE OFFICE OF THE TREASURER. 1828–1919. 19 lin. ft.

These consist of the treasurer's correspondence, daybooks, ledgers, cashbooks, provision returns, payment statements, and other fiscal records.

RECORDS OF THE OFFICE OF THE DEAN. 1801–1966. 798 lin. ft.

General records of the Office include correspondence, cadets' personnel files, personal and school history sheets, engagement for service and oath of allegiance documents, and registers of graduates. Also included is correspondence of the librarian.

RECORDS OF ACADEMIC DEPARTMENTS. 1892–1966. 38 lin. ft.

These include organization and functional charts, rosters, pamphlets, and texts, mostly for the 1930–66 period.

RECORDS OF THE OFFICE OF THE DIRECTOR OF ADMISSIONS AND REGISTRAR. 1818–1966. 38 lin. ft.

These consist of academic board minutes, descriptive lists of new cadets, and cadets' academic records.

MISCELLANEOUS RECORDS. 1819–1966. 463 lin. ft.

These consist of reports of the Board of Visitors and cadets' personnel files of the Department of the Army.

AUDIOVISUAL RECORDS OF THE CHIEF SIGNAL OFFICER. 1900–1964. 24,760 items.

Included are photographs (23,100 items) of events, scenes, and people at West Point; and recordings (1,660 items) of lectures and speeches.

RECORDS OF THE UNITED STATES SOLDIERS' HOME (RECORD GROUP 231)

The U.S. Soldiers' Home originated in an act of March 3, 1851, which provided for a "military asylum" with branches to support invalid and disabled soldiers. Temporary homes were set up in 1851 at New Orleans, La., East Pascagoula, Miss., and Washington, D.C. The New Orleans asylum existed for about a year. The Western Military Asylum at Harrodsburg, Ky., established in 1853, received members of the discontinued East Pascagoula asylum (also called Greenwood's Island) and ceased operations in 1858. An act of March 3, 1859, changed the name of the asylum at Washington to the Soldiers' Home, which in 1947 also began caring for Air Force personnel.

Funds for establishing the asylums were composed of part of the tribute the Army levied on Mexico City during the Mexican War, which the Secretary of War held for a future military asylum, and also of an appropriation for discharged soldiers. The existing home is supported by funds withheld from the pay of Army and Air Force personnel, unclaimed money from deceased servicemen's estates, and forfeitures due to desertions and stoppages by court-martial sentencing. The home is a quasi-official agency administered by a Board of Commissioners, consisting of the Governor of the Home (the Board president), the Adjutant General of the Army, the Surgeons General of the Army and the Air Force, the Judge Advocate Generals of the Army and the Air Force, the Chief of Engineers, the Director of Personnel Planning for the Air Force, the Chief of Finance of the Army, and the officer performing Army quartermaster duties.

There are 37 cubic feet of records dated between 1803 and 1943 in this record group.

CORRESPONDENCE AND ORDERS. 1851-1930. 5 lin. ft.

These comprise letters, 1868-99 and 1902-30, and endorsements, 1879-1902, sent by the Governor of the Soldiers' Home; Board proceedings and letters sent by the secretary of the Board of Commissioners, 1868-83; letters and endorsements sent by the office of the attending surgeon, 1881-1912; letters received, 1899-1903, with a name index; and reports, correspondence, and orders relating to administration of the Military Asylum and the Soldiers' Home, 1851-1909. There are also orders issued by the Governor's office, 1892-1906 and 1915, and administrative memorandums and orders, 1852-1923.

RECORDS OF INMATES. 1803-1943. 37 lin. ft.

Included are general registers, reports, and returns, including descriptive books of men admitted and discharged and returns and muster rolls of inmates, 1851-1941; registers of sick inmates, 1872-1943; registers, death certificates, statements of service, descriptions of deceased inmates, and other records relating to deaths, 1852-1942; warrants, a register of prisoners confined, and records relating to the confining and discharging of prisoners, 1869-1927; and documents generally predating the establishment of the Soldiers' Home that appear to be inmates' personal papers, 1803-58.

RECORDS OF EMPLOYEES. 1851-1941. 1 lin. ft.

These consist of reports of civilian and inmate employees, 1851-62; monthly reports of persons employed at East Pascagoula, 1853, and Harrodsburg, 1853-58; and a register of employee transfers, discharges, absences, and resignations, 1938-41.

Department of the Navy

General

GENERAL RECORDS OF THE DEPARTMENT OF THE NAVY (RECORD GROUP 80)

The Department of the Navy was established by an act of April 30, 1798. Control of naval affairs had previously been exercised by the Congress under the Articles of Confederation and by the Secretary of War. The Board of Navy Commissioners was created February 7, 1815, as part of an expansion of the Navy Department, but its authority was generally confined to procuring stores and materials and to constructing, arming, and equipping vessels of war. The Secretary of the Navy retained charge of naval personnel and discipline, appointments, detailing of officers, and movements of vessels. The Board of Navy Commissioners was abolished in 1842 and replaced by five bureaus. Two additional offices were established in the Secretary's Office—the Office of the Judge Advocate General (see RG 125) in 1880 and the Office of the Chief of Naval Operations (see RG 38) in 1915. In 1947 the Department of the Navy became part of the National Military Establishment, and in 1949 it became part of the Department of Defense. The principal tasks of the Department of the Navy are policy control, naval command, logistics administration and control, and business administration.

Most records of the Secretary's Office before 1885 are in the naval records collection of the Office of Naval Records and Library (see RG 45).

There are 9,266 cubic feet of records dated between 1804 and 1959 in this record group.

RECORDS OF THE OFFICE OF THE SECRETARY OF THE NAVY. 1804-1959. 7,797 lin. ft.

After bureaus were established in 1842 the Office of the Secretary retained overall supervision of the Department but maintained exclusive control over matters of civilian personnel, finance, and public relations. Later the operation of naval petroleum and oil-shale reserves was supervised by this Office.

The records include general correspondence, 1804-1948, consisting of books of letters sent, 1804-1913, and loose copies of letters sent, 1858-86 and 1918-40, with indexes. Included among letters received are those from the Commandant of the Marine Corps, 1828-86, and reports from commissions and boards. There are three large general files of correspondence for the periods 1885-96, 1897-1926, and 1926-46, accompanied by name and subject indexes. Included are office files of Secretaries of the Navy Frank Knox, 1940-44, and James Forrestal, 1944-47. There are also a number of smaller security-classified and unclassified subseries of correspondence, 1917-46, maintained separately from the general files.

Included also are personnel records, 1808-1959, chiefly civilian, with some for Marine Corps officers; fiscal records, 1821-1934, including correspondence sent by the disbursing clerk, bills approved by the Secretary, and daily and summary account records; and public relations records, 1897-1943, including those relating to the Department's participation in national and international expositions, press releases and transcripts of press conferences, and letters received from the public on controversial issues.

RECORDS OF SUBORDINATE OFFICES. 1891-1957. 890 lin. ft.

The Office of the Assistant Secretary of the Navy, originally established in

1861 and abolished in 1869, was re-created in 1890. The records, 1891-1940, relate to civilian personnel and the administration of shore establishments. Most of the correspondence of this office is in the general files of the Secretary's Office, but the records include letters sent and memorandums issued, 1893-1911, some sent by Assistant Secretary Theodore Roosevelt. Also included are office files of Assistant Secretary Franklin D. Roosevelt, 1913-14.

The Office of the Under Secretary was authorized by Congress on June 20, 1940. Its records, some of which are classified, include the office file of Under Secretary James Forrestal, 1940-44, the desk file and correspondence of his aide and special assistant, 1942-44, official histories relating to naval war contracts renegotiations, 1940-47, and transcripts of speeches by Under Secretary Thomas S. Gates, 1954-57.

Among the records of other units are those for the officer in charge of operating the Federal Shipbuilding and Dry-dock Co., Kearney, N.J., 1941-42, Director of Naval Petroleum and Oil-Shale Reserves, 1909-38, Office of Research and Inventions, 1918-45, Administrative Office, 1941-46, Office of Procurement and Material, 1942-45, and Office of Budget and Reports, 1942-45.

RECORDS OF THE BOARD OF NAVY COMMISSIONERS. 1815-42.
7 lin. ft.

Most of the records of the Board are in the naval records collection of the Office of Naval Records and Library (see RG 45). In this record group are inventories of stores in shore establishments, fiscal records, drafts of proposed rules and regulations for the Department, Capt. Matthew C. Perry's report on British dockyards, and instructions for building ships.

RECORDS OF BOARDS AND COMMISSIONS. 1882-1947.
963 lin. ft.

These include minutes or journals, reports received, correspondence, recommendations, and miscellaneous related records; many of the series are fragmentary. The earliest belong to the Naval Advisory Board, 1882-90, which advised the Secretary on the construction of war vessels. Records of the Compensation Board, 1917-41, which supervised costs of vessels built under contract with the Department on a cost-plus-profit basis, include correspondence, audit records, material order data, and records relating to special rentals and plant extension sections. Other board records include those for the Board on Construction, 1889-1909, Naval War Board, 1898, Naval Consulting Board, 1915-23, Submarine Board, 1928-29, Navy Manpower Survey Board, 1943-44, Army-Navy Munitions Board, 1922-42, Navy Board for Production Awards, 1941-45, and Board on Awards to Civil Employees, 1918-47. There are some records of other boards concerned with selection of sites for navy yards, organization of yards, business methods of the Department, hull changes, and fuel oil.

CARTOGRAPHIC AND AUDIOVISUAL RECORDS. ca. 1840-1958. 786,917 items.

Cartographic records (10 items) include a map of an area in the State of Sonora, Mexico, 1913; maps of Guam, 1908, one showing lands purchased by the Navy for a coaling station at Sumay; and published topographic maps of an area in California, annotated to show the flightlines of an aerial photographic survey of Naval Oil Reserves 1 and 2, ca. 1932.

Still pictures (786,872 items) consist of photographs, some of artworks dating back to 1798, of Secretaries and Assistant Secretaries, U.S. Presidents, admirals, commodores, other officers, and enlisted personnel, ca. 1840-1958; women in the Navy Air Force, Navy, and Marine Corps, 1943-45; ships, boats, ordnance, equipment, airfields, naval air stations, navy bases and yards in the United States and foreign countries, blimps, dirigibles, balloons (including the first navy observation balloon), hydroplanes, flying boats, and other types of airplanes, 1896-1958; historic flights, air races, polar expeditions, and trophies, 1896-1939; training activities, 1911-58; the Great White Fleet in Australia, 1908; and the Japanese surrender aboard the U.S.S. *Missouri*, 1945. Included are photographs of plants under contract to supply the Navy with war materials, 1943, and recruiting, Red Cross, and Liberty Loan posters, 1892-1919. There are also photographs of foreign navies and scenes, 1911-58.

There are motion pictures (35 reels) of wreckage of the Navy dirigible *Shenandoah* (ZR-1), 1925; medical training in the United States, 1938; and naval equipment and activities, mainly in the Pacific theater during World War II, including ships, submarines, airplanes, training, mail delivery, defense against kamikaze attacks, the battle of Midway, the battle for the Marianas, the invasions of Saipan, Eniwetok, Solomon Islands, Guam, and Okinawa, preparation for the invasion of the Ryukus, bombing raids over Japan, and the Japanese surrender aboard the U.S.S. *Missouri*. There are also films on the history of naval aviation, Japan, and peace celebrations in several American cities.

Microfilm Publication: *Annual Reports of the Governors of Guam, 1901-1941*, M181, 3 rolls, DP.

SPECIFIC RESTRICTIONS

I. *Records*: Records of the office of James V. Forrestal as Under Secretary and Secretary of the Navy, including records of his special assistant, Eugene S. Duffield, 1941-47.

Restrictions: Permission to examine these records must be obtained from authorized personnel of the Secretary of the Navy's Office.

Specified by: Assistant Vice Chief of Naval Operations/Director of Naval Administration.

II. *Records*: Photographic records of the Department of the Navy accessioned from the Naval Photographic Center, Washington, comprising the Department of the Navy's official "general" still picture history file.

Restrictions: Access may be granted to these photographic records except that when the records are not marked or otherwise stamped "Released," the approval of the Chief of Information, Navy Department, must be obtained before reproductions thereof are furnished.

Specified by: Assistant Vice Chief of Naval Operations/Director of Naval Administration.

NAVAL RECORDS COLLECTION OF THE OFFICE OF NAVAL RECORDS AND LIBRARY (RECORD GROUP 45)

The Naval Records Collection was begun in 1882 when the Librarian of the Navy Department, then in the Office of Naval Intelligence, began to collect for publication naval documents relating to the Civil War. The staff engaged in this task was designated the Naval War Record Office and was known collectively with the library as the Office of Library and Naval War Records. The Office was placed under the Secretary of the Navy in 1899, and shortly thereafter most of the bound records of the Secretary's Office—all dated before 1886—were transferred to the Office of Library and Naval War Records. In the early 1900's the Office collected older records of naval bureaus and records relating to naval personnel and operations during the American Revolution. In 1915 the Office was named the Office of Naval Records and Library, and it was reassigned in 1919 to the Office of Naval Intelligence where it was merged with the Historical Section, created in 1918 to select and arrange records relating to U. S. naval participation in World War I. During the period between World Wars I and II many documents relating to naval history were acquired from private and public sources. In August 1946 the Office of Naval Records and Library was combined with the Office of Naval History, established in 1944 to prepare histories and narratives of naval activities during World War II.

There are 2,962 cubic feet of records dated between 1691 and 1927 in this record group.

RECORDS OF THE OFFICE OF THE SECRETARY OF THE NAVY. 1776-1913. 1,127 lin. ft.

These comprise nearly all existing records that originated in the Office of the Secretary before 1886 and include correspondence, directives, and fiscal, personnel, legal, and miscellaneous records. Most of the records created after 1886 are among the general records of the Department of the Navy (see RG 80).

Correspondence includes letters to officers, to Federal executive agents,

and to the Congress, and miscellaneous letters sent, 1798-1886. There are letters to commandants and Navy agents, 1808-65; confidential letters sent, 1813-22, 1840, 1843-79, and 1893-1908; letters to the Board of Navy Commissioners, 1815-42, and Members of Congress, 1820-31; indexes, 1823-61; letters to Navy Department bureaus, 1842-86, and officers commanding squadrons or vessels, 1861-86; and deciphered messages, 1888-1910. Letters received include miscellaneous letters received, 1801-84; letters from officers below the rank of commander, 1802-48, commanders, 1804-86, captains, 1805-61, officers commanding expeditions, 1818-85, the Congress, 1825-61, the Board of Navy Commissioners, 1827-42, Federal executive agents, 1837-86, officers commanding squadrons, 1841-86, Navy Department Bureaus, 1842-85, Navy agents and naval storekeepers, 1843-65, the Superintendent of the Naval Academy, 1847-84, commandants of Navy yards and shore stations, 1848-86, rear admirals, commodores, and captains, 1862-65, and rear admirals and commodores, 1866-84; and related registers and indexes.

Directives, 1776-1913, include orders, circulars, and regulations; fiscal records, 1794-1893, include correspondence, ledgers, and registers of bills and warrants; and personnel records include correspondence about appointments and resignations, 1803-90, muster rolls and payrolls, 1798-1859, rosters, 1798-1889, registers and indexes of applications and appointments, 1814-87, registers and indexes of regular officers, 1798-1874, registers of volunteer officers, 1861-79, and indexes and registers of officers' orders, 1823-73. Legal records resulted from legal and regulatory functions of the Office of the Secretary, relating to contracts, claims, prize vessels and their cargoes, prisoners, courts-martial, courts of inquiry, and the examination, promotion, and retirement of Navy and Marine officers, 1807-76. Miscellaneous records include letters relating to the Barbary pirates, 1803-8; correspondence relating to the reception of liberated Africans and letters from members of the American Colonization Society; letters relating to the Florida-Indian War, 1835-42, and the Naval Asylum; reports on naval vessels and live-oak lands; and records relating to naval service.

RECORDS OF THE BOARD OF NAVY COMMISSIONERS. 1794-1842. 109 lin. ft.

Included are the journal of the Board, 1815-42, with a register, 1825-42; letters sent, 1815-42, including those to the Secretary of the Navy, Navy agents, and commandants; letters received, 1814-42; reports of the Chief Naval Constructor, 1827-34; and other records, 1794-1842, including contracts, a register of officers, inventories of naval stores, journals of timber expeditions, and records relating to expenditures, supplies, property inventories, and work at navy yards.

RECORDS OF OFFICES AND BUREAUS OF THE NAVY DEPARTMENT. 1811-1914. 48 lin. ft.

These consist of records of the Bureau of Yards and Docks, 1811-79, including letters relating to timber and a history, 1797-1875, of the Boston navy yard by Commodore George Henry Preble; the Bureau of Ordnance and Hydrography, 1842-62, including journals of the North Pacific exploring expedition under Comdrs. Cadwalader Ringgold and John Rodgers, 1853-56; the Bureau of Construction, Equipment, and Repairs, 1825-58, including statistics on building costs of naval vessels, reports on sailing vessel qualities, and reports of engineers; the Bureau of Construction and Repair, 1865-76; the Bureau of Steam Engineering, 1861-86; the Bureau of Navigation, including letters sent relating to appointments and resignations, 1813-42, cruising reports of naval vessels, 1895-1910, and daily reports of vessel arrivals and departures, 1897-1910; and the Office of the Judge Advocate General, the Office of Naval Intelligence, 1888-1914, and the Bureau of Equipment, 1888-1908.

RECORDS OF NAVAL SHORE ESTABLISHMENTS. 1814-1911. 21 lin. ft.

Included are correspondence, orders, logs, and miscellaneous records of the Baltimore, Havana, Mound City, New Orleans, Newport, and Rio Grande Naval Stations; the Boston, Gosport (Norfolk), Mare Island, New York, Pensacola, Philadelphia, Portsmouth, N.H., and Washington navy yards; and the Naval Academy.

RECORDS OF BOARDS AND COMMISSIONS. 1836-1902. 2 lin. ft.

These comprise minutes, letters, journals, and miscellaneous records of the Board for Testing Ordnance, 1836-37, the Board To Prepare a Code of Regulations for the Government of the Navy, 1857-58, the Naval Examining Board, 1861-62, the Permanent Commission, 1861-65, the Joint Army and Navy Board, 1866, the Board for the Examination of Officers for Promotion, 1868-69, the Commission To Ascertain the Cost of Removing the Naval Observatory, 1878, the Naval War Board, 1898, and the Board of Arbitration for Army and Navy Maneuvers, 1902.

RECORDS AND PAPERS FROM GOVERNMENT DEPARTMENTS AND CITIZENS. 1691-1908. 100 lin. ft.

Records transferred from the War Department include letters sent by the Secretary of War to naval officers, constructors, shipbuilders, and others, 1790-98; some records of the Philadelphia Arsenal, concerning military and naval supplies, 1796-1814; and correspondence between the Secretary of War and Samuel Hodgdon and John Harris, storekeepers at the Philadelphia Arsenal, relating to the arming of frigates and warships, 1795-98. Records transferred from the Treasury Department include indexes to bonds executed by Navy paymasters, 1809-65, and notes on naval fiscal matters, 1844-62. Records transferred from the Department of State, 1812-83, include letters from collectors of customs to the Secretary of State, relating to commissions for privateers, 1812-15.

There are originals and transcripts of logs, journals, and diaries of officers of the U.S. Navy at sea, 1776-1910, including copies of logs of the *Wasp*, 1776, *Ranger*, 1777-80, *Bonhomme Richard*, 1779, H.M.S. *Serapis*, 1779, *Alliance*, 1779-80, and *Ariel*, 1780; copies of logs and journals kept aboard the *Constitution*, 1798-1804; a log of the *Monitor*, 1862; logs and journals of American privateers and merchant vessels, 1776-1869; account books of naval vessels, 1777-1879; and a large collection of letter books of naval officers, 1778-1909. Records of the Confederate States of America and its citizens, 1861-67, consist principally of account books of naval vessels and payrolls of civilian personnel at naval shore establishments, 1861-64; muster rolls, payrolls, logs, and journals of naval vessels, 1861-65; and logs of Confederate privateers, 1861.

There are documents and transcripts of documents from foreign sources, 1691-1908, many of them concerning the British Navy, including logs and journals of naval and merchant vessels, 1775-1889; documents relating to John Paul Jones, 1778-91; registers of U.S. prisoners in Halifax, Barbados, Jamaica, and Quebec, 1805-15; and naval manuscripts copied for Capt. Alfred T. Mahan, 1807-15.

"AREA" AND "SUBJECT" FILES. 1775-1927. 1,225 lin. ft.

The "area file" and the "subject file," 1775-1927, include unbound records and documents obtained from private sources, from volumes unbound because of their poor condition, and from the files of the Office of the Secretary, the Office of Detail, and the Bureau of Navigation. The material was augmented with photographs, drawings, clippings, pamphlets, occasional cross-reference sheets, and other items. The "area file" is arranged by region; the "subject file" is arranged by subject.

Microfilm Publications: Many of the series of letters sent and received by the Secretary of the Navy to 1886 are available as microfilm publications. The "area file" for the period 1775-1910 has also been filmed. For a listing of records series and microfilm publication numbers, see the current *List of National Archives Microfilm Publications*.

RECORDS OF THE
OFFICE OF THE CHIEF OF NAVAL OPERATIONS
(RECORD GROUP 38)

The Office of the Chief of Naval Operations was established by an act of March 3, 1915, to coordinate naval operational activities. Under the Office were the Office of Naval Intelligence, the Board of Inspection and Survey, and the Naval Communication Service. On

April 8, 1942, an Executive order placed under this Office the Hydrographic Office (see RG 37) and the Naval Observatory (see RG 78).

The Chief of Naval Operations is the principal naval adviser to the President and the Secretary of the Navy on the conduct of war, the principal naval executive and adviser to the Secretary of the Navy on the administration of the Department, and the naval member of the Joint Chiefs of Staff. He is responsible for the naval operating forces and associated bureaus and offices, manpower and logistical services, research and development plans and activities, naval strategic planning, the organization and training of naval forces, their preparation and readiness, and the maintenance of a high level of quality among personnel and components of the Navy.

The general correspondence of the Office from 1915 to June 30, 1942, is interfiled with that of the Office of the Secretary of the Navy (see RG 80).

See Henry P. Beers, "The Development of the Office of the Chief of Naval Operations," *Military Affairs*, Vols. 10 and 11 (1946-47); Julius Augustus Furer, *Administration of the Navy Department in World War II* (1959); and Vincent Davis, *Postwar Defense Policy and the U.S. Navy, 1943-46* (Chapel Hill, 1966), and *Admirals' Lobby* (Chapel Hill, 1967).

There are 3,120 cubic feet of records dated between 1882 and 1968 in this record group.

RECORDS OF THE CHIEF OF NAVAL OPERATIONS. 1914-46.
585 lin. ft. and 417 rolls of microfilm.

General records consist of correspondence, 1942-46, with an index; and microfilm copies of classified correspondence, 1918-43 (375 rolls), and of history cards and indexes, 1918-42 (42 rolls). There are records that concern the military government established by the Navy in the Dominican Republic from 1916 to 1924, consisting of general correspondence, 1917-24, with a subject index; correspondence of the military governor with High Comissioner Sumner Welles, 1922-23; legal correspondence, 1920-22; correspondence of the naval detachment, 1924; miscellaneous correspondence, registers, and indexes; radio messages, with registers, 1922-24; quarterly reports, Executive orders and regula-

tions, and official publications and issuances of the military government, 1916-24; correspondence, memorandums, and reports relating to the military government and its predecessors, 1914-24; and financial records, 1917-23.

RECORDS OF THE DEPUTY CHIEF OF NAVAL OPERATIONS (ADMINISTRATION). 1885-1963.
650 lin. ft. and 23,061 rolls of microfilm.

The Deputy Chief for Administration is responsible for internal administration of the Office of the Chief of Naval Operations. The records include records of the Division of Naval Communications, consisting of general correspondence of the Director, 1911-26; classified general correspondence, 1917-26; a subject index, 1911-26; microfilm copies (23,061 rolls) of classified messages and dispatches, 1941-63; correspondence of the Postal Affairs Section, 1942-45; general records of the Office of the Atlantic Coast Communications Superintendent, 1917-25; and miscellaneous office files, plans and blueprints, newspaper clippings, and publications.

The Division of Pan American Affairs and U.S. Naval Missions grew out of the Navy's interest in developing ties with foreign naval services through means of naval missions and later in response to wartime conditions. The records consist of reports of secret conversations between U.S. naval representatives and those of other American Republics, 1940-42.

The Military Government Section of the Central Division was organized in 1944 to establish policies for the administration of occupied areas. In 1945 the Section was reorganized as a division under an Assistant Chief of Naval Operations. Its records consist of classified general correspondence, 1943-44, with an index; and classified plans and reports on public finance and health. The Naval District Affairs Division was established October 13, 1945, to administer and organize the shore establishment. The records relate to standardization of terminology, 1943-46.

The Office of Naval Records and Library was established to furnish general library services, administer historically valuable naval records, and prepare historical documents and studies for publication. In 1946 the Office was merged with the Office of Naval History. The records consist of general correspondence, 1885-1925, administrative records, 1918-25, miscellaneous registers and indexes, and records of the Historical Section created in 1918. Material originally held by the Office constitutes the Naval Records Collection of the Office of Naval Records and Library, Record Group 45.

RECORDS OF THE DEPUTY CHIEF OF NAVAL OPERATIONS (OPERATIONS). 1882-1954. 915 lin. ft.

The Deputy Chief for Operations is responsible for preparing strategic plans and policies and for the training, readiness, and employment of naval operating forces. The records include records of the Office of Naval Intelligence, consisting of letters sent, 1899-1911, and received, 1882-83 and 1886-99; general correspondence, 1899-1912; confidential general correspondence, 1913-24; classified special correspondence, 1916-27, general correspondence, 1929-43, administrative correspondence, 1927-44, and outgoing correspondence, 1929-45; registers and indexes to correspondence; miscellaneous classified correspondence, case files, and registers; letters from, 1882-1900, letters to, 1899-1905, reports of, 1886-1922, and secret reports of, 1936-43, naval attaches; registers of attaches' intelligence reports, letters, and other incoming records, 1882-88 and 1897-1929; miscellaneous dispatches and letters received from attaches; miscellaneous records relating to subversive activities, 1917-27, the U.S. Communist Party, 1927-30, and personnel informants, agents, and other individuals, 1882-1925; classified publications of the Office, 1882-1954; classified foreign publications, 1901-42; confidential records relating to camouflaged vessels, 1917-19; records of wartime divisions of the Office, 1917-19; outgoing letters of the Intelligence Branch, 1929-40; general correspondence of the Coastal Information Section, 1939-43; and miscellaneous records of the Foreign Intelligence Branch, 1936-45.

The Operational Readiness Division, established in 1945, assumed functions of the Division of Fleet Training and authority under the Mine Warfare Section. Records of the two offices consist of general correspondence, 1914-41, subject files, 1908-26, reports, 1917-41, issuances, 1919-26, reports of vessel efficiency inspections, 1923-30, and general correspondence of the Mine Warfare Section, 1942-45.

Field activity records include correspondence and other records maintained by naval attaches, missions, and representatives in foreign countries, 1885-1905 and 1917-35. The Office of Aid for Information of the Third Naval District at New York City existed from 1917 to 1919 to administer intelligence work within the district. Its records consist of classified general correspondence, 1917-19; records concerning motion picture censorship, the placing of informants aboard vessels, investigations of ship passengers using the port of New York, and searches of vessels; and records relating to activities of the Branch Naval Intelligence Office at New York City, 1917-18.

RECORDS OF THE DEPUTY CHIEF OF NAVAL OPERATIONS (LOGISTICS). 1882-1964. 375 lin. ft.

Included are records of the Board of Inspection and Survey, consisting of outgoing correspondence, 1882-1937; frag-

mentary incoming correspondence for
certain years between 1882 and 1901;
indexes and registers to the correspondence; administrative records, 1917-35;
inspection reports of naval vessels,
1893-1964, including submarines and
vessels removed from the Navy register; reports on aircraft acceptance trials,
1919-32; and miscellaneous records of
other inspection activities. There are
also general correspondence and reports
of the Board of Inspection for Shore Stations, 1910-14, and of the Joint Merchant
Vessel Board, 1915-20; and correspondence and appraisal records of the Board
of Review, 1917-22. Also included are
records of the Base Maintenance Division, consisting of classified general correspondence and related records of the
Base Defense Section, 1941-45; miscellaneous records of its predecessor, the
Naval Districts Division, 1916-21; and
classified correspondence of the Shore
Station Development Board, 1920-42.

RECORDS OF THE DEPUTY
CHIEF OF NAVAL OPERATIONS
(AIR). 1941-43. 65 lin. ft.

These records consist of general correspondence, 1943, correspondence of
the Naval Air Transport Service, 1941-
43, correspondence relating to airplane
contracts, 1943, and indexes.

CARTOGRAPHIC AND
AUDIOVISUAL RECORDS. 1884-
1968. 8,988 items.

Cartographic records (280 items)
include maps collected and forwarded to
the Office of Naval Intelligence by naval
attaches, showing political boundaries,
economic conditions, world trade, mandates, naval facilities, communications
networks, anglicized versions of place
names, and information relating to the
Sino-Japanese War, 1884-1943; an incomplete set of bound volumes of climatic

charts of the world, prepared by the
Naval Weather Service Division, 1955-
68; and a published handbook relating
to climate of the Northern Hemisphere,
1955.

Still pictures (8,660 items) include photographs of foreign and domestic aircraft and parts, 1917-40; Allied leaders
during World War II; minesweeping
activities, 1941-45; Navy training, 1941-
45; preparation of equipment for shipment overseas, 1941-45; coastal features
of the Marshall, Caroline, and Marianas
Islands, n.d.; U.S. military fortifications,
1918-23; defenses of Valparaiso, Chile,
1897; Italian seaports, 1920; naval armor
tests, 1891-92; Haiti, Veracruz, and
Tampico, Mexico, 1914; construction of
the *Kaiser Wilhelm II* at Bremen, Germany; interiors of captured German submarines, 1918; and maps of Russia and
an aerial mosaic of Nanking, China, 1929.
A motion picture (1 reel) showing tests
of Higgins landing craft, 1941.

Sound recordings, 1942-45 (47 items),
include radio broadcasts made chiefly in
the Pacific theater during World War
II, concerning eyewitness accounts by
war correspondents and members of the
fighting forces of battles, bombing raids,
air operations from aboard a carrier,
Marine jungle operations, the bombard-
ing of Japan and the funeral of Ernie
Pyle on Ie Shima; radio-telephone conversations between tank crews in battle;
interviews with a submarine crew;
greetings from servicemen to their families; broadcasts relating to the war production effort, the role of women in the
shipbuilding industry, and war bond promotion; a report to the Congress on the
progress of the war in Europe by General Eisenhower; and a V-E Day broadcast.

See Charlotte M. Ashby, comp., *Preliminary
Inventory of the Cartographic Records of the Office
of the Chief of Naval Operations*, PI 85 (1955).

RECORDS OF THE UNITED STATES MARINE CORPS
(RECORD GROUP 127)

The U.S. Marine Corps was created by an act of July 11, 1798, which authorized the Commandant of the Corps to appoint an adjutant, a paymaster, and a quartermaster. Around those three staff officers and the Commandant the branches of Marine Corps Headquarters developed. Although the Corps was at first subject to both Army and Navy regulations, an act of June 30, 1834, placed it under exclusive naval control except for units detached by Presidential order for Army service. A staff system in the Headquarters organization was begun in 1918 when the first of many sections and divisions was created in the Office of the Commandant. In 1920 the most important unit, the Division of Operations and Training, was created. That Division was renamed in 1939 the Division of Plans and Policies, subdivisions of which were designated by General Staff letters M-1 through M-5. When Headquarters was reorganized along General Staff lines in 1952, the Division of Plans and Policies was abolished and its sections, now G-1 through G-4, were elevated to divisional status under assistant chiefs of staff.

The Commandant of the Marine Corps is directly responsible to the Secretary of the Navy for all administrative and operational matters affecting the Corps. These include providing amphibious forces for service with the fleet in seizing and defending advanced naval bases, and conducting land operations essential to a naval campaign. Other duties include providing detachments to serve on naval ships and to protect property of naval activities.

There are 2,207 cubic feet of records dated between 1798 and 1950 in this record group.

RECORDS OF THE OFFICE OF THE COMMANDANT. 1798-1939. 1,592 lin. ft.

General records (1,532 lin. ft.) include letter books, with indexes; registers of letters received; letters received; a general correspondence file, with indexes and synopsis cards, 1904-12; a general correspondence file, 1913-38; and orders issued and received. Other records include general correspondence of the officer in charge of recruiting, 1921-39, and of the Intelligence Section, Division of Operations and Training, 1915-37; and letters received, records of overseas units, and scrapbooks accumulated by the Historical Division, 1798-1918.

RECORDS OF THE ADJUTANT AND INSPECTOR'S DEPARTMENT. 1798-1950. 2,169 lin. ft.

In 1943 this Department was designated the Personnel Department. Records include letter books, registers of letters received, letters received, and orders issued; records relating to Marine Corps officers, including rosters, registers, military histories, and monthly reports; records relating to enlisted men, including service records, 1798-1895; size rolls; descriptive lists; and registers of courts-martial, desertions, discharges, and deaths. Other records relate to both officers and enlisted men, including muster rolls, 1798-1945, and general returns. There is also a general correspondence file, 1939-50 (in WNRC).

RECORDS OF THE PAYMASTER'S DEPARTMENT. 1808-1939. 16 lin. ft.

In 1946 this Department was consolidated into the Supply Department under the direction of the Quartermaster. The records include letter books, letters received, and a 1909-39 general correspondence file.

RECORDS OF THE QUARTERMASTER'S DEPARTMENT. 1811-1942. 173 lin. ft.

In 1946 this Department was consolidated with the Supply Department. The records consist of letter books, registers of letters received, and letters received, 1811-1900; and general correspondence files, 1918-42.

RECORDS OF MARINE BARRACKS. 1802-1939. 119 lin. ft. (in WNRC).

These records, mostly fragmentary, relate to routine activities of Marine detachments at shore establishments and include correspondence and orders of commanding officers, muster rolls, and morning reports.

RECORDS OF EXPEDITIONARY FORCES AND DETACHMENTS ABROAD. 1898-1944. 71 lin. ft.

Included are general correspondence of the Marines in China, 1930-34; morning reports and journals of the Marines in Cuba, 1898-1911; general correspondence, intelligence and patrol reports, and miscellaneous records of the Guardia Nacional, 2d Marine Brigade, and 5th Marine Regiment in Nicaragua, 1927-32; general correspondence, intelligence reports, and miscellaneous records of the Garde d'Haiti and the 1st Marine Brigade in Haiti, 1915-34; and correspondence, journals, and other records of the 5th Marine Regiments, 1914, Marine aircraft squadrons, 1931-34, and Marine defense battalions, 1943-44.

CARTOGRAPHIC AND AUDIOVISUAL RECORDS. 1775-1947. 1,325 items.

Cartographic records (999 items) include maps and plans relating to foreign areas, 1883-1943, particularly Central and South America and China, 1904-43, and to Marine Corps installations, 1910-39; and published topographic maps of France and Germany, annotated to show operations of the 4th Marine Infantry Brigade from June 6, 1918, to June 19, 1919.

Audiovisual records include photographs (300 items), some of paintings and sketches of Marine Corps uniforms and insignia, 1775-1947; commandants, generals, adjutants, inspectors, and paymasters of the Corps, 1776-1945; groups of Marines, 1904-38; and emergency landing fields in Santo Domingo, the Dominican Republic, and Haiti, 1923. Motion pictures (21 reels) consist of World War II training films and films of combat in the South Pacific, 1939-45. There are also sound recordings (5 items) of Marine Corps recruiting broadcasts, 1942-43.

See Charlotte M. Ashby, comp., *Preliminary Inventory of the Cartographic Records of the United States Marine Corps*, PI 73 (1954); and Maizie Johnson, comp., *Records of the United States Marine Corps*, Inv. 2 (1970).

Microfilm Publications: *Muster Rolls of the United States Marine Corps, 1798-1815*, T1118, 5 rolls; and *Muster Rolls of the United States Marine Corps, 1893-1958*, T977, 4,074 rolls.

Offices and Bureaus

RECORDS OF THE BUREAU OF MEDICINE AND SURGERY (RECORD GROUP 52)

The Bureau of Medicine and Surgery was created in the Department of the Navy by an act of August 31, 1842. Its functions include administering naval dispensaries and hospitals; caring for the Navy's sick and injured; medically examining prospective and current naval personnel; practicing preventive medicine, including inspecting naval ships and stations to determine the adequacy of health facilities; conducting research in general medicine and dentistry; and giving specialized instruction to medical officers and selected enlisted men.

There are 1,092 cubic feet of records dated between 1812 and 1951 in this record group.

CORRESPONDENCE. 1842-1951. 975 lin. ft.

Included are letters sent, 1842-86, and received, 1842-85, with indexes and registers; general correspondence, 1885-1951, with indexes and registers; and secret and confidential correspondence, 1920-41, with a register.

RECORDS OF NAVAL VESSELS, STATIONS, AND HOSPITALS. 1812-1945. 368 lin. ft.

Included are medical journals of shore stations, 1812-89, ships, 1813-89, and expeditions, 1872-85; lists of patients, 1830-89, and hospital admission papers, 1825-89; lists of medical records, 1813-1912; sick reports, 1851-80; medical certificates and casualty lists, 1828-1939; annual sanitary reports, 1907, 1919, 1927, and 1943; and reports relating to survivors of wrecked ships and aircraft, 1942-45. Personnel records, 1824-1930, include lists of medical officers, 1824-73; statements of medical officers' service, 1842-73; and appointment papers of stewards, apothecaries, and nurses, 1861-84.

MISCELLANEOUS RECORDS. 1812-1946. 45 lin. ft.

These consist of records of the Administrative Division, 1943-46; records of the Naval Medical School and its predecessors, including letters sent, 1880-1909, and received, 1880-1911; and orders and notices, 1905-9. Fiscal records include a journal of expenditures, 1922-26, and security-classified records of the Division of Preventive Medicine, including minutes, publications, reports, and correspondence of subcommittees of the Division of Medical Science of the National Research Council, 1940-44. Field records include registers of patients, 1812-1929; letters sent by ship surgeons, 1859-86, and by the U.S. Naval Hospital at Portsmouth, N.H., 1882-84; and an expenditure book kept on board the U.S. receiving ship *Ontario*, 1844-46.

CARTOGRAPHIC AND AUDIOVISUAL RECORDS. 1900-1946. 1,116 items.

Included are a published atlas illustrating distribution and disease transmission characteristics of mosquito species in the Southwest Pacific, 1946, and photographs (1,115 items) of facilities and methods of treatment at Navy hospitals in Normandy, other parts of France, and southern England, 1944; of Navy hospital construction at Portsmouth, Va., 1918-19; of the Navy Hospital Corps schools at Norfolk, Va., and Washington, D.C., 1900-1910; and of gas warfare equipment and first aid, 1918-19.

See Kenneth F. Bartlett, comp., *Preliminary Inventory of the Records of the Bureau of Medicine and Surgery*, PI 6 (1948).

RECORDS OF THE BUREAU OF ORDNANCE
(RECORD GROUP 74)

The Bureau of Ordnance and Hydrography was established in the Navy Department by an act of August 31, 1842. Its name was changed to Bureau of Ordnance by an act of July 5, 1862, which transferred its duties relating to hydrography to the Bureau of Navigation. The Bureau of Ordnance was responsible for design, manufacture, procurement, maintenance, and issuance of all armament (including armor, torpedoes, mines, depth charges, pyrotechnics, bombs, ammunition, war explosives and chemicals, defensive nets, buoys, and net appliances) and, except as specifically assigned to other agencies within the Navy Department, optical and other devices and material for the control of guns, torpedoes, and bombs. The Bureau also provided for operation, upkeep, and repair of naval gun factories, ordnance plants, torpedo stations, proving grounds, powder factories, ammunition depots, magazines, and mine depots. The Bureau of Ordnance was abolished by an act of August 18, 1959, which transferred its functions to the Bureau of Naval Weapons.

There are 6,481 cubic feet of records dated between 1818 and 1946 in this record group.

GENERAL CORRESPONDENCE. 1842-1944. 7,051 lin. ft.

Included are letters and telegrams sent, 1842-1911, registers of letters received and letters received, 1842-85, general correspondence, 1885-1912, security-classified general correspondence, 1912-44 (in WNRC), secret general correspondence, 1918-41 (in WNRC), indexes to general correspondence, 1914-26 and 1926-43 (in WNRC), history cards for correspondence, 1912-26 (in WNRC), and miscellaneous correspondence, 1906-17.

RECORDS RELATING TO THE MANUFACTURE AND TESTING OF GUNS, GUN PARTS, AMMUNITION, AND ARMOR. 1842-1913. 44 lin. ft.

These consist primarily of reports and correspondence relating to inspection, manufacture, and testing of various types of guns (the 32-pounder, naval,

Wiard Steel, Ames wrought-iron, Gatling, Hotchkiss, XI-XIII and XV-inch, Alger's Foundry, Cold Spring Foundry, Tredegar Foundry, and breech-loading rifles and guns), Puritan gun carriage, metals, machineguns and small arms, Lowell machinegun, torpedoes, carriage castings, gun forgings, armor plate, the Gathman torpedo gun, ballistic tests, cannon, and the Murphy Iron Wheel. There are also reports relating to other arms and ammunition.

RECORDS RELATING TO GUN EXERCISE AND TARGET PRACTICE. 1854-1918. 4 lin. ft.

Included are letters received from gunnery practice ships; correspondence on long-range firing of heavy ordnance; reports of ship inspections, target and ordnance practice, guns and powder, and gun exercises on ships; miscellaneous ordnance reports; instructions for firing large guns; the French *Naval Gun Exercise Manual*; a manual of diagrams of gun crew positions for firing; and a journal of target practice on ships.

RECORDS OF GUNS AND ORDNANCE MATERIAL. 1818-1942. 93 lin. ft.

These include lists, registers, and journals relating to guns at navy yards, stations, and on ships, and to naval ordnance materials supplied to ships and stations; and reports of armament on vessels.

RECORDS RELATING TO PATENTS AND INVENTIONS. 1826-1926. 14 lin. ft.

Included are letters sent; letters received; correspondence relating to examination of patents, license and royalty agreements, and patent infringements; reports on inventions; ordnance patents; a patents and inventions file; and patent specifications.

RECORDS RELATING TO SUPPLIES, ACCOUNTS, CONTRACTS, AND PERSONNEL. 1836-1939. 102 lin. ft.

These consist of letters received relating to methods of purchasing supplies and to civilian personnel duties; correspondence relating to gun shipments; journals of correspondence; and contracts, budget appropriations, and related records.

RECORDS OF UNITS OF THE BUREAU. 1900-1943. 42 lin. ft.

Included are copies of letters sent by bureau desks; security-classified correspondence relating to testing and experiment projects concerning equipment purchased under ordnance contracts; correspondence relating to submarine nets, mine and torpedo inventions, the mine depot at Yorktown, Va., and aviation ordnance; gun and torpedo research data; and workpapers relating to the design, testing, and procurement of aeronautic ordnance materials.

RECORDS OF ORDNANCE BOARDS. 1845-1911. 4 lin. ft.

These consist of reports, correspondence, and other records of the following boards: Navy Armament, 1845; Rifled Guns, 1863; Parrot 100-Pounder Guns, 1865; Permanent Ordnance Board, 1869-71; Breech-Loading Rifles, 1869; Naval Torpedo Boats, 1871-72; Naval Torpedo, 1889, 1891, and 1905-11; Armor Factory, 1891 and 1897; Armor Plate, 1891-93; and the Special Board on Armor Plate, 1895.

SPECIAL COLLECTION OF RECORDS. 1849-1905. 11 lin. ft.

Reports and correspondence arranged by subject and brought together either because of the nature of the work performed by a particular officer or because of his contributions to the work of his bureau.

CARTOGRAPHIC AND AUDIOVISUAL RECORDS. 1842-1946. 14,296 items.

Cartographic records (18 items) include maps showing ownership of land in the District of Columbia along the Potomac River, 1842-68, the track of the U.S.S. *Constitution* along the Massachusetts coast, 1876, and water densities in various seas and oceans, 1905-23; and maps of naval magazine and nitrate plants in the United States, 1905-23.

Audiovisual records (14,278 items) consist of photographs of U.S. and foreign ordnance and ordnance tests, bases, buildings, installations, ships, airships, airplanes, and machinery, 1864-1922; construction and use of naval railway batteries, maps of areas in Europe where the batteries were installed, Allied and German machines and guns, ships and mine laying, Allied and German fleets at Scapa Flow, and Secretary of the Navy Josephus Daniels on a trip to Europe, 1917-21; ordnance tooling equipment, machinery, smoke bomb tests, graphs, charts, and the construction of the Fort Defiance Machinery Co., Defiance, Ohio, 1917; artillery and carriages made in the Creusot works of Schneider 9 Co. of France, 1874-81; and naval ordnance used in Operation Crossroads, Bikini, and resultant underwater damage to ships, 1946.

See William F. Shonkwiler, comp., *Preliminary Inventory of the Records of the Bureau of Ordnance,* PI 33 (1951).

RECORDS OF THE BUREAU OF SHIPS
(RECORD GROUP 19)

The Bureau of Ships had its origin in the Bureau of Construction, Equipment, and Repairs established in the Navy Department by an act of August 31, 1842. The latter Bureau was abolished by an act of July 5, 1862, and its functions were divided among three new bureaus: Equipment and Recruiting (the recruiting function having been transferred from the Office of the Secretary of the Navy), Steam Engineering, and Construction and Repair.

A general order of June 25, 1889, transferred the functions and records of the Bureau of Equipment and Recruiting relating to enlisted men to the Bureau of Navigation, now the Bureau of Naval Personnel (see RG 24). The Bureau of Equipment and Recruiting, renamed the Bureau of Equipment in 1891, was discontinued by an act of June 24, 1910, and its functions were assigned to other bureaus, many of them to the Bureau of Steam Engineering, by a departmental order of June 30, 1910. The Bureau of Equipment was finally abolished by an act of June 30, 1914.

The Bureau of Steam Engineering was renamed the Bureau of Engineering in 1920, and both it and the Bureau of Construction and Repair were abolished by an act of June 20, 1940, which consolidated their functions, personnel, and records to form the Bureau of Ships.

The Bureau of Ships was responsible for design, construction, conversion, procurement, maintenance, and repair of ships and other craft. It also had authority over specifications of fuels and lubricants, conduct of salvage operations, and management of shipyards, repair facilities, laboratories, and other shore facilities. The Bureau was later responsible for purchase of ships for the Departments of the Army and the Air Force, coordination of shipbuilding for the entire Department of Defense, and planning and coordination of departmental repair and conversion programs with other Government agencies. On March 9, 1966, by order of the Department of Defense, the Bureau of Ships was abolished and its functions were transferred to the Secretary of the Navy, who delegated most of them to the Naval Ship Systems Command under the Chief of Naval Operations (see RG 38).

Many of the records of Bureau of Ships predecessors before 1885 and of the Bureau of Equipment before 1889 have not been located. Records relating to vessel construction and repair before 1842 are among the records of the Board of Navy Commissioners (see RG 45). For records of the Naval Observatory, the Nautical Almanac Office, and the Hydrographic Office, all at one time part of the Bureau of Equipment and Recruiting, see Record Groups 37 and 78.

There are 17,194 cubic feet of records dated between 1794 and 1949 in this record group.

RECORDS OF THE BUREAU OF CONSTRUCTION, EQUIPMENT, AND REPAIRS. 1820-62. 5 lin. ft.

Fragmentary in character, most of the records relate to supplies and accounts of ships and shipyards and include descriptions of ship repairs, inventories and memorandums of stores, and data on construction and maintenance costs, 1820-62. Also included are registers for which the correspondence has not been located, 1842-44 and 1846-47; letters received from the Boston navy yard, September-December 1861; and abstracts of letters received and sent, January 1848-January 1849.

RECORDS OF THE BUREAU OF CONSTRUCTION AND REPAIR.
1794-1943. 11,915 lin. ft.

Included are all of the known extant records of the Bureau of Construction, Equipment, and Repairs not described above, as well as letters sent, 1850-80; letters received, 1861-82 and 1886; general and miscellaneous correspondence, 1887-1940, and correspondence relating to ships, 1886-94 and 1896-1925; and to administrative and fiscal matters, 1896-1940. History cards, indexes, and registers accompany the records.

Plans of ships and stations, consisting chiefly of tracings, drawings, blueprints, vandykes, and plans, with indexes, of ships and shore establishments, 1794-1910; plans of foreign naval vessels, 1917-33; and miscellaneous plans, 1890-1940. Records of descriptions, dimensions, weights, tests, and trials of vessels, including data on ship weights, 1886-1921, experiment data, 1895-1925, general information booklets about naval vessels, 1900-1917, and Board of Inspection and Survey tracings prepared to accompany reports containing technical data about ship performances during tests, 1907-11.

Claims involving vessels, concerning Civil War vessels, 1861-1909, post-Civil War vessel construction, 1894-1911, and German merchant vessels, 1928-29; surveys and reports of work, including ship construction and repair reports, 1837-96, boards of survey reports about ships and their equipment, 1854-69, performance and condition of vessel reports, 1864-75, vessel specifications, 1883-1917, construction accounts, 1887-99, and movement of vessel reports, 1895-1914; and fiscal records primarily concerning supplies, equipment, and accounts and consisting of invoices and bills of lading, 1842-88, allowance lists of equipage and supplies, 1893-1934, and copies of contracts and related records, 1852-84 and 1939-43.

Records of the Design Division, relating to weight and stability of ships, 1912-40, and to design data for naval vessels, 1914-27; records of the Camouflage Section, 1917-19, concerning use of camouflage in World War I and consisting of drawings, designs, prints, watercolor sketches, reports, and correspondence; and records of the Scientific and Computing Branch, ca. 1900-1918, consisting of enclosures to correspondence on tonnage calculations and moldloft dimensions.

Other records, consisting of copies of correspondence with Adm. William S. Sims, commanding the U.S. Naval Forces Operating in European Waters, 1917-19; files of Rear Adm. George H. Rock, relating to the International Conference on Safety of Life at Sea to which he was a delegate, 1928-30; records concerning inventions and patents, 1866-85; and fiscal, personnel, and other records, 1842-88.

RECORDS OF THE BUREAU OF ENGINEERING. 1840-1942.
5,773 lin. ft.

General correspondence (in WNRC) relating to the design, construction, maintenance, and repair of machinery and to the Bureau's responsibility, after 1910, for electrical and radio apparatus. It consists of letters sent, 1862-90; letters and reports received, 1861-72; letters sent and received, 1888-1910, with indexes; and general correspondence, 1885-87 and 1910-40, with indexes. Technical records (in WNRC), including reports about laboratory tests of equipment and materials, 1910-41, weight of machinery installed in vessels, 1890-1915, and tests and engineering performances of vessels, 1862-1939.

Plans consisting of tracings, drawings, blueprints, and vandykes of hulls, machinery, and equipment of vessels, 1840-1932. Some of the plans dated before 1910 originated in the Bureau of Equipment, and most of those before 1862 were originally maintained by the Board of Navy Commissioners and the Bureau of Construction, Equipment, and Repairs. Included are indexes to drawings of ship machinery, 1874-1904 (in WNRC). Fiscal records (in WNRC), including records that relate to contracts for engineering materials, 1904-42, ship specifications, 1889-1922, requisitions for machinery and supplies, 1862-65, allowance lists of vessels, 1917-18, and appropriations, 1924-32.

Records of the General Inspector of Machinery (in WNRC), 1905-26, consisting of correspondence and reports that concern tests of equipment and inspections of machinery at naval and private shipyards, and correspondence of Rear Adm. John R. Edwards, relating to the London Radio Telegraphic Conference of June 1912; records of the Division of Logs and Records (in WNRC), consisting of logs of naval steam vessels, 1845-1906, and reference data, with indexes, about vessels, 1887-1935; records of the Radio Division (in WNRC), including orders and memorandums, 1906-30, reports and data about ship radio installations and operational and technological experiments, 1910-42, scrapbooks of the Alaska Radio Expedition, 1912 and 1914, reports concerning naval radio installations in Alaska, 1917-23, and historical and descriptive reports, with illustrative material, from naval radio stations and ships, 1925-40; and records of boards of officers (in WNRC), 1863-1904, consisting of candidates' examinations for promotion in the Engineer Corps of the Navy and minutes and reports of examining boards of naval engineers.

RECORDS OF THE BUREAU OF EQUIPMENT. 1875-1917. 420 lin. ft.

Included are general correspondence, 1899-1910, with indexes, 1875-1910; records relating to naval coaling stations, 1885-1910; records concerning the construction, site, and finances of the Naval Observatory, 1887-1910; records pertaining to homing pigeons and tests of wireless equipment, 1896-1910; and plans, drawings, and descriptive texts of electrical appliances on vessels, 1893-1917.

RECORDS OF THE GENERAL SUPERINTENDENT OF IRONCLADS. 1861-66. 4 lin. ft.

By order of the Secretary of the Navy in 1861, Rear Adm. Francis H. Gregory was made superintendent of the building and equipping of ironclads and monitors. He was succeeded by Commodore Cadwalader Ringgold, his assistant, after his death on October 4, 1866. The office was closed on November 1, 1866. The records include letters sent to and received from the Secretary and Assistant Secretary of the Navy, Navy Department bureaus, naval officers, contractors, and inspectors. Also included are circular letters, telegrams, registers, reports, indexes, lists, and miscellaneous items.

RECORDS OF THE COORDINATOR OF SHIPBUILDING. 1939-40. 1 lin. ft.

On September 14, 1939, the Chief of the Bureau of Engineering was appointed Coordinator of Shipbuilding for the Navy to expedite the construction of ships, and the Chief of the Bureau of Construction and Repair was appointed Assistant Coordinator. When the Bureau of Ships was established the Bureau chief assumed the duties of the Coordinator. The records consist of letters and memorandums received, letters sent, and a card register of correspondence about the shipbuilding program.

RECORDS OF THE BUREAU OF SHIPS. 1890-1949. 8,653 lin. ft. and 1,151 rolls of microfilm.

General records (in WNRC), consisting of correspondence, reports, memorandums, and other materials about the design, construction, and repair of ships and about the design and procurement of radio, radar, and underwater sound equipment for naval vessels, 1940–45; and reports of naval laboratory experiments, 1939–46.

Divisional records consisting of: Records of the Contract Division, including correspondence concerning contracts let by the Bureau of Construction and Repair, 1938–43. Records of the Maintenance Division, including hull and machinery allowance lists, 1911–45. Records of the Electronics Division, 1916–46, including general correspondence; correspondence about research and experimental projects, 1931–42; and specifications, 1937–44. Records of the Publications Division, consisting of reports of performance tests of auxiliary machinery; descriptions of electrical installations on naval vessels, ca. 1900–1948; and publications concerning naval vessels, 1900–1945. Records of the Shipbuilding Division, consisting of plans of naval vessels decommissioned from 1911 through 1949, with microfilm copies (1,151 rolls) of the plans; records relating to ship design, 1890–1942; specifications for materials; weekly reports about labor employed in naval shipbuilding at private yards; and tables of requirements relating to lend-lease materials, 1942–44.

AUDIOVISUAL RECORDS. ca. 1855–1946. 148,181 items.

These consist of photographs and photographs of artworks of naval personnel, 1776–1941; events in naval history and ships silhouettes, constructions, launchings, damages, wrecks, salvages, scrappings, camouflages, and drydocks, 1789–1946; historic sailing ships, ca. 1799–1922; and models of ships, including some American clippers, 1825–1939. There are also photographs of ship fittings including figureheads and ornaments, boilers and accessories, steam turbines, engines, gun mounts, and diagrams of radios and machinery, 1863–1942; foreign ships, including British naval vessels, 1863–1945; commercial ships, some foreign made, that were commissioned by the Navy, 1900–1944; Samoa, 1904; naval installations, including the New York navy yard, ammunition depots, and radio and communication stations and equipment in the United States and abroad, 1905–30; the Atlantic Fleet on review, 1915; harbor and defense installations of Gibraltar, 1922; mockups of ship designs submitted by private firms, 1941–46; and undated blueprints of French vessels.

See Elizabeth Bethel et al., comps., *Records of the Bureau of Ships*, PI 133 (1961).

RECORDS OF THE
BUREAU OF SUPPLIES AND ACCOUNTS (NAVY)
(RECORD GROUP 143)

The Bureau of Provisions and Clothing was established in the Department of the Navy by an act of August 31, 1842, and renamed in 1892 the Bureau of Supplies and Accounts. At first its functions, taken over from the former Board of Navy Commissioners, were to supply the Navy with provisions, clothing, and small stores, and to perform Department accounting. Later many of the duties of the Bureau of Equipment were transferred to it. Until after World

War II the Chief of the Bureau was also Paymaster General of the Navy. The Bureau, among other functions, supervised the procurement, receipt, storage, shipment, and issuance of food, fuel, clothing, general stores, and other materials; maintained and operated naval supply depots and similar units and supervised activities of Supply Corps officers; procured, allocated, and disbursed funds; and kept money and property accounts. The Bureau of Supplies and Accounts was abolished May 1, 1966, as part of a Defense Department reorganization, and its functions were assigned to the Naval Supply Systems Command.

There are 3,969 cubic feet of records (in WNRC) dated between 1885 and 1946 in this record group.

RECORDS. 1885-1946. 5,261 lin. ft.

Most of the records are in successive series of correspondence, 1885-1942, with indexes, 1894-1925. There are separate correspondence series concerning chartered vessels, 1917-23, advance bases, 1942-45, a Supply Corps correspondence course for Reserve officers, 1927-38, and commissions in the Naval Reserve Supply Corps, 1935-38. There is also correspondence of a Board of Survey, Appraisal, and Sale, 1920-26; the Storage, 1939-43, and War Plans, 1940-42, Divisions; and the Logistics Planning Branch, 1943-44. Other records, 1894-1946, include war plans, reports, tables concerning use of materials, data concerning a working fund, appropriation ledgers, and a history of the Bureau during World War I.

RECORDS OF THE BUREAU OF YARDS AND DOCKS
(RECORD GROUP 71)

The Bureau of Yards and Docks in 1862 replaced the Bureau of Naval Yards and Docks, established in the Navy Department by an act of August 31, 1842. Bureau functions included the design, construction, and maintenance of all naval public works and utilities, such as drydocks, marine railways, shipbuilding ways, harbor structures, storage facilities, powerplants, heating and lighting systems, and buildings at shore establishments. The Bureau also operated powerplants, maintained public works and utilities at shore establishments, and obtained real estate for Navy use. At advanced bases and in combat areas Bureau work was performed by construction battalions (Seabees). A Department of Defense reorganization order of March 9, 1966, abolished the Bureau, and the Secretary of the Navy transferred most of its functions to the Naval Facilities Engineering Command.

Records relating to matters under Bureau jurisdiction, particularly to navy yards and shore establishments, may also be found in the naval records collection of the Office of Naval Records and Library (see RG 45) and among records of naval districts and shore establishments (see RG 181).

There are 4,855 cubic feet of records dated between 1820 and 1946 in this record group.

GENERAL CORRESPONDENCE. 1842-1942. 2,437 lin. ft.

This correspondence consists of general files, 1886-1942, confidential correspondence, 1918-41, letters received, 1842-85, and letters sent, 1842-1911.

TECHNICAL RECORDS. 1820-1944. 462 lin. ft. and 33 rolls of microfilm.

These records relate to design and construction of shore establishment facilities and include plans, drawings, and blueprints, with some on microfilm (33 rolls), including an index, 1876-1944; news memorandums on selected projects, 1926-40; a manuscript history of the Naval Asylum at Philadelphia, 1877-78; and journals of daily transactions at navy yards, 1820-1921.

FISCAL RECORDS. 1832-1946.
2,150 lin. ft.

Included are annual reports of estimates and expenditures, 1836-37 and 1842-1911; annual estimates for public works projects, 1921-40; reports of work done to improve yards, 1842-98; Navy agents' vouchers and exhibits, 1842-98; store returns, 1842 and 1844-69; general, 1866-89, and construction, 1832-72, ledgers for major yards; contracts, 1842-1946 (in WNRC), with related correspondence, 1911-42 (in WNRC); correspondence about specifications, 1925-42 (in WNRC); and semimonthly abstracts of work done, 1843-67.

PERSONNEL RECORDS. 1837-1900.
81 lin. ft.

For the most part these records consist of monthly reports of officers, 1842-85, and of beneficiaries at the Naval Asylum (the U.S. Naval Home after 1889), 1850-97; returns of apprentices, 1837-42 and 1853-81; and shore establishment payrolls, 1844-99.

OTHER RECORDS. 1925-44.
10 lin. ft. and 2 rolls of microfilm.

Included are correspondence, blueprints, plans, and memorandums relating to naval air station construction at Seattle, Tongue Point, Oreg., San Diego, and San Pedro, 1925-42; correspondence and related documents concerning Seabees training at Camp Pendleton, Calif., 1942-44; and publicity files (some on microfilm) of the construction battalion's Recruiting Division, 1942-43.

AUDIOVISUAL RECORDS. 1876-1944. 75,927 items.

Included are photographs of shore establishments in the United States, U.S. possessions, and other countries at all stages of construction, including those of navy yards, submarine bases, and air, coaling, and naval training stations; construction and equipment for floating drydocks, lighters, and barges; construction of bridges, docks, breakwaters, and ships; activities of the Public Works Administration, the Work Projects Administration, and private companies at naval bases; Seabees personnel, activities, and training during World War II; and explosion damage at an ammunition dump. Also included are photographs used in planning activities, testing materials, and settling damage claims; and blueprints of powerplant facilities at navy yards.

See Richard G. Wood, comp., *Preliminary Inventory of the Records of the Bureau of Yards and Docks*, PI 10 (1948).

RECORDS OF THE BUREAU OF NAVAL PERSONNEL
(RECORD GROUP 24)

The Bureau of Naval Personnel originated as the Bureau of Navigation, established by an act of July 5, 1862. Naval personnel matters had usually been assigned to the Office of the Secretary of the Navy. The Bureau of Navigation was made responsible for certain personnel functions relating to officers. The Office of Detail, whose duties included appointing and instructing volunteer officers, was under the Bureau of Navigation periodically from 1865 until 1889, when the Bureau finally incorporated the Office and also assumed the personnel functions of the Bureau of Equipment and Recruiting. All nonpersonnel functions of the Bureau of Navigation had been reassigned by 1942 when its name was changed to Bureau of Naval Personnel. The Bureau is responsible for the training and education of officers and enlisted men, including supervision of the U.S. Naval Academy and other schools; establishing complements for Navy ships; and the recruitment, assignment, and separation of naval personnel.

There are 13,141 cubic feet of records dated between 1789 and 1956 in this record group.

CORRESPONDENCE. 1850-1945.
6,727 lin. ft.

Included are letters sent to the President, Congressmen, and executive departments, 1877-1911; the Secretary of the Navy, naval establishments, and officers, 1850-1911; commandants, 1862-1911; enlisted personnel and apprentices, 1864-1911; concerning civilian personnel, 1903-9; and other letters sent, 1862-1912. Also letters received, 1862-89; general correspondence (6,043 lin. ft.), 1889-1945; record cards, 1903-25, subject cards, 1903-43, and history cards, 1925-42; indexes and registers, 1862-1903; and correspondence relating to vessels, personnel, and naval activities, 1885-1921.

LOGS. 1801-1946. 8,232 lin. ft.

Included are logs of U.S. naval ships and stations, 1801-1946, with indexes and lists; logs of the German merchant vessels *Prinz Waldemar* and *Prinz Sigismund*, 1903-14; communication logs and signal record books, 1897-1922; and signal logs and codebooks, 1917-19.

MUSTER ROLLS. 1860-1956.
725 lin. ft. and 34,834 rolls of microfilm.

These include muster rolls of ships, 1860-1900, ships and stations, 1891-1900,

and ships and shore establishments, 1898-1939 (in WNRC); Civil War muster rolls, 1861 and 1863; and microfilm copies (34,834 rolls), with indexes, of muster rolls of ships, stations, and other naval activities, 1939-56.

RECORDS RELATING TO NAVAL OFFICERS, ENLISTED MEN, AND APPRENTICES. 1798-1943.
1,284 lin. ft. and 67 rolls of microfilm.

Records relating to naval officers, 1798-1940, include application, examination, and appointment records, 1838-1940; commissions and warrants, 1844-1936; orders and related records, 1883-1903; identification, 1917-21, and age, 1862-63, certificates; registers, rosters, and records showing complements, 1799-1909; personnel jackets and other records, 1900-1925; service records, 1798-1924; and miscellaneous records, 1863-92.

Records relating to enlisted men include envelopes containing documents about those who served between 1842 and 1885; correspondence jackets for enlisted men, 1904-43; a microfilm copy (67 rolls) of an index to rendezvous reports, muster rolls, and other personnel records, 1846-84; registers and lists of recruits, 1861-73; enlistment returns, changes, and reports, 1846-1942; continuous service certificates, 1865-99; and records concerning discharges and desertions, 1882-1920.

Records that relate to naval apprentices include certificates of consent for minors, 1838-67, "apprentice papers," 1864-89, a journal of enlistments, 1865-68, records relating to training methods, and a register of enlistments, 1864-75.

RECORDS OF THE BUREAU OF EQUIPMENT AND RECRUITING.
1856-1928. 328 lin. ft.

These consist of letters sent to the Secretary of the Navy, the Fourth Auditor of the Treasury, the Commissioner of Pensions, the Superintendent of the

U.S. Naval Academy, and china, glass, and plated ware manufacturers, 1862-89; and to commanders of squadrons and naval forces, 1865-83, and commandants of navy yards and stations and other officers, 1862-85. Also letters received, 1862-92; indexes and registers of correspondence, 1862-90; conduct reports and shipping articles, 1857-1910; records of discharges and desertions, 1856-89; continuous service certificates and records of merit awards, 1863-1928; records relating to naval apprentices, 1880-86; and a record of vessel complements, n.d.

DIVISION RECORDS OF THE BUREAU OF NAVIGATION. 1804-1946. 560 lin. ft.

These consist of records of the Chaplains Division, 1804-1946, including correspondence and miscellaneous records of chaplains; the Division of Naval Militia Affairs, 1891-1918, including general records, an index to correspondence, letters sent, organization reports, summaries of units' enrolled forces, payroll records, certificates, and allowance books; the Divison of Officers and Fleet, 1887-98, including letters received, registers of correspondence, correspondence, appointments of paymaster clerks, and lists of Navy, Marine, and civilian officers at yards and stations; the Naval Academy Division, 1851-1940, including appointment letters and jackets for naval cadets, with registers of cadets; the Morale Division, 1918-24, including reports and correspondence received; and the Training Division, 1917-40, including reports and correspondence.

RECORDS OF FIELD ESTABLISHMENTS. 1836-1946. 173 lin. ft. (in WNRC).

These records comprise regulations, correspondence, and station logs of the Naval Home at Philadelphia, 1838-1942; letters sent, a journal of activities, and admission and discharge registers of the Naval Hospital at Philadelphia, 1855-71;

correspondence and muster cards of the indoctrination school for officers at Fort Schuyler, N.Y., 1941-46, and the Enlisted Naval Training School at Bedford Springs, Pa., 1942-45; and correspondence and other records of the V-12 unit at Dartmouth College, 1942-46, and the Naval Reserve Midshipmen's School at Northwestern University, 1941-45.

OTHER RECORDS. 1861-1946. 179 lin. ft.

Included are records of the Signal Office, 1869-86; the Coast Signal Service, 1898; the Board of Visitors of the U.S. Naval Academy, 1910-13; Bureau of Naval Personnel and Naval Research Personnel Board units, 1940-46; and the Office of Detail, including reports of naval cadets and correspondence, 1865-90. Other miscellaneous records include annual reports of the Chief of the Bureau of Navigation, naval militia bills, applications and registers of employees, records showing complements of ships and shore units, and watch, quarter, and station billbooks, 1861-1945.

CARTOGRAPHIC AND AUDIOVISUAL RECORDS. 1799-1945. 11,526 items.

Cartographic records, 1898-1935 (15 items), consist of manuscript maps showing American and Spanish naval operations in Cuban waters during the Spanish-American War; published maps of the United States, showing naval administrative districts and headquarters, 1919 and 1935; and maps and charts of areas of the world, some giving economic and strategic data, 1905-32.

Still pictures, 1799-1945 (11,409 items), consist of photographs and some photographs of paintings of chaplains, civilian employees, officers and enlisted men and their families, commended or deceased enlisted men, and commissioned, noncommissioned, and Reserve Navy and Marine Corps officers, 1799-1938; photographs and artworks from the Chaplains Division, depicting religious facilities and activities, 1799-1945; photographs of Navy activities, including those of the German surrender on the high seas, 1890-1926; and photographs of ships of the U.S. Navy, 1892-1935, and Spanish Navy, 1895-98.

Motion pictures, 1917-27 (101 reels), relate to Navy World War I activities, including submarine patrols by seaplanes and land-based planes, the airship *Los Angeles* (ZR-3) over New York after a flight from Germany, lighter-than-air craft rescuing fishermen, ship launchings and maintenance, convoy escorts, submarine maneuvers, Marine training, torpedo manufacturing and firing, minelaying, Liberty Loan promotion, and participation in patriotic celebrations, parades, and ceremonies. Films concerning Navy activities between World Wars I and II show demonstrations of aerial mapping techniques at Miami, recreational activities in other countries, maneuvers, rescue of Armenian refugees from Turkey and evacuation of personnel from grounded and burning

ships, escort duties such as President Wilson's trip to Europe after World War I, and training at navy yards, the U.S. Naval Academy, the Great Lakes Naval Training Station, and aboard ship. Also included are films of Armistice celebrations in London and New York; captured German arms, equipment, and a submarine; war damage in Belgium and France; military and civilian leaders of the United States, Great Britain, France, Denmark, and Spain; Italian, British, and Turkish naval ships; the Virgin Islands; and news coverage of Wilson's second inauguration and U.S. Navy, Red Cross, and League of Nations activities in Turkey relating to the Armenian problem.

There is also a sound recording, 1945, dramatizing sailors' roles in World War II.

See Virgil E. Baugh, comp., *Preliminary Inventory of the Records of the Bureau of Naval Personnel*, PI 123 (1960).

Microfilm Publications: For a complete listing see the current *List of National Archives Microfilm Publications*.

RECORDS OF THE HYDROGRAPHIC OFFICE
(RECORD GROUP 37)

The Hydrographic Office originated in the Depot of Charts and Instruments, established in 1830. In 1842 the Depot was assigned to the Bureau of Ordnance and Hydrography, and in 1854 the Depot was designated the U.S. Naval Observatory and Hydrographical Office (see RG 78). In 1862 the Office was transferred to the Bureau of Navigation, and the Hydrographic Office was established in 1866 as a separate administrative unit of that Bureau. After many transitions throughout which it remained virtually autonomous, the Hydrographic Office in 1942 became part of the Office of the Chief of Naval Operations. It was renamed the U.S. Naval Oceanographic

Office on July 10, 1962. This Office conducts hydrographic surveys in foreign waters and on the high seas; collects and disseminates hydrographic and navigational data; prepares maps and charts relating to navigation, including strategic and tactical charts required for naval operations and maneuvers; and issues sailing directions, light lists, pilot charts, navigational manuals, and periodicals.

Records relating to the work of the U.S. Naval Observatory and Hydrographic Office under the Bureau of Navigation and logs of expeditions are among records of the Bureau of Naval Personnel (see RG 24). Other records of the Bureau of Ordnance and Hydrography and of expeditions, including journals of the North Pacific Exploring Expedition, are among records of the Office of Naval Records and Library (see RG 45).

See Gustav A. Weber, *The Hydrographic Office* (Baltimore, 1926); George S. Bryan, "The Naval Hydrographic Office," *Proceedings* of the U.S. Naval Institute, Vol. 72 (November 1946), pp. 1395-1403; and R. O. Glover, "Hydro' Charts in War," *Proceedings* of the U.S. Naval Institute, Vol. 73 (January 1947), pp. 27-37.

There are 2,078 cubic feet of records dated between 1837 and 1968 in this record group.

RECORDS OF THE BUREAU OF ORDNANCE AND HYDROGRAPHY. 1842-63. 2 lin. ft.

These consist of letters received, 1842-62, and sent, 1842-63, relating to requests for and the purchase, production, publication, and distribution of nautical charts and instruments and navigational data.

GENERAL CORRESPONDENCE OF THE HYDROGRAPHIC OFFICE. 1862-1945. 384 lin. ft.

These comprise letters received, some by the U.S. Naval Observatory and Hydrographical Office, 1862-1920; letters sent, 1866-1909; reports, correspondence, and memorandums, 1885-1924; general correspondence, 1924-45; and related registers and indexes.

RECORDS OF EXPLORING EXPEDITIONS AND HYDROGRAPHIC SURVEYS. 1837-1946. 1,046 lin. ft.

Included are journals and logs kept by members of the Wilkes Expedition, which circumnavigated the globe and explored the Antarctic, the Pacific Islands, and the northwest coast of the United States, 1838-42. Also correspondence and reports (with indexes), pamphlets, and notes regarding plans for hydrographic surveys; and exploring expedition and hydrographic survey

field notes (980 lin. ft. in WNRC), consisting of soundings, triangulations, field angles, shore topography and drag records, tide and fathometer rolls, and astronomical and other observations, 1837-1946.

DIVISIONAL RECORDS. 1903-10. 5 lin. in.

These consist of Division of Chart Construction memorandums sent to the Hydrographer ("Memo A") and an office file of the Chief of the Division of Pilot Charts and Branch Offices, relating to the controversy between the Hydrographic Office and the Weather Bureau that concerned publishing, printing, and distributing meteorological data and pilot and navigational charts.

OTHER RECORDS. 1855-1937. 11 lin. ft.

Among these are correspondence concerning Lt. Matthew F. Maury, USN, who was relieved from duty by the "Plucking Board" of 1855; some daily remark books kept by navigation officers aboard U.S. vessels, 1866-75; a journal of the Hydrographic Office, February-June 1879; timeball reports relating to periodic visible time signals, 1885-1905; daily radio station logs, 1936-37; and reports relating to observations at sea and navigational hazards, 1885-1924.

CARTOGRAPHIC AND AUDIOVISUAL RECORDS. 1838-1968. 114,493 items.

Cartographic records (114,312 items) include manuscript survey sheets and chart enclosures from correspondence, 1838-1952, and nautical charts published by the Nautical Chart Division and its predecessors, 1868-1968. The former include "boat" or worksheets, "smooth" or compilation sheets, running survey sheets, reconnaissance sheets, rough field sheets, and sketches of land areas and shoals, particularly of the coast of Central and South America and island areas of the Pacific Ocean. Among chart enclosures are manuscript and annotated maps that relate to the North Atlantic ice patrol, such explorations as Adm. Robert E. Peary's arctic exploration, 1893-1903, weather studies, and ship disasters. The Chart Construction Division records consist of charts of harbors, ports, naval facilities, ocean bottoms, soundings, currents, nautical routes, coastlines, and other hydrographic data, 1868-1968. There are also aeronautical charts of the polar regions, the Southwest Pacific, and the Gulf of Mexico-Caribbean Sea area, showing radio and visual navigation aids, isogonic lines, aircraft facilities, and relief and spot elevations, 1928-65; LORAN charts published by the Navigational Science Division, 1945-61; charts published by the Maritime Safety Division, 1852-1950, that relate to sea and atmospheric conditions, including M. F. Maury's "Wind and Current Charts," 1848-52, and meteorological charts, 1883-84; and aerial photographs (30 rolls in WNRC) of Pacific islands, 1923-50.

There are also photographs (181 items) of lighthouses, lightships, and harbors in Uruguay, Japan, the Bay of Matanzas, Cuba, and Pago Pago, Samoa, 1877-1937; and panoramas of the coast of Lower California made by the U.S.S. *Ranger*, 1889-90.

See Walter W. Weinstein, comp., *Preliminary Inventory of the Records of the Hydrographic Office*, PI 39 (1952).

Microfilm Publication: *Records of the United States Exploring Expedition Under the Command of Lieutenant Charles Wilkes, 1836-1842*, M75, 27 rolls.

RECORDS OF THE NAVAL OBSERVATORY
(RECORD GROUP 78)

The first predecessor of the Naval Observatory was the Naval Depot of Charts and Instruments, established under the Board of Navy Commissioners in 1830. The Depot was transferred to the Bureau of Ordnance and Hydrography in 1842. An observatory was built for the Depot in 1844, and 10 years later it was renamed the U.S. Naval Observatory and Hydrographical Office. The Office was transferred to the Bureau of Navigation in 1862, where 4 years later the Office was divided into the Naval Observatory and the Hydrographic Office. In 1889 the Observatory was transferred to the Bureau of Equipment and Recruiting. When that Bureau was abolished in 1910, the Observatory was restored to the Bureau of Navigation. In 1942 the Observatory was attached to the Office of the Chief of Naval Operations.

The Observatory derives and furnishes the national time; maintains continuous astronomical observations; and develops, inspects, and services astronomical, navigational, and aerological instruments. It also prepares the *American Nautical Almanac*, the *American Air Almanac*, the *American Ephemeris and Nautical Almanac*, and other publications of value to navigators and scientists.

Letters sent by the Depot of Charts and Instruments, 1833-42, some letters received, 1844-54, and other letters, chiefly 1866-95, have been deposited in the Manuscript Division of the Library of Congress by the Naval Historical Foundation.

See Gustav A. Weber, *The Naval Observatory* (Baltimore, 1926).

There are 538 cubic feet of records dated between 1840 and 1943 in this record group.

RECORDS OF THE NAVAL OBSERVATORY. 1840-1943.
572 lin. ft.

Correspondence consisting of letters sent, 1842-1911, letters received, 1840-92, and correspondence, 1885-1943, with indexes. Some of these records relate to the work of Lt. (later Comdr.) Matthew F. Maury, Superintendent of the Depot and its successor office from 1842 to 1861, and concern astronomical, meteorological, and magnetic observations; collection of meteorological data by merchant vessels; production and distribution of sailing directions and wind and current charts; purchase, inspection, and issuance to the Navy of nautical instruments, charts, and books; and Maury's quasi-official activities, such as his travels, lectures, and proposals. Others concern the purchase and distribution of nautical instruments and charts during the Civil War; loss of the hydrographic function; the expansion of astronomical work; the Nautical Almanac Office; the expansion of the Observatory's functions during World War II; the design and development of scientific equipment; the manufacture, repair, and servicing of meteorological instruments; publications; and astronomical observations and reductions.

Records relating to magnetic and telescopic observations, 1843-1907, including records of observations made at Washington, D.C., and Annapolis, Md., consisting of notebooks containing observations of vertical and horizontal force, magnetographic deflections, and temperature reductions in the magnetic vault, 1843-96, with graphic and statistical summaries; and notebooks of data and remarks on astronomical observations, 1845-1907. There are also chronograph tapes and sheets, reduction sheets, and two card catalogs of stars—the *Washington Zone Catalogue* and the *Transit Circle Star Catalogue*.

RECORDS OF THE UNITED STATES NAVAL ASTRONOMICAL EXPEDITION TO THE SOUTHERN HEMISPHERE. 1848-61. 25 lin. ft.

Included are letters sent, 1848-61, and letters received, 1848-59, by Lt. James M. Gilliss, superintendent of the expedition, relating to preparations, activities, and results of the expedition; notebooks of telescopic observations made chiefly in the vicinity of Santiago de Chile, 1849-52, with data sheets on reductions, differential measures, clock corrections, and determinations of latitude and longitude; a card catalog of stars in the Southern Hemisphere; and Gilliss' printed narrative of the expedition, 1849-52.

CORRESPONDENCE OF THE NAUTICAL ALMANAC OFFICE. 1849-1911. 38 lin. ft.

The Nautical Almanac Office, established in 1849 to prepare the *American Ephemeris and Nautical Almanac*, reported directly to the Secretary of the Navy until 1859 when it was transferred to the Bureau of Ordnance and Hydrography. The Office was transferred in 1862 to the Bureau of Navigation and in 1889 to the Bureau of Equipment and Recruiting, where it became part of the Observatory in 1894.

The correspondence relates to the Office's functions of preparing publications, computing astronomical data, and conducting research leading to new tables of celestial motion, and includes letters received, 1849-85 (with gaps before 1868), letters sent, 1852-1911 (with gaps before 1883), and correspondence, 1885-1904. Indexes are available for the correspondence. Gaps in both the letters received and letters sent series are filled by records of the Office, dating from 1849, that have been deposited in the Manuscript Division of the Library of Congress by the Naval Historical Foundation.

AUDIOVISUAL RECORDS. 1840-84. 107 items.

Included are pencil and oil landscape sketches of Greenland made during and after the U.S. *Polaris* Expedition, 1871-73; two unidentified woodcuts of an arctic landscape; unidentified photographs of arctic regions, possibly taken by the members of the Lady Franklin Bay Expedition, 1881-84; 19th-century hand-colored lithographs of arctic areas; and photographic prints made by a member of the Leigh Smith Expedition to Spits-bergen, 1873.

Microfilm Publication: *Correspondence of the Astronomical Expedition to the Southern Hemisphere, 1846-61*, T54, 1 roll.

RECORDS OF THE
OFFICE OF THE JUDGE ADVOCATE GENERAL (NAVY)
(RECORD GROUP 125)

Legal duties of the Department of the Navy were handled by the Office of the Secretary of the Navy until the appointment in 1865 of the Solicitor and Naval Judge-Advocate General, who was transferred in 1870 to the Department of Justice. The Office of the Judge Advocate General was created by an act of June 8, 1880. The Office of the Solicitor was established in 1900 and handled non-military legal matters of the Department between 1908 and 1921. The two Offices were merged in 1921.

The Office of the Judge Advocate General has authority over military, administrative, and applied law concerning the operation of the Navy. It administers military justice, prepares orders for enforcement of court-martial sentences, initiates corrective legal actions, handles matters relating to international and admiralty law and claims against the Navy, drafts departmental legislation, and administers a legal assistance program.

See Henry P. Beers, "Historical Sketch of the Office of the Judge Advocate General, Navy Department," U.S. Naval Institute *Proceedings*, LXVII (May 1941).

There are 2,687 cubic feet of records dated between 1799 and 1943 in this record group.

GENERAL RECORDS. 1865-1918.
400 lin. ft.

These consist principally of general correspondence, 1883-1908, communications to the Secretary of the Navy, 1885-1912, letters received, 1879-83, registers of letters received, 1876-80 and 1883-1904, indexes to letters received, 1880-83 and 1890-1904, unofficial letters sent, 1892-1909, letters sent by the Solicitor, 1908-11, confidential letters sent to military personnel and Congressmen, 1894-1904, other letters sent, 1879-1911, endorsements, 1890-92, miscellaneous letters, 1865-66, and other indexes and registers, 1880-1908.

PERSONNEL RECORDS. 1799-1943.
1,853 lin. ft. (in WNRC).

These consist chiefly of records relating to Navy and Marine Corps courts-martial, courts of inquiry, boards of investigation and inquest, and examining and retiring boards. Included are records of proceedings of general courts-martial and courts of inquiry, 1799-1942, including courts of inquiry convened under a January 16, 1857, act, 1857-59. There are also a register of general courts-martial, 1909-43; indexes, registers, reports, and slip records for summary courts-martial and deck courts, 1855-1930, including the only records of deck court proceedings known to exist, 1910; records of proceedings of boards of investigation and inquest, 1866-1942; and proceedings and registers of examining and retiring boards, 1836-1941. Also included are personnel reports from commanding officers, 1860-95; correspondence relating to desertions and discharges, 1883-1908; memorandums announcing court-martial findings and sentences, 1892-1911; letters sent concerning courts-martial, 1898-1911 and

1929-31; and proceedings, lists, correspondence, registers, orders, indexes,
and other records concerning Office
activities, 1860-1931.

FISCAL RECORDS. 1869-1943.
481 lin. ft.

These consist of correspondence and
other records concerning legal matters
affecting naval vessels, 1887-1906, and
specifications, 1888-1922; records relating to commandeering and release of private vessels, 1917-19; and registers,
indexes, reports, memorandums, transcripts, abstracts, correspondence, and
other records relating to claims, contracts, bids, leases, disposition of real
estate and other property, and monetary
affairs.

PATENT RECORDS. 1893-1942.
452 lin. ft.

These comprise patent case files,
1918-42; correspondence and other
records concerning inventions, 1915-34;
records relating to German claims
resulting from patent infringements,
1918-31, and to interferences, chiefly for
1925-42, with some dated as early as
1893; and indexes and transcripts.

RECORDS OF OPINIONS AND
DECISIONS. 1846-1911. 11 lin. ft.

Included are opinions and decisions of
the Judge Advocate General, the Attorney General, the Comptroller of the
Treasury, and the Solicitor of the Navy,
with indexes and registers, 1846-1911.

RECORDS OF BOARDS AND
OTHER SPECIAL UNITS. 1896-1938.
120 lin. ft.

Included are records of a few examining boards, courts of inquiry, and other
units dated as early as 1896; the naval
disciplinary barracks at Port Royal, S.C.,
1911-15, and Puget Sound, Wash., 1912-
15; Board on Valuation of Commandeered Property, 1918-22; Legal Section, Force Commander's Office, U.S.
Naval Forces Operating in European
Waters, established to handle matters
related to admiralty or other civil law,
including claims for damages resulting
from the presence or operation of U.S.
naval forces in European countries and
waters, 1917-22; the Paris Naval Board
on Claims, 1918-22; the Cancellation
Board, appointed in 1923 to examine
claims resulting from the cancellation of
naval contracts, 1923-24; and the Naval
War Claims Board, established in 1925
to consider contractors' claims for losses
on World War I naval contracts, 1925-
38.

Microfilm Publication: *Records of General
Courts-Martial and Courts of Inquiry of the Navy
Department, 1799-1867*, M273, 198 rolls.

RECORDS OF THE BUREAU OF AERONAUTICS
(RECORD GROUP 72)

The Bureau of Aeronautics was established in the Navy Department by an
act of July 12, 1921, to perform
aeronautical duties as directed by the
Secretary of the Navy. General supervision of naval aeronautics, placed in the
Bureau of Navigation in 1911, was established in the Division of Operations in
1914 as the Office of Naval Aeronautics
and transferred in 1915 to the Office
of the Chief of Naval Operations. In 1917
the name was changed to the Office of
Naval Aviation, and in 1918 to the Aviation Division. Following orders issued in
1916 to distribute functions concerning
construction and equipment of naval aircraft among the Bureaus of Construction and Repair, Steam Engineering,
Ordnance, Yards and Docks, and Navigation, several new units were created

to handle these functions, including the Aircraft Division of the Bureau of Construction and Repair and the Aeronautics Division of the Bureau of Steam Engineering. When the Bureau of Aeronautics was established, functions of these units were transferred to it, including responsibility for testing materials, making contracts, and outfitting bases and other shore establishments. During World War II Bureau functions were expanded, and emphasis was placed on developing naval aircraft designs; purchasing, constructing, and maintaining aircraft and airships; maintaining naval air stations and fleet air bases; and supervising the service, repair, overhaul, and salvage of naval aircraft. The Bureau was abolished by an act of August 18, 1959, and its functions transferred to the Bureau of Naval Weapons. They were reassigned in 1966 to the Air, Weapons, and Electronics Systems Commands.

See Bureau of Aeronautics, *Manual* (1945); and Albert R. Buchanan, ed., *The Navy's Air War, A Mission Completed* (New York, 1946).

There are 4,053 cubic feet of records dated between 1911 and 1946 in this record group.

RECORDS OF PREDECESSORS. 1911-25. 559 lin. ft.

The records include the general correspondence of the Aeronautics Division, with a register and a filing classification guide, relating to airplane engines, fuel, propellers, lights, detectors, kites, balloons, gas, and other aviation matters, 1911-22; Aviation Division correspondence, with indexes, registers, and a filing plan, 1914-21; and Aircraft Division correspondence, with a register and filing classification guide, 1917-25.

GENERAL RECORDS OF THE BUREAU OF AERONAUTICS. 1917-45. 3,500 lin. ft.

These records primarily consist of central correspondence files, 1917-45, with a register and a microprint record of communications received, 1944-45. Included are correspondence and reports concerning contracts, patents, designs, and specifications for aircraft and aircraft instruments, electronic devices, and other equipment; and organization charts, issuances, memorandums, and planning directives for shore activities.

TECHNICAL AND RESEARCH RECORDS. 1916-45. 250 lin. ft.

These comprise records relating to the U.S. Helium Production Plant, Fort Worth, Tex., and the Army and Navy Helium Board, 1919-30; reports and research memorandums of the Lighter-Than-Air Design Branch, 1916-45; test reports and photographs of that Branch, relating to stability tests, flight-test strains and stresses, specifications, and blueprints, 1921-36; test reports and specifications, 1923-40; structural calculation test reports on airplane wing and fuselage parts, 1935-43; test reports on aircraft and aircraft equipment, and contractor descriptive specifications, 1925-42; aircraft manufacturer proposals for rejected aircraft, 1931-41; erection and maintenance instructions, 1928-43; contractor weight and balance reports, 1919-40; reports on naval aircraft engines, 1930-38; and flight logs for experimental engines and aircraft, 1917-42.

OTHER HEADQUARTERS RECORDS. 1926-44. 169 lin. ft.

These consist chiefly of Army Air Corps contracts of joint interest to the Navy Department and related correspondence, 1937-42, a survey of Bureau of Aeronautics civilian personnel, 1944, and monthly reports of the quantity, type, and location of naval aircraft, 1926-40.

RECORDS OF THE U.S. NAVAL AIR STATION, LAKEHURST, N.J. 1918-41. 45 lin. ft.

The records consist primarily of reports, plans, tracings, and photographs of the airships *Shenandoah, Los Angeles, Akron*, and *Macon*.

AUDIOVISUAL RECORDS. 1916-46. 96,950 items.

There are training slides of Navy aviators and photographers, naval air stations, aerial charts and maps, the PN-9 flight to Hawaii, and foreign and domestic ships, aircraft, and equipment, 1916-26. Also photographs of Navy aerial photography trainees, 1917-18; activities at the Dayton and Akron, Ohio, Naval Air Stations, 1917-38; constructing and testing dirigibles, balloons, amphibious planes, parachutes, and other materials at the Philadelphia Naval Aircraft Factory and private plants, 1917-41; and Navy airplanes and their structural details, 1928-46.

See William F. Shonkwiler, comp., *Preliminary Inventory of the Records of the Bureau of Aeronautics*, PI 26 (1951).

Commands and Installations

RECORDS OF NAVAL DISTRICTS AND SHORE ESTABLISHMENTS (RECORD GROUP 181)

The Department of the Navy, soon after its beginning in 1798, created navy yards and other fleet service shore establishments. A system of naval districts for the United States, its territories and possessions, however, was not formally established until 1903 under the Bureau of Navigation, and the Chief of Naval Operations in 1915 assumed supervision over the system. The districts assumed greater responsibility during World War I, and by the end of World War II they exercised almost complete military and administrative control over naval operations within their limits, including naval shipyards (navy yards), stations, training stations, air installations, and advance bases.

For the records of shore establishments under the jurisdiction of a particular bureau see the record group for that bureau.

There are 7,142 cubic feet of records (in WNRC except for nontextual records) dated between 1783 and 1948 in this record group.

RECORDS. 1783-1948. 10,875 lin. ft. and 3 rolls of microfilm.

The records consist chiefly of correspondence, indexes, registers, reports, memorandums, telegrams, cablegrams, orders, circulars, logs, journals, blueprints, and personnel and fiscal and accounting records from the offices of the commandants of naval districts at Boston (1st), 1903-4 and 1917-43, New York (3d), 1917-42, Norfolk, Va. (5th), 1926-43, Charleston, S.C. (6th), 1903-25, New Orleans (8th), 1917-33, Great Lakes, Ill. (9th), 1919-39, San Diego (11th), 1920-43, San Francisco (12th), 1925-39, Seattle (13th), 1918-43, and Pearl Harbor (14th), 1903-44; navy yards at Boston, 1811-1943, Charleston, 1902-33, Mare Island, Calif., 1854-1940, Memphis, 1845-55, New York, 1826 and 1835-1942, Norfolk, 1863-1943, Pearl Harbor, 1899-1942, Philadelphia, 1794-1939, Portsmouth, N.H., 1815-1911, Puget Sound, 1925-43, and Washington D.C., 1783-92 and 1811-1927; the Great Lakes Naval Training Station, Ill., 1914-

23; Mound City Naval Station, Ill., 1873; New Orleans Naval Station, 1865–75; Newport Naval Training Station, R.I., 1883–1948 (including 1 roll of microfilm); Pollok Naval Station, Philippine Islands, 1903–4; Culebra Naval Station, P.R., 1902–11; San Juan Naval Station, P.R., 1898–1912; St. Thomas Naval Station, V.I., 1917–31; Lakehurst Naval Air Station, N.J., 1919–45; Miami Naval Air Station, 1918; Norfolk Naval Air Station, 1922–36; Squantum Naval Reserve Aviation Base, Mass., 1930–43; Grand Cayman Island Naval Air Facility, British West Indies, and La Fe Naval Air Facility, Cuba, 1942–44; Naval Coal Depot, San Diego, 1904–11; Naval Reserve Divisions, Rock Island, Ill., 1924–43; and naval operating bases at Aukland, New Zealand, 1943–44, and Londonderry, Northern Ireland, 1942–44. There are also microfilm copies (2 rolls) of activity location cards of the Fleet Post Office, San Francisco, 1940–45; and records of advanced amphibious bases in Algeria, 1942–44, Salerno, Italy, 1944, and Port Lyautey, Morocco, 1943–44.

AUDIOVISUAL RECORDS. 1891–1945. 20,985 items.

Included are photographs of Navy personnel, ships, aircraft, and facilities at the Washington Navy Yard, 1891–1919; building construction, ship repair and alteration, and other activities of the Philadelphia Navy Yard, 1907–26; construction progress, the installation of equipment, and damaged machinery and ships at the Pearl Harbor Navy Yard, 1914–42; and officers, enlisted men, quarters, and operational activities at the U.S. naval base, Falmouth, England, 1944–45.

See Richard G. Wood, comp., *Preliminary Inventory of the Records of Naval Establishments Created Overseas During World War II*, PI 13 (1948).

RECORDS OF THE UNITED STATES NAVAL ACADEMY (RECORD GROUP 405)

The U.S. Naval Academy, formally opened as the Naval School on October 10, 1845, on the site of Fort Severn at Annapolis, Md., was given its present name in 1850 and transferred from the supervision of the Secretary of the Navy to the Bureau of Ordnance and Hydrography. The Academy has remained at Annapolis except for the period 1861 to 1865, when it was temporarily located at Newport, R.I. In 1862 the Bureau of Navigation acquired responsibility for the Academy, but in 1867, while the Bureau of Navigation continued to conduct the routine administration and financial management of the school, the Department of the Navy assumed direct supervision. The remaining official connection with the Bureau of Navigation was discontinued in 1869, but was restored by a Navy Department general order in 1889. The Academy is now under the supervision of the Bureau of Naval Personnel.

There are 404 cubic feet of records dated between 1836 and 1951 in this record group.

GENERAL RECORDS OF THE OFFICE OF THE SUPERINTENDENT. 1845–1951. 401 lin. ft.

Included are letters sent to the Secretary of the Navy, 1865–88; the Assistant Secretary of the Navy, 1903–5; Navy Department bureaus, 1865–1908; Naval Academy officers, instructors, and cadets, 1881–88 and 1894–1908; the Congress, 1888–1901; and other individuals, 1845–1911. Also letters and telegrams sent by the Superintendent, 1857–1901, and the Assistant Superintendent, 1895–98; letters received from the Secretary of the Navy, naval officers, and private individuals, 1845-86, the Bureau of Navigation, 1862-83, commandants of navy yards, 1877-81, naval officers, 1875-81, midshipmen's parents, 1910, and others, 1875-1906; general correspondence, 1907-27, with indexes and record cards; confidential correspondence of the Superintendent serving concurrently as Commandant of the Severn River Naval Command, 1944-51; and the Superintendent's orders, 1890-1912, and other orders and notices, 1850-88 and 1894-1928.

RECORDS OF BOARDS. 1836-1942. 10 lin. ft.

These consist of proceedings, minutes, and other records of the Board for the Examination of Midshipmen, 1836-80, the Board of Visitors, 1863-1914, the Academic Board, 1854-1942, and the Supervisory Naval Examining Board, 1918.

RECORDS OF DEPARTMENTS. 1845-1920. 8 lin. ft.

These consist of letters sent and contracts relating to buildings and grounds, 1858-1911; and correspondence, orders, sample examinations, grade books, schedules, and sample assignments of departments of instruction, 1845-1920.

PERSONNEL RECORDS. 1846-1945. 82 lin. ft.

Included are correspondence relating to midshipmen, 1846-88, and examining candidates, 1846-76; entrance papers, 1848-53; rolls of midshipmen, 1849-71; registers of misconduct by cadets, 1865-1904; monthly class reports, 1855-83; registers relating to class standings of cadets, 1844-1924, and of candidates admitted to the Academy, 1860-1930; applications and medical records of the U.S. Naval Reserve Midshipmen's School, 1941-45; lists, reports, and registers relating to such subjects as physical fitness, annual examinations, midshipmen's congressional districts, applicants for appointments as naval cadets at large, cadets' academic records, day-books of weekly grades, examinations held for classes of midshipmen, punishments, class reports, midshipmen's term grades, cadets' clothing, midshipmen on leave, and conduct, 1850-1915; and correspondence, orders, and journals of summer cruise ships, 1860-1916. Also orders and notices that concern midshipmen, including orders of practice cruise ships, 1892-1902, regimental orders, 1909-20, and orders relating to midshipmen's dismissals or suspensions, 1856-62.

RECORDS OF RESERVE OFFICER CLASSES. 1917-19 and 1941-45. 26 lin. ft.

These consist of reports, correspondence, orders, and enrollment cards of Reserve officer classes held during World Wars I and II.

OTHER RECORDS. 1847-1950. 2 lin. ft.

These include correspondence, memorandums, and orders of the commandant of midshipmen, 1875-1912; correspondence and proceedings of boards appointed to investigate charges against midshipmen and court-martial proceedings, 1866-1915; financial accounts, including lists of bills paid, requisitions, cadets' messbooks, an expense book of cadets, and a billbook of midshipmen, 1847-1924; registers of visitors to the tomb of John Paul Jones, 1919; minutes of an association of naval officers to erect a monument to Lt. S. W. Preston, 1865-67; publications relating to the Academy, 1941-50; correspondence, memorandums, circulars, and other records of the Chief Clerk's Office, 1915-17; correspondence of the Superintendent's aide, 1917; minutes of the Naval Academy officers club, 1897-1934; and a list of officers on duty at the Academy, 1896-1907.

RECORDS OF NAVAL OPERATING FORCES
(RECORD GROUP 313)

Navy Department General Order 5 of May 14, 1959, defined operating forces as "the several fleets, seagoing forces, sea frontier forces, district forces, Fleet Marine Forces and other assigned Marine Corps forces, the Military Sea Transportation Service, and such shore activities of the Navy and other forces and activities as may be assigned to the Operating Forces of the Navy by the President or the Secretary of the Navy." Military command of shore activities is assigned to operating forces when shore activities contribute operationally to missions at sea. The naval operating forces were organized chiefly on a geographical basis into fleets and squadrons until 1922 when the U. S. Fleet became the principal naval force. A reorganization in 1941 provided for the Pacific, Atlantic, and Asiatic Fleets. This organization was modified during and after World War II. In 1967 the major commands afloat were the Pacific Fleet; the Atlantic Fleet; the Naval Forces, Europe; and the Military Sea Transportation Service. Since May 1915 the Chief of Naval Operations has been responsible to the Secretary of the Navy for fleet operations and readiness for use in war.

There are 249 cubic feet of records dated between 1864 and 1957 in this record group.

RECORDS OF SQUADRONS AND FLEETS. 1865-1940. 174 lin. ft.

These records comprise reports, correspondence, and journals of the Asiatic Squadron, 1898-1905, the Atlantic Fleet, 1905-9 and 1917-18, the Bering Sea Squadron, 1892-95, the Detached Squadron, 1907, the European Squadron, 1869-1905, the Squadron of Evolution, 1889-92, the Nicaraguan Expeditionary Squadron, 1909-10, the North Atlantic Squadron, 1865-1905, the Pacific Fleet, 1904-11, the South Atlantic Squadron, 1892-1905, and the U.S. Fleet, 1936-40; and combined records of two or more naval forces, 1892-1906.

OTHER RECORDS. 1864-1944. 90 lin. ft.

These consist of correspondence of the U.S. Auxiliary Naval Force, 1898; and correspondence and miscellaneous records of individual vessels, 1864-1944, including the cruiser *Augusta*, 1935-44.

CARTOGRAPHIC RECORDS. 1907-57. 39 items.

Included are published charts prepared by the U.S. Atlantic Fleet, relating to its around-the-world cruise, 1907-9, anchorages on the Hudson River, European ports, and British and American mine locations, 1907-18; and annotated base maps of Antarctica and an accompanying published report relating to the Army-Navy Trail Party of Operation Deep Freeze II, prepared by the U.S. Naval Support Force, Antarctica, 1956-57.

Department of the Air Force

RECORDS OF THE ARMY AIR FORCES
(RECORD GROUP 18)

The Army Air Forces (AAF) originated August 1, 1907, as the Aeronautical Division in the Office of the Chief Signal Officer. In July 1914 the Aviation Section was created in the Signal Corps, and in July 1917 the Equipment Division was established in the Office of the Chief Signal Officer. In September 1917 the Aeronautical Division became the Air Division. An Executive order of May 20, 1918, divided the Aviation Section into two separate agencies: the Division of Military Aeronautics and the Bureau of Aircraft Production. A Presidential directive of May 29, 1918, created the Air Service of the Army and separated it from the Signal Corps. In August 1918 the Director of Aircraft Production was appointed Second Assistant Secretary of War and Director of Air Service, responsible for both the Bureau of Aircraft Production and the Division of Military Aeronautics, which were united by an Executive order of March 19, 1919.

The Army reorganization act of June 4, 1920, made the Air Service a combatant arm of the Army, and the Air Corps Act of July 2, 1926, changed the name of the Air Service to the Air Corps. In March 1935 the General Headquarters Air Force was created, and on June 20, 1941, a new position, the Chief of the Army Air Forces, was created. At the same time the General Headquarters Air Force was renamed the Air Force Combat Command. A general reorganization of the War Department united these two agencies as the Army Air Forces on March 9, 1942, placing them directly under the Secretary of War and the War Department General Staff. The National Security Act of 1947 redesignated the Army Air Forces

the U.S. Air Force under the newly created Department of the Air Force.

See *The Army Air Forces in World War II* (7 vols., 1948-58); and H. H. Arnold, *Global Mission* (New York, 1949).

There are 11,439 cubic feet of records dated between 1914 and 1952 in this record group.

GENERAL RECORDS OF THE OFFICE OF THE CHIEF SIGNAL OFFICER. 1914–18. 4 lin. ft.

These consist of compilations of extracts of letters, telegrams, and memorandums of War Department offices, relating to regulations and authorities for U.S. flying schools, including balloon instruction, training, airplane types, and performance. Included are charts, reports, and correspondence relating to the organization and duties of the Planning Section and to a program of airplane production. Other records reflecting the Chief Signal Officer's activities during 1918 are in the AAF central files.

RECORDS OF THE DIVISION OF MILITARY AERONAUTICS. 1914–19. 13 lin. ft.

These include correspondence, memorandums, orders, and other records relating to foreign and domestic air services, airplane construction and equipment, flight training, schools of military aeronautics, radio development, and training of radio officers.

RECORDS OF THE BUREAU OF AIRCRAFT PRODUCTION. 1916–21. 142 lin. ft.

These records consist of issuances, general correspondence, historical data, and other material relating to operation, procurement, and production activities of the Bureau and its subordinate divisions. Included is correspondence of the Executive Department of the Signal Corps Equipment Division, the Director and the Assistant Director of Aircraft Production, and the Chemical Section of the Science and Research Division (1916-19), concerning production problems of the World War I period and aspects of early airplane production and aerial photography.

RECORDS OF THE SPRUCE PRODUCTION DIVISION. 1917-46. 239 lin. ft.

The Spruce Production Division was established in the Office of the Chief Signal Officer on November 15, 1917, to increase the output of timber for airplane construction during World War I. When the Bureau of Aircraft Production was created in May 1918, the Division came under its authority. To carry out the required production program of the Bureau, the Division assumed full control of the logging and lumber industry of the Northwest. An act of July 9, 1918, created a special agency, the U.S. Spruce Production Corporation. On November 1, 1918, the functions and properties of the Division passed to the Corporation, and a dual organization was formed. The Spruce Production Section of the Bureau of Aircraft Production was initially the Washington office of the Spruce Production Division of Portland, Oreg. The Division was officially demobilized on August 31, 1919, but the Section in Washington continued to function until 1921. At the last meeting of the Spruce Production Corporation Directors on November 12, 1946, provision was made for its liquidation. The records consist of issuances, reports, general correspondence, messages, rosters, and other documents relating to functions mainly during World War I. There are also records of the Spruce Production Section, districts, and units, and of the Corporation.

RECORDS OF THE GENERAL HEADQUARTERS AIR FORCE AND THE AIR FORCE COMBAT COMMAND. 1935-42. 207 lin. ft.

For a period of 7 years Air Corps functions in the continental United States were divided between the Office of the Chief of the Air Corps, which was concerned with materiel and noncombat air matters, and the General Headquarters Air Force, established in March 1935 at Langley Field, Va., for unit training and tactical air employment. The General Headquarters Air Force became increasingly independent after 1939, except for the interval between July 1940 and June 1941 when the combat air units in the continental United States reverted to the jurisdiction of the newly created ground-controlled General Headquarters, U.S. Army. In November 1940 Maj. Gen. H. H. Arnold, Chief of the Air Corps, was appointed Deputy Chief of Staff for Air, and in June 1941 he was appointed Chief of the Army Air Forces with control over both the Office of the Chief of the Air Corps and the General Headquarters Air Force. The General Headquarters Air Force was renamed the Air Force Combat Command on June 20, 1941, and was terminated on March 9, 1942. The records consist of issuances, general correspondence, messages, technical and operational records, and office files of the Commanding General, 1935-41, and certain staff files, including those of the Intelligence and Signal Sections, 1935-42.

RECORDS OF THE HEADQUARTERS ARMY AIR FORCES AND ITS PREDECESSORS. 1917-48. 7,072 lin. ft. and 20 rolls of microfilm.

These records consist chiefly of security-classified and unclassified central decimal files of the Army Air Forces, the Office of the Chief of the Air Corps, the Office of the Air Service, and their predecessors, and are organized by several major chronological periods. Included are a "project" series arranged alphabetically by various Air Force organizations, a "foreign file" arranged alphabetically by foreign areas or overseas commands, and an extensive body of "bulk" files that originated in the records offices of various divisions and offices and consist of subseries, narrative and statistical reports, documentary compilations, and selected accumulations of office files that remained intact and separate from the main series. After the reorganization of September 18, 1947, the Headquarters Army Air Forces became the U. S. Air Force, and its central file system was continued until October 1948.

OFFICE FILES OF THE AIR CORPS AND THE ARMY AIR FORCES OFFICERS. 1922–47. 27 lin. ft.

These consist of issuances, reports, messages, and other documents concerning the assignments and activities of Lt. Col. Frank Andrews, 1932, Lt. Gen. Ira C. Eaker, 1945–47, Maj. Gen. James R. Fechet, 1925–30, Maj. Gen. Benjamin F. Giles, 1945–46, Maj. Gen. Millard F. Harmon, 1939–45, Lt. Gen. Harold A. McGinnis, 1944–45, Maj. Gen. Mason M. Patrick, 1922–27, Gen. Carl A. Spaatz, 1946–47, Lt. Gen. George E. Stratemeyer, 1942, and Brig. Gen. Lyman P. Whitten, 1941–46. Also included are briefs of messages of primary interest to the Commanding General of the Army Air Forces, known as General Arnold's Logs, 1942–45.

RECORDS RELATING TO THE AIR CORPS MAIL OPERATIONS. 1934. 80 lin. ft.

These consist mainly of correspondence relating to handling of mail by the Air Corps during the period February–

May 1934. Included are some records of Headquarters of the Eastern, Central, and Western Zones.

OTHER GENERAL RECORDS. 1917–52. 3,037 lin. ft. and 631 rolls of microfilm.

These consist of minutes of the Munitions Assignment Committee and the Joint Munitions Allocation Committee, relating to the allocation of aircraft under the Lend-Lease Act, 1941–48; messages (partly on 631 rolls of microfilm), statistical summaries, and combat operation reports, 1939–47 (in WNRC); records relating to aircraft procurement, 1917–47; civilian and military Air Force personnel records, 1919–47; research and development records, 1941–46; records relating to patents and inventions, 1918–46; records relating to dissemination of information to the public; records relating to inspections of AAF installations, 1944–47 (in WNRC); records relating to medical policy and administration, 1940–47 (in WNRC); and records relating to construction in the European and Mediterranean Theaters of Operations, 1943–46. Included is a document collection, with an index, accumulated by the Air Corps Library and its predecessor, the Air Service Library, 1917–52.

BOARD AND COMMITTEE RECORDS. 1917–47. 29 lin. ft.

These records consist of reports, memorandums, and correspondence of the Reprogramming Committee of the Air Board, and records accumulated by Theodore Von Karman, Director of the Army Air Forces Scientific Advisory Board and its predecessor—the AAF Scientific Advisory Group—relating to the long-range AAF research and development program in various fields of science, 1941–47; minutes, reports, and general correspondence, 1917–18, of the Aircraft Board, formerly the Aircraft Production Board, which was established May 16, 1917, and discontinued

October 1, 1917; Air Service Advisory Board reports and correspondence relating to Air Service policy, organization, programs, and legislation, 1919–21, records relating to claims against the Air Service, 1920–21, and files of the legal adviser, 1920–21; minutes of meetings and miscellaneous records of the Air Service Claims Board, 1918–21; and general decimal correspondence of the Air Service Control Board, 1918–19.

RECORDS OF HEADQUARTERS TWENTIETH AIR FORCE. 1944–45. 53 lin. ft.

Headquarters XX Air Force, located in Washington, D.C., was distinct from its two major components in the Pacific—the 20th and 21st Bomber Commands. Most of the staff members and civilian assistants in Headquarters XX Air Force served at the same time in the major air staff offices of AAF Headquarters, with Gen. H. H. Arnold as Commanding General of the Army Air Forces and of the XX Air Force. These records consist of general correspondence relating to the use of B–29's in the Pacific, incoming and outgoing radio and cable messages, and mission reports of the 20th and 21st Bomber Commands. They include also some correspondence of General Arnold.

RECORDS OF COMMANDS, ACTIVITIES, AND ORGANIZATIONS. 1917–42. 250 lin. ft.

These are mainly records of field installations and commands, consisting of orders, reports, correspondence, messages, and other records relating to maintenance of aircraft and equipment, preparation and distribution of technical orders and other instructions, and training of civilian employees for supply and maintenance work in the continental United States as well as training of military personnel as air service groups and other units for overseas duty. Included

are records of the I Concentration Command Headquarters, located at Luken Field, Cincinnati, Ohio, which was established in June 1942 as the AAF Foreign Service Concentration Command (and renamed in August 1942) to expedite the staging and movement overseas of the AAF combat groups and squadrons that had completed their unit training phase in the First, Second, Third, and Fourth Air Forces. In November 1942 the Command was discontinued and its functions were transferred to the four Air Forces. These records consist of reports, training directives, correspondence, transcripts of telephone conversations, and other records relating to aircraft modifications, weather information, briefing, intelligence, training, and administrative functions.

CARTOGRAPHIC RECORDS. 1917–47. 6,657 items.

There are plans of certain airfields in Texas collected by the Aviation Section of the Office of the Chief Signal Officer, 1917–18; maps prepared by the Army Air Service, 1918–25, and the Army Air Corps, 1929–36, showing proposed airways, various transcontinental and around-the-world flights, landing fields, experimental air navigation maps, photomaps, and airstrip maps of the United States; a series of looseleaf project record books containing reports, illustrations, and correspondence on the methods and equipment used in aerial photography for surveying and mapping, 1922–32; and incomplete sets of aeronautical charts of the world at varying scales and special maps published by the Army Air Forces and its component units, including the Office of the Assistant Chief of Air Staff Intelligence, the Directorate of Weather, Aeronautical Chart Service, and several of the Air Force Commands, 1939–47.

AUDIOVISUAL RECORDS. 1901-64. 452,414 items.

Photographs (446,495 items) include those relating to aviation in World War I; of aviation cadets, graduates of bombardier and navigation and gunnery schools, personnel assigned to various bombardment squadrons in World War II, and Air Force officers and civilians significant to aviation history, 1911-46; of building and runway construction, equipment, sanitary and recreational facilities, target ranges, power stations, airplane squadrons, and radio control rooms made at March Field, Calif., 1928-34; relating to the development of aircraft, both lighter and heavier than air, parachute experimentation, helium repurification plants, accident studies, record flights, Army maneuvers viewed from the air, flood and tornado damage, and personnel at Scott Field, 1928-37; of early aircraft developed by Glen H. Curtiss and Glenn L. Martin and activities of the joint Army and Navy aviation school at Rockwell Field, Calif., 1914-18; of activities at air bases and showing physical features for guiding pilots along military air routes from South America to Africa and Asia, 1943-45; and of foreign and domestic aircraft, 1901-59. There are also photographs of mountain ranges, rivers, and valleys, 1917-64; flood, hurricane, earthquake, and other disaster areas; national parks; historic sites; foreign countries; and logging and other activities of the Spruce Production Corporation, 1917-22.

Motion pictures, 1912-49 (5,828 reels), consist of films concerning the development and use of lighter-than-air craft, 1925-35; World War II training films illustrating the coordination of operational units of the American Eighth Air Force and the combined efforts of these units in preparing and completing a bombing mission, and containing instructions in flight and gunnery and the maintenance and use of planes, helicopters, airfield tractors, forklift trucks, and spray-painting equipment; Air Transport Command briefing films, consisting of aerial and ground views of terrain and flight routes and landing facilities in the North and South Atlantic areas, Europe, India, China, the Caribbean area, South America, Africa, the Pacific area, the British Isles, Alaska, the Canal Zone, and the United States; animation for the briefing films, showing particular flight routes, locations of landing strips, radio beams, and the principal geographic configuration of specific areas; combat films made in all theaters of operations in World War II, concerning activities of the USAAF and containing material on all other aspects of the war, including land and sea battles, amphibious operations, military leaders of the Allied powers at conferences and visiting troops, entertainers, war correspondents, Red Cross activities, rest and recreation activities, native peoples and their customs and participation in the war, captured enemy spies and saboteurs, Allied and Axis prisoners of war and prisoner-of-war camps, internees and internee camps, concentration camps, Axis atrocities, V-E and V-J Days, the occupation of Germany and Japan, atomic scientists, the atomic bomb blast over Nagasaki, and damage to Nagasaki and Hiroshima. There is also a film made by the Air Corps in 1933 of the Arkansas flood; a Coast Guard training film on swimming through burning oil and surf; and a film entitled "Last Rites of the Battleship Maine," made by the Selig Corporation in 1912.

Sound recordings, 1945 (91 items), consist of recordings of radio programs in "The Fighting AAF" and "Your AAF" series, which include actual air combat accounts obtained by radio reporters in all theaters of action, and eyewitness accounts of combat.

Microfilm Publications: *Colonel Gorrell's History of the U.S. Army Air Service*, T619, 58 rolls; and *Cross Indexes to Air Corps Correspondence, January 1939-September 1942*, T914, 20 rolls.

RECORDS OF THE
OFFICE OF THE SECRETARY OF THE AIR FORCE
(RECORD GROUP 340)

The Office of the Secretary of the Air Force had its origin in the National Security Act of July 26, 1947, which established the Department of the Air Force as part of the National Military Establishment and provided that certain functions, property, personnel, and records be transferred to the Department of the Air Force from the Department of the Army. The National Military Establishment was renamed the Department of Defense in 1949. The Secretary of the Air Force is responsible for administration, training, operations, logistical support, welfare, and preparedness of the Air Force, and other activities prescribed by the President or the Secretary of Defense. The Office of the Secretary includes the Under Secretary; Assistant Secretaries for Research and Development, Installations and Logistics, Financial Management, and Manpower and Reserve Affairs; the Administrative Assistant; General Counsel; Director, Office of Legislative Liaison; Director, Office of Information; and various boards or committees reporting to the Secretary.

There are 1,432 cubic feet of records dated between 1942 and 1956 in this record group.

GENERAL RECORDS. 1943-54. 631 lin. ft.

The correspondence file of the Secretary's Office, 1948-54, covers Air Force administration, relations with contractors, budget estimates, departmental communications, research and development, departmental committees, legal affairs, charitable and professional groups, and newspaper clipping files. Included are the numeric "project file," 1947-49; a numeric file, 1948-54; the "special interest and chronological" file for organizations, offices, boards, and committees, 1950-52; a file of Air Force

Printing Board minutes, 1943-54; and Air Force budget estimates, 1948-54.

RECORDS OF THE OFFICE OF THE UNDER SECRETARY OF THE AIR FORCE. 1947-50. 5 lin. ft.

This subject file includes reports, correspondence, contracts, claims, and administrative documents concerning procurement of Air Force supplies and services.

RECORDS OF THE GENERAL COUNSEL. 1949-54. 5 lin. ft.

Records include files relating to procurement, research and development, real property management, family housing, finance, civil aviation, personnel security, and negotiation of international agreements affecting the Air Force, 1945-53, and Air Force Contract Adjustment Board case files, 1951-54.

RECORDS OF THE OFFICE OF THE DIRECTOR OF LEGISLATIVE LIAISON. 1943-56. 673 lin. ft.

These records include reports, correspondence, Senate and House bills from the 78th through the 83d Congresses on the Air Force legislative program, 1943-54, and biweekly status reports on legislation, 1949-54. Congressional correspondence consists of a file concerning inquiries (the "constituent file"), 1948-51, letters received and sent, and reports and documents relating to provisions for air travel of Congressmen (the "travel file"), 1949-56. Included also are case files of the Investigations Division, comprising reports, correspondence, memorandums, and other documents relating to investigations by congressional committees of Air Force personnel, operations, procurement, supply, and morale, 1950-55.

RECORDS OF THE OFFICE OF INFORMATION SERVICES. 1942-53. 13 lin. ft.

These include correspondence, motion picture scripts, contracts, and documents of the Pictorial Branch, Public Information Division, relating to film projects and motion picture production at Air Force facilities, 1947-53; speeches, photographs, press releases, and a subject file, 1942-50; and news comments, 1948-49.

RECORDS OF THE AIR BOARD. 1942-49. 13 lin. ft.

The Air Board was established in 1946 to assist the Commanding General, Army Air Forces, in policy formulation. Records include documents relating to unification of the Armed Forces and to organization and policies of the autonomous Air Force, 1945-48. Included are documents, 1942-49, originating with Gen. Hugh J. Knerr before he became Secretary General of the Board, concerning the development of airpower and the deterrent force concept of war.

RECORDS OF THE AIR COORDINATING COMMITTEE. 1948-51. 36 lin. ft.

This Committee was established in 1945 to coordinate Federal aviation policy; its functions were transferred in 1960 for liquidation to the Federal Aviation Agency. Records consist of reports, correspondence, and studies on aviation problems of participating agencies, development of policy, and liaison between Government and industry in aviation.

RECORDS OF THE AIR FORCE BOARD FOR THE CORRECTION OF MILITARY RECORDS. 1949-55. 45 lin. ft.

Records consist of applicants' case files of petitions to the Air Force to correct military records, including transcripts of hearings, memorandums, vouchers, and related documents.

RECORDS OF THE JOINT AIR DEFENSE BOARD. 1951-55. 4 lin. ft.

Records consist of correspondence, directives, and other documents relating to its establishment; reports and studies of air defense; and records on the dissolution of the Board.

RECORDS OF THE JOINT AIR TRANSPORTATION BOARD. 1952-54. 1 lin. ft.

Records consist of special orders and memorandums, correspondence, and material relating to Joint Air Transportation Board publications.

RECORDS OF THE JOINT AIRBORNE TROOP BOARD. 1952-55. 3 lin. ft.

This Board was established by the U.S. Army, with equal Army and Air Force representation. Records include administrative reports and correspondence.

RECORDS OF THE JOINT TACTICAL AIR SUPPORT BOARD. 1952-55. 13 lin. ft.

This Board, established by the Department of the Air Force, developed joint procedures concerning tactical air support of ground forces. Records consist of reports and correspondence on project activities and the organization and dissolution of the Board.

RECORDS OF THE PHYSICAL SECURITY EQUIPMENT AGENCY. 1951-53. 7 lin. ft.

This joint agency was under Air Force management. Its records comprise reports, correspondence, and other documents relating to policy, development of physical security and investigative equipment for Department of Defense agencies, and coordination with other agencies.

RECORDS OF
HEADQUARTERS UNITED STATES
AIR FORCE
(RECORD GROUP 341)

Headquarters U.S. Air Force, also known as the Air Staff, was established September 18, 1947, under terms of the National Security Act of 1947, to succeed to functions of the Army Air Forces Headquarters and its subordinate organizations in the Zone of Interior and overseas. The Chief of Staff, directly responsible to the Secretary of the Air Force, presides over the Air Staff, exercises command over major air commands, and is responsible for policies and plans. As a member of the Joint Chiefs of Staff he is one of the principal military advisers to the President, the National Security Council, and the Secretary of Defense and is the principal military adviser and executive to the Secretary of the Air Force on activities of the Air Force.

The main organization is divided into five distinct functional groupings—four are headed by Deputy Chiefs of Staff and the fifth by the Comptroller of the Air Force—each of which is subdivided into smaller structures. In addition, certain offices outside the normal chain of command report directly to the Chief of Staff. These are the Director of Administrative Services; the Chief Scientist; the Inspector General; the USAF Scientific Advisory Board; the Surgeon General; the Chief, Operations Analysis; the Judge Advocate General; the Chief of Chaplains; the Assistant Chief of Staff, Intelligence; the Assistant Chief of Staff, Reserve Forces; and the Assistant Chief of Staff, Studies and Analysis.

There are 7,053 cubic feet of records dated between 1935 and 1963 in this record group.

GENERAL RECORDS. 1942-56.
361 lin. ft. and 241 rolls of microfilm.

These consist of record copies of general, special, and letter orders and other issuances, 1943-56; Air Force Council memorandums and decisions, 1951-53; general correspondence, 1942-53, with indexes; congressional correspondence, 1946-52, with indexes; daily staff digests, 1949-52; records relating to unification of the Armed Forces, 1947-49; correspondence relating to operation of the Air Force Postal and Security Courier Service, 1947-55; historical summaries of the Orders Branch mission, 1949-55; agenda and minutes of the Air Staff Committee on Air Force Reserve Policy, 1948-51, the Joint Committee on Reserve and National Guard Policy, 1948-53, and the Reserve Program Review Board, 1946-53; and microfilm copies (241 rolls) of Air Force administrative publications, with background data, 1941-46.

MESSAGES. Sept. 1947-Jan. 1958.
2,164 lin. ft. and 25 rolls of microfilm (in WNRC).

Messages, some on microfilm (25 rolls), received and dispatched, relating to USAF activities.

RECORDS OF THE OFFICE OF THE SURGEON GENERAL. 1940-55. 129 lin. ft.

These include correspondence, 1950-51, studies, 1940-54, statistical health reports, 1947-48, historical data, 1940-55, monthly major air command reports, 1949-55, and publications, 1950-53.

RECORDS OF THE OFFICE OF THE INSPECTOR GENERAL. 1942-56. 463 lin. ft.

Included are general correspondence, 1948-54; correspondence, personnel action memorandums, reports, and publications of the Office of the Director of Special Investigations, 1948-55; and other records relating to military police activities, law enforcement, and internal security, 1942-56.

RECORDS OF THE COMPTROLLER OF THE AIR FORCE. 1935-56. 233 lin. ft. and 450 rolls of microfilm.

These consist of correspondence, studies, and manuals, 1935-56; microfilm copies (450 rolls) of statistical reports, 1944-56; and budget estimates and justifications, 1943-54, relating to the development of accounting and cost systems and related financial matters.

RECORDS RELATING TO PERSONNEL. 1943-56. 245 lin. ft.

Included are general correspondence, 1947-55, management studies and reports, 1950-52, personnel status reports, 1949-52, "chapel records," July 1, 1949-December 31, 1955, accident reports and case files, 1943-55, and correspondence concerning Wage Board employees, 1951-55.

RECORDS RELATING TO RESEARCH AND DEVELOPMENT. 1940-54. 143 lin. ft.

Research and development records were created in various divisions and branches of the Office of the Deputy Chief of Staff, Development, and its predecessor offices. Included are records of the Chief Scientific Advisor, consisting of board reports, with minutes and agenda; general correspondence; and messages, studies, and other reports relating to research and development, testing new air weapons systems, strategic aircraft and aircraft armament, guided missiles, rockets, bombs, other ordnance materiel, and radar and other devices.

RECORDS OF THE OFFICE OF THE DEPUTY CHIEF OF STAFF, OPERATIONS. 1941-57.

Included are general records, 1947-57 (952 lin. ft.), consisting of correspondence of the Executive Office, 1947-48, and the Office of the Assistant for Atomic Energy, 1950-53; publications, flight data, and case files of the 1009th Special Weapons Squadron, 1948-57; and records of the Office of the Assistant for Guided Missiles, 1947-49, and of the Assistant for Programming, 1948-53. Operations records, 1947-56 (211 lin. ft.), include correspondence, 1947-55, messages, 1949-50, air rescue mission reports, 1955-56, movement orders, 1946-54, and reports, 1952-56.

Records of the Director of Plans, 1942-55 (606 lin. ft. and 74 rolls of microfilm), include general decimal files relating to USAF participation in joint planning and operations, 1942-54, and microfilm copies of an accompanying index; civil aviation case files and related records, 1942-55; records relating to the National Security Act, 1948; and Air Coordinating Committee records, 1945-55. Intelligence records, 1942-56 (1,492 lin. ft. and 5 sound recordings), include general records, 1945-55 (in WNRC); Korean daily reports, 1951-53; records of the Air Technical Intelligence Center, Wright-Patterson Air Force Base, 1948-55; records of Air Attache offices, 1948-55; dossiers of foreign military visitors to Air Force bases, 1948-55; military intelligence interpretation reports, with index, 1942-56 (in WNRC); field photographic intelligence reports on Korea, 1950-56 (in WNRC); an "AF document file," 1942-51 (in WNRC); technical reports, 1951-53; and digests and periodicals, 1948-55.

Installation records, 1948-55 (421 lin. ft. in WNRC), consist of general correspondence, 1948-55; Construction Division policy records, 1950-51; housing studies; Air Force Academy site selection reports, January-June 1950;

and real estate planning reports, reports of visits, regional airfield correspondence, and reports of the USAF Installations Representative Office, 1948-55. Records of the Director of Manpower and Organization, 1941-55 (199 lin. ft.), consist of general decimal correspondence, 1948-53; "Air Force base" files, 1948-49; incoming and outgoing messages, 1952; a historical file, 1951-53; tables of organization and equipment, 1941-53, and distribution, 1941-53; troop program records, 1943-48; vouchers and supporting documents, 1950-54; Air Force Organization military order letters, 1953; personnel allotment vouchers, 1948-53; and strength reports, September 1944-July 1955.

RECORDS OF THE OFFICE OF THE DEPUTY CHIEF OF STAFF, MATERIEL. 1939-56. 822 lin. ft.

Included are general correspondence, 1939-52; records relating to policies and procedures of the Air Force atomic energy materiel program, 1951-53, and the mutual security program, 1950-56; records relating to design, development, and testing of ordnance materiel, 1941-51; logistics planning records, including Project Redhead, with index, July 1952-January 1953; case files and correspondence relating to mortuary and grave registration activities during the Korean conflict, 1946-56; traffic management and transportation service records, 1947-54; and correspondence relating to aircraft development, production, and industrial planning, 1941-54.

CARTOGRAPHIC RECORDS. 1947-63. 4,458 items.

These include published aeronautical charts and special maps issued by the Aeronautical Chart and Information Center, showing political boundaries, time zones, climate, vegetation, population density, economic activities, transportation routes, and radar and navigational information; and photographs and charts of the moon.

RECORDS OF UNITED STATES AIR FORCE COMMANDS, ACTIVITIES, AND ORGANIZATIONS (RECORD GROUP 342)

The U.S. Air Force (USAF) was established in 1947 as the successor of the Army Air Forces (AAF), which had developed from a series of military air services dating back to 1907. This record group consists of the records of the field organization of the USAF and its predecessors. The USAF field organization is currently composed of 15 major commands and additional separate operating agencies. The commands are organized on a functional basis in the United States and on an area basis overseas. Each is responsible for certain phases of the worldwide activities of the USAF and for organizing, administering, equipping, and training its subordinate elements.

The following are examples of current USAF commands, activities, and organizations that illustrate the general pattern of past years: the Aerospace Defense Command, a major command whose primary mission is the aerospace defense of the United States; the Air Training Command, which performs most of the training missions of the USAF; the Air University, which is primarily concerned with the higher education of Air Force officers; the Headquarters Command, which provides administrative and logistic support for Headquarters, USAF, and other units in the Washington, D.C., area; the Strategic Air Command and the Tactical Air

Command, which prepare for and conduct strategic operations and tactical operations, respectively; the Overseas Command, which is composed of the U.S. Air Forces in Europe, Pacific Air Forces, Alaskan Air Command, and the U.S. Air Forces Southern Command; and the separate operating agencies, which are the Air Force Accounting and Finance Center, the Aeronautical Chart and Information Center, the Office of Aerospace Research, the Air Force Academy, the Air Force Data Systems Design Center, the Air Reserve Personnel Center, and the Air Force Reserve.

There are 1,276 cubic feet of records dated between 1900 and 1964 in this record group.

RECORDS. 1934–55. 1 lin. ft. and 4,759 rolls of microfilm.

Microfilm (in WNRC) of the Historical Collection of the Historical Division, Air University, Maxwell Air Force Base, Ala., 1935–52, consisting of histories of some units of the USAF and its predecessors, the AAF and the Air Corps, in the Zone of Interior and overseas. The histories are accompanied by mission directives; general and movement orders; and operational plans, tables, charts, and photographs. Also on microfilm are monographs, studies, and reports. Original records and other materials dating from 1907 to the present are in the custody of the Historical Division of the Air University.

In the Center for Polar Archives are selected official records and personal papers from the Arctic, Desert, and Tropic Information Center at the Air University, concerning polar explorations and related activities, 1934, 1943–45, and 1953–55.

AUDIOVISUAL RECORDS. 1900–1964. 4,384 items.

Motion pictures, 1900–1964 (4,370 reels), made or collected by the USAF, relating to the history of the development of flight, including activities of the Wright brothers beginning in 1900, such as demonstration flights in France, Italy, and the United States; to the development of airplanes, gliders, balloons, dirigibles, autogiros, helicopters, rockets, jets, satellites, aeronautical oddities, parachutes from 1495 to modern times, ballistic cameras, and radar; to early air races, air shows, distance and altitude records, the flight by Richard E. Byrd and Floyd Bennett to the North Pole, 1926, the Hindenburg crash, 1937, and Finn Ronne's antarctic expedition, 1946–48; to the dedication of the New York International Airport, 1948; and to people in the history of aviation, including Wilbur and Orville Wright, Edward V. Rickenbacker, William Mitchell, Charles A. Lindbergh, Richard E. Byrd, Floyd Bennett, Igor Sikorsky, and Wiley Post. Included are films concerning noncombat activities of the USAF and its predecessors, 1920's–64, including the airmail service; rescue and assistance missions in natural disaster areas at home and abroad; hurricane hunting; the Berlin airlift; training and maneuvers; airbase construction; the opening of the Air Force Academy, 1955; participation in the preparations for and activities of the International Geophysical Year, 1953–59; atomic bomb tests in the Pacific and elsewhere; and research and development work in the fields of guided missiles, remote control weapons, supersonic flight, and space technology. World War I films illustrate the activities of the Army Air Service in France.

There are World War II films concerning AAF activities abroad and at home; women in the AAF; Axis concentration and prisoner-of-war camps and atrocities; Allied bombing missions over Europe and Africa and in the Pacific theater; the defense of Britain and Moscow; the effects of bombing raids on Japan, including the atomic bombings of Hiroshima and Nagasaki; the surrender of Germany and Japan; and the customs, religion, and industry of Japan, the black market, and the Allied occupation. There are films on the Korean conflict and the truce-signing ceremonies and a few of Vietnam combat. Included are films of inaugurations of Presidents Franklin D. Roosevelt and Harry S. Truman; of the Presidency of John F. Kennedy, his inaugural, many of his activities, and worldwide memorial services for and tributes to him; of the funeral of Gen. John J. Pershing, 1948; and of the 1952 Olympic games. There are also captured German films depicting the war in Poland and covering research and development of planes, gliders, helicopters, jets, rockets, and ballistic missiles, 1912-44; captured Japanese films relating to preparations for the Pearl Harbor attack and World War II combat; and a Russian film of the 1949 May Day celebration. Many military and civilian leaders appear in these films, including Theodore Roosevelt, Dwight D. Eisenhower, Fiorello La Guardia, Winston Churchill, Richard M. Nixon, Chiang Kai-shek, Syngman Rhee, Paul von Hindenburg, Josef Stalin, and V. M. Molotov.

Sound recordings, 1961 (14 items), of two radio broadcast series on aerospace technology.

DEPARTMENT OF JUSTICE

GENERAL RECORDS OF THE DEPARTMENT OF JUSTICE
(RECORD GROUP 60)

The Department of Justice was established by an act of June 22, 1870, which continued and expanded the legal and administrative duties of the Attorney General, provided for by an act of September 24, 1789, to conduct suits in the Supreme Court, give opinions on questions of law at the request of the President or heads of Departments, and make recommendations to the President on appointments and pardons.

The new Department, with the Attorney General at its head, was given general supervision of U.S. attorneys and marshals, and to it were transferred the Solicitor of the Treasury, law officers of the State and Navy Departments and Bureau of Internal Revenue, and, from the Interior Department, supervision of the accounts of U.S. attorneys and marshals and other officers of the courts and the control of the judiciary fund from which court expenses and the safekeeping of prisoners were paid.

The duties of the Department include providing means for the enforcement of Federal laws, representing the Government in any court, supervising Federal penal institutions, detecting violations of Federal laws except those assigned to other agencies, and administering immigration and naturalization laws and registration of aliens.

See *Annual Reports* of the Attorneys General, 1870- ; *Registers* of the Department of Justice and the Federal Courts, 1871- ; Homer Cummings and Carl McFarland, *Federal Justice* (New York, 1937); Albert Langeluttig, *The Department of Justice of the United States* (Baltimore, 1927); and James S. Easby-Smith, *Department of Justice, Its History and Functions* (1904).

There are 18,107 cubic feet of records dated between 1790 and 1970 in this record group.

ATTORNEY GENERAL'S RECORDS. 1790-1870. 96 lin. ft.

These records, few of which antedate 1818, consist chiefly of incoming correspondence but include some drafts of outgoing letters and opinions of the Attorney General; records relating to requests for opinions of the Attorney General; records of cases appealed from lower courts; notes and briefs of arguments before the Supreme Court and other courts; drafts of legislation; records relating to land titles (including transcripts of proceedings before a commission for settling private claims in California, 1851-56), pardons, claims, and appointments to office; office accounts and payrolls; and some personal papers of Attorneys General. The records relate, among other matters, to the powers and duties of Government officers; establishment of the Department; treaty interpretations; courts, including courts-martial; claims against the United States; territorial government; banks, including Banks of the United States; neutrality laws, including violations during the Napoleonic wars, Latin American struggles for independence, the Crimean War, and the Fenian disturbances; nonintercourse legislation of the Jefferson-Madison period; the War of 1812; public land problems, including validity of prior titles to land in Louisiana, Florida, and California; pardons; customs-law violations; piracy; slavery and the slave trade; and the Civil War and Reconstruction.

OPINIONS ON QUESTIONS OF LAW. 1817-1934. 7 lin. ft.

Copies of official opinions on questions of law rendered to the President,

Department heads, and chairmen of congressional committees. No existing collection of opinions is complete.

See Justice Department, *Official Opinions of the Attorneys General* (1852-   ).

OPINIONS ON TITLE QUESTIONS.
1841-43 and 1853-1904. 3 lin. ft.

Copies of opinions rendered in compliance with a joint congressional resolution directing the Attorney General to give his opinion as to the validity of title to land or sites purchased or proposed for purchase by the United States. Title opinions after 1904 are in the Department's central files.

LETTERS SENT. 1818-1918.

Letters sent were generally preserved in bound form until 1904. Since then copies of letters sent have been filed with the related correspondence in subject or case files, but letters sent were recorded in press copy books until 1912. The practice that prevailed from 1867 to 1904 of segregating letters to different classes of persons in different series of letter books resulted in the distribution of letters on the same subject among several series. The letters sent books are grouped as follows.

General and Miscellaneous Letters. 1818-1912. 87 lin. ft. Included are letters to the President, Members and officers of Congress, Department heads, judges, district attorneys, marshals, and clerks of courts. Letter books contain all the Attorney General's outgoing correspondence other than opinions, 1818-67, letters sent to the Solicitor of the Treasury, 1830-42, and those for which there are drafts or copies among the Attorney General's records, chiefly for the period between October 1, 1850, and May 25, 1857, when letters sent were not contained in letter books. The special series of letter books initiated between 1867 and 1874 narrowed the coverage of the parent series to letters to miscellaneous persons. The letter books were

discontinued in 1904, except that a particular series of letters, 1871-1904, was succeeded by a general series of letterpress books in which outgoing letters of the Department of Justice were copied, 1904-12.

Letters Concerning Judiciary Expenses. 1849-84. 5 lin. ft. Included are letters sent by the Departments of the Interior, 1849-70, and Justice, 1870-84, concerning administration of the judiciary fund and supervision of accounts of U.S. attorneys, marshals, clerks, and other officers of U.S. courts. The Interior series includes replies to all letters relating to this function, but the Department of Justice series is limited almost entirely to letters sent to officers whose accounts were involved. These letters show the effort of the central authorities to require exact accounting from field officers in such matters as the care and conveyance of prisoners, employment of deputy U.S. marshals, payment of witness fees, and the rental and equipment of buildings for U.S. courts, attorneys, and marshals. They relate to such matters as the enforcement of the laws prohibiting the slave trade, the return of blacks to Africa, and the suppression of counterfeiting. After 1884 such letters were included with instructions to district attorneys and marshals, letters to judges and clerks, and in Accounts Division letter books.

Instructions to U.S. Attorneys and Marshals. 1867-1904. 72 lin. ft. These are letters regarding general policy and action to be taken in particular cases; they may authorize expenditures or the leasing of quarters. Many of the letters to marshals concern prisoners. Between 1861, when the power to direct district attorneys and marshals was conferred upon the Attorney General, and 1867, when instructions were segregated in a separate series, similar letters are recorded in the general letter book series.

Letters to Executive Officers and Members of Congress. 1871-1904.

120 lin. ft. The letters concern legislative matters, the initiation and conduct of civil and criminal litigation, directions to district attorneys and marshals, appointments to office and other personnel matters, expenditures, and other subjects relating to law enforcement, the Federal judiciary, and routine business. There are reports to Congress on special subjects, letters relating to questions and complaints referred to the Attorney General by Members of Congress, and recommendations regarding the approval of legislation by the President.

Letters to Judges and Clerks. 1874-1904. 15 lin. ft. Included are letters to Federal and territorial court judges and clerks concerning such matters as the transmittal of court reports, supplying transcripts of case records, and settling accounts; others relate to less routine matters, such as charges against judges and other court officials, policy on the bench, qualifications for judicial offices, need for legislation, and the relationship between judges and the Attorney General in the interpretation of law. Similar letters dated before 1874 are with those concerning judiciary expenses and general and miscellaneous letters.

Letters Concerning Specific Subjects. 1869-1918. 8 lin. ft. The subjects relate to internal revenue cases, 1869-1904, suits in circuit and district courts, 1889-1913, French spoliation claims, 1899-1902, advice to the Solicitor of the Treasury, 1830-42, and expositions, bankruptcy, and suspended land entries, 1888-1918.

A number of the Attorney General's letters were published in the congressional series before 1881 and are listed in S. Ex. Doc. 109, 47th Cong., 1st sess., Serial 1990.

LETTERS RECEIVED. 1849-1904. 2,690 lin. ft.

These include letters relating to administration of the judiciary fund and supervision of the accounts of marshals, clerks, and other judicial officers, 1849-89 (for the 1849-70 period inherited from the Department of the Interior); letters, 1870-84 ("source-chronological files"), filed by source from which received (President, executive department, Congress, or U.S. judicial districts); and letters, 1884-1904 ("year files"), filed by number in subject or case files. These communications, some having indexes and registers, relate to a great variety of subjects, such as Southern Reconstruction, including the Enforcement Act of 1870, the Ku Klux Klan Act of 1871, and the Civil Rights Act of 1875; litigation with Pacific railroads; frauds, including violation of banking and election laws and operations of the Credit Mobilier, "Whiskey Ring," and "Star Route" manipulators; enforcement of neutrality legislation, particularly against filibustering expeditions such as those of William Walker and invaders of Cuba; protection of the public domain, expecially timber and mineral resources; labor disturbances threatening interstate commerce or mail transportation; monopolies, including the telephone patent litigation of the 1880's and efforts to apply the Antitrust Act of 1890; war with Spain; administration of appropriations under the Attorney General's control, including transportation, treatment, and housing of prisoners; and enforcement of laws relating to polygamy, peonage, trading with Indians, and immigration.

NUMERICAL FILES. 1904-37.

In 1904 a straight numerical filing system was adopted whereby letters received and sent were placed in subject or case files. From 1904 until 1912 they constituted the Department's central files, although copies of outgoing letters frequently were placed in bound volumes as well. The subject matter in the files for this period is similar to that in earlier and later files. Administration files for judicial districts classified by subject were established in 1912 and a general series of central files classified by subject in 1914. The numerical files (2,758 lin. ft.), however, were continued as a depository for materials not subject to these classifications.

Administrative Records Relating to Judicial Districts. 1907-38. 218 lin. ft. These consist chiefly of administration files for judicial districts, 1912-38, containing correspondence, memorandums, and reports concerning the administration of judicial districts through the offices of U.S. attorneys and marshals. Some related correspondence, 1907-34, and examiners' reports are filed separately as records of the Examiner's Unit of the Administrative Division (and predecessors).

Classified Subject Files. 1914-41 and 1945-49. 11,500 lin. ft. More than 160 class or subject numbers were assigned to the central files, most of which comprise case materials. Included, for example, are classes for insecticides and fungicides, plant quarantine, the Harrison Narcotic Act, the National Prohibition Act, copyrights, the Packers and Stockyards Act, the Mortgage and Lien Foreclosure Act, the Railroad Labor Act, and the antitrust laws. There are also subject classes for Department functions concerning particular commodities, types of transactions, Government units, and general internal administration. These include strikes, immigration, customs violations, kidnappings, the TVA, the Farm Credit Administration, civil rights, bankruptcy, Court of Claims cases (1945-49), and Department administration. For these records there are card indexes, file classification schemes, and correspondence registration slips.

Administrative Orders, Circulars, and Memorandums. 1856-1953. 30 lin. ft. These relate to the internal administration and procedures of the Department of Justice and are accompanied by a card index, 1908-52.

Confidential Telegrams of U.S. Attorneys. 1930-53. 5 lin. ft. These consist of coded telegrams with decoded versions received by the Department of Justice from U.S. attorneys, 1930-53, and the Department's codebooks used in 1916 and from 1930 to 1953. The telegrams relate to evidence in court cases; propaganda and security matters, particularly regarding the activities of the Japanese in Hawaii before December 7, 1941; and administrative problems of U.S. attorneys.

Records of the Latin American Section of the War Division. 1942-45. 6 lin. ft. This section acted as the technical legal staff of the U.S. representative on the Emergency Advisory Committee for Political Defense (also known as the Inter-American Advisory Committee for Political Defense). The records consist of official record and memorandum files, a country file, the subject file of Miguel A. de Capriles, Committee and subcommittee records, reports of technical sessions, resolutions, and an administrative file.

RECORDS OF THE APPOINTMENT CLERK AND PERSONNEL DIVISION. 1853-1965. 1,300 lin. ft.

These records relate chiefly to district attorneys, marshals, wardens and trustees of penal institutions, officials of the Department in Washington, and judges of U.S. courts. They include applications and endorsements for and protests against appointments to the Supreme Court, 1853-1924, U.S. circuit courts, 1869-1901, U.S. circuit courts of appeals, 1903-29, and U.S. courts of claims, 1855-1928; the same for U.S. district and territorial court judges, attorneys, and marshals, 1853-1933, and for Federal judicial candidates who were not commissioned, 1960-65; a general file of "departmental" applications for positions, 1850-1933; letters sent concerning appointments, 1884-1912; registers of nominations submitted to the Senate by the President,

1877-89 and 1893-1905; and lists of judges, district attorneys, and marshals for different periods from 1846 to 1883.

RECORDS OF THE ASSISTANT ATTORNEY GENERAL FOR THE SPANISH TREATY CLAIMS COMMISSION. 1901-10. 25 lin. ft.

The treaty concluding the Spanish-American War obligated the United States to adjudicate and settle all claims of its citizens against Spain from the outbreak of the Cuban insurrection in 1895 to the exchange of ratification. A Spanish Treaty Claims Commission was established in 1901, and an Assistant Attorney General was provided to defend U.S. interests before the Commission. Both that office and the Commission ceased to exist on May 2, 1910. The records consist chiefly of correspondence with the Departments of State and War, docket books, and special reports. Duplicates of the Assistant Attorney General's case files are in case files of the Spanish Treaty Claims Commission (see RG 76).

RECORDS OF THE INSULAR AND TERRITORIAL AFFAIRS BUREAU. 1902-6. 2 lin. ft.

This Bureau, in existence from 1902 to 1906, had charge of Department business relating to insular and territorial possessions, the Isle of Pines, the Isthmus of Panama, Indian reservations, ocean cables, and other matters. Its records consist of letters sent relating to such subjects as extradition of criminals, legislative proposals relating to territories and insular possessions, and marriage customs in Puerto Rico.

RECORDS OF THE HIGH COST OF LIVING DIVISION. 1919-20. 6 lin. ft.

This Division was established to combat profiteering and price practices following World War I. Most of its records are in the classified subject files, while these separately maintained records consist mainly of correspondence.

RECORDS OF THE WAR TRANSACTIONS SECTION. 1922-26. 10 lin. ft.

This Section was established in 1922 to investigate and prosecute frauds arising from wartime contracts. Most of its records make up class 70 of the classified subject files for 1918-33, while these separately maintained records consist chiefly of the legal files of the office of the directors and minutes of the Joint Board of Survey.

RECORDS OF THE HUGHES AIRCRAFT INVESTIGATION OFFICE. 1918-19. 17 lin. ft.

An investigation of charges of dishonesty and malversation in the production of aircraft was conducted in 1918 by Charles Evans Hughes with Justice Department cooperation. The records consist of correspondence, copies of testimony of about 200 witnesses, and exhibits of aircraft producers.

CLAIMS DIVISION RECORDS CONCERNING PATENT CLAIMS. 1919-46. 110 lin. ft.

Under the Settlement of War Claims Act of 1928 a claims arbiter was appointed to determine fair compensation due German, Austrian, and Hungarian owners whose patents or patent applications had been seized during World War I by the Alien Property Custodian under the Trading With the Enemy Act. The records, 1928-31, are those created and separately maintained by the Department's Claims Division in defending the Government against claims brought by nationals of former enemy countries before the arbiter. Also included are records of the Albert Jensen claims cases involving ships taken over by the Allies in World War I, 1919-42, and the survey of Federal patent practices, 1943-46.

RECORDS OF NAVAL OIL RESERVE INVESTIGATIONS. 1924-39. 59 lin. ft.

These records relate to civil and criminal cases resulting from investigations of leases on naval oil reserves conducted by the Senate Committee on Public Lands and Surveys, 1922-24. Involved were Naval Oil Reserve No. 1, Elk Hill, Calif., No. 2, Buena Vista Hills, Calif., and No. 3, Teapot Dome, Wyo. The files, created by Atlee Pomerene and Owen J. Roberts, special counsel, and Justice Department officials, consist of correspondence, newspaper clippings, memorandums, evidential materials, pleadings, briefs, transcripts, and related records.

RECORDS OF THE LANDS DIVISION'S ALABAMA FIELD OFFICE. 1926-40. 12 lin. ft.

The records are chiefly correspondence and legal documents concerning land titles of Federal projects in Alabama.

RECORDS OF INVESTIGATIONS OF BANKRUPTCY ADMINISTRATION. 1929-31 and 1939-40. 8 lin. ft.

These consist of reports, letters, and memorandums resulting from investigations conducted by Col. William J. Donovan in 1929 and Solicitor General Thomas D. Thatcher in 1930 and 1931, which were later used by the Attorney General's Committee on Bankruptcy Administration. They include returns and reports from referees in bankruptcy, clerks of court, and business firms on such subjects as the reelection of trustees, subpoena practices, adjustment of scheduled liabilities, emoluments received by referees, and first meetings of creditors.

See *Administration of the Bankruptcy Act: Report of the Attorney General's Committee on Bankruptcy Administration* (1941).

RECORDS OF THE ATTORNEY GENERAL'S SURVEY OF RELEASE PROCEDURES. 1935-38. 130 lin. ft.

This was a research project to devise a more uniform system of probation, parole, and pardon in Federal and State jurisdictions. Its records consist primarily of correspondence and research materials on probation, parole, and pardon procedures in the States.

See Department of Justice, *Attorney General's Survey of Release Procedures* (Washington and Leavenworth, 1939-40).

RECORDS OF THE ATTORNEY GENERAL'S ADVISORY COMMITTEE ON CRIME. 1934-38. 28 lin. ft.

This Committee surveyed conditions and developments in the field of criminal justice generally, prepared a study of crime prevention work, planned a Federal crime prevention bureau, and acted as a clearinghouse for information. Its records consist chiefly of correspondence and information files.

RECORDS OF THE ATTORNEY GENERAL'S COMMITTEE ON ADMINISTRATIVE PROCEDURE. 1939-41. 63 lin. ft.

This Committee examined procedural practices of 28 Federal administrative agencies that made decisions directly affecting private rights and property. Its records consist of monographs, transcripts of hearings, minutes, correspondence, and material used in preparing its final report.

See the *Final Report* of the Committee (1941) and its monographs published as *Administrative Procedure in Government Agencies* (S. Doc. 10, 77th Cong., 1st sess., Serial 10563).

RECORDS OF THE GENERAL AGENT. 1877-1907. 15 lin. ft.

The General Agent conducted investigations for the Attorney General, managed Department business concerning prisons and prisoners, and supervised examiners and special agents. The special agents investigated Indian matters, and the examiners investigated official acts, records, and accounts of marshals, district attorneys, clerks of courts, U.S. commissioners, and other officers. In 1894 the newly organized Division of Accounts was placed under the supervision of the General Agent, and in about 1895 he was given charge of construction and maintenance of Federal penal institutions that were beginning to replace State, territorial, and local prisons and jails as places of detention for Federal prisoners convicted of serious offenses. On October 1, 1907, the position of General Agent was abolished and its functions divided among a Chief Examiner, a Superintendent of Prisons and Prisoners, and the Division of Accounts.

The records include letters to the Attorney General, 1882–93, wardens and marshals, 1881–85, examiners and special agents concerning expenses and operations, 1882–1907, and miscellaneous letters sent, 1882–1907. There are also records relating to the construction of Federal prisons, reports of the Department's earliest examinations of Federal prisoners in State and local penal institutions, 1879–81, reports and correspondence of examiners, 1882–90 and 1893, and documents relating to "Star Route" and mail and pension frauds, 1878–82. Incoming correspondence addressed or referred to the General Agent and outgoing letters from 1904 are in the central files of the Department.

RECORDS OF THE SPECIAL EXECUTIVE ASSISTANT TO THE ATTORNEY GENERAL. 1935–40. 46 lin. ft.

These are office files of the special assistant for publicity. They contain information on Department organization and operations.

RECORDS OF THE CHIEF CLERK'S OFFICE. 1903–17. 10 lin. ft.

These records, chiefly letters sent, reflect the activities of the Chief Clerk when he was responsible for most of the purely administrative activities of the Department.

RECORDS OF THE OFFICE OF THE DISBURSING CLERK. 1870–1924. 24 lin. ft.

The Chief Clerk served as Disbursing Clerk from 1870 until 1875, when that function was transferred to another clerk. In 1896 the fee system for district attorneys and marshals was abolished, and the Disbursing Clerk was made responsible for disbursement of funds from more than 40 appropriations covering Department salaries and expenses and salaries of district attorneys, marshals, judges, and certain other officers. In 1914 Congress designated marshals as disbursing officers for the payment of their own salaries and those of district attorneys, active judges of the lower Federal courts, and employees of these officers and courts. In 1934 the Treasury Department was made responsible for disbursements, and this Office was abolished. Its records consist chiefly of payrolls, 1870–87 and 1892–1908, disbursements made under specific appropriations, 1898–1908, quarterly and monthly accounts current, 1870–1907, and an appropriation ledger, 1907–24.

RECORDS OF THE DIVISION OF ACCOUNTS. 1855–1912. 8 lin. ft.

The Chief Clerk supervised accounting functions until October 1894 when a Division of Accounts was organized to conduct the audit—initiated by the Dockery Act of July 31, 1894—of accounts of district attorneys, assistant attorneys, marshals, commissioners, and clerks of courts, and accounts relating to U.S. prisoners. Its records include fee and expense books of U.S. marshals and deputies, 1896-1912, a summary of emolument returns of U.S. attorneys and marshals, 1855-63 and 1869-84, copies of leases approved for quarters to be used by U.S. courts and attorneys and marshals, 1872-94, and photographs of U.S. penitentiaries at Atlanta and Leavenworth.

CARTOGRAPHIC RECORDS. ca. 1900-1920. 10 items.

Maps of the United States and of individual States, showing railroad systems, oil company lands, and locations of oil refineries and pipelines; a map of New York Harbor; a plan of a lock and dam on the Yamhill River in Oregon; a plan of Walter Reed Hospital, Washington, D.C.; and graphs pertaining to oil production, 1890-1906.

AUDIOVISUAL RECORDS. 1941-44. 584 items.

These are sound recordings of broadcasts over facilities of the German Radio Broadcasting Corp. during World War II by Herbert J. Burgman, Douglas Chandler, Frederick W. Kaltenbach, and Robert Best. They were used as evidence in treason trials of these individuals.

Microfilm Publications: Included are records relating to the appointment of Federal judges, attorneys, and marshals for the Territories and States of Idaho, 1861-99, Oregon, 1853-1903, Utah, 1853-1901, and Washington, 1853-1902. For a complete listing see the current *List of National Archives Microfilm Publications.*

SPECIFIC RESTRICTIONS

Records: All records less than 25 years old except the following classes of the central files:
Class 3. Weeks Forestry Act
Class 22. Food and Drug
Class 33. Federal Buildings Act
Class 38. Naturalization
Class 39. Immigration
Class 66. Rentals and Leases
Class 76. Opinions of Courts
Class 77. Claims in Favor of the United States
Class 100. Miscellaneous Correspondence
Class 101. Mortgage and Lien Foreclosure Act
Class 103. Wills, Bequests, Gifts
Class 154. Court of Claims Cases

Restrictions: Only authorized employees of the Department of Justice and other persons specifically authorized by the Attorney General or his alternate in archival matters may have access to the restricted records.

Specified by: Department of Justice.

RECORDS OF UNITED STATES ATTORNEYS AND MARSHALS (RECORD GROUP 118)

Provision for U.S. attorneys and marshals was made by the Judiciary Act of September 24, 1789. Under authority of the act of June 22, 1870, that created the Department of Justice, the Attorney General exercises general supervision over U.S. attorneys and marshals, who are appointed by the President for each judicial district.

U.S. attorneys investigate violations of Federal criminal laws, present evidence to grand juries, prosecute Federal criminal cases, and serve as the Government's attorney in civil litigation in which the United States is involved or has an interest (see RG 21).

U.S. marshals execute and serve writs, processes, and orders issued by

U.S. courts and U.S. commissioners and commissions; notify the Department of Justice of defiance of Federal authority; and serve as local disbursing officers for salaries and expenses of U.S. attorneys, marshals, and Federal courts within their districts. Since the establishment of the Administrative Office of the U.S. Courts in 1939, marshals have disbursed funds appropriated for Federal courts only at the discretion of that Office.

There are 125 cubic feet of records dated between 1821 and 1943 in this record group.

RECORDS OF U.S. ATTORNEYS. 1821–1943. 118 lin. ft.

Included are the following:

Southern District of Alabama: correspondence, 1826–1921, case records, 1824–1912, and docket books, 1867–1918, relating chiefly to election fraud, land, timber trespass, lottery, peonage, and internal revenue cases.

District of Arizona: correspondence, 1903–12, relating to naturalization, deportation of aliens, sale of liquor to Indians, illegal stock grazing, and the corporation excise tax law.

Western District of Arkansas: grand jury dockets, 1895–1934, and minutes, 1898–1935.

Northern District of California: neutrality violation case files, 1913–20.

District of China: correspondence, 1933–41, and case files, 1934–41.

District of Minnesota: criminal dockets, 1882–85, Indian land allotment fraud cases, 1910–12, letters sent, 1876–87, and letters received, 1869–99.

Eastern District of Missouri: letters sent, 1853–61 and 1863–89, grand jury dockets, 1887–1932, and grand jury minutes, 1876 and 1890–1918.

Southern District of New York: antitrust and other case files, 1847–1918, records of cases in local and State courts of New York, ca. 1821–80, and letters received, 1821–47 and 1876–78.

Eastern District of North Carolina: case files, 1919–41, and correspondence, 1921–32.

Eastern District of Pennsylvania: case files relating chiefly to Government land, Indian questions, Socialist activities, Federal-State jurisdiction, and to such World War I matters as the high cost of living, 1911–43.

Eastern District of Virginia: orders for confiscation of property, 1865, and correspondence, 1865–85.

Western District of Wisconsin: case files, 1892–1908, and correspondence relating to public land, Indian, and national bank matters, 1894–1908.

RECORDS OF U.S. MARSHALS. 1845–1941. 4 lin. ft.

These records include:

Southern District of Alabama: letters sent, 1885–87, and a subject file of correspondence, 1907–23.

District of Arizona: correspondence concerning Indian cases, 1917–23.

District of China: case files relating to investigations of complaints involving U.S. citizens in China, 1935–41.

Southern District of New York: letters received, 1845–48 and 1868, and orders relating to prisoners and witnesses, 1848–52.

Eastern District of Virginia: letters sent, 1869–72, a bankruptcy docket, 1867–68, and applications and reports of census takers, 1859–61.

RECORDS OF THE OFFICE OF THE PARDON ATTORNEY (RECORD GROUP 204)

The Office of the Pardon Attorney, originally called the Office of Attorney in Charge of Pardons, was established in the Attorney General's Office by an act of March 3, 1891. It succeeded to the functions of a pardon clerk, a position that had been established in the Office by an act of March 3, 1865. Before 1865 responsibility for recommending action on Federal pardon applications to the President had been shared by the Attorney General and the Secretary of State. The Office currently receives all requests for Executive clemency except in military cases; conducts all appropriate correspondence; receives reports from U.S. attorneys, trial judges, and others; and submits recommendations to the Attorney General and the President.

There are 848 cubic feet of records dated between 1853 and 1946 in this record group.

RECORDS. 1853-1946. 1,130 lin. ft.

These consist primarily of closed files for formal pardon cases, including endorsements, protests, and reports filed with requests for Executive clemency, 1853-1946, with an index to cases for the period 1853-89 (936 lin. ft., in WNRC). Other records include pardon

dockets, 1853-1923, requisitions for pardon warrants ("recitals") sent to the Secretary of State, 1861-93, copies of pardon warrants issued, 1893-1936, records of pardon cases denied, 1893-1918, records relating to pardons and commutations for "political prisoners" of World War I, ca. 1918-33, copies of letters sent relating to general pardon matters, 1868-1934, records of Utah amnesty cases, 1882-92, and a volume of abstracts of pardon cases from State Department records, 1793-1853.

See Gaiselle Kerner, comp., *Preliminary Inventory of the Records of the Office of the Pardon Attorney*, PI 87 (1955).

SPECIFIC RESTRICTIONS

Records: All records less than 25 years old.

Restrictions: Only authorized employees of the Department of Justice and other persons specifically authorized by the Attorney General or his alternate in archival matters may have access to these records.

Specified by: Department of Justice.

RECORDS OF THE
IMMIGRATION AND NATURALIZATION SERVICE
(RECORD GROUP 85)

Between 1882 and 1891 the Secretary of the Treasury had general supervision over immigration. The Office of Superintendent of Immigration of the Department of the Treasury was established under an act of March 3, 1891, and was designated a bureau in 1895 with responsibility for administering the alien contract-labor laws. In 1900 administration of the Chinese-exclusion laws was added. In 1903 the Bureau became part of the Department of Commerce and Labor. Functions relating to naturalization were assigned to the Bureau in 1906

and its name was changed to the Bureau of Immigration and Naturalization. It was transferred to the Department of Labor by an act of March 4, 1913, as the Bureau of Immigration and the Bureau of Naturalization. Executive Order 6166 of June 10, 1933, reunited those Bureaus to form the Immigration and Naturalization Service, which was transferred in 1940 to the Department of Justice.

The Service administers laws relating to admission, exclusion, deportation, and naturalization of aliens, and investigates alleged violations of those laws; patrols U.S. borders to prevent unlawful entry of aliens; supervises naturalization work in designated courts; cooperates with public schools to provide citizenship textbooks and other services that prepare candidates for naturalization; and registers and fingerprints aliens in the United States.

See Darrell H. Smith and H. Guy Herring, *The Bureau of Immigration* (Baltimore, 1924); and Smith, *The Bureau of Naturalization* (Baltimore, 1926).

There are 956 cubic feet of records dated between 1787 and 1954 in this record group.

GENERAL IMMIGRATION RECORDS. 1882-1952. 150 lin. ft. and 5,865 rolls of microfilm.

These consist chiefly of letters received, 1882-1906, subject correspondence files, 1906-32, letters sent, 1882-1912, registration of refugee alien case files, 1934-37, microfilm copies (5,865 rolls) of alien registration forms, 1940-44, records concerning Fiorello H. La Guardia, 1907-48, appropriation ledgers, 1911-39, statistical and administrative records, 1902-39, and registers and indexes, 1882-1952.

CHINESE IMMIGRATION RECORDS. 1882-1925. 99 lin. ft.

These records from the central files of the Service and its predecessors relate to the administration of regulations concerning Chinese immigration to and residence in the United States, including general files, 1898-1908, applications for residence certificates, 1897-1920, other records relating to residence certificates, 1892-1903, correspondence relating to the use of Chinese identification certificates under the Chinese Exclusion Acts, 1882-91, and correspondence concerning Chinese entering the United States from Canada, ca. 1914-20, and the admission of individual Chinese immigrants, 1924-25.

PASSENGER ARRIVAL RECORDS. 1883-1954. 11,476 rolls of microfilm.

These are microfilm copies (11,476 rolls) of ship and airplane passenger and crew lists, 1883-1945; passenger list indexes, 1883-1954; and passenger lists for Baltimore, 1891-1909, Boston, 1891-1943, New Orleans, 1903-45, New York, 1897-1942, Philadelphia, 1883-1945, and minor ports, 1893-1945.

"AMERICANIZATION" RECORDS. 1913-36. 197 lin. ft.

These consist of correspondence and other records, which include those of the Federal Council of Citizenship Training, created in an education and Americanization program for aliens who wished U.S. citizenship. The records relate to textbooks, textbook revisions, and the appointment of teachers for the program; suggestions to petitioners for naturalization; special naturalization schools; citizenship preparation; and the activities of patriotic organizations, schools, churches, trade unions, and governmental units in the program.

NATURALIZATION RECORDS. 1906-40. 580 lin. ft.

There are correspondence and other records of the centralized administration of the naturalization laws of the United States that relate chiefly to identification of courts that issued naturalization certificates, interpretations of naturalization laws, and procedural instructions; collected naturalization fees; and examined naturalization declarations, petitions, and certificates, 1906-40. Included are indexes to fraudulent naturalizations, 1906-15, and to naturalizations of World War I soldiers, 1918.

FIELD OFFICE RECORDS. 1787-1944. 808 lin. ft.

Records of Hartford, Conn., and Boston offices consist of copies of naturalization proceedings in Federal and non-

Federal courts of Maine, Massachusetts, New Hampshire, and Rhode Island, 1787-1906, with indexes; records of the New York office include letters sent, 1903-12, and correspondence concerning citizenship education programs, 1906-44; records of the Philadelphia office consist chiefly of letters received, 1882-1903, letters sent, 1884-1911, case files of applicants who wished admittance to the United States as contract laborers, 1929-45, shipmaster reports on deserters, 1909-16, Pennsylvania Board of Public Charities records, 1872-90, and correspondence of the Gloucester City N.J., suboffice and station, 1882-1944, records of the Baltimore office include correspondence of the Norfolk inspector's office, 1904-40; records of the El Paso office include correspondence concerning alleged violations of neutrality laws along the Mexican border, 1916-21; and records of the San Francisco office chiefly concern operations of the Angel Island immigration station, 1910-41.

RECORDS OF ALIEN ENEMY INTERNMENT CAMPS. 1917-18 and 1941-48. 550 lin. ft.

Included are administrative records of the Hot Springs, N.C., camp for the internment of civilian enemy aliens, 1917-18; and administrative records and internee case files of 16 alien enemy internment facilities, 1941-48 (in WNRC).

AUDIOVISUAL RECORDS. 1940-45. 61 items.

These consist of sound recordings of such radio series as "You and Your Citizenship"; "Heirs of Liberty," which instructed aliens in U.S. citizenship laws; and those about the Immigration Border Patrol and aliens' obligations under the Alien Registration Act of 1940.

SPECIFIC RESTRICTIONS

I. *Records*: Microfilm copies of alien registration forms executed by aliens in the United States.

Restrictions: These records are restricted by the terms of the Immigration and Nationality Act of 1952 (66 Stat. 163), section 264 (b), which reads: "All registration and fingerprint records made under the provisions of this title shall be confidential, and shall be made available only to such persons or agencies as may be designated by the Attorney General."

Specified by: Congress of the United States.

II. *Records*: Microfilmed index to correspondence case files of the Immigration and Naturalization Service, 1903-52.

Restrictions: Until the year 1977 the use of this index, unless otherwise authorized by the Immigration and Naturalization Service, is limited to personnel of the National Archives and no information from the index as to the existence of records not in the custody of the National Archives is to be given.

Specified by: Department of Justice.

III. *Records*: Microfilm copies of ship and airplane passenger manifests and crew lists that are less than 50 years old.

Restrictions: No one may examine these records and no information from them or copies of them may be furnished to anyone except authorized employees of the Department of Justice or other persons specifically authorized by the Attorney General or his alternate in archival matters.

Specified by: Department of Justice.

IV. *Records*: All other records of the Immigration and Naturalization Service that are less than 25 years old.
  Restrictions: Only authorized employees of the Department of Justice and other persons specif-

ically authorized by the Attorney General or his alternate in archival matters may have access to these records.

Specified by: Department of Justice.

RECORDS OF THE FEDERAL BUREAU OF INVESTIGATION (RECORD GROUP 65)

The Federal Bureau of Investigation (FBI) traces its origin to October 1, 1907, when the Attorney General appointed a Chief Examiner for the Department of Justice (see RG 60). An order of July 26, 1908, authorized the Chief Examiner to administer all the Department's investigative matters, and the following year the Chief Examiner's organization was renamed the Bureau of Investigation. In 1923 the Bureau inherited the functions and records of the Bureau of Criminal Identification, which had been created in 1907 and had operated under the Superintendent of Prisons as a clearinghouse for exchanging criminal records. The functions of the Bureau of Investigation were consolidated with the investigative functions of the Bureau of Prohibition to form the Division of Investigation by an Executive order of June 10, 1933. The Division was designated the Federal Bureau of Investigation by an act of March 22, 1935. The FBI investigates Federal law violations within the jurisdiction of the Department, operates a technical laboratory and a national police academy, and gathers, classifies, preserves, and exchanges criminal identification records.

Records concerning the identification of criminals and maintained by the National Bureau of Criminal Identification of the International Association of Chiefs of Police, and records of the American Protective League, which

served as a reserve force for the Bureau in World War I, were placed in the custody of the Bureau of Investigation. The FBI has retained in its own custody most of its records.

See Federal Bureau of Investigation, *The Federal Bureau of Investigation* (1935); A. C. Millspaugh, *Crime Control of the National Government* (1937); and Frederick L. Collins, *The FBI in Peace and War* (New York, 1943).

There are 28 cubic feet of records dated between 1897 and 1936 in this record group.

RECORDS. 1897-1936. 34 lin. ft.

Included are letters sent by the Chief Examiner and the Chief of the Bureau, 1908-11, and the Attorney General, 1910-12; administrative reports to the Attorney General, 1908-11, and daily reports from special agents, 1908-9; applications for special agent positions, ca. 1915-18; samples of Bertillon criminal identification cards collected by the Bureau of Criminal Identification and the National Bureau of Criminal Identification, 1898-1924; and miscellaneous records relating to criminal identification, 1899-1924. Other records of the National Bureau of Criminal Identification consist of letters sent, 1897-1923, an album of classified pictures and information concerning criminals, 1906, criminals pictures, 1898-1910, and foreign-language pamphlets about criminology, 1906-21. Headquarters records of the American Protective League include its news bulletin, *The Spy Glass*, 1918-19;

and samples of investigation requests, correspondence with field offices, and badge-holding members' record cards, 1917-19.

Also included is a motion picture (3 reels) entitled "You Can't Get Away With It," 1936, illustrating FBI crime detection activities.

RECORDS OF THE BUREAU OF PRISONS
(RECORD GROUP 129)

The Bureau of Prisons was established in the Department of Justice by an act of May 14, 1930. To it were transferred the personnel, records, and duties of the Superintendent of Prisons, who had been made responsible for Federal prison matters in 1907 by the Attorney General. The Bureau was made responsible for the administration of Federal penal and correctional institutions and for Federal prisoners in non-Federal institutions.

A central Board of Parole, also established in 1930 with authority in parole matters over all Federal prisoners, succeeded separate boards of parole for each institution housing Federal prisoners. An act of September 30, 1950, changed authority for appointment of members of the Board from the Attorney General to the President of the United States. The Department of Justice now handles certain administrative functions for the Board that were previously performed by the Bureau of Prisons.

The Federal Prison Industries, Inc., was created by an Executive order of December 11, 1934, to provide employment and to control industrial operations in Federal penal and correctional institutions, functions previously vested in the Industrial Division of the Bureau of Prisons. This corporation was transferred in 1939 to the Department of Justice where it operates under the supervision of the Director of the Bureau of Prisons, with its policies controlled by a board of six directors appointed by the President.

There are 1,008 cubic feet of records dated between 1907 and 1946 in this record group.

RECORDS OF THE
SUPERINTENDENT OF PRISONS
AND PRESIDENTS OF BOARDS
OF PAROLE. 1907-31. 17 lin. ft.

These include correspondence and related records of the Office of the Superintendent of Prisons, 1907-12, correspondence relating to parole matters, 1910-28, minutes of parole boards, 1910-27, monthly reports of marshals, 1921, and records concerning Leavenworth Penitentiary, the National Training School for Boys, and conditional commutations of sentences, 1907-31.

GENERAL RECORDS OF THE
BUREAU OF PRISONS. 1929-46.
614 lin. ft.

These consist chiefly of correspondence and other records relating to general administration of the Bureau, 1930-37; records relating to the administration, construction, furnishing, and supplying of Federal penal and correctional institutions, 1930-37; correspondence on libraries in Federal prisons, 1929-36; and a sample of inspection reports on non-Federal jails holding Federal prisoners in Indiana, Massachusetts, Oregon, and South Carolina, 1931-46.

RECORDS RELATING TO
PAROLES. 1910-43. 413 lin. ft.

There are parole case files (in WNRC) of Federal prisoners in certain Federal institutions (chiefly those that have been discontinued), 1915-43, in State institutions of States without a parole system, 1927-40, and of States with a parole system, 1910-27; and sound recordings of three National Parole Conference programs, 1939.

RECORDS OF THE FEDERAL PRISON INDUSTRIES, INC. 1930-43. 100 lin. ft.

Headquarters records of this corporation and its predecessor, the Industrial Division of the Bureau of Prisons, relate chiefly to the establishment and operation of manufacturing plants for prison industries, procurement of raw materials, sale of products, and exchange of prison-made products with Government agencies. Included is a motion picture entitled "Protecting the Public."

SPECIFIC RESTRICTIONS

I. *Records*: Inmate records less than 25 years older than the date of termination of sentence.

Restrictions: Only authorized employees of the Department of Justice and other persons specifically authorized by the Attorney General or his alternate in archival matters may have access to these records.

Specified by: Department of Justice.

II. *Records*: All other records of the Bureau of Prisons that are less than 25 years old.

Restrictions: Only authorized employees of the Department of Justice and other persons specifically authorized by the Attorney General or his alternate in archival matters may have access to these records.

Specified by: Department of Justice.

RECORDS OF THE BUREAU OF NARCOTICS AND DANGEROUS DRUGS (RECORD GROUP 170)

The Bureau of Narcotics and Dangerous Drugs was established in the Department of Justice April 8, 1968. To it were transferred the duties and functions of the Bureau of Narcotics and the Bureau of Drug Abuse Control. The Bureau of Narcotics, established by an act of June 14, 1930, had replaced the Federal Narcotics Control Board (which had authority to "make and publish all proper regulations" to prohibit the importation and exportation of certain narcotics specified in an act of May 26, 1922) and the Narcotic Division (which had inherited functions vested in the Commissioner of Internal Revenue by the Harrison Act of 1914 to regulate domestic use of opium and coca and their derivatives) of the Bureau of Prohibition. The Bureau of Drug Abuse Control was established in the Food and Drug Administration of the Department of Health, Education, and Welfare to carry out functions of the Drug Abuse Control Amendments of 1965.

The Bureau of Narcotics and Dangerous Drugs is responsible for preventing illicit traffic in narcotic, stimulant, and depressant drugs; controlling the legitimate manufacture and auditing manufacturers and other handlers of such drugs for medicinal purposes; and providing educational programs in the use and abuse of drugs.

There are 654 cubic feet of records (in WNRC except for nontextual records) dated between 1915 and 1940 in this record group.

RECORDS. 1915-40. 785 lin. ft.

Relating mainly to applications and permits to import and export narcotics, registrations of dealers in narcotics, and violations of narcotics laws, these records include correspondence of the Narcotic Division of the Bureau of Prohibition, 1919-28, the Commissioner of Internal Revenue with collectors of customs, 1919-35, the Federal Narcotics Control Board, 1915-26, and the Bureau of Narcotics, 1927-40; case files of the Narcotic Division concerning narcotic law violations, 1915-27; reports, 1918-19, record cards, 1920-27, and import licenses, 1923-25; and motion picture films (14 reels) relating to drug traffic and enforcement of narcotics laws in Egypt, China, and the United States, and a British instructional film (1 reel) on the culture of the poppy plant, 1928-37.

SPECIFIC RESTRICTIONS

Records: Motion picture files relating to drug traffic, enforcement of narcotics laws, and the culture of the poppy plant, 1928-37.

Restrictions: These films, so long as they are less than 50 years old, may not be loaned to or duplicated for anyone for any purpose whatsoever without the permission of the Commissioner of Narcotics.

Specified by: Commissioner of Narcotics.

RECORDS OF THE COURT OF CLAIMS SECTION (JUSTICE) (RECORD GROUP 205)

The Office of Solicitor for the U.S. Court of Claims, created with the court in 1855, was abolished in 1868 and its functions transferred to the Attorney General, who, with his assistants, was charged with prosecuting and defending all matters and suits in the court on behalf of the United States. Claims matters in the Department of Justice have since been handled by a unit directed by an Assistant Attorney General. That unit, formally designated the Claims Division in 1934, has supervised all suits in the U.S. Court of Claims except land and tax cases. In 1937 the Claims Division was divided into several sections, including the Court of Claims Section, which handled all suits in the court defended by the Claims Division except those relating to patents and copyrights. The name of the Claims Division was changed to the Civil Division in February 1953.

There are 1,679 cubic feet of records dated between 1793 and 1947 in this record group.

RECORDS. 1793-1947. 2,015 lin. ft.

These include general claims correspondence, consisting of letters sent, 1868-1914, and received, 1888-1914, with fragmentary items dated as early as 1860; correspondence and related records on claims cases accumulated by defense attorneys, 1860-1926; dockets (books and cards), indexes, and correspondence for general jurisdiction cases, 1855-1938, and congressional jurisdiction cases, 1884-1941; case files that generally include the petition of reference, pleadings, briefs, depositions, findings or opinions of the court, and exhibits for general jurisdiction cases, 1855-1945 (in WNRC), and for congressional jurisdiction cases, 1884-1944 (in WNRC); case files and dockets for departmental cases (including naval bounty cases arising from the Spanish-American War), 1883-

1943; case files and a docket for District of Columbia cases, 1880–87; dockets, indexes, and records submitted as evidence in French spoliation cases, 1885–1903 (with a few records dated as early as 1793); case files, correspondence, dockets, and indexes for Indian depredation cases, 1891–1917; cases and reports for claims brought before U.S. district and circuit courts under jurisdiction concurrent with the general jurisdiction of the Court of Claims, 1887–1910; records relating to cotton linters' cases, 1916–40, and to claims arising out of recisions of airmail contracts, 1934–42; and administrative records, 1930–47.

See Gaiselle Kerner and Ira N. Kellogg, Jr., comps., *Preliminary Inventory of the Records of the Court of Claims Section of the Department of Justice*, PI 47 (1952).

Discontinued Agencies

RECORDS OF THE SOLICITOR OF THE TREASURY (RECORD GROUP 206)

The Office of the Solicitor of the Treasury was created in the Department of the Treasury by an act of May 29, 1830, to supervise all legal proceedings involving the collection of debts due the United States. Previously that power had been vested successively in the Comptroller of the Treasury, 1789–1817, the First Comptroller of the Treasury, 1817–20, and the Agent of the Treasury, 1820–30.

The Solicitor directed, instructed, and required reports from all U.S. attorneys, marshals, and clerks of courts in matters relating to suits and proceedings for recovering debts due the United States; established regulations to guide customs collectors and required reports from the collectors concerning suits; issued distress warrants to direct proceedings against delinquent revenue collectors or receivers of public money; customarily examined all Treasury officers' official bonds, contracts, contractor bonds, and related legal documents; served as the Treasury Department law officer, which included advising Department officials on any legal question not involving the Constitution; and administered lands acquired by the United States in payment for debts and, with the approval of the Secretary of the Treasury, leased or sold such lands. The Solicitor, together with the U.S. district attorney in charge of the claim and the Secretary of the Treasury, made compromise agreements involving U.S. claims.

An act of June 22, 1870, transferred the Office to the Department of Justice, and in later years the Solicitor's functions were to some extent absorbed by other subordinates of the Attorney General. An Executive order of June 10, 1933, transferred the Office back to the Treasury Department and divested it of functions relating to the conduct of litigation and the supervision of U. S. attorneys, marshals, and clerks of courts. The Office was abolished May 10, 1934, and its functions were transferred to the Office of the General Counsel for the Department of the Treasury.

There are 770 cubic feet of records dated between 1791 and 1934 in this record group.

GENERAL CORRESPONDENCE.
1801-1934. 763 lin. ft.

Included are letters from the President, 1833-95, the Secretary of the Treasury, 1822-96, and the Attorney General, 1822-98, with opinions for the Secretary of the Treasury and advice and directions to the Solicitor on instructions to district attorneys. There are also letters from U.S. district attorneys, marshals, and clerks, 1801-1908, with reports relating to cases, suggestions concerning actions, requests for advice, explanations of official conduct, and information about such matters as the organization of the Federal judiciary, the problems of extending Federal authority into new territories and States, and frontier conditions; reports and letters from officers in judicial districts, concerning customs suits, 1865-91; letters from the U.S. attorney for the Southern District of New York, 1896-1910; letters from Treasury special agents, 1858-95, and revenue agents, 1862-69, concerning investigations; letters from coordinate Treasury officials and officials of other agencies, 1815-95, concerning litigation and other legal matters; and miscellaneous letters received, 1803-95.

Numerical case files ("Letters Received"), 1896-1934, consist of most letters received for this period and copies of letters sent incorporated into the files after 1910. Letters sent, 1820-1934, consist of letters, opinions, and other communications. Miscellaneous letters sent, 1830-70, consist chiefly of form replies to attorneys, marshals, collectors, and others responsible to the Solicitor that provide information on bonds and new regulations, and also include letters relating to the sale and lease of lands owned by the United States.

Also included are indexes and registers, which are fragmentary until the mid-1860's, to letters received, 1845-1910 (indexes dated after 1910 are to both letters received and sent); letters sent, 1836-1934; and letters referred, 1831-36 and 1866-75.

LEGAL OPINIONS AND BRIEFS.
1820-1933. 20 lin. ft.

These opinions were prepared by the Solicitor in response to requests from officials of Government departments. Included are a card digest to opinions included in the numerical case files; opinions of the Solicitor of the Department of Labor, 1915, and other officials; indexes to sources cited in opinions; and briefs and memorandums concerning the Solicitor's work and activities.

CASE FILES AND SUIT RECORDS. 1791-1929. 110 lin. ft.

These records, formed by withdrawing letters, reports, and other items from incoming material, are not official files for suits tried in Federal courts. The case files and suit papers, 1805-1926 (86 lin. ft.), were maintained by the Solicitor for some of the suits under his charge, which concerned such matters as banking regulations, customs laws, cases that were compromised, lands conveyed to the United States and the sale of these lands, and postmasters and other officials in default. There are also registers and indexes, 1791-1929, some of which relate to the case files, that list all important actions affecting progress of suits in which the Solicitor had an interest. These suits involve such additional matters as recovery of U.S. property, opium smuggling, postal regulations, and the enforcement of such statutes as the Pure Food and Drug Act, the Safety Appliance Acts, and the Twenty-Eight Hour Law.

REPORTS ON LITIGATION AND RELATED LETTERS. 1821-1934.
229 lin. ft.

These form reports concern suits to recover debts due the United States, civil suits after 1830 in which the United States generally was a party or was otherwise interested and in which the reporting officers participated, and criminal prosecutions. The reports include letters related to early cases, names of persons sued or prosecuted and vessels or objects libeled, comments on cases and information about the amounts involved, steps taken, judgments or sentences, and case settlements. They are from district attorneys, 1821-1921 (125 lin. ft.), clerks of courts, 1821-1929, marshals, 1821-85, and collectors of customs, 1839-45, reporting their activities in conducting cases to the Agent of the Treasury and the Solicitor. Closely related letters from these reporting officers, 1839-45, usually explaining why formal reports have not been made, are found in the general correspondence series of the Solicitor's Office.

MISCELLANEOUS RECORDS.
1791-1934. 8 lin. ft.

These consist chiefly of administrative records and include circulars; transmittal letters; warrants of distress; a record of deposits made to the U.S. Treasurer's credit as a result of suits; and lists of debts due the United States, bonds, salary payments, powers of attorney, and district attorneys' and court clerks' accounts.

See George S. Ulibarri, comp., *Preliminary Inventory of the Records of the Solicitor of the Treasury*, PI 171 (1968).

RECORDS OF THE OFFICE OF ALIEN PROPERTY (RECORD GROUP 131)

The World War I Office of Alien Property Custodian was created by an Executive order of October 12, 1917. The Trading With the Enemy Act of October 6, 1917, authorized the Custodian to assume control and dispose of enemy-owned property in the United States and its possessions. The Office was abolished May 1, 1934, and its functions and records transferred to the newly established Alien Property Bureau in the Claims Division of the Justice Department. On December 9, 1941, the Bureau was replaced by the Alien Property Division, established to handle problems concerning enemy property resulting from U.S. entry into World War II and to liquidate the affairs of the World War I Office.

The World War II Office of Alien Property Custodian was established within the Office for Emergency Management on March 11, 1942, under authority of the Trading With the Enemy Act of 1917 and the First War Powers Act of December 18, 1941. An Executive order of April 21, 1942, transferred to it the functions, personnel, and property of the Alien Property Division of the Department of Justice. The Custodian was empowered to control or vest, use, administer, liquidate, or sell foreign-owned properties that were productive resources requiring active management, such as business enterprises and patents. Authority over foreign-owned properties that constituted general purchasing power and required no active management, such as cash and securities, was delegated to the Secretary of the Treasury. An Executive order of June 8, 1945, extended the jurisdiction of the Custodian to all property in the United States owned by Germany and Japan or their nationals. An Executive order of October 14, 1946, terminated the Office of Alien Property Custodian and transferred its functions, except those relating to property in the Philippine Islands, to the Department of Justice, Office of Alien Property. Another Executive order of that date created the

Philippine Alien Property Administration, which was abolished June 15, 1951, and its functions also transferred to the Office of Alien Property. This Office was transferred to the Civil Division of the Department on September 1, 1961, and it was terminated on June 30, 1966. Foreign-funds-control functions at that time were transferred to the Office of Foreign Assets Control of the Treasury Department. The Assistant Attorney General in charge of the Civil Division is responsible for other alien property functions and has the title of Director of the Office of Alien Property.

There are 1,545 cubic feet of records (in WNRC except for nontextual records) dated between 1917 and 1957, with some dated as early as 1878, in this record group.

RECORDS RELATING TO ACTIVITIES ARISING FROM WORLD WAR I. 1917-57.
1,578 lin. ft.

These consist of office files of the Custodian and other officials; general and administrative records, including minutes of conferences, reports, and procedural and reference material; general correspondence; and records concerning personnel and disbursements, 1917-43. Records of units of the World War I Office and its successors consist of investigative records, 1917-27 (including seized records dated as early as 1914), relating to enemy-owned property. There are also records of the Bureau of Trusts and related units, concerning the seizure, administration, and disposition of property held in trust, 1917-41, including ships, radio stations, patents, trademarks, copyrights, real estate, mortgages, insurance companies and policies, and securities; records concerning property in territories and possessions, property in estates, and banks and other depository institutions; and records relating to the management and disposition of seized concerns, 1917-34 (including some seized records dated as early as 1890), accounting and auditing, 1917-57, claims for the return of or compensation for property, 1918-42, and legal matters, 1917-46.

There are many record and index cards, docket books, lists, and other forms of information digests. Case files for individual trustees or corporations generally include correspondence, reports, memorandums, minutes, orders, demands for surrender of property, financial statements, ledgers and other accounting records, audits, licenses, transcripts of testimony at hearings, legal documents, and exhibits. There are also records of seized concerns, including articles of incorporation, bylaws, minutes of directors meetings, annual reports, correspondence, contracts, insurance policies, legal and financial records, and radiograms.

RECORDS RELATING TO ACTIVITIES ARISING FROM WORLD WAR II. 1941-51. 290 lin. ft.

Included are prevesting reports, case files for interned persons with assets, records of a research project on Japanese economic operations, inventories of records, and reference material. Records seized from enemy organizations, dating from 1878 to 1946, include the German Railroads Information Office, German-American Bund, Deutsches Haus, Deutscher Klub of Dallas, German American Athletic Union of North America, the Federation of Italian War Veterans in the United States, and the Dante Alighieri Society. They include organizational documents, minutes, reports, correspondence, membership records, legal and financial records, pamphlets, programs, books, periodicals, press releases, newspaper clippings, songbooks, and musical scores.

CARTOGRAPHIC AND AUDIOVISUAL RECORDS. 1908-41. 54,448 items.

Charts and maps, 1927-39 (27 items), of U.S. harbors annotated to show facilities used by sales agents for the Franco-German potash cartel.

Photographs, 1908-41 (54,280 items), of German works of art, cities, industries, festivals, customs, Nazi officials, and military operations in Europe and Africa from the German Railroads Information Office in New York, 1930-41; personnel and activities of the German-American Bund, 1932-41; interiors and exteriors of ships of the Hamburg-American Line—North German Lloyd, 1908-39, and of cities, natives, and buildings at ports visited by its ships, 1920-39; imported steel products sold by the Seamless Steel Equipment Corp. of New York, and other German and American steel products, 1926-40; farms, quarries, chemical plants, and related industries in the United States from the records of Chemnyco, Inc., of New York, 1928-35; and performers and scenes from Ufa-Films, Inc., ca. 1939-40.

Motion pictures of the 1930's (36 reels), concerning travel in Germany and other countries from the records of the Hamburg-American Line—North German Lloyd, and Japanese film dramas from the records of Haruta and Co., Inc.

Sound recordings, ca. 1930-41 (105 items), from the German-American Bund of German nationalist songs, symphonies, and operatic selections used at entertainments and rallies; speeches by Hitler and other Nazi leaders; and Bund rallies held in Madison Square Garden and the Hippodrome in New York.

SPECIFIC RESTRICTIONS

Records: Seized corporate records dated after the time of seizure by the Office of Alien Property and all other records that are less than 50 years old.

Restrictions: These records may be used only by authorized employees of the Department of Justice and by other persons who have obtained the permission of the Office of Alien Property.

Specified by: Department of Justice.

RECORDS OF THE BUREAU OF WAR RISK LITIGATION (RECORD GROUP 190)

The Bureau of War Risk Litigation was established in the Department of Justice on September 11, 1933, to perform legal functions related to the defense of suits against the United States that concerned war risk and life insurance contracts authorized by the War Risk Insurance Act of October 6, 1917, and later acts. Those functions had been performed by the Bureau of War Risk Insurance of the Treasury Department before 1921, the U.S. Veterans Bureau from 1921 to 1930, and the Veterans Administration from 1930 to 1933. The Bureau was headed by a director who, until July 1, 1942, was under the general supervision of the Assistant to the Attorney General and subsequently the Assistant Attorney General in charge of the Claims Division. On June 30, 1945, the Bureau was abolished, and its functions were transferred to the Claims Division of the Department of Justice.

The General Claims Section of the Civil Division (the Claims Division before 1953) has retained headquarters litigation files dated from ca. 1940, with card indexes from 1919 and docket cards from 1932. Some field records relating to war risk insurance cases have been retained in U.S. attorneys' offices. Departmental World War II insurance litigation records are among general records of the Department of Justice (see RG 60).

There are 98 cubic feet of records dated between 1924 and 1946 in this record group.

RECORDS. 1924-46. 130 lin. ft.

These include a reference file, 1924-37; central office dockets and indexes, 1930-44; closed headquarters case files, 1925-46; printed briefs and records on appeal or transcripts of testimony, 1925-46; a card index to names of plaintiffs, 1925-46; and correspondence, reports, and dockets of the District of Columbia, Mississippi, and New York offices, 1929-45.

SPECIFIC RESTRICTIONS

Records: All records less than 25 years old.

Restrictions: Only authorized employees of the Department of Justice and other persons specifically authorized by the Attorney General or his alternate in archïval matters may have access to these records.

Specified by: Department of Justice.

POST OFFICE DEPARTMENT

RECORDS OF THE POST OFFICE DEPARTMENT
(RECORD GROUP 28)

The Office of the Postmaster General was created by an act of September 22, 1789, which continued regulations that originated with the appointment on July 26, 1775, of Benjamin Franklin as Postmaster General by the Continental Congress. The first act to provide in detail for a Post Office Department was passed February 20, 1792, and subsequent legislation enlarged its duties. The Postmaster General has been a member of the Cabinet since 1829, but the Post Office Department did not attain the status of an executive department until June 8, 1872. Assistant Postmasters General, authorized by acts of 1792, 1810, 1836, and 1891, were assigned administrative supervision over specific functions of the Department.

See Wesley E. Rich, *The History of the United States Post Office Department to the Year 1829* (Cambridge, Mass., 1924).

There are 2,893 cubic feet of records dated between 1773 and 1968 in this record group.

RECORDS OF THE OFFICE OF THE POSTMASTER GENERAL.
1773-1953. 877 lin. ft.

The functions of this Office, which is responsible for the general supervision, direction, and management of the Department, include the appointment of departmental officers and employees; issuance of orders and promulgation of rules and regulations concerning the organization and operations of the postal service; determination of appeals from decisions of the Assistant Postmasters General; and consideration of claims against the Department. The records include journals containing orders of the Postmaster General, 1835-1953; outgoing correspondence, 1789-1952 (with

gaps); a few incoming letters, 1837-43; and correspondence sent by the private secretary, 1867-1901 (with gaps), the administrative assistant, July-December 1929, and the executive assistant, 1930-35. Records of the Office of the Chief Clerk, whose duties originally concerned field and investigative activities but after 1872 related almost solely to administrative and housekeeping functions, include a fair copy of the journal of Hugh Finlay, Surveyor of Post Roads and Post Offices for the British Post Office Department, containing reports and comments about post offices and their services in the northern and southern districts of the North American Col onies, 1773-74; sample cashbooks, bonus, forms, and printed material relating to American and foreign post offices, 1794-1894; manuscript copies of Department annual reports, 1836-40 and 1846; some congressional correspondence, 1839-58 (with gaps); inquiries of the Keep Commission about administrative procedures, 1906-7; outgoing correspondence, 1873-1910; records relating to buildings occupied by the Department, 1827-55; records concerning the experimental telegraph line built in 1843 under the general direction of S. F. B. Morse and the Postmaster General, 1837-46; telegraph rate agreements under an act of July 24, 1866, authorizing the Postmaster General to set rates for telegrams sent by the Government, 1866-1913; correspondence concerning personnel and operation of the Censorship Board, 1917-18; general correspondence and reports relating to personnel, 1904-13; and a scrapbook of circulars, notices, instructions, and newspaper clippings relating to postal activities, 1823-71.

Records of the Disbursing Officer include correspondence, inventories, and fiscal records relating to the purchase of office supplies and equipment, sale of property, payment of salaries, and maintenance of buildings and equipment, 1862-1913; records of the Division of Service Relations relate to a cooperative store operated for the benefit of Department employees at Washington, D.C., 1917-21, and to postal employee welfare programs developed through national, county, local, and departmental councils and boards, 1921-30. Records of the Office of the Solicitor consist of case files with indexes, docket books, registers, and transcripts of hearings concerning use of the mails for fraud, sedition, lotteries, false advertising, transportation of obscene matter, and other violations of postal laws and regulations, 1905-51; records relating to Federal operation of telephone, telegraph, and cable companies, 1918-21, with related indexes; records relating to enforcement of the Espionage Acts of World War I, 1917-21, and World War II, 1942-45, which denied second-class mailing privileges to certain publications; correspondence and reports relating to investigations of airmail and ocean mail contracts, 1934-40; office files of the Solicitor, 1912-22; opinions, 1868-74 and 1895-97; outgoing letters, 1877-79 and 1906; registers of postmasters' claims for reimbursement, 1882-1929; and records relating to bonding of mail route carriers, 1901-2 and 1908. Records of the Office of the Purchasing Agent consist of letters sent relating to supply and equipment purchases, 1904 and 1910.

RECORDS OF THE BUREAU OF THE FIRST ASSISTANT POSTMASTER GENERAL. 1789-1950. 337 lin. ft.

This Bureau establishes and manages post offices; selects and nominates postmasters for first-, second-, and third-class post offices; and appoints postmasters to fourth-class post offices. It administers city, village, rural, and spe-cial delivery service and handles unmailable and undeliverable mail. The title of the Bureau was changed to the Bureau of Post Office Operations in 1950. The records include letters sent, 1793-1800, journals (orders), 1867-1905, and miscellaneous correspondence and statements, 1911-41, relating to legislation, appropriations, credit unions for postal employees, and postmaster conventions; records of the Division of Postmasters consist of a record of first returns received from postmasters, 1789-1818, and records relating to appointments of postmasters and to the establishment, discontinuance, and change of name and site of post offices, 1815-1950; records of the Division of Post Office Clerical Service relate to appointments and salaries of clerks and other personnel in first- and second-class post offices, 1889-1907, and operations of second- and third-class post offices, 1916-36, of contract stations and branches, 1916-35, and of Sunday service at post offices, 1911-12.

Records of the Division of City Delivery Service relate to mail carriers employed in first- and second-class post offices, 1888-1907; carriers separated from the postal service, 1863-99; inspections of city delivery service at Baltimore, Md., Kalamazoo, Mich., and Pittsburgh, Pa., 1929-31; and Detroit River steamboat service, 1895-1928. Records of the Division of Rural Delivery Service consist of correspondence, 1898-1936, issuances of the Superintendent of the Free Delivery System, 1901-6, and statistical data, 1896-1910; records of the Division of Rural Mails consist of correspondence, memorandums, reports, issuances, and accounting records concerning the operation of rural mail routes and the administration of the Division, 1906-34, and records relating to the employment of rural mail carriers, 1901-20; records of the Division of Post Office Service consist of correspondence and reports relating to classification of employees and measurement of work in post offices, 1912–34; and a small quantity of records relating to the Division of Dead Letters, 1897–1930.

RECORDS OF THE BUREAU OF THE SECOND ASSISTANT POSTMASTER GENERAL. 1814–1966. 929 lin. ft.

This Bureau supervises transportation, routing, and distribution of mail and manages the international postal service. Its title was changed in 1949 to the Bureau of Transportation. The records include administrative records, 1889–1957, reports, 1911–31, memorandums, 1914–29, letters sent, 1891–1934, correspondence concerning airmail service, 1921–27, notices to railway companies concerning mail transportation, 1885–1909, and a roster of Bureau employees, 1893–1912; and records of the special administrative aide, consisting of budget estimates and reports relating to appropriations, 1920–33, and reports of personnel changes, 1918–33. Records of the Division of Railway Mail Service include correspondence, 1902–29; issuances, 1912–55; rosters of clerks and agents, 1855–97; divisional newsletters, 1918–51; registers of railroad and electric car mail route contracts, 1877–1948, and star route mail contracts, 1814–1960 (with gaps), containing information about service to small post offices not on railroad lines; records relating to special service contracts, 1920–41; lists of star route mail contractors, 1833–77; paybooks for star route service, 1851–66; records relating to Government-operated star service by motortrucks, 1917–24, and establishment of highway post office routes, 1940–59; orders, contracts, and correspondence relating to powerboat and steamboat mail route

service, 1859–1953; and records relating to construction and maintenance of railway post office cars, 1930–62.

Records of the Division of Railway Adjustments consist of correspondence relating to rates paid for mail transportation, 1907–46, case files and correspondence concerning transportation of mail matter by means other than the Postal Service in violation of Federal statutes, 1896–1933, public carriers' reports of railway mail service performed, 1916–22, and registers of the employment of mail messengers, 1877–81 and 1900–1947. Records of the Division of International Postal Service include record copies of postal conventions with foreign countries, 1857–1929; records relating to postal congresses and conventions, 1847–1927; correspondence, reports, and questionnaires relating to vessels and routes employed in the ocean mail service, 1929–39; correspondence relating to military postal service during the Spanish-American War, 1898–1902; records relating to the operation of postal services in Cuba, 1896–1908, the Philippine Islands, 1895–1903, and Puerto Rico, 1899–1900; and correspondence, airline schedules, financial statements, surveys, and performance reports relating to the foreign airmail service, 1918–39.

Records of the Division of Airmail Service consist of correspondence, reports, and memorandums of the Service, 1918–25, of the general superintendent of the Service, 1926–42, and of the Second Assistant Postmaster General concerning air transport, 1926–52; publicity material about airmail service, 1918–37; records relating to airmail routes and autogiro and helicopter service, 1919–49; correspondence and reports concerning National Airmail Week, 1938–39; performance and efficiency reports on domestic airmail service, 1920–41; and blueprints and specifications for airplanes, hangars, and equipment, 1918–25.

RECORDS OF THE BUREAU OF THE THIRD ASSISTANT POSTMASTER GENERAL. 1775-1968. 112 lin. ft.

This Bureau collects and deposits postal revenues, receives and disposes of all moneys coming directly to the Department, and keeps accounts showing the fiscal operations of the postal, money order, and postal savings systems. The title of the Bureau was changed in 1949 to the Bureau of Finance. The records include those of the Division of Finance, consisting of accounts, ledgers, and journals of the General Post Office, 1775-1803; cashbooks used by the General Post Office, 1791-95; correspondence of the Division, 1922-37; and records showing quarterly receipts of post offices, 1895-1956. Records of the Postal Savings System consist of correspondence relating to the establishment and operation of the system, 1913-20, annual reports, 1913-36, and records relating to post office boxes, 1894-1934. Records of the Division of Money Orders consist of correspondence, memorandums, reports, and accounts, 1868-1936; and copies of international money order conventions, with related correspondence, 1856-1966. Records of the Division of Stamps consist of plate-proof stamp sheets, 1870-1962 (on permanent loan to the Smithsonian Institution), and stamp billbooks, 1870-97; a ledger showing quantities and costs of stamps furnished to postal services in Cuba, Puerto Rico, the Philippine Islands, and Guam, 1898-1900; records of the postal card agent, 1893-1923; and a historical file on early postage stamps, 1847-1901. There are a few records of the Division of Newspaper and Periodical Mail relating to an increase in second-class rates, 1917-20; and records of the Division of Parcel Post, consisting of international parcel post agreements, with related correspondence, 1887-1966, and miscellaneous records relating to foreign parcel post facilities, 1911-12.

RECORDS OF THE BUREAU OF THE FOURTH ASSISTANT POSTMASTER GENERAL. 1834-1953. 580 lin. ft.

This Bureau administers, operates, and maintains Government-owned post office buildings; authorizes allowances for operating non-Government-owned postal quarters and vehicles used for collection and delivery services; distributes equipment and supplies; supervises the screen wagon, pneumatic tube, and Government-owned motor vehicle services; supervises shops for the manufacture and repair of mail equipment; and produces and distributes post route maps and parcel post zone keys. In 1949 the Bureau became the Bureau of Facilities. The records include correspondence, memorandums, reports, and issuances of the Fourth Assistant Postmaster General, 1905-32; records of the Division of Topography, consisting of letters sent, 1901-11, reports of site locations (ca. 1837-1950), and geographical information forms submitted by postmasters to aid the Department in the preparation of postal maps; and records of the Division of Motor Vehicle Services, consisting of advertisements, contracts, and correspondence concerning manufacture and operation of mail transportation vehicles, 1858-1939, and correspondence relating to shipment of farm products by postal trucks, 1919-29.

Records of the Pneumatic Tube Service consist of correspondence, contracts, reports, surveys, issuances, statistical data, and blueprints relating to the establishment and operation of the Service, 1892-1953; and records of a congressional commission established to investigate the desirability of Government ownership of the Service, 1912-14. Records of the Division of Post Office Quarters consist of correspondence and reports, 1916-42; records relating to leases of postal quarters, 1916-32; blueprints, plans, and estimates for construction of postal quarters, and reports concerning space accommodations and conditions of Federal buildings, 1911-30; and records relating to dedications of post office buildings, 1933-42. Records of the Division of Equipment and Supplies consist of periodic reports of work performed in mail-equipment shops, 1915-24, and miscellaneous records relating to operations of the Division, 1868-1911.

RECORDS OF THE BUREAU OF ACCOUNTS. 1836-1942. 69 lin. ft.

Established in 1921 to perform auditing functions previously handled by the Treasury Department, this Bureau examined accounts of the postal services and certified quarterly to the Postmaster General accounts of postmasters' funds and general expenses of the services. The Bureau was terminated in 1953, and its functions were assigned to the Bureau of Finance. The records consist of correspondence, memorandums, and issuances, 1862-1924; a register of mail routes, ca. 1838-61; accounts relating to postal services between the United States and foreign countries, 1883-1915; and accounts of postmasters, 1862-74.

RECORDS OF THE BUREAU OF THE CHIEF INSPECTOR. 1864-1935. 177 lin. ft.

The Bureau investigates mail depredations and violations of postal laws and regulations and inspects Department finances, property, and equipment. The records consist of letters sent by the Chief Special Agent, Office of Mail Depredations, 1875-77; case files of investigations, 1877-1903; statements of arrests for offenses against postal laws, with related registers and indexes, 1864-99; records relating to an investigation of the Railway Mail Service, 1925; annual reports, 1905-35; rosters of inspectors and other employees, 1898-1909; records of Inspection Offices at St. Louis, 1876-78, Denver, 1879-1907, Philadelphia, 1896-1909, and New York, 1907-8; and a collection of bimonthly general intelligence press reports of the Justice Department, relating to radical publications, 1918-22.

CARTOGRAPHIC AND AUDIOVISUAL RECORDS. 1839-1966. 3,920 items.

Cartographic records (2,948 items) include a post route atlas of the United States and individual States and territories compiled under the direction of David Burr, 1839; several series of State, county, city, and rural post delivery route maps, 1867-1966, prepared by the Division of Topography and its predecessors, showing post offices, mail delivery routes, frequency of mail service, distances between post offices, mail-carrying railroads, navigable waters (1917), and congressional districts (1935-40); and maps and plans of landing fields and airmail routes, prepared by the Division of Airmail Service, 1918-41.

Photographs, 1920-52 (903 items), relating mainly to airmail service, of pilots, including Charles A. Lindbergh; planes; accidents; the Pan American Airline Service; airports and mail facilities; and exhibits and trophies.

Motion pictures, 1921-57 (69 reels), showing activities and facilities of the Department, including the Dead Letter Office; mail handling and delivery; transportation of mail by air, land, and water; parcel post; manufacture and repair of mail bags; printing and issuing stamps; protection of the mails from use for purposes of defrauding the public and from robbery; the postal savings system; instructions to mail users; post office buildings and the construction and dedication of the New Post Office, Washington, D.C., 1931-34; and Presidents Hoover and Roosevelt, Postmasters General, and other prominent persons. A scenic film about Mt. Rainier National Park and German propaganda films relating to the conquest of Belgium, Holland, France, and Poland during World War II are included.

See Arthur Hecht et al., comps., rev. by Forrest R. Holdcamper, *Preliminary Inventory of the Records of the Post Office Department*, PI 168 (1967).

Microfilm Publications: *Letters Sent by the Postmaster General, 1789-1836,* M601, 50 rolls, DP; *The Territorial Papers of the United States: The Territory of Wisconsin, 1836-1848*, M236, 122 rolls; and *Journal of Hugh Finlay, 1773-74, and General Postoffice Ledger—"Ledger of Benjamin Franklin," 1776-78*, T268, 1 roll.

DEPARTMENT OF THE INTERIOR

RECORDS OF THE
OFFICE OF THE SECRETARY OF THE INTERIOR
(RECORD GROUP 48)

The Department of the Interior was established by an act of March 3, 1849, which provided that the Secretary of the Interior should assume powers previously exercised by the Secretary of War over the Commissioner of Indian Affairs, by the Secretary of the Treasury over the General Land Office, by the Secretaries of War and the Navy over the Commissioner of Pensions, by the Secretary of State over the Commissioner of Patents, and by the President over the Commissioner of Public Buildings. Jurisdiction over census taking, marshals and court officers, Federal buildings and grounds throughout the United States, and charitable and penal institutions in the District of Columbia was also placed in the Department.

Agencies that have since been transferred from the Department include the Patent Office, Pension Office (Veterans Administration), Census Bureau, Office of Education, Office of the Commissioner of Railroads, Capitol Buildings and Grounds, Freedmen's Hospital, St. Elizabeth's Hospital, the Columbia Institution for the Deaf (Gallaudet College), and Howard University. Separate record groups have been established for the records of many operating units of the Department.

There are 4,296 cubic feet of records dated between ca. 1833 and 1964 in this record group.

RECORDS OF THE DIVISION OF APPOINTMENTS. 1849-1908. 580 lin. ft.

This Division had charge of those Department personnel matters central-ized in the Secretary's office. The records include reports to the Congress and the Secretary; incoming letters, with registers and indexes, 1849-1907; letters sent; formal communications to the Civil Service Commission; Presidential and Departmental appointment papers; and records relating to political charges against employees and files of boards of inquiry. There are also orders and circulars, 1852-1908, personnel statistics, information on appointment methods, and examinations for clerks.

RECORDS OF THE DIVISION OF FINANCE. 1849-1935. 158 lin. ft.

The Finance Division or Disbursing Office was established in 1853, and some of the Secretary's records for earlier years have been kept with those of the Division. Most records are those of the disbursing clerk, who from 1871 to 1883 was Chief of the Disbursement Division and from 1883 to 1921 Chief of the Division of Finance. Records include correspondence, chiefly 1857-1910, with indexes and registers of letters sent and received, and letters sent with indexes, 1849-1907, appropriation ledgers, 1853-1923, cashbooks, 1853-1935, journals, 1879-99, and chief disbursing clerks' certificates of settlement of accounts, 1911-28.

RECORDS OF THE OFFICE OF THE ASSISTANT ATTORNEY GENERAL. 1890-1909. 10 lin. ft.

An act of 1871 authorized an Assistant Attorney General to advise the Secretary of the Interior while remaining an official of the Department of Justice. His incomplete files include letters sent, 1890-1907; letters received, 1895-1903; briefs, exhibits, and digests of court cases, 1893-1909; and a docket of Department cases, 1901-7.

RECORDS OF THE PATENTS AND MISCELLANEOUS DIVISION. 1849-1943. 392 lin. ft.

The Patents and Miscellaneous Division (formerly known as the Pension and Miscellaneous Division and briefly in 1907 as the Miscellaneous Division) has records dating from 1849, although the Division was not formally established until much later. There are records concerning Patent Office agricultural business until 1862, and Pension Office business, 1849-1907. Usually the Patents and Miscellaneous Division handled census work in the Office of the Secretary; there are no separate records of the temporary Census Division.

The Patents and Miscellaneous Division administered public buildings and grounds work, welfare institutions, prisons, and affairs of the District of Columbia. It directed court officers, suppression of the African slave trade, and black colonization. The Division directed the Office of Education, national parks, administration of territories, the Geological Survey and its predecessors (except reclamation work assigned to the Lands and Railroads Division), legislation, the Executive Mansion, census taking, creation of forest reserves, 1891-95, building construction, and admission of attorneys and agents to practice before the Department. The Patents and Miscellaneous Division was abolished in 1907 and some of its duties were transferred to Department bureaus, others to the Chief Clerk.

Among records of this Division are (1) letters received, 1849-ca. 1880, from the President, the Congress, and Government departments; letters received about the Executive Mansion, patents, the Department of Agriculture, the Pat-

ent Office Building, pension legislation, bounty land claims, prisons and convicts, the Government Hospital for the Insane, and charitable institutions; a file of miscellaneous letters received, 1881-1907, with indexes and registers; decennial census records, 1849-1904; records relating to the administration of the territories, 1850-1911; and smaller series of letters received and sent, 1849-1906, with indexes. (2) Records relating to Pension Office business, 1849-1920, include letters sent and received, 1896-1907, with indexes and registers; letters sent, 1849-83, with indexes, 1849-69; digests of decisions, 1852-64 and 1861-75; appeal books, 1867-1918, with indexes, 1881-1911; and records relating to pension claims. (3) Records relating to suppression of African slave trade and to black colonization include letters received, 1854-72, letters sent, 1858-72, and a "Steward's Weekly Returns of Provisions" for the U.S.S. *Atlanta,* 1858-59. (4) Records concerning attorneys and agents include rolls of attorneys and agents, 1884-1923, and a roll of those suspended and disbarred, 1869-1923; name indexes, 1869-1943; and records concerning admitted attorneys and agents, 1884-1907. (5) There are records relating to Government participation in the Philadelphia Centennial Exposition, 1876; the World's Columbian Exposition at Chicago, 1893; the Louisiana Purchase Exposition at St. Louis, 1904, with documentation on the Alaska Exhibit and the Indian Territory Exhibit; the Lewis and Clark Centennial Exposition, Portland, Oreg., 1905, including the District of Alaska Exhibit; the Jamestown Ter-Centennial Exposition, Norfolk, Va., 1907; the Alaska-Yukon-Pacific Exposition, Seattle, 1909, including records of the Office of the Alaskan Exhibit; and the Panama-Pacific International Exposition, San Francisco, 1915. (6) Records of the Returns Office, 1881-1904, consist of letters received and financial records. (7) Records of the U.S. Penitentiary for the District of Columbia, 1829-76, include minutes, annual reports, correspondence, and records of visits of the Board of Inspectors; incoming letters and records of the warden's office; sentences of convicts; and financial and administrative records. (8) There are records, 1852-65, of the Office of Explorations and Surveys, created by an act of March 3, 1853, which authorized the Secretary of War to determine "the most practicable and economical route for a railroad from the Mississippi River to the Pacific Ocean." The records consist of correspondence relating to expeditions and surveys, scientific work, printing and engraving, and applications for employment, 1852-61; and correspondence and other records concerning the Isaac Stevens expedition, 1853-61. (9) Records of the engineer and architect (Brig. Gen. Montgomery C. Meigs) supervising construction of the Pension Office Building, 1881-89, include letters sent and received, with index and register of letters received, 1882-89; daily reports of the superintendent and a volume of plans, 1882-87; financial records, 1882-88; and personal records of General Meigs, 1882-89.

RECORDS OF THE LANDS AND RAILROADS DIVISION. 1849-1907. 570 lin. ft.

This Division, formally established about 1870, had functioned since 1849, administering the public domain and the General Land Office, mostly handling appeals to the Secretary from decisions of the Commissioner of the General Land Office.

A Pacific Wagon Road Office in the Office of the Secretary was discontinued at the beginning of the Civil War. In 1865 an Engineer office was established to handle matters concerning the Pacific railroads, land-grant railroads, Government wagon roads, the Washington aqueduct and other public works in the District of Columbia, and the Capitol

Extension. In 1867 this Office was replaced by the Pacific Railroad Division, which in 1870 was merged into the Lands and Railroads Division.

Records of the Division include letters sent and received and related records in numerous series, 1849-1907, with indexes, 1881-1905, and registers; railroad packages, 1849-1901, arranged by name of land-grant railroad; records of timber trespasses and fraudulent land entries, 1887-1901; letters and reports received from land inspectors, 1891-1907; and records concerning the settlement of Oklahoma, 1889-92. Letters sent relating to boundary surveys, the Engineer Office, Pacific railroads, land-grant railroads and wagon roads, and inspectors, 1849-1907.

General records, 1849-1907, include histories of bills and joint resolutions of Congress, 1899-1907, appeal books, 1859-1907, decisions of the Secretary of the Interior, 1849-55, opinions of the Assistant Attorney General for the Department, 1886-1901, and account books of "Oklahoma town lot funds," 1901-7. Records relating to Des Moines River Land Claims, 1895-1906, include claims decided, 1895-99, claims submitted, 1895-1906, letters sent, 1896-1900, and action and award books, 1896-1904. Records concerning wagon roads, 1856-87, include letters received, accounts, and other records, 1856-87, with a register of letters received, 1857-67; letters sent, 1857-71; and copies of letters sent concerning boundary surveys, 1857-63 and 1865-71. There are also records concerning reclamation, 1889-1907, with an index to correspondence, 1906-7, and "miscellaneous projects" records, 1901-7.

RECORDS OF THE INDIAN DIVISION. 1849-1907, with a few dated as early as 1833. 308 lin. ft.

The Division handled the Secretary's correspondence and kept records concerning Indian affairs. There are administrative records dating from 1849; general records, 1849-1907, including letters received, 1849-80 and 1881-1907, with registers and indexes; special files, ca. 1833-1907; letters sent, 1849-1907, with indexes; letters sent to officials and departments, 1873-83; proceedings of the Indian Peace Commission, 1867-68; and records relating to inspectors, 1878-1907, claims, 1873-85, and allotments, 1886-1906. Records relating to Indian Trust Funds, 1849-98, include letters received, 1851-80, with registers; special files, 1849-83; letters sent, 1857-80; ledgers, 1857-83; and other records concerning allotments and stocks and bonds, 1857-98.

RECORDS OF THE INDIAN TERRITORY DIVISION. 1898-1907. 203 lin. ft.

After 1898 this Division conducted the business of the Office of the Secretary relating to the Indian Territory and the Five Civilized Tribes. The records consist of letters sent and received, 1898-1907, with indexes and registers, including an index of letters to Federal officials, 1898-99; memorandums and regulations, 1898-1907; Final Rolls of the Five Civilized Tribes, 1899-1907 and 1914; records of allotments, contests, and leases, 1898-1907; and miscellaneous records.

CENTRAL CLASSIFIED FILES. 1907-53. 1,982 lin. ft.

In 1907 the Office of the Secretary was reorganized, several divisions were abolished, and a central filing system established. The records consist of narrative and statistical reports, circulars, manuals, opinions, decisions, briefs and other legal documents, Executive orders, correspondence, memorandums, press releases, charts, maps and plats, and other records arranged according to a numeric-subject classification system, with a subject and name index.

RECORDS OF THE PERSONNEL MANAGEMENT DIVISION. 1907-53. 262 lin. ft.

These records are designated as File No. 15 of the central files, but were kept separately by the Division of Personnel Management and its predecessors. The records concern personnel administration and include a subject index.

RECORDS RELATING TO LEGISLATION. 1907-58. 339 lin. ft.

These include reports, copies of legislation, records relating to legislation of interest to the Department, and correspondence.

MISCELLANEOUS GENERAL FILES. 1872-1939. 24 lin. ft.

These consist of a file of building plans for Federal and other buildings; press releases, 1923-39; and records of the Departmental Committee on Economy and Efficiency, 1908-12.

SPECIAL FILES OF DEPARTMENT OFFICIALS. 1918-61. 165 lin. ft.

These comprise records of Secretaries of the Interior Hubert Work, 1923-28, Harold Ickes, 1933-42, Oscar L. Chapman, 1933-53, and Douglas McKay, 1952-56; Under Secretaries Abe Fortas, 1942-46, Richard Searles, 1951-52, Clarence A. Davis, 1953-56, and Elmer F. Bennett, 1957-61; Assistant Secretaries Theodore A. Walters, 1933-39, Michael W. Straus, 1943-45, C. Girard Davidson, 1946-50, Robert R. Rose, Jr., 1951-52, Felix E. Wormser, 1953-58, Fred G. Aandahl, 1953-60, and Ross L. Leffler, 1957-61; Special Assistant Herbert Kaufman, 1918-19; Ernest Walker Sawyer, 1929-33, relating to matters in Alaska; the War Minerals Relief Commissioner, 1933-38; the special adviser on labor relations, 1936-47; other special files, including ones on conservation, 1928-45, on labor relations, 1951-52, on electric power, 1951-52, and on expositions, 1926–28; and records of the Office of the Executive Assistant to the Secretary, including press releases, 1923–32, and policy statements of the Secretary, 1922–33.

RECORDS OF THE OFFICE OF THE SOLICITOR. 1906–59. 163 lin. ft.

The Office of the Solicitor is a continuation of the Office of the Assistant Attorney General for the Department of the Interior established in 1871. The title was changed in 1914. The records include correspondence and memorandums, 1930–58; records of the associate solicitor, 1928–48, relating to Boulder Dam, Hetch Hetchy Dam, coal mines, oil and gas, territories, and other subjects, 1906–59; the assistant solicitor for land matters, 1933–40; chief counsels of bureaus and other legal officers, 1933–54; decisions of the Secretary or his deputies, 1935–42; records of court cases, 1915–41, and Indian cases, 1934–58; Oklahoma Indian cases, 1942–50, with index and registers, 1942–47; records concerning land cases, 1950–59, reclamation cases, 1953–59, and Board of Appeals cases, 1941–47; and other records of litigation involving the Department.

RECORDS OF THE INSPECTION DIVISION. 1906–28. 12 lin. ft.

Between 1924 and 1928 an Inspection Division functioned in the Office of the Secretary, directed by a Chief Inspector. Records of inspections date from 1906. There are general records, 1924–27, inspection reports for bureaus, 1906–27, reports and records concerning inspectors, 1924–28, and correspondence, reports with exhibits, and other records concerning inspections and investigations, 1924–28.

RECORDS OF THE PURCHASING OFFICE. 1932–47. 3 lin. ft.

The Purchasing Office was estab-

lished by the Secretary in 1932 and was discontinued in 1947. Records consist of orders, 1932–46, and circulars, 1932–47.

RECORDS OF THE DIVISION OF INFORMATION. 1933–47. 18 lin. ft.

The information office existing in the Office of the Secretary since 1923 was organized in 1937 as the Division of Information to handle public relations. The records include correspondence and other records, 1933–43; a program file, 1943–47; and Radio Section scripts, reference materials, and general records, 1938–47.

RECORDS OF THE PUBLICATIONS SECTION. 1941–49. 7 lin. ft.

The records consist of general records on the printing, binding, and distribution of publications, 1942–49; and records concerning a Departmental War History, 1941–48, including reports, drafts, correspondence, and press releases.

RECORDS OF THE DIVISION OF LAND UTILIZATION. 1935–56. 183 lin. ft.

On April 15, 1940, the Office of Land Utilization was created to plan land use for the Department. In 1950 the name of the Office was changed to Division of Land Utilization. It provided a technical staff for the Assistant Secretary for Public Land Management until it was abolished in 1953. The records include classified files, 1937–56, reference material, 1944–50, records concerning soil conservation and land use, 1935–41, and records concerning a public lands study, 1950.

RECORDS OF THE DIVISION OF WATER AND POWER. 1941–52. 186 lin. ft.

The Division of Power was established in 1941 to supervise electric power work of the Department. In 1943 the functions of the National Power Policy Committee were transferred to the Division. This Division was replaced in 1950 by the Division of Water and Power and served as technical staff to the Assistant Secretary for Water and Power Development. Included are records of the Division of Water and Power, 1941–51; records concerning legislation, 1945–51, and disposal of surplus property, 1944–46; reports concerning river basin and reclamation projects, 1941–50; and power contracts and related records, 1941–51. Also records on legislation and legal matters, 1941–44; records concerning the development of Alaska, 1947–52; records relating to water resources policy, 1950–52; records of the Branch of Economics and Statistics, with a reference file, 1941–47; and records concerning the President's Materials Policy Commission, 1952.

RECORDS OF OTHER DIVISIONS. 1943–53. 18 lin. ft.

These include records of the Division of Management Research, 1943–52; the Minerals and Fuels Division, consisting of general records, 1946–51, documentation on the President's Materials Policy Commission, 1951–53, and reports, correspondence, and other records of the National Minerals Advisory Council, 1947–51; and records of the Division of International Activities, comprising general records, 1948–53, records relating to training programs, 1949–53, and financial records, 1949–53.

RECORDS OF DEPARTMENTAL COMMITTEES AND STAFFS. 1910–60. 95 lin. ft.

Included are reports, correspondence, and other records of the Departmental Committee on Economy and Efficiency, 1910–13. Records of the Coordination Committee, 1946–47. Records of the Program Staff, including central files, 1946–

53; records and reports of regional field committees, 1947–53; records relating to interagency committees, 1947–53, the Water Resources Policy Review, 1950–52, the Missouri Basin Survey Commission, 1951–53, and the President's Materials Policy Commission, 1951–53; reference material kept by the Staff, 1947–53; records of the Director of the Program Staff, 1947–50; files of a staff member, 1947–53; and records of the Defense and Synthetic Liquid Fuels Operation, 1950–53. There are also records, 1948–51, of the Director of the Alaska Field Staff, established to coordinate programs in Alaska.

The Technical Review Staff, established in 1953, took over certain activities of the Program Staff, Division of Land Utilization, Division of Water and Power, Minerals and Fuels Division, and Division of International Activities. Its records consist of minutes, reports, correspondence, and other records relating to field committees, 1953; regional field committee reports, 1950–60; and correspondence, instructions, and copies of diplomatic despatches relating to economics, 1953–57.

RECORDS OF INTERDEPARTMENTAL COMMISSIONS AND COMMITTEES. 1908–56. 35 lin. ft.

The records include those of the National Conservation Commission, concerning water rights, 1908–9; reports, hearings, and other records of the San Gabriel River Commission, 1925–26; records of the National Power Policy Committee, consisting of classified files, 1934–35, records of the General Counsel, 1934–41, and the War Department's National Defense Power Committee, 1938–39; correspondence and other records of the U.S. Coronado Exposition Commission, 1939–41; and records of the Presidential Advisory Committee on Water Resources Policy, 1954–56.

CARTOGRAPHIC RECORDS. 1849–1923. 616 items.

Included are maps of the United States, relating to natural resources, national parks and forests, the public domain, Indian reservations, mining districts and claims, railroads, and reclamation projects, 1865–1923; maps and records relating to the Lower Colorado River project, 1906–12; maps of the four railroad routes surveyed from the Mississippi River to the Pacific Ocean, 1849–57; and a map prepared by the Pacific Wagon Roads Office, showing part of a wagon road to the Pacific, 1857.

AUDIOVISUAL RECORDS. 1862–1964. 3,000 items.

Still pictures, 1862–1964 (2,318 items), include photographs and a few charcoal drawings of officials of the Department, 1862–1933; public buildings under construction in Washington, D.C., 1878–1907, and original boundary markers of the District of Columbia; public buildings in Muskogee and Tulsa, Okla.; the Louisiana Purchase Exposition, St. Louis, 1904; the Alaskan Agricultural Fair, 1918; earthquake damage in Alaska, 1964; agriculture, industry, and schools in several of the territories, 1893–1909; a sewage system plan for Hawaii; mines and mining at Jerome and Prescott, Ariz., ca. 1900; oilfields and refineries, Los Angeles, 1927; national parks in the western territories, 1875–1907; Governors of the Five Civilized Tribes, 1863–1919; Pueblo artist Marie Chiwiwi; and prints used in reports. There are also photographs of damage to the U.S. Capitol, part of a report of the Architect, 1899; exhibits at the Milwaukee Public Museum, ca. 1900; the U.S.S. *Maine* and her captain; the S.S. *George Loomis;* and an ancient Latin tract.

Motion pictures, 1929–62 (179 reels), relate to the overall activities of the Department; power development, irrigation, soil conservation, and manufacturing in the TVA area; the Bureau of Reclamation; national monuments; national parks; wildlife conservation; Indian economy, training, and assistance; Southwest Indians, their homes and culture; economic and social conditions in the Virgin Islands; the Carpenter-Whitney expedition to Alaska, 1929, and the operation of the Alaska railroad, 1962; and the history of the westward expansion, depletion of natural resources, and development of irrigation in connection with activities of the General Land Office and the Geological Survey. There are also films concerning State parks; CCC work in national and State parks; recreation for underprivileged children; scenic and historic sites in the United States and its territories; forest fires and firefighting; University of Chicago studies on effects of erosion; fishing and recreation on Lake Superior; and African wildlife.

Sound recordings, 1936–52 (504 items), include speeches, discussions, interviews, news, ceremonies, and musical programs, many of them of broadcasts made by the Department or collected by it from Government agencies and commercial sources. They relate to functions of the Department; activities of the Bureau of Biological Survey and the U.S. Fish and Wildlife Service; the Bureau of Mines; the Bureau of Reclamation; dedication ceremonies at several reclamation projects; dust bowl migration and reclamation of dust bowl land; the Division of Territories and Island Possessions; the work of the General Land Office; the Geological Survey; an interview in 1941 with William Henry Jackson, pioneer photographer with the Survey; the national park system; the Office of Indian Affairs; the Petroleum Administration Board; and the Solid Fuels Administration for War. There are recordings relating to the Work Projects Administration disease control programs; the Public Works Administration projects to combat the depression; the public housing program and postwar housing; the work of the Civilian Conservation Corps; child labor, and wages and hours legislation; the role of women and other civilians in the war effort; the Social Security system; Department of Agriculture; Office of Price Administration; War Resources Planning Board; War Production Board; National Defense Advisory Commission; Civil Service Commission; Office of Civilian Defense; Bureau of the Budget; Treasury Department; Public Health Service; Federal Communications Commission; State Department; Veterans Administration; Office of Alien Property; Selective Service System; and wartime development of industry, aeronautics, scientific research, and atomic energy. There are also recordings concerning the National Education Association; President Roosevelt's birthday celebration in 1945 and the dedication of Hyde Park, 1946; a dramatization of U.S. history from the Revolution to World War II; presidential campaign speeches of 1940; newscasts of World War II; Allied cooperation during the war; Hitler's Sudeten, 1938, and Danzig, 1939, speeches; President Roosevelt's "Day of Infamy" speech, December 8, 1941; discussions about the UN, UNRRA, and UNESCO; and musical programs including folk and religious music and Marian Anderson's concert at the Lincoln Memorial, 1939, and at the dedication of the Anderson Memorial at the Department of the Interior, 1943.

See Laura E. Kelsay, comp., *Preliminary Inventory of the Cartographic Records of the Office of the Secretary of the Interior*, PI 81 (1955); John H. Martin, comp., *List of Documents Concerning the Negotiation of Ratified Indian Treaties, 1801-1869*, SL 6 (1949); and Catherine H. Rowland, comp., *Index to Appropriation Ledgers in the Records of the Office of the Secretary of the Interior, Division of Finance, 1853-1923*, SL 18 (1963).

Microfilm Publications: Included are Department territorial papers, ca. 1850-1914, for Alaska, Arizona, Colorado, Dakota, Idaho, Montana, New Mexico, Utah, Washington, and Wyoming; appointment papers, 1849-1907, consisting of applications and recommendations for positions in Arizona, California, Idaho, New Mexico, and Wisconsin; letters sent by the Indian Division, 1849-1903, and by the Lands and Railroads Division, 1849-1904; records relating to the African slave trade and black colonization, 1854-72; and records relating to wagon roads, 1857-81, and to the administration of Yellowstone National Park, 1872-86. For a complete listing see the current *List of National Archives Microfilm Publications*.

RECORDS OF THE BUREAU OF LAND MANAGEMENT
(RECORD GROUP 49)

The Offices of the Secretary and the Register of the Treasury at first handled the disposition of the public domain, but an act of April 25, 1812, established the General Land Office (GLO) as a bureau in the Department of the Treasury to administer all public land transactions except surveying and mapping work. Surveyors general (the first surveyor general had been appointed under an act of May 18, 1796; thereafter surveyors general were appointed for new areas as needed) conducted surveys and mapped public lands almost independently of other Government agencies until 1836 when they were placed in the GLO. In 1849 the GLO was transferred to the Department of the Interior.

Reorganization Plan No. 3 of 1946 consolidated the GLO and the Grazing Service, also in the Department of the Interior, to form the Bureau of Land Management. The Bureau classifies, manages, and disposes of public lands and their resources according to principles of multiple-use management. It also administers federally owned mineral resources on non-Federal lands and on the Outer Continental Shelf.

See Thomas Donaldson, *The Public Domain* (1884); and General Land Office, *Public Land System of the United States* (1924).

There are 36,312 cubic feet of records dated between 1770 and 1966 in this record group.

GENERAL RECORDS. 1796-1938.
6,429 lin. ft.

Included are general correspondence of the Washington land offices dated before 1908 (6,400 lin. ft.), including telegrams, reports, and other communications sent, 1796-1908, that relate to surveys; military bounty land warrants and scrip; private land, preemption, homestead, mineral, timber, and stone claims; Indian and swamp lands; railroad grants; agricultural college scrip and school lands; forest reserves; townsites; reclamation; timber trespasses; preparing, recording, and transmitting patents; and fiscal, personnel, and other administrative matters. Letters received, 1803-1908, with registers and indexes, including separately filed letters from registers and receivers, 1803-49; from surveyors general, 1803-71; and relating to railroad rights-of-way and land grants, canal improvement and irrigation rights, timbercutting permits, timber trespasses and sales, and military, lighthouse, and other reservations.

Other Washington office records concern special grants to immigrants and refugees (in WNRC), 1830; railroad mortgages, 1886-1938; a register of mining entries (in WNRC), 1875-1907; Federal reimbursements for tax revenues lost by counties in Oregon and California when railroad land grant titles were revested in the United States, 1916-31; valuation of Indian lands acquired by the United States, 1864-1908; records of the Board of Commissioners for the Hot Springs, Ark., Reservation, 1877-79; correspondence concerning Alabama selec-

tions under the May 23, 1928, Muscle Shoals Grant, 1915-28; and records relating to the Kaweah Cooperative Colony of California, 1934-35.

RECORDS RELATING TO PUBLIC LAND SURVEYS. 1796-ca. 1962.
728 lin. ft.

Public lands (the public domain) are federally owned or managed lands acquired by the Government through treaties, cessions by States, and purchases; they are disposed of under congressional authority. These records consist of records from Division "E" (the Division of Surveys, GLO), including letters received by the Secretary of the Treasury and the Commisssioner of the GLO from the Surveyor General of the Territory Northwest of the River Ohio, 1797-1849; reports, letters, and memorandums received from surveyors general of public land States, including records of the Surveyors General of Mississippi (south of Tennessee), 1803-31, Missouri, 1813-32, Alabama, 1817-32, and Florida, 1824-32; letters, with registers and indexes, and other records received from all surveyors general, ca. 1826-83; contracts with deputy surveyors, 1817-32, and surveyors contracts and bonds with surveyors general, 1851-1913, including correspondence, special instructions, and diagrams; records relating to surveys of State boundaries, military reservations, islands, townsites, private land claims, and national parks, 1860-1940; group survey records (in WNRC) created after surveyors general discontinued hiring deputy surveyors in 1910, including reports, correspondence, special instructions, and plats and copies of progress reports, 1910-62; records that relate to surveying small islands, 1910-26; field notes from survey examinations, ca. 1883-1913; plats, field notes, correspondence, and other records relating to rejected and abandoned surveys, ca. 1847-1915; letters sent to executive departments, 1864-1903; letters sent to registers and receivers, 1883-94; and records relating to Alaskan surveys, 1918-53, and to homestead entry and forest exchange surveys in national forests, 1910-53.

Locally maintained records include letters received, 1797-1856, and sent, 1797-1854, by the Surveyor General of the Territory Northwest of the River Ohio; correspondence of the Surveyor General of Arkansas, 1831-59; and letters sent by the Surveyor General of Montana, 1892-1922, and the Surveyor General of South Dakota, 1920-22.

RECORDS RELATING TO PUBLIC LAND DISPOSALS. ca. 1796-1951, with a few dated as early as 1770. 32,950 lin. ft.

Control records include Executive orders and proclamations relating to notices of land sales, opening and closing of land offices, withdrawal or restoration of land for military reservations, national parks and forests, wildlife refuges, and reservoirs, 1806-1949; "selection" and "adjustment" lists reflecting selection of land for railroads and wagon roads, 1829-1935; monthly abstracts of entries (in WNRC) submitted to the central land office by district land office registers and receivers, 1796-1908; and GLO tractbooks (in WNRC), ca. 1800-1930.

There are records relating to military bounty land warrants (in WNRC), 1788-1855, including Virginia military bounty land warrants used to obtain patents for lands in the Virginia Military District in Ohio and warrants, assignments, identifications, wills, location certificates, and other records concerning the conveyances or locations of warrants granting public lands to veterans and heirs of veterans of the Revolutionary War, the War of 1812, the Mexican War, Indian wars, and frontier skirmishes. Name indexes (in WNRC) for Virginia military warrants and for warrants issued under acts of 1788, 1803, and 1812 are available.

Records relating to the issuance of land scrip (in WNRC), 1830-62, were created under various laws beginning with an act of May 30, 1830, that provided for the exchange of unused military bounty land warrants for scrip that could be traded for public lands. They include exchanged warrants, applications for scrip, scrip stubs, indexes, lists, copies of the scrip issued for warrants, "Agricultural College Scrip" (authorized by an act of July 2, 1862), "Chippewa Halfbreed Scrip" (provided for by a treaty of April 12, 1864), "Choctaw Scrip" (issued under an act of August 23, 1842), and "Surveyor General Scrip" (authorized by an act of July 4, 1836).

Nonmilitary land entry papers (in WNRC), 1788-1951, consist chiefly of records accumulated before the GLO issued patents for entries (including cash and credit purchases, preemption entries, and entries under the Graduation Act, Homestead Act, Timber Culture Act, Timber and Stone Act, and Desert Land Act) made under general land laws. These case files usually include financial records; records showing successive steps taken before a patent was issued; records containing claimant's age, residence, and citizenship; and land descriptions, information concerning land improvements, and records concerning uses of land required by various laws.

Records concerning private land claims (claims originating in grants or other concessions from governments possessing sovereignty over territory that later became part of the United States) include extensive docket files for claims in California, Louisiana, Mississippi, and elsewhere, 1803-1908 (with some material dated as late as 1951), containing survey notes, transcripts of court proceedings, reports, correspondence, plats, and other records concerning administrative review and final adjudication of claims by the Washington office. Records, 1803-60, of special boards appointed to accumulate evidence and settle claims—especially those whose work covered areas now in Alabama, Mississippi, and California—include records of the Office of the Surveyor General of California, concerning the rancho period in California and consisting of "complete expedientes" (1-579), "incomplete expedientes" (1-315), transcripts and translations of documents for cases 1-809 presented to the Board of California Land Claims Commissioners to support titles, a journal and minutes of Board proceedings, and lists or indexes to land grants, 1852-56. Records relating to private land claims in Florida include warrants and survey plats, chiefly about British private grants, 1824-98; a few records of the Governor and Council of West Florida, 1770-79; and reports, correspondence, and lists concerning the Spanish archives of East and West Florida and the attempts by the Department of the Interior to trace and acquire them, 1848-98.

Records relating to Federal townsites, 1888-1925, with indexes, include minutes, deed applications, contest records, accounts, and diagrams of the boards of townsite trustees established (particularly in Oklahoma and Alaska) to subdivide sites and sell townlots under supervision of the GLO Commissioner; and docket files of the GLO Washington office containing reports, correspondence, plats, and diagrams of townsites.

Files concerning abandoned military reservations and some nonmilitary reservations, such as lighthouses and lifesaving stations, 1822-1937, with an index, include Executive orders, correspondence, title papers, plats, maps, blueprints, and tracings that document the GLO's role in the creation of military reservations from public lands and its responsibility for the disposal of reservations abandoned by the War and Navy Departments.

Other records relating to disposal of public lands include school selection and school indemnity selection lists and other records concerning grants to States for schools and other purposes, 1826-1938; reports, correspondence, and other records relating to swamp lands granted to States, 1849-1909; "Indian Reserve files" (in WNRC) relating to Indian allotment applications for land, 1839-1916, with a register, 1855-1916; "canal and reservoir grants," with an index, relating to lands granted under an act of March 3, 1891, to provide irrigation, 1891-1922; "railroad rights-of-way files," 1878-1931, concerning rights-of-way to cross public lands granted railroads under an act of March 3, 1875; and "reclamation project files" relating to projects created on public lands for reclamation purposes, 1901-45.

Records of GLO units concerned with public land disposals include letters sent by the Recorder's ("B") Division, concerning patents, 1817-1908; letters sent by the Public Lands ("C") Division, relating to public land disposals, 1796-1908; records of the Private Land Claims ("D") Division, concerning private land claims, 1788-1909; letters sent by the Railroad, Rights-of-Way, and Reclamation ("F") Division, concerning lands granted for railroads, canals, and reservoirs, 1856-1909; letters sent by the Pre-Emption ("G") Division, relating to preemption and grants to States for schools, townsites, and other State selections, 1832-1908; letters sent by the Homestead Contests ("H") Division, 1887-1908, and the Indian and Swamp Land ("K") Division, 1849-1908; records relating to accounting and financial matters of the Accounting ("M") Division, 1853-1908; letters sent by the Mineral Contest ("N") Division, 1844-1908; records of the Forestry ("R") Division, relating to use of military bounty land warrants and scrip on the public domain, 1788-1908; dockets (in WNRC) relating chiefly to contests concerning mineral lands and railroad land grants that conflicted with private entries, 1870-1909; and Field Service Division case files and trespass cases (in WNRC), 1910-49.

There are also records of closed district land offices, including records relating to ceded Chickasaw land, 1823-1908, and reports, correspondence, and other records, 1820-1919, of land offices in Mississippi; records of offices in Missouri and Arizona, including applications to purchase land in Missouri, 1818-1908; correspondence of the office at Gainesville, Fla., 1932-33; and local office tractbooks (in WNRC), ca. 1800-1935.

RECORDS RELATING TO MANAGEMENT OF THE PUBLIC DOMAIN. 1818-1946. 40 lin. ft.

Included are a journal and correspondence of James L. Cathcart and James Hutton, agents appointed under an act of March 1, 1817, to report on the public lands reserved to supply timber for naval purposes, 1818-19; a reports register of special (timber) agents, 1882-1903; correspondence, permits and leases, lists of mineral lands, and accounting records of War Department officers in charge of leasing lead and copper land in Illinois, Wisconsin, and Michigan, 1824-47 (chiefly for the period after 1842, when most of these lands were ceded by the Chippewa Indians); correspondence, accounting records, contracts, maps, and related records of the GLO Washington office, 1897-1938, and the Office of the Superintendent of Logging at Cass Lake, Minn., 1903-38, relating to logging on Chippewa ceded lands in Minnesota; and records of the Grazing Service, chiefly notices concerning decisions on applications for grazing licenses in New Mexico, Oregon, Utah, and Wyoming, 1935-46.

RECORDS RELATING TO ADMINISTRATION. 1813-1950. 125 lin. ft.

Records of the Administrative ("A") Division, established as the Chief Clerk's Office, consist of the records of Divisions "A" and "M," including correspondence relating to GLO operations, 1813-1950; personnel records, 1820-1926; accounting records maintained by Division "M," relating to such special accounts as those for timber depredation, contingent surveying, and Indian and swamp lands, ca. 1813-1909; divisional scrapbooks containing office orders, circulars, memorandums, clippings, and other records, 1904-20; appointment notices to registers and receivers, 1841-44; circulars sent, 1850-54; and letters sent by the receiving clerk, 1871-1910.

Office files of the associate director, 1938-47, and of the Chief of Division "A," 1924-47; investigation files concerning oil shale lands, maintained by the chief of the GLO field division at Denver, 1920-33; and "stock driveway files" relating to public lands in the Western States used as stock driveways or trails, 1916-50.

RECORDS OF STATE OFFICES OF THE BUREAU OF LAND MANAGEMENT. 1851-1961. 2,468 lin. ft.

Included are letters sent and received by State offices and suboffices, reports of special agents, registers of homestead receipts, records of agricultural surveys, and plats for the following State offices: Arizona, 1860-1960, and California, 1853-1961 (in FRC Los Angeles); Oregon, 1851-1946 (in FRC Seattle); and Utah, 1855-1957, and Wyoming (including suboffices at Cheyenne, Douglas, Evanston, Lander, and Sundance), 1867-1946 (in FRC Denver).

CARTOGRAPHIC AND AUDIOVISUAL RECORDS. 1785-1966. 114,451 items.

GLO mapping activities included platting townships from field survey data and reproducing the plats for official and public use, compiling maps to show the extent of surveys and other data concerning management of the public domain, and maintaining maps and plats prepared for GLO operations as well as those submitted for rights-of-way grants through public lands.

Cartographic records, 1785-1966 (114,351 items), consist of Division "B" plats of townships in California, Colorado, Oregon, Idaho, Montana, New Mexico, Wyoming, and South Dakota, showing mines and mining claims and, in some instances, patent numbers and dates and survey and document numbers, 1872-96; Division "E" records include manuscript and annotated maps (the "old map file") showing development and disposal of public lands in the United States and in individual States and territories, 1790-1946; field notes and related textual records (the "old case F file") of State, territorial, and Indian-land boundaries, 1809-72; manuscript plats and diagrams of Indian lands and boundaries in Kansas, 1857-65, the Indian Territory, 1856-92, and Indiana, Michigan, and Ohio, 1807-49; plats and field notes for townsites, city parks, cemeteries, and Government properties in public land States; township plats showing naval timber reserve requirements in Alabama, Florida, Louisiana, and Mississippi, and public land withdrawals in California, Colorado, Montana, and New Mexico, 1908-31; and plats of private land claims in Arizona, California, Colorado, Florida, New Mexico, Louisiana, Illinois, and Missouri, 1853-1915. Most manuscript plats and field notes from the original public land surveys are in the custody of the Bureau of Land Management, but Division "E" records also include plats and field notes from the survey of the seven ranges in Ohio (the first public land survey), 1785-87. Also included among Division "E" records are plats of township surveys made by deputy surveyors supervised by a surveyor general, including headquarters plats for Illinois, Indiana, Iowa, Kansas, Missouri, and Ohio, 1785-1946;

and local office plats for Alabama, Indiana, Iowa, Kansas, Mississippi, Missouri, Wisconsin, Ohio, the Indian Territory, and Washington, 1803-91. Some of the local office plats include land entry numbers and entrymen's names.

Included are Division "F" manuscript and annotated maps (the signed copies authorizing companies to construct facilities on public lands) showing railroad land grants and rights-of-way through public lands for railroads, military and other wagon roads, canals, irrigation ditches, transmission lines, reservoirs, and quarries, 1851-1939.

There are Division "K" township plats and diagrams of lands on Indian reservations that show the classification and status of lands offered for settlement, 1904-31.

The map file of Division "N" consists of survey plats of mineral claims in Alabama, Alaska, Arizona, Arkansas, California, Colorado, Idaho, Montana, Nevada, New Mexico, Oregon, South Dakota, Utah, Washington, and Wyoming, 1872-1908.

Cartographic records prepared by the Grazing Service include maps and diagrams of grazing districts in Arizona, Colorado, and New Mexico, 1934-45. Also included are the Bureau of Land Management's published atlas of Alaska, showing Federal land withdrawals and reservations, 1952; and detailed maps and aerial survey photoprints, with photo-index negatives and prints, of the Louisiana coastline, 1953-57.

Audiovisual records (100 items) consist of photographs of the opening of the Cherokee Strip, Oklahoma Territory, 1893; and photographs relating to the ecologic survey of Ferry Lake, Caddo Parish, La., 1914.

See Harry P. Yoshpe and Philip P. Brower, comps., *Preliminary Inventory of the Land-Entry Papers of the General Land Office*, PI 22 (1949); Laura E. Kelsay, comp., *List of Cartographic Records of the General Land Office*, SL 19 (1964);

and Kelsay and Charlotte M. Ashby, comps., *Cartographic Records Relating to the Territory of Wisconsin, 1836-1848*, SL 23 (1970).

Microfilm Publications: For a complete listing see the current *List of National Archives Microfilm Publications.*

RECORDS OF THE BUREAU OF INDIAN AFFAIRS
(RECORD GROUP 75)

The Bureau of Indian Affairs was established in 1824 within the War Department, which from the establishment of the Federal Government had exercised jurisdiction over Indian affairs in their civilian aspects. Known as the Office of Indian Affairs until 1947 when it was officially designated the Bureau of Indian Affairs, it operated informally within the War Department from 1824 until 1832 when the Congress authorized appointment of a Commissioner of Indian Affairs. In 1849 the Bureau was transferred from the War Department to the newly created Department of the Interior.

The Bureau of Indian Affairs is responsible for most of the Federal Government's relations with Indians, including their economic development, education, and legal rights. The Bureau's responsibility has, however, never extended to all Indians, but only to Indians living on reservations or maintaining their tribal affiliation in some manner. Some tribes, particularly in the East, have been under State rather than Federal authority. The Indians and Eskimos of Alaska came under the Bureau's jurisdiction in 1931 with the transfer to the Bureau of the Alaska Division of the Office of Education, which had been established in 1885 to administer matters relating to the education and health of natives of Alaska. In 1955 the Bureau's health activities, including those in Alaska, were transferred to the Public Health Service.

In 1824 the Bureau inherited a well-established system of Indian superintendencies and agencies, and the basic organizational structure has remained unchanged. The Bureau now consists of the central office, area offices, and field installations including Indian agencies, boarding schools, and irrigation projects.

There are 16,329 cubic feet of records dated between 1794 and 1967 in this record group.

RECORDS OF THE OFFICE OF THE SECRETARY OF WAR RELATING TO INDIAN AFFAIRS. 1800-1824. 3 lin. ft.

Although most records of the Office of the Secretary of War relating to Indian affairs were transferred to the Bureau after 1824, some correspondence dated between 1800 and 1824 remained with the records of the Office of the Secretary of War (see RG 107). Records dated before November 1800 were destroyed by a fire in the War Department. Letters received, 1800-1823, concern negotiations of Indian treaties, land reserves of individual Indians, mission schools, Government trading posts, issue of licenses, and distribution of annuities. Letters sent, 1800-1824, include copies of addresses to Indian delegations, appointments, passports issued for travel in Indian country, and instructions to treaty commissioners.

RECORDS OF THE OFFICE OF INDIAN TRADE. 1795-1824. 27 lin. ft.

The Office of Indian Trade was formally established in 1806, although two Government trading houses had begun operating in 1795 among the Creek and Cherokee Indians. An act of April 18,

1796, which was reenacted from time to time with slight changes until 1822, authorized the President to establish Government trading houses or factories, and some 28 factories were in existence at different times under this system. Headquarters for supplying the factories and for receiving furs and peltries was at Philadelphia, and the system was operated mainly through the facilities of the War Department. In 1806 provision was made for a Superintendent of Indian Trade, who maintained a warehouse in Georgetown, D.C., and was responsible for purchasing and transporting goods to the factories until the system was abolished in 1822.

There are records of the Office and individual factories. Most of the Office records are for the period after its removal to Georgetown in 1807. They include letters received, 1806–24, letters sent, 1807–30, and accounting records. There are records, chiefly accounting records, for the following factories: Arkansas, 1805–10, Belle Fontaine, 1805–9, Cherokee (Tellico and Hiwassee), 1796–1810, Chicago, 1805–22, Chickasaw Bluffs, 1806–18, Choctaw, 1803–25, Creek, 1795–1820, Detroit, 1802–4, Fort Edwards, 1818–23, Fort Madison, 1808–15, Fort Wayne, 1804–12, Green Bay, 1815–23, Mackinac (Michilimackinac), 1808–12, Natchitoches-Sulphur Fort, 1806–23, Osage, 1808–23, Prairie du Chien, 1818–22, Sandusky, 1806–12, and Spadre Bluffs (Illinois Bayou), 1818–24. A few records of other Government units and some private records are intermingled with these.

GENERAL CORRESPONDENCE AND OTHER RECORDS OF THE BUREAU. 1801–1939. 14,007 lin. ft.

The general correspondence files document all aspects of the Bureau's functions and, in almost every instance, contain materials relevant to divisional records. Throughout the period 1824–1907 the basic records of the Bureau were maintained in separate series of incoming and outgoing correspondence. For the period 1824–80 the incoming records are arranged by field jursidictions and by special subjects. From 1881 until 1907 incoming letters and reports were filed as records of the Land Division and of the Education and other Divisions. Letter books of letters sent, 1824–86, comprise one chronological series. The Commissioner's reports to the Secretary of War appear in the series before 1838, but thereafter the reports to the Secretary of War and the Secretary of the Interior are in separate volumes, 1838–85. With the introduction of the letterpress, press copies were separately maintained by divisions; there are copies, ca. 1870–1908, for the Land, Civilization, Depredation, Finance, Accounts, Medical and Educational, Education, and Miscellaneous Divisions. After the system of classified files was inaugurated in 1907, copies of outgoing letters were placed in these files, but in addition a straight chronological file of outgoing letters, 1900–1936, was maintained. Since these letters were duplicated in the central classified files only a sample has been retained. Most of the correspondence dated between 1907 and 1939 was filed according to a decimal-subject classification system. Letters sent, letters received in reply, and other records relating to the same subject were filed with the initial incoming letter to form a dossier or file. Records in these central classified files were grouped as follows: records relating to the central office of the Bureau ("Indian Office"); general administrative records ("General Service"); and records relating to individual field units of the Bureau, with a few subject designations arranged alphabetically by name of jurisdiction or subject. In 1936 a numerical subject classification scheme known as the Shaeffer, or "New," System was adopted, but the following year the decimal classification system was restored.

Many incoming letters were removed from the general files and filed separately in other series or groupings of Bureau records. Certain incoming letters and papers relating chiefly to claims and investigations were separated and maintained in 303 special files, 1807–1904. Some of the most important documents relating to problems at particular reservations or in connection with certain tribes or persons were placed in 203 special case files, 1821–1907. They concern such matters as railroad rights-of-way, cattle and timber trespass, logging, special claims, schools, contracts, surveys, unathorized settlement, and the sale of liquor. A similar group of segregated records, identified as special series A, ca. 1859–1934, consists of correspondence, records of the Land and Inspection Divisions, special reports, materials prepared for congressional hearings, and related records concerning land matters, heirship cases, claims, personnel matters, estimates, enrollments, investigations, and schools.

Some correspondence concerning negotiation of Indian treaties was filed with related journals, council proceedings, reports and other records in a ratified treaty file, 1801–68, and an unratified treaty file, 1821–69. Correspondence, maps, and other records concerning Executive orders relating to Indian reservations, 1850–92, were also segregated. "Authorities," comprising letters from the Secretary of the Interior or his representative authorizing actions that usually concerned expenditures, were registered and indexed separately from other incoming correspondence and were assigned their own series of numbers. The indexes and registers are among the records.

Also filed separately are copies of orders and circulars issued and replies received by the Bureau. A separate series of indexes and registers, 1877–1907, was maintained for incoming letters that constituted claims against the

Bureau and contracts made by Bureau officials. The claims for this period were destroyed by authority of the Congress while the records were still in Bureau custody. A series of volumes identified as Miscellaneous Records, 1836–87, contains copies of commissions, treaties, regulations, reports, memorandums, circular letters, and public notices; lists of employees, schools, contracts, land locations, patentees, claimants, and population figures; and statements of funds and other financial information.

OFFICE RECORDS OF BUREAU OFFICIALS. 1837–1950. 21 lin. ft.

These comprise chiefly letters sent, memorandums, and miscellaneous documents dating from 1837 and include the office file of Commissioner of Indian Affairs John Collier, 1933–45, and some records of the Chief Clerk, assistant commissioners of Indian affairs, 1935–50, assistants to the Commissioner, 1935–41, the finance officer, and the chief administrative officer.

RECORDS RELATING TO INDIAN REMOVAL. 1817–1906. 45 lin. ft.

Indian removal to an Indian Territory west of the Mississippi River became an explicit policy during the administration of President Andrew Jackson. A number of treaties were negotiated whereby tribes agreed to give up their lands in the East and move west. All the treaties contained provisions for compensating the Indians for their land and property. The actual work of removal was assigned to the Office of the Commissary General of Subsistence in the War Department, but private companies managed some of the removals.

Most of the records relate to the removal of the Five Civilized Tribes, though there are a few documents concerning the removal of Indians from the Old Northwest. Many of the records relate not to actual removal but to the enforcement of those provisions of treaties concerning reservations in the East and compensation of Indians for losses.

The records include reports, correspondence, contracts, and financial records of the Commisssary General of Subsistence who, before October 1836, furnished transportation, rations, rifles, and other articles specified by removal treaties. The Cherokee removal records include a register of Cherokees who wished to remain in the East, 1817-19, eastern Cherokee census rolls, 1835-84, emigration rolls, 1817-38, and records of four boards of commissioners established to adjudicate claims. The Chickasaw removal records include letters sent, 1832-61, census and muster rolls, 1837-39, and land location and sale records under articles of the treaty of 1834. Records relating to Choctaw removal include census rolls for 1831 and 1856, emigration lists, 1831-57, land reserve and land sale records, records of commissions appointed to adjudicate claims under articles of the treaty of 1830, and some statements and schedules dated as late as 1906. The Creek removal records include a census, 1833, emigration lists, 1836-38, an index to Creek land reserves and land location registers, and records concerning the sales of Creek lands and of a commission appointed to investigate reports of frauds in the sale of Creek lands.

Records relating to the removal of other tribes consist of muster rolls of the Apalachicola and Seminole, Kickapoo, New York, Ottawa, Potawatomi, Quapaw, and Wyandot Indians.

RECORDS OF THE LAND DIVISION. 1797-1967. 534 lin. ft.

These consist of general records, including registers, 1855-80, and indexes, 1881-96, to letters received and docket books for the Five Civilized Tribes, 1897-1910; surveying and allotting records, 1797-1919; platbooks, 1858-1923, allotment schedules, 1856-1935, and allotment records, 1856-89, of the Chippewa of Lake Superior and the Mississippi, the Red Lake and Pembina Chippewa mixed bloods, the Indians of Michigan, and the mixed bloods allotted on the Nemeha Half-breed Reserve, 1856-89; land sale and lease records, including appraisements, 1844-1922, schedules of appraisements and reports, and records, 1861-85, relating to certificates of indebtedness for the Kansa (Kaw), Sauk and Fox of the Mississippi, Osage, and Winnebago Indians; records relating to the disposal of the Cherokee neutral lands, 1866-89, and to trust lands for the Chippewa and Munsee, the Kaw, the Confederated Kaskaskia, Peoria, Piankeshaw, Wea, and Iowa, the Kickapoo, Omaha, Osage, Ottawa, Pawnee, Potawatomi, Sauk and Fox of the Mississippi and the Missouri, and the Winnebago Indians, 1857-1900; records concerning removals of restrictions on land sales and certificates of competency; patent, deed, and land lease records, 1855-1967; land reserve files comprise chiefly correspondence and legal documents relating to lands reserved by treaty or law for individual Indians, 1825-1907; Choctaw Net Proceeds Case records, 1875-98; military bounty land records, 1855-82; Indian Civil War military service claims, 1865-90; claims of white settlers evicted from the Crow, Creek, and Winnebago Reservations, 1890-1900; and Sioux property and allotment claims records, 1891-1946.

There are enrollment records prepared in connection with land matters, including registers of Indian families of certain tribes; records, 1828-32, relating to the enrollment of California Indians authorized by an act of May 18, 1928; records relating to Cherokee citizenship and to enrollment of the eastern Cherokee, Choctaw Freedmen, Mississippi Choctaw, Flathead, Osage, Ottawa in Kansas, Stockbridge and Munsee, and Indians of Washington State; applications and records concerning registration under the Indian Reorganization

Act of 1934; and rolls for revisions of names of Indians at several agencies in North Dakota, South Dakota, and Montana.

Other records of the Division relate to the right of attorneys to represent claimants before the Department of the Interior and its bureaus, 1876-1907, concern bonds and banks, 1904-24, or constitute miscellaneous reference material.

RECORDS OF THE LAW AND PROBATE DIVISIONS AND PREDECESSORS. 1848-1923. 14 lin. ft.

The Law Office was established in 1908 under the supervision of a law clerk, formerly of the Land Division, and by 1911 was usually referred to as the Law Division. In 1913 the Heirship Section of the Land Division was transferred to the Law Division, which thereafter was chiefly concerned with probate work, and by 1917 was known as the Probate Division.

The records of these Divisions comprise letters sent, 1907-13; Indian wills, 1911-21; reports of examiners of inheritance, 1919-23; court decisions, 1904-12; opinions of the Attorney General, 1848-66, the Comptroller, and other officials, 1911-23; probate work and appropriation reference notes and material, 1911-23; and acts of the Congress, 1867-1917, relating to Indian administration.

RECORDS OF THE IRRIGATION DIVISION. 1891-1946. 129 lin. ft.

The Irrigation Division was established in 1924, but administrative units concerned with irrigation had been set up in the Bureau much earlier. Most of the correspondence concerning Indian irrigation activities before 1924 was handled by the Office of the Chief Engineer, established by an act of March 3, 1905. The Office of the Chief Engineer was located in Los Angeles until 1912 when it was moved to Washington, D.C.

The records of the Division, its prede-

cessors, and the Office of the Chief Engineer include miscellaneous reports and related records prepared by Bureau officials and other agencies, such as the Bureau of Reclamation, 1891-1946; Chief Engineers' annual reports, 1908-24 and 1932; annual district and project reports, 1908-40; monthly progress reports, 1907-35; general correspondence, 1901-31; and a small quantity of photographs and maps.

RECORDS OF THE FORESTRY DIVISION. 1908-44. 6 lin. ft.

The Forestry Division was not formally established until 1924. Fragmentary records relating primarily to timber surveys and valuations are chiefly those of predecessor units. Most of the reports, correspondence, and other records concerning forestry are in the central classified files of the Bureau. Among Division records are reports of inspection and appraisal of timberlands on the Flathead Reservation, 1908-9, field notebooks relating to an examination of the Red Lake Reservation, 1909-10, plats of the Spokane Reservation, 1910, and forestry reports for the Menominee agency, 1907-44.

RECORDS OF THE CIVILIZATION DIVISION. 1800-1882. 4 lin. ft.

Established in 1846 as one of the original Divisions of the Bureau, the Civilization and General Statistics Division maintained information concerning Indian population, tribal wealth, missionary establishments, traders, and advancement in agricultural and mechanical arts and in schools and education. Later, responsibility for matters concerning depredation claims, conduct of the Indians, liquor control, intrusions on Indian lands, and field personnel was added. In 1881 educational matters came under its jurisdiction, and in 1885 it became the Education Division with all of its noneducational responsibilities assigned to other divisions. Since its records were transferred to the divisions inheriting its functions, the records of the Civilization Division are fragmentary.

The records consist primarily of miscellaneous documents, among which are some census rolls, 1835–69, population figures, 1800–1853, investigative records of the Fort Phil Kearney (or Fetterman) massacre, 1867, correspondence relating to the Ute Commission appointed to supervise the removal of the Ute Indians in Colorado to a new reservation, 1881–82, and Civil War claims of loyal Indians driven from their homes or who suffered property damage, 1866–70.

RECORDS OF THE DEPREDATION DIVISION. 1835–96. 28 lin. ft.

The Division was established in October 1885 to investigate claims against the Indians for depredations. In 1891 the investigation and determination of the Indian depredation claims were transferred to the United States Court of Claims. The Depredation Division continued to answer inquiries and to service records until it was abolished in 1893. The records include registers of depredation claims, 1862–91, docket books, 1885–91, evidence concerning depredation claims, 1835–96, and records relating to claims for depredations committed by the Sioux Indians in Minnesota in 1862.

RECORDS OF THE EDUCATION DIVISION. 1859–1947. 180 lin. ft.

Established in 1885 to replace the Civilization and Education (Civilization) Division, this Division was responsible for school administration, agricultural and mechanical training, matters concerning law and order (including liquor suppression), and health and sanitation. The Division by 1914 consisted of Employees, Law and Order, Health, Schools, Industries, Construction, and Statistics Sections. In 1926 the Education Division was designated the Administrative Division and was abolished in 1931, the Schools Section of the Adminis-

trative Division having become the Education Division in 1930.

The records of the Administrative and Education Divisions relate to school and educational activities; records relating to other activities of the two divisions were transferred to new divisions or other units when those units were separated from the Education and Administrative Divisions. Exceptions are certain records of the Industries and Law and Order Sections. Also included are records of the Civilization Division and the Medical and Educational Division (established in 1873 and consolidated with the Civilization Division in 1881). Most of the Division's general records comprise periodic school attendance reports, 1910–39, and annual school census reports, 1912–39. Also included are indexes and registers for letters received by the Education Division; a register of letters received by the Medical and Educational Division, 1878–81; indexes to letters received by the Superintendent of Indian Schools, 1895–1907; circulars, 1897–1909; authorities, 1902–5; office files of several Division officials, including the Chief Supervisor of Education and General Superintendent, 1910–27, and the Director of Education, 1931–35; various statistical compilations, 1859–1910; school calendars, 1930–34; and miscellaneous reports, memorandums, and other records.

Records of the Industries Section, 1910–29, consist of reports of industrial surveys, 1922–29, and some reports concerning graduates of Indian schools, 1914–16, and former students, 1910–25. Records of the Law and Order Section, 1908–47, include the chief special officer's general correspondence, 1933–47, his correspondence with special officers, 1933–47, and his correspondence relating to the use of peyote, 1908–11 and 1915–18. There are case reports relating chiefly to liquor law violations, 1923–33, and some weekly narrative reports of special officers and deputies, 1915–17.

RECORDS OF THE HEALTH DIVISION. 1923-43. 53 lin. ft.

The Health Division was established in 1924 to conduct health activities formerly handled by the Education Division. From July 1924 until 1931 it was called the Medical Division. The records consist chiefly of periodic statistical and narrative reports, 1925-43 (submitted by physicians, dentists, and field matrons and nurses), and hospital reports, 1923-38; reports of health surveys of the Eastern Cherokee of North Carolina, 1933, the Potawatomi of Kansas, 1928, the Indians of the Fort Totten Agency, N. Dak., 1929, and of the Zuni Reservation, N. Mex., 1934; and some reports relating to examinations and treatments for trachoma.

RECORDS OF THE DIVISION OF EXTENSION AND INDUSTRY. 1930-53. 24 lin. ft.

Established December 5, 1930, as a successor to the Industries Section of the Administrative (Education) Division, this Division first was known as the Division of Agricultural Extension and Industry, but it was often called the Extension Division. It was organized to assist the Indians in solving domestic and economic problems through instruction and guidance classes, demonstrations, visits, and work supervision. Agricultural extension agents or the agency superintendents supervised the work at the agencies.

The records include the Director's annual reports, 1932-39, periodic narrative and statistical reports and correspondence, 1930-34; annual reports and work programs, 1934-43; and records relating to a social and economic survey, 1933-34, a land use survey, 1934-35, noxious weed surveys, 1932 and 1941, and the Alaska Reindeer Service, 1939-42 and 1950-53.

RECORDS OF THE ALASKA DIVISION. 1877-1940. 161 lin. ft.

This Division was established in 1885 in the Office of Education chiefly to supervise the education of Eskimo and Indian children in Alaska, but its duties were not limited to educational matters. Its representatives served as law-enforcement agents, collected data for Government agencies, directed the Alaska Reindeer Service, and supplied medical aid to the natives. In 1931 the Division was transferred from the Office of Education to the Office of Indian Affairs.

The records from both Offices include letters received, 1883-1907, and sent, 1877-1908; correspondence files, 1908-35, with a separate file relating to the Metlakahtla Controversy, 1897-1931; budget and accounting records; reports and statistical records, including some periodic school reports, 1933-40; a reference file of the Assistant Chief of the Division, 1888-1926; newspaper clippings, 1897-1908; photographic negatives and prints, 1894-1932; and a file on Alaskan school matters, 1886-89.

RECORDS OF THE FINANCE DIVISION. 1817-1949. 501 lin. ft.

The Finance Division, one of the original divisions organized in 1846, was responsible for administrative examination of accounts, appropriations, remittances, stock investments, settlement of claims, and generally for all matters involving expenditure of money for or on account of Indians. The records, created by several divisions involved in financial matters, concern affairs of the Mexican Kickapoo, 1895-1914; appropriation ledgers, 1837-1921; liability registers, 1901-16; tabular statements of funds remitted to field officials, 1870-1908; appropriation warrants, estimates, statements, and vouchers; accounts; contracts and bonds, 1836-77; claim records, 1921-35; and records concerning claims of traders, 1819-64, and the Kansas claims of New York Indians, 1901-7. Records concerning tribal and individual moneys and payments to Indians include annuity payment rolls, 1841-1949; rolls compiled for payments made to the Old Settler Cherokee, the Cherokee freedmen, self-emigrant Creeks, and citizen Potawatomi; and a list of Sioux scouts, soldiers, and heirs, 1892. There are also records concerning Indian trust funds, 1837-1909, and a few miscellaneous documents, including a ledger for the centennial exhibition, a journal of the Ute Indian Commission, 1894-96, and records relating to requisitions, 1817-35.

RECORDS OF THE MISCELLANEOUS DIVISION. 1847-1909. 12 lin. ft.

The Miscellaneous Division was established in 1889 to be responsible for trade with the Indians and for office supplies, duties formerly assigned to the Office of the Assistant Commissioner and, before 1886, the Office of the Chief Clerk. Additional duties were assigned concerning the Bureau library, procurement and distribution of publications, preparation of the *Annual Report of the Commissioner of Indian Affairs*, expositions and exhibitions, office personnel, activities of field matrons, and other matters not assigned to any other division. It was abolished in 1908, and its duties not allocated to one of the other divisions were assigned to the Office of the Chief Clerk.

The records of the Division relate to traders' licenses, including letters received, 1878-80 and 1889-1905, applications, 1892-99, registers, 1847-73 and 1876-82, copies of licenses, 1865-98, and rosters of licensed traders, 1885-1909.

RECORDS OF THE INSPECTION DIVISION. 1873-1948. 148 lin. ft.

Inspectors for the Indian service were first appointed on July 1, 1873, and were responsible to the Commissioner of Indian Affairs until March 25, 1880, when they were placed under the supervision of the Secretary of the Interior. In 1909 an inspection service, under a chief supervisor, was established in the Office of the Commissioner; this service developed into the Inspection Division. All officers not assigned to a particular agency or school were considered to be inspecting officers. No inspectors were actually assigned to the Bureau until 1915 when an inspection force, with a chief inspector and several district inspectors, was established. In 1924 these inspectors were transferred to the Office of the Secretary of the Interior to form part of a new Inspection Division for the entire Department. There continued to be an Inspection Division in the Bureau of Indian Affairs until 1931.

Among the records are inspectors' reports, 1873-80, special agent files, 1907-48, and reports of inspections made at agencies, schools, hospitals, and other facilities, 1908-40.

RECORDS OF THE STATISTICS DIVISION. 1885-1948. 604 lin. ft.

A Statistics Section was organized as part of the Library Section of the Office of the Chief Clerk on March 8, 1909, to handle duties transferred from the Miscellaneous Division. In 1939 the Section, then assigned to the Office of the Finance Officer, was made a Division. It was abolished in 1947.

The Statistics Division processed census rolls, reports, and statistical data, and compiled information for the *Annual Report of the Commissioner of Indian Affairs*. The records of the Division include correspondence concerning reports, 1930-35; superintendents' annual narrative reports, 1910-38, and annual statistical reports, 1920-35; reports and other records, 1933-48, relating to extension activities, land tenure, individual Indian income, land acreage verification, Federal real estate, population and vital statistics, and law and order; and census rolls and supplements, 1885-1940.

RECORDS OF THE EMPLOYEES SECTION. 1833-1940. 45 lin. ft.

The Employees Section, known as the Appointments Section until 1911, was established in the Education Division on March 8, 1909, to handle appointments, transfers, separations, and promotions and other personnel actions of field employees. It was abolished in 1939, and the personnel work of the Bureau was centralized in a Personnel Division. Records of the Section include the pre-1909 records of the Civilization, Accounts, and Education Divisions, concerning employee matters and consisting of registers of applications and recommendations, 1833-68; copies of commissions, 1866-1909; rosters of field employees, 1848-50, superintendents and agents, 1853-63, field officials, 1849-1911, agency employees, 1853-1909, school employees, 1884-1909, and Indian police, 1878-1909; personnel organization (salary) lists, 1912-40; and correspondence concerning personnel, 1930-36 and 1939.

RECORDS OF THE LIBRARY SECTION. 1856-1950. 22 lin. ft.

In 1908 responsibility for the Bureau library was transferred from the Miscellaneous Division to the newly created Library Section in the Office of the Clerk. After the latter was abolished in 1934, the Section was, successively, under the Finance Officer and the Chief Administrative Officer. The records include congressional reports and documents, 1856-1914; correspondence and clippings concerning memorials; a publications file, 1907-50, including copies of *The Native American* and *Indians at Work*; and newspaper clippings.

RECORDS OF THE CONSTRUCTION DIVISION. 1931-43. 73 lin. ft.

The Construction Division was established in 1939, but a predecessor Division had operated from April 1908 until March 1909, when it became the Construction Section of the Education Division. The Division was responsible for construction and repair of schools, hospitals, agency buildings, water and sewerage systems, housing facilities for employees, and heating and power plants. It functioned until about 1948 when it was replaced by the Division of Buildings and Facilities. A single series of records relates to construction work financed by the Public Works Administration and contains reports, correspondence, memorandums, financial documents, photographs, blueprints, and related material, 1931-43.

RECORDS OF THE CIVILIAN CONSERVATION CORPS—INDIAN DIVISION. 1933-44. 98 lin. ft.

The Indian Emergency Conservation Work Division (IECW) was established May 22, 1933, but was renamed Civilian Conservation Corps—Indian Division (CCC-ID) when Emergency Conservation Work became the Civilian Conservation Corps on July 1, 1937. The objectives of the CCC-ID program were to provide employment for Indians and to accomplish useful conservation work. An enrollee program provided training, recreation, and welfare for the Indians. CCC-ID fieldwork was terminated July 10, 1942, but the Washington office continued to operate in order to conclude its affairs. The records include general files, 1933-44, records concerning the enrollee program, 1937-42, narrative and pictorial reports of CCC-ID activities, 1937-42, and some records relating to the magazine *Indians at Work*, 1936-42.

RECORDS OF THE REHABILITATION DIVISION. 1935-44. 25 lin. ft.

The Rehabilitation Division was established in 1936 to carry out an Indian relief and rehabilitation program. Funds were provided through the Work

Projects Administration, the Resettlement Administration, and its successor, the Farm Security Administration. On October 29, 1941, the Rehabilitation Division was consolidated with the Extension Division, but separate records for the Rehabilitation Division were maintained until 1944. The records include general files, 1935-44, project records, 1935-44, and a few pictorial reports, 1936-42.

RECORDS OF THE INDIAN ORGANIZATION DIVISION. 1933-56. 21 lin. ft.

The Indian Organization Division was established in 1934 to supervise the organization of Indian tribes as provided by the Indian Reorganization Act (Wheeler-Howard Act) of June 18, 1934. In 1943 the Division became the Division of Tribal Relations. Included are records concerning the Wheeler-Howard Act, 1933-37, records concerning Indian organization, 1934-56, correspondence, 1934-46, and some questionnaires concerning tribal organization in Alaska, 1934-35.

FIELD OFFICE RECORDS. 1794-1956. 5,698 lin. ft.

These records were created mainly by superintendencies, agencies, and nonreservation schools, most of which were discontinued and their records transferred to Washington, D.C. The kinds of records maintained by the superintendencies and agencies varied little between jurisdictions, although there are great differences in the quantities that survived. For the most part they consist chiefly of correspondence, frequently with indexes and registers to letters received and sent and to financial documents.

There are records for the periods indicated for the following superintendencies: Arizona, 1863-73, Dakota, 1860-78, Idaho, 1863-70, Minnesota, 1849-56, Montana, 1867-79, Nevada, 1869-70, New Mexico, 1849-74, Northern, 1851-76, Oregon, 1848-78, Utah, 1855-70, Washington, 1853-74, Wisconsin, 1836-48, and Wyoming, 1870. Field records of the Central Superintendency, 1813-78, include some records for its predecessors, the Missouri and St. Louis Superintendencies. Records of the Southern Superintendency, 1832-70, include materials for its predecessor, the Western Superintendency, and some of the Arkansas Superintendency and the Wichita Agency, which were established by the Confederacy during the Civil War. Records of the Michigan Superintendency, the Mackinac Agency, and the Sault St. Marie Agency and Subagency, 1814-85, are filed together.

There are field records for the following agencies: Cherokee, East, 1798-1838, Cherokee, West, 1816-19, Chickasaw, 1812-16, Choctaw, East, 1817-21, Consolidated Chippewa, 1913-35, Creek, East, 1794-1818, Green Bay Subagency, 1850, Leech Lake, 1889-1922, Malheur, 1875-82, Moqui Pueblo, 1875-83, Nett Lake, 1908-17, New York, 1938-49, Southern Apache, 1871-78, Union, 1867-1911, and White Earth, 1875-1922. Among the White Earth Agency records are the records of the Chippewa Commission of 1889, established to negotiate with the Chippewa in Minnesota for the cession and relinquishment of certain reservations and the reduction in size of the White Earth and Red Lake Reservations.

There are also field records in archives branches, Federal records centers, for the following agencies and activities: Cherokee (North Carolina), 1889-1952, and Seminole, 1934-50 (in FRC Atlanta); Great Lakes Consolidated, 1869-1950, Keshena, 1879-1953, Menominee, 1873-1945, and Tama, 1896-1943 (in FRC Chicago); Potawatomi, 1851-1942, and Winnebago, 1861-1949 (in FRC Kansas City); Cheyenne Arapaho, 1892-1930, Five Civilized Tribes (Dawes Commission), 1898-1914, Old

Quapaw (Seneca), 1867-1900, and Osage, 1876-1950 (in FRC Fort Worth); Albuquerque Indian School, 1917-36, Division of Forestry and Grazing, 1932-49, Fifth Irrigation District, 1908-36, Fort Lewis Indian School, 1892-1916, Jicarilla, 1890-1952, Mescalero, 1874-1946, Navajo (including Navajo Extension, Northern Navajo, Leupp Training School, Toadlena Day School, Shiprock Boarding School, and Charles H. Burke Indian School), 1884-1952, Pueblo (including Pueblo and Jicarilla, Pueblo Day Schools, Northern Pueblo, Santa Fe Subagency, Southern Pueblo, Laguna Sanatorium, United Pueblo, Pueblo Lands Board, and Departmental Rio Grande Board), 1865-1952, Santa Fe Indian School, 1890-1934, Uintah and Ouray, 1892-1952, Ute, 1878-1952, Wind River, 1873-1952, and Zuni, 1899-1935 (in FRC Denver); Nevada and Northern California agencies, 1864-1930 (in FRC San Francisco); Chinle Subagency, 1938-56, Colorado River, 1867-1950, Fort Apache, 1875-1949, Fort Defiance Subagency, 1880-1939, Hopi, 1907-56, Pala, 1893-1953, Palm Springs, 1937-56, Papago, 1870-1946, Phoenix Area Field Office, 1891-1943, Pima, 1888-1950, Riverside Area Field Office, 1906-56, San Carlos, 1898-1948, Shiprock Subagency, 1936-55, Truxton Canyon Subagency, 1895-1947, Tuba City Subagency, 1915-49, Uintah and Ouray, 1930-54, and Window Rock, 1911-45 (in FRC Los Angeles); and Billings Area Office, 1912-52, Blackfeet, 1875-1952, Chemawa Indian School, 1882-1952, Colville, 1865-1952, Crow, 1877-1952, Flathead, 1875-1952, Fort Belknap, 1878-1952, Fort Hall, 1882-1952, Fort Peck, 1877-1952, Grande Ronde-Siletz, 1863-1952, Juneau Area Office, 1905-52, Klamath, 1865-1952, Northern Cheyenne, 1884-1952, Northern Idaho, 1875-1952, Portland Area Office, 1902-52, Spokane (Wellpinit Subagency), 1885-1950, Umatilla, 1865-1952, Wapato Irrigation Project, 1906-56, Warm Springs, 1900-1952, Western Washington (including Puget Sound,

Tulalip, Taholah, Puyallup, and Near Bay), 1854-1950, and Yakima, 1878-1952 (in FRC Seattle).

The nonreservation schools for which there are records include: the Carlisle Indian Industrial School, 1879-1918, the Chamberlain Indian School, 1901-9, the Fort Shaw Indian School, 1892-1910, the Springfield (Hope) Indian School , 1901-20, and the Wittenburg Indian School, 1895-1917. Some school records are also found among field records of the Leech Lake and White Earth agencies. Most of these nonreservation school records were created at the Carlisle School, but they are very incomplete, with little correspondence and large gaps in other records. Relating chiefly to individual students, they include student record files, 1879-1918, indexes to student records, student record and information cards, enrollment and attendance records, and financial records.

Miscellaneous field records consist of correspondence of Special Commissioner to the Navajo Indians Herbert J. Hagerman, 1923-32, and a special agent. There is also a cashbook of the industrial teacher and special disbursing agent for the Seminole in Florida.

RECORDS OF THE BOARD OF INDIAN COMMISSIONERS. 1869-1933. 35 lin. ft.

The Board of Indian Commissioners was established June 3, 1869, and given the right to inspect records of the Bureau of Indian Affairs, to visit and inspect superintendencies and agencies, to be present when goods were purchased for the Indian Service, and to inspect goods and make recommendations on matters concerning administration of Indian affairs. In its later years the Board limited its activities chiefly to inspections and surveys and to making recommendations. It was abolished by an Executive order of May 25, 1933. Its records include minutes, 1869-1933, letters received, 1869-99, letters sent, 1870-91 and 1893-1909, general correspondence, 1899-1933, special reports, 1915-33, reports of the Pueblo Lands Board, 1925-31, and reference material.

OTHER RECORDS. 1794-1941. 169 lin. ft.

Other records include those of the Indian Arts and Crafts Board, concerning a 1941 exhibit of Indian art at the Museum of Modern Art in New York City, 1939-41; a Revenue Office letter book, 1794-96, relating to the Treasury business of the War Department, which contains some information about purchase of goods for Indians; a calendar of papers relating to the Black Hawk War; a record of the distribution of Henry R. Schoolcraft's *Historical and Statistical Information Respecting the History, Condition, and Prospects of the Indian Tribes of the United States;* and a set of index cards identified as a "Biographical and Historical Index of American Indians and Persons Involved in Indian Affairs," which was published in eight volumes by the G. K. Hall Co.

CARTOGRAPHIC RECORDS. 1800-1944. 37,779 items.

The central map file of the Bureau consists of four series of maps. The maps in the first two series, numbered by the Bureau from 1 to 13,799, contain information about Indians and Indian lands, 1800-1939. The third series consists of small-scale administrative maps, 1878-1941. The maps in the fourth series are the record set of published maps of Indian reservations, 1908-44. The map file of the Irrigation Division includes maps of Indian reservations relating to allotments, irrigation projects, cultivated areas, canals and ditches, and classification, 1872-1943. The map file of the Forestry Branch consists of fire control maps relating to ranger and fireguard stations, lookout stations, and reserved lands, 1920-44. The Realty Branch map

file contains township plats relating to land disposition within reservations, 1846-1937.

AUDIOVISUAL RECORDS. 1862-1959. 13,810 items.

There are photographs, 1862-1959 (13,797 items), relating to almost all aspects of the work of the Bureau of Indian Affairs, including activities and facilities at the agencies and on the reservations and Bureau personnel; and to the lives of American Indians, including family groups, farms, homes, schools, and hospitals. They show Indian living conditions, customs, dress, dances, industry, and service in the Armed Forces; irrigation projects on Indian reservations, 1919; industrial progress of Indians in Arizona, 1922; Indian conferences in Minnesota, Oklahoma, and Montana, 1914-27; the sale of Oklahoma Indian lands, 1919-25; classrooms and activities at Bureau schools, including the Indian Industrial School at Genoa, Nebr., 1910, and the Carlisle, Pa., Indian School, ca. 1914; and health problems and the treatment of tuberculosis in Indians, ca. 1915. There are portrait photographs of individual Indian chiefs and tribal leaders, ca. 1880-96, and members of tribal delegations to the Federal Government, 1872; and watercolors, crayon drawings, and needlework of Indian school pupils, ca. 1926. There are also X-rays of the human body, hand-colored lantern slides used at the Carlisle Indian School, including Dore illustrations of the Bible, scenes from the life of Columbus, illustrations of selected fables and comic stories, scenes in Japan, and black and white slides of historic buildings and sites in England and France. Some of the tribes represented are Sioux, Apache, Delaware, Kiowa, Comanche, Arapaho, Caddo, Wichita, Waco, Keechie, Towoccaroo, Cheyenne, Seminole, Yankton, Blackfoot, Ute, and Navajo.

Motion pictures, 1908-20 (13 reels), illustrate the life, religious customs, dances, and warfare techniques of American Indians; the flag-raising ceremony held on the visits of the Wanamaker Exposition to the tribes; the adoption of Marshal Ferdinand Foch by the Crow; the groundbreaking ceremony for the Indian Memorial in New York, with President William H. Taft and his Cabinet in attendance; the declaration of allegiance made by the tribes on becoming American citizens; the adoption of a Dr. Dixon by the Wolf Clan of the Mohawk Nation Iroquois Confederacy; and Eskimos and their homes and customs.

See Edward E. Hill, comp., *Preliminary Inventory of the Records of the Bureau of Indian Affairs*, PI 163 (2 vols., 1965); Laura E. Kelsay, comp., *List of Cartographic Records of the Bureau of Indian Affairs*, SL 13 (1954); and Kelsay and

Charlotte M. Ashby, comps., *Cartographic Records Relating to the Territory of Wisconsin, 1836-1848*, SL 23 (1970).

Microfilm Publications: Many records relating to Indian affairs are available as microfilm publications, including letters received, 1806-24, and letters sent, 1807-23, by the Superintendent of Indian Trade; letters received, 1800-1823, and letters sent, 1800-1824, by the Secretary of War relating to Indian affairs; letters received by the Office of Indian Affairs relating to various jurisdictions, 1824-80; general letters sent by the Office, 1824-81, and report books, 1838-49; special files, 1807-1904; records relating to the negotiation of ratified and unratified Indian treaties, 1801-1823, periodic Indian census rolls, 1885-1940; and certain special census rolls. Among field office records on microfilm are those of the Cherokee in Tennessee, 1801-35, and the following superintendencies: Arizona, 1863-73, Michigan, 1814-51, New Mexico, 1849-80, Oregon, 1848-73, Southern, 1832-70, and Washington, 1853-74. For a complete listing see the current *List of National Archives Microfilm Publications.*

RECORDS OF THE GEOLOGICAL SURVEY (RECORD GROUP 57)

The Geological Survey was established in the Department of the Interior by an act of March 3, 1879, which provided for "the classification of the public lands and the examination of the geological structure, mineral resources, and products of the national domain." An act of September 5, 1962, expanded this authorization to examinations outside the national domain, while topographic mapping and chemical and physical research were authorized by an act of October 2, 1888. The Survey's chief functions are to survey, investigate, and conduct research on the Nation's topography, geology, and mineral and water resources; classify land according to mineral composition and water and power resources; furnish engineering supervision for power permits and Federal Power Commission licenses; supervise naval petroleum reserves and mineral leasing operations on public and Indian lands; and disseminate data relat-

ing to these activities. Several statutes have provided authorization for publication, sale, and distribution of maps, atlases, monographs, bulletins, water supply papers, and other documents prepared by the Survey.

Upon its establishment the Geological Survey took over some personnel, functions, and records of four earlier surveys. Two of them, the U.S. Geological and Geographical Survey of the Territories (the Hayden Survey), 1867-79, and the U.S. Geographical and Geological Survey of the Rocky Mountain Region (the Powell Survey), 1869-79, operated under the Interior Department. The other two, the U.S. Geographical Surveys West of the One Hundredth Meridian (the Wheeler Survey), 1872-79, and the Geological Exploration of the Fortieth Parallel (the King Survey), 1867-79, operated under the Office of the Chief of Engineers of the War Department. The Geological Survey early initiated irrigation surveys and reclamation planning, but this responsibility was transferred in 1907 to the newly established Bureau of Reclamation. Similarly, the Technologic Branch of the Survey, which had been responsible for technologic, as opposed to geologic, aspects of mineral industries, was transferred in 1910 to the Bureau of Mines. By an Executive order of June 4, 1925, the Mineral Resources Division of the Survey, which since 1882 had compiled and published annual statistics on mineral production, was also transferred to the Bureau of Mines.

The Geological Survey consists of a headquarters organization, most of which is in Washington, D.C., and a field organization made up of separate area offices and their subordinate field offices.

There are 1,480 cubic feet of records dated between 1853 and 1971 in this record group.

RECORDS OF EARLY SURVEYS.
1853-81. 9 lin. ft.

The Hayden Survey, under the direction of Ferdinand V. Hayden, was authorized by an act of March 2, 1867, that provided for a geological survey of Nebraska. This was later extended to all the territories, and work was done in Wyoming, Idaho, Montana, New Mexico, and Colorado. The records include general letters received, 1864-79; letters received from persons in foreign governments, 1853-79, and from Government agencies, 1867-79; personal letters received, 1853-66 and 1872-79; military records, 1867-74; incomplete files of accounting records, 1872-79; and applications for positions and recommendations, 1872-79.

The Powell Survey, under the direction of Maj. John W. Powell, was authorized by an act of July 11, 1868, that ordered the "Secretary of War to issue rations for 25 men of an expedition engaged in exploration of the river Colo-

rado." An act of June 23, 1874, authorized the survey to continue in Utah and extended its activities to the Rocky Mountain region. The records consist of letters received, 1869-79, and letters sent, 1876-79.

The King Survey, under the direction of Clarence King, was authorized by an act of March 2, 1867, that provided for exploration of the territory between the Rocky Mountains and the Sierra Nevada Mountains, including possible routes for the Pacific Railroad. The records include communications received from the Corps of Engineers and the Treasury Department, 1867-70; letters and reports from King to the Chief of Engineers, 1867-79; and letters from the Engineer Department, 1870-81, and the Treasury Department and the Public Printer, 1870-79.

The Wheeler Survey, under the direction of Lt. George M. Wheeler, was authorized by an act of June 1, 1872, to continue "military and geographical surveys and explorations west of the one hundredth meridian." The records consist solely of the handwritten report "Progress Report upon Geographical and Geological Explorations and Surveys West of the 100th Meridian in 1872, under the direction of Brigadier General A. A. Humphreys, Chief of Engineers, by 1st Lieutenant George M. Wheeler, Corps of Engineers, in Charge."

RECORDS OF THE OFFICE OF THE DIRECTOR. 1874-1952.
314 lin. ft.

Included are classified correspondence files, 1912-50, with indexes to letters received, 1918-49; a director's file, 1905-47, relating to Survey administration, policy, and programs; a branch, section, and division reports file, 1900-1912, consisting of annual and monthly reports; personnel data files, 1921-41; office file of the Information Section, 1942-45; and records concerning the work of the vertebrate paleontologist of the Survey, 1882-99. Also records of the Section of Illustrations, including letters sent and reports, 1884-1938, illustrations for professional papers, 1902-38, bulletins, 1884-1948, water supply papers, 1905-48, annual reports, 1882-1932, circulars, 1933-34, monographs, 1890-1915, and other Survey publications, 1874-1925; letters sent by the Editorial Division, 1888-1906; summaries of articles concerning stratigraphy, 1876-1940; letters received by the Division of Engraving and Printing, 1940-48; files accumulated by the staff geologist of territories and island possessions, 1946-52; and records relating to the Federal Interagency River Basin Committee and other interagency committees, 1949.

GENERAL CORRESPONDENCE OF THE GEOLOGICAL SURVEY. 1879-1901. 53 lin. ft.

Included are letters received with registers, 1879-1901, and indexes, 1880-89; letters sent, 1879-95, with indexes, 1879-83; monthly reports, 1882-90; a register of applications for appointment to geologic and ethnologic positions, 1879-86; and a register of communications received and letters sent, 1879-87.

RECORDS OF THE GEOLOGIC DIVISION. 1867-1951. 269 lin. ft.

In 1901 the work of the Geological Survey was decentralized, and thereafter principal records were maintained by various branches. The Geologic Branch, which became a division in 1949, conducted surveys and investigations to determine the distribution, structure, composition, history, interrelationships, and uses of rock and mineral deposits, and carried on research in geologic and related chemical and physical problems.

The records include general correspondence, 1901-51, with an index, 1901-16; a collection of geologists' field notebooks, 1867-1939, consisting of notes, usually in diary form, rough sketches, maps, and diagrams made in the course of geologic investigations or in the examination of individual mines; summaries relating to stratigraphy compiled for the Committee on Geologic Names, 1894-1938; and records relating to the Arkansas bauxite program, 1942-46.

There are also records of the Section of Areal Geology, consisting of correspondence relating to folios for the *Geologic Atlas of the United States*, 1907-20, and records relating to the Section of Western Areal Geology, 1912-16; records of the Mineral Resources Division, including correspondence relating to war activities, 1917-18, a general file, 1918-19, and fiscal records, 1887-88; general records of the Mineral Deposits Branch, 1910-52, relating to chromite deposits, 1941-45, potassium nitrate, 1916-18, potash, 1944-49, and other metals, 1942-46; records relating to western dolomite investigations, 1942-45; records of the Section of Geology of Iron and Aluminum Deposits, including staff correspondence, 1915-45; records of the Fuel Branch, consisting of correspondence concerning fuel development, 1943-48; and records of the Foreign Geology Branch, including a report file on strategic minerals in Brazil, 1941-46, and records concerning the Brazil mica and quartz programs, 1943-45. Also records of Arnold Hague, including a general file of letters, memorandums, and reports, 1881-86; letters received and sent, 1880-1916; records relating to proposed legislation for forest reserves, 1890-97; records concerning meteorology, 1885-87; manuscripts and reference material, 1883-1915; and publications relating chiefly to Yellowstone Park, 1869-1912.

RECORDS OF THE TOPOGRAPHIC DIVISION. 1880-1948. 75 lin. ft.

First organized as a branch in 1889, the Topographic Division was established in 1947. Its records include general correspondence, 1880-1948, reports concerning Forest Service mapping projects, 1934-38, records relating to Work

Projects Administration activities, 1938-41, letters sent regarding public works appointments, 1933-40, memorandums and other records relating to public works projects, 1933-41, correspondence of the engineering consultant, 1938-41, and records of the Map Information Office, comprising those of the Federal Board of Surveys and Maps and other units, 1919-42. Also an office file of Col. Claude H. Birdseye, relating to mapping programs of the Federal Board of Surveys and Maps, 1934-36; correspondence and reports relating to the American Society of Photogrammetry, 1939-41; reports, minutes of meetings, and other records relating to an inter-American cultural conference, 1939-40; and copies of patents, 1929-39.

RECORDS OF THE WATER RESOURCES DIVISION. 1888-1959. 270 lin. ft.

The Water Resources Branch was established in 1906 and became a division in 1949. It studies all aspects of water resources, including surface and ground water and quality, quantity, and utilization of water. Its records include general and administrative correspondence, 1907-58; correspondence with Survey offices, 1931-51, other Federal agencies, 1916-51, and district engineers and field employees, 1910-46; annual narrative and statistical reports, 1933-47, and monthly progress reports, 1934-35; vital records inventories from field offices, 1951; accounting records, 1888-1912; records concerning the Great Falls waterpower project, 1908-11; records relating to cooperation with the Corps of Engineers, 1915-45; and records relating to public works projects, 1933-42. Also records relating to the White Mountain water resources investigation, including field notes and precipitation and hydrographic data, rating tables, graphs, charts, and correspondence, 1909-13; records of the superpower survey, a study of a system for generation and

distribution of electricity between Boston and Washington, D.C., including correspondence, 1920-23, minutes of meetings of the advisory board, 1920-21, and newspaper clippings, 1921-22; records concerning cooperation with State governments, 1903-30; records relating to water supply publications, 1935-40; a published report of the Lake Mead Comprehensive Survey of 1948-49, issued in 1954; and stock water reports and related correspondence, 1942-59.

Records relating to specific investigations of water problems involving States or foreign governments include those relating to the Kootenai River investigations carried out by the International Joint Commission of the United States and Canada, 1934-50; those maintained by Brig. Gen. Hans Kramer as Chairman of the Colorado-Kansas Arkansas River Compact Commission, 1946-49, and as Chairman of and representative of the United States on the Arkansas River Compact Administration, 1949-56; and minutes of the Arkansas River Compact Commission, 1946-48, and the Arkansas River Compact Administration, 1949-55. Closely related are the records of chief hydraulic engineers, 1934-59.

Records of the Surface Water Branch include records relating to the Ohio River special report, 1904-17, stream control data, 1900-1939, a special investigations report file, 1931-48, and records relating to floods, 1935-42. Records of the Quality of Water Branch include records of the chemist in charge, 1913-46; an inventory of analyses of surface waters for irrigation, 1947-48; administrative correspondence relating to field offices and laboratories, 1946-52; and records relating to research and development, 1946-51. Records of the Ground Water Branch include general correspondence and reports, 1920-47; reports of branch and field offices, 1914-42; records concerning public water supplies, 1930-39, and mineral waters, ca. 1895-1930; records of the geologist in charge, relating to the Section of Hydrology of the American Geophysical Union, 1937-48; correspondence relating to the International Union of Geodesy and Geophysics, International Association of Hydrology, 1937-48; and diaries of field trips on Geological Survey business, 1938-44. Records of the Water Utilization Branch include letters sent, 1933-40, and accounting records, 1940-42. Records of the Division of Power Resources include records concerning cooperation of the Geological Survey in Federal Power Commission projects, 1921-42; consular reports regarding foreign water supplies, 1924-38; reports on developed U.S. waterpower, 1921-30, and annual reports concerning developed and potential waterpower, 1923-45; and records relating to the production of electricity, 1919-43.

RECORDS OF THE CONSERVATION DIVISION. 1912-48. 31 lin. ft.

The Conservation Branch was created July 1, 1925, by Survey Order 115, which consolidated the former Land Classification Branch with the Oil Leasing Organization and Mineral Leasing Division transferred from the Bureau of Mines. It became a division in 1949. Its records include administrative correspondence concerning Survey cooperation with other Federal works agencies, 1933-41, reports and a file by State relating to public works projects, 1933-36, an Indian lands file, 1933-37, public utilities annual reports, 1912-48, and records concerning Red River oil operations, 1924-26.

RECORDS OF OTHER DIVISIONS AND BRANCHES. 1888-1952. 4 lin. ft.

Included are records of a branch known as the "Powell Irrigation Survey," consisting solely of abstracts of disbursements for irrigation expenses, 1888-89; records of the Division of Hydrography, including an Irrigation Branch report file, 1890-98; records of expenditures of the Irrigation Branch, 1894-99, an operations ledger, 1901-5, and accounting records, 1897-1906; and records of the Alaskan Branch, including a general file, 1900-1946, relating to activities in Alaska.

OTHER RECORDS. 1917-65. 1 lin. ft.

These consist of records relating to the Geological Survey of the Dominican Republic, 1917-22, and of Haiti, 1917-24; records concerning the President's Commission on Oil Reserves, 1924-27; and minutes of the Compact Committee of the Kansas-Oklahoma Arkansas River Commission, 1956-65.

CARTOGRAPHIC AND AUDIOVISUAL RECORDS. 1868-1971. 77,940 items.

Cartographic records (71,842 items) include manuscript and published topographic, geological, and land use maps of areas in the Western United States from the Hayden and Powell Surveys, 1869-81; administrative maps relating to Survey mapping activities and maps published to accompany annual reports, professional papers, bulletins, and monographs, 1881-1955; manuscript and published river surveys and topographic maps, at varying scales, of areas in the United States and its dependencies, and special maps of States, national parks and forests, military reservations and battlefields, mining districts, and urban areas, 1879-1969; geological maps and maps showing mineral deposits, 1879-1969; published maps and graphs relating to streamflow and the distribution and availability of ground water, 1911-69; published maps and related publications concerning land classification in the Western United States, 1930; aerial photographs and photoindexes principally covering areas in the Northeastern United States, 1938-42; and published topographic maps, at two different scales, of selected areas in Antarctica, 1956-71.

Audiovisual records (6,098 items) include photographs by William H. Jackson and drawings by Henry W. Elliott of the Yellowstone, Grand Teton, and adjacent areas for the Hayden Survey, 1869-83; photographs of E. O. Beaman, J. Fennemore, and John K. Hillers of the Colorado River and adjacent areas for the Powell Survey, 1871-78; photo-graphs by Hillers and others of geological formations in the Carolinas, Georgia, Tennessee, New York, Florida, and along the Potomac River, 1878-86; photographs of the Colorado River and its tributaries made during the Robert Stanton Survey for a railroad route from the Colorado coalfields to the Pacific coast, 1889-90; and aerial mosaic photographs of coastal areas of Louisiana, Alabama, Georgia, Mississippi, and South Carolina, 1934.

RECORDS OF THE FISH AND WILDLIFE SERVICE
(RECORD GROUP 22)

The Fish and Wildlife Service was formed June 30, 1940, by a merger of the Bureau of Fisheries and the Bureau of Biological Survey. The Office of U.S. Commissioner of Fish and Fisheries (often called the U.S. Fish Commission), established February 9, 1871, was transferred to the newly created Department of Commerce and Labor in 1903 and became the Bureau of Fisheries. Regulation of the salmon and fur seal industries in Alaska, a function of the Treasury Department since 1868, also was transferred in 1903 to the new Department and exercised by the Division of Alaskan Fisheries and the Alaska Fur Seal Service, which were merged with the Bureau of Fisheries in 1905 and 1908, respectively. The Bureau of Fisheries was placed in the Department of Commerce in 1913 and was transferred to the Department of the Interior July 1, 1939. On that date the Bureau of Biological Survey, whose function of research in ornithology and mammalogy had originated in the Department of Agriculture in 1885, and which subsequently had become a Bureau charged with general administration of laws to protect wildlife, was also transferred to the Department of the Interior.

The Fish and Wildlife Service is responsible for carrying out plans and administering Federal laws for the control and conservation of fish, game birds, and other forms of wildlife. Since 1937 the Service and its predecessors have supervised an extensive program of Federal aid to the States in wildlife restoration; it also administers national wildlife refuges.

There are 870 cubic feet of records dated between 1868 and 1960 in this record group.

RECORDS OF THE BUREAU OF FISHERIES. 1868-1942.

General Records.   1870-1942. 368 lin. ft. Included are general correspondence and related records comprising letters received, 1870-81, including those from Livingston Stone, who was in charge of U.S. Fish Commission activities on the Pacific coast; letters received, 1882-1900, with related registers and alphabetical indexes, 1882-1917; letters sent, 1871-1906, with registers, 1881-94, and alphabetical indexes, 1882-1906; letters sent by Commissioners G. Brown Goode, 1887-88, and Marshall McDonald, 1888-95; and letters sent by the Office of Engineer and Architect,

1886-1906, relating to construction at field stations.

The records also include part of the general classified files, 1902–42 (earlier material was drawn into central files established in the Bureau in 1937), relating to comments and criticisms, emergency relief, conservation, black bass and angling, whaling operations, and inspections; station histories, 1875-1931, consisting chiefly of correspondence relating to construction, operation, and termination of field stations; records relating to legislation and legal questions, 1892-1937; records concerning operation of Bureau vessels, 1879-1940; correspondence and other records concerning participation in national and international expositions, 1881-1927, including account books, 1880-1916; records concerning fishways and fish protection on Federal power and irrigation projects, 1919-35, including an earlier project on the Great Falls of the Potomac, 1884-95; and correspondence and other records concerning relations with Canada and Mexico, 1905-37.

Records of the Joint Commission Relative to the Preservation of the Fisheries in Waters Contiguous to Canada and the United States, 1893-95; logs of the schooner *Grampus*, 1886-93, the steamer *Fish Hawk*, 1889, and the *Pelican*, 1933, 1937, and 1940; working papers of Statistical Agent Charles H. Lyles, relating to the fishing industry in the Greater New York area, 1935-39; statistical bulletins and tables, 1892-1920; clippings from the *Daily Times*, Gloucester, Mass., 1900-1915 and 1929-37; and reference material on trawl fisheries and British fishing, 1912-15.

Records of the Deputy Commissioner include general correspondence, 1916-21; records concerning the use of crayfish and eulachon as food, 1903-19, and oil pollution of waters, 1920-23; correspondence and other records concerning the National Research Council, 1917-24;

and correspondence and clippings concerning fish cookery, 1923-25.

Financial records include a file of "accounts," 1871-1906, consisting chiefly of statements of expenditures under appropriations; "journals," 1871-87, comprising records of disbursements, with alphabetical indexes; statements of account current, 1880-1906; abstracts of disbursements, 1883-1919; "voucher indexes," 1887-1919; a record of disbursements relating to participation in the Tenth Decennial Census, 1879-81; and account books for expositions, 1880-1916.

Alaska File of the Secretary of the Treasury. 1868-1903. 12 lin. ft. The Secretary of the Treasury was responsible for the protection and conservation of Alaskan fur seals, 1868-1903, and Alaskan salmon fisheries, 1889-1903. Records in the "Alaska file," accumulated by the Secretary of the Treasury and later inherited by the Department of the Interior, consist of letters received, with an index, relating to fur seal activities, 1868-1903, in the vicinity of the Pribilof Islands and, after 1890, to pelagic sealing in the North Pacific Ocean and the Bering Sea; letters received relating to salmon fisheries, 1889-1903, and to salmon preservation; reports from collectors of customs, 1895-1902, on fur seal catches, sealskin importation, and vessel clearances; and printed documents and maps.

Records of the Division of Alaska Fisheries. 1869-1940. 80 lin. ft. Included are reports, correspondence, and other records, 1869-1937; general records, 1902-40; records concerning legislation and regulations, 1871-1937; copies of proclamations and Executive orders, 1892-1930; transcripts and other records concerning hearings, 1907-22; annual reports of field officials, 1917-35; records concerning vessels operated by the Bureau, 1914-40; the sealing log of the schooner *Golden Fleece*, 1896; and logs of the steamers *Homer*, 1910-13,

Melville Dollar, 1914, and *Elihu Thomson*, 1916. There are also monthly reports of vessels, 1918-40, with some logs; permits for fishery operations, 1914-24; licenses for fur farms, 1914-15, and reports concerning the killing of fur seals, 1914-39; statistical reports, tables, and other records concerning the Alaskan fishing industry and fishing industries in general, 1904-39; reports on Alaska salmon streams, 1923-40; inventories of property on St. George and St. Paul Islands, 1910-12; and personnel records, 1913-39.

Records of the Division of Scientific Inquiry. 1900-1935. 15 lin. ft. Included are correspondence concerning geographical areas, species, and administration and personnel, 1900-1935; correspondence concerning cruises and the disposition of scientific collections, 1901-28; and reports on the pathology of fishes and pollution of waters, 1903-23.

RECORDS OF THE BUREAU OF BIOLOGICAL SURVEY. 1890-1944. 466 lin. ft.

These records include the general correspondence, 1902-25, known as the "old alphabetical file"; general correspondence and other records, 1890-1944; a reference file, 1934-35; records relating to the Water Resources Committee of the National Resources Committee, 1935-36; records concerning farming and protection of fur-bearing animals in Alaska, 1911-30, relating chiefly to fox farming; permits for the collection and shipping of Alaskan birds and animals, 1914-21; commissions and bonds for appointments under the Alaska Game Commission, 1925-33; records concerning Migratory Bird Treaty Act cases, 1918-39; registers of bands issued by the American Bird Banding Association, 1912-22; reports from hunting clubs concerning wild fowl hunting, 1927-28; records and reference material on game reserves, 1904-39; monthly and weekly reports of field workers on wildlife refuges, 1922-

35; records relating to Public Works Administration and Civil Works Administration projects on bird and game reservations, 1933-35, Emergency Conservation Work projects on reservations, 1934-37, Civilian Conservation Corps work, 1935-42, and construction work at reservation headquarters, 1934-39; records of the associate architect, concerning construction and repair work on reservations, 1935-37; records documenting a cooperative program of the Division of Cooperative Extension and Bureau of Biological Survey for the conservation and restoration of wildlife, 1935-37; and correspondence of the President's Committee on Wildlife Restoration, 1934, relating to a program for wildlife restoration.

CARTOGRAPHIC AND AUDIOVISUAL RECORDS. 1870-1960. 53,007 items.

Cartographic records (250 items) include published and photoprocessed maps of Alaskan and coastal waters, 1888-90, many of which were compiled from surveys made on the *Albatross*; maps, 1908-19, annotated by the Alaska Fisheries Division, showing fishtraps, fisheries, and fish canneries and packing plants; maps of seal rookeries in the Pribilof Islands, 1872-98, with later maps, 1904-37, annotated to show boundaries of hauling and breeding grounds, the number of seals at the height of the season, and positions from which photographs were taken; a map showing the routes of the Death Valley Biological Expedition of 1891; and maps of the United States and certain regions, showing principal life areas, Federal wildlife and bird refuges, and game preserves, 1891-1941.

Still pictures, 1870-1960 (52,744 items), include photographs relating to the fishing industry, including shrimp and oyster fishing, sponging, hatchery spawning, and the pearl button industry in Iowa; of wharves, nets, domestic and foreign boats and fishermen, and marine life species; of shores and ports along the Atlantic coast (including the Chesapeake Bay and the Roanoke River in North Carolina), the Gulf of Mexico (including Louisiana and Florida), the west coast (including Oregon and Washington), Lake Superior (including Michigan and Minnesota), and the Mediterranean; and of Alaskan wildlife, 1888-1960. There are hand-colored stereopticans of game birds, beaver, and ermine, 1870; photographs of paintings, 1872-90, by Henry W. Elliott, illustrating fur seal and sea otter industries in the Pribilof Islands; and photographs taken by expeditions of the U.S. Fish Commission schooner *Albatross* to the Pribilofs, Alaska, the South Sea Islands, and Hawaii, 1898-1904. There are Biological Survey photographs of birds, mammals, reptiles, persons, plants, maps, refuges, and topography in the United States and Alaska. There are also posters, leaflets, original drawings, and photographs used as illustrations for publications of the Departments of the Interior and Agriculture, such as *North American Fauna, Service Survey, Conservation Bulletins, Farmers' Bulletin,* and *Journal of Agricultural Research,* 1888-1955.

Motion pictures, 1915-37 (13 reels), include films on control of rats, prairie dogs, and porcupines; concerning cooperative fish culture in the United States and pearl culture in Japan; relating to an inspection trip to Alaska by Service officials; and of life in a Boy Scout camp. There is also a film illustrating aerial bombing techniques of the Air Service, 1921.

Microfilm Publication: *Alaska File of the Office of the Secretary of the Treasury, 1868-1903,* M720, 25 rolls, DP.

RECORDS OF THE NATIONAL PARK SERVICE
(RECORD GROUP 79)

The National Park Service was established in the Department of the Interior by an act of August 25, 1916, and was assigned duties relating to the national parks and monuments previously performed by the Office of the Secretary of the Interior. In 1933 the Service was expanded and redesignated the Office of National Parks, Buildings, and Reservations; the name National Park Service was restored in 1934. The expanded Service was placed in charge of national monuments formerly administered by the Forest Service of the Department of Agriculture and national monuments, military and battlefield parks and sites, and some national cemeteries formerly administered by the War Department. An act of August 21, 1935, provided for the establishment of national historic sites, including some owned by private organizations. Other areas established under the supervision of the Service are a national memorial park, historical parks, memorials, parkways, recreation areas, and seashores.

It is the responsibility of the National Park Service to promote and regulate use of national parks, monuments, and similar reservations in order to conserve scenery, natural and historic objects, and wildlife for the enjoyment of future generations. The Service establishes and enforces regulations for park use, protects parks from fire and other dangers, regulates concession operators, investigates and recommends proposed new areas, acquires land (including the termination of private land titles within park boundaries), and constructs and maintains roads, trails, and buildings. The Service also engages in research and educational work, such as managing guided tours and lectures, marking nature trails, maintaining museums and libraries, and preparing publications and studies in history, archeology, natural history, and wildlife.

There are 2,899 cubic feet of records dated between 1872 and 1966 in this record group.

RECORDS OF THE OFFICE OF THE SECRETARY OF THE INTERIOR RELATING TO NATIONAL PARKS AND MONUMENTS. 1872-1916. 38 lin. ft.

Included are letters received, 1872-1907; an index to and registers of letters received by the Patents and Miscellaneous Division, 1905-7; and records of the Office of the Chief Clerk of the Department of the Interior, consisting chiefly of reports and correspondence relating to legislation and legal questions, 1887-1916.

RECORDS OF THE WAR DEPARTMENT RELATING TO NATIONAL PARKS. 1892-1937. 36 lin. ft.

These records, most of which were created in the Offices of the Quartermaster General and the Chief of Engineers, 1925-33, consist of reports, administrative records, and correspondence relating to plans for military parks and monuments, purchase of land, development of the areas, and administration of completed projects. Much of the material concerns Civil War battle sites and includes some detailed studies of the battles in relationship to topography and buildings.

RECORDS OF THE NATIONAL PARK SERVICE. 1901-64.

General Records. 1907-64. 1,790 lin. ft. These include central files, 1907-39; central classified files, 1907-49;

processed issuances consisting chiefly of memorandums sent to regional directors, other field officers, and central office employees, 1940-47; records concerning the National Capital Park and Planning Commission, 1923-34; *Nature Notes*, 1927-35; newspaper and magazine clippings, 1915-25; an appropriation expenditure record, 1915-21; abstracts of disbursements, 1921-25; an allotment ledger, 1924-30; and summary financial statements, 1925-32.

Also included are records of Horace M. Albright, simultaneously Assistant Field Director and Superintendent of Yellowstone National Park, 1926-29, and Director of the Service, 1929-33; Arno B. Cammerer, Assistant Director, 1919-29, Associate Director, 1929-33, and Director, 1933-40; Newton B. Drury, Director of the Service, 1940-51; Conrad L. Wirth, Director, 1952-64; and Roger W. Toll, Superintendent of Rocky Mountain National Park until 1929 and of Yellowstone National Park, 1929-36.

Records of the Office of the Chief Counsel. 1932-50. 49 lin. ft. These comprise a legislative file including letters received; letters sent by the Service and the Office of the Secretary of the Interior; reports; memorandums; maps; photographs; and other records concerning proposed legislation in which the Service was interested.

Records of the Branch of Engineering. 1901-42. 19 lin. ft. The Engineering Division was established in 1917, renamed the Branch of Engineering in 1933, and merged with the Branch of Plans and Design in 1946 to form the Branch of Development. Included are general records of the Engineering Division, 1917-26; records relating to the Hetch Hetchy project, 1901-34; reports on the water supply of San Francisco and neighboring areas, 1902-12; contracts, proposals, and specifications, 1920-26; and road survey reports, 1925-39, final construction reports, 1934-42, and monthly narrative reports of the

Bureau of Public Roads engineers, 1936-37.

Records of the Field Headquarters at San Francisco. 1925-36. 23 lin. ft. The Field Headquarters at San Francisco was organized in 1927 to coordinate work of the several field divisions and was placed under the chief engineer of the Engineering Division. Technical functions were gradually transferred from the field to Washington, and in 1935 the use of the term "Field Headquarters" was discontinued. The records consist of classified files, 1925-36, divided into general records, records relating to individual parks, and records relating to monuments.

Records of the Branch of Plans and Design. 1914-41. 41 lin. ft. This Branch originated as the Landscape Engineering Division in 1918 and was renamed Landscape Architecture Division in 1928 and the Branch of Plans and Design in 1933. From 1931 it prepared master plans for national parks and monuments, and in 1946 it was merged with the Branch of Engineering to form the Branch of Development. The records consist of monthly narrative reports, 1936-38, plans and inscriptions, 1914-30, and master plans, 1931-41.

Records of the Branch of Forestry. 1928-49. 3 lin. ft. The Forestry Division, established in the Berkeley Office of the Service in 1927, was transferred to Washington in November 1933 as the Branch of Forestry and redesignated the Forestry Division in 1947. The Branch was concerned chiefly with protecting forests from fires, insects, diseases, and other dangers. Its records consist of forest fire reports, 1928-49, which include information concerning location, cause, physical conditions, actions taken, and damage. Also included are some narrative reports, memorandums, and correspondence.

Records of the Wildlife Division. 1930-39. 9 lin. ft. The Wild Life Survey, organized in the Berkeley Office of the Service in 1929, was formally established in the Washington Office in 1934 as the Wildlife Division to direct conservation and management of wildlife. In December 1939 its duties and personnel were transferred to the Bureau of Biological Survey and the Bureau of Fisheries, which merged in 1940 to form the Fish and Wildlife Service. There are records of the Wildlife Division, 1934-36; records of David H. Madsen, who served as Assistant Land Purchaser, Supervisor of Wild Life Resources, Wild Life Expert, Fish Culturist, and Supervisor of Fish Resources, 1930-39; and separate records maintained by Madsen as Supervisor of Fish Resources, 1935-39.

Records of the Branch of Recreation, Land Planning, and State Cooperation. 1933-50. 483 lin. ft. The Branch of Lands, also known as Lands and Maps, was established in 1928 to investigate proposed park areas and supervise land acquisition. It was renamed the Branch of Planning in 1932, and supervision of land acquisition was transferred to the Branch of Lands and Use. In 1933 the Branch, with a succession of name changes, was put in charge of Emergency Conservation Work (ECW) activities in State and local parks, and in 1936 it was authorized to supervise Civilian Conservation Corps (CCC) work in national park areas. The Branch was also in charge of Work Projects Administration (WPA) Emergency Relief Appropriation (ERA) projects; the recreational demonstration area program; the park, parkway, and recreation area study; and, for a time, the U.S. Travel Bureau.

The records include a State park file, 1933-47; procedural issuances concerning CCC and Civil Works Administration (CWA) work, 1933-34; reports of district officers and inspectors on State park emergency conservation work, 1933-35, and State park ECW work, 1935-36; project reports on CCC projects in State and local parks, 1933-37;

narrative reports of ECW projects in National Park Service areas, 1933-35; records concerning WPA projects, 1935-43; and records concerning water, 1936-49.

There are also records on recreational demonstration areas, including program files, 1934-47, and project reports, 1934-36; land purchase control cards and records, 1934-36; project records of the Project Planning and Control Section, Land Utilization Division, Resettlement Administration, 1935-36; managers' narrative and statistical reports, 1941-42; and land transfer records, 1943-50.

Records concerning the Recreation-Area Study include classified files, 1936-47, monthly reports, 1936-41, competitive recreational development records, 1935-40, and reports on recreational developments under the supervision of the Department of Agriculture, 1940. Records of the Development Division consist of notices of Presidential authorization for ERA projects, 1938-42, memorandums sent to field officers, 1936-42, and records relating to Civilian Public Service Camps, 1941-48.

Records of the Project Application Section include general records, 1935-43; inspection reports, 1934-39; and memorandums, correspondence, and other records concerning CCC camps, 1935-44. Records of the Work Control Section include Federal, 1934-43, and State and local project reports, 1937-44; records of the Progress Records and Cost Analyses Section consist of project progress and cost records, 1934-42, statistical compilation records, 1935-41, and ECW work progress and cost reports, 1933-37; and records of the supervisor of project training consist of general records, 1935-42, and correspondence and memorandums, 1935-42.

RECORDS OF REGIONAL OFFICES. 1865-1954. 341 lin. ft.

Included are records of Region I, established in 1937 with headquarters in Richmond, including central classified files, 1936-52; records concerning work in the 23 States comprising Region I, 1935-44; correspondence of regional officers with district offices, 1936-37; records concerning WPA projects, 1936-42; inspection reports, 1938-43; monthly reports, 1936-41; master plans, 1935-42; and records of the landscape architect, 1934-38, of the regional engineer on dam construction, 1936-43, and of the regional geologist, 1935-42. There are also records of the regional wildlife technician, consisting of general records, 1936-42, monthly reports, 1936-40, weekly reports of the regional biologist, 1940-42, special reports, 1936-41, and reports of student technicians, 1937-38.

Also included are records of the regional supervisor of the recreation area study, including general records, 1936-43, monthly reports, 1937-42, Federal park use study reports, 1940-41, and records concerning the first national report on the recreation study, 1939-40; records concerning recreational demonstration areas, including records of land acquisitions, 1934-45, correspondence on projects with Resettlement Administration regional offices, 1935-36, and records relating to individual projects, 1934-41; records of Colonial National Historical Park, consisting of classified files, 1930-54, and relating chiefly to the observance of the Yorktown sesquicentennial in 1931 and subsequent annual celebrations; records relating to Yorktown National Cemetery, consisting of letters received, 1915-32 (with an index, 1922-29), letters sent, 1916-32 (with an index, 1922-29), and quarterly, 1917-25, and interment, 1910-29, reports; records of Petersburg National Battlefield, consisting of general records, 1935-53; and correspondence of the Petersburg National Military Park Commission and the Fredericksburg and Spotsylvania County Battlefields Memorial Park Commission, 1928-33.

The system of National Capital Parks

has been operated as a separate unit of the Park Service since 1933, and in 1962 it was made the sixth region, the National Capital Region. Its records include those relating to repairs and alterations of the White House and the Executive Office Building, 1925-37; drawings and tables of alterations and additions to executive offices, 1934; "Cabinet sketches" of the Thomas Jefferson Memorial, n.d.; registers of burials, n.d., and visitors, 1879-1903, at Battleground National Cemetery; clippings about Washington, D. C., 1934-37; records of the Vicksburg National Cemetery, 1868-1913; and selected records from the "deed file" of the Land and Water Rights Division, 1865-1952.

RECORDS OF THE POTOMAC COMPANY AND THE CHESAPEAKE AND OHIO CANAL COMPANY. 1785-1938. 116 lin. ft.

The Potomac Company, incorporated in Maryland and Virginia, was organized in 1785, with George Washington as president, to improve navigation of the Potomac River by deepening the channel and cutting canals around the falls. The company never succeeded, and in 1828 its property was transferred to the newly organized Chesapeake and Ohio Canal Company. The latter company proposed to build a canal from Washington to the navigable water of the Ohio River or one of its tributaries. Construction on the canal began July 4, 1828, and continued sporadically until 1850, when the canal was completed to Cumberland, Md. In 1889 the canal passed into receivership and was operated by a receiver until it was closed in 1924. In 1938 the property was purchased by the United States and placed under the jurisdiction of the National Park Service, which received the records of both companies.

Records of the Potomac Company include proceedings, 1785-96; minutes, correspondence, and reports, 1785-1828; letters sent, 1817-28; legal records, 1792-1828; records concerning transfer of shares of stock, 1791-1828; a stock ledger, 1787-1828; ledgers, 1796 and 1800-1807; a cashbook, 1823-28; letters sent and other records relating to the Potomac and Shenandoah Navigation Lottery, 1810-19; and miscellaneous accounts, 1785-1828.

Records of the Chesapeake and Ohio Canal Company include proceedings of stockholders, 1828-89, with an index, 1828-83; proceedings of the president and directors, 1828-90, with indexes; subscription books, 1827-30; lists of shareholders, ca. 1829-37; letters received by the office of the president and directors, 1828-89, with registers, 1828-88; letters sent by the office of the president and directors, 1828-70 and 1879-81, with a register, 1828-70; letters sent by the office of the trustees, 1897-1938, and correspondence, 1913-38, with an index; letters received by the Commissioner of the Chesapeake and Ohio Canal, 1835-42, and letter books of the Commissioner, 1835-42; letters received by the chief engineer, 1834-52, with a register, 1835-40; letters sent by the chief engineer, 1838-52; and records of resident and assistant engineers, 1828-42.

There are also records concerning legal matters and land, including legal records, 1828-1900, deeds and other records concerning land titles, 1828-78, and land surveys and descriptions of land, 1828-73; records concerning construction and maintenance, including drawings and calculations for the Paw Paw Tunnel, ca. 1836, and for sections of the canal, 1836-41, field notebooks, 1827-96, records relating to bids for construction work, 1836 and 1841, assessment books, 1828-33, and accounting records relating to construction and maintenance, 1828-82; records concerning traffic on the canal, including a record of boat registrations, 1851-74, a register of boats employed on the canal, 1878, statements of articles transported,

1850-78, registers of tolls collected at Georgetown, 1845-54, registers of ascending and descending boats, 1869-80, returns of manifests, 1851-77, returns of waybills, 1878-87, and ledgers for toll accounts, 1855-92; financial records, including journals, and ledgers, 1828-90, treasurers' journals, 1853-70 and 1872, treasurers' ledgers, 1828-70 and 1881-89, abstracts of receipts and expenditures, 1828-80, records relating to bonds and coupons, 1838-84, payrolls, 1873-74 and 1884-85, record of payrolls, 1913-38, records relating to leases, 1870-1938, accounts, 1872-90, financial statements, 1893-98 and 1909-24, and miscellaneous accounting records, ca. 1828-89; and records relating to a proposed extension of the canal, 1874, memorandums concerning the coal trade, 1893, and printed materials, 1816-1907.

RECORDS RELATING TO COMMISSIONS. 1935-66. 9 lin. ft.

Included are correspondence and other records of the U.S. Commission for the Celebration of the Two Hundredth Anniversary of the Birth of John Marshall, 1955-57, the Jamestown-Williamsburg-Yorktown Celebration Commission, 1954-60, the Battle of New Orleans Sesquicentennial Celebration Commission, 1963-66, the Jefferson Memorial Commission, 1935-42, and the Civil War Centennial Commission, 1957-65.

CARTOGRAPHIC RECORDS. 1791-1958. 8,861 items.

Included are maps and plans prepared by the Chesapeake and Ohio Canal Company and its predecessor, the Potomac Company, 1791-1937; the "numbered map file" prepared by the National Capital Parks and its predecessors, the Office of Public Buildings and Grounds and the Office of Public Buildings and Public Parks of the National Capital, consisting of maps relating to public lands, buildings, and monuments in the National Capital area, 1797-1958; master and progress plans for Washington, D.C., compiled in the Branch of Plans and Design of the National Park Service, 1936-37; maps and plans of the District of Columbia recreation system, 1930-41, prepared as part of the D.C. Work Projects Administration; maps, diagrams, and tables relating to Rock Creek pollution studies in Washington, D.C., prepared for the Eastern Division, Branch of Engineering, National Park Service, 1935; maps and plans prepared by the Arlington Memorial Bridge Commission, 1923-42; and large-scale aerial photographic prints of northwest Washington, 1937.

AUDIOVISUAL RECORDS. 1871-1965. 17,330 items.

Still pictures, 1871-1965 (17,298 items), include photographs, some made as early as 1860, of tourists, park officials, scenery and activities in national parks in the United States and Hawaii, and national monuments; of scenic areas in parks including Glacier, Yellowstone, Grand Teton, Great Smoky Mountains, National Capital, and Colonial National Historical Park; illustrating the history, geology, botany, and physical features of Zion and Bryce Canyon National Parks; engineering projects in several national parks, at the Salem Maritime National Historic Site, Washington Monument, Executive Office Building, North Interior Building, Mount Vernon Memorial Highway, and other areas in the District of Columbia, Maryland, and Virginia; documenting the work of CCC, WPA, and NYA workers in museum development programs; of the W. H. Tipton collection of Civil War photographs relating to the Battle of Gettysburg and the development of the battleground, city, and surrounding area; of Civil War sites in northern Virginia and Harpers Ferry, W. Va., 1863-94; and those accumulated by or made for the Civil War Centennial Commission, 1957-65. There are also photographs collected by the U.S. Commission for the Celebration of the Two Hundredth Anniversary of the Birth of John Marshall, 1955, including photographs of Supreme Court Justices and exteriors and interiors of buildings used by the Court; photographs of the San Francisco Exposition, 1939-40, and of park areas in the Congo and Spain; and "Alberttypes" of the Hayden Geological Survey of the Territories, 1871-72.

Motion pictures, 1930-37 (15 reels), of Shenandoah and Great Smoky Mountains National Parks, parks in Georgia and Washington, and Camp Roosevelt.

Sound recordings, 1932-51 (17 items), of the memorial service in honor of Stephen T. Mather at the Bohemian Club, San Francisco, 1932; the dedication of Mammoth Cave National Park, 1946; the dedication of the equestrian statues at the Arlington Memorial Bridge, Wash-

ington, D.C., 1951; and a speech of Newton B. Drury to the Commonwealth Club of California, 1947.

See Edward E. Hill, comp., *Preliminary Inventory of the Records of the National Park Service*, PI 166 (1966).

SPECIFIC RESTRICTIONS

Records: Office files of Conrad L. Wirth, former Director of the National Park Service, consisting of correspondence, memorandums, and other material, 1931-64.

Restrictions: No one may examine these records or be given information from them or copies of them except by permission of the Assistant Director, Administration, of the National Park Service.

Specified by: Director of the National Park Service.

RECORDS OF THE OFFICE OF TERRITORIES
(RECORD GROUP 126)

The Office of Territories was established July 28, 1950, by administrative order of the Secretary of the Interior to carry out certain of his responsibilities pertaining to areas noncontiguous to the United States and under U.S. jurisdiction. The Office, the successor to the Division of Territories and Island Possessions, established by Executive order of May 29, 1934, is concerned with the development of the economic, social, and political life of the territories and with the advancement of international peace and security by the close coordination of territorial affairs with the defense and foreign policies of the United States. Before 1873 it was a function of the Secretary of State to serve as the channel through which officers of the territorial governments communi-

cated with the Government in Washington and to act in a supervisory capacity over these officers. By an act of March 1, 1873, these powers and duties were transferred to the Secretary of the Interior, who exercised them through his immediate office until the newly established Division of Territories and Island Possessions was made responsible for them in 1934. The accelerated acquisition of territorial possessions outside the continental United States after the Spanish-American War, although offset to some extent by the creation of new States from former territories, emphasized the need for a centralized administration of territorial governments. In 1907 President Theodore Roosevelt directed that all Government activities relating to the territorial possessions of the United States, except the Philippine Islands, should be handled by the Department of the Interior. Between 1907 and 1934, however, the Department's territorial functions were considerably decentralized. Although the functions of the Bureau of Insular Affairs relating to the administration of the government of Puerto Rico were transferred to the new Division of Territories and Island Possessions in 1934, it was not until the Bureau was terminated in 1939 that the Division inherited the last territorial responsibilities of the War Department, many of which related to the Philippine Islands. Control of the government of the Virgin Islands was transferred in 1931 from the Department of the Navy to the Department of the Interior. Direct supervision of certain territorial governments by the Navy Department was continued until 1951 when the control of American Samoa and the Trust Territory of the Pacific Islands was transferred to the Interior Department. Territorial functions of that Department have included not only supervisory responsibilities of the respective Governors' offices, but also those relating to the insane in Alaska, Alaskan reindeer, the Government-owned Bluebeard Castle Hotel at St. Thomas in the Virgin Islands, and the operations of Government units, such as the U.S. Antarctic Service, the Office of the U.S. High Commissioner to the Philippine Islands, the Alaska Railroad, the Alaska Road Commission, the Virgin Islands Company, the Puerto Rican Hurricane Relief Commission and Loan Section, and the Hawaiian Homes Commission.

There are 753 cubic feet of records dated between 1878 and 1953 in this record group.

GENERAL RECORDS OF THE OFFICE AND ITS PREDECESSORS. 1907-51. 710 lin. ft.

These consist of central classified files relating to departmental administration of Alaska, Arizona, Guam, Hawaii, New Mexico, Oklahoma, the Philippine Islands, Puerto Rico, American Samoa, the District of Columbia, the Virgin Islands, equatorial islands, Antarctica, the civilian food reserve program, trust territories, and the Alaska Railroad, 1907-51; an index relating to the Philippine Islands, 1939-46; letters and memorandums concerning the Virgin Islands, 1931-34; cables sent and received from Puerto Rico, 1934-40; and office files of the Director of the Division of Territories and Island Possessions, 1942-45, of the Executive Assistant to the Secretary of the Interior relating to Alaska, 1929-31, and of the Chief Counsel, 1939-46.

FUNCTIONAL RECORDS OF THE OFFICE AND ITS PREDECESSORS. 1920-53. 62 lin. ft.

Included are office files of the Special Disbursing Officer of Puerto Rico, 1920-51; administrative records, records relating to loans, quarterly reports of the Puerto Rican Hurricane Relief Commission, and monthly reports of the Commission's Board of Alternates, 1929-35; annual reports of the Commission and its successor, the Puerto Rican Hurricane Relief Loan Section, 1929-36, and administrative records and quarterly and semiannual reports of the Section, 1935-46; correspondence relating to settlement in Matanuska Valley, Alaska, 1934-39; a reference file of the Director of the Research Unit on Territorial Policy, 1941-44; general records of the Civilian Food Reserve Section, relating to the War Food Administration and the Office of Price Administration, 1942-45, and an office file of its field representative in Alaska, 1942-44; records of the West Indian Conference on problems in the Caribbean area, 1944-46; records relating to Federal Inter-Agency Alaskan Development Committee activities, 1947-49; general administrative records of the Pacific islands recruitment program, relating to displaced persons, 1949-51; and records relating to allotments for and priorities of projects in the territories, 1950-53.

RECORDS OF THE OFFICE OF THE U.S. HIGH COMMISSIONER TO THE PHILIPPINE ISLANDS. 1935-49. 18 lin. ft.

Included are records of the High Commissioner's offices at Manila, 1935-46, and Washington, D.C., 1942-48; a list of persons interned by the Japanese, 1942; correspondence concerning internees, 1942-47; radiograms sent and received, February-September 1946; and claims of staff members in the High Commissioner's Office for losses suffered during World War II, July 1949.

RECORDS OF THE U.S. ANTARCTIC SERVICE. 1939-43. 47 lin. ft.

These consist of an office file of the Executive Secretary of the Executive Committee; reports, general correspondence, and informational and special subject files; the administrative assistant's letters sent; radiograms; records relating to appropriations; scientific and technical reports; fiscal and supply correspondence, with a classified requisition file; contracts; purchase orders; vouchers; a name index, with a personnel data file; and an index of equipment.

CARTOGRAPHIC AND AUDIOVISUAL RECORDS. 1878-1948. 33,744 items.

Cartographic records, 1878-1942 (12,379 items), consist of maps relating to the Hawaiian Islands, 1878-1906, and Alaska, 1923-27; and manuscript and annotated maps and charts and aerial photographs of Antarctica from the U.S. Antarctic Service Expedition, 1939-41.

Audiovisual records include photographs, 1908-48 (21,268 items), of the Copper River Railroad, Alaska, 1908; the survey, construction, and operation of the Alaska Railroad and Alaskan agricultural production, 1914-23; President Warren G. Harding in Alaska and his funeral; Puerto Rico Reconstruction

Administration activities and Puerto Rican terrain, vegetation, animals, buildings, and people, 1935-48; and the 1939-41 U.S. Antarctic Service (Byrd) Expedition. There are also motion pictures (97 reels) of the Byrd expedition, 1939-41.

See Charles E. Dewing and Laura E. Kelsay, comps., *Preliminary Inventory of the Records of the United States Antarctic Service*, PI 90 (1955); Richard S. Maxwell, comp., *Preliminary Inventory of the Records of the Office of the U.S. High Commissioner to the Philippine Islands*, PI 151 (1963); and Maxwell and Evans Walker, comps., *Preliminary Inventory of the Records of the Office of Territories*, PI 154 (1963).

Microfilm Publications: *Interior Department, U.S. Antarctic Service Picture File*, T834, 7 rolls; and *Interior Department, U.S. Antarctic Service Selected Logs and Reports*, T834, 2 rolls.

SPECIFIC RESTRICTIONS

Records: Records of and relating to the program of the Office of the U.S. High Commissioner to the Philippine Islands for the safekeeping of currency, gold, securities, and other valuables, including records relating to the destruction of currency by U.S. authorities.

Records sent by the Office to the Bureau of Accounts, Department of the Treasury, and records created by the Bureau in providing control over the valuables after their transfer to the continental United States and in acting on claims arising from the safekeeping program of the Office, 1941-59.

Lists (counterparts) of documents received by the Bureau of Accounts from the Office and an index of important Japanese properties in the Philippine Islands, 1942.

Restrictions: No one may examine these records or be given information from them or copies of them except as authorized by the Secretary of the Treasury, the Commissioner of Accounts, or their duly authorized representatives.

Specified by: Department of the Treasury.

RECORDS OF THE BUREAU OF RECLAMATION
(RECORD GROUP 115)

The Bureau of Reclamation, first known as the Reclamation Service, was created under the Reclamation or Newlands Act of June 17, 1902, which established a reclamation fund from the sale of public lands to finance the location, construction, and maintenance of irrigation works that would store, divert, and develop waters for reclaiming arid and semiarid lands in the States and territories. The act gave responsibility for administering the fund to the Secretary of the Interior, who established the Reclamation Service to exercise that function under the jurisdiction of, but not as a part of, the Geological Survey. On March 9, 1907, the Service was separated from the Survey and was made directly responsible to the Secretary. It was renamed the Bureau of Reclamation on June 20, 1923. The Bureau plans, constructs, and operates irrigation works in 17 contiguous Western States and Hawaii; builds and operates hydroelectric powerplants; and distributes electric power and energy generated at certain powerplants, reservoirs, projects, and dams.

See Institute for Government Research, *The U.S. Reclamation Service* (New York, 1919).

There are 2,418 cubic feet of records dated between 1891 and 1963 in this record group.

GENERAL RECORDS. 1891-1960. 2,431 lin. ft.

These consist of general administrative and project correspondence, with indexes, 1902-45; accident and injury reports, 1902-29; project and feature histories, reports of engineering boards, reports to the Board of Army Engineers, project operation and maintenance reports, and other special reports, 1902-60; summary cost reports and narrative statements concerning construction at reclamation projects, 1916-49; Service and Bureau specifications for reclamation projects, 1902-55 (in WNRC); public land withdrawal and restoration files, 1891-1945; a personnel correspondence file, 1902-40; and records relating to Bureau administration of Civilian Conservation Corps activities, 1934-43.

RECORDS OF THE COMMITTEE OF SPECIAL ADVISERS ON RECLAMATION. 1923-24. 13 lin. ft.

The Secretary of the Interior appointed this factfinding committee in September 1923 to study Federal methods for reclaiming land through irrigation. On April 10, 1924, it submitted its report, which was published as Senate Document 92, 68th Congress, 1st session. Committee records include reports, correspondence, and exhibits accompanying the final report.

RECORDS OF ORGANIZATIONS CONCERNED WITH RECLAMATION. 1899-1934. 43 lin. ft.

The Bureau acquired the records of several private organizations interested in reclamation. Included are records of the National Irrigation Association, including clippings about irrigation, 1899-1906, land law repeal, 1903, and agriculture, 1905-10; press releases, 1903-6; drafts of legislation relating to river control, 1911; and records of the Mitchell News Bureau, 1902-3. Records of the National Reclamation Association consist of general correspondence, 1911-34, correspondence with Government officials, 1914-18, miscellaneous records and correspondence, 1912-14 and 1918-33, George H. Maxwell's scrapbooks relating to Association activities, 1912, court decrees and claims for water rights in Utah and Wyoming, 1904-16, clippings relating to flood control, 1912-14, and Government reports and publications, 1907-20. Also records of the American Homecroft Society, relating to the use of yards and vacant lots for gardens, 1920-21, and publicity material of the *Talisman*, the Society's magazine, 1920.

CARTOGRAPHIC AND AUDIOVISUAL RECORDS. 1897-1963. 75,971 items.

Cartographic records, 1904-63 (2,482 items), include plats of townships in Federal irrigation project areas, showing farm units; maps of the United States and western areas, showing irrigation and hydroelectric development, dams, reservoirs, and reclamation projects; and aerial survey film, with indexes, covering western areas.

Audiovisual records, 1897-1955 (75,089 items), include photographs of Bureau activities in developing power and irrigation projects in Washington, Oregon, Idaho, Montana, North and South Dakota, Wyoming, Utah, Colorado, Nebraska, Oklahoma, Texas, New Mexico, Arizona, Nevada, and California; of towns, transportation, agricultural activities, industries, roads, bridges, rivers, floods, drought conditions, and economic and physical results of projects in the Western States, Hawaii, and the Southern States, including Alabama, Florida, Georgia, Louisiana, Mississippi, North Carolina, South Carolina, and Tennessee; relating to the development of the engineering progress on dams, reservoirs, canals, tunnels, flumes, pumping plants, and powerplants; and of Civilian Conservation Corps activities at Bureau projects, project maps and diagrams, Bureau exhibits and displays, Western Indian culture, national parks, and irrigation in other countries.

See Edward E. Hill, comp., *Preliminary Inventory of the Records of the Bureau of Reclamation*, PI 109 (1958); and Emma B. Haas, Anne Harris Henry, and Thomas W. Ray, comps., *List of Photographs of Irrigation Projects of the Bureau of Reclamation*, SL 15 (1959).

Microfilm Publication: *Project Histories and Reports of Reclamation Bureau Projects* [1902-25], M96, 141 rolls.

RECORDS OF THE BUREAU OF MINES
(RECORD GROUP 70)

The Bureau of Mines was established in the Department of the Interior by an act of May 16, 1910. In 1925 the Division of Mineral Resources of the Geological Survey and the Coal Division of the Bureau of Foreign and Domestic Commerce were transferred to the Bureau of Mines, which became part of the Department of Commerce. The Bureau was returned in 1934 to the Department of the Interior. The Bureau is the Federal scientific and engineering agency responsible for safeguarding lives of workers in mineral industries and for developing efficient methods of mining, preparation, distribution, and use of mineral resources. Its functions include inspecting mines, mills, and smelters; testing fuels for Government use; issuing licenses that control production and use of nonmilitary explosives; operating experimental and other plants to produce helium and synthetic liquid fuels; collecting information about production and consumption of mineral resources, employment, and accidents in mines; and conducting research on mining methods, improvement of mining conditions, and production of essential minerals. Included in this record group are records of the interdepartmental Joint Information Board on Minerals and Derivatives, created in 1918 to coordinate and distribute information concerning minerals important for war purposes; and of the Committee on Mineral Imports and Exports of the U.S. Shipping Board, which operated in 1919 to plan a program for restricting mineral imports and exports to conserve shipping space.

See Fred W. Powell, *The Bureau of Mines* (New York, 1922).

There are 3,181 cubic feet of records dated between 1895 and 1955 in this record group.

GENERAL RECORDS. 1910-50. 3,447 lin. ft. (in WNRC).

Included are central correspondence, with indexes, 1910-50, and records relating to Bureau organization; general policy; legislation; rules and regulations; cooperative relationships with other Government agencies and private institutions; rescue and general fieldwork; mining operations, safety, and health; management and labor; ores and ore dressing; metallurgy; helium; mineral technology; fuel lands and their leasing; coal technology; lignite; peat; Government fuel yards; petroleum and natural gas; and activities of the War Minerals Division, the Division of Mineral Resources and Statistics, field stations, and laboratories.

DIVISION AND FIELD RECORDS. 1895-1954. 382 lin. ft. and 230 rolls of microfilm.

Included are reports, correspondence, statistical data, and reference files of the Divisions of Explosives Regulation, 1917-21, Explosives, 1926-33, Coal Economics, 1907-48, Petroleum and Fuel, 1905-45, Foreign Activities ("foreign company reports file"), 1913-45, Minerals, 1917-53, and Mineral Production Security, 1941-45; and Branches of Non-Metal Economics, 1905-54, Construction

and Chemical Materials, 1923-54, and Health and Safety, 1911-49.

Miscellaneous records of the Bureau include coal production tabulation sheets, 1900-1937; petroleum information files, 1915-30; blueprints and drawings relating to helium and early helium development; war gas investigation reports, 1917-18; negative microfilm copies (230 rolls) of employment and accident schedules, 1915-35; coal mine inspection releases, 1942-49; a public works file, 1934-41, relating to construction of Federal projects and a point 4 program file, 1950-51; records of the Tin, Lead, and Zinc Division of the War Production Board, 1942-47; and records of the Division of Mineral Resources of the Geological Survey, 1895-1925, the Coal Division of the Bureau of Foreign and Domestic Commerce, 1920-25, the Joint Information Board on Minerals and Derivatives, 1918, and the Committee on Mineral Imports and Exports, 1918.

CARTOGRAPHIC AND AUDIOVISUAL RECORDS. 1908-55. 576 items.

Cartographic records (241 items) consist of maps of the United States and of individual States, showing distribution of mineral deposits, locations of mines, and graphic statistical data relating to economic aspects of the mining industry, 1908-44; maps of the world, showing petroleum marketing systems and distribution of oil reserves, 1919; a map of the United States, showing natural gas pipelines and plants, 1929; and maps of the United States, showing production, by State, of metallic ores and bituminous coals, 1928-29.

Audiovisual records include photographs (100 items) of Chemical Warfare Service tests of war gases and gas masks at the American University Experiment Station, Washington, D.C., 1917-18.

Motion pictures, 1913-39 (235 reels), relate to mining methods, processing, refining, manufacturing, products, and use of nickel, silver, lead, iron, copper, aluminum, magnesium, sulfur, clay, asbestos, carborundum, and sillimanite, 1919-38 and ca. 1943; coal mining methods, 1919-38; oil well drilling and petroleum refining chiefly in the United States and Mexico, 1923-36; drilling rocks and quarrying sandstone, granite, and limestone for portland cement, 1915-31; automobile manufacturing and assembly, including explanations of internal combustion engines and automobile lubrication, 1926-36; manufacturing, testing, and using dynamite, electric detonators and meters, safety glass, spark plugs, steel, storage batteries, valves, and watches, 1922-38; employing steam, water, and electric power, 1922-28 and ca. 1943; and using the oxyacetylene torch, 1922 and 1938. There are films used in Bureau safety and health education programs concerning industry, 1913-17; gas, fires, dust explosions, handling equipment, and excavating in coal mines, and shoring, blasting, handling equipment, and loading ore in metal mines, 1914-30; oil well fires and oil industry safety, 1923-24; carbon monoxide poisoning, 1928; rescue and first aid, 1915-31; traffic, 1924 and 1937; and sani-

tation in mining towns. There are films about the natural resources and scenery of Arizona and Texas, and national parks, including Yellowstone, Yosemite, Grand Canyon, Rocky Mountain, and Shenandoah, 1925-55. Also included is news coverage of the Royalton, Ill., mine disaster, 1914; the testing of railway guns at Fort Story, Va., 1929; and of President Franklin D. Roosevelt aboard the U.S.S. *Houston*, arriving at Cartagena, Colombia, 1934.

SPECIFIC RESTRICTIONS

Records: Statistical tabulations of sales, production, employment, and accidents in mineral industries; microfilm copies of the schedules from which some of these tabulations were made; and monthly reports of fatalities in coal mines submitted by State agencies.

Restrictions: Use of these records is restricted to employees of the Bureau of Mines and to persons authorized to consult them by appropriate Bureau officials.

Specified by: Bureau of Mines.

RECORDS OF THE GOVERNMENT OF AMERICAN SAMOA
(RECORD GROUP 284)

Under the 1899 Treaty of Berlin the seven eastern islands of Samoa were to be a U.S. possession and Western Samoa a German possession. The treaty was ratified by the U.S. Senate on February 16, 1900. An Executive order placed American Samoa under control of the Department of the Navy and directed the Secretary of the Navy to take necessary steps to establish U.S. authority and give the islands protection. U.S. naval control of American Samoa lasted until June 29, 1951, when, by Executive order, the President transferred control

to the Department of the Interior. In 1960 the Secretary of the Interior approved a constitution for American Samoa.

There are 155 cubic feet of records dated between 1899 and 1966 (in FRC San Francisco) in this record group:

RECORDS OF THE OFFICE OF THE GOVERNOR. 1900-1961.
94 lin. ft.

These consist of annual reports of the Governor to the Secretary of the Navy, 1902-51; regulations, proclamations, and orders issued by the Governor, 1900–1956; compilations of the laws and regulations of American Samoa, 1900–1946; general correspondence file, 1900–1958; general subject file, 1941–61; records relating to the Samoan legislative body (Fono) and copies of its proceedings, 1902–49; special studies of Samoa prepared by the Governor's office, 1912, 1916, and 1940; copies of speeches of the Governors and documents relating to special ceremonies, 1908–56; and other records, including correspondence with U.S. Presidents, a journal, 1900, of the activities of the Commandant's office, and copies of treaties and agreements, 1900–1948. Also included are copies of proceedings of a special congressional commission to investigate Samoa and recommend legislation, 1930; correspondence, petitions, and other records concerning charges made against Gov. Waldo Evans, 1921–27; copies of records of investigative bodies, 1947–53; records relating to the motor vessel *Samoa*, 1942–47; four color plates of designs for the Samoan flag, 1960; and World War II intelligence files, 1941–45.

RECORDS OF THE OFFICE OF THE SECRETARY OF NATIVE AFFAIRS AND SUCCESSOR AGENCIES. 1900–1966. 31 lin. ft.

The Office of the Secretary of Native Affairs was created in 1903 under the direction of the naval governor of American Samoa. This Office directed the judiciary, acted as liaison between the naval governor and the Samoan people, and supervised district governors, judges, magistrates, police, the copra industry, and collection of taxes. It was abolished in 1931. Administrative duties were taken over by the newly created Office of the Attorney General, and a separate judicial branch was created under a chief justice. The records comprise general files of the Office of the Secretary of Native Affairs and successors, 1907–66, annual reports of the Secretary of Native Affairs, 1901 and 1905–25, regulations and orders issued by the Government of American Samoa, 1900–1946, copies of proceedings of the Fono, 1905–47, and miscellaneous records of the Secretary of Native Affairs, 1902–37. Also included are census returns, 1900–1945, and applications for claims against the U.S. Government for damages caused by U.S. Marines, 1953.

RECORDS OF THE HIGH COURT. 1899–1962. 8 lin. ft.

These consist of criminal and civil case files, 1901–29; probate case files, 1902–45; copies of wills, 1906–61; papers concerning the bankruptcy of E. W. Carr, first Secretary of Native Affairs, 1899–1908; a list of persons committed to prison, 1904–30; copies of contracts between Samoans and merchants, 1905–25; alien registration forms, 1940; petitions for naturalization, 1946; petitions for divorce and copies of divorce orders, 1900–1962; and correspondence of the Clerk of the High Court, 1951–52.

RECORDS OF THE OFFICE OF THE ATTORNEY GENERAL. 1900–1965. 54 lin. ft.

The records comprise a general correspondence file, 1931–64, a correspondence file relating primarily to district and village matters, 1939–55, outgoing letters, 1942–63, a register of letters received, 1949–58 and 1961, and copies of regulations and orders issued by the Government of American Samoa, 1938–61. Also included are police investigative case files, 1932–62; police station logbooks, 1957 and 1962; daily record of prisoners, expenditures for prison mess, and arrest records, 1935–51; copies of immigration and emigration rules and regulations, 1934–61; records concerning immigration and emigration, 1937–65; copies of proceedings, correspondence, and other records of various boards and commissions, 1941–59; records documenting prices received for copra and showing prices paid to producers and names of contractors, 1908–48; and copies of personnel records, 1900–1963.

RECORDS OF THE
SOUTHWESTERN POWER ADMINISTRATION
(RECORD GROUP 387)

The Southwestern Power Administration was created by the Secretary of the Interior in 1943 to sell and dispose of electric energy generated at certain federally constructed and operated projects. The Administration carries out functions assigned to the Secretary by the Flood Control Act of 1944 with respect to specific projects.

There are 17 cubic feet of records dated between 1946 and 1954 in this record group.

RECORDS. 1946-54. 20 lin. ft.

These consist of progress reports, general correspondence, and a contract file of the Administration's Washington liaison office.

Discontinued Agencies

RECORDS OF THE COMMISSIONER OF RAILROADS
(RECORD GROUP 193)

The Pacific Railroad Act of July 1, 1862, which provided for the establishment of a Government corporation to "lay out, locate, construct, furnish, maintain, and enjoy a continuous railroad," also required the corporation and each railroad connected with it to file annual reports with the Secretary of the Treasury setting forth names of directors and stockholders and amounts of stock subscribed, money received, and debts. An act of June 25, 1868, required that reports also be filed by other railroads aided by the Government, that the scope of the reports be enlarged, and that thereafter the reports be submitted to the Secretary of the Interior. In June 1878 the Congress created the Office of the Auditor of Railroad Accounts in the Department of the Interior to receive and examine these reports. An act of March 3, 1881, changed the title to the Office of the Commissioner of Railroads. The Office was terminated by the Congress on June 30, 1904, and its records were transferred to the Secretary of the Interior.

There are 49 cubic feet of records dated between 1862 and 1904 in this record group.

RECORDS OF THE COMMISSIONER OF RAILROADS. 1862-1904. 63 lin. ft.

These include annual reports of the Auditor of Railroad Accounts, 1878-80, and of the Commissioner of Railroads, 1881-1903; reports of railroads that received Federal aid, 1864-1904; minutes of the Board of Directors, the Executive Committee of the Board, and the stockholders of railroads, 1885-87; correspondence, 1878-1904, with registers and indexes; a record of U.S. bonds issued to railroad companies, 1865-80; a scrapbook of newspaper clippings, 1879-80; and correspondence and reports received after the Commissioner's office was terminated, 1904-7.

RECORDS OF THE U.S. PACIFIC RAILWAY COMMISSION. Apr.-Oct. 1887. 6 lin. ft.

The U.S. Pacific Railway Commission

was created by an act of March 3, 1887, to examine the affairs of Pacific railroads that had received Federal aid. The commissioners submitted their report to the President in December 1887. The records of the Commission were transferred to the Secretary of the Interior, who placed them with the Commissioner of Railroads.

The records consist of correspondence, April-October 1887, testimony and exhibits, answers of Leland Stanford as president of the Central Pacific Railroad to questions sent by the commissioners, and reference material, 1875-87.

See Marion M. Johnson, comp., *Preliminary Inventory of the Records of the Commissioner of Railroads*, PI 158 (1964).

RECORDS OF THE ALASKAN TERRITORIAL GOVERNMENT (RECORD GROUP 348)

From the time the United States purchased Alaska from Russia in 1867 to the passage of an act of May 17, 1884, there was no formal civil government in Alaska. Limited control of the area was exercised by the U.S. Army, 1867-77; the Department of the Treasury through the Collector of Customs at Sitka, other collectors, and the Revenue-Cutter Service, ca. 1877-79; and the Department of the Navy, 1879-84.

The 1884 act provided for the civil government of Alaska under a Governor, established the temporary seat of that government at Sitka, and conferred district status on Alaska. It also empowered the Secretary of the Interior to regulate the enforcement of Federal laws relating to mining claims and provide for education in the area. Under an act of July 24, 1897, a surveyor general was appointed for the U.S. District of Alaska. Homestead laws were extended to the District and provisions were made for railroad rights-of-way by an act of May 14, 1898. An act of June 6, 1900, assigned to the civil government responsibility for the care of the insane under the direction of the Secretary of the Interior. Provisions of that act also extended and defined the organization of the civil government and the courts. Alaska was

formally designated a U.S. Territory and its capital was established at Juneau by an act of August 24, 1912. The Alaska Mental Health Enabling Act of July 28, 1956, transferred the Interior Department's responsibility for the care of the insane to the Territorial government. Provisions for admitting Alaska into the Union as a State were included in an act of July 7, 1958, and the formal admission was completed January 3, 1959, under Presidential Proclamation 3269.

There are 297 cubic feet of records (in FRC Seattle) dated between 1884 and 1958 in this record group.

RECORDS. 1884-1958. 356 lin. ft.

These include the Executive Office central file ("Term of Office File"), 1884-1920; administrative records, 1885-1912; the Governors' annual reports, 1917-57; letters received and sent by the Secretary of Alaska, 1900-1913; general correspondence, 1909-58; Territorial government legislative records, 1913-39; reports from surveys and studies, 1910-58; records relating to emergency relief programs, 1934-41, and to the Alaska rural rehabilitation project, 1935-49; expenditure and accounting records, 1913-52; and correspondence relating to the care of the insane, 1905-33.

RECORDS OF THE BUREAU OF INSULAR AFFAIRS
(RECORD GROUP 350)

The Bureau of Insular Affairs had its origin December 13, 1898, as the Division of Customs and Insular Affairs in the Office of the Secretary of War to assist in administering customs and other civil affairs in Puerto Rico, Cuba, and the Philippine Islands. A War Department order of December 10, 1900, designated the Division of Customs and Insular Affairs the Division of Insular Affairs. The latter Division was named the Bureau of Insular Affairs by an act of July 1, 1902. Reorganization Plan No. II of 1939 consolidated the Bureau with the Division of Territories and Island Possessions, Department of the Interior (see RG 126).

The functions of the Bureau and its predecessors included supervising civil affairs of the Governments of the Philippine Islands, 1898-1939, and Puerto Rico, 1898-1900 and 1909-34; and the Cuban Military, 1898-1902, and Provisional, 1906-9, Governments (see RG's 140 and 199). The Bureau also supervised the Dominican, 1905-39 (see RG 139), and Haitian, 1920-24, Customs Receiverships and performed duties relating to the Panama Canal, March-May 1904 and January-April 1905. To some extent it acted as a central clearinghouse for information concerning all U.S. territories and insular possessions. The records in this record group interpret the purpose and intent of orders, laws, and rulings, and document the Secretary's determinations on civil questions in island governments.

There are 1,645 cubic feet of records dated between 1868 and 1945 in this record group.

GENERAL RECORDS. 1898-1945. 922 lin. ft.

Included are general classified files, with indexes and record cards, relating to the Philippines, 1898-1939; Puerto Rico, 1898-1900 and 1909-34; the Military, 1898-1902, and Provisional, 1906-9, Governments of Cuba; the Dominican, 1905-39, and Haitian, 1920-24, Customs Receiverships; the Virgin Islands, 1917-45; the Panama Canal, 1904-5; and aspects of territorial administration. Also a confidential file, 1914-35; classified files relating to customs matters, 1898-1941, and the Dominican Customs Receivership, 1905-35; a personal name file, 1914-45; letters sent, 1899-1913; and maps (57 items) primarily relating to the Philippine Islands, with a few of Puerto Rico, 1911-34.

OTHER RECORDS RELATING TO THE PHILIPPINE ISLANDS. 1897-1938. 47 lin. ft.

These include executive orders and proclamations of the Governor General of the Philippine Islands, 1898-1935, and the President of the Commonwealth of the Philippine Islands, 1935-36; correspondence of the Philippine (Taft) Commission, 1900-1906; acts of the Commission, 1900-1907, the Philippine Legislature, 1907-35, and the Philippine National Assembly, 1936-37; House and Senate bills of the Philippine Legislature, 1928-35; galley proofs of *A History of the Philippine Insurrection Against the United States, 1899-1903,* 1906, with related records of the War Department project to publish the history, 1899-1916; correspondence and reports relating to Gen. Mariano Noriel and Apolinario Mabini, 1916; and records of the Philippine Exposition Board, 1904-5, and the Manila Railroad Co., 1905-17.

LIBRARY RECORDS. 1868-1945. 685 lin. ft.

As an adjunct to its general correspondence files, the Bureau accumulated a library that consists chiefly of official documents relating to all noncontiguous U.S. territory and includes published documents issued by the U.S. Government and the Bureau of Printing at Manila, relating to the administration of U.S. insular possessions, 1900-1934; copies of the *Gaceta de Manila*, 1868-98, and the *Official Gazette* of Manila, 1902-32; and manuscript reports of the Philippine Commission, 1900-1915, and the Governors General of the Philippines, 1916-40, and Puerto Rico, 1909-31. There is also a card index to the library, 1898-1935.

MISCELLANEOUS RECORDS. 1898-1937. 49 lin. ft.

Included are the U.S. President's Executive orders relating to island possessions, 1903-32; a code translation volume, n.d.; records relating to the Spanish Treaty Claims Commission, 1910; correspondence between Gen. Leonard Wood and the Secretary of War, relating to Cuba, 1899-1902; notes on Secretary of War Henry L. Stimson's trip to the West Indies and Panama, 1911; laws, ordinances, decrees, and military orders effective in Puerto Rico, 1900-1934; records relating to sugar production, 1930-33; and records of the Statistical Branch, relating to the occupation of Cuba, 1901-2. Also scrapbooks relating to Bureau activities, 1905-17; summaries of newspaper articles published in the Dominican Republic, 1905-6, and of newspaper and magazine articles about territorial affairs, 1931-36; abstracts of newspaper and magazine articles published in the Philippines, 1929-35; and

a list of periodicals received by the Bureau, 1918-34.

AUDIOVISUAL RECORDS. 1898-1939. 14,570 items.

These consist primarily of photographs relating to Cuba, including the first military governor, a jail, and other subjects; Puerto Rican Governors, census enumerators, police, schools, and roads; places and persons in Haiti, Santo Domingo, Panama, and the Virgin Islands; Philippine agricultural products and methods, tribes, customs, crafts, industries, modes of transportation, railroad development, educational facilities, public roads and buildings, political bodies, historical events, geographical features, and cities; and Philippine and American military organizations and officials.

See Richard S. Maxwell, comp., *Preliminary Inventory of the Records of the Bureau of Insular Affairs*, PI 130 (1960); Kenneth Munden, comp., *Records of the Bureau of Insular Affairs Relating to the Philippine Islands, 1898-1935, a List of Selected Files*, SL 2 (1942); Munden, comp., *Records of the Bureau of Insular Affairs Relating to the United States Military Government of Cuba, 1898-1902, and the United States Provisional Government of Cuba, 1906-1909, a List of Selected Files*, SL 3 (1943); Munden and Milton Greenbaum, comps., *Records of the Bureau of Insular Affairs Relating to Puerto Rico, 1898-1934, a List of Selected Files*, SL 4 (1943); and Munden, comp., *List of Records of the Bureau of Insular Affairs Relating to the Dominican Customs Receivership, 1905-1940*, SL 5 (1943).

Microfilm Publications: *Bureau of Insular Affairs: Index to Official Published Documents Relating to Cuba and the Insular Possessions of the United States, 1876-1906*, M24, 3 rolls; and *History of the Philippine Insurrection Against the United States, 1899-1903, and Documents Relating to the War Department Project for Publishing the History*, M719, 9 rolls, DP.

RECORDS OF THE WAR MINERALS RELIEF COMMISSION (RECORD GROUP 194)

The War Minerals Relief Commission (WMRC) was established under the War Minerals Relief Act of 1919 to assist the

Secretary of the Interior in adjudicating mineowners' claims for losses relating to the production of manganese, chrome, pyrite, or tungsten in compliance with Government requests or demands during World War I. Although by 1926 final settlements had been made on all claims submitted, an act of February 13, 1929, authorized claimants to petition the Supreme Court of the District of Columbia to review the Secretary's decisions. The Secretary was directed by an act of May 18, 1936, to reopen certain claims and include in his adjustments interest paid by or accrued against the claimant to 1936. After May 1, 1923, the Commission functioned as part of the Office of the Secretary, under the Solicitor's direction. The Commission was abolished April 15, 1940, and its functions were performed by the Office of the Chief Clerk of the Department of the Interior until June 30, 1941.

There are 155 cubic feet of records (in WNRC) dated between 1917 and 1941 in this record group.

RECORDS. 1917–41. 195 lin. ft.

The records include those relating to the completion of Commission activities by the Chief Clerk of the Department of the Interior. There are records relating to administration, legislation, and Government promotion of the production program, 1917–29; correspondence and other records of Commissioner John Briar, 1919–36; correspondence, reports, and other records of the Chief Engineer of the Commission, 1918–23; correspondence and other records of the Chief Clerk and the Chief Accountant of the Commission, 1918–25, including weekly reports of field auditors, 1922–25; claims files containing questionnaires, correspondence, supporting papers, and other documents relating to individual claims, 1919–41; claims lists and indexes; records relating to recommendations, decisions, and awards; and general correspondence and related Commission records, 1919–41.

RECORDS OF THE PETROLEUM ADMINISTRATIVE BOARD (RECORD GROUP 232)

By a series of Executive orders issued in the summer of 1933, the Secretary of the Interior was designated Administrator of the Code of Fair Competition for the Petroleum Industry and was delegated responsibility for administering the provisions of the National Industrial Recovery Act, which authorized the President to prohibit transporting in interstate or foreign commerce petroleum and petroleum products exceeding amounts permitted by State laws or regulations. On September 11, 1933, the Secretary established the Petroleum Administrative Board to enforce regulations issued under authority of the National Industrial Recovery Act and the petroleum code. The Board assumed most functions of the Federal Oil Con-

servation Board, 1924–34, which had investigated petroleum production, refining, distribution methods, and sources of supply; studied and recommended Government activities concerning petroleum; and cooperated with oil industry and State authorities in conservation work. Although the U.S. Supreme Court on May 27, 1935, invalidated code-making provisions of the act, the Board continued to exist as the agent of the Secretary in enforcing the Connally "Hot Oil" Act of February 22, 1935, which also prohibited foreign and interstate commerce in petroleum and its products produced in violation of State laws. The Board worked closely with the Petroleum Labor Policy Board, 1933–36, which assisted the Secretary in enforcing the labor provisions of the petroleum code. The Petroleum Administrative Board was terminated March 31, 1936, and replaced by the Petroleum Conservation Division.

There are 405 cubic feet of records (in WNRC) dated between 1924 and 1943 in this record group.

RECORDS. 1924-43. 623 lin. ft.

These consist of reports, correspondence, studies, press releases, clippings, reference material, and other records of the Federal Oil Conservation Board, 1924-34; reports, briefs, hearings, orders, correspondence, and other records transferred from the National Recovery Administration, concerning the preparation of the petroleum code, 1933-35; records of the Petroleum Administrative Board, including correspondence, office files, orders and other procedural issuances, production and cost schedules, other statistical and accounting records, transcripts and other records concerning hearings, compliance case files, reference material, and field office records, 1933-36; correspondence and other records of the Petroleum Labor Policy Board, 1934-35; case files, administrative correspondence, and other records of the Oil Enforcement Section of the Division of Investigations, Department of the Interior, 1933-35; and records of the Petroleum Conservation Division, 1934-43, some of which were created by the Petroleum Administrative Board, including general subject files, proration studies, and reading files of communications sent by the Division and by the Federal Tender Board and its successor, Federal Tender Board No. 1, Kilgore, Tex., concerning the issuance of clearance certificates for shipping petroleum and petroleum products.

RECORDS OF THE
PUERTO RICO RECONSTRUCTION ADMINISTRATION
(RECORD GROUP 323)

The Puerto Rico Reconstruction Administration was established in the Department of the Interior by Executive Order 7057 of May 28, 1935, in accordance with the Emergency Relief Appropriation Act of 1935, to provide relief, increase employment, and rehabilitate the agricultural economy in Puerto Rico. It initiated and administered urban and rural housing projects, granted loans to farmers, assisted in establishing cooperatives, and constructed a cement plant and hydroelectric plants. By a joint resolution of August 15, 1953, the Secretary of the Interior was authorized to liquidate the Administration, and it was terminated February 15, 1955.

There are 65 cubic feet of records dated between 1935 and 1953 in this record group.

RECORDS. 1935-53. 72 lin. ft.

Included are general files of the Washington office, consisting of correspondence, progress reports, financial statements, and other records relating to agency administration and projects, 1935-45; records of the Office of the Assistant Administrator in Puerto Rico, including correspondence, 1935-45, investigative files, 1937-40, radiograms received and sent, 1935-50, legal opinions, 1935-39, and administrative orders, 1935-44; records relating to Administration-sponsored cooperatives, such as the Cooperativa Azucarera Los Canos and the Cooperative Lafayette, 1935-45; records of the Administrative, 1935-50, Rural Electrification, 1935-42, Finance, 1935-45, Forestry, 1935-41, Engineering, 1935-53, Legal, 1935-40, and Rural Rehabilitation, 1935-41, Divisions;

records of the Office of Housing Management, 1935-47; and records relating to the Guaynabo cement plant project, 1935-45.

See Mary Jane Schmittou and Mario D. Fenyo, comps., *Preliminary Inventory of the Records of the Puerto Rico Reconstruction Administration*, PI 152 (1963).

RECORDS OF THE
NATIONAL BITUMINOUS COAL COMMISSION, 1935-36
(RECORD GROUP 150)

The first National Bituminous Coal Commission was established in the Department of the Interior by the Bituminous Coal Conservation Act of August 30, 1935 (the Guffey Act). The Commission was to determine average production costs for bituminous coal in each of nine minimum-price areas and establish minimum prices based on those costs, guarantee collective-bargaining rights to miners, provide for adoption of maximum hours and minimum wages in the bituminous industry, and constitute marketing regulations and conduct research on the production, use, conservation, and distribution of bituminous coal. On May 18, 1936, the U.S. Supreme Court declared unconstitutional the principal provisions of the Guffey Act and the Commission ceased most of its activities. An act of April 26, 1937, created the second National Bituminous Coal Commission (see RG 222). Records of the Office of Consumers' Counsel of the Commissions are among records of the Office of the Bituminous Coal Consumers' Counsel (see RG 223).

There are 70 cubic feet of records (in WNRC except for nontextual records) dated between 1935 and 1936 in this record group.

RECORDS. 1935-36. 86 lin. ft.

Included are records of the Office of the Secretary of the first National Bituminous Coal Commission and its Code Membership, District Board, and Docket Sections and Business Manager's Office, including drafts of minutes, orders and other Commission issuances, transcripts of hearings before the Commission, correspondence, code acceptance certificates, affidavits of tonnage production, and materials relating to organization, administration, and work of district boards; records of the Commission's director of research; and general records and office files of its Legal Division. Records of the Bituminous Coal Labor Board of the Department of Labor, which from 1935 to 1936 mediated labor disputes in the bituminous coal industry under the Guffey Act, consist of minutes, correspondence, and records concerning a wage dispute in Illinois.

CARTOGRAPHIC RECORDS. 1935-36. 60 items.

These consist of maps and graphs relating to petroleum and coal production, Commission districts, pipelines, railroads, and coal sales.

See Wallace B. Goebel, comp., and Charles Zaid,

rev., *Preliminary Inventory of the Records of the National Bituminous Coal Commission, 1935-36,* PI 156 (1963).

SPECIFIC RESTRICTIONS

Records: Records less than 50 years old containing "information obtained from a producer disclosing costs of production or sales realization."

Restrictions: "No information obtained from a producer disclosing costs of production or sales realization shall be made public without the consent of the producer from whom the same shall have been obtained, except where such disclosure is warranted by a controversy with the producer over any order of the Commission and except that such information may be compiled in composite form in such manner as shall not be injurious to the interests of any producer and, as so compiled, may be published by the Commission." (49 Stat. 1006.)

Specified by: Congress of the United States.

RECORDS OF THE BITUMINOUS COAL DIVISION
(RECORD GROUP 222)

The second National Bituminous Coal Commission was established in the Department of the Interior by the Bituminous Coal Act of April 26, 1937, after the principal provisions of the Bituminous Coal Conservation Act of 1935 were declared unconstitutional (see RG 150). The second Commission operated as an independent agency until Reorganization Plan No. II of 1939 abolished it and transferred its functions to the Secretary of the Interior, who then established the Bituminous Coal Division. Both the Commission and the Division determined average production costs for bituminous coal in each production area and established minimum and maximum prices based on those costs, established marketing regulations, assisted in adopting maximum hours and minimum wages in the bituminous coal industry, and conducted research relating to the production, use, conservation, and distribution of bituminous coal. The Division also assisted the Office of Price Administration (OPA) in enforcing wartime regulations for coal producers, sales agents, and distributors. With the expiration in August 1943 of congressional authorization, the Division was terminated; its field organization and most of its records were transferred to the Solid Fuels Administration for War (see RG 245).

There are 1,526 cubic feet of records (in WNRC except for nontextual records) dated between 1937 and 1943 in this record group.

RECORDS. 1937-43. 2,150 lin. ft.

These consist of records of the second National Bituminous Coal Commission and the Bituminous Coal Division and include minutes, administrative records, transcripts of hearings, orders and other issuances, general and special correspondence files, officials' office files, contracts, code membership files, case files and other records concerning compliance with regulations and petitions for exemption (including OPA regulations), and records concerning field operations, the determination of costs and the establishment of prices, and statistics. Maps, 1937-43 (10 items), relate to coal production, distribution, market areas, and shipment and price rates in the United States.

SPECIFIC RESTRICTIONS

Records: Records containing information obtained from a producer disclosing costs of production or sales realization.

Restrictions: "No information obtained from a producer disclosing cost of production or sales realization shall be made public without the consent of the producer from whom the same shall have been obtained, except where such disclosure is made in evidence in any hearing before the Commission or any court and except that such information may be compiled in composite form in such manner as shall not be injurious to the interests of any producer and, as so compiled, may be published by the Commission." (50 Stat. 88.)

Specified by: Congress of the United States.

RECORDS OF THE
SOLID FUELS ADMINISTRATION FOR WAR
(RECORD GROUP 245)

On November 5, 1941, the President named the Secretary of the Interior the Solid Fuels Coordinator for National Defense, redesignated Solid Fuels Coordinator for War in May 1942. The Office of Coordinator was basically an information-gathering and advisory body. It was replaced on April 19, 1943, by the more powerful Solid Fuels Administration for War. Although the Secretary of the Interior was Administrator, the Deputy Administrator directed agency operations. In August 1943 the Administration inherited some functions and the field organization of the Bituminous Coal Division (see RG 222). The Administration was the chief Government instrument for wartime control of solid fuels industries. It issued and enforced policy and operating directives to those industries, recommended to the Office of Price Administration maximum prices for solid fuels, advised other agencies on such matters as transportation of solid fuels and manpower needs of solid fuels industries, and formulated general policies and specific programs for development, conservation, distribution, and use of coal and (by 1944) coke.

The Administration also participated in the operation of Government-seized coal mines. For the first two seizures, 1943-44, the Secretary of the Interior organized Coal Mines Administrations (often considered one Administration with separated periods of activity), with himself as Administrator, to operate the mines in close association with the Solid Fuels Administration for War. During the third seizure, May-June 1945, employees of the Solid Fuels Administration for War administered the mines. A Coal Mines Administration, conducted almost entirely by Navy personnel and often referred to as the Coal Mines Administration—Navy, was established in May 1946 for the fourth seizure. At first the Secretary of the Interior served as its administrator, but in June 1946 a separate administrator was appointed. Executive Order 9847 of May 6, 1946, terminated the Solid Fuels Administration for War, and the Coal Mines Administration—Navy ceased to exist on June 30, 1947.

There are 1,223 cubic feet of records (in WNRC) dated between 1937 and 1948 in this record group.

RECORDS. 1937-48. 1,517 lin. ft.

Central office records include general records of the Solid Fuels Administration for War and records of the Office of the Deputy Administrator and divisions of the Administration, and comprise administrative records, orders and other procedural issuances, reports, correspondence, compliance case files and other legal records, statistical tabulations, and press releases, 1941-47. Also the Coal Mines Administrations' reports, correspondence, legal records, financial and accounting records for claims arising from mine seizures, and records relating to a medical survey in mining regions, 1943-48.

Field office records chiefly comprise reports and correspondence of the second National Bituminous Coal Commission, the Bituminous Coal Division, the Solid Fuels Administration for War, and the Coal Mines Administrations, 1937-47.

See Edward F. Martin, comp., *Preliminary Inventory of the Records of the Solid Fuels Administration for War*, PI 34 (1951).

SPECIFIC RESTRICTIONS

Records: Records of the former Bituminous Coal Division and its predecessor, the second National Bituminous Coal Commission, that contain information obtained from a producer disclosing costs of production or sales realization and are included among the records of the Solid Fuels Administration for War.

Restrictions: "No information obtained from a producer disclosing cost of production or sales realization shall be made public without the consent of the producer from whom the same shall have been obtained, except where such disclosure is made in evidence in any hearing before the Commission or any court and except that such information may be compiled in composite form in such manner as shall not be injurious to the interests of any producer and, as so compiled, may be published by the Commission." (50 Stat. 88.)

Specified by: Congress of the United States.

RECORDS OF THE
FEDERAL INTERAGENCY RIVER BASIN COMMITTEE
(RECORD GROUP 315)

The Federal Interagency River Basin Committee was created by an agreement of December 29, 1943, between the Federal Power Commission and the Interior, War, and Agriculture Departments. Membership was later extended to the Departments of Commerce, Labor, and Health, Education, and Welfare. Committee objectives were the exchange of information on activities involving water use and control, cooper-

ation in the preparation of reports on multiple-purpose projects, and correlation of project results. The Committee also coordinated interagency projects and programs. The agreement was its sole charter, and it remained a voluntary unit. Funds were provided by member agencies whose unanimous consent was necessary for any proposed action. Eight technical subcommittees and five regional committees were established to carry out the Committee's specialized functions. On May 26, 1954, the President abolished the Committee and created as its successor the Interagency Committee on Water Resources.

There are 14 cubic feet of records dated between 1940 and 1954 in this record group.

RECORDS. 1940-54. 17 lin. ft.

These consist of minutes, 1944-54, with an index, 1944-53; reports, 1948-51; general correspondence, 1945-54; records of the Subcommittee on Hydrology, including minutes, 1946-54, reports, 1950, and maps and atlases showing hydrologic stations, 1947 and 1949; minutes, 1946-54, and reports, 1940-53, of the Subcommittee on Sedimentation and the Subcommittee on Benefits and Costs, 1946-53 and 1940-53; a semiannual report of the Subcommittee on Energy Conversion Procedures, Factors, and Empirical Constants, 1950; minutes, reports, and maps of the New England-New York Interagency Committee, 1950-54; and minutes of the Pacific Southwest Federal Interagency Technical Committee, 1948-54, and of the Columbia Basin, 1946-54, Missouri Basin, 1945-54, and Arkansas-White-Red River Basins, 1950-53, Interagency Committees.

CARTOGRAPHIC RECORDS. 1947-54. 27 items.

Records of the Subcommittee on Hydrology include two atlases of river basin maps; and records of the New England-New York Interagency Committee include maps of river basins, showing land use.

RECORDS OF THE OFFICE OF GEOGRAPHY
(RECORD GROUP 324)

The Office of Geography provides research and other staff services for the interdepartmental Board on Geographic Names and the Secretary of the Interior on foreign geographic nomenclature. The Office inherited functions and records of earlier boards and committees engaged in similar work. The earliest of these, the U.S. Board on Geographic Names, was created by an Executive order of September 4, 1890, to ensure uniform usage of geographic nomenclature throughout the executive departments of the Government. The title of the Board was changed to the U.S. Geographic Board in 1906, and the Board itself was abolished in 1934. Its records and functions were transferred to the Department of the Interior, where the Secretary created the Division of Geographic Names and the Advisory Committee on Geographic Names. The two units together were designated as the U.S. Board on Geographic Names. This Board was abolished by an act of July 25, 1947, and the new Board on Geographic Names was created. By order of the Secretary of the Interior of June 17, 1948, the Division of Geography was established in his office and made responsible for performing all staff functions for the Board of Geographic Names and its committees. The Division became the Office of Geography in 1955. The functions and records relating to domestic geographic names were transferred from the Office to the Geological Survey in 1958, while functions and records relating to foreign names remained in the Office. The latter were transferred in 1968 to the Department of Defense.

There are 75 cubic feet of records dated between 1890 and 1968 in this record group.

RECORDS. 1890–1968. 90 lin. ft.

These consist chiefly of reports and decision lists of the U.S. Board on Geographic Names and successor agencies, 1890–1968, including both domestic and foreign names, 1943–68; an incomplete set of rules for treating foreign geographic names, 1944–48; catalogs, 1949–53; gazeteers, 1955–56; and maps, 1907 and 1943–47 (971 items), prepared chiefly as aids in making nomenclature decisions.

RECORDS OF THE
DEFENSE ELECTRIC POWER ADMINISTRATION
(RECORD GROUP 327)

The Defense Electric Power Administration (DEPA), known briefly as the Defense Power Administration, was established December 4, 1950, by order of the Secretary of the Interior. Its principal purpose was to mobilize electric utility companies for defense production. The DEPA was authorized to allocate critical materials to electric utility companies and to exercise defense control and expansion functions over the power industry. These functions included scheduling major power equipment production, evaluating needs for materials, distributing materials within the power industry, issuing power priorities, requisitioning power facilities where necessary, and reviewing certificates of necessity for accelerated tax amortization, loans, and loan guarantees required in power expansion. An order of the Secretary of the Interior of May 7, 1953, abolished the DEPA and delegated certain of its defense functions to the Assistant Secretary of the Interior for Water and Power.

There are 41 cubic feet of records dated between 1950 and 1953 in this record group.

RECORDS. 1950–53. 49 lin. ft.

These consist of a general subject file of the Office of the Administrator; procedural issuances; letters sent; a detailed narrative history of the DEPA with 27 appendixes, one of which contains a history of the northwest electricity conservation program, 1952–53; speeches and press releases; files of the Office of the General Counsel; general records of the Power Supply Division, relating to power resources and requirements, and office files of the Division Chief; records relating to powerplants and to the preparation of a report on power requirements; office files of the Chief of the Utilities Conservation Branch, and correspondence with utility companies in the northwest region; and general files of the Construction Expediting Branch and of the Major Equipment Scheduling Branch.

Department of Agriculture

RECORDS OF THE
OFFICE OF THE SECRETARY OF AGRICULTURE
(RECORD GROUP 16)

The Department of Agriculture, established by an act of May 15, 1862, continued and expanded the agricultural activities engaged in by the Patent Office since 1836. The Department was headed by a commissioner without Cabinet rank until an act of February 9, 1889, enlarged the agency's powers and duties and made it an executive department under a Secretary. For several decades the Department was engaged chiefly in the distribution of seeds and plants and in scientific and educational work to increase agricultural production or decrease unit costs, to prevent damage by disease and insects, and to select the best varieties and breeds of plants and animals. The work of the Department has steadily expanded and numerous changes have been made in its organization to provide for new functions, to bring together related scientific and economic work, and to coordinate various research, extension, and regulatory activities. The Department now performs functions relating to research, conservation, production, education, marketing, regulation, surplus disposal, rural development, and agricultural adjustment.

See Department of Agriculture, *Yearbook 1940: Farmers in a Changing World* (1940), and *Century of Service, the First 100 Years of the United States Department of Agriculture* (1963); and George McGovern, ed., *Agricultural Thought in the Twentieth Century* (Indianapolis, 1967).

There are 7,642 cubic feet of records dated between 1839 and 1964 in this record group.

RECORDS OF THE
AGRICULTURAL SECTION OF
THE PATENT OFFICE. 1839-60.
5 lin. ft.

These records concern the preparation and distribution of annual reports and the collection and distribution of seeds and plants. Records relating to annual reports include letters from farmers about crop prospects and agricultural practices, completed questionnaires, and articles and essays, with correspondence. Records relating to seed and plant distribution include reports from consular officials, foreign seed firms, and missionaries; requests from agricultural societies and farmers; and reports about cultivating seeds and plants. Also included are reports and letters concerning studies of native grasses and European markets for cotton, collecting tea seeds in China and native grape cuttings, and developing sprays for orange trees.

RECORDS OF THE
COMMISSIONER AND THE
SECRETARY OF AGRICULTURE.
1879-1964. 5,006 lin. ft.

These records consist chiefly of the subject files of the Office of the Secretary, 1906-64, and letters sent by the Secretary, 1893-1941. The reports, letters, memorandums, and other records received, with letters sent, are filed under the names of objects, commodities, events, transactions, and activities of interest to the Department. These files include not only correspondence of the Secretary but also a large part of the correspondence received or prepared by the Assistant and Under Secretaries; by property, fiscal, and personnel officers attached to the Secretary's Office; and by special assistants and committees. Many of these records are concerned with policy, organization, and procedure rather than with details of research or program execution.

The letters sent form a separate and nearly complete set of all letters signed by the Secretary from 1893 through 1941. Many such letters were prepared in the bureaus of the Department, and the main file on a particular transaction may be among the records of the bureau most concerned or in the subject files of the Office of the Secretary.

There are also three small series of letters sent, 1879-97, chiefly concerning requests for seeds, publications, special reports, and information. For the years before the initiation of the subject files in 1906, the only incoming correspondence is a small series covering the years 1893-1906.

Other records of this Office include transcripts of press conferences, 1933-40; speeches of Secretary Ezra Taft Benson, 1953-60; orders, circulars, and memorandums, 1897-1942; records relating to the national agricultural achievement "A" awards program, 1943-44; and minutes of Rural Electrification Administration's local electric cooperatives, 1941-44.

RECORDS OF THE OFFICE OF THE ASSISTANT SECRETARIES, THE UNDER SECRETARY OF AGRICULTURE, AND SPECIAL ASSISTANTS. 1889-1943. 33 lin. ft.

Included are letters sent by Assistant Secretaries and special assistants, 1889-1929; reports and correspondence of Under Secretary Paul H. Appleby, concerning wartime food management, 1942-43; office files of Assistant and Under Secretary Milburn L. Wilson, 1934-40; office files, 1932-36, and

records relating to emergency relief work, 1933-35, of the Assistant to the Secretary in Charge of Civil Works; and office files of the special assistant, 1933-35, and the scientific adviser to the Secretary, 1933-38.

RECORDS OF THE OFFICE OF THE SOLICITOR. 1891-1945. 1,700 lin. ft.

The Office of the Solicitor was renamed the Office of General Counsel in 1955. General records consist of correspondence, 1900-1942, and records relating to real or alleged violations of laws enforced by the Department, 1891-1943, national defense and food control during World War I, and applications for patents by Department employees, 1922-44. There are also case files relating to land acquisition for resettlement and rehabilitation projects, 1935-42, and national forestry purposes, 1920-38.

The functions and records of the Agricultural Adjustment Administration's Legal Division were taken over in 1935 by the Solicitor's Office. Included are records relating to enforcement of the Agricultural Adjustment Act, 1933-37, correspondence concerning licenses, 1933-37, and orders, notices, transcripts of hearings, and marketing agreements, 1933-41. In similar fashion the legal work and records of the General Counsel of the Resettlement Administration were taken over in 1937 by the Solicitor's Office. Its records consist of case files, 1935-37, and newspaper clippings relating to housing projects, 1935-36.

RECORDS OF THE OFFICE OF INFORMATION. 1913-63. 723 lin. ft.

In July 1913 the Office of Information was established to publicize the discoveries and recommendations of Department scientists, specialists, and field workers. Its records include correspondence, 1913-44, press releases, 1913-63, radio releases, 1926-54, the *Daily Digest*, 1921-42, the *Official Record*, 1922-33, and the *Weekly News Letter*, 1913-21.

RECORDS OF THE OFFICE OF
THE CIVILIAN CONSERVATION
CORPS (CCC) ACTIVITIES. 1933-42.
24 lin. ft.

Many CCC camps were under technical supervision of Department bureaus,
especially the Forest and Soil Conservation Services. The Secretary delegated
to the Forest Service responsibility for
liaison with the Office of the Director
of the CCC and for coordinating and
supervising CCC work of the Department as a whole. It was not until
July 27, 1938, that the Office of the
Civilian Conservation Corps Activities
was established to perform those functions. Its records include correspondence, memorandums, camp directories,
and maps.

RECORDS OF THE OFFICE FOR
AGRICULTURAL WAR
RELATIONS. 1940-43. 99 lin. ft.

In May 1941 the functions of the Division of Agriculture in the Advisory Commission to the Council of National
Defense were transferred to the Office
of Agricultural Defense Relations under
the Secretary of Agriculture. The Office,
the name of which was changed in 1942
to the Office for Agricultural War Relations, adjusted the agricultural program
to meet defense needs, disseminated
information about agricultural defense
problems, coordinated defense efforts in
the Department, and assisted the Secretary in communicating with defense
agencies about production, procurement,
and prices. These records consist chiefly
of correspondence relating to Division
activities, 1940-41, and to agricultural
defense programs and problems, 1941-
43.

RECORDS OF OTHER UNITS.
1862-1948. 433 lin. ft.

Included are records of the Office of
Irrigation Inquiry, 1890-95; letters sent
by the Director of Scientific Work, 1920-
29; records relating to the Department's

emergency relief work performed in
cooperation with the Works Progress
Administration; correspondence and
reports concerning labor relations in the
meatpacking industry and other records
of the Office of the Government Representative for Meat Supply, 1946; correspondence and letters sent by the Office
of Feed and Food Conservation, 1948;
letters sent by the Office of the Chief
Clerk, 1893-1929; cashbooks, ledgers,
employee salary records, money
receipts, and appropriation ledgers of
the Office of the Disbursing Clerk, 1868-
1921; and records of the Office of Budget
and Finance, 1933-42, including correspondence of the Director of Finance,
1935-37. Records of the Office of Plant
and Operations, 1903-43, include warranty deeds, 1913-41, and reports and
correspondence of its Real Estate Division about buildings owned or occupied
by the Department in and near the District of Columbia, 1906-39; the operation
of the Administration Building and the
construction and operation of the South
Building, 1926-39; and the construction
of the Beltsville Research Center, 1939-
42. Records of the Office of Personnel,
1862-1940, include folders for certain
Department employees.

There are also correspondence,
reports, and minutes of the Joint Committee on Projects, 1914-15; correspondence about the Department representative on the Committee on Food Supply
and Prices, 1917-18; correspondence and
reports of the President's Agricultural
Conference, 1919-25; reports of the
Committee on Fire and Explosion Risks,
1921; records relating to the General
Supply Committee, 1914-18, Federal
Board for Vocational Education, 1917-
32, Federal Power Commission, 1923-30,
Federal Real Estate Board, 1921-34 and
1939-42, and Federal Traffic Board,
1932; correspondence of the National
Drought Relief Committee secretary,
1930-32; reports exchanged between the
Department and the National Emergen-

cy Council, 1933–36; minutes of the Combined Food Board, 1941–42; correspondence and reports of the Interbureau Committee on Post War Planning, 1941–45; correspondence, minutes, reports, and speeches relating to the Famine Emergency Committee, 1946; and correspondence of the Cabinet Food Committee, 1947–48.

RECORDS OF THE WAR FOOD ADMINISTRATION. 1943–45.
140 lin. ft.

In March 1943, to assure an adequate supply and efficient distribution of food, the Food Production Administration (except the Farm Credit Administration), Food Distribution Administration, Commodity Credit Corporation, and Extension Service were consolidated to form the Administration of Food Production and Distribution, renamed the War Food Administration the following month. It was abolished in 1945. The records consist chiefly of the Administrator's correspondence, reports, and memorandums.

CARTOGRAPHIC AND AUDIOVISUAL RECORDS. 1886–1959. 25,463 items.

Cartographic records (2,081 items) include atlases relating to agricultural statistics and farm taxation and tenure, 1889 and 1922–37; regional maps of the United States prepared by postwar planning committees, showing industrial development, transportation facilities, and soil-type, crop, livestock, and population distributions, 1941–45; maps of the United States published decennially that show State, territorial, and county boundaries from 1840 to 1940; and maps showing the progress of aerial photographic surveys, 1944–47.

Audiovisual records (23,382 items) consist of engravings and portrait photographs of scientists, 1886–1925; the Erwin F. Smith collection of portrait photographs of scientists, 1886–1927; photographs of agricultural research activities, Government buildings, and scenes in and near Washington, D.C., 1899–1938; photographs received by the Office of Information from the Extension Service, Forest Service, Rural Electrification Administration, Biological Survey, Bureau of Entomology, Federal Crop Insurance Corporation, Agricultural Adjustment Administration, and other departmental units, 1900–1959; the Frank Lamson-Scribner collection of photographs of exhibits and plantlife, 1901–36; and hand-colored lantern slides of the halls, buildings, streets, statuary, and exhibits of the Department in the Panama-Pacific International Exposition at San Francisco, 1915.

See Harold T. Pinkett, comp., *Preliminary Inventory of the Records of the Office for Agricultural War Relations*, PI 37 (1952).

Microfilm Publication: *Letters Sent by the Secretary of Agriculture, 1893–1929*, M440, 563 rolls, DP.

RECORDS OF THE FOREST SERVICE
(RECORD GROUP 95)

The Forest Service of the Department of Agriculture originated in 1881 as the Division of Forestry. By an act of March 2, 1901, the Division was designated the Bureau of Forestry, and in 1905 was renamed the Forest Service. The Congress in 1891 authorized forest reserves (national forests) from timberlands of the public domain; in 1905 responsibility for their administration was transferred from the Department of the Interior (see RG's 48 and 49) to the Department of Agriculture and vested in the Forest Service. The Weeks Act of 1911 and the Clarke-McNary Act of 1924 gave impetus to programs of land acquisition, fire control, and State cooperation. Responsibilities for forest research and utilization were increased by the McNary-McSweeney Act of 1928. From 1933 to 1942 the Service supervised a large part of the Civilian Conservation Corps (CCC) work program (see RG 35). Under the Emergency Appropriation Act of June 19, 1934, the Service carried out the Prairie States forestry ("Shelterbelt") project until it was transferred to the Soil Conservation Service in 1942 (see RG 114). During World War II the Service was assigned several major war-related programs. The Service is now responsible for promoting conservation and the best use of national forests and grasslands. Its activities are oriented around the administration and development of the national forest system, cooperation with and assistance to administrators of State and private forests, and forest and range research.

There are 2,439 cubic feet of records dated between 1882 and 1965 in this record group.

GENERAL RECORDS. 1882-1958.
268 lin. ft.

These records concern legislation, cooperation with private organizations and Federal and State governmental agencies, working plans, administration, and testing, measuring, and identifying timber, and comprise Division of Forestry letters received, 1888-99, and sent, 1886-99; general correspondence of the Division, Bureau, and Service, 1898-1908; correspondence of the Office of the Chief (known as the Forester before 1935), 1908-48; and miscellaneous records, 1882-1934. There are also records relating to the Ballinger-Pinchot controversy, 1904-10, Forester Gifford Pinchot's administration, 1905-10, the Keep Commission, 1904-8, National Conservation Commission, 1908-9, National Conservation Congress, 1909, National Conservation Exposition, 1912-13, National Forest Reservation Commission, 1911-58, emergency rubber project

administered by the Service, 1942-46, and the Northeastern Timber Salvage Administration, 1938-41.

Minutes of the Service Committee provide information about Service administration, 1903-35; correspondence and reports of the Section of Inspection, 1906-8, and "general integrating inspection reports," 1937-55, concern field evaluations of policies, programs, and regulations; and correspondence of the Law Office, relating to administration, legislation, claims, and litigation concerning forest lands, 1905-9. Selected official diaries illustrate activities of district and assistant district rangers, nursery superintendents, and prominent Service officials, 1906-44.

RECORDS RELATING TO ADMINISTRATIVE MANAGEMENT AND INFORMATION. 1900-1951.
302 lin. ft.

Included are records, 1900-1944, of the Division of Operation (the Branch of Operation before 1935), comprising reports, memorandums, and correspondence relating chiefly to administrative operations, compilation of administrative statistics, purchases of equipment and supplies, maintenance of buildings, and budgetary matters; and records relating to forest reserves, 1905-7, and to the 10th and 20th Regiments of forest engineers activated for service in World War I, 1917-18.

Records, 1927-51, of the Division of Fiscal Control (the Office of Fiscal Control in the Branch of Operation before 1935), include reports and correspondence relating to allotments, budgets, and audits.

The Division of Information and Education was created in 1935; its records and those of its predecessors—the Office of Publication and Education (established in 1905), the Office of Editor (established in 1910), and the Branch of Public Relations (created in 1920)—include general correspondence, 1907-41, news articles and press releases, 1900-1933 and 1937-46, regional office publications, 1910-41, and radio scripts for "Uncle Sam's Forest Rangers," 1932-44.

RECORDS RELATING TO THE ADMINISTRATION OF NATIONAL FOREST RESOURCES. 1896-1952. 591 lin. ft.

Included are records, 1904-52, of the Division of Engineering and its predecessors, including general correspondence, 1932-52, and Region 7 reports, correspondence, maps, and blueprints, 1920-35, relating to surveying, mapping, and photographing forest lands; constructing roads, trails, telephone lines, bridges, dams, and buildings; and supervising engineering work performed in national forests by private individuals or companies.

Records, 1909-41, of the Division of Fire Control, established in 1935 as the Division of Fire Control and Improvement (functions of which had originated under the Branch of Operation), consist chiefly of reports, correspondence, memorandums, and exhibits relating to Federal and State legislation and research studies on fire control, educational campaigns to prevent fires, claims due to fires, plans for and construction of rapid transportation and communication facilities to be used in fires, and development and use of methods, machines, and equipment for detecting and fighting fires.

The Division of Range Management was established in 1935. Its predecessors were the Branch of Grazing, created in 1907, and the Branch of Range Management, created in 1927. The records, 1905-52, relate to administration of grazing permits, range legislation, organization and administration of the Division and its predecessors, work plans, studies, special surveys, inspection activities, cooperative projects, and trespassing. A few relate to wildlife management before 1935.

Records, 1939-50, of the Division of Watershed Management, established in 1945, include reports, correspondence, surveys, inventories, and studies relating to plans and programs for land and water control and conservation in national forests; and records concerning the emergency rubber project, 1942-46, inherited by the Division after the liquidation of the project.

Records of the Division of Timber Management, established in 1936, include general correspondence, 1905-52, relating to development of plans for supervision of timber sales, surveys, planting, and improvement, and insect and disease control performed by the Division and its major predecessors—the Branch of Silviculture, 1907-20, and the Branch of Forest Management, 1920-36. Also fragmentary records of other predecessor units, including the Office of Forest Management, 1901-9, Office of Forest Extension, 1899-1908, Office of Federal Cooperation, 1908-11, and Office of State and Private Cooperation, 1896-1908.

Records, 1914-50, of the Division of Wildlife Management, established in 1935 (the Division of Range Management and its predecessors had been responsible for wildlife in national forests before that date), include general correspondence concerning quantity, distribution, and importance of wildlife in national forests, relation of wildlife to other forest uses, wildlife protection, establishment of refuges, restocking depleted areas, and interagency cooperation.

RECORDS RELATING TO LAND ACQUISITION AND ADMINISTRATION. 1906-65. 736 lin. ft.

In 1908 the Branch of Lands replaced the Office of Lands of the Branch of

Operation. The Branch of Lands assisted in interpreting application to forest lands of mineral, forest, and homestead legislation; surveyed and classified lands; administered purchase, sale, exchange, and use permits; and determined the legality of property claims. In 1920 the Branch was also given control over acquisitioning lands for national forests, which had been performed by the "Appalachian Work" unit and its successor, the Branch of Acquisition. The Branch of Lands was abolished in 1935, and its functions were transferred to a division later known as the Division of Land Acquisition and to the Division of Recreation and Lands. The Division of Land Acquisition, which in 1954 was divided into the Division of Lands and the Division of Land Utilization, was reunited in 1956 as the Division of Lands but divided again in 1957 into the Division of Land Adjustments and the Division of Land Classification. The Division of Recreation and Lands was redesignated the Division of Recreation and Land Uses in 1954.

The records include general correspondence of these divisions; purchase, exchange, and donation cases, 1922-51; deeds, judgments, and condemnations of land acquired for national forests, 1913-65; records relating to land utilization projects, 1934-43, and the Northern Pacific Railroad land-grant suit, 1906-40; miscellaneous records relating to Service activities in the Appalachian region, 1906-21; and a case file about homesteads granted in national forests under the Forest Homestead Act of 1906.

RECORDS RELATING TO STATE AND PRIVATE FORESTRY COOPERATION. 1913-51. 56 lin. ft.

From the beginning the Forest Service cooperated with State and private owners of forest lands to prevent forest fires, conserve and increase productivity of forest lands and resources, and control forest pests. These functions were performed by the Office of State and Private Cooperation, later known as the State and Private Division and the Division of State Cooperation. In 1935 a State and Private Forestry Branch was established to supervise cooperative work carried on in several divisions, and by 1949 cooperative activities were consolidated in the Division of Cooperative Forest Management and the Division of Cooperative Forest Protection. The records of the divisions and their predecessors include reports, correspondence, and plans relating to efforts to fulfill fire prevention and control provisions of the Weeks Act and the Clarke-McNary Act.

RECORDS RELATING TO RESEARCH ACTIVITIES. 1890-1954. 493 lin. ft.

Before 1905 the work of the Bureau of Forestry was mostly that of research and investigation. In 1904 a Section of Silvics (later the Office of Silvics) was organized, and the Office of Forest Products (later the Branch of Products) was established in 1905 to study timber utilization. In 1908 the first of several experiment stations was established, and in 1910 the Forest Products Laboratory at Madison, Wis., was established in cooperation with the University of Wisconsin. In 1913 the Office of Silvics was superseded by the Office of Forest Investigations. During 1915 Forest Service research activities were consolidated in the Branch of Research, which was replaced in 1935 by five research divisions authorized to conduct research relating to forest management, protection, economics, influences, and products.

The records include the "research compilation file," 1897-1935, a collection of special documents, usually unpublished, relating to forest production, management, and utilization; project files of the Forest Products Laboratory, consisting of technical reports of kiln drying, glues, wood fireproofing, wood as a colloid, and shrinkage control, 1917-35 and 1937-49; records accumulated in preparing the Copeland report *National Plan for American Forestry* (S. Doc. 12, 73d Cong., 1st sess.), relating to public forest policy and coordination of Federal and State forest activities, 1923-33; administrative and research files of the Forest Taxation Inquiry, concerning the relation of tax laws to timber growth and conservation, 1926-37; and records of the divisions and their predecessors, including correspondence, reports, and research studies relating to silviculture, dendrology, botany, and entomology.

RECORDS RELATING TO CCC WORK. 1933-42. 371 lin. ft.

CCC camps in Federal, State, and private forests were supervised by the Forest Service. Records of the Washington office of the Service concern activities of the Coordinating, Enrollee Training, and Camp Program Divisions in planning, supervising, and executing projects to prevent fires, exterminate pests, compile maps, construct recreational and other facilities, reseed lands, and develop wildlife. The records of 34 representative CCC camps contain detailed information on fieldwork, 1933-42.

CARTOGRAPHIC AND AUDIOVISUAL RECORDS. 1890-1962. 19,400 items.

Cartographic records (16,032 items) include topographic, planimetric, and special maps of the Division of Engineering, including published atlases relating to individual national forests, 1908-25; project files containing manu-

script, photoprocessed, and published maps, graphs, and charts used as illustrations, 1910-59; large-scale standard published maps of national forests, game refuges, and other reservations, 1911-60; maps relating to fire control activities and road systems, 1931-62; and aerial survey film negatives of major forest areas, 1934-38. Map files of other Forest Service divisions usually consist of base maps prepared by either the Division of Engineering or other Government agencies to illustrate lumber production and consumption, 1909-35; forest planning, 1910-52; tree species, timber surveys, and timber-sale areas in national forests, 1913-40; grazing districts, rangelands, land use, "Shelterbelt" project areas, and range management plans, 1915-45; recreational facilities in national forests, 1917-30; and county range surveys, 1935-38.

Audiovisual records (3,368 items) include photographs, posters, and prints of posters illustrating Forest Service activities, 1898-1941; photographs of forest reserves in Arizona, California, Colorado, Idaho, Montana, Oregon, and South Dakota, 1898-1900; illustrations of war-related activities of the Forest Products Laboratory, 1917-18; pictures of forest cover, streams, lookouts, fires, reforestation, and trails, 1933-39; and photographs of raising and harvesting guayule rubber in the United States and Mexico during the emergency rubber project, 1942-45.

See Charlotte M. Ashby, comp., *Preliminary Inventory of the Cartographic Records of the Forest Service*, PI 167 (1967); and Harold T. Pinkett, comp., and Terry W. Good, rev., *Preliminary Inventory of the Records of the Forest Service*, PI 18 (1969).

RECORDS OF THE FOREIGN AGRICULTURAL SERVICE (RECORD GROUP 166)

A Section of Foreign Markets was established in the Department of Agriculture in 1895 to collect information on

production, consumption, and prices of foreign farm products. Its functions were continued successively by the

Bureau of Statistics, the Office of Markets (later designated the Bureau of Markets), and the Division of Statistical and Historical Research of the Bureau of Agricultural Economics, which from 1922 to 1930 received and analyzed reports relating to foreign agriculture. An act of June 5, 1930, created the Foreign Agricultural Service, whose officers reported directly to the newly formed Foreign Agricultural Service Division of the Bureau of Agricultural Economics and represented the Department of Agriculture in world trade centers. The Service was transferred from the Department of Agriculture to the Department of State by Reorganization Plan No. II of 1939. Other Division personnel and its economic research functions and records were assigned to the Office of Foreign Agricultural Relations, a separate unit established in the Office of the Secretary of Agriculture.

By a Secretary's memorandum of March 10, 1953, the Office of Foreign Agricultural Relations became the Foreign Agricultural Service. The primary purpose of the Service is to develop foreign markets for U.S. farm products. Through its network of agricultural attaches stationed in principal countries and agricultural marketing specialists who make investigations abroad, the Service maintains current information on world agricultural production, policy situations, and trade competition. It also makes available to farm and business interests in the United States published information concerning agricultural commodities in world trade.

There are 961 cubic feet of records dated between 1901 and 1954 in this record group.

RECORDS. 1901-54. 1,028 lin. ft.

The records of the Service and its predecessors consist of correspondence of the Office of Foreign Agricultural Relations that relates to Office administration, coordination of departmental activities in the area of foreign trade, and agricultural production and marketing, 1942-49. There are also reports (826 lin. ft.) from abroad prepared by American consuls, agricultural attaches, and special agents that relate to such phases of foreign agriculture as production, market trends, imports, exports, and trade regulations, and to international agricultural conferences and agreements, 1904-54; reports concerning forestry and forest products, 1901-41; entomological and quarantine reports, 1911-39; statistical compilations of agricultural commodities imported and exported by the United States, 1930-41; and records relating to the Italian land utilization program, 1933. Records of field offices in the Union of South Africa and Sydney, Australia, consist chiefly of correspondence, field reports, and special studies, 1931-33. Included also are reports, correspondence, and other records relating to American participation in international agricultural conferences, including the International Institute of Agriculture at Rome, 1922-41; and records of the Foreign Agricultural Service's Technical Collaboration Branch, consisting of organizational, administrative, and technical reports relating to agricultural assistance programs in Latin American countries, 1942-53.

CARTOGRAPHIC RECORDS. 1945 and 1948. 2 items.

These consist of atlases compiled by the Office of Foreign Agricultural Relations: the *Agricultural Geography of the Philippine Islands, A Graphic Summary* (1945) and the *Agricultural Geography of Europe and the Near East* (1948), which contain maps showing climate, land elevation, soils, crops, livestock, and population.

RECORDS OF THE COMMODITY EXCHANGE AUTHORITY
(RECORD GROUP 180)

The Commodity Exchange Administration was established in the Department of Agriculture by a Secretary's memorandum, effective July 1, 1936, under the Commodity Exchange Act of June 15, 1936. It succeeded the Grain Futures Administration, created to enforce the Grain Futures Act of 1922, but its jurisdiction was extended to cover dealings in additional commodities. By an Executive order of February 23, 1942, the Commodity Exchange Administration was merged with other agencies to form the Agricultural Marketing Administration. On February 1, 1947, the Commodity Exchange Authority was established as an agency of the Department of Agriculture.

The chief function of the Authority is maintaining fair and honest trading practices on commodity exchanges designated as contract markets under the Commodity Exchange Act. Other responsibilities of the Authority are to protect market users against cheating, fraud, and abusive practices in commodity transactions; to safeguard the handling of traders margin money and equities by preventing misuse of such funds by brokers; and to ensure benefits of membership privileges on contract markets to cooperative associations or producers. The agency also investigates trading and market operations and provides information, statistics, and reports to the public on trading, marketing, and conditions affecting markets. Its supervision of trading currently covers 22 commodities in which one or more exchanges are conducting markets.

There are 232 cubic feet of records dated between 1921 and 1952 in this record group.

RECORDS. 1921–52. 278 lin. ft.

Included are correspondence and records relating to work of the Authority and its predecessors, 1921–42 and 1945–52; Grain Futures Administration case files ("dockets"), 1922–36; "Administrative Dockets," 1936–42, and "Criminal Cases," 1936–41, of the Commodity Exchange Administration; arbitration proceedings, 1926–27; an office file relating to the grain situation and a study of futures markets made by the Soviet Government, 1927–38; progress reports of the Chicago office, 1931–39; and monthly reports of trading in grain futures in the Chicago market, 1934–35 and 1937–40.

See Stanley W. Brown and Virgil E. Baugh, comps., *Preliminary Inventory of the Records of the Commodity Exchange Authority*, PI 112 (1959).

SPECIFIC RESTRICTIONS

Records: Docket files, 1922–42.

Restrictions: These records may not be examined by or information from or copies of them furnished to any person except by permission of an appropriate official of the Commodity Exchange Authority.

Specified by: Commodity Exchange Authority.

RECORDS OF THE FEDERAL EXTENSION SERVICE
(RECORD GROUP 33)

The Extension Service of the Department of Agriculture was organized July 1, 1923, to bring together Department extension activities handled by the States Relations Service, the Office of Exhibits of the Assistant Secretary's

Office, and the Office of Motion Pictures of the Division of Publications. The States Relations Service had been established in 1915 as a consolidation of the Office of Experiment Stations and the farmers cooperative demonstration work of the Bureau of Plant Industry. The Secretary of Agriculture renamed the Extension Service the Federal Extension Service in 1953, but in 1970 its name reverted to Extension Service.

The Service coordinates extension activities of Department bureaus with those of State agricultural colleges, helps farmers carry out new farming and home enterprises through the services of county agricultural and home demonstration agents, makes known results of agricultural research, and presents displays and exhibits at fairs and expositions. In periods of crisis, such as drought, depression, or war, local agents of the Service perform emergency activities.

See Alfred Charles True, *A History of Agricultural Extension Work in the United States, 1785–1923,* Department of Agriculture Miscellaneous Publications 15 (1938).

There are 911 cubic feet of records dated between 1888 and 1952 in this record group.

ANNUAL NARRATIVE AND STATISTICAL REPORTS. 1908–47.
197 lin. ft. and 3,577 rolls of microfilm.

Included are annual narrative and statistical reports of the Extension Service, 1908–45, all of which are on microfilm (3,577 rolls) except those for 1945; exhibits and other material submitted with the reports, 1914–44; annual narrative and statistical reports for North Carolina, 1908–17; national indexes to annual narrative reports of field workers, 1924–28; Smith-Lever annual inspection reports of cooperative field extension work, 1914–47; and reports and other records on activities of boys and girls clubs, 1911–22.

CORRESPONDENCE. 1906–49.
879 lin. ft.

Included are general correspondence of the Extension Service and its predecessors, 1907–49, with subject and author indexes; correspondence of Alfred C. True, Director, States Relations Service, 1914–23; letters sent by the Washington office, 1943–44, and by extension specialists, 1943–45; correspondence of the Division of Agricultural Instruction, 1906–26; and correspondence of the Office of Demonstrations on Reclamation Projects, chiefly with field offices and project personnel, 1914–26.

RECORDS RELATING TO FAIRS AND EXPOSITIONS. 1888–1909.
5 lin. ft.

These records consist of correspondence and related records, 1888–90, concerning the Paris Universal Exposition of 1889; letters received by the Chairman, Board of Management, 1891–99, for the World's Columbian Exposition, Chicago, 1893; letters sent by the Chairman, Board of Management, 1895–97, for the Cotton States and International Exposition, Atlanta, 1895; reports and letters sent by the Chairman, Board of Management, 1897–99, for the Tennessee Centennial Exposition, Nashville, 1897; letters sent and received by the Chairman, Board of Management, 1897–99, for the Trans-Mississippi International Exposition at Omaha, 1898; correspondence of the Secretary of Agriculture, 1898–1902, concerning the Paris Universal Exposition, 1900; and letters sent and received, 1899–1902, relating to the Pan American Exposition, Buffalo, 1901. There are also a few records concerning the South Carolina Interstate and West Indian Exposition, Charleston, 1901–2; the Louisiana Purchase Exposition, St. Louis, 1904; the Jamestown Tercentennial Exposition, 1907; the Alaska-Yukon-Pacific Exposition, Seattle, 1909; and the National Ecuadorian Exposition, Quito, Ecuador, 1909.

RECORDS RELATING TO THE
FARM LABOR PROGRAM. 1943-48.
31 lin. ft.

These consist primarily of correspondence, 1943-48, histories of divisional activities relating to the program, 1943-47, annual narrative and statistical reports on workers under the program, 1943-47, and a map of the United States showing major crop areas requiring imported labor, 1947.

OTHER RECORDS. 1905-44.
49 lin. ft.

Included are memorandums issued by the Secretary of Agriculture, 1913-44; circular letters issued by the Extension Service, 1908-44, with an index; reports of farmers cooperative demonstration work in the South, 1906-13; letters received from cooperating farmers, 1905-6, and from county demonstration agents, 1905-12; reports on the European corn borer control project, 1925-29; correspondence of the Federal Drought Relief Committee, 1930-31; and records of the Puerto Rican Hurricane Relief Commission, consisting principally of minutes, orders, reports of the Board of Alternates, and reference material, 1928-35.

AUDIOVISUAL RECORDS. 1906-52.
5,565 items.

Photographs (5,000 items) illustrating rural life and farm activities, 1906-42.

Motion pictures, 1913-52 (565 reels), made or acquired by the Department of Agriculture, relating chiefly to the activities of the Extension Service, and including assistance and advice to farmers and ranchers; home economics instruction; sponsorship of and cooperation with 4-H Clubs, American Farm Bureau Federations, the National Grange, and State farm organizations and extension services; work with land-grant colleges in agricultural education; and cooperation with the Federal Emergency Relief Administration in the establishment and operation of cooperative farm communities. Films of departmental organization, facilities, and personnel, including a number of Secretaries; the Department's role in enforcing the Pure Food and Drug Act and in both World Wars; explorations for plants that can be grown in the United States; the inspection of imported seeds and plants; and the Department's roadbuilding activities, conservation of wildlife, and promotion of fur-bearing animal farming. There are also films of Forest Service activities, Civilian Conservation Corps work, national parks, Weather Bureau work, highlights of the Coolidge and Hoover administrations, activities of important persons, and events.

See Virgil E. Baugh, comp., *Preliminary Inventory of the Records of the Extension Service*, PI 83 (1955).

Microfilm Publications: The annual reports of Federal Extension Service field representatives for all States, 1908-44, the District of Columbia, 1917-19, and the Commonwealth of Puerto Rico, 1930-44, have been microfilmed. For a complete listing see the current *List of National Archives Microfilm Publications*.

RECORDS OF THE COMMODITY CREDIT CORPORATION
(RECORD GROUP 161)

Creation of the Commodity Credit Corporation was authorized by Executive Order 6340 of October 16, 1933. It was managed by and operated in close affiliation with the Reconstruction Finance Corporation until it was transferred to the Department of Agriculture in 1939. The Corporation made loans to producers to increase and stabilize farm prices and assure adequate farm products. Loans were generally made by existing local banks in accordance with Corporation instructions. After the outbreak of World War II the Corporation's operations were expanded to facilitate increased production of war-scarce commodities and the lend-lease export of agricultural products. It worked closely with the Reconstruction Finance Corporation, the Agricultural Adjustment Agency, and the Soil Conservation Service. Since 1945 the operating functions of the Commodity Credit Corporation have been performed by the Agriculture Department's Production and Marketing Administration and its successors, the Commodity Stabilization Service and the Agricultural Stabilization and Conservation Service. The Corporation acquired a permanent Federal charter by an act of June 29, 1948, and is managed by a six-member Board of Directors subject to general supervision and direction of the Secretary of Agriculture, who is an ex officio director and Chairman of the Board.

There are 1,232 cubic feet of records dated between 1933 and 1948 in this record group.

RECORDS. 1933–48. 1,478 lin. ft.

These consist of the central files, 1933–43, with indexes, relating to all phases of the Corporation's activities; cables sent and received by the State Department, 1939–41, concerning the Cotton-Rubber Exchange Agreement between the United States and the United Kingdom, 1939; samples of program records, 1939–48; and records of the war hemp program, 1942–46. The records include information on loans, setoffs, price supports, commodity purchases, prices, marketing, and facilities.

RECORDS OF THE AGRICULTURAL STABILIZATION AND CONSERVATION SERVICE (RECORD GROUP 145)

The Agricultural Stabilization and Conservation Service had its beginnings in the Agricultural Adjustment Administration (AAA), established in the Department of Agriculture under the Agricultural Adjustment Act of May 12, 1933. The AAA administered aid to farmers through programs and parity payments designed to conserve soil resources, stabilize market prices of farm products, and bring about an equitable relationship between incomes of farmers and nonfarm groups. The AAA was reorganized by the Soil Conservation and Domestic Allotment Act of February 29, 1936, and its later programs were conducted under authority of the Agricultural Adjustment Act of 1938 and related legislation. In 1943 the AAA (renamed the Agricultural Adjustment Agency in 1942) was transferred to the War Food Administration. The Production and Marketing Administration, established in 1945, assumed most functions of the War Food Administration. In 1953 the Production and Marketing Administration was designated the Commodity Stabilization Service, which was renamed the Agricultural Stabilization and Conservation Service on June 5, 1961.

See Persia C. Campbell, *Consumer Representation in the New Deal* (New York, 1940).

There are 5,082 cubic feet of records dated between 1933 and 1955 in this record group.

GENERAL RECORDS OF THE AAA. 1933–47. 1,447 lin. ft.

These consist of a central correspondence file (1,400 lin. ft.), including some records created by the War Food and the Production and Marketing Administrations, 1933–47; a subject correspondence file, 1933–38; the comptroller's office file, 1933–42; press releases, 1933–40; docket files, 1933–38; and reports concerning governmental assistance to farmers, 1934-36.

RECORDS OF THE AAA CONSUMERS' COUNSEL DIVISION. 1933-43. 141 lin. ft.

This Division presented consumer viewpoints to aid in formulating agency policies. Its records include general correspondence, with indexes, 1933-43; office files of consumer counsels, 1933-42, and other officials, 1934-38; correspondence relating to price racketeering, 1933; records relating to National Recovery Administration codes, 1933-35; records concerning the national milk survey conducted to determine per capita milk consumption of school children, 1935; records relating to a nonfarm income study, 1937-38; and a reference file consisting chiefly of publications concerning consumers, 1940-43.

RECORDS OF THE PRODUCTION AND MARKETING ADMINISTRATION. 1942-54. 101 lin. ft.

Included are records of the Office of the Administrator, consisting primarily of correspondence, management improvement surveys, and organization charts, 1942-53; minutes, correspondence, and audit reports relating to commodity offices, 1951-54; and correspondence of the Grain Division, 1945-53.

RECORDS OF WAR BOARDS. 1942-48. 4 lin. ft.

State and county defense boards, which correlated farmers' efforts in meeting food production goals, were established July 5, 1941. They were renamed war boards January 7, 1942. These records consist of records of the California War Board, consisting chiefly of requisitions for machinery seized from Japanese-American farmers and appraisal reports evaluating seized equipment, 1942-48; and information and policy memorandums issued by the Department of Agriculture War Board to State war boards, 1942-44.

RECORDS OF THE COMMODITY STABILIZATION SERVICE. 1952-55. 21 lin. ft.

These include reports and memorandums concerning drought relief, 1952-55; correspondence of the Grain Division, 1953-54; and correspondence with State agricultural mobilization committees, 1952-54.

CARTOGRAPHIC AND AUDIOVISUAL RECORDS. 1931-52. 60,017 items.

Cartographic records, 1931-52 (58,186 items), comprise aerial photographs, most of which are on a scale of 1:20,000 and cover a large part of the United States; they include 17,000 rolls of negatives containing approximately 1,735,000 images, 18,000 prints, and 14,000 photoindexes, 1935-42. There are regional maps of the United States, showing climate, land purchase projects, crop regions, and areas covered by aerial survey contracts, 1931-52.

Audiovisual records consist of photographs (1,800 items) of civilian and military defense activities, 1940-45; filmstrips (26 items) relating to AAA soil conservation activities, marketing quotas for grain, and the ever-normal granary program, 1935-41; and motion pictures, 1941 (5 reels), consisting of "The Land," a film produced by Robert Flaherty of the AAA Documentary Film Section, Division of Information, concerning the reclamation and conservation of farmland depleted by poor agricultural practices.

See Carl J. Kulsrud, "The Archival Records of the Agricultural Adjustment Program," *Agricultural History*, XXII (July 1948).

RECORDS OF THE SOIL CONSERVATION SERVICE
(RECORD GROUP 114)

The Soil Conservation Service (SCS) was established in the Department of Agriculture by an act of April 27, 1935, to provide a permanent program for preventing and controlling soil erosion. Its predecessor, the Soil Erosion Service (SES) created in the Department of the Interior by the National Industrial Recovery Act of June 16, 1933, had been transferred on March 25, 1935, to the Department of Agriculture.

The SCS, which inherited many functions from other Government agencies, began in 1937 to provide technical and other assistance to farmers in soil conservation districts organized under State laws. In 1938 the Secretary of Agriculture gave the SCS some responsibilities for the program authorized by the Cooperative Farm Forestry Act of 1937. Reorganization Plan No. IV of 1940 transferred the soil and moisture conservation operations conducted by the SCS on lands under Department of the Interior jurisdiction to that Department. The SCS was given responsibility for assisting in water conservation programs in 1944, and in 1952 was authorized to assume the soil survey program of the Bureau of Plant Industry, Soils, and Agricultural Engineering. Duties of the SCS include conducting soil and snow surveys, watershed activities, and river basin surveys and investigations; promoting agricultural stability in the Great Plains area; assisting local groups in planning and developing land and water resources in multiple county areas; and giving technical help to landowners and operators who participate in the Department's agricultural conservation, cropland conversion, and cropland adjustment programs.

See Robert J. Morgan, *Governing Soil Conservation: Thirty Years of the New Decentralization* (Baltimore, 1965); and Department of Agriculture Economic Research Service, *The Land Utilization Program, 1934-64*, Agricultural Economic Report 85 (1965).

There are 5,117 cubic feet of records dated between 1900 and 1969 in this record group.

CENTRAL OFFICE RECORDS.
1900-1952. 1,974 lin. ft. and 290 rolls of microfilm.

General records (1,047 lin. ft.) of the SES and SCS include general correspondence, 1933-41; letters sent by Director Hugh H. Bennett, 1937-38, and other officials, 1933-39; organization and function charts, 1935-43; scientific studies and administrative reports, 1935-41; and reports concerning emergency conservation work projects, 1935-37.

Records of the Office of Research comprise correspondence and other records of Hugh H. Bennett, 1926-34 (including his correspondence as Director of the Soil Erosion and Moisture Conservation Investigations in the Bureau of Chemistry and Soils, 1928-34); reports and correspondence of the Soil Erosion and Moisture Conservation Investigations, 1929-35; annual reports, memorandums, organization charts, manuals of procedure, and other Office administrative records, 1935-40; research information files, 1929-40; correspondence with regional offices, 1935-39; records relating to projects, 1935-38; and a catalog of publications relating to the SCS, ca. 1920-40.

Records of divisions with specialized functions include general records of the Hydrologic Division, consisting chiefly of correspondence, work plans, and weekly reports, 1935-40, and correspondence with hydrologic laboratories, 1935-42; classified files of the Hillculture Division, concerning prevention of erosion in hilly country and including information on terracing, grading, machinery, and crop rotation, 1937-39; and meteorological charts (in WNRC) for New Philadelphia and Zanesville, Ohio, of the Climatic and Physiograhic

Division, 1936-43. There are also records of the Division of Engineering, which inherited responsibility for certain drainage and irrigation investigations carried on by the Bureau of Agricultural Engineering before 1938, consisting primarily of State project files, 1930-40 and 1947-52, with a partial index; technical files and rain and precipitation charts, 1900-1940; bulletins, speeches, articles, scientific papers, and manuscripts, 1937-46; summaries of weekly reports, 1942-52; drainage studies, 1923-40; articles and studies relating to terracing, ca. 1920-40; the field office records of a Mississippi State drainage survey, ca. 1937-42; reports and correspondence regarding slopes, 1937-43; and inspection reports of Civilian Conservation Corps (CCC) drainage camps, and correspondence and reports of the Hydrologic and Hydraulic Section, 1937-42.

Land utilization records include records acquired in 1938 when land utilization programs conducted successively by the Federal Emergency Relief Administration, the Resettlement Administration, and the Bureau of Agricultural Economics were transferred to the SCS. They consist primarily of a program historical file, 1933-40; general files, reports, job plans, instructions, forms, correspondence, memorandums, technical papers, and other documents relating to specific projects, 1934-39; case files of unapproved projects, 1934-36; narrative reports containing data on project histories, locations, objectives, work plans, and costs, 1935-37; regional directors' semimonthly and monthly narrative reports of land utilization activities, 1937; project appraisal reports, 1938; records regarding the Lost Pines conservation project in Bastrop County, Tex., and the Jack Fork Mountain conservation project in Oklahoma, 1936; and microfilm copies (290 rolls) of vendors' case files that concern acquiring and establishing land titles, 1933-39.

Records relating to experiment stations include records acquired in 1935 when the erosion control experiment stations of the Bureau of Chemistry and Soils and the Bureau of Agricultural Engineering were transferred to the SCS. They consist primarily of correspondence concerning scientific and administrative supervision of the stations, 1929-40, annual reports, 1929-37, monthly progress reports, 1940-41, summary reports, 1931-35, project study outlines, 1936, correspondence about fiscal matters, 1935, and progress reports, 1937. Many of the records concern the experiment stations at Amarillo and Tyler, Tex., Bethany, Mo., Fort Hays, Kans., Guthrie, Okla., La Crosse, Wis., Pullman, Wash., Statesville, N.C., and Zanesville, Ohio.

FIELD RECORDS. ca. 1933-42.
1,021 lin. ft.

In 1935 regional offices were established to supervise conservation work in large geographic areas, and in 1938 and 1939 area offices were created to function immediately under regional offices. Originally SCS representatives in the States (State cooperators or coordinators) functioned as liaison officers who coordinated Federal and State work. In 1942 State offices replaced area offices as intermediate units between regional and project offices, which had immediate technical supervision over soil conservation projects. SCS regional offices were discontinued in 1954. State offices and a Caribbean office now give technical and administrative supervision to local work units where conservation technicians work directly with landowners and operators.

Records of regional offices, 1934-42 (705 lin. ft.), consist primarily of reports, correspondence, cooperative agreements, memorandums, and statistical materials. Records are most extensive for regional offices at Rapid City, S. Dak., Salina, Kans., Spartanburg, S.C. (in FRC Atlanta), and Fort Worth and Amarillo, Tex. The Amarillo office had jurisdiction over the Dust Bowl area, and its records reflect participation in cooperative emergency programs.

Records of area offices, 1934-42, consist chiefly of reports from and correspondence with local units, concerning soil conservation demonstration projects, soil conservation districts, CCC camps, water facility and wind erosion projects, and plant nurseries. Included are records (in FRC Atlanta) of area offices at Birmingham and Montgomery, Ala., Columbia, S.C., Raleigh and Salisbury, N.C., and Athens, Rome, and Tifton, Ga. Records are most extensive for offices at Bath, N.Y., Casper, Wyo., and Indiana and Lancaster, Pa.

Records of State offices, ca. 1933-42, include reports, fragmentary correspondence, project proposals, and cooperative agreements from offices in Maryland, Mississippi (in WNRC), Montana, Nebraska, Pennsylvania, Texas, Wisconsin, and Wyoming.

Selected records of project offices, 1933-41, include periodic and other reports, correspondence, project plans, cooperative agreements, and work programs. The records are most extensive for offices at Albion, Nebr., Faribault, Minn., and Huron and Rapid City, S. Dak. Also included are records of the Prairie States forestry (Shelterbelt) project, 1934-41, established to ameliorate drought conditions by planting protective belts of forest in the Plains region.

The Project for Technical Cooperation with the Bureau of Indian Affairs, which was supervised by the Technical Cooperation—Bureau of Indian Affairs, was created in the SCS in December 1935 to make physical and economic surveys of all Indian lands west of the Mississippi except the Navajo-Hopi Reservation. Its records include classified general headquarters records, 1935-39; the files of the Director of the Technical Cooperation—Bureau of Indian Affairs, relating chiefly to office administration and relations with cooperating agencies, 1937-39; and project correspondence and survey records relating to individual reservations and base maps of Indian reservations, 1936-39.

The Ames, Iowa, nursery, one of the experimental erosion nurseries established by the Bureau of Plant Industry to collect and develop plants used in conservation activities, was transferred in 1935 to the SCS. Its records comprise administrative and technical files concerning organization, personnel, finances, cooperative relations, seed testing, and other phases of nursery operation, 1934-39.

Land utilization records, 1934-42, separately maintained by field offices at Amarillo and Dallas, Tex., Lincoln, Nebr., and Little Rock, Ark., consist primarily of reports, general correspondence, project proposals, plans, and records relating to individual land utilization projects.

RECORDS OF CCC CAMPS. 1933-42. 79 lin. ft.

In 1935 supervision of the Emergency Conservation Work (later known as the CCC) camps assigned to the Forest Service for erosion control work on agricultural lands was transferred to the SES and then to the SCS. The records relate to administration, informational and educational activities, labor problems, and technical activities concerning wind and water erosion, drainage, irrigation-grazing, dam construction, dune control, and nursery development projects of selected CCC camps given technical direction by the SCS. They include extensive records for camps at Cartersville, Ga., Clanton, Ala., Lancaster, Pa., Memphis, Tex., and New Madrid, Mo. There are also selected documents from camps and their supervisory units in Alabama, Arizona, Colorado, Kentucky, Mississippi, New Mexico, North and South Carolina, Tennessee, Utah, Virginia, and West Virginia.

CARTOGRAPHIC AND
AUDIOVISUAL RECORDS. 1915-69.
216,992 items.

Cartographic records (212,692 items)
comprise aerial photographs and photoindexes of areas in the United States,
1933-39, and manuscript and published
maps of the United States and its
regions and States compiled by the SCS
and its predecessors, 1915-69, showing
climatic patterns; water resources and
streamflows; lake and reservoir sedi-
mentations; geological formations; soil
types and erosions; the distribution of
natural vegetation and cultivated crops;
potential and existing land uses; and the
location, extent, and status of projects

established to control floods, improve
drainage and irrigation, conduct land use
experiments, develop recreational facilities, and conserve soils, forests, and
game.

Audiovisual records (4,300 photographs) consist of aerial photographs
taken for a soil erosion study, 1934-37,
and photographs of farming operations
and techniques and soil conservation
activities in Arizona, Colorado, New
Mexico, Kansas, Utah, Montana, North
and South Dakota, and Wyoming, 1934-
55; Indians and reservation life, CCC
activities, landscapes, and geographic
features in Arizona, Colorado, New Mexico, Kansas, Utah, and Wyoming, 1934-
55; and a snow survey, ca. 1950.

RECORDS OF THE
RURAL ELECTRIFICATION ADMINISTRATION
(RECORD GROUP 221)

The Rural Electrification Administration (REA) was established as an emergency agency by Executive Order 7037
of May 11, 1935. To it were transferred
rural electrification projects initiated by
the Public Works Administration under
an act of June 16, 1933. The REA
became a permanent Government agency in 1936 and was transferred to the
Department of Agriculture by the President's Reorganization Plan No. II of
1939. The chief REA function is to make
self-liquidating loans at low interest
rates to individual farmers, farm cooperatives, and utility districts for financing
construction and operation of electric
generating plants and transmission lines,
wiring of rural premises, and acquisition
and installation of electrical and plumbing appliances and equipment. An act
of October 28, 1949, authorized the
REA to make loans also to telephone
organizations for extension and
improvement of rural telephone service.

There are 1,255 cubic feet of records
dated between 1934 and 1954 in this
record group.

RECORDS OF THE OFFICE OF
THE ADMINISTRATOR. 1934-54.
387 lin. ft. and 75 rolls of microfilm.

Included are minutes of the Administrative Policy Advisory Committee,
1939-45; general correspondence, 1935-
53; correspondence with State organizations concerning State and territorial
programs, 1938-42, loans to REA borrowers, 1935-40 and 1946-51, engineering aspects of REA projects, 1935-40,
and projects that supplied power to
defense agencies, 1941-43; REA project
case files, some of them on microfilm
(75 rolls), 1934-42; and special reports,
1939-43. Records of REA officials
include records of Administrator Morris
L. Cooke, 1935-37; correspondence and
related records of Administrators John
L. Carmody, 1936-40, Harry Slattery,

1939-45, and Claude R. Wickard, 1947-53; and records of the Assistant Administrator, 1936-54, and the consulting economist, 1936-53.

DIVISIONAL RECORDS. 1935-54. 806 lin. ft.

These include records of the Management Division, consisting of minutes of meetings of REA borrowers, 1943-51, electric power retail rate reports, 1935-51, correspondence of the Division Chief, 1937-50, and management survey reports, 1948-53; Application and Loans Division, consisting of reports on economic qualifications of users of electrification facilities, 1937-50, correspondence and reports regarding property acquisition by REA electric and telephone borrowers, 1939-54, field activity reports, 1946-51, and records of the Assistant Chief of the Division, 1946-53; Engineering Division, consisting of correspondence, 1939-53, of the Chief (with cooperative associations, 1948-53), and reports, 1946-51; correspondence with telephone associations, 1952-53, of the Telephone Engineering Division; reports on wholesale rates of electricity, 1935-51, of the Power Division; correspondence relating to electrical service rates to national defense users, 1940-45, of the Cooperative Operation Division; correspondence of the Chief of the Administrative and Loan Accounting Division, 1935-54; correspondence and reports of the Chief and Assistant Chief of the Finance Division, 1936-50; correspondence and memorandums concerning training, 1949-52, of the Personnel Division; correspondence of the Chief of the Information Service Division, 1937-53, and records of the Chief of the Cooperative Education Section, 1937-54, correspondence and reports concerning information programs, 1937-40, minutes and correspondence of committees and conferences, 1935-52, correspondence concerning the telephone program, 1937-53, and news releases, bulletins, and reports, 1936-54; Technical Standards Division, consisting of correspondence, 1936-52, technical reports, 1939-51, and records of committees, 1936-52; and correspondence of the Utilities Division, relating to more efficient use of electric energy by REA cooperative members, 1938-40.

RECORDS OF AREA OFFICES. 1952-53. 142 lin. ft.

These consist primarily of minutes of meetings of REA borrowers, 1952-53; general correspondence (arranged alphabetically by name of State or territory) relating to REA borrowers, 1952-53; and reports concerning field activities, 1952-53, and retail and wholesale power rates, 1952-53.

CARTOGRAPHIC RECORDS. 1939-52. 1,285 items.

Maps of the United States and of individual States, showing electrical transmission lines, stations, and generating plants (particularly REA-financed facilities); and maps showing distribution of telephones in rural areas.

RECORDS OF THE FEDERAL CROP INSURANCE CORPORATION (RECORD GROUP 258)

The Federal Crop Insurance Corporation was created in the Department of Agriculture by the Agricultural Adjustment Act of February 16, 1938. Corporation functions have been modified by subsequent legislation, the latest of which was approved September 12, 1964. Under its programs the Corporation insures wheat, cotton, tobacco, corn, flax, peaches, peanuts, peas, potatoes, raisins, apples, grapes, dry beans, soybeans, barley, grain sorghums, oats, rice, citrus fruit, tomatoes, sugar beets, sugarcane, tung nuts, and the investment in several crops under a combined crop protection plan. The Corporation develops crop insurance so that farmer premiums cover the indemnities paid for crop failures.

There are 27 cubic feet of records (in WNRC) dated between 1938 and 1944 in this record group.

RECORDS. 1938-44. 34 lin. ft.

These consist chiefly of general correspondence, but include records used by an insurance consultant, the Ekern and Meyers Insurance Co., and records relating to the Cutsinger Elevator Firm at Edinburgh, Ind.

RECORDS OF THE FARMERS HOME ADMINISTRATION (RECORD GROUP 96)

The Farmers Home Administration (FHA), was established in the Department of Agriculture by an act of August 14, 1946, to succeed the Farm Security Administration (FSA). The FSA was established in 1937 in the Department of Agriculture to succeed the Resettlement Administration, which had been established in 1935 to administer rural rehabilitation and land programs begun in 1933 under the Subsistence Homesteads Division of the Department of the Interior and the Federal Emergency Relief Administration. The FHA provides small farmers with credit to construct or repair homes and farm buildings, improve farming operations, or become farmowners, and gives individual guidance in farm and home management.

There are 2,195 cubic feet of records dated between 1931 and 1959 in this record group.

CENTRAL OFFICE RECORDS.
1931-59. 920 lin. ft.

These consist of general correspondence of the Washington office, 1935-38, and of the Cincinnati office, 1935-42; correspondence relating to FSA participation in the defense program, 1940-42; records of the Rural Rehabilitation Division, consisting of general correspondence, 1935-38, and sample complaint correspondence between the Adminis-

trators of the Resettlement and the Farm Security Administrations and rural rehabilitation applicants, 1935-42; reports and correspondence of the Cooperative Division, relating to cooperative associations, 1935-59; records of the Division of Subsistence Homesteads, including correspondence with the general public, correspondence concerning proposed subsistence homestead projects, and a census of part-time farming, 1933-35; records of the Resettlement Division, concerning farm community and homestead projects, 1935-42, migratory labor camps, 1935-43, and the operation of defense relocation corporations, 1941-53; case files of the Project Management Division, concerning payments in lieu of taxes, 1935-48; general correspondence of the Farm Ownership Division, 1937-42; and selected case files of the Emergency Crop and Feed Loan Division, 1931-46.

FIELD OFFICE RECORDS. 1934-47.
1,629 lin. ft.

These comprise records of the 12 regional offices of the Resettlement and Farm Security Administrations and consist primarily of general correspondence of regional directors, land acquisition case files, and records concerning resettlement projects of regional resettlement divisions, 1934-47; farm ownership case files of regional rural rehabilitation divisions, 1937-46; and case files for paid rural rehabilitation loans made in 134 selected counties, 1934-44.

CARTOGRAPHIC AND AUDIOVISUAL RECORDS. 1934-40. 69 items.

Cartographic records, 1935-40 (26 items), consist of maps of the United States, including those of areas in the South and Southwest showing land use and ownership, irrigation, drainage, reclamation, and homestead projects.

Audiovisual records consist of motion pictures, 1936-37 (11 reels), including two films directed by Pare Lorentz and produced by the Documentary Film Section of the Division of Information, "The Plow That Broke the Plains" and "The River." Also films concerning migratory labor camps; agricultural and industrial cooperatives in Russia, England, Sweden, Finland, and Scotland; and the construction of typical houses and barns.

Sound recordings, 1934 and 1936 (32 items), include radio programs that emphasize the role of the Resettlement Administration in introducing scientific farming methods and giving financial assistance to farmers; a dramatization of the sinking of the *Lusitania*, with a commentary on attempts to salvage her cargo; and a discussion of extortion practices in the United States.

See Stanley W. Brown and Virgil E. Baugh, comps., *Preliminary Inventory of the Records of the Farmers Home Administration*, PI 118 (1959).

RECORDS OF THE AGRICULTURAL RESEARCH SERVICE (RECORD GROUP 310)

The Agricultural Research Administration (ARA) was established in the Department of Agriculture by an Executive order of February 23, 1942, to coordinate the functions of several long-established scientific bureaus. Its activities were chiefly administrative, with the bureaus continuing to function as before, and on November 2, 1953, the ARA and the bureaus were consolidated by the Secretary of Agriculture as the Agricultural Research Service. The Service plans, administers, and conducts research and related regulatory programs. The records of the ARA were inherited by the Service.

There are 224 cubic feet of records dated between 1918 and 1953 in this record group.

RECORDS OF THE AGRICULTURAL RESEARCH ADMINISTRATION. 1918-53. 315 lin. ft.

These consist of general correspondence of the Office of the Administrator, 1942-53; records relating to research and administration, 1938-48; memorandums, 1942-43 and 1949-53; correspondence and reports, 1946-53, concerning the administration of the Research and Marketing Act of 1946; records of staff assistants, 1946-53; two maps published by the ARA, showing land assignments at the Agricultural Research Center in Beltsville, Md., to Department of Agriculture offices; blueprints for buildings and equipment of the Bureau of Entomology and Plant Quarantine, 1918-42; and motion pictures, 1933-49 (11 reels), illustrating methods of cultivating and harvesting sugar beets.

RECORDS OF THE FARMER COOPERATIVE SERVICE
(RECORD GROUP 314)

The Farmer Cooperative Service was established in the Department of Agriculture under the Secretary's Memorandum 1320 of November 2, 1953. The Service was to continue work authorized by the Cooperative Marketing Act of July 2, 1926, and performed by the Cooperative Research and Service Division of the Farm Credit Administration. When the Administration was made independent of the Department in August 1953, the functions of its Cooperative Research and Service Division were transferred to the Secretary of Agriculture.

The Service performs educational and advisory work to improve the organization and effectiveness of marketing, farm supply, and related cooperatives; conducts and publishes studies on problems of cooperative financing, organization, merchandising, product quality, costs, efficiency, and membership; and works with cooperatives, State agencies, colleges, extension services, and other educational agencies to disseminate information about cooperative principles and practices and to improve the efficiency of farmer cooperatives.

There is less than 1 cubic foot of records dated between 1948 and 1951 in this record group.

RECORDS. 1948-51. 4 items.

Photocopied and published maps of the Cooperative Research and Service Division, with related textual records, showing the locations of cooperatives that handled farm supplies.

RECORDS OF THE ECONOMIC RESEARCH SERVICE
(RECORD GROUP 354)

The Economic Research Service (ERS) was established by the Secretary of Agriculture on April 3, 1961, to consolidate research in domestic and foreign agricultural economics and marketing previously conducted by the Agricultural Research Service, Agricultural Marketing Service, and Foreign Agricultural Service. Domestic research by the Bureau of Agricultural Economics was divided between the Agricultural Research Service and the Agricultural Marketing Service when the Bureau was abolished in 1953. ERS activities relate to seven major areas: economic and statistical analysis, marketing economics, farm production economics, natural resource economics, economic development, foreign regional analysis, and foreign development and trade.

There are 3 cubic feet of records (in WNRC) dated between 1934 and 1964 in this record group.

RECORDS. 1934-64. 4 lin. ft.

These consist of minutes, correspondence, tabulations, reports, publications, and other records of the Production Resources Branch of the Farm Production Economics Division, ERS, and predecessors in the Agricultural Research Service, and the Bureau of Agricultural Economics, concerning participation in the Northeast Production Advisory Group, 1939-53, Northeast Farm Management Research Committee, 1951-64, and New England Research Council on Marketing and Food Supply, 1934-55. There are also office files of an official of the Agricultural Research Service, 1954-60.

Discontinued Agencies

RECORDS OF THE BUREAU OF ANIMAL INDUSTRY
(RECORD GROUP 17)

The Bureau of Animal Industry was established in May 1884 to prevent the exportation of diseased cattle and eradicate contagious diseases among domestic animals. It replaced the Veterinary Division, created by the Commissioner of Agriculture in 1883. The Bureau conducted scientific investigations and administered statutes and regulations to protect the public from infected or diseased meat products, eradicate animal diseases, and improve the livestock of the country. It enforced such regulatory measures as the Meat Inspection Act of 1891, under which it inspected meat processing; the Diseased Animal Transportation Act of 1903, under which it used quarantines to prevent interstate and foreign commerce in diseased animals; the Virus Serum Act of 1913, under which it supervised the preparation, sale, import, export, and interstate shipment of veterinary biological products; and the Twenty-Eight Hour Act of 1873, which required that animals in interstate transit be unloaded, fed, and watered every 28 hours. From 1927 to 1939 it also enforced the Packers and Stockyards Act of 1921. In 1953 the Bureau was abolished, and its functions were divided among the Branches of Animal Disease and Parasite Research, Animal and Poultry Husbandry Research, Animal Disease Eradication, Animal Inspection and Quarantine, and Meat Inspection of the Agricultural Research Service. Some records relating to the enforcement of the Packers and Stockyards and Meat Inspection Acts and to the Bureau's dairy cattle work are, respectively, among the records of the Agricultural Marketing Service (see RG 136) and the records of the Bureau of Dairy Industry (see RG 152).

There are 693 cubic feet of records (in WNRC except for one map) dated between 1874 and 1950 in this record group.

RECORDS. 1874-1950. 865 lin. ft.

The Bureau operated through an extensive field service supervised by several headquarters divisions. The following divisions were chiefly responsible for the creation of the records described below: Meat Inspection, Field Inspection, Tuberculosis Eradication, Biochemic, Pathological, Zoological, Field Inspection and Quarantine, Tick Eradication, Hog Cholera Control, Virus-Serum Control, and Animal Husbandry.

Included are central correspondence, 1895-1939; general correspondence of the Division of Animal Husbandry, 1901-14; miscellaneous letters sent, 1911-18; letters sent to the Department of State, 1892-97, and to the Solicitor of the Department of Agriculture, 1913-18; letters sent concerning the eradication of foot-and-mouth disease, 1912-18, and the control of viruses and serums used in treating animals, 1913-18; deeds and other title records, including records transferred from the Department of the Army, that relate to land acquired for Bureau fieldwork, 1874-1950; reports; personnel records; orders; circular letters; project statements; an office file of George M. Rommel, Chief of the Division of Animal Husbandry, concerning the Agricultural Commission to Europe, 1918, and the Committee on Live Stock Drouth Relief, 1919; and letters and reports of the Baltimore field station, 1887-1918. Also included is an undated map of the United States, showing locations of Bureau field stations.

See Harold T. Pinkett, comp., *Preliminary Inventory of the Records of the Bureau of Animal Industry*, PI 106 (1958).

RECORDS OF THE OFFICE OF EXPERIMENT STATIONS
(RECORD GROUP 164)

The Office of Experiment Stations was established in the Department of Agriculture on October .1, 1888, to popularize the results of agricultural experiments and to disseminate scientific information among experiment stations created under the Hatch Act of 1887. Subsequent legislation increased the control of the Office over the finances and work of the stations. The Office also promoted agricultural education, administered experiment stations in Alaska and the insular possessions, and conducted investigations concerning irrigation, nutrition, and drainage. In 1915 the Office was combined with other offices carrying out extension and home economics work to form the States Relations Service. When that Service was abolished in 1923, the Office of Experiment Stations resumed its separate identity. The Office administered funds provided by the Bankhead-Jones Act of 1935 for the support of research in agriculture and rural life by experiment stations and Federal agencies, and coordinated agricultural research. From 1936 to 1941 the head of the Office also served as research director for the Department of Agriculture. The Office was under the supervision of the Agricultural Research Administration from December 1941 to November 1953; it was abolished on November 2, 1953, and its functions were transferred to the Agricultural Research Service.

There are 467 cubic feet of records dated between 1888 and 1960 in this record group.

RECORDS OF THE OFFICE OF EXPERIMENT STATIONS.
1888-1960. 418 lin. ft.

Included are administrative records, 1894-1937; correspondence of Alfred Charles True, head of the Office, 1893-1929, of the assistant head of the Office,

1910-29, and of Robert W. Trullinger, agricultural engineer, 1913-27; correspondence with bureaus of the Department of Agriculture, Federal agencies, State and insular experiment stations, and agricultural colleges, 1888-1943; departmental rulings, 1923-37; records concerning State, Soil Conservation Service, and Civil Works Administration projects, 1927-37, and appeals for regional research laboratories, 1937-39; completed registration forms concerning the *Agricultural Science Register*, 1904-26; annual financial reports of the Office, 1889-1928, and of stations, 1907-46; and agenda of meetings of the Committee on Experiment Station Organization, concerning the policy of land-grant colleges and universities, 1940-46.

Records relating to publications include a "card index of Experiment Station literature," material used to prepare *State Agricultural Experiment Stations*, 1930-60, and notes of Alfred Charles True, 1923-29, for a *History of Agricultural Experimentation and Research in the United States* and for a *History of Agricultural Education in the United States*.

RECORDS OF EXPERIMENT STATIONS. 1898-1938. 140 lin. ft.

Records of headquarters in Alaska for experiment stations include administrative records, 1898-1932, including appropriation ledgers and accounts of expenditures, 1898-1914; letters received, 1900-1927, and sent, 1898-1927; and personal letters of Charles C. Georgeson, chief of experiment station work in Alaska, 1900-1920. Also included are administrative records and correspondence for the substations of Fairbanks, 1906–32, Kenai, 1899–1908, Kodiak, 1907–31, Matanuska, 1917–32, and Rampart, 1904–26.

Records of the experiment station at Guam include annual reports, 1917–32, and correspondence, 1908–32; those of the station at Mayaguez, P.R., include correspondence, 1901–38.

CARTOGRAPHIC RECORDS. 1908–41. 15 items.

Maps prepared by State agricultural experiment stations in Maryland, n.d., West Virginia, 1937, and Nevada, 1940–41, relating to soils, slope, vegetation, and land classification; and maps relating to drainage and flood control projects in several States, 1908–15.

RECORDS OF THE BUREAU OF DAIRY INDUSTRY
(RECORD GROUP 152)

The Bureau of Dairy Industry originated in the Department of Agriculture in 1895 as the Dairy Division of the Bureau of Animal Industry, in 1924 became the Bureau of Dairying, and was renamed the Bureau of Dairy Industry by an act of May 11, 1926. The Bureau conducted research in dairy products and byproducts, dairy industry market practices, and the breeding, nutrition, and management of dairy cattle. The Secretary of Agriculture's Memorandum 1320 of November 2, 1953, abolished the Bureau and transferred its functions to the Agricultural Research Service.

There are 103 cubic feet of records (in WNRC) dated between 1907 and 1939 in this record group.

RECORDS OF THE DAIRY DIVISION. 1907–24. 24 lin. ft.

Included are reports, agenda, memorandums, and correspondence relating to international dairy congresses, intraagency projects, assistance given individuals and institutions purchasing cattle, special projects, and experimentation, 1907–22; and to appropriations, patents on employees' findings, experiment stations, the 1923 World Dairy Congress held in the United States, Government regulations on milk, breeding experiments, milk surveys and inspections, supply purchases, and personnel matters, 1922–24.

RECORDS OF THE BUREAU OF DAIRY INDUSTRY. 1925–39. 79 lin. ft.

Included are correspondence concerning annual appropriations, organization, personnel, publications, exhibits, meetings and congresses, cost studies, dairy and breeding experiments, investigations, and milk products; and a reading file, with an index.

RECORDS OF THE BUREAU OF AGRICULTURAL ENGINEERING
(RECORD GROUP 8)

The Office of Experiment Stations of the Department of Agriculture began irrigation investigations in 1898 and drainage investigations in 1903. In 1915 this work, the farm architecture and machinery work of the Office of Farm Management, and the functions of the Office of Public Roads were consolidated in the Office of Public Roads and Rural Engineering, which in 1918 was renamed the Bureau of Public Roads, This reorganization brought most of the civil and mechanical engineering work of the Department of Agriculture into one bureau. The drainage, irrigation, and rural engineering (structures and machinery) investigations were continued under separate units within the Bureau until 1921, when they were brought together in the Division of Agricultural Engineering. In 1931 the Division was given bureau status, and in 1938 it was merged with the Bureau of Chemistry and Soils to form the Bureau of Agricultural Chemistry and Engineering. Some of the functions and records of the Bureau of Agricultural Engineering were later transferred to the Soil Conservation Service (see RG 114) and the Bureau of Plant Industry (see RG 54).

There are 418 cubic feet of records (in WNRC except for nontextual records) dated between 1898 and 1939, with a few dated as late as 1941, in this record group.

RECORDS OF THE OFFICE OF EXPERIMENT STATIONS RELATING TO IRRIGATION AND DRAINAGE INVESTIGATIONS. 1898-1915. 43 lin. ft.

These include general and staff correspondence and field office records relating to the utilization, flow, and measurement of water; irrigation appliances; irrigation customs and laws; the establishment of drainage districts; drain construction; and erosion control.

RECORDS OF THE DIVISION OF AGRICULTURAL ENGINEERING OF THE BUREAU OF PUBLIC ROADS. 1915-31. 171 lin. ft.

Chiefly general correspondence of the Division and its predecessors—the irrigation, drainage, and rural engineering investigation units—with a card index. There are also records relating to surplus war explosives, 1921-25, including minutes of the War Materials Board.

RECORDS OF THE BUREAU OF AGRICULTURAL ENGINEERING. 1907-41. 320 lin. ft.

These consist of general correspondence, 1931-39, with a card index; records of Chief of the Bureau S. H. McCrory, ca. 1922-38; correspondence of the Irrigation Division, 1933-39; records of the Chief of the Drainage Division, 1931-39; fieldbooks of drainage engineers, 1907-38; files concerning rainfall, waterflow, the history of the tractor, and farm operating efficiency, 1929-41; and correspondence and publications on agricultural extension work, 1926-39.

RECORDS OF THE OFFICE OF FARM EQUIPMENT CONTROL. 1918. 1 lin. ft.

This wartime agency controlled the production and distribution of farm equipment; its records include reports to the Secretary of Agriculture, correspondence, and a list of licensed manufacturers.

CARTOGRAPHIC AND AUDIOVISUAL RECORDS. 1901-39. 6,157 items.

Maps and related cross sections and profiles (2,157 items) prepared by the Bureau and its predecessors, relating to planning, drainage, irrigation, and farm development; and maps of individual farms prepared from the Farm Development Investigations throughout the United States, showing farm layouts, soils, crop acreages, and production. Also photographs (4,000 items) illustrating the drainage and irrigation activities of the Division of Drainage.

See Nathan Reingold, comp., *Preliminary Inventory of the Records of the Bureau of Agricultural Engineering*, PI 53 (1953).

RECORDS OF THE BUREAU OF AGRICULTURAL AND INDUSTRIAL CHEMISTRY
(RECORD GROUP 97)

The Bureau of Agricultural and Industrial Chemistry, which engaged in chemical and technological research on the use of agricultural commodities, was the successor agency of several units in the Department of Agriculture. The Division of Chemistry, established in 1862, was primarily concerned with analysis of soil until 1894, and then of food and drugs. In 1901 the Division was designated the Bureau of Chemistry, and after 1906 it was assigned regulatory functions, such as enforcing the Food and Drugs Act. In 1927 its regulatory functions were transferred to the Food, Drug, and Insecticide Administration (see RG 88), and its research functions were consolidated with those of other departmental units to form the Bureau of Chemistry and Soils.

In 1938 the chemical research functions of the Bureau of Chemistry and Soils were combined with the engineering functions of the Bureau of Agricultural Engineering (see RG 8) to form the Bureau of Agricultural Chemistry and Engineering. Its soil research functions that had not been transferred previously were delegated to the Bureau of Plant Industry (see RG 54), and some of its responsibility for irrigation and drainage research was assumed by the Soil Conservation Service (see RG 114).

In 1943 the Bureau of Agricultural Engineering and Chemistry was renamed the Bureau of Agricultural and Industrial Chemistry, and its engineering research functions were transferred to the Bureau of Plant Industry, Soils, and Agricultural Engineering (formerly the Bureau of Plant Industry) (see RG 54). The Secretary of Agriculture's Memorandum 1320 of November 2, 1953, which abolished the Bureau of Agricultural and Industrial Chemistry,

delegated its responsibilities to the Agricultural Research Service.

See Gustavus A. Weber, *The Bureau of Chemistry and Soils* (Baltimore, 1928).

There are 1,358 cubic feet of records dated between 1862 and 1942 in this record group.

RECORDS OF THE DIVISION AND THE BUREAU OF CHEMISTRY.
1862-1927. 1,186 lin. ft.

These consist of reports and letters received, 1862-1909; letters sent, 1878-1907; general correspondence (820 lin. ft.), 1907-18, with indexes; letters sent relating to the World's Columbian Exposition, 1893, the Paris Exposition, 1900, and the St. Louis World's Fair, 1904; bulletins describing Division and Bureau experiments, 1883-1913; notebooks and letters sent regarding experiments with sorghum, 1887-92; notebooks relating to experiments with sugar beets, 1883-1902, and food adulterants, 1890-1905; records about enforcement work, including test reports on imported sugar, 1901-4, letters relating to imported food, 1903-9, and circulars and memorandums, 1908-23; and articles and lectures by Harvey W. Wiley, 1890-1906, copies of published papers, 1911-27, and a bibliography concerning agricultural chemical research, 1915-27.

RECORDS OF THE BUREAU OF CHEMISTRY AND SOILS. 1901-42.
574 lin. ft.

These records include general correspondence, 1935-39, laboratory project reports, 1901-38, papers published in scientific journals, 1927-41, radio scripts and press releases, 1930-42, records relating to manufacture of phthalic anhydride, 1917-41, and correspondence of the Chemical and Technological

Research Branch, 1927-35, with an index.

Records of the Chemical Engineering Research Division, consisting chiefly of correspondence, 1914-42; records relating to committees and councils, 1921-42; and reports on straw gas experiments, 1918, and on investigations concerning smut control, 1914-18, industrial plant dust explosions, 1914-42, cotton gin fires, 1918, and the spontaneous heating and igniting of hay, 1929-32. Correspondence, 1914-36, with an index, and laboratory notebooks, 1917-39, of the Color Laboratory and the Color and Farm Waste Division. Records of the Industrial Farm Products Research Division, including correspondence, 1908-35; office files of the senior chemist, 1936-40; and records relating to committees, 1904-36, and to agricultural waste utilization, 1927-30. Records of the Naval Stores Research Division, consisting of correspondence, 1903-35; and records relating to naval stores demonstration work, 1914-36, specifications, 1915-39, and patent applications, 1934-41. Records relating to the Trail smelter fumes investigations, including maps, reference files, briefs, exhibits, a report of damages awarded by the International Joint Commission, and other reports, 1924-39.

RECORDS OF THE BUREAU OF AGRICULTURAL CHEMISTRY AND ENGINEERING.
1920-42. 22 lin. ft.

These records comprise office files of the assistant chief, relating to engineering research, 1920-42; and an office file of Associate Chief W. W. Skinner, relating to smelter fumes investigations and chemical utilization research, 1927-41.

AUDIOVISUAL RECORDS. ca. 1878-1942. 4,800 items.

Included are photographs and photographs of artworks depicting the history of the American sugar, oil, and other chemical industries beginning in 1671; the prevention and causes of and the damage from dust and boiler explosions and fires in grain and feed elevators and mills, on farms, and in schools, 1878-1939; Bureau personnel and laboratories, 1908-42; and smelter fume investigations and erosion control, 1929-38. There are also general views of Alaska, ca. 1889, and of Holland and the Scandinavian countries, n.d.

See Helen T. Finneran, comp., *Preliminary Inventory of the Records of the Bureau of Agricultural and Industrial Chemistry*, PI 149 (1962).

RECORDS OF THE BUREAU OF PLANT INDUSTRY, SOILS, AND AGRICULTURAL ENGINEERING
(RECORD GROUP 54)

The Bureau of Plant Industry, Soils, and Agricultural Engineering was established February 13, 1943, in the Agricultural Research Administration. Government procurement, propagation, and distribution of seeds and plants began in the Agricultural Section established in the Patent Office in 1839. These activities were transferred to the Department of Agriculture Division of Gardens and Grounds in 1862 and to the Division of Seeds in 1868. As plant work became more specialized, Divisions of Botany, Pomology, Vegetable Physiology and Pathology, and Agrostology were established in the Department from 1869 to 1895. To coordinate and develop plant investigations conducted by these Divisions, the Bureau of Plant Industry was established in 1901. In 1938 soil investigations were transferred to the Bureau. These investigations had originated in the Division of Soils, established in 1894, and had expanded in the Bureau of Soils and the Bureau of Chemistry and Soils, established in 1901 and 1927, respectively. In 1943 engineering research was transferred from the Bureau of Agricultural Chemistry and Engineering to the newly designated Bureau of Plant Industry, Soils, and Agricultural Engineering. The Secretary of Agriculture abolished this Bureau on November 2, 1953, and transferred its functions to the Agricultural Research Service.

See Fred W. Powell, *The Bureau of Plant Industry* (Baltimore, 1927); and Gustavus A. Weber, *The Bureau of Chemistry and Soils* (Baltimore, 1928).

There are 2,896 cubic feet of records dated between 1881 and 1953 in this record group.

GENERAL RECORDS OF THE BUREAU OF PLANT INDUSTRY. 1900-1953. 1,642 lin. ft. and 57 rolls of microfilm.

These consist of annual reports; general correspondence of the office of the Chief, 1900-1953, with indexes; letters sent by the office of the Chief, 1901-29, the Assistant Chief, 1904-53, and the Executive Assistant, 1911-13; letters sent to the Solicitor of the Department, 1906-21; notes relating to plant pathological work, 1917-20; records relating to budget estimates, 1920-33; progress reports, 1921-25; microfilm copies (57 rolls) of catalogs of botanical, paleobotanical, and plant pathology literature, 1937; and records relating to the Roerich expedition to Mongolia and Northern Manchuria regarding drought resistant grasses, 1934-37.

OFFICE AND DIVISIONAL RECORDS OF THE BUREAU OF PLANT INDUSTRY. 1881-1953. 2,773 lin. ft.

These include general correspondence of the Office of Agricultural Technology, 1906-14; records of the Biophysical Laboratory, consisting of general correspondence, 1906-20, and climatological data and soil-moisture records, 1907-17; correspondence of the Division of Cereal Crops and Diseases, 1895-1939, and records relating to corn yield investigations, 1924-36, and European corn borer investigations, 1925-35; correspondence, reports, and other records of the Office of Congressional Seed Distribution, 1881-1925; records of the Division of Cotton, Rubber, and Other Tropical Plants, consisting of correspondence, 1896-1933, field reports, 1905-32, and papers prepared for publication, 1932-35; records of the Division of Drug and Related Plants, consisting chiefly of general correspondence, 1920-29, correspondence relating to castor beans and camphor trees, 1917-20, and ledgers of expenditures, 1903-8; records of the Division of Forage Crops and Diseases, including general correspondence, 1905-29, and correspondence with State agricultural experiment stations, 1899-1928; records of the Division of Forest Pathology, consisting primarily of general correspondence and correspondence with field personnel, 1907-38; records of the Division of Fruit and Vegetable Crops and Diseases, including correspondence, with an index, 1917-41, and correspondence of the Division of Pomology, 1887-1907, the Office of Field Investigations in Pomology, 1902-13, and the Office of Horticultural and Pomological Investigations, 1901-17.

There are also records of the Division of Soil Fertility Investigations, consisting largely of general correspondence, 1915-40, correspondence relating to fertilizer experiments, 1919-36, and papers for publication, 1930-40; records of the Division of Sugar Plant Investigations, consisting of general and intra-Bureau correspondence, 1914-32, and correspondence and reports of the Sugar-Plant Field Experiment Station at Cairo, Ga., 1913-29; correspondence, 1901-26, and crop experiment reports, 1907-20, of the Division of Tobacco and

Plant Nutrition Investigations; letters received, 1891-1908, letters sent, 1885-1911. and other records of the Division of Vegetable Pathological and Physiological Investigations; records of the Division of Western Irrigation Agriculture, consisting chiefly of correspondence, 1901-37, annual and miscellaneous reports and notes relating to experiment farms, 1907-32, and weekly bulletins, 1911-37; records of the Division of Agricultural Engineering, including correspondence, 1943-50, and records relating to the U.S. Department of Agriculture Rubber Survey, 1938-46; records of the Division of Botany, consisting chiefly of letters sent by the botanist, 1893-1936, general correspondence, 1894-1934, and correspondence with scientific institutions and organizations, 1894-1934; reports, 1928-45, and reference files, 1898-1945, of the Division of Farm Machinery; annual reports of the Division of Farm Power and Machinery, 1933-53; correspondence, 1939-49, and records concerning construction projects, 1937-50, of the Division of Plans and Services, records of the Division of Plant Exploration and Introduction, consisting chiefly of correspondence, 1900-1940, and project studies, 1902-32; reports, correspondence, and related records of the office of the chief chemist, 1928-48; and reports and correspondence of the Beltsville, Md., research center, 1933-45.

GENERAL RECORDS OF THE BUREAU OF CHEMISTRY AND SOILS. 1894-1936. 655 lin. ft.

Included are letters received, 1984-1901, and general correspondence of the Bureau of Soils, 1901-36, with indexes; records relating to investigations of soil types, research in soil microbiology, and problems of soil erosion, 1927-35; organization charts of the Bureau of Chemistry and Soils, 1929-33; and correspondence and reports relating to the Committee on Department Methods (the Keep Commission), 1905.

RECORDS OF THE FERTILIZER RESEARCH DIVISION. 1912-35. 44 lin. ft.

These include correspondence relating to potash and kelp investigations, 1916-35; correspondence of the Office of Fertilizer Control, 1918-19, with indexes; office and personal files of J. W. Turrentine, regarding his chemical fertilization work, 1912-26; reports of city waste disposal, 1914; correspondence and reports regarding potash and organic fertilizer investigations, 1919-30; State laws concerning manufacture and sale of fertilizers, 1918-25; reports relating to proposed Federal legislation for sale and shipment of fertilizer, 1920-21; and a bibliography relating to fertilizers, ca. 1920.

RECORDS OF THE FIXED NITROGEN RESEARCH LABORATORY. 1916-27. 30 lin. ft.

These consist primarily of reports and correspondence of the Nitrate Division of the Office of Ordnance of the War Department, 1916-19; reports and correspondence of the Laboratory, including work undertaken at the Muscle Shoals nitrate plant, 1919-25; technical reports, 1919-25; letters sent, 1919-27; correspondence with Government agencies, 1924-25; correspondence of the Physics, Chemical, Synthetic Ammonia, and Engineering Divisions, 1920-27; and an office file of the Associate Director of the Laboratory, 1923-26.

OTHER RECORDS. 1899-1936. 415 lin. ft.

Included are records of the Soil Chemistry and Physics Research Division, consisting of data relating to moisture studies, 1903, a well survey, 1910, and a card record relating to the examination of soil samples, 1917-26. Also records of the Soil Survey Division, consisting largely of reports on soil surveys, 1899-1927; correspondence relating to soil management at Goldsboro, N.C., 1902, reports on soils of Georgia farms, 1907; reports on field investigations, including forest land classification and soil investigations in Maryland, New Jersey, and New York, 1914-19; correspondence relating to peat investigations, 1933-36; and clippings relating to soil surveys, ca. 1912.

CARTOGRAPHIC AND AUDIOVISUAL RECORDS. 1884-1953. 65,275 items.

Cartographic records include maps, 1900-1953 (1,280 items), of the United States and specific areas, showing distribution of soil groups and types, land use, and water resources.

Audiovisual records consist of photographs (63,995 items) of farming machinery and operations; relating to crop improvement, harvesting, handling, storage and preservation, transportation, and marketing of sugar beets, sweet potatoes, other vegetables, corn and other cereal crops, tobacco, fruits, and ornamental plants, 1892-1951; of landscape design projects for Federal installations, 1884-1933; of parks and the Panama Pacific Exposition, 1913-16; and concerning the investigations of suitable lands for cultivating rubber-producing and hemp substitute plants in Central and South America, 1942-48.

See Harold T. Pinkett, comp., *Preliminary Inventory of the Records of the Bureau of Plant Industry, Soils, and Agricultural Engineering*, PI 66 (1954).

RECORDS OF THE BUREAU OF ENTOMOLOGY AND PLANT QUARANTINE (RECORD GROUP 7)

The Bureau of Entomology and Plant Quarantine was established in the Department of Agriculture July 1, 1934, by authority of the Agricultural Appropriation Act of March 26, 1934. Under the Bureau were consolidated the principal entomological research and plant quarantine and control work formerly conducted by various Department agencies. Entomological work originated in the Office of the Entomologist, established in the Agricultural Section of the Patent Office in 1854. In 1863 a Division of Entomology was created, and in 1904 it was given bureau status. Legislation to prevent importation and interstate transportation of insect-infested plants was first enacted in the Plant Quarantine Act of 1912. This act created the Federal Horticultural Board, composed of representatives of Department of Agriculture bureaus, to regulate plant importation and enforce quarantine

measures. In 1928 the Board was abolished, and its functions were transferred to the new Plant Quarantine and Control Administration, which became the Bureau of Plant Quarantine in 1932.

The Bureau of Entomology and Plant Quarantine cooperated with the States in studying and controlling insects to prevent plant diseases. It was responsible for the enforcement of the Plant Quarantine, Insect Pest, Honeybees Importation, Mexican Border Inspection, and Export Certification Acts and, in cooperation with the Post Office, the Terminal Inspection Act. The Bureau was abolished in 1953, and its functions were distributed among the Branches of Entomology Research, Plant Pest Control, and Plant Quarantine of the Agricultural Research Service (see RG 310), and the Divisions of Forest Insect Research and Blister Rust Control of the Forest Service.

See Gustavus A. Weber, *The Bureau of Entomology* (1930).

There are 1,680 cubic feet of records dated between 1863 and 1953 in this record group.

ENTOMOLOGICAL RECORDS.
1863-1953. 1,395 lin. ft.

General records consist of correspondence of the Bureau and its predecessors, 1878-1953; transcripts of minutes, 1925-51; office files of the Bureau Chief, 1880-1950, and of the Assistant Chief and other officials, 1931-53; narrative reports of divisions, 1927-53; notes of the Division of Entomology, relating to the history and description of insects, 1863-1903; notes on entomological specimens collected in Florida, 1881-82; letters received relating to grasshopper fungus, 1901-2; correspondence relating to silk culture, 1883 and 1901-4, and to investigations of gypsy and browntail moths, 1905-8; letters and reports from field agents, 1881-1907; records of the Mediterranean Fruit Fly Board, 1929-46; a data file on a Food and Drug Administration hearing on tolerance of insecticide residue in or on fresh fruits and vegetables, 1933-51; and correspondence with State and Federal agencies, 1934-51.

There are records of the Division of Bee Culture, consisting of letters sent, 1922-32, and office files, 1936-51; of the Division of Cereal and Forage Insects, consisting chiefly of letters and reports of Francis M. Webster, 1881-1908, notes on field investigations, 1903-34, reports from field stations, 1918-46, and reports and correspondence on selected subjects, 1933-46; of the Division of Control Investigations, consisting primarily of reports and correspondence, 1929-51; of the Division of Fruit Insect Investigations, 1907-51, consisting principally of reports and correspondence concerning research of U.S. field stations and reports from Division employees working in foreign countries; and the Insect

Identification and Introduction Branch, 1887-1952. There are also records relating to special activities of the Divisions of Cooperative Field Relations, 1936-42, Cotton Insect Investigations, 1900-1952, Foreign Parasite Control, 1935-39, Fruit Fly Investigations, 1917-51, Grasshopper Control, 1934-51, Gypsy and Brown-tail Moth Control, 1927-51, Japanese Beetle Control, 1928-51, Mexican Fruit Fly Control, 1928-51, Pink Bollworm and Thurberia Weevil Control, 1930-51, Plant Disease Control, 1923-52, Screwworm Control, 1934-51, Southern Field Crop Insect Investigations, 1894-1924, Taxonomic Investigations, 1910-29, and Tropical and Subtropical Fruit Insect Investigations, 1906-21.

PLANT QUARANTINE RECORDS.
1912-52. 465 lin. ft.

These include records of the Federal Horticulture Board, consisting primarily of minutes and correspondence, 1912-28; the Branch of Domestic Plant Quarantines, consisting chiefly of correspondence concerning insects and plant diseases, 1928-51, correspondence with State officials, 1935-39, correspondence relating to the control of the pink bollworm and thurberia, 1912-28, sweet potato weevil project files, 1936-51, and white fringe beetle project files, 1936-52; and the Branch of Foreign Plant Quarantines, consisting of correspondence relating to the work of inspectors at major U.S. ports and important Mexico-Texas border localities, 1913-28. Also included are records relating to Quarantines 1-75, 1912-52, sample records showing typical operations under Plant Quarantine 37, 1912-32, records relating to the eradication of the Mediterranean fruit fly, 1929-32, records concerning insect identification and parasite introduction, 1919-43, control files relating to the European corn borer, 1928-50, and project files on Dutch elm disease, 1935-50.

CARTOGRAPHIC AND AUDIOVISUAL RECORDS. 1870-1950. 4,466 items.

Maps, 1930-50 (1,640 items), prepared by the Bureau and its predecessors, showing distribution of pest infestations and plant diseases in the United States and the status of projects to eradicate them. Most maps relate to the Mediterranean fruit fly eradication campaign in Florida, 1930-33.

Photographs, 1870-1946 (2,825 items), of portraits, including some of artworks of the 1700's; group photographs of American and foreign natural scientists, particularly Department of Agriculture entomologists, assembled or made by Leland O. Howard; and a 1939 sound recording of Howard.

See Harold T. Pinkett, comp., *Preliminary Inventory of the Records of the Bureau of Entomology and Plant Quarantine*, PI 94 (1956).

RECORDS OF THE BUREAU OF AGRICULTURAL ECONOMICS (RECORD GROUP 83)

The Bureau of Agricultural Economics was established in the Department of Agriculture on July 1, 1922, by consolidation of the Bureau of Markets and Crop Estimates with the Office of Farm Management and Farm Economics. The Bureau of Markets, which had originated in 1913 as the Office of Markets, and the Bureau of Crop Estimates, known from 1903 to 1914 as the Bureau of Statistics, had been combined in 1921. The Office of Farm Management and Farm Economics had originated in the Bureau of Plant Industry in 1904 as the Office of Farm Management. Until 1939 the Bureau of Agricultural Economics conducted studies and disseminated information relating to agricultural production, crop estimates, marketing, finance, labor, and other agricultural problems, and administered several regulatory statutes. The Bureau was designated as the central planning agency for the Department in 1938. It was reorganized in 1939, and its marketing functions and records were transferred to the Agricultural Marketing Service; most of its land-utilization work was transferred to the Soil Conservation Service. At this time the Program Planning Division was moved to the Bureau from the Agricultural Adjustment Administration, and

when the reorganization was complete the Program Surveys, State and Local Planning, Program Development and Coordination, and Program Study and Discussion Divisions had been established. In 1945 program planning was transferred to the Office of the Secretary, and public discussion duties were transferred to the Extension Service. The Bureau supervised and coordinated economic and statistical research in the Department under four assistant chiefs who were in charge of agricultural statistics, income and distribution research, production research, and program analysis and rural life research. In 1953 the Bureau was abolished and its functions were transferred to the Agricultural Research Service and the Agricultural Marketing Service.

There are 2,959 cubic feet of records dated between 1886 and 1953 in this record group.

RECORDS OF PREDECESSOR BUREAUS AND OF THE ADMINISTRATOR. 1906-53. 2,929 lin. ft.

Records of the Bureau of Markets and Crop Estimates and its predecessors consist primarily of correspondence and related name and subject indexes of the

Office of Markets, the Bureau of Markets, and the Bureau of Markets and Crop Estimates, 1912-22; and records relating to studies, projects, and surveys, 1906-21.

Records of the Bureau of Agricultural Economics, 1922-53, consist of general and regional correspondence, 1922-53, partially indexed by subject; office files of the Chief of the Bureau, 1934-46, and the Associate Chief, 1934-53; study project and survey records, including those documenting the effect on farm labor of farm machinery and changing farm practices between 1909 and 1936 (accumulated 1936-39); records concerning the operation of the Center Market, Washington, D.C., 1921-30, cooperative agreements between the Bureau and other agencies and institutions, 1917-46, project files, 1907-53, and a manuscript file of published and unpublished studies and reports, 1913-46, partially indexed by author or title; records concerning international organizations, committees, and conferences, relating to postwar foreign relief requirements, 1941-43, to the United Nations Conference on Food and Agriculture at Hot Springs, Va., 1943, Interim Commission on Food and Agriculture, 1943-45, Food and Agriculture Organization, 1945-53, and World Food Council, 1947-52; and files and ledgers of the Bureau's budget officer, 1920-45, and annual reports of the librarian, 1912-42.

RECORDS OF DIVISIONS.
1886-1953. 775 lin. ft.

Records of units primarily responsible for agricultural estimates consist of Bureau of Crop Estimates correspondence, 1915-21; livestock estimating files, 1922-38; general crop reports, 1897-1927; crop damage records, 1919-37; livestock, fruit, and vegetable tabulations, ca. 1912-53; "comments" on general crop, cotton, and poultry reports, 1907-49; and sample reporting schedule forms and questionnaires, 1886-1940.

Records of the Division of Farm Management and Costs and its predecessors consist of the records of Chiefs of the Division, 1923-33; of the Chief of the Office of Farm Management and Farm Economics, 1919-21; staff correspondence, 1910-36; farm management reports, speeches, and articles, 1902-20; project files, 1906-21; research reports, 1937-42; regional planning and adjustment reports, 1935-37; and records relating to farm business surveys, 1909-26, cost of production studies, 1912-25, and farm labor surveys, 1909-22.

Records of the Division of Farm Population and Rural Life and its predecessors consist chiefly of correspondence, 1913-34, a manuscript file of studies on sociological aspects of rural life, 1917-35, field trip reports, 1915-17, project files, 1919-22, State reports on rural problem areas, 1934-35, and records relating to surveys of rural communities, 1921-32.

Records of the Division of Land Economics consist of records of the head of the Division, 1921-32; general correspondence, 1935-43; land policy, 1925-37, and land use planning records, 1931-38; land utilization reports, 1934-36; records relating to the President's Special Committee on Farm Tenancy, 1936-37; water facilities and flood control policy records, 1936-43; manuscript file of Division staff articles and reports, 1919-36; project files and related records, 1934-43; narrative reports on projects and staff activities, 1934-40; records relating to the Trail smelter fumes investigations, 1926-37; and records of the Flood Control, 1937-43, Land Tenure, 1934-43, Land Utilization, 1936-43, Public Finance, 1934-43, and Water Utilization, 1933-44, Sections.

Records of the Division of Marketing and Transportation Research comprise correspondence, reports, and articles accumulated by the agricultural economist, 1934-41.

Records of the Division of Program Analysis and Development consist of narrative and statistical reports relating to a survey of production goals, 1941-42.

Records of the Division of Program Surveys consist of project files, 1940-45. Included are authorizations for studies, questionnaires, records of interviews, and reports on studies of attitudes of rural and urban people toward the war and war-related problems.

Records of the Division of State and Local Planning consist principally of records of the Division Chief, 1938-42, minutes, 1939-41, County Land Use Planning Committee reports, 1938-42, county agicultural planning project records, 1935-38, records of the southeastern regional planning assistant, 1938-42, and Planning Analysis Unit records, 1941-42.

Records of the Division of Statistical and Historical Research consist of general correspondence, 1917-46; records of the Division Chief, 1923-46; War Records project quarterly reports, 1941-45; a reference file, 1939-46; records concerning the history of agricultural economics, 1915-45; and Central Statistical Board, 1933-40, and National Agricultural Conference, 1922-23, records.

Records of the Domestic Wool Section consist of reports and correspondence, 1918-37.

RECORDS OF STATE AND REGIONAL OFFICES. 1934-46.
54 lin. ft.

Extant State records include minutes, correspondence, and other records of the Bureau's representatives in Arizona, Colorado, New Mexico, and Utah, 1934-42; and general correspondence of the Land Utilization Office at Amarillo, Tex., 1936-38, with an index. Extant regional records consist principally of the correspondence of the Appalachian Regional Office, Washington, D.C., 1934-45; office file of the north-central region-

al farm management leader, Milwaukee, Wis., 1935-46; records of the northeastern regional office, Upper Darby, Pa., consisting of general correspondence, 1939-45, correspondence and reports maintained by a regional farm management representative, 1940-46, and records of the Northeast Postwar Planning Committee, 1941-46, and the Northeast Regional Committee on Production Goals, 1941-45; correspondence of the northern Great Plains regional office, Lincoln, Nebr., relating to land use planning and water utilization, 1935-39; postwar planning records of the southeastern regional office, Atlanta, Ga., 1941-45; general correspondence of the southern Great Plains regional office, Albuquerque, N. Mex., 1936-42; and records of the western regional office, Berkeley, Calif., consisting principally of an office file maintained by th regional representative, 1937-42.

CARTOGRAPHIC AND AUDIOVISUAL RECORDS. 1896-53.
31,307 items.

Cartographic records (4,600 items) include maps of the United States and foreign countries, relating to climate, irrigation, crops, and rural population, 1910-20; maps of the United States and of various States and regions, showing aspects of climate, land ownership and use, irrigation and drainage, crops, livestock, employment, and rural population and migration, 1920-50; and maps accumulated or produced by Francis J. Marschner in the Bureau of Agricultural Economics and its successor units in the Department of Agriculture, 1920-53.

There are photographs (26,660 items) relating to farming operations and rural life in the United States, including planning, tillage, crops, livestock, buildings, equipment, office management, marketing, and social studies of rural communities, 1896-1947; farming operations in Argentina, Chile, and Peru, 1921-23; and the major functional activities of the

Bureau, 1911–47. There are also photographs of charts showing population trends, commodities, and prices, 1939–42; and of illustrations used in the Department of Agriculture yearbook, 1921–34.

Filmstrips, 1939–44 (36 items), are those used as illustrations for recorded lectures on general agricultural subjects, the history of agriculture in the United States, and special war-related phases of agriculture.

Sound recordings, 1939–44 (11 items), are of lectures recorded in English and Spanish for use with some filmstrips.

See Vivian Wiser, comp., *Preliminary Inventory of the Records of the Bureau of Agricultural Economics*, PI 104 (1958); and Wiser, comp., *Writings Relevant to Farm Management in the Records of the Bureau of Agricultural Economics*, SL 17 (1963).

RECORDS OF THE BUREAU OF HUMAN NUTRITION AND HOME ECONOMICS
(RECORD GROUP 176)

The Bureau of Human Nutrition and Home Economics began as the Office of Home Economics, established in 1915 when the States Relations Service was organized in the Department of Agriculture. Created to carry out certain provisions of the Smith-Lever Act of 1914 and to continue nutrition studies conducted since 1894 in the Office of Experiment Stations, the Office was given bureau status in 1923. Its name was changed in 1943 to the Bureau of Human Nutrition and Home Economics. The Bureau conducted research on food, fiber, and other agricultural products; housing and household buying; textiles and clothing; use of income; and household management and equipment. It disseminated information through publications, correspondence, and cooperation with other agencies. On November 2, 1953, the Bureau was abolished and its functions were transferred to the Agricultural Research Service.

There are 253 cubic feet of records (in WNRC) dated between 1913 and 1941 in this record group.

RECORDS. 1913–41. 304 lin. ft.

Correspondence of the Bureau and its predecessors, 1917–41, and correspondence, reports, and studies relating to the White House Conference on Child Health and Protection, 1929–31. Records of the Division of Economics include correspondence, 1923–35; reports of a "Use of Time on Farms" study, 1925–30; studies of employer-employee relationships, 1928–33, and of women living in towns and on farms, 1926–27; and surveys of farm homes in Illinois, Indiana, and Michigan, 1913–17. There are also correspondence and summary reports of clothing studies, 1923–27, of the Textiles and Clothing Division; general correspondence, 1923–30, and correspondence relating to a study of refrigerated food, 1927–30, of the Food and Nutrition Division; and correspondence of the Farm Housing Survey, 1933–34.

RECORDS OF THE SURPLUS MARKETING ADMINISTRATION
(RECORD GROUP 124)

The Surplus Marketing Administration was formed July 1, 1940, by combining the Division of Marketing and Marketing Agreements of the Agricultural Adjustment Administration (AAA) and the Federal Surplus Commodities Corporation. The Federal Surplus Commodities Corporation in 1935 had succeeded the Federal Surplus Relief Corporation, organized in 1933 to divert from the open market to destitute families surplus agricultural commodities that were depressing prices of farm products. Under the Agricultural Adjustment Act of 1933 and an act of August 24, 1935, the AAA was given funds and authority to remove agricultural surpluses from ordinary market channels and to encourage domestic and foreign consumption of these commodities. The work of the Purchase Section, established to administer this function, was coordinated in 1935 with the work of the Procurement Division of the Federal Surplus Commodities Corporation; both offices were subsequently staffed by the same personnel. After 1935 the Corporation's basic programs were formulated by the AAA Division of Marketing and Marketing Agreements. Removal of surpluses continued to be the chief function of the Surplus Marketing Administration, but its operations were expanded in 1939 with inauguration of a food stamp plan for use by the needy in normal domestic trade channels, and by the assumption of new duties in 1941 and 1942 relating to lend-lease shipments abroad. In February 1942 the Surplus Marketing Administration was merged with the Agricultural Marketing Service and the Commodity Exchange Administration to form the Agricultural Marketing Administration.

There are 521 cubic feet of records dated between 1933 and 1943 in this record group.

RECORDS. 1933-43. 625 lin. ft.

Records of the Federal Surplus Relief Corporation and its successor, the Federal Surplus Commodities Corporation, consist of office files of the president, 1939-41, the assistant to the president, 1933-34, and the business manager and assistant administrator, 1935-40; reports and correspondence of the executive officer, 1933-40; reports, correspondence, memorandums, statistical summaries, and other records of the livestock disposal and drought cattle program, 1934-38; correspondence and accounts of the Purchases and Distribution Division and of the Commodities Purchase Section, 1933-40; records of the school lunch program, 1933-40; correspondence and summaries of the Divisions of Marketing Agreements and Procurement, 1933-40; correspondence and auditing records of the Division of Investigations, 1933-40; and administrative files of the AAA Commodities Purchase Section, 1933-37. There are also records of the Surplus Marketing Administration, 1939-43, consisting of reports and correspondence of the Special Commodities Section, records of the wheat and corn export programs and the food and cotton stamp programs (chiefly docket files, 1939-43), and records of the Procurement Branch, 1940-43.

RECORDS OF THE OFFICE OF LABOR (WAR FOOD ADMINISTRATION) (RECORD GROUP 224)

The Office of Labor was created March 1, 1943, as the Agricultural Labor Administration in the Department of Agriculture. On March 26 this Administration was made a part of the War Food Administration, and on June 23 it was designated the Office of Labor. The Office was responsible for farm labor supply, recruitment, and wage stabilization. It supervised importation of farmworkers from abroad and the transportation and care of both foreign and domestic interstate farmworkers. Its chief activity was the operation of camps for migratory and foreign farm laborers. When the War Food Administration was abolished on June 29, 1945, the Office of Labor was terminated. Some of its functions were continued by the Labor Branch of the Production and Marketing Administration of the Department of Agriculture until 1948.

There are 38 cubic feet of records dated between 1941 and 1947 in this record group.

RECORDS. 1941-47. 46 lin. ft.

Included are a "precedent file," correspondence, and indexes of the Agricultural Labor Administration and the Office of Labor, 1943; annotated copies of minutes of the production urgency committees of the War Production Board (see RG 179) and of field manpower priorities committees of the War Manpower Commission (see RG 211), concerning labor allocations to food industries, 1943-45; narrative reports, correspondence, and selected records concerning health associations, 1941-47; records of the Labor Branch, Production and Marketing Administration, consisting of transcripts of hearings on wage adjustments before State USDA wage stabilization boards and reports on investigations of the agricultural wage stabilization program in various localities, 1942-46; and two small-scale maps showing basic land resource areas in the United States, 1944.

See Harold T. Pinkett, comp., *Preliminary Inventory of the Records of the Office of Labor of the War Food Administration*, PI 51 (1953).

RECORDS OF THE AGRICULTURAL MARKETING SERVICE (RECORD GROUP 136)

The Agricultural Marketing Service was established in the Department of Agriculture by a Secretary's memorandum in 1939 to consolidate agricultural marketing and related activities. Its predecessors included the Office of Markets, 1913-15, the Office of Markets and Rural Organization, 1915-17, the Bureau of Markets, 1917-21, the Bureau of Markets and Crop Estimates, 1921-22, and, with respect to its early marketing functions, the Bureau of Agricultural Economics, 1922-53. The Service and its predecessors regulated the producing and marketing of agricultural commodities, conducted market research, prepared and disseminated market news, collected and interpreted agricultural statistics, performed market inspection and grading services, and established official grade standards for many farm products.

The Service was discontinued by Executive order in February 1942, but its functions were performed by the Agricultural Marketing Administration, February-December 1942; the Food Distribution Administration, which in 1944 was renamed the Office of Distribution, 1942-44; the Office of Marketing Services, January-August 1945; and the Production and Marketing Administration, 1945-53. A Secretary's memorandum in 1953 established a new Agricultural Marketing Service, renamed in 1965 the Consumer and Marketing Service.

See T. Swann Harding, *Constituent Agencies of the U.S. Department of Agriculture* (1946).

There are 2,434 cubic feet of records dated between 1894 and 1952 in this record group.

GENERAL RECORDS. 1913-44. 1,365 lin. ft.

These consist of fragmentary correspondence and other records relating to activities of the Bureau of Agricultural Economics and earlier marketing units and including miscellaneous marketing correspondence, 1914-31; general correspondence (550 lin. ft.) of the Bureau of Agricultural Economics, concerning marketing, 1922–39; general correspondence of the Director of the Food Distribution Office, 1943–44, with an index; letters sent by the Food Distribution Administration central office and its predecessors to regional offices, concerning operations and administration, and by the Administrator and divisions, relating to marketing, 1940–43; a confidential file containing rules, regulations, Secretary's orders, transcripts of hearings, and other records relating to functions of the Agricultural Marketing Administration and its predecessors, 1913–42; and publications and proposed publications concerning agricultural marketing, 1931–43.

RECORDS CONCERNING PROGRAM PLANNING AND ADMINISTRATION. 1939–45. 73 lin. ft.

These consist of subject (65 lin. ft.), 1942–45, and administrative, 1943, correspondence of the Office of Materials and Facilities, War Food Administration; administrative correspondence, 1943–44, and records of the territorial emergency program, 1939–43, of the Program Liaison Branch, Office of Distribution; general and administrative correspondence, 1943–44, of the Program Appraisal Branch, Office of Distribution; and miscellaneous correspondence, 1940–42, concerning programs and activities of the Agricultural Marketing Service and the Agricultural Marketing Administration.

RECORDS RELATING TO MARKETING REGULATION AND CONTROL OF AGRICULTURAL COMMODITIES. 1927–40. 432 lin. ft.

These include central office records of the Division of Marketing and Marketing Agreements, consisting of codes, agreements, orders, and licenses concerning milk producers, 1933–36; records concerning suspended and relinquished marketing agreements and licenses,

1933–38; files of milk-marketing areas, 1933–37; records concerning milk-marketing studies and surveys, 1927–40; letters sent by the Chief and Assistant Chief, 1934–35, and audit reports and related accounting records, 1934–38, of the Field Investigation Section; records of the Honey Bee Control Committee, 1933–39; and correspondence, reports, and other records of field offices, 1935–40.

RECORDS OF COMMODITY DIVISIONS, BRANCHES, AND OTHER UNITS. 1905–51. 586 lin. ft.

These comprise the records of specialized units and include the reference file of the Chairman, 1933–35, and other records, 1933–34, of the Alcoholic Beverages Committee, Agricultural Adjustment Administration, concerning regulation of brewing, distilling, and allied industries; general correspondence of the Beverages and Tobacco Division, 1942, and an administrative file of its Director, 1943–44; and correspondence of the Dairy and Poultry Branch, Office of Distribution, 1939–44. Central office records of the Fruit and Vegetable Branch consist of minutes, agreements, licenses, orders, reports, and correspondence relating to enforcement of marketing agreements that affected fruits and vegetables, 1933–51; annual reports of the Fruit and Vegetable Division, 1919–36; and such records of the Standard Container Section as a subject file, the Solicitor's case files, and investigators' files relating to violations of the Standard Container Acts, 1919–42. Records of the Grain Division, Bureau of Agricultural Economics, consist primarily of correspondence on administration of Federal grain, 1916–22, with an index; field reports of grain investigations, 1906–25; correspondence of Division officials, 1918–32; a subject file on grain standardization work, 1906–33; and library reference material concerning grain supervision, 1905-30. Correspondence of the Grain Branch, Production and Marketing Administration, 1942-44. Records of the Hay, Feed, and Seed Division, Bureau of Agricultural Economics, consist of central office correspondence concerning the establishment and revision of hay grades, 1922-26; records of field offices at San Antonio, Tex., 1928-33, and Kansas City, Mo., 1934-37; and correspondence of the Seed Verification Section, 1927-37.

Records of the Packers and Stockyard Administration consist chiefly of case files, 1921-45, correspondence, 1921-38, and audit reports, 1922-36. Also correspondence of the Livestock, Meats, and Wool Division, 1916-39; Livestock and Meats Branch, 1943-44; and Special Commodities Branch, 1943-44.

RECORDS CONCERNING ACTIVITIES UNDER FOOD AND NUTRITION PROGRAMS. 1939-47. 102 lin. ft.

Included are records of the Food Division, consisting of correspondence and other records of the Sugar Section, 1942-44, and correspondence of the Food Conversion Section and a file of the Chief of the Grain Products Section, 1942-43. Correspondence of the Civilian Food Requirements Branch, concerning food requirements and school lunch and milk programs, 1941-44. Subject correspondence of the Requirements and Allocations Control Branch and the Nutrition Programs Branch, 1943-44; the Economic Analysis Section, Food Distribution Branch, 1940-43; and the Nutrition Division, 1940-42. Correspondence, 1943-44, and records concerning the "A" awards program, 1943-46, of the Industry Operations Branch; correspondence of the Food Industries Labor Branch, 1942-44, and the Nutrition and Food Conservation Branch, 1939-44; and correspondence, reports, and other records of the industrial feeding and nutrition program, 1941-47.

RECORDS CONCERNING THE ADMINISTRATION OF COMMODITY PROCUREMENT AND PRICE CONTROL PROGRAMS. 1936-44. 14 lin. ft.

Included are records of the general commodities purchase program, consisting chiefly of correspondence, requisitions, memorandums, designations, agreements, orders, and recommendations, 1936-44; correspondence of the Procurement and Price Support Branch, 1944; and subject correspondence of the Office of Price, Food Distribution Administration, 1943-44.

RECORDS RELATING TO THE REGULATION OF MARKETING FACILITIES. 1930-44. 14 lin. ft.

These consist primarily of the records of the Warehouse Division, including correspondence concerning administration of the U.S. Warehouse Act, 1930-39, subject correspondence of the Marketing Facilities Branch, 1944, and correspondence of the Shipping and Storage Branch, 1943-44.

RECORDS CONCERNING SEED INVESTIGATIONS. 1894-1948. 97 lin. ft.

These comprise the records of the Seed Investigations Division of the Bureau of Plant Industry and the Agricultural Marketing Service, including a central correspondence file (56 lin. ft.), 1917-37; correspondence of the Seed Laboratory at Washington, D.C., with U.S. consuls, concerning seed importation, 1913-18; correspondence of the Division with State agencies engaged in seed testing, with seed dealers, and other persons, 1929-39; letters sent by Bureau of Plant Industry officials, concerning pure seed investigations and enforcement of the Federal Seed Act, 1894-1938; record books of seeds received and placed in the National Herbarium seed collection, 1894-1906; case files regarding violations of Federal seed laws, 1933–39; and proceedings and other publications of the Association of Official Seed Analysts of North America, 1915–48.

CARTOGRAPHIC AND AUDIOVISUAL RECORDS. 1909–52. 1,316 items.

Cartographic records (16 items) comprise maps of the United States published under the Production and Marketing Administration, showing loan-purchase agreement rates for crops in 1951 and price support rates in 1952.

Audiovisual records, 1909–19 (1,300 items), consist of photographs relating to cooperative studies of the egg and poultry industry conducted by the Bureau of Chemistry, the Bureau of Animal Industry, and the Bureau of Markets.

SPECIFIC RESTRICTIONS

Records: Records of the Honey Bee Control Committee.

Restrictions: These records may not be examined by or information from or copies of them provided to any person other than an employee of the Department of Agriculture except by permission of an appropriate official of the Department.

Specified by: Department of Agriculture.

DEPARTMENT OF COMMERCE

GENERAL RECORDS OF THE DEPARTMENT OF COMMERCE (RECORD GROUP 40)

The Department of Commerce and Labor was established by an act of February 14, 1903, which transferred to it a number of previously existing offices. Separate Labor and Commerce Departments were established in 1913.

The functions of the Commerce Department are to promote foreign and domestic commerce, the manufacturing and shipping industries, and the transportation facilities of the United States. Most of these functions are performed by bureaus of the Department, whose records constitute separate record groups. This record group includes general records of the immediate Office of the Secretary of Commerce and of officials and offices performing staff and administrative functions for the Department as a whole. It also includes records of various related commissions, boards, and other special bodies.

There are 807 cubic feet of records dated between 1898 and 1954 in this record group.

GENERAL RECORDS OF THE OFFICE OF THE SECRETARY. 1903-54. 883 lin. ft.

These include general correspondence, 1903-50 (612 lin. ft.), with related indexes, 1903-50; letters relating chiefly to labor matters, sent by President Taft to the Department of Commerce and Labor, 1910-12; correspondence of Secretaries of Commerce Robert P. Lamont, 1929-32, Daniel P. Roper, 1933-39, and Jesse H. Jones, 1941-44; separately maintained files relating to bureaus and functions no longer in the

Department, including the Bureaus of Corporations, Mines, Lighthouses, Alaskan Fur Seal Fisheries, and Marine Inspection and Navigation, ca. 1907-42; monthly bureau reports to the Secretary, 1913-50; records of the Appointment Division, 1903-41; records of the Division of Personnel Management and Supervision, 1907-42; reports and correspondence of Coordinator, International Cooperation Programs, J. Clayton Miller, 1945-48; records of the chief regional economist, 1944-47; records of Advisor on Negro Affairs Emmer Martin Lancaster, consisting of correspondence and reports concerning blacks' small businesses, 1940-53; legislative files of the Office of the General Counsel, 1932-40; general records of the Clearing Office for Foreign Transactions and Reports and its successor, the Balance of Payments Division, 1942-54; a map published by the Office of Area Development, showing urban target areas of the national industrial dispersion program; and photographs (125 items) of departmental exhibits, 1926-29, and buildings and office space occupied by the Department.

RECORDS OF COMMISSIONS AND OTHER SPECIAL BODIES. 1898-1949. 105 lin. ft.

Included are minutes of the Industrial Commission, created to investigate labor and industrial practices, 1898-1902; records relating to the Taft Commission, chiefly reports prepared by Department of Commerce bureaus for Commission use, 1910-11; correspondence and reports of the Waste-Reclamation Service and its successors, the Industrial Board and the Industrial Cooperation Service, ca. 1917-20; records of the President's Committee on Foreign Aid, consisting chiefly of correspondence and reports on specific foreign aid programs, 1949 (in HSTL); and records, 1948-49, of the Office of Industry Cooperation, created to promote voluntary price and wage control, consisting primarily of correspondence of the Director, voluntary plans to stabilize wages and prices, transcripts of hearings, and files of staff members and administrative units established to formulate plans for voluntary regulation of specific industries.

Microfilm Publication: *Minutes of the Industrial Commission, 1898-1902*, T10, 1 roll.

SPECIFIC RESTRICTIONS

I. *Records*: Records of the Office of Industry Cooperation.

Restrictions: Records that contain information of a confidential nature about the operations of trade associations and private business firms will not be made available without the prior approval of the Office of the General Counsel of the Department of Commerce.

Specified by: Department of Commerce.

II. *Records*: Legislative files of the Office of the General Counsel of the Department of Commerce.

Restrictions: Only authorized employees of the Office of the General Counsel or others specifically approved by that Office may have access to these records.

Specified by: Department of Commerce.

RECORDS OF THE BUREAU OF THE CENSUS
(RECORD GROUP 29)

The Census Office was established in 1902 as a permanent bureau in the Department of the Interior, but the terms "Census Bureau" and "Census Office" were used interchangeably until the term "Bureau of the Census" was formally fixed by legislation in 1954. Before 1902 a census office was established for each decennial census and disbanded when work on the census was completed. The first nine censuses were taken by U.S. district marshals. In 1790 census returns were submitted directly to the President, those from 1800 to 1840 to the Secretary of State, and those from 1850 to 1870 to the Secretary of the Interior. From 1880 to 1900 the censuses were taken by enumerators under supervisors responsible through the Superintendent of the Census to the

Secretary of the Interior. In 1903 the Census Bureau was transferred from the Department of the Interior to the Department of Commerce and Labor. Since 1913 it has been in the Department of Commerce. The compilation of the *Statistical Abstract of the United States* and responsibility for collecting and compiling foreign trade statistics were transferred from the Bureau of Foreign and Domestic Commerce to the Census Bureau in 1937 and 1941, respectively. In 1946 the functions and records of the Census Bureau relating to vital statistics were transferred to the U.S. Public Health Service of the Federal Security Agency.

The Census Bureau is responsible for providing basic statistics about the people and economy of the Nation to assist the Congress, Government, and public in planning, carrying out, and evaluating programs. It collects, tabulates, and publishes a wide variety of statistical data for Government and private users.

See Carroll D. Wright, *The History and Growth of the United States Census* (1900), and W. Stull Holt, *The Bureau of the Census* (1929).

There are 8,434 cubic feet of records dated between 1790 and 1965 in this record group.

ADMINISTRATIVE RECORDS OF THE CENSUS OFFICE. 1820–1905. 35 lin. ft.

These consist of records relating to administration of the 4th–12th decennial censuses. Most records for each census relate to personnel, including appointment data and lists of marshals, assistant marshals, enumerators, special agents, and Census Office employees; fiscal matters, including payrolls and expenditure accounts; and the enumeration process, including descriptions of enumeration districts, letters and instructions sent by the Census Office, and registers of schedule receipts.

Few administrative records of the earliest censuses have survived. Records of the fourth census consist of only a few miscellaneous documents, 1820–21. Those for the fifth and sixth censuses consist of an account of compensation to marshals and their assistants, 1830–31 and 1840–41, and a register of census return receipts, 1840–41. Thereafter, the records are progressively more voluminous and varied. Records for the 10th and 11th censuses include an alphabetical list of occupations, 1880, a list of Louisiana sugar planters, 1881–82, record books of special agents investigating fisheries and meat production, 1869–80, statistics relating to congregations of Lutheran synods, 1890, the logbook of a special agent containing population statistics and an account of his activities in Alaska, 1890, and lists of names and addresses of State prisons,

orphanages, asylums, hospitals, insane asylums, and schools for the deaf, dumb, and blind, 1890–91.

ADMINISTRATIVE RECORDS OF THE BUREAU OF THE CENSUS. 1882–1965. 573 lin. ft.

Records of the Office of the Director include correspondence, statistical studies, and related records, 1882–1914 and 1922–47. Records of the Census Advisory Committee, 1919–49, consist of minutes, resolutions, reports, and correspondence relating to census legislation, personnel, publications, and Bureau organization.

Records of the assistant director for operations include disbursing ledgers, 1902–23; correspondence, memorandums, and reports of the Administrative Service Division, 1900–1953; records of the Appointments Division, 1898–1929; Publication Division records relating to the World War II history project, 1946; Field Division records concerning problems encountered by field personnel, 1948–50; and the subject file of the Geography Division, consisting chiefly of reports, correspondence, studies, and tabulations, 1889–1950.

Records of the Office of Assistant Director of Statistical Standards include general Bureau records, consisting of periodic reports, 1899–1956; records relating to activities of staff members, such as trips, speeches, presentation of papers, and meetings, 1934–49; general records of the chief statistician and other officials, consisting of reports, correspondence, studies, tabulations, memorandums, and notes, 1905–43; a collection of schedule forms, instructions for gathering and compiling data, form letters, and other issuances prepared for censuses, 1900–1964; legal reports on proposed Federal legislation concerning the Census Bureau, 1936–52; general records relating to the taking of the 1948 census of business, 1944–53; records concerning a study of the decreasing number of farms enumerated, 1940-41, and a survey of the publication program for special studies and monographs relating to the 16th census, 1940-41; minutes, correspondence, reports, schedules, and published monographs relating to the 17th decennial census, 1946-56; correspondence, studies, and workpapers relating to apportionment computation and procedures, 1900-1941; and minutes, reports, correspondence, and instructions relating to the collection of vital statistics, 1936-46.

Records of the assistant director for demographic fields, who was in charge of the decennial census enumerations for agriculture, population, and housing, include scrapbooks of schedule forms, instructions, form letters, and other issuances relating to the census of agriculture, 1935-45; records of the Population Division, relating principally to the development of classification methods for occupations, 1870-1950; a general file of the population and housing program coordinator and expediter, 1947-56; scrapbooks of schedules, instructions, forms, plans, worksheets, and other materials prepared for the census of housing, 1940, the census of religious bodies, 1926, statistics of marriage and divorce, 1922-29, and population, 1920-40; hand and machine data tabulations relating to minority groups, prepared from 1930 census population schedules; and records of the Division of Territorial, Insular, and Foreign Statistics, consisting of a general subject file, 1935-42, and files of schedules, forms, instructions, memorandums, reports, publicity material, tabulations, and other records relating to planning, conducting, and publishing the results of territorial censuses, 1900-1948. Included are records relating to the 1937 census of unemployment, consisting of a general file; publicity material; files of the administrator, technical assistants, and consultants; and records relating to collecting and compiling data, 1937-39.

Records of the assistant director for economic fields include office files of Howard C. Grieves, documenting his Bureau service as the chief economist, 1945-47, and assistant director for economic fields, 1947-65; records of the Business Division, relating to the collection and compilation of data for business censuses, 1929-52; tabulations and compilations of the Division of Foreign Trade Statistics, 1914-16 and 1918-38 (in WNRC); records of the Governments Division and its predecessor units, consisting of files of the chief legal office of the Bureau, relating to census legislation, security classification of census data, and the interpretation of State laws concerning taxation, revenue, pension funds, voting, elections, and the nature of public records; questionnaires and other records relating to election surveys, 1939-47; records relating to general program planning and evaluation, 1945-65, and to finance and employment surveys, 1947-62; records of the Industry Division, consisting of schedules, forms and instructions for censuses of manufactures, 1890-1947; a historical file on the development of reporting forms for the 1947 census of manufactures, 1945-48; records relating to the collection and tabulation of data on special industries and industrial products, 1900-1946; and fragmentary records relating to the Bureau machine shop, 1917-22.

CENSUS SCHEDULES AND SUPPLEMENTARY RECORDS.
1790-1950. 1,275 lin. ft. and 27,988 rolls of microfilm.

These include schedules of population, manufacturing, agriculture, business, and special censuses. Population schedules include those for decennial population censuses, 1790-1870. Most of the schedules for the census of 1890 have been destroyed. Schedules for censuses before 1850 give only the name of the head of each family, followed by such family information as the number of dependents by age and sex. Beginning with the 1850 census the schedules contain the name of each individual and his age, sex, State or country of birth, and occupation. The censuses of 1850 and 1860 contain separate schedules of the slave population. There are schedules of a special census of Indians, 1880. Territorial population schedules are available for Minnesota, 1857-58, Arizona, 1864, and Seminole County, Okla., 1907.

Manufacturing schedules include those for the census of 1820 and for the censuses of manufactures of 1932 (in WNRC) and 1934 (in WNRC). Agricultural schedules consist of those relating to tobacco crops, 1910, general farm schedules, 1920, agricultural schedules for outlying territories and possessions, 1920 and 1930 (in WNRC), schedules of special fruits and nuts, 1930 (in WNRC), horticultural schedules, 1930 (in WNRC), and drainage and irrigation schedules, 1930 (in WNRC). Business schedules (in WNRC) consist of those of the 1929 census of distribution, 1930, and the 1935 business census, 1936.

There are schedules of special censuses of religious bodies, 1926-28 (in WNRC); of Colorado, Florida, Nebraska, and New Mexico, 1885; population and agricultural schedules of Puerto Rico, 1935-36; schedules containing aggregate data, by State and county, for the census of mines, agriculture, commerce, and manufacturing, 1840; schedules of municipal population enumerations, 1932-38; microfilm (400 rolls) of nonpopulation schedules (agriculture, industry and manufacture, mortality, and social statistics) for certain States, 1850-80, the originals of which are in the custody of State and private institutions; and microfilm (20,851 rolls) of population schedules for the 1880-1950 censuses. Supplementary records consist primarily of microfilm (42 rolls) of census publications, 1792-1917; abstracts of decennial population returns, 1791-1841; lists of contents of volumes of 1800-1870 population schedules, 1901-3; and microfilm (6,695 rolls) of an index ("soundex") to names appearing in the 1900 population schedules, 1939.

CARTOGRAPHIC AND AUDIOVISUAL RECORDS. 1850-1960. ca. 57,514 items.

Maps (ca. 50,000 items) annotated to show boundaries and numbers of enumeration districts by county decennially, 1880-1950, and a series of bound volumes containing written descriptions of enumeration district boundaries, 1850-1950. Very few of the maps are dated before 1900. Some descriptions also include names, addresses, special instructions, and rates of pay for enumerators; and population and number of dwellings and farms in each district.

There are also maps and graphs (ca. 7,426 items) showing statistical information relating to cultural, social, and economic activities and population growth, 1860-1957; editions of the *Statistical Atlas of the United States* for the years 1870, 1890, 1900, 1914, and 1924; textual material relating to Bureau mapping activities; and manuscript maps and other graphic illustrations prepared by the International Statistical Program Office, showing information about population distribution and vital statistics of Central America, 1940-46.

Photographs (67 items) relating to the Navajo Indian enumeration, 1930, and to tabulating machinery, 1890-1910.

Motion pictures, 1937-39 and 1960 (16 reels), encouraging the public to cooperate with the national unemployment census of 1937 and the 1940 census; training films for enumerators for the 1940 census; and a National Educational Television series concerning the 1960 census, illustrating Bureau work, tracing the history of U.S. census taking, and explaining the kind of information sought and its uses.

Sound recordings, 1940 (5 items), of the radio series "Uncle Sam Calling— Story of the 1940 Census."

See Katherine H. Davidson and Charlotte M. Ashby, comps., *Preliminary Inventory of the Records of the Bureau of the Census*, PI 161 (1964); *Population Schedules, 1800-1870, Volume Index to Counties and Major Cities*, SL 8 (1951); and James Berton Rhoads and Ashby, comps., *Preliminary Inventory of the Cartographic Records of the Bureau of the Census*, PI 103 (1958).

Microfilm Publications: Records of the Bureau published on microfilm consist chiefly of Federal population census schedules, 1790-1880, and surviving fragments of schedules for the census of 1890 (indexes to the 1880 population schedules and to the 1810 schedules for Virginia are also available); population, agriculture, industry, and mortality schedules for special State censuses of Colorado and Nebraska, 1885; schedules of the 1820 census of manufactures; and publications of the Bureau of the Census, 1793-1917. Federal nonpopulation census schedules (agriculture, industry, mortality, and social statistics), 1850-80, now in the custody of various State depositories, are available for certain States. A listing of these States will be furnished on request.

SPECIFIC RESTRICTIONS

I. *Records*: Schedules of the censuses of population, 1900, 1910, and 1920; and schedules of the censuses of agriculture, 1910, 1920, and 1925.

Restrictions: These records may not be examined by or copies of or information from them provided to any person except by permission of the Director of the Census.

Specified by: Director of the Census.

II. *Records*: Schedules of the censuses of population, 1930, 1940, and 1950; of religious bodies, 1926; of agriculture, 1930 and 1935; of distribution, 1929; of business, 1935; and of manufactures, 1931 and 1933.

Restrictions: These records may not be examined by or copies of or information from them provided to any person other than sworn employees of the Census Office having proper authorization from the Secretary of Commerce.

Specified by: Congress of the United States.

RECORDS OF THE PATENT OFFICE
(RECORD GROUP 241)

The granting of patents for inventions was made a function of the Federal Government by the Constitution. On April 10, 1790, the first patent act created a board consisting of the Secretaries of State and War and the Attorney General to issue patents. It placed related administrative responsibility in the Department of State. In 1793 the board was abolished and its functions given to the Secretary of State. In 1802 a Superintendent of Patents was appointed in the Department to issue patents and administer patent laws. The Patent Office under the Commissioner of Patents was set up in the Department of State by an act of July 4, 1836, transferred to the Department of the Interior by an act of March 3, 1849, and placed under the Department of Commerce by Executive Order 4175 of March 17, 1925. The Office administers patent laws and Federal trademark laws.

There are 18,681 cubic feet of records dated between 1791 and 1923 in this record group.

RECONSTRUCTED RECORDS RELATING TO PATENTS ("NAME AND DATE PATENTS"). 1791-1836. 12 lin. ft.

Most original patent records were destroyed by fire in 1836, but their restoration was provided for in 1837. The records consist of copies of applications, patent heads, drawings, and specifications for original patent grants and reissues.

RECORDS RELATING TO "NUMBERED PATENTS." 1836-1923. 10,800 lin. ft.

These consist of patent application files (7,781 lin. ft.), which include inventors' specifications, patent examiners' reports, legal documents, correspondence with inventors and attorneys, and notices of allowances and fees paid, 1837-1900; drawings, 1837-70; copies of specifications, 1837-40; interference case files, 1836-1900 (in WNRC); registers of interferences, 1839-1905 (in WNRC); drawings, 1838-61, and copies of specifications, 1837-61, relating to claims for additional improvements; case files, 1836-75, and copies of specifications and certificates, 1839-77, with registers, concerning extensions of patent rights; specifications, 1838-48, and drawings, 1838-70, relating to reissued patents; digests, 1837-1900, with indexes, 1837-1923, about assignments of patent property rights; specifications, 1857-64, and drawings, 1843-77, relating to design patents; miscellaneous correspondence and rejected petitions, 1837-54; letters received, 1872-82; and abandoned applications, 1894-1912.

RECORDS OF THE COAST AND GEODETIC SURVEY (RECORD GROUP 23)

The Coast and Geodetic Survey had its origin in an act of February 10, 1807, which authorized the President to have a survey made of U.S. coasts. The first Superintendent of the Survey of the Coast was appointed in the Treasury Department August 3, 1816. In 1818 the earlier act was repealed in part, work was suspended for lack of appropriations, and "work and instruments" were turned over to the Navy Department. In 1832 the act was revived, and the Superintendent of the Survey of the Coast was reappointed in the Treasury Department. The Survey of the Coast was transferred in 1834 to the Navy Department, returned in 1836 to the Treasury Department (where it was known as Coast Survey until it was designated Coast and Geodetic Survey by an act of June 20, 1878), and transferred in 1903 to the Department of Commerce and Labor. It became part of the Department of Commerce in 1913, and in 1965 part of the Environmental Sciences Administration within the Department. Its functions include surveying and charting the coasts of the United States and its possessions, establishing a primary network of vertical and horizontal control in the Nation, studying tides and currents, compiling aeronautical charts, and conducting research in terrestrial magnetism, gravity, and seismology.

There are 3,235 cubic feet of records dated between 1806 and 1957 in this record group.

TREASURY DEPARTMENT RECORDS RELATING TO THE COAST SURVEY. 1806 and 1832-1901. 7 lin. ft.

These consist of a narrative report of a survey of the North Carolina coast from Cape Fear to Cape Hatteras by William Tatham, 1806; letters received, 1832-64, and sent, 1834-73, by the Office of the Secretary; and correspondence of the Appointment Division, 1860-1901.

RECORDS OF THE OFFICE OF THE DIRECTOR. 1843-1950. 256 lin. ft.

These comprise minutes and proceedings of a board created to study the organization and procedures of the Coast Survey, 1843. Also records created during the superintendency of Alexander Dallas Bache, 1844-65, consisting of a general file of correspondence with the staff; administrative records relating to Washington Office operations and field activities; records relating to scientific subjects and activities; private correspondence of Superintendent Bache; a correspondence register for the period 1860-67; miscellaneous scientific and business records of the Superintendent, 1844-49; Bache manuscripts of publications on magnetism, 1859-64; records used in preparing the 1849 annual report; records relating to observations of solar eclipses, May 26, 1854, and July 18, 1860; records relating to surveys and improvements of New York Harbor, 1855-59, Boston Harbor, a proposed Cape Cod ship canal and Provincetown Harbor, 1859-61, Mobile Harbor, 1860, proposed sites for a navy yard, 1862-63, and Philadelphia defenses, 1863-64; records relating to land surveys, 1848-54; an unpublished manuscript "Sailing Directions and List of Harbors," describing bays, harbors, and anchorages on the Atlantic, gulf, and Pacific coasts, 1856-57; "Notes on the Coast of the United States," prepared for the Navy Department, 1861; miscel-laneous statistical data, publications, notes, and correspondence relating to the work of the Coast Survey, 1857-63; and record (duplicate) copies of correspondence, 1848-62.

There are also a "Superintendent's file" comprising general correspondence, with related registers and indexes, 1866-1910; assignments and instructions to Survey personnel, 1855-92; monthly reports and journals of field parties, 1868-75; records relating to observations of the solar eclipse, December 22, 1870, and to surveys in insular possessions, 1900-1906; and a compiled "Abstract of Provisions of the Civil Service Law and Rules With Decisions Affecting the Coast and Geodetic Survey," 1903.

Records for the period 1911-50 reflect changes in the recordkeeping practices of the Survey resulting from recommendations made by the Taft Commission in 1910. They consist of general correspondence, 1911-31; a miscellaneous subject file, 1917-50, relating to activities of directors and assistant directors; periodical narrative and statistical reports from Washington Office units and field parties; and records relating to Taft Commission inquiries into Survey administrative procedures, 1909-11.

RECORDS OF WASHINGTON OFFICE UNITS. 1816-1946. 316 lin. ft.

The Office of the Assistant in Charge of the Washington Office was established in 1843 to supervise Washington Office units. For most of the 19th century this official acted as assistant superintendent and chief administrative officer for the Survey, supervising many operations both in the Washington Office and in the field. In 1899 his duties were limited to supervision of Washington Office units and routine administrative matters. The position was abolished in 1920. The records consist of letters received, 1845-1908, and sent, 1850-1908; indexes, registers, and some correspondence relating to fiscal matters, 1833-36; general correspondence, 1909-14; drafts of annual reports, 1851-52; circulars, 1854-98; reports of the Computing Division, 1869-86; abstracts of personnel records, 1844-1902; and office rollbooks containing personnel information, 1885-1900.

A naval officer detailed in 1859 to the Survey was designated Hydrographic Inspector and assigned responsibility for examining all vessels used by the Survey. The duties of the office were later enlarged to include the examination of data submitted by hydrographic parties and administrative and substantive control over all hydrographic work. The office was superseded in 1899 by the Division of Hydrography and Topography. The records include letters sent, 1854-88, and received, 1863-98; a list of correspondence referred to the Hydrographic Inspector by other Government offices, 1892-95; and a record of the service of naval officers with the Coast Survey, 1866-99.

The Division of Hydrography and Topography was responsible for planning, administering, and reviewing field operations. In 1941 it became the Division of Coastal Surveys. The records consist of letters received, 1899-1909, and sent, 1901-10, with related registers; general correspondence, 1901-25; correspondence with private firms and individuals, 1924-29; circulars, 1899-1903; Survey vessel specifications, 1885-1900; rollbooks of Division officers, 1910-16; lists of personnel on Survey vessels in the Philippines, 1911-17; registers to surveys and vessel logs, 1841-1917; and miscellaneous records relating to surveys and vessels, 1910-17.

Records of the Office of the Disbursing Agent include incoming, 1847-65, and outgoing, 1851-77, letters; letters received, 1879-81 and 1885-97, and sent, 1873-77 and 1881-82; registers of "authorities" for expenditures, 1843-94, with related indexes; disbursing records,

1881-87; personnel and payroll records, 1816-1911; and property inventories, 1841-60.

Records of the Division of Geodesy, which processed field data and performed computations and adjustments of data, consist of reports and correspondence relating to scientific and administrative matters, 1851-1911, correspondence of the inspector of geodetic work and of the Computing Division, 1901-14, monthly and annual reports, 1897-1912, records relating to standards of length used in measurements of base lines, 1844-98, and lists of geographical positions based on Bessel's spheroid, n.d.

Records of the Charts Division, which compiled, produced, and distributed Survey charts, consist of letters sent by the Engraving Division, 1885-90, records of labor costs for the preparation of engraved plates, 1844-1904, records of additions to and corrections of engraved plates, 1877-1904, and records relating to the Committee on Chart Publication, 1916.

Other records consist of letters received by the assistant in charge of State surveys, relating to cooperation with State geological and topographical surveys, 1886-90; minutes of the Chart Board, 1893-94, which advised the Superintendent on preparing and issuing charts; records of the Geophysics Division, comprising reports and data prepared by or based on observations in areas affected by earthquakes, 1912-35; building plans, 1870-1924, maintained by the Office of the Chief Clerk; and narrative project reports prepared by the Aeronautical Charts Branch in cooperation with the U.S. Army Air Forces, documenting the compilation and drafting of aeronautical charts, 1941-46.

RECORDS OF FIELD PARTIES AND STATIONS. 1844-1947.
133 lin. ft.

Ship records, 1846-1947, consist of deck logbooks of Survey vessels, physicians journals, shipping articles, engineer logs, and records relating to property and funds. The deck logbooks, which provide data relating to vessel movements, supplement records of scientific observations by giving dates and conditions under which surveys were taken.

Records of Survey assistants and heads of field parties consist of letter books, reports to the Superintendent, journals of surveys, and accounts of Assistant F. H. Gerdes, 1844-69, while he was in charge of field parties in the Florida Keys, the gulf coast, New England, and the Mississippi Valley (the materials for the period of the Civil War include accounts of military and naval operations); letters sent by J. G. Oltmann, 1855-61, who served under Gerdes in surveying parties along the gulf coast; letters received by Lt. G. H. Elliot, 1859, relating to administration of work on tidal observations on the Pacific coast; letters sent by military assistants in San Francisco, 1856-58 and 1860-67, relating to tidal observations; administrative letters sent by Lt. J. E. Pillsbury, Commanding Officer of the steamer *Blake*, 1885-89, while conducting surveys of the Gulf Stream; letters sent by Assistant Stehman Fourney, 1888-91, relating mainly to Survey operations along the Gulf of Mexico; letters sent by W. D. Alexander, 1901-7, relating to surveys in the Hawaiian Islands; and administrative letters sent by the commander of the *Patterson*, 1904-11, while engaged in surveys in Alaskan waters.

SCIENTIFIC RECORDS. 1816-1948. 3,685 lin. ft. (in WNRC).

Notebooks, unbound portfolios, and packages of sheets produced by recording devices, consisting chiefly of observations made by Survey parties in the continental United States, territories, and insular possessions. Among these records, however, are observations made in other parts of the world in connection with international boundary surveys, observations of eclipses and transits of Venus, expeditions to polar regions, and comparative observations. They also include a few observations made by private citizens and by other Government organizations, or copies of such observations, and office computations of field data. The records comprise azimuth observations, 1844-1919; latitude observations, 1833-1933; longitude records, 1844-1939; time observations, 1831-1912, and computations, 1845-1920; and "astronomical miscellany," 1838-1920, including observations of eclipses of the sun and of sunspots, records of the standardization of instruments, an undated "Paper on the Prime Vertical" by Ferdinand Rudolph Hassler, and an 1852 "Plan for Work on Moon Culminations" by Benjamin Peirce. Also descriptions of stations, 1834-1937, consisting of narrative descriptions; numerical data; drawings; maps locating and identifying stations in triangulation and traverse surveys; "reconnoitering journals" of Ferdinand Rudolph Hassler recording observations in New England, 1816-34, and the District of Columbia and Annapolis, 1835; and an 1869 manuscript of an article by E. Ballard on Indian place names in Maine.

Also included are reconnaissance notes, 1843-1912; base measurements, 1833-1935; computations of base lines, 1857-1937; observations of horizontal directions and angles, 1817-1948; computations of plane coordinates, leveling computations and abstracts, and leveling adjustments, 1934-37, consisting of records created in the course of traverse and leveling surveys conducted in South Carolina by the Civil Works Administration and its successors under the direction of the Coast and Geodetic Survey; descriptions of bench marks, 1878-1938; spirit level observations, 1844-1939; leveling-rod books, 1877-98; leveling miscellany, 1905, consisting of numerical data of "levels for determining the difference of elevation of the tape measuring stakes of the Isthmian Canal Base Line" at Mangrove Beach, Panama; observations of vertical angles, 1833-1929; field observations of terrestrial magnetism, 1832-1930; observations at magnetic observatories, 1854-1935; seismograms, 1903-30; and data for the 1945 magnetic charts of the world, compiled by the Carnegie Institution of Washington for the Navy Hydrographic Office, 1945; gravity observations, 1873-1919; hydrographic survey soundings, 1835-1929; Philippine sounding records, 1901-18; tide-staff readings, 1835-1939; descriptions of tidal bench marks, 1854-1908; observations of currents, 1844-1914; "leveling record—tide station," 1846-1936; related registers; and field notes on Gulf Stream observations, 1843-91, prepared by Lt. J. E. Pillsbury, USN, in command of the *George S. Blake.*

CARTOGRAPHIC AND AUDIOVISUAL RECORDS. 1839-1965. 59,591 items.

Cartographic records, 1839-1965 (59,580 items), include reports and publications relating to maps and mapping activities; an atlas of the Philippine Islands (based on surveys conducted by Jesuit Fathers, 1899-1900, and nautical charts of individual islands), published in the Survey's Manila office, 1913-34;

published aeronautical charts of the United States, including sectional, flight, local, instrument approach and landing, radio facility, danger area, direction finding, and planning charts, aircraft position charts of the North Atlantic Ocean and adjacent land areas, route charts, jet navigation and world aeronautical charts of North America, and airways route charts, 1926-65; published nautical charts of U.S. coasts, its territories and island possessions, including sailing charts covering large ocean areas, general nautical charts designed for offshore coastwise navigation, coast charts for inshore coastwise navigation, and harbor charts, 1839-1965; reproductions of plans of Washington, D.C.; maps and charts prepared during the Civil War by the Survey; and prints of maps constructed from aerial photographs covering the coastal United States, 1927-61.

Audiovisual records, n.d. (11 items), consist of photographs and drawings of Hudson River areas and dredging activities and machinery.

See Nathan Reingold, comp., *Preliminary Inventory of the Records of the Coast and Geodetic Survey,* PI 105 (1958).

Microfilm Publications: *Correspondence of A. D. Bache, Superintendent of the Coast and Geodetic Survey, 1843-1865,* M642, 281 rolls, DP; *U.S. Coast and Geodetic Survey: Nautical Charts, Aid Proofs, and Standards (Chart Nos. 50-1-9100),* T274, 15 rolls; and *Tides Observation Books—Polar Regions,* T296, 2 rolls.

RECORDS OF THE NATIONAL BUREAU OF STANDARDS (RECORD GROUP 167)

The National Bureau of Standards was created in the Department of the Treasury by an act of March 3, 1901, to succeed the Office of Standard Weights and Measures, established in 1830 as a section of the Coast Survey. The Bureau was transferred to the Department of Commerce and Labor by

an act of February 14, 1903. When separate Departments of Commerce and Labor were created in 1913, the Bureau remained in the Department of Commerce. The Bureau provides the central basis in the United States for a complete and consistent system of physical measurements, conducts tests on the properties of materials, develops technological standards and testing methodology, performs research on radiation and in computer technology, and promotes the dissemination of scientific and technological information.

See Gustavus A. Weber, *The Bureau of Standards* (Baltimore, 1925); and John Perry, *The Story of Standards* (New York, 1955).

There are 645 cubic feet of records dated between 1830 and 1968 in this record group.

RECORDS OF THE OFFICE OF STANDARD WEIGHTS AND MEASURES. 1830-1901. 27 lin. ft.

These comprise computations for tests, comparisons, and observations and notes made on weights and measures to determine whether they met desired standards, 1840-1901; reports, fiscal records, correspondence including letters sent to the Treasury Department, 1830-53, and letters received by the Office, 1845-93; reports concerning weights and measures, ca. 1870; and quarterly accounting reports, abstracts of expenditures, and vouchers, 1845-66. There are a few papers of Superintendent Ferdinand R. Hassler, chiefly correspondence and reports regarding fieldwork for a survey of the U.S. coast, production and distribution of standard weights and measures, and administration, 1832-44. Records of Jonathan H. Lane consist of letters from scientists and scientific papers on physics, astronomy, electricity, telegraphy, optics, and weights and measures, 1836-78. There are also minutes and reports of the International Standards Commission, 1870-75.

RECORDS OF THE NATIONAL BUREAU OF STANDARDS. 1875-1968. 886 lin. ft.

Included are a general correspondence file (660 lin. ft.) containing reports and other records relating to administration, finance, publicity, research, and other

Bureau activities, 1901-52, with an index; summary sheets and notebooks containing calibrations of weights, scales, and measures made from direct observations by the Mass and Scale Section, 1901-45; correspondence and other records of the Division of Applied Mathematics, relating to electronic computers, 1947-54; and consolidated reports of the Management Planning Division concerning scientific and technical projects, 1949-65. Published reports and other Bureau publications include *National Bureau of Standards Reports*, consisting of interim and final reports on research projects, 1951-68, *Bulletin of the Bureau of Standards*, 1904-18, *Scientific Papers*, 1919-28, *Technological Papers*, 1910-28, and *Journal of Research of the National Bureau of Standards*, 1928-59. Miscellaneous records, 1906-48, of J. Howard Dellinger, Chief of the Radio Section, and office files, 1907-62, of Lyman J. Briggs, Director of the National Bureau of Standards.

OTHER RECORDS. 1918-33. 80 lin. ft.

These comprise records of the 1931 President's Conference on Home Building and Home Ownership (much supportive work for the Conference was handled by the Bureau's Division of Building and Housing, 1930-33); related reports, correspondence, and memorandums concerning the work of the Committees on Types of Dwellings, Blighted Areas and Slums, and City Planning and Zoning, 1931-33; and correspondence, publications, and other records of Conference committees, 1930-33. Statistical and other records concerning a study of business cycles, 1926-28; correspondence, memorandums, and other records concerning the history and work of the Division of Building and Housing, 1921-30; and administrative reports, correspondence, and related records of the Division of Public Construction, 1929-

33. Records of the National Screw Thread Commission, abolished by Executive Order 6166 of June 10, 1933, consist primarily of minutes, reports, and correspondence, ca. 1918-33, including the final report summarizing the work and history of the Commission, 1933.

CARTOGRAPHIC AND AUDIOVISUAL RECORDS. 1901-59. 502 items.

Cartographic records consist of two maps of the United States and adjacent areas in Canada and Mexico, overprinted to show standard time zones established by the Interstate Commerce Commission, 1935 and 1948.

Audiovisual records, 1901-59 (500 items), consist of photographs of Bureau buildings, equipment, and personnel; and of scientific research and achievements in the study of velocity, diffraction, and the stratosphere.

SPECIFIC RESTRICTIONS

Records: "National Bureau of Standards Reports" maintained by the Office of Technical Information and Publications, 1951-68.

Restrictions: Authorization for access to these reports must be secured from the Office of Technical Information and Publications of the National Bureau of Standards or from the individual sponsors of the reports.

Specified by: Director of the National Bureau of Standards.

RECORDS OF THE WEATHER BUREAU (RECORD GROUP 27)

The Weather Bureau was established by an act of October 1, 1890, in the Department of Agriculture. It took over the weather service that had been established in the Office of the Chief Signal Officer of the War Department in 1870, which itself had taken over the meteorological observation systems and records of the Office of the Surgeon General, begun in 1818, and of the Smithsonian Institution, begun in 1847. The authority of the Weather Bureau was expanded in 1904 to include marine meteorological functions of the Hydrographic Office of the Navy Department. The Bureau was transferred to the Department of Commerce in 1940 and was consolidated in 1965 with the Coast and Geodetic Survey to form the Environmental Science Services Administration (see RG 370). The Weather Bureau's basic climatological records of surface land and air observations since 1872 and its principal records of marine observations since 1904 are in the National Weather Records Center, Asheville, N.C.

See Gustavus A. Weber, *The Weather Bureau* (New York, 1922).

There are 2,605 cubic feet of records dated between 1819 and 1965 in this record group.

CORRESPONDENCE OF THE METEOROLOGICAL DIVISION OF THE SMITHSONIAN INSTITUTION. 1847-67. 4 lin. ft.

Letters received, 1847 and 1859-67, and letters sent, 1850-53.

METEOROLOGICAL CORRESPONDENCE OF THE SIGNAL OFFICE. 1870-95. 495 lin. ft.

Letters sent, 1870-92, and received, 1870-95; observers' letters sent and received, 1872-93; voluntary observers' letters sent, 1874-84, and received, 1874-84 and 1888-93; and letters received from the State Weather Service, 1891-94.

GENERAL CORRESPONDENCE OF THE WEATHER BUREAU. 1894-1942. 855 lin. ft.

Letters received, 1894-1911, with indexes; general correspondence arranged according to the Dewey decimal classification scheme, 1912-42; and letters received by Special Agent R. A. Fessenden, 1901-3.

RECORDS OF SURFACE LAND OBSERVATIONS. 1819-1941. 671 lin. ft. and 564 rolls of microfilm.

Under the leadership of Joseph Henry, the Smithsonian Institution in 1847 began collecting records of meteorological observations and started a system of obtaining weather data from voluntary observers throughout the country. After the meteorological service of the Signal Corps was established in 1870, the meteorological work of the Smithsonian Institution declined. In 1874 the Institution's collection of meteorological reports was transferred to the Signal Office with the approval of the Secretary of War. These records and those collected by the Signal Office include microfilm copies (564 rolls) of surface land observations, 1819-92; surface land observations made outside the United States, 1843-87; daily meteorological observations of surgeons general at military posts, 1819-1916; coast survey notebooks, 1843-73; journals of daily observations at the Naval Observatory, Washington, D.C., 1842-1913; lake survey records, 1859-76; weekly meteorological records arranged alphabetically by name of State, 1870-81; daily journals and abstracts, 1870-1907; records of hourly wind movement, 1872-1904, and wind direction, 1891-1904; records of experimental self-registering instruments, 1870-88, and international simultaneous observations, 1874-92; reports of observers in cotton regions, 1883-1902, and corn and wheat regions, 1896-1902; reports of special rainfall stations, 1887-88, and of observations in Alaska, 1881-92, 1898-1913, and 1918-24; annual reports of Signal Office stations, 1888-96; monthly reports of Weather Bureau stations, 1905-7; records of solar and sky radiation measurements, ca. 1908-41; and reports of observations taken during the transit of Halley's Comet, 1910.

RECORDS OF MARINE OBSERVATIONS. 1842-1930. 342 lin. ft.

The Depot of Charts and Instruments of the Navy Department under command of Lt. Matthew Fontaine Maury began the systematic collection of ocean weather data in 1842. The work was continued and expanded by the Depot's successor, the Hydrographic Office. In 1904 marine weather work and related records were transferred to the Climatology Division of the Weather Bureau. These records include abstracts of ships logs ("Abstract Logs"), 1842-93, with an index; records of marine observations by ocean square, 1873-86, and of simultaneous meteorological observations on ships, 1886-1902; ships abstract storm logs, 1896-1910, gale and storm reports, 1895-1910, and fog reports, 1896-1910; marine meteorological journals, 1879-93, with an index; records containing summary weather data for the North Pacific and North Atlantic Oceans, 1890-1904; and records of observations at the Guam Naval Station, 1902-8 and 1913-19, the Gulf of Mexico and North Atlantic and North Pacific Ocean areas, 1890-1930, and the Azores Islands, 1896-99 and 1912-21.

DIARIES, JOURNALS, AND MISCELLANEOUS PAPERS. 1792-1946. 93 lin. ft.

These consist primarily of records containing miscellaneous meteorological, hydrological, and other scientific information, ca. 1847-91; diaries and journals of meteorological information, 1792-1889; scientific papers of Cleveland Abbe, ca. 1872-1909; and reminiscences of employees and miscellaneous historical information, 1907-46.

RECORDS OF POLAR EXPEDITIONS. 1881-1923. 19 lin. ft.

Included are correspondence, reports, journals, and scientific records of the Lady Franklin Bay Expedition, 1881-86; letter books and journals of the expedition to Point Barrow, Alaska, 1881-83; and records of the expedition to Franz Joseph Land, 1898-99, and of the expedition to Refuge Harbor, Greenland, 1923.

ADMINISTRATIVE AND FISCAL RECORDS. 1871-1930. 36 lin. ft.

These records include station inspection reports, ca. 1871-1930, records describing weather stations, 1883-1904, annual reports of stations, 1888-96, building plans of Weather Bureau stations, 1896-1924, and letters received at Kitty Hawk, N.C., 1879-81, 1887-89, and 1895-96.

CARTOGRAPHIC AND AUDIOVISUAL RECORDS. 1870-1965. 270,268 items.

Cartographic records include maps of the United States (175,757 items) annotated to show surface weather conditions daily from 1870 to 1965, prepared by the Office of the Chief Signal Officer, 1870-91, by the Weather Bureau Forecast Division, 1891-1941, and the Division of Synoptic Reports and Forecasts, 1941-65; historical synoptic maps (58,000 items) showing weather and related information for the Northern Hemisphere, prepared by the Meteorological Research Office in cooperation with the Army, Navy, Air Force, and certain colleges and universities, 1941-56; maps (19,506 items) published by the Division of Hydrologic Services and its predecessors, relating to U.S. river basins, 1897-1956; and charts (844 items) of the oceans and the Great Lakes relating to climatic conditions, which were published monthly by the Marine Section of the Division of Operations and Reports, 1909-14.

Audiovisual records (16,161 items) include photographs of personnel, facilities, projects, and meteorological instruments and apparatus of the Bureau, 1871-1945; of natural disasters, cloud formations, and freakish atmospheric conditions, 1871-1945; and of the Philippine rehabilitation project, 1947-50.

See Lewis J. Darter, Jr., comp., *List of Climatological Records in the National Archives*, SL 1 (1942); and Harold T. Pinkett, Helen T. Finneran, and Katherine H. Davidson, comps., *Preliminary Inventory of the Climatological and Hydrological Records of the Weather Bureau*, PI 38 (1952).

Microfilm Publications: *Journal of Lockwood Expedition on North Coast of Greenland, April 3-June 1, 1882*, T298, 1 roll; and *Climatological Records of the Weather Bureau, 1819-1892*, T907, 564 rolls.

RECORDS OF THE MARITIME ADMINISTRATION
(RECORD GROUP 357)

The Maritime Administration was established by Reorganization Plan No. 21, effective May 24, 1950, as one of the successor agencies to the U.S. Maritime Commission (see RG 178). It administers financial programs to develop, promote, and operate the U.S. merchant marine; determines services and routes necessary to develop and maintain American foreign commerce and requirements of ships necessary to provide adequate service on such routes; conducts research and development activities in the maritime field; regulates the transfer of U.S. documented vessels to foreign registry; maintains equipment, shipyard facilities, and reserve fleets of Government-owned ships essential for national defense; operates the U.S. Merchant Marine Academy at Kings Point, N.Y.; and administers a grant-in-aid program for State-operated maritime academies in California, Maine, Massachusetts, New York, and Texas.

When the Federal Maritime Board (see RG 358) was abolished in 1961, its functions relating to the subsidization of the merchant marine were transferred to the Secretary of Commerce, who established the Maritime Subsidy Board within the Administration to perform these functions. This latter Board negotiates contracts for ship construction and grants operating-differential subsidies to shipping and shipbuilding companies.

The Maritime Administrator is vested with the residual powers of the Director of the National Shipping Authority, which was established in 1951 in the Administration to organize and direct emergency merchant marine operations.

There are 62 cubic feet of records dated between 1950 and 1962 in this record group.

RECORDS. 1950-62. 74 lin. ft.

These include the original directives and administrative orders or "actions" of the Administrator and Deputy Administrator, 1950-60, consisting of reports, letters, and memorandums having the force of regulations; "actions" of the National Shipping Authority, 1951-61, concerning the operation of vessels; transfer-of-registry orders, 1950-62, relating to sale and mortgage of U.S. ships abroad; surrender-of-document orders, 1950-62, with supporting memorandums, relating to changes in ownership, home port, tonnage, or name of owning company, owning company official, or vessel; the manual of orders of the Administrator; and the manual of management orders relating to the organization and functions of administrative units in the Administration (some of which relate to the Federal Maritime Board).

RECORDS OF THE
ENVIRONMENTAL SCIENCE SERVICES ADMINISTRATION
(RECORD GROUP 370)

The Environmental Science Services Administration (ESSA), established in the Department of Commerce by Reorganization Plan No. 2 of 1965, is a consolidation of the Coast and Geodetic Survey (see RG 23) and the Weather Bureau (see RG 27). The Administration studies the oceans, the lower and upper atmosphere, and the size and shape of the earth to further the safety and welfare of the public, enhance and improve the Nation's economy, and assist those Federal departments concerned with national defense, exploration of outer space, and management of natural resources. Its operations include basic and applied research, observations, processing data, and disseminating weather forecasts and warnings and information about other phenomena within its areas of study. ESSA consists of staff offices and the Environmental Data Service, the Weather Bureau, the Research Laboratories, the Coast and Geodetic Survey, and the National Environmental Satellite Center. Its field organization includes Weather Bureau regional offices and Coast and Geodetic Survey field directors and marine centers.

There are 58 cubic feet of cartographic records dated between 1965 and 1968 in this record group.

CARTOGRAPHIC RECORDS. 1965–68. 18,649 items.

Maps of the United States and Canada published by the Weather Analysis and Prediction Division of the Weather Bureau, showing daily surface weather conditions, 1965–67; and nautical and aeronautical charts published by the Offices of Aeronautical Charting and Cartography, Hydrography and Oceanography, and Geodesy and Photogrammetry of the Coast and Geodetic Survey, 1965–68.

Discontinued Agencies

RECORDS OF THE
BUREAU OF MARINE INSPECTION AND NAVIGATION
(RECORD GROUP 41)

Navigation laws were passed by the First Congress in 1789 and were enforced by customs officers under the supervision of the Treasury Department. Federal circuit courts directly handled matters relating to shipment, care, and discharge of seamen until this work was taken over in 1872 by shipping commissioners appointed and supervised by the courts. In 1884 responsibility for the administration of navigation laws, including those administered by the shipping commissioners, was given to the Commissioner of Navigation, who, with the Bureau of Navigation established under his control, was placed under the general supervision of the Secretary of the Treasury. Congress in 1838 had provided for inspection of ship hulls and boilers by local inspectors appointed by U.S. district court judges and for the promulgation of minimum standards regarding lifesaving and firefighting equipment. By the Steamboat Act of 1852 the Steamboat-Inspection Service was formally established to formulate rules and regulations for uniform administration of steamboat inspection laws. A Supervising Inspector General for the Service, directly accountable to the Treasury Department, was provided for by an act of 1871.

In 1903 both the Bureau of Navigation and the Steamboat-Inspection Service were transferred to the Department of Commerce and Labor. In 1913, when a separate Department of Labor was established, they remained in the Department of Commerce, but customs officers of the Treasury Department continued to serve as a part of the field force of the Bureau of Navigation. The two units were combined in 1932 to form the Bureau of Navigation and Steamboat Inspection, to which was transferred in 1934 the Sea Service Section of the U.S. Shipping Board Bureau of the Department of Commerce, which had inherited the functions and records of the Shipping Board Recruiting Service. The Bureau in 1936 was renamed the Bureau of Marine Inspection and Navigation, and in 1942 its functions relating to merchant vessel documentation were transferred to the Bureau of Customs while those relating to merchant vessel inspection, safety of life at sea, and merchant vessel personnel were transferred to the U.S. Coast Guard. By Reorganization Plan No. 3 of 1946 this separation was made permanent and the Bureau was abolished. On February 4, 1967, the merchant vessel documentation function was transferred to the U.S. Coast Guard, which on April 1, 1967, became part of the newly created Department of Transportation.

See Lloyd M. Short, *The Bureau of Navigation* (Baltimore, 1923), and *The Steamboat Inspection Service* (New York, 1922).

There are 11,659 cubic feet of records dated between 1774 and 1958 in this record group.

GENERAL RECORDS OF THE BUREAU OF NAVIGATION. 1791–1935, with a few dated as late as 1937. 1,750 lin. ft.

Included are volumes of letters sent, chiefly from the Secretary of the Treasury and the Commissioner of Navigation, 1865–1907, with one volume for the period 1814–27 and some letters to 1850; letters received, 1884–1906; and general correspondence, 1906–35. Many of the early volumes are indexed individually, and there is a comprehensive index for the period 1905–34. There are also dockets, 1884–1906, listing most letters and other records received, summarizing their contents, and noting action taken; and dockets of incoming letters and other records relating to navigation, tonnage, fines, penalties, and forfeitures, 1867–87, for which the original records are missing. The correspondence relates to remissions and mitigations of fines

and penalties imposed under navigation laws, official numbers assigned to merchant vessels, vessel documents, international conferences on maritime matters, and safety regulations concerning motorboats and dangerous cargoes. Although a large part of the material relates to routine administration and functions of the Bureau, much of it has value for the historian and social scientist. For instance, there are letters relating to Cuban filibustering, 1895–96, negotiations of a fisheries treaty with Great Britain, 1880's, and "crimping" and other maritime labor practices, 1884–1906.

There are also reference lists and volumes, 1791–1931, including a digest of decisions of the first comptroller, 1791–1819, and of decisions and instructions of the Secretary of the Treasury, 1833–63; records relating to navigation and tonnage statistics, 1793–1926; accounting records, 1833–1932, dealing chiefly with the collection of the tonnage tax, fines, and penalties; correspondence and other records relating to adoption of international regulations on safety of life at sea, 1813–32; records concerning codification of navigation laws and various international conventions on maritime regulations, 1919–30; logbooks of patrol vessels used in enforcing navigation laws, 1920–37; and a few photographs of Bureau officials.

RECORDS OF THE STEAMBOAT INSPECTION SERVICE. 1838–1942.

Records of the Supervising Inspector General. 1852–1941. 750 lin. ft. These consist of letters sent by the Supervising Inspector General, 1873–1905, a few letters received relating chiefly to personnel, 1852–1902, registers of letters received, 1866–1907, general correspondence, 1905–34, and letters sent by the Secretaries of the Treasury and of Commerce and Labor, 1852–1907. Many of the early volumes are indexed individually, and there is a comprehensive index for the period 1905-34. These records relate to Service inspection of vessels, licensing of officers, certification of crewmembers, and administration of laws and regulations for protection of life and property at sea.

Also included are annual reports of local and supervising inspectors, 1852-1941; annual statistical statements, 1911-39; issuances, 1917-38; records relating to personnel and accounts, 1866-1933, and vessel casualties, 1871-1939; reports on foreign steam vessels inspected, 1882-1900; commissions issued to local inspectors, 1852-96; a bibliography of articles relating to steam vessels, printed in nautical magazines, 1937-41; correspondence and technical sketches of committees, principally the U.S. Load Line Committee appointed in 1928 by the Secretary of Commerce to study ship construction and loading, 1919-29; loadline certificates, 1921-40; and correspondence and other records regarding the adoption and enforcement of the international loadline convention signed at a 1930 conference at London, 1930-34.

Records of the Board of Supervising Inspectors. 1852-1942. 75 lin. ft. This Board, established in 1852, formulated rules and regulations for administering steamboat inspection laws and approved equipment for merchant vessels. The records consist of journals of proceedings at annual and special meetings, 1852-1942, including minutes, annual inspection reports, decisions, and general rules and regulations; journals of the executive committee, 1936-38 and 1941; correspondence and blueprints relating to Regulations 1-3826 concerning proposed safety devices, 1911-42; circular letters and instructions implementing Board decisions, 1877-1941; samples of forms and placards, 1897-1941, many of which were posted by law in merchant vessels; and compendiums of Board rules and regulations relating to pilots, vessel inspections, and safety devices, 1852-1941.

Records of the Offices of Supervising and Local Inspectors of Steam Vessels. 1838-1942. 75 lin. ft. After 1852 local inspectors formed boards that were grouped geographically into supervising inspection districts, each under a supervising inspector. Supervising inspectors collectively constituted the Board of Supervising Inspectors. Duties of local inspectors included inspecting hulls, boilers, machinery, and lifesaving, firefighting, and other equipment to ensure safety on merchant vessels; examining, licensing, and certifying officers and crewmembers; investigating and trying licensed officers and certified personnel charged with negligence, misconduct, and other infractions of law; and conducting boat and fire drills.

The records, which are fragmentary, comprise certificates of inspection of steam vessels issued by local inspectors at New Haven and Middletown, Conn., 1838-52; a journal, records relating to the issuance of licenses and certificates, and correspondence of local boards at Juneau and Sitka, Alaska, 1898-1942; orders of the Secretary of the Treasury kept by the local New York board, 1883-86; reports and certificates of inspection of the local Philadelphia board, 1845-71; correspondence and reports of the Supervising Inspector of the 3d District, Norfolk, 1869-71; records relating to licenses issued, revoked, and surrendered at the local Baltimore board, 1865-70; loyalty oaths and affidavits for officers of steam vessels, 1862-65, applications and certifications for licenses, 1861-67, and correspondence, blueprints of equipment, decisions on appeals, and an office diary of the office of the Supervising Inspector of the 6th District, Louisville, chiefly 1907-36; reports of investigations of the local Louisville board, 1895-1909; correspondence of the Supervising Inspector of the 7th District, Cincinnati and Pittsburgh, 1908-

36, and of the 8th District, Detroit, 1906–10; reports of investigations and circular letters kept by the local Detroit board, 1861–91; reports of investigations of the local board at Grand Haven, Mich., 1911–35; and a journal, 1853–71, records relating to an insurance surveyor who operated in the Great Lakes area, 1845–49, and applications for able seaman certificates, 1915–36, maintained by the local Cleveland board.

GENERAL RECORDS OF THE BUREAU OF MARINE INSPECTION AND NAVIGATION. 1935–42. 100 lin. ft.

Although the Bureau of Navigation and the Steamboat Inspection Service were combined in 1932, their correspondence continued to be filed separately until March 1935. For the period 1935–42 the records consist of reports, correspondence, and memorandums relating to remissions and mitigations of fines and penalties imposed under navigation acts, official numbers assigned to merchant vessels, vessel documents, international conferences regarding maritime matters, the licensing of officers and certification of crewmembers, and the administration of laws and regulations for protection of life and property at sea. These records are indexed by subject, name of correspondent, and name of vessel. Early in 1943 the files were separated into two parts reflecting the 1942 division of functions.

RECORDS RELATING TO MERCHANT VESSEL DOCUMENTATION. 1774–1958. 5,000 lin. ft.

The records consist of certificates of enrollment, license, and registry, and yacht licenses granted to American-flag merchant vessels. The certificates contain information about vessel owners and masters; date and place of construction; dimensions, rig, and other descriptive details; home port; and dates, place,

and reason for the issuance and surrender of the document. Mortgages, bills of sale, and conveyances are also noted on the documents. Washington headquarters copies of these certificates are arranged by port, essentially in a geographical sequence and thereunder chronologically through ca. 1915, thereafter by the official number assigned to each vessel. All headquarters copies were destroyed by fire in 1814, and many of them for the years 1815–70 were badly damaged by fire in 1921. Certificates for vessels numbered after February 1942 and removed from documentation by June 1958 are among records of the Bureau of Customs (see RG 36). The documents are supplemented by "master abstracts," arranged chronologically and thereunder by port of issue, 1815–1911. Headquarters records also include abstracts of certificates of registry issued at Boston, New York, Philadelphia, and Baltimore, 1789–1811; applications for official numbers and awards showing numbers assigned, 1867–1942; and registers of vessels arranged by official numbers. Annual volumes of *List of Merchant Vessels of the United States*, beginning in 1868, serve as an alphabetical index by name of vessel.

Copies of these certificates, kept by the collector of customs, have been received from customhouses. One volume begins in 1774, several antedate 1815, and there are some for the 20th century. These certificates are arranged by port of issue, type of certificate, and thereunder chronologically. Many certificates of registry for the years 1791–1801 were called in by the Treasury Department in 1885 for use with the French spoliation claims and are now among records of the Bureau of Customs (see RG 36). Coverage for individual ports varies greatly. Supplemental records include master carpenter certificates, 1790–1955, tonnage admeasurement certificates, 1789–1931, bills of sale, 1850–1900 (with a few dated as early as 1804 and some for the 20th century), mortgages and mortgage releases, chiefly 1850-1900, and various types of bonds and oaths.

RECORDS RELATING TO MERCHANT MARINE CASUALTIES AND VIOLATIONS OF INSPECTION LAWS. 1852-1941. 175 lin. ft.

These consist chiefly of closed merchant marine inspection case files, 1937-41, and include minutes of hearings, reports, transcripts of testimony, and correspondence. An index has been retained by the Coast Guard. Records dated before 1937 consist of card records and lists of marine casualties, with particular reference to steam vessels, 1852-1937, that may be used as an index to reports and extant records of local inspectors; and summaries of casualties investigated by local inspectors, 1911-37. Those dated before 1911 were printed in annual reports of the Board of Supervising Inspectors.

RECORDS RELATING TO MERCHANT VESSEL PERSONNEL. 1872-1940.

Applications for Seamen's Protection Certificates. 1916-40. 375 lin. ft. These applications, with affidavits and occasionally other material offered as proof of citizenship, were submitted by seamen in the American merchant marine to collectors of customs acting as field agents for the Commissioner of Navigation (later for the Director of the Bureau of Marine Inspection and Navigation) in the issuance of seaman's protection certificates required by law for sailing in foreign waters. The applications usually contain name and address of the seaman, date and place of his birth, place and date of naturalization if applicable, name of ship on which last employed, and name of ship of his prospective employment. In addition, they contain his signature, left thumb print, photograph, and description of physical characteristics. There are also some applications for certificates for aliens, who, during the period 1918-35, were allowed special certificates after 3 years of service. Similar records for the 19th century are among records of the Bureau of Customs (see RG 36).

Records of U.S. Shipping Commissioners. 1872-1938. 5,000 lin. ft. Since July 1872 shipping commissioners in various ports have administered laws on protection and welfare of seamen, including those relating to their shipping and discharge. The records consist of most of the shipping articles collected by shipping commissioners, 1872-1938, and of official merchant marine logbooks filed with the commissioner at the conclusion of voyages, 1872-1938. In many instances these are the only extant proof of a seaman's service. Coverage for individual ports varies greatly, and these records do not include articles and logs for all American ports. Most of the records before 1915 are for Baltimore, Boston, New York, Portland, Oreg., and San Francisco. The shipping articles for each voyage usually give name and type of vessel, date and port of departure, destination, and the signature, rank or rating, birthplace, height and complexion, wage, date of signing on, and name and address of next of kin of each crewmember. Copies of the articles were filed at the port where crewmembers signed on and at the port where they were paid. Official logbooks contain crew lists, crew slop and cash accounts, loadline information, and entries relating to events on the voyage, such as conduct, health, and discipline of the crew; collisions and other accidents; and deaths, marriages, and births. Articles and logbooks for coastwise voyages were optional until the middle of 1937. Records for many ports are indexed by name of vessel. For many ports there are also chronological registers of services performed for American vessels that serve as guides to the articles and logbooks.

Records of the Former U.S. Shipping Board Recruiting Service and Sea Service Bureau. 1917-34. 550 lin. ft. The Recruiting Service was established in the U.S. Shipping Board June 1, 1917, with headquarters in Boston, to recruit and train merchant marine crews. The Service organized and maintained navigation and engineering schools and training stations and operated several training ships. The organization included the Sea Training, Social Service, and Sea Service Bureaus, the latter serving as a placement agency not only for men trained by the Recruiting Service but also for other merchant ship personnel. In 1919 much of the work was terminated, and in 1921 the schools and training stations were closed. The Sea Service Bureau, however, existed until 1934, when its functions and most of its records, with those of the Recruiting Service, were transferred to the Bureau of Navigation and Steamboat Inspection.

The records include general administrative files and correspondence of the Recruiting Service and the Sea Service Bureau, 1917-34 (with some as late as 1937), including records of the New Orleans, San Francisco, and Seattle offices; special files on officer training, recruitment, training ships, training with turbine engines, draft deferment of seamen, medical matters, and publicity (including photographs pertaining to the activities of the Service); and personnel jackets, 1918-21. Records relating to recruits who were discharged, 1918-20, form a separate series. Applications for appointment, 1918-19, were kept separately for seamen awaiting positions; and there are also applications for training in navigation and engineering schools and training records of enrollees, 1917-21.

AUDIOVISUAL RECORDS. 1884-1938. 411 items.

These consist of photographs relating to recruitment of merchant seamen during World War I and of Bureau commissioners and personnel, 1884-1938.

See Forrest R. Holdcamper, "Registers, Enrollments and Licenses in the National Archives," *American Neptune,* I (July 1941), 275-94; Holdcamper, comp., *List of American-Flag Merchant Vessels That Received Certificates of Enrollment of Registry at the Port of New York, 1798-1867,* SL 22 (2 vols., 1968); and Elmer W. Lindgard, comp., *Preliminary Inventory of the Records of the Collector of Customs, Puget Sound District, in the Federal Records Center, Seattle, Washington,* PI 122 (1960).

Microfilm Publication: *Certificates of Registry, Enrollment, and License Issued at Edgartown, Mass., 1815-1913,* M130, 9 rolls.

SPECIFIC RESTRICTIONS

Records: Official merchant marine logbooks that were deposited with U.S. Shipping Commissioners, shipping articles (form 705, 705A, 705B, or equivalent), and reports of ship personnel not shipped or discharged before U.S. Shipping Commissioners (form 735T or equivalent).

Restrictions: These records may not be examined or consulted except by agents or operators of the vessels concerned, seamen or their duly authorized counsels or agents, qualified scholars engaged in research who agree to make no disclosure injurious to persons or organizations, and such other persons as are authorized by the Commandant of the Coast Guard or his representative.

Specified by: U.S. Coast Guard.

RECORDS OF THE
BUREAU OF FOREIGN AND DOMESTIC COMMERCE
(RECORD GROUP 151)

The Bureau of Foreign and Domestic Commerce was created in the Department of Commerce and Labor August 23, 1912, by consolidating the Department's Bureau of Statistics and Bureau of Manufactures. The Bureau was established to promote the development of U.S. commerce and industry by compiling and distributing information on domestic and foreign trade, manufacturing, and markets. In 1923 the Bureau of Customs Statistics of the Treasury Department was transferred to the Department of Commerce and made a part of the Bureau of Foreign and Domestic Commerce. The Foreign Commerce Service, established within the Bureau in 1927 to investigate foreign commercial and industrial conditions, was transferred to the Department of State in 1939. The functions and records of the Bureau's Division of Foreign Trade Statistics were transferred to the Bureau of the Census in 1941. Five major offices were formed within the Bureau in 1945—the Offices of International Trade, Small Business, Domestic Commerce, Business Economics, and Field Service. In 1948 the functions of the Office of Small Business were absorbed by the Office of Domestic Commerce, which became known as the Office of Industry and Commerce. No Director of the Bureau was appointed after 1945, but the major offices continued under the title of the Bureau of Foreign and Domestic Commerce until a departmental reorganization in 1952 placed the offices under Assistant Secretaries of Commerce.

There are 1,419 cubic feet of records dated between 1899 and 1958 in this record group.

RECORDS OF THE BUREAU.
1913-58. 1,526 lin ft.

Most of the records comprise a central file, 1914-58, arranged primarily by topics, commodities, and geographic areas within a decimal classification system, with indexes. The file includes information about concessions, consortiums, foreign trade and economic relations, and foreign and domestic raw materials and manufactured products. Also records of Directors, Assistant Directors, and other officials of the Bureau, 1929-44, relating to policies and procedures, relations with other Government agencies and the public, and surveys and economic research carried out by the Bureau; reports relating to legislation affecting the Bureau, 1920-40; copies of the Bureau's *Survey of Current Business*, 1920-43; a card index to material in Bureau publications, 1914-40; reports and other communications received from commercial attaches, foreign offices, and trade commissioners, 1920-40; Bureau reports of foreign trade opportunities, 1936-38; records of annual forest industries conferences, 1920-33; and publications of the Bureau, containing information of interest primarily to geographers, 1931-33.

There are also administrative and operational records of administrative units, including the Puerto Rico Office, 1920-50, the Specialty Division, 1928-35, the Motion Picture Division, 1929-30, the Division of Metals and Minerals, 1928-40, the Transportation Division, 1933-40, the Division of Economic Research, 1940-43, and the Publications Committee, 1920-25; working papers and materials used in preparing published reports, including surveys of retail drug stores in St. Louis, Mo., 1929-32, credit, 1933, commodity movements, 1930-33, natural gas, 1930, and the Bureau's usefulness to business, 1933; and accounting ledgers, 1914-33.

RECORDS OF THE MARKETING LAWS SURVEY AND THE MARKETING LAWS UNIT. 1938-43. 100 lin. ft.

The Survey was established in the Works Progress Administration in 1938 to study State laws and court decisions affecting the marketing of goods. In 1941 the President transferred the work of the Survey to the Bureau of Foreign and Domestic Commerce, where it was set up as the Marketing Laws Unit in the Division of Regional Economy. The Chief of the Survey (and later of the Unit) acted as Chairman of the informal Interdepartmental Committee on Interstate Trade Barriers and also of the Federal War Agencies Committee established by the President in 1942 to work with the Executive Committee of the Governor's Conference on problems of wartime restrictions on marketing. Records of these committees are included with those of the Survey and the Unit.

The records include, in addition to administrative files, general correspondence and correspondence with regional offices; records relating to Federal-State conferences; correspondence of officials of the Marketing Laws Survey and Unit; and workpapers, manuscripts, and galley proofs used in preparing the published survey.

RECORDS OF THE NATIONAL COMMITTEE ON WOOD UTILIZATION AND OF THE TIMBER CONSERVATION BOARD. 1925-33. 22 lin. ft.

Both the Committee and the Board were cooperative bodies made up of representatives of Government and private organizations, financed by private funds, and operated through facilities and services contributed by the Federal Government. The National Committee on Wood Utilization was established by the President in 1925 to promote stabilization of lumber production through more effective and economical use of timber and forest resources. The Secretary of Commerce acted as Chairman of the Committee. The Timber Conservation Board was appointed by the President in 1930 to develop a comprehensive plan for maintaining the growth, management, and protection of forests. Both agencies were terminated in 1933 and their property and records transferred to the Lumber Division of the Bureau of Foreign and Domestic Commerce. The records of the National Committee on Wood Utilization, with indexes, relate to the administration and operations of the Committee, the organization and financing of the lumber industry, and the processing and distribution of lumber products. The records of the Timber Conservation Board consist of minutes of the Board and its committees; a general file with information about the administration and work of the Board, world timber supply, laws relating to forest conservation, and conservation methods used in the lumber industry; outgoing correspondence kept by the Board's secretary; and records relating to the Board's research projects, including correspondence, tabulations, and statistical data.

RECORDS OF THE INTERDEPARTMENTAL COMMITTEE ON SHIPPING POLICY AND OCEAN MAIL CONTRACTS. 1928-32. 7 lin. ft.

The Committee, composed of the Secretary of Commerce (as Chairman) and representatives of the U.S. Shipping Board, the Treasury Department, the Post Office Department, and the Interstate Commerce Commission, was established in 1928 to investigate ocean mail contracts and devise policies on shipping rates and subsidies for ocean shipping.

The Committee became inactive after 1932, and its records were transferred to the Transportation Division of the Bureau of Foreign and Domestic Commerce. The records consist of minutes, general files, and replies to a questionnaire regarding subsidies, cost differentials, and facilities of steamship lines.

CARTOGRAPHIC AND
AUDIOVISUAL RECORDS.
1899-1939. 10,132 items.

Cartographic records, 1905-33 (32 items), consist of world maps, showing principal land and sea transportation routes, 1905-8; a map of the United States, showing consumer trading areas, ca. 1929; an incomplete set of mimeographed publications entitled "Geographic News," containing information about map, atlas, and geographic book accessions, 1931-33; and an atlas, showing changes in the economic development of States and regions during the period 1929-48.

Audiovisual records, 1899-1939 (10,100 items), consist of photographs relating to Bureau functions and made in more than 80 countries of people, institutions, ways of life, transportation facilities, and agricultural and industrial commodities, 1899-1939; and of Bureau personnel, 1913-30.

RECORDS OF THE INLAND WATERWAYS CORPORATION
(RECORD GROUP 91)

The Inland Waterways Corporation, with the Secretary of War as incorporator, was created by an act of June 3, 1924. It was given responsibility for functions assigned to the Secretary by the Transportation Act of 1920 (amended in 1924, 1928, and 1934), including administration of U.S. inland water transportation facilities and coordination of rail and water transportation in the United States. Reorganization Plan No. II of 1939 transferred the Corporation to the Department of Commerce. It was sold to the Federal Waterways Corporation under a contract of July 24, 1953, and renamed the Federal Barge Lines, Inc. An act of July 19, 1963, provided for the liquidation of the Corporation.

The Corporation, on funds derived from its transactions, operated barge lines on the Mississippi, Missouri, and Warrior Rivers and the Warrior River Terminal Company short-rail line. It also sold and leased its transportation facilities to private management, conducted investigations of waterway traffic and types of equipment suitable for waterways, and constructed water terminals.

There are 45 cubic feet of records dated between 1932 and 1953 in this record group.

RECORDS. 1932-53. 54 lin. ft.

Records of the Washington office consist of correspondence of Department of Commerce officials, relating to Corporation affairs, 1938-44; correspondence of the Corporation with other Government agencies, 1939-44, and with private inland waterway operators and others concerning the appointment of the Advisory Board, 1939-42; minutes of the Advisory Board, 1944-52; correspondence of Advisory Board Chairman South Trimble, Jr., 1939-53; subject and reference files, 1939-52; labor agreements, 1940-46; records relating to construction programs, 1946-50; proposals by private groups to purchase the Corporation, 1950-53; periodic and operation reports, statistics, and issuances, 1935-53; operation accounts and fiscal records, 1945–53; and organization charts, 1940–53. Also specifications and blueprints of towboats and drawings and blueprints relating to river terminals, 1938–46, and charts relating to hydrographic surveys of the Mississippi River, 1948–52. There are photographs of operations of barge lines, 1948–52, and a motion picture (1 reel) portraying a map of inland waterway routes in the Mississippi River region from Minnesota and Lake Michigan to New Orleans and showing the christening of the packet boat *Mark Twain* at Jeffersonville, Ind., 1932.

SPECIFIC RESTRICTIONS

Records: Records of the Washington office, Inland Waterways Corporation, 1939–53.

Restrictions: No one may examine these records or be given information from them or copies of them except by permission of the records officer of the Department of Commerce.

Specified by: Department of Commerce.

RECORDS OF THE NATIONAL PRODUCTION AUTHORITY (RECORD GROUP 277)

The National Production Authority (NPA) was established in the Department of Commerce on September 11, 1950. The NPA was responsible for developing and promoting production and supply of materials and facilities necessary for military defense, for determining that needs of the civilian economy were adequately represented in the defense effort, and for ensuring that small businesses were participating in defense contracts. It was abolished and its functions were merged with those of the Business and Defense Services Administration by an order of the Secretary of Commerce, October 1, 1953.

There are 546 cubic feet of records dated between 1950 and 1953 in this record group.

RECORDS. 1950–53. 564 lin. ft.

These comprise general records of the Office of the Administrator, 1950–53, consisting of reports, directives, memorandums, and letters concerning legislation, delegation of authority, organization, meetings and conferences, deliberations of advisory and planning committees, managerial problems, program planning, interagency and congressional relations, and general policies with regard to the allocation of scarce commodities; subject files of special assistants to the Administrator, 1950–53; records of the Office of the Executive Secretary, 1951–53, consisting of files relating to the operations review program, and historical reports on defense production; Appeals Board case files, 1951–53, with a related index; case records and subject files, 1951–53, of the Office of the Chief Hearing Commissioner; records of the Office of Public Information, 1950–53, consisting of press releases, delegations, motion pictures, and sound recordings; and records of the Office of the General Counsel, 1950–53, consisting of general correspondence, subject files of assistants, and compliance and enforcement case files of the Compliance Division.

There are also records of the Office of the Assistant Administrator for Administration, consisting of administrative orders and instructions, 1950–53, of the Administrative Coordination Branch, Budget and Management Division; files of the Office of Industry Advisory Committees, relating to committee meetings, 1950–53; records of the Office of Small Business, relating to production equipment in small plant modernization, 1950–52; case files, 1950–51, of the Tax Amortization Division, Facilities and Construction Bureau; records of the Chemical, Rubber, and Forest Products Bureau, consisting of policy files and regulations, 1942–53, of the Containers and Packaging Division, and files of the Lumber and Wood Products Division, 1941–53, including correspondence relating to NPA dealings with foreign governments and statistical records; records of the Industrial and Agricultural Equipment Bureau, including subject files of the Metalworking Equipment Division, 1950–53, and tax amortization case files and requirement summaries of the General Industrial Equipment Division, 1950–53; and records of the Textile, Leather, and Specialty Equipment Bureau, consisting of tax amortization case files of the Service Equipment Division, 1950–53, and subject files, 1951–52, of the Textile and Clothing Division. Also records of the Policy Coordination Bureau, including minutes

and administrative issuances, 1950–53; subject files of the Administrative Office, 1942–53; controlled materials reports and other files of the Program Coordination Division, relating to mobilization and requirements, 1951–53; subject files and issuances of the Control Operations Division, 1950–53; general and procedures development files, 1941–53, of the Priorities and Directives Division; subject files, 1951–53, of the Foreign Division; files of the Director of the Civilian Requirements Division, 1951–52; and statistical reports, publications, and administrative issuances of the Statistical Standards Division, 1942–53.

Also included are Defense Production Administration planning and programing records, 1952; NPA records arranged and maintained by the Executive Secretary of the Defense Production Administration, including copies of organizational statements, orders, regulations, rules of procedure and practice, records concerning the organization and operation of interagency and advisory committees, and transcripts of interviews with officials prepared for historic documentation, 1950–53; and a set of manuals, project authorizations, office notices, and general progress reports, 1950–53.

DEPARTMENT OF LABOR

GENERAL RECORDS OF THE DEPARTMENT OF LABOR
(RECORD GROUP 174)

The present Department of Labor was created by an act of March 4, 1913, as one of the successor agencies of the Department of Commerce and Labor. Although a Department of Labor had previously existed, it was without Cabinet rank and was the predecessor agency of the Bureau of Labor Statistics (see RG 257). The Department has jurisdiction over matters relating to the welfare of American wage earners, including the improvement of their working conditions and the advancement of profitable employment opportunities.

See U.S. Department of Labor, *The Anvil and the Plow: A History of the United States Department of Labor* (n.d.).

There are 1,021 cubic feet of records dated between 1907 and 1968 in this record group.

RECORDS. 1907-68. 1,426 lin. ft.

These consist of minutes of departmental and other committees, reports, correspondence, memorandums, issuances, and press clippings comprising a central file of the Office of the Secretary of Labor, 1913-33 (with a few records dated as early as 1907 and administrative records to 1942).

Records of Secretaries William B. Wilson, 1913-21, Frances Perkins, 1933-45, Lewis B. Schwellenbach, 1945-48, Maurice J. Tobin, 1948-53, Martin P. Durkin, 1953, James P. Mitchell, 1953-60, Arthur J. Goldberg, 1961-62, and Willard W. Wirtz, 1962-67; of Under Secretaries Michael J. Galvin, 1941-50, David A. Morse, 1946-48, Lloyd A. Mashburn, 1953, Arthur Larson, 1954-57, and James T. O'Connell, 1957-60; of Deputy Under Secretary Millard Cass, 1947-66; of Assistant Secretaries Charles V. McLaughlin, 1938-41, Marshall E.

Dimock, 1939, Daniel Tracy, 1940-46, Edward C. Moran, Jr., 1945, John W. Gibson, 1945-51, Philip M. Kaiser, 1948-53, Ralph Wright, 1949, Robert T. Creasey, 1949-52, Spencer Miller, Jr., 1953-54, John J. Gilhooley, 1957-60, Jerry R. Holleman, 1961-62, and James J. Reynolds, 1961-65; of the assistant secretary for administration and his predecessors, the chief clerk, and the budget officer, 1942-68; and of Special Assistants to the Secretaries Hugh L. Kerwin, 1913-20, Richardson Saunders, 1933-39, Louis Sherman, 1945-47, Charles W. Straub, 1948-52, Thacher Winslow, 1948-52, Charles O'Dell, 1954-56, Albert L. McDermott, 1954-60, Aryness Joy Wickens, 1956-59, Stephen N. Shulman, 1961-62, Samuel V. Merrick, 1961-63, and Seymour Wolfbein, 1962-67. Records of Secretaries of Labor, relating to their memberships on the Trade Policy Committee, 1958-63.

Records of the Wage Determination Branch of the Office of the Solicitor, relating to the enforcement of the Davis-Bacon Act of 1931, consist of administrative files, 1941-43, prevailing wage-rate case files, 1931-45, and "county files" containing data from which wage rates on Government contracts were determined, 1941-47 (in WNRC). Also records relating to the Conciliation Service, 1919, and the Division of Negro Economics, 1919-21. Office of Information records, consisting of correspondence and subject classified files, 1933-62; texts of speeches and other public statements, including scripts for radio broadcasts of Secretaries Perkins, 1933-45, and Schwellenbach, 1945-48, and of Assistant Secretaries D. A. Morse, Philip Hannah, and John T. Kmetz, 1946-48; informational issuances, such as press releases and statements, 1948-60; and records of the departmental World War II historical program, consisting of reports, correspondence, memorandums, and drafts of histories, 1942-47. A general file of the Chairman of the Departmental Committee on Economic Policy and Programs, 1949-50; files of the Management-Labor Policy Committee on Defense Manpower, consisting of agenda, summary and verbatim minutes, documents submitted for consideration, correspondence, and issuances, 1950-51; case files of the departmental Defense Manpower Administration on its advisory reports to the Wage Stabilization Board, regarding the latter's "rare and unusual" wage adjustment cases, 1951-53; and records of the Program Planning and Review Committee, including agenda, minutes, summaries of actions, memorandums, issuances, reports, and correspondence, 1955-62.

Reports, studies, and administrative files of the Division of Research and Investigation, U.S. Commission on Industrial Relations, 1912-15; records of the President's Mediation Commission, including transcripts of hearings at Globe, Clifton, and Bisbee, Ariz., 1917; and reports, correspondence, and memorandums relating to Commission activities, 1917-18.

Photographs (19 items) of Secretaries M. J. Tobin and M. P. Durkin and of the 40th anniversary celebration of the Department, 1949-54, and a sound recording of President Truman's address to the President's Conference on Industrial Safety, 1949.

Microfilm Publication: *Reports of the United States Commission on Industrial Relations, 1912-15*, T4, 15 rolls.

SPECIFIC RESTRICTIONS

I. *Records*: Records of the immediate offices of the Secretaries of Labor, Under Secretaries of Labor, Assistant Secretaries, and special assistants to the Secretaries of Labor.

Restrictions: For a period of 20 years subsequent to the accession of such records by the National Archives, unless a shorter or longer period of time is specified in the transfer agreement, no one may examine these records or be given information from them or copies of them except as authorized by the Secretary of Labor, the Assistant Secretary for Administration, or a representative of either. *Provided further*: that where a different restriction is specified for any other records of the Department of Labor accessioned by the National Archives, such restriction shall also apply to any related correspondence, references, etc., which may be included in records described above in part I *Records*.

Specified by: Secretary of Labor.

II. *Records*: General file of the Chairman of the Departmental Committee on Economic Policy and Programs, 1949-50.

Restrictions: Before January 1, 1974, no one may examine these records or be given information from them or copies of them except as authorized by the Secretary of Labor, the Assistant Secretary for Administration, or a representative of either.

Specified by: Secretary of Labor.

III. *Records*: Records of the Program Planning and Review Committee, 1955-62.

Restrictions: Before January 1, 1972, no one may examine these records or be given information from them or copies of them except as authorized by the Secretary of Labor, the Assistant Secretary for Administration, or a representative of either.

Specified by: Secretary of Labor.

IV. *Records*: Davis-Bacon "county files."

Restrictions: No one may examine these records or be given information from them or copies of them except as authorized by the Secretary of Labor, the Assistant Secretary for Administration, or a representative of either.

Specified by: Secretary of Labor.

RECORDS OF THE BUREAU OF LABOR STATISTICS (RECORD GROUP 257)

The Bureau of Labor Statistics originated as the Bureau of Labor, established in the Department of the Interior by an act of June 27, 1884. In 1888 the Bureau became an independent Department of Labor without Cabinet status. It was incorporated into the Department of Commerce and Labor in 1903 as a bureau, and when the present Department of Labor was organized in 1913 the Bureau was transferred to it as the Bureau of Labor Statistics.

As the Federal Government's principal factfinding agency in the field of labor economics, the Bureau gathers and analyzes data and publishes reports concerning the labor force, employment, and unemployment; long-range occupational employment prospects, wage rates, earnings, hours of work, and labor productivity; industrial hazards, accidents, and work injuries; rent; labor unions, collective bargaining, and work stoppages; and foreign labor conditions. The Bureau is also the principal Government agency concerned with price statistics outside the field of agriculture. It publishes periodical indexes of consumer and wholesale prices and conducts studies of consumer expenditures and incomes.

There are 238 cubic feet of records dated between 1885 and 1945 in this record group.

RECORDS. 1885-1945. 286 lin. ft.

These records include letters sent, 1901-6, and telegrams, 1897-1904; administrative orders, letters, and issuances, 1885-1906; appropriation, voucher, and other ledgers, 1885-1913; memorandums and statistical compilations concerning labor, economics, and demography, 1896-1905; transcripts of the Anthracite Coal Strike Commission proceedings, 1902-3; records relating to personnel, chiefly job applications, 1885-1919; correspondence concerning the Bureau's participation in the Pan American Exposition at Buffalo, N.Y., and the Louisiana Purchase Exposition at St. Louis, Mo., 1899-1904; Department and Bureau forms, 1885-1916; collective-bargaining agreements filed by employers, trade associations, and trade unions, 1912-45; selected general correspondence of the Bureau, 1908-39; correspondence with other Federal agencies, 1933-34; the Commissioner's general correspondence, 1923-43, and his correspondence with the Secretary of Labor, 1925-29, the Bureau staff, 1933-35, and other Labor Department units, 1935; the files of Commissioner Ethelbert Stewart, 1904-31; correspondence and other records relating to National Recovery Administration programs, 1933-34; records concerning a survey of Federal statistical activities, 1932; and appropriation ledgers and financial statements, 1913–34.

SPECIFIC RESTRICTIONS

I. *Records*: Collective-bargaining agreements designated as "Confidential" when filed with the Bureau of Labor Statistics by employers, trade associations, and trade unions, 1941-45.

Restrictions: These records shall not be made available to private inquirers unless, in any particular case, the inquirer has obtained prior written permission from the parties to the agreement or agreements in question.

Specified by: Commissioner of Labor Statistics.

II. *Records*: Central correspondence file of the Bureau of Labor Statistics, 1939-49; and correspondence of the Commissioner, of Labor Statistics, 1933 and 1935-43.

Restrictions: No one may examine these records or be given copies of or information from them except by permission of the Commissioner of Labor Statistics or his authorized representatives.

Specified by: Bureau of Labor Statistics.

RECORDS OF THE WOMEN'S BUREAU
(RECORD GROUP 86)

The Women's Bureau, established in the Department of Labor by an act of June 5, 1920, succeeded the Woman-In-Industry Service, a war emergency agency authorized in 1918 to ensure effective employment of women while conserving their health and welfare. Many of the records of the Woman-In-Industry Service were destroyed by fire on August 31, 1930.

The Women's Bureau develops standards, policies, and programs to promote the welfare of working women, increase their efficiency, improve their working conditions, and advance their opportunities for profitable employment. It publishes reports on trends in the employment of women and the characteristics of the female working force; women's employment opportunities, wages, and conditions of work in occupations and industries; the dual role of women as workers and homemakers; and factors affecting women's income, financial

responsibilities, and needs. The Bureau analyzes and makes recommendations concerning existing and proposed labor laws and regulations applicable to women and laws affecting their civil and political status. In cooperation with other Labor Department bureaus it assists in coordinating activities of the Department for wider implementation of programs affecting all workers. The Bureau also plans programs of study and observation for women community leaders, provides technical materials to international agencies, and advises U.S. delegates attending international conferences concerned with women's status in political, social, economic, legal, and educational fields.

See *Activities of the Women's Bureau of the United States*, Women's Bureau Bulletin 86 (1931).

There are 17 cubic feet of records dated between 1918 and 1956 in this record group.

RECORDS OF THE WOMAN-IN-
INDUSTRY SERVICE. 1918-20.
5 lin. ft.

These consist of general correspondence of Director Mary Van Kleek, 1918-
20, and her correspondence with members of the War Labor Policies Board,
1918; minutes of the War Labor Policies
Board, relating to women in industry,
1918-19; minutes of an October 1918
conference sponsored by the War Labor
Policies Board for State labor law
enforcement officials; records relating to
hearings before the National War Labor
Board, 1918; and bulletins issued by the
Service, 1918-19.

RECORDS OF THE WOMEN'S
BUREAU. 1919-56. 18 lin. ft.

These consist of records relating to
a survey of immigrant women in industry, 1925; reports and related records
concerning women in administrative
positions in State labor law enforcement
agencies, 1931-33; reports, bulletins, and
copies of *Newsletter* and *The Woman
Worker* issued by the Bureau, 1919-56;
and charts, graphs, posters, and special
subject maps prepared by the Bureau.

AUDIOVISUAL RECORDS.
1845-1945. 2,131 items.

Photographs, 1845-1945 (2,125 items),
of women at work in defense and peacetime industries, in agriculture, and in the
professions, 1892-1945; and photographs
and photographic copies of artworks
illustrating improvement in working
conditions and of equipment used by
women in the home and in industry from
colonial to modern times, documenting
the struggle for women's rights, and
showing women's fashions.

Motion picures, 1928-38 (6 reels), consisting of dramas on the role of women
in industry and the impact of labor laws
and union activity on working conditions
for women.

RECORDS OF THE BUREAU OF LABOR STANDARDS
(RECORD GROUP 100)

The Division of Labor Standards was
established in November 1934 in the
Department of Labor; its name was
changed in 1948 to the Bureau of Labor
Standards. The Bureau promotes industrial safety and health and gives technical advice in this field to State labor
departments, labor unions, and trade
associations. It develops national standards for labor legislation and labor law
administration and assists the Bureau
of International Labor Affairs in implementing international labor standards.
Through agreements negotiated
between Federal and State agencies, it
coordinates the enforcement of laws concerning wage rates, work hours, industrial homework, child labor, and safety
and health. The Bureau serves as a center of information and as an advisory
service on conditions and programs in
the area of child labor and youth employment standards, and prepares publications and exhibits for public information.

There are 597 cubic feet of records
(in WNRC except for nontextual
records) dated between 1934 and 1957
in this record group.

RECORDS. 1934-57. 877 lin. ft. and 6
rolls of microfilm.

These consist of general classified
files, with a card index, including minutes, reports, correspondence, memorandums, surveys, and publicity material,
1934-49; case files for registrations of

labor organizations as required by the Taft-Hartley Labor Management Relations Act, 1946-57, with a microfilm copy (6 rolls) of a card index for the years 1946-48; data concerning State legislative action prepared by Commerce Clearing House, Inc., a private reference service, and by the Division of Labor Standards, 1936-40; maps (18 items) of the United States showing the extent of occupational disease insurance coverage, 1935-38; and the motion picture "Stop Silicosis," 1938.

SPECIFIC RESTRICTIONS

Records: Labor organization registration case files covering union fiscal years 1946-57 submitted in conformance with the Taft-Hartley Labor Management Relations Act of 1947.

Restrictions: The use of these records is restricted to personnel assigned to the Labor-Management Services Administration of the Department of Labor, and such other persons as have obtained the written permission of the Secretary of Labor, the Assistant Secretary for Labor-Management Relations or his deputy, the Director of the Office of Labor-Management and Welfare-Pension Reports or his deputy, the Assistant Director for Reports and Analysis or his deputy, or the Records Officer of the Labor-Management Services Administration.

Specified by: Labor-Management Services Administration, Department of Labor.

RECORDS OF THE WAGE AND HOUR AND PUBLIC CONTRACTS DIVISIONS (RECORD GROUP 155)

The Wage and Hour Division was established in the Department of Labor to administer the wage and hour provisions of the Fair Labor Standards Act of June 25, 1938. The act establishes (subject to certain exemptions) minimum wage, overtime compensation, equal pay, and child labor standards for persons employed in interstate or foreign commerce, in the production of goods for such commerce, and for certain other activities. The Division originally was empowered to establish industry committees—equally representative of employers, employees, and the public— to recommend minimum wages. An amendment, effective January 25, 1950, limited the industry committee procedure to Puerto Rico and the Virgin Islands, where it was to be used for establishing wage rates below the statutory minimum.

The Public Contracts Division was created in the Labor Department to administer the Walsh-Healey Public Contracts Act of June 30, 1936, which required Government supply contracts exceeding $10,000 to stipulate minimum wage, overtime pay, nonemployment of child and convict labor, and safety and health standards.

The two Divisions were consolidated by order of the Secretary of Labor on August 21, 1942. The Wage and Hour and Public Contracts Divisions also administer and enforce the minimum wage and fringe benefit provisions of the McNamara-O'Hara Service Contract Act of 1965, the wage provisions of the National Foundation on the Arts and the Humanities Act applicable to grants-in-aid for the arts, and the Age Discrimination in Employment Act of 1967.

There are 518 cubic feet of records dated between 1938 and 1952 in this record group.

RECORDS OF THE WAGE AND HOUR DIVISION. 1938-42. 88 lin. ft.

These consist of records relating chiefly to personnel, but including copies of administrative orders and issuances, 1938-42; regulations, 1938-42; materials relating to cooperative agreements with several State governments that had wage and hour legislation, 1940-41; orders of investigations of individual violations of the Fair Labor Standards Act, 1939-42; files of 41 industry committees, including transcripts of hearings, briefs, exhibits, recommendations on minimum wages and maximum hours, and the official orders of the Division's administrator, 1938-42; Puerto Rico Industry Committee records, 1940-42; records relating to establishment of minimum wage rates for apprentices in 17 industries, including transcripts of hearings, briefs, exhibits, final decisions, and materials relating to certificates permitting employment of apprentices at less than the statutory minimum wage, 1938-42; records relating to exemptions from provisions of the Fair Labor Standards Act for operators of seasonal industries, 1938-42; "special industry" investigation files on industries partially exempted from provisions of the act, 1938-42; records of hearings on claims for exemptions for facilities furnished by employers to employees, 1940-41; records relating to hearings on amendments to recordkeeping regulations for employers, 1940-41, and to regulations regarding employees in areas of production exempt from provisions of the act, 1939-42; and press releases, 1938-40.

RECORDS OF THE WAGE AND HOUR AND PUBLIC CONTRACTS DIVISIONS. 1938-52. 592 lin. ft. and 9 rolls of microfilm.

Included are records relating to organization, budget, and congressional and interagency relations, 1938-47; samples of significant inspection case files, including 9 rolls of microfilm, 1939-45 (textual records in WNRC); correspondence with unions, trade associations, national organizations, and Members of Congress, 1938-52; and records relating to the Special Industry Committee for Puerto Rico, 1938-46.

Records of the Public Contracts Division consist of inspection case files and are included with the corresponding series of the Wage and Hour and Public Contracts Divisions. None are dated before 1939.

SPECIFIC RESTRICTIONS

Records: Inspection case files of the Wage and Hour and Public Contracts Divisions.

Restrictions: These records shall not be available to researchers until 30 years after the closing year of the cases except as authorized by the Secretary of Labor, the Administrative Assistant Secretary, or a representative of either.

Specified by: Secretary of Labor.

Discontinued Agencies

RECORDS OF THE WAGE ADJUSTMENT BOARD (RECORD GROUP 236)

The Wage Adjustment Board (WAB) was established by the Secretary of Labor on May 29, 1942, as the Government's principal wage stabilization agency for the building and construction industry during World War II. The WAB was the direct result of an agreement of May 22, 1942, between Federal contracting agencies and the Building and Construction Trades Department of the American Federation of Labor, which stipulated that wage rates on all war construction work controlled or financed by the Government were to be frozen at levels prevailing on July 1, 1942, and provided for the creation of a wage adjustment board. The WAB was composed of representatives of Federal contracting agencies and labor organizations participating in the wage stabilization agreement.

On October 13, 1943, the WAB was given authority to stabilize wages in the private sector of the building construction industry and to adjudicate labor disputes involving the industry. Under its broadened jurisdiction the WAB was reorganized to include representatives of labor, industry, and the public. Thereafter the WAB operated as an industry commission of the National War Labor Board (NWLB) and its successor, the National Wage Stabilization Board (NWSB), with its decisions subject to review by those agencies. When the NWSB was established in 1946 the WAB

lost its authority to adjudicate labor disputes. The WAB was dissolved when the NWSB was terminated February 24, 1947. Despite its close connection with the NWLB and the NWSB, the WAB remained administratively a separate unit in the Labor Department.

There are 174 cubic feet of records dated between 1942 and 1947 in this record group.

RECORDS. 1942–47. 209 lin. ft.

These consist of minutes of the Board, 1942–46; correspondence, 1942–46; case files, 1942–47, with indexes to 1946, and a case docket, 1942–44 (in WNRC); and budgetary records, workload reports, and issuances. The case files include wage-adjustment cases relating to Government and private construction work and some dispute cases relating to private construction work. Each case file generally contains the initial application for a ruling, background and supporting documents filed by the interested parties, reports and recommendations of the investigation agent, the decision of the Board, and related correspondence and memorandums.

See Leonard Rapport, comp., *Preliminary Inventory of the Records of the Wage Adjustment Board*, PI 72 (1954).

RECORDS OF THE BUREAU OF EMPLOYMENT SECURITY
(RECORD GROUP 183)

The Bureau of Employment Security was preceded by the Division of Information created in 1907 in the Bureau of Immigration and Naturalization of the Department of Commerce and Labor. On January 3, 1918, this Division, which had become a general placement agency in the Labor Department's Immigration Service, was made a separate administrative unit under the name United States Employment Service (USES). An act of June 6, 1933, reorganized USES

as a Bureau to administer public employment service provisions of the Wagner-Peyser Act, and during the mid-1930's its subsidiary, the National Reemployment Service, operated public employment service agencies in the States on an emergency basis until they were absorbed by State agencies.

The Bureau of Unemployment Compensation of the Social Security Board, established as an independent agency under the Social Security Act of 1935, initially administered the unemployment insurance program. On July 1, 1939, USES and the Bureau of Unemployment Compensation were merged in the Bureau of Employment Security of the Social Security Board (which became part of the Federal Security Agency on the same date) to administer public employment service and unemployment insurance programs. In 1942 USES, including the State employment services, was absorbed by the War Manpower Commission but was transferred to the Labor Department in 1945 when the Commission was terminated. On November 16, 1946, the State employment services were returned to State control. On July 1, 1948, USES was attached to the Bureau of Employment Security of the Social Security Administration, Federal Security Agency, and on August 19, 1949, the Bureau of Employment Security was transferred to the Labor Department. Under other legislative programs the Bureau administered functions relating to the operation of veterans and farm placement services and manpower development and training projects. The Bureau of Employment Security was abolished on March 14, 1969, and its functions assigned to the Office of the Assistant Secretary for Manpower, where they were divided between the U.S. Training and Employment Service and the Unemployment Insurance Service.

There are 859 cubic feet of records dated between 1907 and 1949 in this record group.

RECORDS OF THE U.S.
EMPLOYMENT SERVICE. 1907-49.
1,000 lin. ft.

Included is a small body of material, 1907-32, relating to the origin, organization, and operations of USES, including files of the office of the Federal State Director, Omaha, Nebr., 1917-19. For the period 1933-42 the records comprise

subject-classified general files and files of various units, including the Operations, Veterans', Standards and Research, and Business Administration Divisions and the Farm Placement Service; National Reemployment Service headquarters correspondence; proceedings of conferences; press releases; records relating to personnel, including material on the Civil Service merit system; special files of orders and circulars; fiscal and financial records, including budget analyses and financial reports on State offices; files of staff officials; State employment service plans of operation, with related correspondence; headquarters and State employment service handbooks, manuals, bulletins, analyses, and reports; labor market survey reports for certain States, cities, and metropolitan areas; and other surveys, reports, and statistical materials.

There is research data that includes materials relating to USES industry studies; surveys of the Upper Monongahela Valley and of rural youth in Maryland; an occupational research program; and an inventory of registrants at USES offices taken for a study of unemployment, with related administrative correspondence, progress and cost reports, and analyses of applicants by occupational classifications. Also included are subject-classified files, with an index, and miscellaneous records of Washington headquarters offices, 1942-47; narrative and statistical labor market area reports, 1940-49; area office reports of the War Manpower Commission, 1942-45; and reports, correspondence, publications, and related records concerning labor markets in industries, 1941-47.

RECORDS OF THE SOCIAL
SECURITY BOARD. 1936-42.
300 lin. ft.

These consist of subject-classified files of the Bureau of Unemployment Compensation, Social Security Board, 1936–39; and of the Bureau of Employment Security, Social Security Board, Federal Security Agency, relating to unemployment compensation functions of the Bureau, 1939–42.

DEPARTMENT OF HEALTH, EDUCATION, AND WELFARE

GENERAL RECORDS OF THE DEPARTMENT OF HEALTH, EDUCATION, AND WELFARE (RECORD GROUP 235)

The Department of Health, Education, and Welfare (HEW) was established by Reorganization Plan No. 1 of 1953. This plan abolished the Federal Security Agency (FSA), created in 1939, and transferred its functions and components to HEW. HEW administers Federal and Federal-State programs in public health, education, and social and economic security. It also carries out Federal responsibilities in relation to the American Printing House for the Blind, Gallaudet College, and Howard University.

There are 391 cubic feet of records (including less than 1 cu. ft. in JFKL) dated between 1857 and ca. 1963 in this record group.

RECORDS. 1857-ca. 1963. 469 lin. ft.

These include records of the Office of the FSA Administrator and the Office of the HEW Secretary, consisting of minutes, reports, memorandums, issuances, correspondence, publications, statistical studies, and related materials about programs, operations, and units of those agencies, 1939-55. FSA records also include files of the Assistant Administrator, relating to agency programs, 1941-45; general subject files of and field agents' reports to the Office of War Property Distribution, 1945-47; reports and studies of the Division of Personnel Management, 1936-44; speeches, articles, press releases, and other issuances of the Information Division, 1936-42; and legal opinions relating to social security programs, 1936-39, transcripts of regional attorneys conferences, 1938-39, and reports and opinions about proposed

legislation, 1936-42, of the Office of the General Counsel and its predecessor, the Office of the General Counsel of the Social Security Board. There are also (in JFKL) letters of condolences from foreign students and teachers on the death of President Kennedy.

The records of Gallaudet College, established in 1857 as the Columbia Institution for the Deaf and given its present name in 1954, consist of minutes of directors meetings, 1864-65; correspondence, 1868-1954 (with gaps); ledgers, journals, accounts, financial statements, and other fiscal records concerning Government contributions and college expenditures for supplies, food, salaries, books, and activities, 1857-1952; and a record of funds received by the Kendall School, an elementary and secondary institution associated with the college, 1912-30.

AUDIOVISUAL RECORDS. 1861-1963. 122 items.

Included are photographs (113 items) from "Brady's Album Gallery" and "Photographic Incidents of the War," depicting military bridges, camp activities, battle scenes, fortifications, gunboats, and street scenes; photographs of artworks of hospitals and rest homes in and near Washington, D.C., 1861-65; a motion picture (1 reel) illustrating language teaching techniques, ca. 1963; and sound recordings (8 items) of the broadcasted speeches of FSA Administrator Paul V. McNutt, ca. 1942, and of a radio series concerning the training and rehabilitation of the handicapped, 1947.

RECORDS OF THE PUBLIC HEALTH SERVICE
(RECORD GROUP 90)

The Public Health Service (PHS), originally called the Marine Hospital Service, has its origin in an act of July 16, 1798, which authorized hospitals for the care of sick and disabled American merchant seamen. Subsequent legislation greatly broadened the scope of its activities. In 1902 its name was changed to Public Health and Marine Hospital Service, and in 1912 to Public Health Service. The PHS was under the jurisdiction of the Treasury Department from 1798 to July 1, 1939, when it was placed in the newly created Federal Security Agency, which became in 1953 the Department of Health, Education, and Welfare. In 1966 the PHS was expanded and reorganized into three operating agencies: the Consumer Protection and Environmental Health Service, the Health Services and Mental Health Administration, and the National Institutes of Health (NIH). In 1968 the Food and Drug Administration was made part of the Consumer Protection and Environmental Health Service.

The PHS, under the direction of a Surgeon General, is responsible for medical care of personnel of the Coast Guard, the Coast and Geodetic Survey, and the merchant marine; providing health services to American Indians; preventing the spread of disease; research in the cause, prevention, and control of disease; extending and improving State and local health services through technical assistance and financial aid; collaborating with foreign governments and international organizations in world health activities; supervising manufacture of biologic products; collecting, analysing, and publishing vital and health statistics; and disseminating health information. To perform these functions the PHS operates marine hospitals, hospitals for specific diseases, medical facilities for Federal penal institutions, research institutes and laboratories, the National Library of Medicine, and quarantine and health stations throughout the United States. It also administers Freedmen's Hospital and St. Elizabeth's Hospital in the District of Columbia.

See Ralph Chester Williams, M.D., *The United States Public Health Service, 1798-1950* (1951).

There are 1,382 cubic feet of records dated between 1802 and 1965 in this record group.

GENERAL RECORDS OF THE PUBLIC HEALTH SERVICE.
1833-1946. 1,200 lin. ft.

These consist of general files and correspondence, with registers and indexes, including letters sent and received by the Marine Hospital Service, 1833-78, and by the Office of the Supervising Surgeon General, 1872-97 (with some material as early as 1860 and as late as 1899), and a PHS central file of general correspondence, 1897-1946. The central files are grouped in three main segments: 1897-1923, arranged numerically; and 1924-35 and 1936-46, arranged by class of correspondent and subject-numeric thereunder. The records to 1878 deal mainly with the operation of marine hospitals. The central files from 1897 include correspondence, reports, memorandums, and other records about medical officers, foreign ports, boards of officers, diseases, drugs, serums and vaccines, control of water supplies used by interstate carriers, the Hygienic Laboratory, conferences, public health education, hygiene and sanitation, inspection of immigrants, cooperation with State and local agencies, marine hospitals, and relief and quarantine stations.

RECORDS OF THE NATIONAL BOARD OF HEALTH. 1879–84. 44 lin. ft.

The Board, composed of seven members appointed by the President and three medical officers detailed from the Army, the Navy, and the Marine Hospital Service, was established by an act of March 3, 1879, to advise the Federal and State Governments on public health preservation and improvement. The Board was terminated in 1886. Its records include minutes of the Board and its Executive Committee; the secretary's journal; committee reports; correspondence, with related registers; form letters and questionnaires sent to municipal health authorities; published bulletins; a report of the Yellow Fever Commission on the epidemic of 1878; proceedings of the 1881 International Sanitary Conference held at Washington, D.C., and of the 1884 National Conference of State Boards of Health at St. Louis; and a disbursement ledger.

RECORDS OF THE HOSPITAL DIVISION. 1877–1935. 100 lin. ft.

As the Marine Hospital Service acquired public health functions, this Division (originally the Division of Marine Hospitals and Relief) was organized to supervise hospitals and medical facilities. Records include correspondence, 1918–35, patient registers, 1877–1920, and medical officer reports, 1923–35.

RECORDS OF THE QUARANTINE DIVISIONS. 1878–1936. 70 lin. ft.

Quarantine functions under an act of 1878 requiring inspection of vessels exposed to diseases in foreign ports and later quarantine measures affecting interstate control of diseases were administered by the Division of Foreign and Insular Quarantine and the Domestic Quarantine Division. Records include correspondence with quarantine stations, 1878–1936, and with foreign stations, 1893–1936; and records relating to vessels inspected and fumigated, 1892–1929.

RECORDS OF THE TRACHOMA SERVICE. 1916–33. 50 lin. ft.

Organized in 1913 to treat trachoma, this Service functioned through field clinics, largely in rural areas in the Appalachians and Ozarks. The Service was administered by the Domestic Quarantine Division. The records include correspondence, 1926–30, caseworker reports, 1926–33, and clinical treatment records, 1916–32.

RECORDS OF THE GENERAL INSPECTION SERVICE. 1919–41. 140 lin. ft. (in WNRC).

This Service was organized in 1920 to make systematic inspections of PHS stations and activities and to investigate complaints regarding the administration of hospitals. The records include hospital inspection and other reports (including reports on hospitals operated by PHS under contract), correspondence, and newspaper clippings providing information on physical facilities, equipment, treatment facilities, and services furnished by public and private institutions, and, after World War I, information on treatment of ex-servicemen and relations between the PHS and the American Legion.

RECORDS OF VENEREAL DISEASE CONTROL ORGANIZATIONS. 1918–36. 115 lin. ft.

Included are records of the U.S. Interdepartmental Social Hygiene Board and of the PHS Division of Venereal Diseases, both established under the Chamberlain-Kahn Act of July 9, 1918. The Interdepartmental Social Hygiene Board made grants to universities and associations for medical and educational research and allocated funds to States for control, prevention, and treatment of venereal diseases. The Board was terminated in 1923. Its records consist of fragmentary minutes, memorandums, correspondence, allotment ledgers, account books, and publications, 1918-22. Some files of the Board have been incorporated with records of the Division of Venereal Diseases. The Division's records include reports, correspondence, studies, publications, and newspaper clippings, 1918-36 (in WNRC).

RECORDS OF THE NATIONAL INSTITUTES OF HEALTH. 1915-60. 76 lin. ft.

The NIH and its predecessors, the Hygienic Laboratory, 1887-1930, and the National Institute of Health, 1930-48, have been the principal PHS medical research laboratory. The records of the Office of the Director include a subject-classified general file arranged similarly to the PHS central file, relating to the organization, administration, and activities of NIH and its predecessors, ca. 1915-51 (chiefly 1935-49); a "divisions file," ca. 1920-39, on administration and operations of NIH divisions and sections before establishment of the specialized institutes (with the exception of the National Cancer Institute, established in 1937); an "organization file," 1938-51, on individual institutes; a "PHS divisions file," 1920-39, on relations with PHS headquarters units; a "station file," 1930-49 (chiefly 1939-49), concerning field operations and activities; a "government file," 1924-50, on relations with other Federal agencies; a "geographic file," 1924-50, of correspondence and related records on activities of and in conjunction with State and foreign public health and medical research facilities and officials; and a "disease investigation file," 1920-37 (with some records dated as early as 1917), relating to research on particular diseases. The records also include small files of former medical directors L. R. Thompson, 1920-37, and A. M. Stimson, 1937-39,

and a series of program activity reports, 1960.

OTHER HEADQUARTERS RECORDS. 1802-1965. 100 lin. ft.

These include records of the White House Conference on Health, 1965, consisting of texts of speeches and papers presented, transcripts of proceedings and panel discussions, and press releases; correspondence of administrative units, such as the Division of Scientific Research, 1917, and the Office of the Medical Purveyor, 1877-81; correspondence with other Federal agencies, ca. 1917-29; records relating to international health activities, ca. 1903-41; correspondence regarding applications and nominations for appointments and charges against PHS officers, 1868-1910; publications relating to vital statistics, 1854-1945; reports of the Philippine rehabilitation program, 1946-49, covering maternal and child care, diseases, sanitation, and restoration of medical facilities; and fiscal and property accounting records relating to 19th century PHS operations, including statements of the Marine Hospital Fund, 1802-48 and 1861-64, hospital returns, 1833-50, records concerning the building and maintenance of marine hospitals, and records of appropriations, disbursements, accounts, allotments, purchases, and issuances of medical supplies.

FIELD RECORDS. 1809-1939. 65 lin. ft.

Included are prescription and case books, correspondence, medical and surgical reports, registers of hospital and relief patients, inventories, statements of expenditures, and journals relating to a number of hospitals, quarantine and relief stations, and other PHS facilities.

CARTOGRAPHIC AND AUDIOVISUAL RECORDS.
1878-1965. 12,922 items.

Cartographic records (19 items) include maps prepared from sanitary engineering surveys of military camps and airfields in Texas, 1918; and maps of drainage basins located primarily in the Western United States, relating to water uses and water pollution, 1942-51.

Photographs, 1878-1954 (12,777 items), of marine and other hospitals, quarantine stations, other PHS facilities, and administrative and scientific personnel, relating to research in communicable and epidemic diseases and child hygiene, and to the study and treatment of malaria, yellow fever, and other diseases spread by insects.

Motion pictures (49 reels) include a series entitled "Science of Life," produced in 1924 for educational use in the life sciences and personal hygiene for young men and women; and films relating to the causes, treatment, and control of cancer and of malaria, syphilis, and other communicable diseases, 1924-50.

Sound recordings (77 items) consist of a recording of a radio broadcast about National Negro Health Week, 1942, and recordings of the proceedings of the 1965 White House Conference on Health.

See Charles Zaid, comp., *Preliminary Inventory of the Records of the National Board of Health*, PI 141 (1962).

RECORDS OF THE OFFICE OF EDUCATION
(RECORD GROUP 12)

A Department of Education, headed by a Commissioner, was established by an act of March 2, 1867. It was abolished as an independent agency on July 20, 1868, and reestablished as the Office of Education in the Department of the Interior. The original statutory function of both the Department and the Office was to collect and disseminate information on education in the United States and abroad and to promote better education throughout the country. Later legislation and Executive orders have added functions, including responsibility for Federal financial assistance to education and special studies and programs. Among the programs is the vocational education program initiated under the Federal Board for Vocational Education in 1917 and transferred to the Office of Education on October 10, 1933. In 1931 the functions and records of the Alaska Division were transferred to the Office (now the Bureau) of Indian Affairs (see RG 75). In 1939 the Office of Education was transferred to the Federal Security Agency, which became in 1953 the Department of Health, Education, and Welfare.

There are 639 cubic feet of records dated between 1870 and 1965 in this record group.

RECORDS OF THE OFFICE OF THE COMMISSIONER OF EDUCATION. 1870-1953. 100 lin. ft.

These include an incomplete set of letters sent, 1870-1908; an incomplete index to unlocated letters received, 1893-1907; correspondence with Government agencies and private organizations, 1905-42; minutes, reports, memorandums, and publications relating to the work of the Federal Board for Vocational Education, 1918-31; field service reports, 1923-29; monthly reports of division chiefs, 1932-35; records documenting special programs administered by the Office during World War II, 1940-45; records relating to efficiency and economy, 1887-1912, research and experiment stations, 1915–26, education conventions, 1926–32, professional education and college standards, 1909–30, education in foreign countries, 1912–24, secondary education, 1915–23, conferences and meetings participated in by the Commissioner, 1909–36, and American Education Week, 1924–28; and an incomplete set of *School Life*, 1918–24. There are also records on the organization and administration of the Office of Education, immigrant and black education, international congresses and conventions, adult education, junior colleges, conservation education, and schools on Government reservations, including Indian schools, 1870–1953.

RECORDS OF THE DIVISION OF VOCATIONAL EDUCATION.
1917–42. 530 lin. ft. (in WNRC).

When the functions of the Federal Board for Vocational Education were transferred to the Office of Education in 1933, the Division of Vocational Education was created to take over the Board's organization and staff. The records comprise files of both the Board and Division, including correspondence and related records of division chiefs and administrators with State and Federal officials and agencies, private organizations, and schools concerning the program, 1917–42; records relating to State programs, 1917–32; and reports and correspondence of field agents, documenting the establishment and administration of programs in trade, industrial, agricultural, and commercial education, home economics, and vocational rehabilitation, 1917–42.

RECORDS OF OTHER DIVISIONS AND OFFICES. 1919–62. 60 lin. ft.

Included are reports, correspondence, and publicity material of the Highway Education Board, 1919–26; reports, correspondence, and surveys of the Home Economics Division, 1923–33; correspondence of the Chief Clerk, 1928–32;

files of the Advisory Committee on Education by Radio, 1928–33; reports, plans, correspondence, scripts, publicity material, and budget records of the Radio Education Division, 1936–40; and office files of Specialist in Negro Education and Chief of the Adult Education Section Ambrose Caliver, 1931–62.

RECORDS OF SURVEYS, STUDIES, AND SPECIAL PROJECTS. 1911–46. 300 lin. ft.

These include reports, correspondence, and schedules relating to surveys of public schools in States and cities, 1911–30; records relating to World War I programs, such as Americanization projects, home and school gardens, and Flag Day; records of a survey of engineering schools, 1923, the "Platoon Plan" in public schools, 1925–38, land grant colleges, 1929–30, private commercial and business schools, 1929, and the national survey of teacher's education, 1930–33; records relating to educational projects in CCC camps, 1933–45, including minutes of meetings and conferences, reports, plans, correspondence, and records used in preparing a program history; records documenting the National Survey of Vocational Education and Guidance of Negroes, 1935–37, including minutes, reports, correspondence, memorandums, questionnaires, and office files of staff members; correspondence, project proposals, instructions, and drafts of completed studies and reports relating to the project in research in universities, 1935–37; correspondence, issuances, State project and data files, publicity material, and budget records relating to the Federal forum project, 1936–41; files concerning vocational education programs under the George-Deen Act, 1935–38; reports, correspondence, course plans, reports, historical files, and financial records relating to the engineering, science, and management war training program, 1940–45; correspondence, plans, and financial records of State programs, and reports, issuances, and other records relating to vocational training for war production workers, 1940-46 (in WNRC); reports, correspondence, and publicity material of the School and College Civilian Morale Service, 1941-43; records relating to projects for financing construction and maintenance of schools in congested production areas under the Lanham Act, 1941-45; and correspondence, publicity material, and radio scripts relating to the High School Victory Corps, 1942-45.

AUDIOVISUAL RECORDS. 1912-65. 187 items.

Motion pictures, 1940-55 (15 reels), consist of a film on the industrial skills of blind persons; a drama, entitled "Fight for Life," produced and directed by Pare Lorentz, about obstetrical training and practice in the slums of a large city, films for use in supervisory training, and a film of the address of President Dwight D. Eisenhower to the 1955 White House Conference on Education.

Sound recordings (172 items) of a radio broadcast of December 15, 1941, commemorating the 150th anniversary of the Bill of Rights; selected radio broadcasts produced by the Office of Education from 1934 to 1953, containing voices of prominent persons recorded between 1912 and 1951; accounts of historical events, 1937-50, and programs of educational significance, 1938-49; the proceedings of the White House Conferences on Education, 1955 and 1965; speeches and discussions by Commissioners of Education, 1955-64; and the swearing in ceremony of Francis Keppel as Assistant Secretary for Education, October 4, 1965.

Microfilm Publication: *Letters Sent by the Commissioner of Education, 1870-1909*, M635, 71 rolls, DP.

RECORDS OF THE FOOD AND DRUG ADMINISTRATION (RECORD GROUP 88)

The Food and Drug Administration was designated by the Agricultural Appropriation Act of 1931 to continue the regulatory functions performed by the Bureau of Chemistry, the Board of Food and Drug Inspection, and the Food, Drug, and Insecticide Administration, established under the Food and Drugs Act of 1906. The Food and Drug Administration and its functions—except those relating to the enforcement of the Insecticide Act of 1910 and the Naval Stores Act—were transferred in 1940 from the Department of Agriculture to the Federal Security Agency, which became the Department of Health, Education, and Welfare in 1953. The Administration enforces the Federal Food, Drug, and Cosmetic Act; the Tea Importation Act; the Import Milk Act; the Caustic Poison Act; the Hazardous Substances Labeling Act; and the Filled Milk Act. It is responsible for promoting purity, standard potency, and honest and informative labeling of consumer products covered by these acts.

There are 979 cubic feet of records dated between 1877 and 1946 in this record group.

GENERAL RECORDS OF THE FOOD AND DRUG ADMINISTRATION AND ITS PREDECESSORS. 1897-1946. 1,688 lin. ft.

Included are records of the Food Standards Committee, relating to investigations of the manufacture of food products, 1897-1938; records relating to foreign food and drug legislation, 1910-40, with a card index; correspondence (in WNRC) on the administration of the Food and Drugs Act of 1906 by the Bureau of Chemistry and its successor, the Food, Drug, and Insecticide Administration, 1919-29, and an index (in WNRC); records concerning Consumers' Research, Inc., 1922-40; a file relating to an importer of chemicals used in fruit and vegetable sprays and pharmaceuticals, 1925-38; records relating to the proposed importation of medicinal and food substances, 1922-38; project schedules and reports on the enforcement of the Food and Drugs Act, 1916-38; summary information cards about seizure recommendations, 1907-37, and analyses of food product samples, 1905-32; charge and status cards (in WNRC) showing charges against products, dealers, or manufactures, and the status of the product according to the Food and Drugs Act; import detention notices, 1907-38 (in WNRC); an index to articles seized because of Food and Drugs Act violations (in WNRC); an index of manufacturers charged with violations, 1907-38 (in WNRC); a card index to correspondence on the detention of imports, 1906-42 (in WNRC); and allotment and disbursement ledgers, 1914-40.

Records of the Food, Drug, and Insecticide and the Food and Drug Administrations include records of commissioners, relating to proposed food and drug legislation, 1927-40; general correspondence, 1930-37 (in WNRC), and an index (in WNRC); transcript of a hearing before the Senate Committee on Agriculture and Forestry, concerning the administration of the Federal Food and Drugs Act, June 3-30, 1930; reports, correspondence, and memorandums relating to a survey of orange beverages and the effects of shellac on animal organisms, 1935-36; records of the Food Division, 1929-41, and of its Beverage Branch, 1907-45, concerning tests and analyses of foods; import milk permit case files of reports and correspondence on plant inspections and milk sample

tests, 1927-41, with an index (in WNRC); minutes, reports, correspondence, and memorandums relating to the Division's work with the National Research Council committees on medical research and on drugs and medical supplies, 1941-46; and advertising material for patent medicines and health devices, demonstrating the need for regulation of food and drug advertising, 1933-37.

RECORDS OF THE BOARD OF FOOD AND DRUG INSPECTION. 1904-13. 23 lin. ft.

This Board, created by the Secretary of Agriculture on April 25, 1907, to act on all questions arising from the enforcement of the Food and Drugs Act of 1906, handled correspondence involving interpretation and conducted hearings based on alleged violations of the act. The Board was abolished in 1914, and its functions were divided between the Bureau of Chemistry and the Office of the Solicitor. The Board's records consist of minutes of executive sessions, 1907-13; records relating to hearings, 1907-13; correspondence of the Chairman, 1908-10; food inspection decisions, 1904-13; transcripts of hearings on bleached flour, November 18-23, 1908; notices of judgments obtained by the Board, 1908-10; reports by the Bureau of Chemistry, the Solicitor of the Department of Agriculture, U.S. consuls abroad, and others, 1908-12; and records relating to recommendations on the seizure and condemnation of food and drug shipments on grounds of adulteration or mislabeling, 1908-12.

RECORDS OF THE REFEREE BOARD OF CONSULTING SCIENTIFIC EXPERTS. 1911-13. 9 lin. ft.

The Board of Referees, established by the Secretary of Agriculture as an independent, unbiased group of five experts, reported to the Secretary on the wholesome or deleterious character of foods and drugs. This Board was discontinued after June 30, 1915. The records consist of reports, food charts, blood analyses, and correspondence relating to the use of sulfur dioxide as a food preservative and the use of alum in certain foods.

RECORDS OF THE BUREAU OF CHEMISTRY. 1877-1920. 40 lin. ft.

Until 1927, analytical and regulatory work concerning purity standards for food and drugs as well as the enforcement of the 1906 act were performed mainly by the Bureau staff. The Bureau Chief served as Chairman of the Board of Food and Drug Inspection. A reorganization of July 1, 1927, transferred regulatory work to the newly established Food, Drug, and Insecticide Administration. The records consist of transcripts of hearings to determine the legal definition of whiskey, 1906-9; records relating to a court case involving the seizure of a shipment of phenacetine (or acetphenetidine), 1906-14; minutes of the Committee on Business Methods, 1907-13; the "special file" comprising reports and correspondence relating to enforcement of the Food and Drugs Act, with related index, 1907-20; letters sent to inspection districts, 1916-17; World War I project files on problems of conservation, preservation, and development of new food sources, 1917-19; a card index to publications and manuscripts of former staff members; and miscellaneous records, 1877-1910, including copies of correspondence, articles, and speeches by Harvey W. Wiley, Chief, Bureau of Chemistry.

RECORDS OF THE SUPERVISING TEA EXAMINER. 1912-37. 20 lin. ft.

The Tea Act of March 2, 1897, provided that the Secretary of the Treasury, assisted by a board of tea experts, should establish standards of purity and quality for imported teas. A tea inspection service, headed by the Supervising Tea Examiner, was established to enforce the act. On July 1, 1920, the administration of the Tea Act was transferred to the Bureau of Chemistry. The records comprise periodical and special statistical reports, 1912-37, and correspondence, 1913-29.

FIELD RECORDS. 1906-46. 57 lin. ft.

Records of the Philadelphia Station consist of reports, correspondence, and memorandums relating to manufacturers and distributors of foods, drugs, and insecticides within its jurisdiction.

RECORDS RELATING TO THE UNITED STATES PHARMACOPOEIA. 1880-1940. 15 lin. ft.

The *United States Pharmacopoeia*, a publication of the U.S. Pharmacopoeia Convention, which is an agency of American scientists interested in drugs, chemicals, and medicinal preparations, contains lists of drugs and formulas for their preparation. The standards promulgated by the Convention were adopted as official U.S. standards by the Food and Drugs Act of 1906. The records consist of reports, circulars, bulletins, and related material of the committees engaged in the publication of the *United States Pharmacopoeia*, such as the Committee on Revision, the Executive Committee, the General Committee, and their subcomittees.

AUDIOVISUAL RECORDS. 1906-35. 3,800 items.

These include photographs relating to chemical analysis and fraudulent labeling of drugs; inspection of milk, fish, and other foods; the seizure and destruction of contaminated foods; and the manufacture of sugar candy, liquors, and other commodities, 1906-35 (with a few dated as early as 1885).

SPECIFIC RESTRICTIONS

Records: Import detention case summary cards, records of the Office of the Supervising Tea Examiner, and Federal Import Milk Act permit files.

Restrictions: No one may examine these records or be given information from them or copies of them except persons authorized by the Records Officer of the Food and Drug Administration. *Specified by*: Food and Drug Administration.

RECORDS OF THE CHILDREN'S BUREAU
(RECORD GROUP 102)

The Children's Bureau was established as part of the Department of Commerce and Labor by an act of April 9, 1912, and was transferred to the newly created Department of Labor the following year. In 1946 the Bureau, exclusive of the child labor functions centered in its Industrial Division, was transferred to the Social Security Administration of the Federal Security Agency. When that agency was abolished in 1953, its functions and units, including the Social Security Administration and the Children's Bureau, were transferred to the newly created Department of Health, Education, and Welfare.

The Children's Bureau compiles reports on all matters relating to child-life and implements programs to promote child health and welfare, especially those relating to infant and maternal mortality, working mothers, the birth rate, orphanages, juvenile delinquency, desertion, dangerous occupations, accidents, child diseases, employment, and State and community measures for the protection and care of children. It administers Federal aid to State agencies for child welfare, maternal and child health,

and crippled children. It also plans with public and voluntary national, State, and local organizations and agencies for the development and extension of services for children and youth.

See Children's Bureau, *History and Functions of the Children's Bureau, United States Department of Labor* (1944) and *Five Decades of Action for Children, A History of the Children's Bureau* (1962).

There are 500 cubic feet of records dated between 1912 and 1949 in this record group.

RECORDS. 1912–49. 600 lin. ft.

These consist of a classified central file, 1912–40; correspondence and reports relating to child labor, with indexes, 1916–43; operating plans and budget estimates (in WNRC) relating to Federal aid to State agencies for crippled children, 1936–47, for child welfare services, 1936–49, and for maternal and child health, 1936–45; and motion pictures (7 reels) and filmstrips (4 items) relating to prenatal care, training midwives, and infant and child care and diseases, 1919–26.

RECORDS OF THE SOCIAL SECURITY ADMINISTRATION
(RECORD GROUP 47)

The Social Security Act of August 14, 1935, established a three-member Social Security Board as an independent agency. The Board administered provisions of the act relating to Federal old-age and survivors insurance and authorizing grants-in-aid to States for administration of unemployment compensation, old-age assistance, and assistance to the blind and to dependent children. The Board also made studies and recommendations for providing economic security through social insurance. Under Reorganization Plan No. I of 1939, the Board became part of the Federal Security Agency, and the U.S. Employment Service, formerly in the Labor Department, was consolidated with the Board's Bureau of Employment Security. Reorganization Plan No. 2 of 1946 abolished the Social Security Board and transferred its functions to the Federal Security Administrator. The Administrator established the Social Security Administration as successor to the Board and delegated to it the functions of the Children's Bureau, which had been transferred from the Department of Labor. In 1948 the U.S. Employment Service, which had been transferred to the War Manpower Commission in 1942 and to the Department of Labor in 1945, was returned to the Bureau of Employment Security in the Social Security Administration. Also in 1948 the Bureau of Federal Credit Unions, formerly part of the Federal Deposit Insurance Corporation, was transferred to the Social Security Administration. Under Reorganization Plan No. 2 of 1949, the Bureau of Employment Security, including the U.S. Employment Service, was transferred to the Department of Labor. The Social Security Administration became part of the Department of Health, Education, and Welfare in 1953. In 1963 the Bureau of Family Services and the Children's Bureau were transferred to the Department's new Welfare Administration.

There are 346 cubic feet of records dated between 1934 and 1963 in this record group.

RECORDS OF THE COMMITTEE ON ECONOMIC SECURITY.
1934-35. 48 lin. ft.

The Committee was created by Executive Order 6757 on June 29, 1934, under provisions of the National Industrial Recovery Act, to study economic and social security and to develop a legislative program. The Social Security Act of 1935 and amendments adopted in 1939 resulted from its work. Terminated as a formal agency in April 1936, the Committee continued informally for a number of years. Its records include minutes, reports (including drafts and copies of the Committee's report to the President), issuances, correspondence, and copies of speeches concerning the work of the Committee and its boards, advisory committees, and subcommittees; records relating to congressional hearings and to drafting the social security bill and amendments; staff reports, studies, and correspondence; and files of collected materials on social security plans and proposals, pension plans, social insurance, and related State legislation.

RECORDS OF THE SOCIAL SECURITY BOARD. 1935-46.
281 lin. ft.

Minutes and agenda of the Board's meetings, 1935-46; the Board's central files, including reports and correspondence arranged by a decimal classification system, 1935-46; files of the Chairman, 1935-42, and the Executive Director, 1935-40; and reports of the Bureau of Old-Age and Survivors Insurance and its divisions, the Bureau of Federal Old-Age Benefits, and other administrative units of the Board, 1935-40.

RECORDS OF THE SOCIAL SECURITY ADMINISTRATION.
1946-63. 1 lin. ft.

Minutes and agenda of commissioners meetings.

AUDIOVISUAL RECORDS. 1936-44. 40 items.

Motion pictures, 1936-44 (23 reels), illustrating procedures to obtain social security coverage for old-age and survivors insurance, disability insurance, and unemployment benefits. Also newsreels on activities of President Franklin D. Roosevelt, Secretary of State Cordell Hull, Gov. Alfred M. Landon, and others. Filmstrips, 1936-44 (11 items), to accompany lectures on social security benefits, on procedures for obtaining coverage, and on recruiting war workers.

Sound recordings, 1936-40 (6 items), consisting of lectures to accompany the above filmstrips.

SPECIFIC RESTRICTIONS

I. *Records*: Records defined in Title 20, Code of Federal Regulations, section 401.1, as ". . . any return or portion of a return (including information returns or other written statements) filed with the Commissioner of Internal Revenue under Title VIII of the Social Security Act, the Federal Insurance Contributions Act or the Self Employment Contributions Acts, or under regulations made under authority thereof, which has been transmitted to the Department of Health, Education, and Welfare by the Commissioner of Internal Revenue, or . . . any file, record, report, or other paper or any information obtained at any time by the Department or by any officer or employee of the Department, or from the Department or any officer or employee thereof by any other person or by any other agency or officer or employee thereof, which in any way relates to, or is necessary to, or is used in or in connection with, the administration of the old-age and survivors insurance program conducted pursuant to title II of the Social Security Act . . ."

Restrictions: No disclosure of such records or of information from them shall be made unless authorized under 20 CFR 401.3 or by the Commissioner of Social Security.

Specified by: Secretary of Health, Education, and Welfare.

II. *Records*: Minutes and agenda of the Social Security Board from October 16, 1935, to July 15, 1946, and of the Commissioner of Social Security from July 18, 1946, to January 28, 1963.

Restrictions: No one may examine these records or be given information from them or copies of them except by permission of the Records Management Officer of the Department of Health, Education, and Welfare.

Specified by: Secretary of Health, Education, and Welfare.

DEPARTMENT OF HOUSING AND URBAN DEVELOPMENT

GENERAL RECORDS OF THE DEPARTMENT OF HOUSING AND URBAN DEVELOPMENT (RECORD GROUP 207)

The Department of Housing and Urban Development succeeded the Housing and Home Finance Agency (HHFA), which had been established by Reorganization Plan No. 3 of 1947 to coordinate Federal housing activities. The HHFA had, in turn, replaced the National Housing Agency (NHA), established by Executive order in 1942 to coordinate wartime housing activities, and was responsible for implementing the Housing Act of 1949. Included within the HHFA were the Federal Housing Administration (see RG 31); the Public Housing Administration (see RG 196); the Federal National Mortgage Association (see RG 294); the Urban Renewal Administration and the Community Facilities Administration (formerly the Community Facilities Service of the General Services Administration), which were established as constituent units by the HHFA Administrator's Organizational Order 1 of December 23, 1954; and the Home Loan Bank Board, which became independent in 1955 as the Federal Home Loan Bank Board (see RG 195). Under provisions of the Housing Act of 1954 the National Voluntary Mortgage Credit Extension Committee was created with the HHFA Administrator as Chairman. The act of September 9, 1965, creating the Department of Housing and Urban Development, transferred the functions, powers, and duties of the HHFA to the Department.

There are 269 cubic feet of records dated between 1931 and 1969 in this record group.

RECORDS OF PREDECESSORS OF HHFA. 1931–47. 175 lin. ft.

Records of the Central Housing Committee, established in 1935 to coordinate Federal housing activities, include correspondence relating to Committee organization, 1933–35; minutes and reports, 1935–42; general records of the Executive Secretary, 1935–42; and records of several specialized and technical committees, first known as subcommittees, including the Appraisal and Mortgage Analysis, Economics and Statistics, Law and Legislation, Public Relations, and Research, Design, and Construction Committees, 1935–42.

Records of the Division of Defense Housing Coordination, Office for Emergency Management, include policy and administrative records and general records ("Subject File"), 1940–42, and correspondence relating to defense housing, 1941–42.

Records of the National Housing Agency consist of general files relating primarily to NHA activities and operations, 1942–47; correspondence, memorandums, and directives of Assistant Administrator Coleman Woodbury, 1942–45; a subject file of the war housing program and a 5-percent sample of local program operating files, 1942–46; and minutes, procedural issuances, correspondence, memorandums, and other records of the Homes Use Division, 1942–46.

Records of the Division of Research and Statistics, Federal Housing Administration, include reports, maps, and issuances, 1937-45, containing data about cities compiled from sources dated from 1850 to 1945; housing monographs, 1939-42; and reports containing data on construction contracts, 1931-41.

Case files relating to Resettlement Administration and Farm Security Administration housing projects, 1934-42; and basic construction plans for Greendale, Wis., Greenhills, Ohio, and Greenbelt, Md., 1933-35.

RECORDS OF THE HOUSING AND HOME FINANCE AGENCY.
1942-65. 95 lin. ft.

Included are general records of the Division of Housing Research and its predecessors, including unpublished reports comparing the quality of privately produced materials or containing critical comments on proprietary products or technology, 1942-54; minutes, memorandums, and other records relating to the allocation of scarce building materials, 1942-45; sample case files relating to the construction of prefabricated houses and the production of new building materials, 1946-47; reports, memorandums, and correspondence about contract research projects, chiefly with the National Bureau of Standards, 1945-54; and a record set of research and technical publications, 1943-54.

Records of the Division of Plans and Programs include a general subject file, 1950-53; correspondence relating to mobile, demountable housing, 1950-51; a subject file relating to the controlled materials plan, 1950-52; and "locality files" relating to housing in critical defense areas in accordance with the Defense Housing and Community Facilities and Services Act of 1951 and an act of July 31, 1951, extending the Federal rent control law to critical areas, 1950-54.

There are also records of the Division of Community Facilities and Operations, consisting of a general subject file and project files relating to the disaster relief program, 1947-53; and project files relating to a 1946 Hawaiian relief program, which provided assistance in repairing and constructing municipal buildings damaged or destroyed by a tidal wave.

Records, 1954-65, relating to the National Voluntary Mortgage Credit Extension Program, established in 1954 to facilitate location of private mortgage credit for federally insured or guaranteed mortgages in areas with inadequate facilities for access to such loans, or for minority groups to whom such funds were not readily available. The records comprise files of executive secretaries of the national committee and of regional subcommittees.

AUDIOVISUAL RECORDS. 1963-69.
54 items.

Motion pictures, 1963-69 (43 reels), document the creation of the Department of Housing and Urban Development and the appointment by President Johnson of Robert C. Weaver as the Department's first Secretary, and show several ceremonies relating to the establishment and early activities of the Department.

Sound recordings, 1966-68 (11 items), consist of radio spot announcements and speeches by Secretary Weaver.

See Katherine H. Davidson, *Preliminary Inventory of the General Records of the Housing and Home Finance Agency*, PI 164 (1965).

SPECIFIC RESTRICTIONS

I. *Records*: "Locality files" (1950-54) that relate to providing housing in critical defense areas in accordance with the Defense Housing and Community Facilities and Services Act of 1951 and an act of July 31, 1951, extending the Federal rent control law to critical areas.

Restrictions: No one may examine these records or be given information from them or copies of them except persons approved by the Security Officer of the Department of Housing and Urban Development.

Specified by: Department of Defense.

II. *Records*: Unpublished reports among the general records of the Division of Housing Research of the Office of the Aministrator and its predecessors that compare the quality of privately produced materials or that contain unfavorable comments about proprietary products or technology.

Restrictions: No one may examine these records or be given information from them or copies of them without the written permission of the Secretary of the Department of Housing and Urban Development or his authorized representative.

Specified by: Department of Housing and Urban Development.

RECORDS OF THE FEDERAL HOUSING ADMINISTRATION (RECORD GROUP 31)

The Federal Housing Administration (FHA) was created by the National Housing Act of June 27, 1934. By Reorganization Plan No. I of 1939, it was grouped with other agencies to form the Federal Loan Agency. The FHA was transferred to the National Housing Agency in 1942, the Housing and Home Finance Agency in 1947, and the Department of Housing and Urban Development in 1965.

The FHA carries out programs authorized by the National Housing Act to insure private lending institutions against loss on mortgage loans for one- to four-family dwellings, rental housing projects of eight or more units, and property repair or improvement. It also insures advances for housing in nonurban and disaster areas and housing for the elderly and military personnel, for nursing homes, and for the improvement of housing standards—with particular emphasis on the rehabilitation of slums and blighted areas. During World War II FHA field offices accepted, processed, and forwarded to the War Production Board applications from private sources for scarce materials to be used in war housing and utility lines and systems, issued allotments and preference ratings for priorities, and inspected projects for conformity with regulations regarding the use of critical materials. The issuance of building permits and priorities for building materials and the inspection of construction were assumed by the FHA under the veterans emergency housing program in 1946.

There are 96 cubic feet of records dated between 1930 and 1958 in this record group.

RECORDS. 1930-58. 56 lin. ft.

Included are organizational charts and a procedural manual, 1958; project files consisting of sample dossiers for 12 representative multiunit housing development projects, selected on a geographical basis, that illustrate Government procedures to insure various types of rental projects, 1936-46; sample case files containing plans and specifications for typical American homes insured by the 58 FHA regional offices, 1934-38; a city data file of reports, tabulations, and charts gathered between 1938 and 1945 (a few covering the years 1930-38) by the Research and Statistics Division to forecast housing demands and mortgage values (for other records of this Division see RG 207); and audit and financial reports and an appropriation digest of the Reports Section, Controller's Division, 1935–54.

CARTOGRAPHIC AND AUDIOVISUAL RECORDS. 1934–42. 4,000 items.

Maps, 1934–42 (3,972 items), prepared by the Division of Research and Statistics from Real Property Surveys conducted in about 260 cities, showing, by blocks, certain aspects of housing, and from the Housing Market Analysis, showing areas around selected cities considered financially safe for underwriting mortgages.

Motion pictures, 1935–36 (10 reels), relating to construction, renovation, and modernization of homes, farm buildings, and commercial properties under FHA; low-cost home construction; home hazards and their remedies; and the effect of FHA on building industries.

Sound recordings, ca. 1934 (18 items), of radio programs explaining FHA operations and benefits.

See Charlotte Munchmeyer, comp., *Preliminary Inventory of the Cartographic Records of the Federal Housing Administration*, PI 45 (1952).

Discontinued Agencies

RECORDS OF THE FEDERAL NATIONAL MORTGAGE ASSOCIATION (RECORD GROUP 294)

The Federal National Mortgage Association (FNMA), originally chartered February 10, 1938, as the National Mortgage Association of Washington under title III of the National Housing Act, was given its present name in April 1938. Operating as a subsidiary of the Reconstruction Finance Corporation (RFC), FNMA was placed under the Federal Loan Agency (FLA) in 1939, transferred to the Department of Commerce in 1942, and returned to the FLA in 1945. Reorganization Plan No. 22 of 1950 transferred the Association from the RFC (an independent agency after June 1947) to the Housing and Home Finance Agency (see RG 207). The FNMA was placed under the Department of Housing and Urban Development by an act of September 9, 1965.

The FNMA initially provided a nationwide general secondary market for mortgages insured by the Federal Housing Administration and, after July 1948, for some mortgages guaranteed by the Veterans Administration. The Federal National Mortgage Association Charter Act of August 2, 1954, rechartered the FNMA; provided that its mortgage portfolio be managed and liquidated; and authorized it to establish a secondary market facility for home mortgages, which was to be transformed gradually into a privately financed and operated organization. The FNMA then functioned as a mixed-ownership corporation, with common stock owned by private investors and preferred stock owned by the Government, until it became two separate corporations under title VIII of the 1968 Housing and Urban Development Act. One corporation, the Federal National Mortgage Association, is a Government-sponsored private corporation that manages secondary mortgage market operations. The other, the Government National Mortgage Association in the Department of Housing and Urban Development, continues to exercise the functions of the original FNMA in financing federally underwritten mortgages, managing and liquidating Federal trusts and mortgages, and guaranteeing securities backed by federally insured housing mortgages.

There are 11 cubic feet of records dated between 1938 and 1954 in this record group.

RECORDS. 1938-54. 13 lin. ft.

These include general records relating to legislation, organization, budget, and operations; correspondence on marketing mortgages insured by the Federal Housing Administration, and with field agents; case files of declined and canceled loans; and periodic financial statements, with supplementary materials. Records of the FNMA after it became a part of the Housing and Home Finance Agency, 1950-54, consist of records of Budget Officer Walter C. Hand, 1950-53, and other budget records.

SPECIFIC RESTRICTIONS
Records: Records containing information about private firms.

Restrictions: These records will be available to officials of the Federal Government for official purposes and to others only with the permission of the President of the Federal National Mortgage Association.

Specified by: President of the Federal National Mortgage Association.

RECORDS OF THE OFFICE OF THE HOUSING EXPEDITER (RECORD GROUP 252)

The Office of the Housing Expediter (OHE) originated December 12, 1945, when the President appointed a Housing Expediter in the Office of War Mobilization and Reconversion to plan, coordinate, and expedite postwar housing programs. An Executive order in January 1946 authorized the Expediter to plan a veterans housing program and coordinate activities of executive agencies in implementing that plan. Congressional authorization for the OHE was given in the Veterans' Emergency Housing Act of May 22, 1946. The OHE was merged with the National Housing Agency from May 1946 to January 1947, when it was made an independent executive agency. A few months later Civilian Production Administration (CPA) functions relating to the veterans emergency housing program and rent control functions of the Office of Price Administration were transferred to OHE. The veterans emergency housing program—which had stimulated production of building materials, directed those materials into housing construction, and provided veterans with priorities for houses so built—was curtailed by the Housing and Rent Act of 1947 and its amendments. The OHE was terminated by Executive Order 10276 of July 31, 1951, and its functions were transferred to the Office of Rent Stabilization (ORS) of the Economic Stabilization Agency and to the Housing and Home Finance Agency.

There are 1,655 cubic feet of records dated between 1941 and 1953 in this record group.

CENTRAL OFFICE RECORDS.
1941-53. 1,061 lin. ft.

These include records of OHE predecessor units and consist of minutes, reports, correspondence, and related records of the Western Log and Lumber Administration inherited by the OHE from the CPA, 1942-47; a subject file of the CPA Office of Production, consisting of memorandums, reports, correspondence, and other records documenting efforts to stimulate production of building materials, 1943-47; plans and specifications for prefabricated houses, 1946-47; and records of the Office of the Chief Compliance Commissioner, consisting of memorandums that relate to policy and procedures, 1943-44, compliance surveys, 1942-45, and various officials' general records, 1942-47. Also central subject files of the OHE, 1946-47 and 1950-51; records of Housing Expediter Tighe E. Woods, 1947-52, and other officials, ca. 1942-48; bulletins, brochures, and other publications relating to Government housing and rent programs, 1945-53; records of the Office of General Counsel, Compliance Division, consisting primarily of case files, 1944-48, and organization charts and related records, 1946-53; and records of the Office of Deputy Director for Administration, including general records, 1947-52, budgetary records, 1944-53, and memorandums and instructions relating to liquidation, 1945-50.

There are also general records of the Office of Operations, 1946-47; subject and locality files and publicity materials of the Director of the Community Action Advisory Service, 1946-47; reports concerning Land and Public Utilities Advisory Service activities, and correspondence and memorandums maintained by Service officials, 1946-47; reports, correspondence, and memorandums of the Director of the Labor Advisory Service, 1944-47; administrative records of the Office of Industry Advisory Committees, 1945-47; and correspondence, memorandums, and reports of industrial labor specialists, 1946-47. Records of the Non-Residential Construction Branch, including reports and memorandums, 1946-48, and general records, 1946-47; and selected case files of the national office, 1946-48, and district construction offices, 1946-47. Reports, memorandums, charts, tables, and other records documenting Statistics and Analysis Branch activities, 1946-47. Also minutes of staff meetings of the OHE Policy Council and the National Housing Agency, and administrative orders, memorandums, monographs, and other records documenting the administration, operation, and policy of the veterans emergency housing program, 1946-47; and orders, monographs, reports, and related records on the history of rent control, 1941-50.

REGIONAL AND AREA OFFICE RECORDS. 1942-53. 642 lin. ft.

Eight regional offices administered OHE field projects. These records (those of OHE Region IV are in FRC Atlanta) include those of all regional offices except for Region VII, which had its headquarters in Seattle, and generally consist of Office of Price Administration, 1942-46, and ORS, 1947-53, general rent records; minutes of rent advisory boards, 1947-53; records of the regional attorney and other officials, 1942-53; serial memorandums, 1942-46; and policy, procedural, and statistical materials maintained by regional and area officials, 1942-51. Records (in WNRC) of area offices include narrative reports and related records of area rent offices, 1942-51, sample case files, 1942-52, sample rent enforcement case files, 1942-53, interpretations of rent regulations, 1942-43, rent advisory board decontrol files, 1947-52, and publications and issuances relating to the housing and rent program, 1947-53.

AUDIOVISUAL RECORDS. 1946–52. 74 items.

These consist of a motion picture about housing for veterans, 1946, and sound recordings (73 items) of public hearings on rent control and broadcasts of speeches, interviews, and panel discussions by housing officials, Congressmen, and others on rent control, 1950–52.

SPECIFIC RESTRICTIONS

Records: All records relating to the rent control and veterans emergency housing programs that contain information that was deemed confidential by the Rent Stabilizer or with reference to which a request for confidential treatment was made by the person supplying such information.

Restrictions: Such information may not be published or disclosed in any way, unless the Archivist of the United States determines that the withholding of such information is contrary to the interest of the national defense and security. In general, the types of information so restricted are data about the technical and financial operations of individual firms. Statu-

tory exceptions to these restrictions are as follows: information may be released in statistical totals or summaries in such manner that the source thereof is not disclosed or identified directly or indirectly; information may be released if the persons who supplied the information agree to its release; the Defense Department and the Maritime Administration may obtain such data and information as may be requested by them for use in the performance of their official duties; and information may be released to any Federal agency that has authority supported by provisions of legal penalties to collect the same information itself. Statutory authority for the imposition of these restrictions is contained in the Emergency Price Control Act of 1942, title II, section 202(h) (56 Stat. 23); Federal Reports Act of 1942, section 4(b) (56 Stat. 1078); Second Deficiency Appropriation Act, 1945, title I, section providing for the Office of Price Administration (59 Stat. 412); and the Housing and Rent Act of 1949, title II, section 206(g)(63 Stat. 18).

Specified by: Congress of the United States.

RECORDS OF THE PUBLIC HOUSING ADMINISTRATION
(RECORD GROUP 196)

The Public Housing Administration was a successor to the U.S. Housing Authority (USHA), established in the Department of the Interior to administer the U.S. Housing Act of 1937. This act authorized a system of loans, grants, and subsidies to assist local housing authorities develop low-rent housing projects. In 1939 the USHA, which had assumed responsibility for the public housing projects of the Federal Emergency Administration of Public Works,

was transferred from the Department of the Interior to the Federal Works Agency (see RG 162). In 1942 USHA functions were consolidated with public housing functions of the Federal Works Agency and its subordinate units (the U.S. Housing Authority, the Public Buildings Administration, the Division of Defense Housing, and the Mutual Ownership Defense Housing Division), the War and Navy Departments, the Farm Security Administration, and the

Defense Homes Corporation into the Federal Public Housing Authority (FPHA) under the National Housing Agency. During World War II the FPHA chiefly provided housing for workers in war industries under such legislation as the Lanham Act. In 1947 the FPHA was succeeded by the Public Housing Administration (PHA) under the Housing and Home Finance Agency (see RG 207). The PHA resumed public housing functions authorized by the 1937 act, liquidated properties constructed under the Lanham Act, converted barracks into temporary housing for World War II veterans, and, during Korean hostilities, performed defense housing activities under the Defense Housing and Community Facilities and Services Act of 1951. The PHA lapsed when the functions, powers, and duties of the Housing and Home Finance Agency were transferred to the Department of Housing and Urban Development in 1965.

There are 257 cubic feet of records dated between 1895 and 1962 in this record group.

RECORDS OF PREDECESSOR AGENCIES. 1932-58. 227 lin. ft. and 783 rolls of microfilm.

These include records of the Housing Division of the Federal Emergency Administration of Public Works, consisting chiefly of loan applications under the limited dividend program, and correspondence, reports, surveys, and an analysis of the program and of housing conditions, 1932-34; records about the "Carl Mackley houses," an approved limited dividend housing project in the Philadelphia area, 1933-58; Federal program project files (in WNRC) of correspondence, reports, surveys, and related records documenting applications by cities for Federal aid, the construction of approved projects, and the transfer of completed projects to local housing authorities, 1933-42; and microfilmed

construction plans (106 rolls) for housing projects, 1933-37. Records of the Farm Security Administration include histories of projects in Greenbelt, Md., and Greendale, Wis., prepared in 1938; and microfilmed construction plans (24 rolls) of subsistence homestead and "greentown" programs, 1933-37. Records of the USHA consist of orders, bulletins, other issuances, and general records, 1937-42; microfilmed press clippings (4 rolls) relating to various housing programs, 1938-40; and microfilmed construction plans of housing projects under USHA programs, 1938-41 (254 rolls), and under the Lanham Act war housing program, 1940-45 (392 rolls).

RECORDS OF THE PUBLIC HOUSING ADMINISTRATION. 1938-62. 61 lin. ft.

Included are reports and correspondence maintained by the Commissioner, 1947-48; reports, surveys, and general records of the Division of Statistical Standards, 1942-49; and reports of the Statistics Division, 1945-47. Records of the Administrative Planning Division consist of general records and bulletins, circulars, directives, manuals, and other policy and procedural issuances, 1938-49; reports, memorandums, and issuances relating to organizational and operational procedures, 1942-47; monthly reports, 1943-47; memorandums and other records relating to 1947 and 1948 reorganizations, 1946-49; issuances of the National Housing Agency, including those of the Federal Public Housing Authority, 1942-47; forms, with amendments and revisions, 1938-47; site acquisition records and land plats for projects, 1941-55; project operating budgets, fiscal year 1957; and financial statements, fiscal years 1953-62.

There are also sample field records, consisting of housing managers' files on the administration of two projects in the war housing program, 1943-47; five sample case files from publicly funded projects under which housing units were converted into multiple-family dwellings, 1943-49; and sample case files of correspondence, reports, and plans relating to proposed constructions, finances, and equipment for project houses, 1942-46.

AUDIOVISUAL RECORDS.
1898-1946. 285 items.

Photographs, collected ca. 1937 (210 items), showing slum conditions in the United States and London, 1898-1903. Sound recordings (75 items) of "Slums Cost You Money," "Famous Homes of Famous Americans," "Agency Series," and other radio broadcasts, concerning defense housing and the need for low-cost housing, explaining the Federal housing program and the role of local government in its implementation, describing famous Americans' homes, and containing reports from several executive agencies, 1938-46.

DEPARTMENT OF TRANSPORTATION

RECORDS OF THE UNITED STATES COAST GUARD
(RECORD GROUP 26)

The U.S. Coast Guard, established in the Department of the Treasury by an act of January 28, 1915, was formed by consolidating the Department's Revenue-Cutter and Lifesaving Services. It took over lighthouse administration in 1939, and in 1942 functions of the Bureau of Marine Inspection and Navigation (see RG 41) relating to navigation and vessel inspection laws and to merchant seamen were transferred to the Coast Guard. On April 1, 1967, under an act of October 15, 1966, the Coast Guard became a part of the Department of Transportation. Under the same act, the functions of admeasuring and documenting American vessels were transferred from the Bureau of Customs to the Coast Guard.

The Coast Guard, which operates on the high seas and navigable waters of the United States and its territories and possessions, is a military service and operates as part of the Navy in time of war or when the President directs. In 1946 an International Air-Sea Rescue Service was established, and the Coast Guard was made responsible for international civil aviation over water. In 1948 it became responsible for operating LORAN and other warning stations. Its major duties include enforcing customs and navigation laws, supervising vessel anchorages and movements, reporting marine casualties, protecting life and property at sea, installing and maintaining aids to navigation and to transoceanic aviation, and carrying on oceanographic observations as part of an interagency program.

There are 10,290 cubic feet of records

dated between 1789 and 1963 in this record group.

RECORDS OF THE BUREAU OF LIGHTHOUSES AND ITS PREDECESSORS. 1789–1939.
3,642 lin. ft.

The maintenance of lighthouses was performed by Treasury Department officials from 1789 until the Light-House Board was organized in 1852. This Board, transferred to the Department of Commerce and Labor in 1903, was superseded in 1910 by the Bureau of Lighthouses, which remained in the Department of Commerce when the Department of Labor became a separate agency in 1913. It was consolidated with the Coast Guard in 1939. The records include correspondence, with indexes, of Board predecessors, including letters received, 1789–1852, and sent, 1792–1852, and general correspondence of the Board, 1852–1910, and the Bureau, 1910–39 (2,122 lin. ft.); and minutes and journals of the Board and the naval and engineer secretaries, 1852–1910. Other records, 1789–1939, comprise legal case files on the acquisition and disposition of sites; deeds and contracts for lighthouse construction, equipment, and supplies; drawings of lighthouses and lighthouse sites (including some lifesaving stations), 1840–1935; logbooks (in WNRC) of lighthouses, tenders, and light vessels, 1873–1939; title papers to vessels owned by the Board, 1853–95; appointment and salary registers and miscellaneous personnel records, 1833–1912; and accounting records, ca. 1852–1912.

Records, 1838-1939, of the 3d, 4th, 5th, 6th, 7th, 8th, 9th, 10th, 12th, and 17th Lighthouse Districts (460 lin. ft.) consist primarily of correspondence and wreck reports and often substitute for headquarters records destroyed by fire. The records of the 3d District, New York, 1852-1939, are the most complete. Also included are records of lighthouses in the Virgin Islands, 1910-17, and Puerto Rico, including some Spanish colonial government records, 1838-98.

RECORDS OF THE REVENUE-CUTTER SERVICE. 1790-1915, with a few dated as late as 1920. 606 lin. ft.

This Service originated under an act of August 4, 1790, authorizing the construction and equipment of cutters to enforce laws governing the collection of customs and tonnage duties. Customs collectors supervised the cutters from 1791 until 1843, when a Revenue Marine Division in the Office of the Secretary of the Treasury took over that function. In 1849 control of cutters was again transferred to the collectors, but in 1871 a new Revenue Marine Division was established. It became the Revenue-Cutter Service on July 31, 1894. Its functions include suppressing smuggling, the slave trade, and piracy; assisting ships in distress; removing and destroying wrecks and other navigation hazards; and enforcing quarantine regulations, neutrality laws, and laws forbidding the importation of unskilled Chinese labor. After 1867 it enforced regulations in Alaska concerning the unauthorized killing of fur-bearing animals, fishery protection, and traffic in firearms, ammunition, and liquor. It was authorized in 1914 to furnish medical and surgical aid to crewmembers of American deep-sea fishing vessels. It was also responsible for furnishing the vessels for the International Ice Patrol, established in 1914.

The records include correspondence, with registers and indexes, 1833-1910, but including copies of letters sent dated as early as 1790; muster rolls, 1833-1913; applications for positions, 1844-80; correspondence, 1880-1920, and specifications for vessels dating from 1845 of the Construction and Repair Division; records relating to Alaskan cruises and police work in Alaska, 1867-1914, including the rescue by the *Bear* of icebound whalers in 1897-98 and the *Nunivak's* ethnological and meteorological studies and collection of botanical and geological data in the Yukon River area in 1899; wreck reports, 1894-1913; reports of assistance rendered, 1903-14; and account books.

RECORDS OF THE LIFESAVING SERVICE. 1847-1915. 880 lin. ft.

This Service was established in 1871 in the Revenue-Marine Division of the Treasury Department. It was placed under a general superintendent immediately responsible to the Secretary of the Treasury by an act of June 18, 1878, but its relationship to the Revenue-Cutter Service remained close. In 1882 a Board of Life-Saving Appliances was established to examine, test, and report on all lifesaving equipment.

The records include correspondence concerning Service personnel, fiscal matters, procedures, programs, and sea disasters and rescues, 1847-1914; journals, 1881-1914; accounting records, wreck reports from lifesaving stations, and abstracts of wreck reports, 1878-85; records relating to awarding lifesaving medals; articles of engagement for surfmen, and miscellaneous personnel records, 1878-1915; and correspondence and reports of the Board of Life-Saving Appliances, 1888-1911.

U.S. COAST GUARD RECORDS. 1828-1947, with a few dated as early as 1790. 7,441 lin. ft. and 308 rolls of microfilm.

Included are reports, correspondence, and memorandums, 1910-41, of Coast

Guard headquarters, relating to administrative and legal matters, including site files for lifesaving and lifeboat stations and records about constructing, equipping, and repairing vessels and shore establishments; the Bering Sea and International Ice Patrols; seized vessels; marine disasters, prohibition, and operations; and personnel and communications.

Personnel records include registers for officers, 1790–1919; World War I cards for enlisted men (with surnames beginning A through H) and honorable discharges, 1917–37; muster rolls, 1833–1932; officer personnel files (in WNRC), 1890–1929; and records (in WNRC) of general, summary, and deck courts-martial, 1906–41.

Logbooks, 1828–1941, include logbooks, journals, and weekly transcripts of logbooks of named vessels in the Revenue-Cutter Service and the Coast Guard; Coast Guard logs (in WNRC) for vessels and shore units, 1942–47; and logs (in WNRC) for lifesaving and lifeboat stations, lighthouses, lightships, and miscellaneous shore units, 1873–1941.

Marine engineering records, 1924–40, include blueprints, tracings, and construction reports of vessels in the *Tampa* class and small boats constructed by the Work Projects Administration.

Included are microfilm copies of casualty and wreck reports submitted under an act of June 20, 1874, by masters, agents, or owners of U.S. vessels that sustained or caused accidents involving the loss of life, serious bodily injury, or loss of property, and related indexes, 1913–39 (28 rolls). There are also microfilm copies of indexes to and reports of assistance to individuals and vessels by Coast Guard units, which contain dates, names of stations or vessels concerned, and vessels, persons, or planes assisted, 1916–40 (280 rolls). Also reports, correspondence, and related records, 1922–41, of the Coast Guard Intelligence Division, relating to violations of customs and navigation laws, including the Volstead Act.

Case histories of individuals and vessels engaged in or suspected of smuggling rum, 1928–35, consist of reports of seizures and court actions, copies of log entries, newspaper clippings, and correspondence. Similar and related records are among the correspondence files, 1910–41, and among those of the Intelligence Division.

Records of the Bering Sea Patrol, 1926–40 (now the Alaska Patrol), consist of correspondence and communications between patrol units. Earlier records relating to the Patrol are among Revenue-Cutter Service records. Records of the Public Relations Division, the Coast Guard Information Service, and predecessor agencies, 1917–46, include narrative and statistical reports and monographs of Coast Guard operations in the two World Wars; war diaries, 1942–45; and miscellaneous reference material.

CARTOGRAPHIC AND AUDIOVISUAL RECORDS.
ca. 1855–1963. 41,277 items.

Cartographic records, 1915–41 (183 items), include annotated maps of the North Atlantic coastline of the United States that show harbor and coast facilities, 1915–41, including a few original blackout charts, 1940–41; a plan of the Navassa Island Lighthouse Station, 1916; and maps of air routes, 1929.

Audiovisual records consist of still pictures, 1812–1963 (41,000 items), including photographs of officers of the Revenue-Cutter Service and Coast Guard, 1860–1945, admirals and commandants, 1843–1960, ships and boats used by the Coast Guard, including the cutter *Bear* and officers, 1886–1963, and Maritime Service training stations, enrollees, and personnel. There are also photographs, plans, paintings, and drawings of lighthouses, lights, fog signals, lighthouse tenders, lightships, and light service personnel, 1852–1945; photographs relating to Coast Guard activities that depict flood relief work, training, port security duties, firefighting, lifesaving, radio equipment use and maintenance, icebreaking, weather observation, supervision of fishing and whaling industries, gunnery, aviation, and work of the Maritime Service and SPARS, 1886-1947; and activities in the War of 1812, Mexican War, Civil War, Spanish-American War, and the two World Wars. Included are photographs of captured rumrunners, 1923-35, and of Allied and neutral vessels and Japanese merchant vessels that entered San Francisco Bay, 1937-43.

Motion pictures, 1918-55 (84 reels), consist of films relating to the history of the Coast Guard that illustrate peacetime activities, such as making rescues at sea and in disaster areas, cooperating with the Fish and Wildlife Service in the whaling and fur seal industries, protecting and enforcing laws at waterfronts and harbors, enforcing ship safety regulations, patrolling beaches and offshore areas to guard against smuggling, performing icebreaking and lighthouse duties in the Great Lakes, conducting iceberg patrols, constructing and maintaining lighthouses and light buoys, assisting ships in U.S. coastal and other waters, taking weather observations, training at the Coast Guard Academy and other institutions, and participating in recreational activities; relating to Coast Guard domestic activities during World War II that included patrolling docks and harbors, inspecting ships, investigating ship sinkings, fighting fires, taking weather observations, and patrolling beaches; relating to such Coast Guard overseas activities during

World War II as amphibious operations in all theaters, transporting war materiel and troops, making rescues at sea, patrolling for submarines, and escorting convoys; and that show FBI agents with captured German spies, a yacht race, and U.S. political and military leaders.

There are sound recordings, 1937-39 (10 items), of radio broadcasts concerning Coast Guard administration and its role in training merchant seamen; its history, traditions, and activities; graduation exercises at the Coast Guard Academy; and award ceremonies for ham radio operators who maintained communications in disaster areas.

Microfilm Publications: Included are *Alaska File of the Revenue-Cutter Service, 1867-1914*, M641, 20 rolls, DP; *U.S. Coast Guard Reports of Assistance to Individuals and Vessels, 1916-40*, T720, 247 rolls; *Index by District to U.S. Coast Guard Reports of Assistance, 1917-1938*, T919, 19 rolls; *Index by Station to U.S. Coast Guard Reports of Assistance, 1924-1938*, T920, 9 rolls; *Index by Floating Unit to U.S. Coast Guard Reports of Assistance, 1917-1935*, T921, 5 rolls; *U.S. Coast Guard Casualty and Wreck Reports, 1913-1939*, T925, 21 rolls; and *Index to U.S. Coast Guard Casualty and Wreck Reports, 1913-1939*, T926, 7 rolls.

SPECIFIC RESTRICTIONS

Records: Case histories of individuals and vessels engaged in or suspected of smuggling rum, 1928-35.

Restrictions: Until these records are 50 years old no one may examine them or obtain information from them except with the permission of the Chief, Public Information Division, U.S. Coast Guard.

Specified by: Commandant of the U.S. Coast Guard.

RECORDS OF THE BUREAU OF PUBLIC ROADS
(RECORD GROUP 30)

The Bureau of Public Roads had its origin in the Office of Road Inquiry, created by the Secretary of Agriculture on October 3, 1893, under authority of an act of March 3, 1893. Within the Department of Agriculture it was known successively as the Office of Public Roads Inquiries, 1899-1905, Office of Public Roads, 1905-15, Office of Public Roads and Rural Engineering, 1915-18, and Bureau of Public Roads, 1918-39. By the President's Reorganization Plan No. I of 1939, it became part of the new Federal Works Agency and was renamed the Public Roads Administration. On July 1, 1949, it was transferred to the General Services Administration and its name changed back to Bureau of Public Roads, and on August 20, 1949, it was transferred to the Department of Commerce by Reorganization Plan No. 7 of 1949. An act of October 15, 1966, transferred the Bureau to the Department of Transportation.

Until 1912 the functions of the Bureau were limited to collecting and disseminating information on roadbuilding and management. The Post Office Appropriation Act for fiscal year 1913, however, allotted $500,000 for the improvement of post roads, "to be expended by the Secretary of Agriculture in cooperation with the Postmaster General." The Federal Aid Road Act of 1916 began a large-scale program of Federal-State cooperation in road construction, reconstruction, and improvement under the supervision of the Bureau. Subsequent acts provided for participation in the construction of the Inter-American Highway, the Alcan Highway, and the Interstate Highway System. The administration of the Federal-aid highway program remains the major function of the Bureau. It also administers the highway beautification program and the highway construction phase of the Appalachian regional development program. It is responsible for developing and administering a highway safety program, constructing defense highways and roads in national parks and forests, conducting research in transportation and highway design, providing assistance to foreign governments, and participating with other Government agencies in special projects.

For records of the Division of Agricultural Engineering, which until 1931 was part of the Bureau of Public Roads, see Records of the Bureau of Agricultural Engineering, Record Group 8.

There are 2,483 cubic feet of records dated between 1892 and 1970 in this record group.

RECORDS. 1892-1967. 2,959 lin. ft. (in WNRC).

These consist primarily of correspondence and other records, 1893-1952, with related indexes to 1955. There are also files of Capt. P. St. J. Wilson, Chief Engineer, 1916-34; certificates appointing private citizens as volunteer "public roads correspondents" to help the Bureau investigate and collect information, 1905-9, with related correspondence; other certificates of appointment, 1905-11; reports of highway studies, 1910-52; correspondence and other records of the War Department's Highway Traffic Advisory Committee, 1941-45; and letters sent by the National League for Good Roads, a private group organized by Gen. Roy Stone, who in 1893 became the first head of the Office of Road Inquiry, 1892-93.

CARTOGRAPHIC AND AUDIOVISUAL RECORDS. 1900-1970. ca. 97,850 items.

These consist of published and annotated highway and traffic maps (ca. 3,200 items) compiled and maintained by the Bureau's central office and related to the federally aided system of interstate and defense highways and to the Inter-American Highway, 1920-65; published county and State roadmaps (ca. 54,000 items) prepared by State highway departments following the Bureau's standard specifications, 1920-70; and photographs (40,650 items) illustrating the evolution of transportation since 312

B.C., highways and methods of transportation, the Mount Vernon Memorial Highway, and results of the 1906 San Francisco earthquake, 1900-1963.

See Truman R. Strobridge, comp., *Preliminary Inventory of the Records of the Bureau of Public Roads*, PI 134 (1962).

RECORDS OF THE FEDERAL AVIATION ADMINISTRATION (RECORD GROUP 237)

The Civil Aeronautics Act of June 23, 1938, established an independent Civil Aeronautics Authority "to promote the development and safety and to provide for the regulation of civil aeronautics." It also provided for the transfer to the Authority of the functions of the Bureau of Air Commerce, which had been established in 1926 as the Aeronautics Branch of the Department of Commerce, and of the Bureau of Air Mail of the Interstate Commerce Commission. By Reorganization Plans Nos. III and IV of 1940 the Authority was divided into the Civil Aeronautics Board and the Civil Aeronautics Administration (CAA), which were placed in the Department of Commerce. The CAA enforced most civil air regulations, aided the development of a national airport system and of aviation education, promoted air commerce abroad, coordinated civil aviation defense and war production requirements, and planned, constructed, and operated the Federal Airways System. The Federal Aviation Act of 1958 created the Federal Aviation Agency and transferred to it the functions of the CAA, the Airways Modernization Board (established by an act of August 14, 1957), and the safety regulatory authority of the Civil Aeronautics Board. Under the Department of Transportation Act of October 15, 1966, the Federal Aviation Agency became the Federal Aviation Administration, a component of the Department of Transportation.

There are 569 cubic feet of records dated between 1926 and 1957 in this record group.

RECORDS. 1926–57. 590 lin. ft.

Included are a general file of the CAA and its predecessors, 1926–43, consisting of policy, fiscal, and administrative records, reports, correspondence, and material relating to developing civil aeronautics, air commerce, and Federal airways; establishing civil airways, landing areas and other facilities, and navigational aids; and controlling and protecting commercial air traffic. Also a reference file relating to aspects of airport construction, such as soil problems, construction material, equipment, lighting systems, navigational facilities, and installation specifications, 1935–47; project files, including correspondence, reports, specifications, blueprints, charts, and related material concerning planning, designing, and constructing airports and airport facilities, civil landing areas, and landing areas for national defense programs, 1941–47; and files of Col. Sumpter Smith, a member of an interdepartmental engineering committee, relating to the establishment, planning, and construction of the Washington National Airport, 1936–40. A "Memorandum of Understanding," ca. 1949, between the CAA and the Army, and one, 1954, between the CAA and the Navy, regarding Army and Navy navigational facilities and radar in the continental United States.

CARTOGRAPHIC AND AUDIOVISUAL RECORDS. 1926–57. 2,565 items.

Cartographic records (162 items) include maps of commercial, military, airmail, and other U.S. air routes, prepared by the Aeronautics Branch of the Department of Commerce, 1926-36; airway maps of the United States, prepared by the Bureau of Air Commerce, showing scheduled airlines, aeronautical communication stations, and plans for airfield and beacon sites, 1934-38; field notebooks prepared by the Civil Aeronautics Authority, relating to surveys of an alternate airport at Washington, D.C., and of Alvin Field, Colo., 1939-40; plans and profiles, prepared by the Authority, of U.S. airfields, 1939; and a radio facilities planning chart published by the CAA, 1941.

Audiovisual records (2,403 items) consist of motion pictures (3 reels) illustrating CAA functions and activities, 1957, and portrait photographs (2,400 items) of CAA War Training Service air cadets, 1942-44.

RECORDS OF INDEPENDENT AGENCIES

RECORDS OF THE AMERICAN BATTLE MONUMENTS COMMISSION (RECORD GROUP 117)

The American Battle Monuments Commission, created by an act of March 4, 1923, erects and maintains memorials at suitable sites (except in national cemeteries) commemorating the services of American Armed Forces since April 6, 1917; designs, constructs, administers, and maintains permanent American military cemeteries located outside the United States and its possessions; maintains at overseas cemeteries rosters of men recorded as missing and of burials; and provides regulations for the erection of American war memorials by other sponsors.

In 1939 the Commission issued *American Armies and Battlefields in Europe*, a revision of *A Guide to the American Battlefields in Europe* (1927). The Commission also published in 1944 a series of 28 volumes titled *Summary of Operations in the World War*.

There are 79 cubic feet of records dated between 1922 and 1961, with some as early as 1850, in this record group.

RECORDS. 1922–61. 56 lin. ft. (in WNRC).

These include correspondence with former division officers of the American Expeditionary Forces in France, relating to operations on the Western Front, 1923–30, with a name index; drafts of "Summaries of Operations" and background papers, 1922–31; records relating to the revision of "Summaries of Operations," 1931–39; proofs of division front-line maps compiled for publication with the *Summary of Operations in the World War*, 1937; correspondence of Secretary of the Commission Maj. Xenophon H. Price, 1926–33; and records relating to the rights of occupation by the U.S. Government of military cemeteries in Belgium, France, Great Britain, and Mexico City, 1850–1961.

CARTOGRAPHIC AND AUDIOVISUAL RECORDS. 1923–44. 2,038 items.

Maps (456 items) summarizing the European operations of the American Expeditionary Forces during World War I, 1923–44; and maps and ground plans (64 items) of U.S. military cemeteries in Europe, 1937–39.

Photographs and sketches (1,489 items) of memorials and monuments erected in Europe to honor U.S. Armed Forces that served in World War I, prepared by or submitted to the Commission, 1923–38; and terrain photographs of European battlefields on which 29 U.S. divisions served, with key maps and annotations to identify the terrain, 1923–25. A motion picture (8 reels), 1937, "America Honors Her War Dead," show-ing parts of dedications of American war memorials and chapels in Europe. Sound recordings (21 items) of the dedication ceremony of the Meuse-Argonne War Memorial at Montfaucon, France, 1937.

RECORDS OF THE CIVIL AERONAUTICS BOARD
(RECORD GROUP 197)

The Civil Aeronautics Board (CAB), an independent agency established under Reorganization Plans Nos. III and IV of 1940, functioned under the Civil Aeronautics Act of 1938, as amended. It succeeded to certain functions of the Civil Aeronautics Authority, established under the act, and its predecessors, the Bureau of Air Commerce of the Department of Commerce and the Bureau of Air Mail of the Interstate Commerce Commission. The CAB was given responsibility for regulating economic aspects of air carrier operations, promulgating safety standards, investigating accidents, and promoting international air transportation. The Federal Aviation Act of 1958 continued the Board, but the Administrator of the Federal Aviation Agency assumed CAB functions related to safety rulemaking. The Department of Transportation Act of 1966 transferred to the National Transportation Safety Board CAB functions related to civil aircraft accident investigations and safety enforcement. The CAB authorizes domestic air carriers to engage in interstate and foreign transportation and regulates the operations of foreign air carriers in the United States. It has jurisdiction over subsidies paid air carriers and over tariffs, rates, and fares charged for air transportation and for carrying the mail. The Board, which regulates the accounting procedures of air carriers and their financial and business relationships, requires the carriers to file regular financial and operating reports and makes that data available to other Government agencies and the public. It also advises the Department of State in negotiating agreements with foreign governments for the development of international civil aviation.

There are 197 cubic feet of records dated between 1934 and 1962 in this record group.

RECORDS. 1934–62. 236 lin. ft.

These consist of records of the CAB and its predecessors, including minutes (in WNRC) of the Civil Aeronautics Authority, 1938–40, and the CAB, 1940–62; transcripts of testimony, reports, and correspondence of the Bureau of Air Commerce, relating to investigation of the *Hindenburg* disaster, 1937–38; and a case file relating to the investigation of the 1935 aircraft accident in which Will Rogers and Wiley Post were killed.

Records of the Federal Aviation Commission, a temporary body appointed by the President in 1934 to study aviation conditions and make policy recommendations to the Congress, consist of minutes, transcripts of testimony and related exhibits, and correspondence regarding proposed- legislation, reports on the Commission's work and recommendations, and fiscal and operations records relating to airlines, 1934–35.

SPECIFIC RESTRICTIONS

Records: Minutes of the Civil Aeronautics Board and its predecessor agency, the Civil Aeronautics Authority (dating from 1938).

Restrictions: No one may examine these records or be given information from them or copies of them except by permission of the Civil Aeronautics Board or its Secretary.

Specified by: Civil Aeronautics Board.

RECORDS OF THE COMMISSION OF FINE ARTS
(RECORD GROUP 66)

The Commission of Fine Arts was established as an independent agency by an act of May 17, 1910. It is composed of "seven well-qualified judges of the fine arts" appointed by the President, who serve 4-year terms or until their successors are appointed. The Commission's duties include advising, at the request of the President or any congressional committee, on all matters of art with which the Federal Government is concerned. Specifically it advises on the location of statues, fountains, and monuments in the District of Columbia; the plans and designs for public structures and parks in the District; the selection of artists and models for statues, fountains, and monuments erected by the United States; and the design and execution of medals, insignia, and coins. In accordance with congressional acts of 1930 and 1950, the Commission advises on the height, color, design, and exterior appearance of private buildings in specified areas of the District and reviews permits for the construction, alteration, reconstruction, or razing of any buildings in "Old Georgetown." Since March 2, 1944, expenditures for the Commission have been administered by the Department of the Interior.

Records relating to the location of monuments, statues, and memorials in the District before 1910 are chiefly among records of the Office of Public Buildings and Grounds (see RG 42).

There are 198 cubic feet of records dated between 1901 and 1960 in this record group.

RECORDS OF THE COMMISSION. 1910-52. 183 lin. ft.

Included are reports, memorandums, and other records relating to the Commission's financial obligations, art projects, and other activities; correspondence concerning Commission meetings, 1910-40; general correspondence of the Commission, 1910-42; correspondence of the Secretary, 1910-21 and 1928-40, and the Executive Officer, 1910-40, with members of the Commission, and relating to general administration, 1920-22 and 1927-40; project files consisting of correspondence, drawings, plans, sketches, and other records, 1910-52; and case files consisting of brief formal statements and related sketches or blueprints made under the Shipstead-Luce Act, 1930-52.

The completed project files contain information on hundreds of projects, such as the Argonne Cemetery, an Arkansas Centennial Coin, the Arlington Memorial Bridge, the Lincoln Memorial, the House Office Annex, Union Station Plaza, and the Ferdinand de Lesseps Monument. A list of these projects has been compiled and is available as an appendix to Preliminary Inventory 79.

CARTOGRAPHIC AND
AUDIOVISUAL RECORDS. 1901-60.
10,139 items.

There are two maps of Washington,
D.C., showing the development of the
central area west of the Capitol, 1941,
and land improvements, 1920-28.

Audiovisual records, 1901-60 (10,137
items), include photographs of plans and
completed projects of the Commission;
photographs of landscaping, art, architecture, and sculpture in the United
States and in foreign capitals; and aerial
photographs of Washington, D.C. There
are photographs of drawings and paintings of memorials; American flag displays; Army insignia; designs for medals
and coins; personalities; colonial
America; early Washington, D.C., including St. John's Church and the White
House in 1816, the White House green-
houses, and city plans; and the World's
Columbian Exposition, 1776-1950. There
are also architects' sketches of the Pentagon and the Chicago Century of Progress Building, and panoramas of the Panama Canal construction, ca. 1915.

See Richard S. Maxwell, comp., *Preliminary
Inventory of the Records of the Commission of
Fine Arts*, PI 79 (1955).

RECORDS OF THE
EXPORT-IMPORT BANK OF THE UNITED STATES
(RECORD GROUP 275)

The Export-Import Bank of the
United States originated as the Export-
Import Bank of Washington, which was
organized as a District of Columbia
banking corporation in accordance with
Executive Order 6581 of February 2,
1934. Reorganization Plan No. I of 1939
grouped the Bank with other agencies
to form the Federal Loan Agency. The
Bank was transferred to the Department of Commerce on February 24,
1942; the Office of Economic Warfare
on July 15, 1943; and the Foreign Economic Administration on September 25,
1943. It was made an independent agency by the Export-Import Bank Act of
1945, which was amended in 1947 to rein-
corporate the Bank under Federal charter. By an act of March 13, 1968, its
name was changed to the Export-Import
Bank of the United States, the capital
stock of which is held by the U.S. Government.

The purpose of the Bank is to help
finance and facilitate exports and
imports between the United States and
foreign countries or their agencies or
nationals. One of its major programs is
to finance exports for developmental
projects and programs. The Bank supplements private capital by making loans
and by extending other credits that private lending institutions cannot grant
without Government assistance.

There are 5 cubic feet of records dated
between 1934 and 1951 in this record
group.

RECORDS. 1934-51. 6 lin. ft.

Case files relating to credit granted
to foreign nations and domestic or foreign private firms to aid the foreign
trade of the United States, containing
applications for credit, synopses of
actions taken, agreements, memorandums and other supporting records, and
related correspondence.

SPECIFIC RESTRICTIONS

Records: Case files relating to credit
granted to foreign nations and domes-

tic or foreign firms to aid the foreign trade of the United States, 1934-51.

Restrictions: No one may examine these records or be given information from them or copies of them except by permission of the Administrative Officer

of the Export-Import Bank of the United States.

Specified by: Administrative Officer, Export-Import Bank of the United States.

RECORDS OF THE FARM CREDIT ADMINISTRATION (RECORD GROUP 103)

The Farm Credit Administration (FCA) was created March 27, 1933, as an independent agency to consolidate the functions of all Federal agencies concerned primarily with agricultural credit. The FCA assumed functions of the Federal Farm Loan Bureau, directed by the Federal Farm Loan Board; the Federal Farm Board; the Crop Production and Seed Loan Offices of the Department of Agriculture; and regional agricultural credit corporations. Under provisions of the Farm Credit Act of June 16, 1933, the FCA established production credit corporations and associations providing credit for farm and ranch operations and created banks for cooperatives as a permanent source of credit for farmers' cooperative associations. An act of January 31, 1934, made the FCA responsible for the management of the Federal Farm Mortgage Corporation, and from 1934 to 1942 it also supervised Federal credit unions. On July 1, 1939, the FCA was placed under the Department of Agriculture, but on December 4, 1953, with the exception of its Cooperative Research and Service Division (renamed Farm Cooperative Service), it again became an independent agency.

There are 851 cubic feet of records dated between 1913 and 1961 in this record group.

RECORDS OF THE FARM CREDIT ADMINISTRATION. 1913-61.
838 lin. ft. and 38 rolls of microfilm.

These records (with some from FCA predecessor units) include Administrative Division reports on the organization and operation of the FCA, 1934-49, records on the organization and operation of Federal land banks, 1934-47, and reports on the organization and operation of miscellaneous field offices, 1935-57; Finance and Research Division records concerning budget programs of credit institutions, 1946-52; Examination Division reports and related records concerning financial and administrative operations of credit institutions under supervision of the FCA and its predecessor, the Federal Farm Loan Board, 1917-42; Land Bank Division correspondence regarding Federal land banks, 1916-39, monthly reports of Federal land banks, 1933-38, selected loan case files, 1933-44, National Farm Loan Association records, 1917-57, records of liquidated National Farm Loan Associations, 1918-41, and reappraisal reports concerning value of farmland and buildings on which defaulted loans were held, 1917-39; Intermediate Credit Division records, 1923-39; Production Credit Division records concerning production credit corporations and associations, 1933-39, and selected loan case files,

1934-43; Cooperative Division minutes of the Decision Committee, and a microfilm (38 rolls) of farmer marketing and purchasing cooperatives, compiled between 1913 and 1942, containing tabulated information for the period 1862-1942; Regional Agricultural Credit Division periodic and special reports relating to agricultural credit corporations, 1934-38 and 1943-44, and Regional Agricultural Credit Corporation of Sioux City selected loan case files, 1932-35; and Federal Farm Mortgage Corporation minutes, 1934-61, and correspondence, 1933-42.

RECORDS RELATING TO JOINT STOCK LAND BANKS. 1918-37. 7 lin. ft.

Joint stock land banks were privately capitalized stock institutions offering farmers long-term first mortgage amortized loans. The Federal Farm Loan Board supervised financial and administrative operation of the banks through inspectors, who examined accounts, and appraisers, who examined securities offered for loans. The records consist chiefly of minutes of meetings of stockholders and bank officials, and correspondence and other records relating to banks, including the Bankers Joint Stock Land Bank, Milwaukee, 1918-37, and the Ohio Joint Stock Land Bank, Cincinnati, 1922-32.

RECORDS OF THE FEDERAL FARM LOAN BOARD. 1916-33. 139 lin. ft.

These consist primarily of minutes, 1927-33, records of hearings held with local officials, 1916, Board correspondence, 1916-26, and correspondence relating to the location of Federal land banks and concerning the appointment of bank directors, 1916-17.

RECORDS OF THE FEDERAL FARM BOARD. 1928-33. 19 lin. ft.

These include minutes, correspondence, memorandums, statistical studies, survey reports, and other documents relating to the administration and operation of the Federal Farm Board, 1929-33; and correspondence (in FRC Seattle) of the Portland, Oreg., regional office, 1928-32, and of its western representatives, 1929-32.

RECORDS OF THE GRAIN STABILIZATION CORPORATION. 1930-34. 58 lin. ft.

These consist of general correspondence, 1930-33; the Corporation president's correspondence concerning exports to Brazil, 1931-32; the treasurer's general records, Collateral and Finance Department correspondence and related records, and Accounting and Stock Record Department records, 1930-33; Futures Department memorandums on operation and procedures, 1930-31; Insurance Department correspondence and reports, 1933; Export, Purchase, and Sales Department records, and Brazil Coffee-Wheat Department correspondence and report, 1931-33; New York Coffee Office correspondence, 1931-34; correspondence and accounting records of the Drought Relief Department of the Farmers National Grain Corporation, 1930-31; and records of branch offices of the Pacific Coast Division, 1930-32 (in FRC Seattle), and of Branch offices in Duluth, 1930-31, Buffalo, 1931-33, and Minneapolis, 1930-33. There are also some records relating to the liquidation of the Grain Stabilization Corporation, 1932-34.

RECORDS OF THE COTTON STABILIZATION CORPORATION. 1930-35. 11 lin. ft.

These include incorporation records, 1930-31, general correspondence, 1930-33, correspondence with the Red Cross, 1932, and financial reports, 1931-35.

CARTOGRAPHIC AND AUDIOVISUAL RECORDS. 1931-42. 69 items.

Cartographic records, 1931-42 (63 items), include published maps of the 12 FCA districts, showing counties and crop reporting districts; Office of the Land Bank Commissioner maps of drainage districts in Clay and Green Counties, Ark., and the Grand Prairie rice region; and Division of Finance and Research maps showing county and township boundaries and values of farmlands and buildings in certain States.

Audiovisual records, 1936-37, include motion pictures (4 reels) promoting cooperative marketing of wool, President Franklin D. Roosevelt at his desk in the White House, the FCA building and several other buildings in Washington, D.C.; and sound recordings (2 items) of 15-minute radio programs entitled "Homes on the Land."

RECORDS OF THE FEDERAL COMMUNICATIONS COMMISSION (RECORD GROUP 173)

The Federal Communications Commission (FCC) was established by the Communications Act of June 19, 1934, to regulate radio broadcasting and interstate and foreign communications by radio and wire. Under the creating act the FCC succeeded the Federal Radio Commission, established in 1927, and also acquired functions of the Postmaster General in fixing rates for Government use of wire facilities and certain regulatory functions of the Interstate Commerce Commission. The Federal Radio Commission in 1932 had been given the functions of the Radio Division of the Department of Commerce, originating in an act of 1910 requiring radio installations on certain merchant ships. At present the FCC supervises the charges and operating practices of common carriers engaged in interstate or foreign communications, issues broadcasting licenses, assigns broadcast frequencies, classifies radio and television stations and prescribes the nature of their services, and enforces radio requirements for some classes of vessels. The FCC is authorized to conduct investigations, has additional regulatory jurisdiction under provisions of the Communications Satellite Act of 1962, and is represented on the Interdepartment Radio Advisory Committee.

There are 3,666 cubic feet of records dated between 1910 and 1964 in this record group.

RECORDS OF FCC PREDECESSORS. 1910-62. 265 lin. ft.

These consist of records of the Radio Division of the Department of Commerce and the Federal Radio Commission, comprising correspondence files on early radio regulation, with indexes, 1910-34, and correspondence relating to applications for broadcast station licenses, 1928-32. Records of the Interstate Commerce Commission consist of regulations, 1912-32; "formal docketed," 1912-62, "finance," 1921-34, and "valuation," 1918-27, case files; and records relating to valuation procedures, comprising minutes, corporate history statements, transcripts of hearings, reports of property appraisals and unit labor costs, forms, working papers, inventories, and other records relating chiefly to the Western Union Telegraph Co. and the McKay Companies Land Line System (Postal Telegraph System), 1914–34, with copies of documents dated as early as 1888.

RECORDS OF THE OFFICE OF THE SECRETARY. 1927–64. 2,521 lin. ft.

Included are minutes (in WNRC) of the Federal Radio Commission, 1927–34, and the FCC, 1934–64; docketed case files (in WNRC) of the Federal Radio Commission and the FCC, 1927–63; histories of FCC activities during the Korean war period, 1952; records of a 1936 special investigation of companies engaged in interstate telephone communications conducted under a joint resolution of the Congress; and exhibits presented by the National Association of Broadcasters in a hearing on the Communications Act of 1934.

RECORDS OF THE OFFICE OF THE CHIEF ACCOUNTANT. 1934–49. 6 lin. ft. (in WNRC).

This Office acquired the fiscal records of predecessor agencies, relating to wire and wireless communications. It was abolished October 31, 1955, and accounting functions were integrated into the operating bureaus. The Office's Accounting Systems Division was assigned to the Common Carriers Bureau, and its Economics Division was placed under the Broadcast Bureau. The records consist of completed questionnaires (statistical circulars) from communications common carriers that relate to company histories, corporate relationships, fiscal matters, and operations.

RECORDS OF THE COMMON CARRIERS BUREAU. 1914–60. 355 lin. ft.

These consist of annual financial reports (in WNRC) by communications common carriers to the Accounting Systems Division. Also correspondence and other records relating to the administration, finances, and operations of broadcasting stations and networks, 1939–50.

RECORDS OF THE BROADCAST BUREAU. 1937–61. 142 lin. ft. (in WNRC).

Included are financial reports of broadcasting stations collected by the Economics Division. (In 1961 the Economics Division was terminated, and the collecting of these reports was assigned to the Research and Education Division.)

RECORDS OF THE RADIO INTELLIGENCE DIVISION. 1940–47. 30 lin. ft.

This Division was established in 1940 to investigate and monitor clandestine wireless operations in the United States and its possessions and to train military personnel and intelligence agents in monitoring techniques. It was discontinued in 1946. The records comprise a subject-classified general file, 1942–45; reports, correspondence, and other records relating to congressional investigations of the FCC and the attack on Pearl Harbor and to the security classification of records, 1942–46; files of George E. Sterling, Chief of the Division, 1940–47; and records relating to clandestine stations, intercepted radio transmissions, and cooperation with British and Canadian security organizations, 1940–45.

RECORDS OF THE INTERDEPARTMENT RADIO ADVISORY COMMITTEE. 1922–52. 88 lin. ft.

This committee was established in 1922 as an independent agency to assign radio frequencies to Government radio stations. It also implements international telecommunications treaties. During World War II the Committee was attached to the Board of War Communications (originally the Defense Communications Board), but was reassigned independent status after the Board was terminated in 1947. These records comprise minutes of the subcommittees, 1922-52; reports, drafts of Executive orders, and supplements relating to assignments of radio frequencies, 1923-49; and reports, correspondence, and other records relating to the Committee's policies, operations, and history, 1922-49.

CARTOGRAPHIC AND AUDIOVISUAL RECORDS. 1934-45. 312 items.

Cartographic records (7 items) consist of maps of Cuba and the United States, showing radio facilities, 1937-42, and annotated Hydrographic Office tracking and outline charts relating to activities of the Radio Intelligence Division, 1942-43.

Audiovisual records consist of sound recordings, 1934-45 (305 items), of cases heard and decided by the FCC (concerning petitions, complaints, or FCC motions) chiefly involving telephone, telegraph, cable, and radio broadcasting companies and concerning such matters as rates, facilities, the quality of services, corporate organizations, assignments of radio frequencies, and ownership transfers.

See Albert W. Winthrop, comp., *Preliminary Inventory of the Records of the Federal Communications Commission,* PI 93 (1956).

SPECIFIC RESTRICTIONS

I. *Records*: Microfilm copies of the formal official minutes of the FCC bearing security or other classification mark.

Restrictions: No one may examine these records or be given information from them or copies of them except by permission of the FCC.

Specified by: Federal Communications Commission.

II. *Records*: Annual financial reports filed by licensees and permittees of standard, FM, television, and international broadcast stations with the FCC in accordance with section 0.417 of the FCC Rules and Regulations.

Restrictions: These records are not open to public inspection unless special permission is granted by the FCC upon written request describing in detail the documents to be inspected and the reasons therefor.

Specified by: Federal Communications Commission.

III. *Records*: Records of the Interdepartment Radio Advisory Committee, 1922-49.

Restrictions: No one may examine these records or be given information from them or copies of them except by permission of the Interdepartment Radio Advisory Committee.

Specified by: Interdepartment Radio Advisory Committee.

RECORDS OF THE FEDERAL DEPOSIT INSURANCE CORPORATION (RECORD GROUP 34)

The Federal Deposit Insurance Corporation (FDIC) was created by the Federal Reserve Act of June 16, 1933, primarily to insure deposits of all banks entitled to insurance under the law. FDIC major functions are to pay depositors of insured banks that have been closed without adequate provision having been made for such payments; to act as receiver for national banks placed in receivership and, when appointed by Staff authorities, for State banks placed in receivership; and to prevent unsound banking practices. The FDIC is authorized to make loans to or purchase assets of an insured bank to facilitate a merger or prevent it from closing, to reopen a closed bank when its continued operation is essential to the economy of the community, to pass on mergers between insured and noninsured banks, and to examine insured banks to determine their condition for insurance purposes. The FDIC is managed by a three-member Board of Directors. The President appoints two members, one of whom is elected chairman, for 6-year terms. The Comptroller of the Currency serves ex officio as the third member. No more than two members may belong to the same political party.

There are 98 cubic feet of records (in WNRC) dated between 1933 and 1935 in this record group.

RECORDS. 1933-35. 118 lin. ft.

Included are assessment remittance letters, certified and amended statements, assessment and amended assessment adjustments, schedules of remittance, and trial balance tapes.

RECORDS OF THE FEDERAL HOME LOAN BANK SYSTEM (RECORD GROUP 195)

The Federal Home Loan Bank Board (FHLBB) was established by an act of July 22, 1932, to provide credit reserves for savings and home financing institutions. The FHLBB governs the Federal Home Loan Bank System, which consists of 12 regional Federal Home Loan banks and other member institutions; supervises the operations of the Federal Savings and Loan System established under provisions of the Home Owners Loan Act of 1933 (as amended); and serves as the Board of Trustees for the Federal Savings and Loan Insurance Corporation, established by the National Housing Act of 1934 to insure accounts in thrift and home financing institutions in the System. In 1939 the FHLBB and its subsidiaries became part of the Federal Loan Agency. They were placed under the National Housing Agency in 1942, and under the Agency's successor, the Housing and Home Finance Agency (see RG 207), in 1947. The FHLBB again became independent in 1955. Some administrative functions of the Board were transferred to its Chairman by Reorganization Plan No. 6 of 1961.

There are 173 cubic feet of records dated between 1933 and 1947 in this record group.

RECORDS OF THE FEDERAL HOME LOAN BANK BOARD.
1933-47. 10 lin. ft.

These consist of minutes, correspondence, and reports relating to the Board's representation on the Central Housing Committee, 1935-39; correspondence on financing local banks, 1933-35; a few reports of the chief accountant and comptroller, 1933-47; and reports of local economic and financial conditions made by member banks, 1942-45.

RECORDS OF THE HOME OWNERS' LOAN CORPORATION
(HOLC). 1933-45. 180 lin. ft. and 482 rolls of microfilm.

The HOLC was established in 1933 to grant long term mortgage loans at low interest rates to homeowners unable to procure financing through normal channels. The FHLBB served as its Board of Directors until the HOLC was dissolved in 1954. The records include congressional correspondence concerning policies and procedures, 1934–45; microfilm (482 rolls) of general administrative correspondence, chiefly with regional and local offices, 1933–36; sample general loan correspondence of central and field offices filed under the letter "C," 1933–36; "HOLC city survey file" of reports, maps, questionnaires, transcripts of interviews, and working papers from a survey made to determine current and future values of real estate, 1935–40; and property management files, 1941–44.

CARTOGRAPHIC RECORDS. 1933–41. 14 items.

Maps of selected U.S. cities, annotated to show business, industrial, and residential districts, 1933–39; and a map showing areas allocated defense housing funds, 1941.

SPECIFIC RESTRICTIONS

Records: Records showing the sources for the information, including questionnaires, memorandums, notes, and other work materials in the "HOLC city survey file," 1935–40, which relates to a survey and a partial resurvey of cities of more than 40,000 population to determine current and future values of real estate.

Restrictions: These records may not be examined by or copies of or information from them furnished to any person except by permission of the Federal Home Loan Bank Board.

Specified by: Federal Home Loan Bank Board.

RECORDS OF THE FEDERAL MARITIME COMMISSION (RECORD GROUP 358)

The Federal Maritime Commission was established as an independent agency by Reorganization Plan No. 7, effective August 12, 1961. The Commission regulates services (including rates and classifications), practices, and agreements of common carriers by water engaged in the foreign and domestic offshore commerce of the United States, terminal operators, freight forwarders, and other persons subject to shipping statutes. It investigates discriminatory practices in such commerce and accepts or rejects tariff filings of common carriers engaged in foreign trade.

The reorganization plan that established the Commission also abolished the Federal Maritime Board and transferred its regulatory functions to the Commission and its subsidiary functions to the Secretary of Commerce (see RG 357). The Board had been created in the Department of Commerce in 1950 as one of the successor agencies of the U.S. Maritime Commission (see RG 178).

There are 6 cubic feet of records dated between 1950 and 1957 in this record group.

RECORDS. 1950–57. 7 lin. ft.

These consist of the original signed minutes, with indexes, of the Federal Maritime Board, 1950–57, which name the members present, outline the agenda, and summarize discussions and actions taken; and copies of memorandums presented for discussion and of orders, regulations, decisions, and other formally adopted issuances.

SPECIFIC RESTRICTIONS
Records: Original signed minutes, including indexes, of the Federal Maritime Board, 1950-57.

Restrictions: No one may examine these records or be given information from them or copies of them except by permission of the Office of the Secretary, Federal Maritime Commission.
Specified by: Federal Maritime Commission.

RECORDS OF THE FEDERAL MEDIATION AND CONCILIATION SERVICE
(RECORD GROUP 280)

The Federal Mediation and Conciliation Service (FMCS), created by the Labor Management Relations Act of 1947, assumed the functions that had been performed by the U.S. Conciliation Service. This Service had developed in the Department of Labor under provisions of the act of March 4, 1913, creating the Department and authorizing the Secretary of Labor to act as a mediator or to appoint commissioners of conciliation in labor disputes. The FMCS has no enforcement authority. Its mediators assist representatives of labor and management in settling disputes. The National Labor-Management Panel, which equally represents management and labor, advises the Director of the Service.

There are 1,297 cubic feet of records dated between 1913 and 1965 in this record group.

RECORDS OF THE U.S.
CONCILIATION SERVICE. 1913-48.
1,403 lin. ft.

Included are correspondence, 1913-48; dispute, 1913-48, arbitration, 1937-48, and technical, 1938-48, case files (in WNRC); technical case reports, 1940-47 (in WNRC); administrative files of the Technical Division, 1937-48; and related indexes, 1913-48.

RECORDS OF BOARDS, PANELS, AND COMMISSIONS. 1945-59.
14 lin. ft. (in WNRC).

Included are records of factfinding boards and panels appointed by the Secretary of Labor after World War II to investigate disputes involving the oil industry and the Greyhound Corp., 1945-46, and the International Harvester Co., the packinghouse industry, Pacific coast longshoremen, the nonferrous metal and sugar refining industries, Pacific Gas and Electric Co., Western Union Telegraph Co., and Milwaukee Gas Light Co., 1946. Records of panels and boards appointed by the President, including a panel to investigate a dispute involving General Motors Corp., 1945-46, and a board to investigate a dispute in the steel industry, 1959. Records of an FMCS factfinding board to investigate a dispute in the steel industry, 1949; and of the National Trucking Commission, established to mediate disputes in the trucking industry, 1946-47.

RECORDS OF THE FEDERAL MEDIATION AND CONCILIATION SERVICE. 1948-65. 233 lin. ft. (in WNRC).

These consist of dispute case records, with related indexes, 1948-62; "special assignment" case files, 1957-59; and "related activities" case files, 1960-65.

AUDIOVISUAL RECORDS. 1959.
70 items.

These consist of slides (69 items) illustrating preventive mediation work of the Service, and an accompanying explanatory sound recording.

SPECIFIC RESTRICTIONS

Records: Dispute case records of the U.S. Conciliation Service and the Federal Mediation and Conciliation Service, 1913-59; and "special assignment" and "related activities" case files pertaining to labor-management media-

tion and internal assignments of various types, 1957-63.

Restrictions: These records may not be examined by or copies of or information from them furnished to any person except by permission of the Director of Administrative Management, Federal Mediation and Conciliation Service, or his authorized representatives.

Specified by: Federal Mediation and Conciliation Service.

RECORDS OF THE FEDERAL POWER COMMISSION
(RECORD GROUP 138)

The Federal Power Commission (FPC) is an independent agency operating under the Federal Water Power Act of 1920 and the Natural Gas Act of 1938. Subsequent legislation and Executive orders have increased its functions and authority. Originally composed of the Secretaries of War, the Interior, and Agriculture, the Commission was reorganized in 1930 to include five full-time commissioners appointed by the President, with the Chairman designated by the President from among the five members.

The FPC regulates interstate aspects of the electric power and natural gas industries, including licensing construction and operation of non-Federal hydroelectric power projects on Government lands or navigable U.S. waters, regulating rates and other aspects of interstate wholesale transactions, and issuing certificates for gas sales to and from interstate pipelines and construction and operation of pipeline facilities. It gathers, analyzes, maintains, and publishes information concerning companies subject to its jurisdiction. The FPC con-

trols the holding of interlocking positions in these companies by requiring its approval of appointment or election to such positions.

The FPC also regulates securities, mergers, consolidations, and acquisition of public utilities companies. It studies plans for construction of dams by the Department of Defense and other Government agencies and makes recommendations concerning their installation, allocates costs of certain Federal projects and participates in allocation of costs of others, and approves and confirms proposed rates for the sale of electric power from certain Federal and international projects.

There are 56 cubic feet of records dated between 1920 and 1954 in this record group.

RECORDS. 1920-54. 67 lin. ft.

Included are notarized applications and related correspondence concerning interlocking directorates, 1920-41, records relating to the Wheeler-Rayburn public utilities holding company bill, May 17-27, 1935, and general records of the National Defense Power Staff, 1940–44.

Cartographic records include maps (879 items), most of which relate to surveys of river basins in the investigation of power potential in flood control projects, 1925–54.

SPECIFIC RESTRICTIONS
Records: Applications for authorization to hold positions in more than one public utility, with related correspondence.

Restrictions: Records not filed in the "Formal" section of individual application folders may not be examined by or information from or copies of them furnished to the public except by permission of the Federal Power Commission.

Specified by: Federal Power Commission.

RECORDS OF THE FEDERAL RESERVE SYSTEM
(RECORD GROUP 82)

The Federal Reserve System, established by an act of December 23, 1913, comprises the Board of Governors of the Federal Reserve System, the Federal Open Market Committee, the Federal Advisory Council, 12 Federal Reserve banks and their 24 branches, and member banks (all national banks in the 50 States and State banks and trust companies that have been admitted to the System). The Board of Governors determines general monetary, credit, and operating policies for the System and formulates rules and regulations to carry out the purposes of the organic act. The Board influences credit conditions in the Nation to control credit expansion or contraction by setting requirements for reserves maintained by member banks against deposits and reviewing and determining the discount rate charged by Reserve banks on their discounts and advances. It supervises Reserve banks and member State banks and trust companies. Members of the Board of Governors and five representatives of the Reserve banks form the Federal Open Market Committee. Reserve banks act as depositories and fiscal agents for the United States and issue Federal Reserve notes.

There are 9 cubic feet of records dated between 1936 and 1965 in this record group.

RECORDS. 1936–65. 10 lin. ft.

The records consist of minutes of the Federal Open Market Committee, 1936–65, and its Executive Committee, 1936–55; a newsreel of dedication ceremonies for the Federal Reserve Building at Washington, October 20, 1937; and a sound recording of President Roosevelt's speech on that occasion.

Microfilm Publication: *Minutes of Meetings of the Federal Open Market Committee, 1936– , and of Its Executive Committee, 1936–55*, M591, 27 rolls, DP.

RECORDS OF THE FEDERAL TRADE COMMISSION
(RECORD GROUP 122)

The Federal Trade Commission (FTC) is the successor agency to the Bureau of Corporations, established in the Department of Commerce and Labor in

1903 to investigate and report on the operations of interstate corporations except common carriers. When separate Departments of Commerce and Labor were established in 1913, the Bureau remained in the Department of Commerce.

By an act of September 26, 1914, the FTC was made into an independent agency. The functions of the FTC have been enlarged by a series of acts beginning with the Clayton Act of October 15, 1914. By these acts the FTC is authorized to prevent unfair methods of competition and undue restraint of trade in interstate commerce; compile data concerning U.S. economic and business conditions as a basis for remedial legislation and for the public's protection; prohibit false advertising of food, drugs, curative devices, and cosmetics to safeguard life and health; and promote the adoption of trade-practice rules to elevate business ethics.

There are 5,324 cubic feet of records dated between 1903 and 1959 in this record group.

RECORDS OF THE BUREAU OF CORPORATIONS. 1903-14.
543 lin. ft.

These consist of records and related indexes of the Bureau of Corporations transferred to the FTC, including administrative records; studies, reports, and correspondence concerning the jurisdiction, powers, and operating methods of the Bureau; special investigations of particular industries; and Federal, State, and foreign incorporation, taxation, trust, and insurance laws.

RECORDS OF THE FEDERAL TRADE COMMISSION. 1914-59.
8,086 lin. ft.

Included is the general file of the FTC, containing correspondence, reports, memorandums, issuances, transcripts, speeches, and legislation relating to the powers, duties, organization, procedures, investigations (including letters to and from complainants and documents containing trade secrets or information supplied in confidence), conferences, and fiscal matters, 1914-21. Also records relating to administration of the program for licensing patents, trademarks, and copyrights owned during World War I by nationals of the Central Powers, 1916-24; press releases, 1914-59; and press clippings, ca. 1918-44.

Records of the Economic Division (4,789 lin. ft. in WNRC) relate to FTC economic investigations and consist of procedural rules and instructions, transcripts of hearings, progress resumes, agents' reports, correspondence, statements of persons interviewed, lists of firms investigated, schedules submitted by those firms about their organizations and operations, statistical data, drafts of final reports, and working papers and reference material, 1915-38.

Foreign trade complaint files (in WNRC) of the Export Trade Section relate to complaints about business practices of American exporters and importers, 1921-29. Records of the Docket Section include "formal" docketed case files (in WNRC) of complaints of unfair methods of competition or undue restraint of trade, 1916-52, and auxiliary case files (in WNRC), 1915-36, documenting the investigations; docketed, 1915-26, and undocketed, 1916-36, applications (in WNRC) for issuing complaints; and a classified general file, with an index, containing minutes, correspondence, memorandums, reports, questionnaires, and transcripts relating to administrative procedures and investigatory activities, 1918-41. Records of the Special Board of Investigation, created in 1929 to examine charges of false and misleading advertising, consist of radio program scripts containing advertisements passed upon by the Board, 1936-38.

CARTOGRAPHIC RECORDS.
1923-36. 293 items.

Included are maps relating to utility companies, prepared by the Mail and Files Section, Administrative Division, 1923-34, and by the Chief Counsel, 1931-36; and diagrams, graphs, and maps prepared by the Economic Division, relating to public utilities, farm products, petroleum production, and manufacturers of farm machinery, 1928-36.

See Estelle Rebec, comp., *Preliminary Inventory of the Records of the Federal Trade Commission*, PI 7 (1948).

Microfilm Publication: *Report of the Commissioner of Corporations on the Petroleum Industry, Part III, Foreign Trade, April 1909*, T154, 1 roll.

SPECIFIC RESTRICTIONS

Records: All records except the files of the Bureau of Corporations, Department of Commerce, 1903-14, that were transferred to the FTC; portions of the numerical file (Nos. 8000-9989) of the FTC, 1914-21, that do not comprise correspondence with complainants or documents containing trade secrets or information given in confidence; the formal dockets; records relating to radio program scripts containing advertisements passed upon by the Special Board of Investigation, 1936-38; press releases, 1914-59; and press clippings, ca. 1918-44.

Restrictions: Except for the material listed above, no one may examine FTC records or be given information from them or copies of them except by permission of the FTC.

Specified by: Federal Trade Commission.

GENERAL RECORDS OF THE GENERAL SERVICES ADMINISTRATION (RECORD GROUP 269)

The General Services Administration (GSA) was established as an independent agency by the Federal Property and Administrative Services Act of June 30, 1949. The act consolidated and transferred to the GSA certain real and personal property and related functions formerly assigned to various agencies. Its purpose is to provide an economical and efficient system for managing Government property and records, including such services as constructing and operating buildings, procuring and distributing supplies, disposing of surplus property, managing traffic and communications, stockpiling strategic and critical materials, and managing, preserving, and disposing of records. Records of the component services that constitute the GSA have been allocated to separate record groups.

There are 61 cubic feet of records dated between 1953 and 1967 in this record group.

RECORDS. 1953-67. 73 lin. ft.

These consist chiefly of inventory listings of Federal real estate leased or owned by civilian or defense agencies in the United States, U.S. territories, and other countries, giving for each property listed the agency of custody, the location, an area description, the date of acquisition or lease, the number and size of buildings on the property, the acreage, and the cost.

RECORDS OF THE PUBLIC BUILDINGS SERVICE (GSA)
(RECORD GROUP 121)

The Public Buildings Service designs, constructs, manages, maintains, and protects most federally owned and leased buildings. It is also responsible for the acquisition, utilization, and custody of General Services Administration (GSA) real and related personal property.

Federal building outside the District of Columbia was performed by Federal agencies and, to some extent, by special commissions and officers appointed by the Secretary of the Treasury until 1853, when a Construction Branch was created in the Department of the Treasury. The Branch later became the Bureau of Construction in the Office of the Supervising Architect, and that Office, in turn, was transferred in 1933 to the Public Buildings Branch of the Procurement Division. The Public Buildings Administration was created in the Federal Works Agency in 1939 by consolidating the Public Buildings Branch and the National Park Service's Branch of Buildings Management. The latter Branch had inherited responsibilities for Federal construction in the District of Columbia from the Office of Public Buildings and Public Parks of the National Capital (see RG 42). An act of June 30, 1949, abolished the Public Buildings Administration and transferred its functions to the GSA. The Public Buildings Service was established December 11, 1949, by the Administrator of General Services to supersede the Public Buildings Administration.

See Department of the Treasury, *A History of Public Buildings Under the Control of the Treasury Department* (1901); and Darrell H. Smith, *The Office of the Supervising Architect of the Treasury* (Baltimore, 1923).

There are 8,593 cubic feet of records dated between 1801 and 1968 in this record group.

GENERAL CORRESPONDENCE.
1843-1945. 11,988 lin. ft.

Included are letters sent by the Secretary of the Treasury, concerning customhouses and other buildings, 1851-63; letters sent, 1852-1930 (with gaps), and registers of letters sent, 1852-1901, chiefly by the Supervising Architect; letters sent, chiefly by the Supervising Architect, 1888-1912 (in WNRC); letters and telegrams sent by the Technical Division, Office of the Supervising Architect, 1897-1908; letters sent and received by the construction superintendent, concerning the erection of the Washington, D.C., Post Office, 1891-99; letters sent concerning the construction of the Treasury Extension Building, 1855-63, a hygienic laboratory at Washington, D.C., 1902-3 and 1908-9, and other buildings; letters received, chiefly by the Supervising Architect, 1843-1910 (in WNRC); general correspondence and related records, 1910-39 (in WNRC); correspondence and related records concerning operation and maintenance of Federal buildings outside the District of Columbia, 1933-45; and general correspondence of the Administrative Office, Section of Space Control, Procurement Division, 1935-39.

DRAWINGS, PLANS, AND SPECIFICATIONS OF PUBLIC BUILDINGS. ca. 1833-1945.
234 lin. ft.

These records, which relate primarily to public buildings throughout the United States that have been sold, traded, or demolished, consist of original drawings, tracings, and prints of sites and interior and exterior plans, 1840-1943; construction drawings of U.S. Government buildings at expositions, 1891-1940; architectural sketches and drawings principally of front elevation and simple floor plans and plumbing, heating, electric conduit, painting, and repair specifications, 1840-1943; plans and charts showing room assignments and floor plans, and blueprints of maps showing building locations, 1870-1945; and drawings, photographs, and other records of the Office of the Supervising Architect, concerning the design, construction, alteration, and management of Treasury Department headquarters buildings in Washington, ca. 1833-1910, and other Federal buildings, ca. 1870-1931.

RECORDS CONCERNING LAND ACQUISITIONS AND SALES BY THE UNITED STATES. 1801-1968. 855 lin. ft.

Land acquired by the United States for debts was often redeemed by the owner or his heirs, or relief was given by congressional acts. During 1936 and 1937 some effort was made by the Procurement Division to clear up disputed titles and dispose of those lands. The Solicitor of the Treasury's records concerning land the Government acquired in payment for debts, chiefly for defaults in payment to the Government, consist primarily of warranty deeds to land acquired, 1801-78, and conveyed, 1830-1927; a register of lands, 1830-59; letters sent by the Solicitor about lands, 1842-45; letters and memorandums sent by the Section of Space Control about disposing of Government land, 1936-37; closed land disposal case files, 1885-1939; and case files of lawsuits brought by the United States to acquire land in payment for debts, 1821-1911. Records concerning Government purchase and sale of land at Harpers Ferry consist principally of correspondence, 1845-87, warranty deeds to land conveyed, 1852-1902, and records about abatement cases, 1878-88.

Records relating to a Federal real estate inventory consist of correspondence and related material of the Section of Space Control, Procurement Division, about conducting the inventory, and a departmental and agency file consisting largely of correspondence, memorandums, minutes, and special reports on parcels of real estate that Federal departments and agencies owned, 1936-38; and questionnaires sent by the Section to determine names, dates acquired, areas, locations, and costs of Federal properties, 1929-39.

Other records relating to land include correspondence and related material about land in the District of Columbia, 1930-39; title papers and site registers, including warranty deeds, abstracts and certificates of title, site proposals, and related title papers, 1838-1968 (in WNRC); and miscellaneous documents concerning sites ("Site Registers"), ca. 1845-1903.

MISCELLANEOUS AND FISCAL RECORDS. 1816-1940. 14 lin. ft.

These consist primarily of registers of bonds to contractors, 1889-97, and to construction superintendents, 1889-94; construction contracts, 1854-60; a contract docket, 1882-92; an inspection file of construction and inspection engineers, 1935-40; appropriation account ledgers and daybooks, 1816-1906; a ledger about constructing, altering, and repairing hospital facilities, 1921-22; accounting ledgers and journals about constructing the Treasury Extension Building, 1855-71; an Office of the Supervising Architect appointment book, 1900-1902; property record for furniture and fixtures in public buildings, 1896-1906; James Stewart and Co.'s claims file, 1937; and an office file of the Procurement Division technical officer, concerning construction and administration, 1923-35.

RECORDS CONCERNING FEDERAL ART ACTIVITIES. 1933-43. 95 lin. ft.

The public works of art project was established late in 1933 to furnish work decorating non-Federal public buildings and parks for unemployed artists. The records of the project, which ceased functioning at the end of fiscal year 1934, consist primarily of the central file of the Advisory Committee to the Treasury on Fine Arts; final reports, 1933-36; central office correspondence, including that with artists, and related records; a file of publicity material and newspaper clippings; a card list of completed artworks received by the Washington office from project artists; correspondence of the Business Director, selected regional office records, and Region 2 correspondence with artists, 1933-34; correspondence of the Assistant Technical Director, 1934-35; and card lists of paintings and sculptures executed under the project and allocated to Government agencies, Congressmen, public buildings, art galleries, and other institutions, with fragmentary related correspondence, 1934.

Records of the Treasury relief art project, established on July 21, 1935, to employ competent, unemployed artists in decorating both new and old Federal buildings, consist primarily of the chief's general administrative and reference file, 1935-37; central office correspondence with field offices, State supervisors, and others, 1935-39; and correspondence of the New York City supervisor with the Washington office, 1935-38.

Records of a unit successively known as the Treasury Department Section of Painting and Sculpture, the Treasury Department Section of Fine Arts, and the Public Buildings Administration Section of Fine Arts (1934-43), which cooperated with other offices of the Treasury Department and subsequently of the Public Buildings Administration in providing newly constructed Federal buildings with murals and sculpture, consist principally of correspondence of section heads and case files, 1934-43; correspondence with artists ("Artists' Let-

ters"), 1939-42; annual and miscellaneous reports, letters received, and other records concerning completed murals and sculpture and their artists, 1935-42; bulletins of the Section of Painting and Sculpture, 1935-41; biographical data on artists, 1938; records concerning exhibitions, 1939-42, the decoration of New York World's Fair buildings, 1937-41, National Art Week, 1940-41, and national defense and war art projects, 1941-42; and correspondence with and about artists in Civilian Conservation Corps camps, 1934-37.

RECORDS CONCERNING CONTRACTORS' CLAIMS AGAINST THE FEDERAL GOVERNMENT. 1919-26. 4 lin. ft.

These comprise claims of public building contractors who incurred losses under prewar contracts due to World War I price and priority conditions, including war claims case files that consist of reports, correspondence, subcontracts, and other records; a summary card file on claims; and a reference file on claims, including correspondence and memorandums.

RECORDS OF COLLABORATING BOARDS AND COMMITTEES. 1921-41. 29 lin. ft.

These consist of records of the Board of Consultants on Hospitalization, established in 1921 to advise the Secretary of the Treasury on locating and expanding hospital facilities for World War I veterans, including correspondence that consists largely of reference material and statistical data accumulated during surveys and studies, 1921-23, correspondence concerning prospective purchases and donations of land and buildings, 1921-22, and records about proposed sites and buildings, 1921-27; and the Advisory Committee for the National Archives Building, appointed in 1930 to advise and assist the Supervising Architect in determining the size and character of the proposed archives building, including the file of the Chairman that consists of sketches, drawings, notes, surveys, and reference materials, 1929-41, and records of the Subcommittee on Documents that concern a survey of records held by Federal agencies, 1930.

AUDIOVISUAL RECORDS.
1855-1966. 121,240 items.

Still pictures (121,238 items) include photographs that illustrate plans for and construction, alteration, and completion of Federal and other public buildings, monuments, and memorials in the United States and abroad, including defense housing, Government buildings and exhibits at national and international expositions, schools, and health and recreational facilities, 1855-1966. Also included are photographs of paintings, murals, and sculpture produced for public buildings and of sketches submitted in several competitions, 1933-43. There are also photographs of Henry W. Elliott's paintings of the fur seal industry in the Pribilof Islands, 1872-90; some Cabinet officials and postmasters appointed during President Rutherford B. Hayes' administration, 1877; the children of President Grover Cleveland, 1895-1903; and drawings and paintings of war industries, civilian defense activities, and military personnel and equipment, 1941-45.

Motion pictures (2 reels) of President Franklin D. Roosevelt dedicating the Washington National Airport, 1940, and of clearing the site for and constructing the Pentagon, 1940-43.

See W. Lane Van Neste and Virgil E. Baugh, comps., *Preliminary Inventory of the Records of the Public Buildings Service*, PI 110 (1958).

RECORDS OF THE FEDERAL SUPPLY SERVICE (GSA)
(RECORD GROUP 137)

The General Supply Committee, established in the Department of the Treasury by an act of July 17, 1910, replaced the General Supply Committee of the Board of Awards, formed in January 1909. The Committee aided in contracting for supplies used by two or more Departments or independent agencies in the District of Columbia, disposed of surplus war material in the District, and acted as a central clearinghouse for information concerning surplus war material throughout the United States. After 1929 it performed additional procurement functions for agencies in the District and, on request, for field offices. The Federal Coordinating Service, established in the Bureau of the Budget in 1921, coordinated Government disposal of surplus war material, purchase and liquidation of supplies, and specifications for materials.

Executive Order 6166 of June 10, 1933, abolished both the Committee and the Service and transferred their functions to the Procurement Division of the Treasury Department. The Procurement Division was divided into the Supply and the Public Works (later Public Buildings) Branches. The Public Buildings Branch, which had been given some functions of the Office of the Supervising Architect, was transferred to the Federal Works Agency on July 1, 1939. Procurement functions for all Federal civilian agencies were consolidated in 1939 in the Procurement Division, renamed the Bureau of Federal Supply in 1946.

The Federal Property and Administrative Services Act of 1949 abolished the Bureau and transferred its responsibilities to the General Services Administration. On December 11, 1949, the

Administrator of General Services established the Federal Supply Service to supersede the Bureau. Responsibility for procuring strategic and critical materials was transferred in 1950 from the Federal Supply Service to the Emergency Procurement Service (now the Property Management and Disposal Service). The Federal Supply Service determines policies and methods for and engages in procuring, warehousing, and distributing supplies and services required by Federal agencies; regulates the supply functions performed by other agencies; and standardizes purchase specifications.

There are 280 cubic feet of records dated between 1909 and 1936 in this record group.

RECORDS. 1909-36. 336 lin. ft.

Records of the General Supply Committee include minutes, 1909-26 and 1929-31, correspondence, 1927-30, and circulars, 1924-28; those of the Federal Coordinating Service consist chiefly of classified files (270 lin. ft.), 1921-33, and reference material, 1918-33; and those of the Federal Traffic Board, a subsidiary of the Federal Coordinating Service, comprise classified files, 1921-33, a reading file, 1923-30 and 1933, letters and memorandums received from and sent to the chief coordinator, 1924-30, a daily mail register, 1929-30, reading files of the Rail Routing Division, 1922-25, and of the Rate, Classification, and Tariff Division, August 1922, and records of the Federal Traffic Section of the Procurement Division, 1933-36.

RECORDS OF THE
NATIONAL ARCHIVES AND RECORDS SERVICE (GSA)
(RECORD GROUP 64)

The National Archives and Records Service (NARS) was established December 11, 1949, by the Administrator of General Services to succeed the National Archives Establishment, created by an act of June 19, 1934. Under the direction of the Archivist of the United States, the Office of the National Archives selects, preserves, arranges, describes, and makes available to the Government and public noncurrent Government records that have continuing value. The Office of Records Management administers Federal records centers, promotes improved Federal records management and paperwork practices, and conducts research in the creation, maintenance, and disposition (including automatic data processing) of Federal records. The Office of Presidential Libraries adminis-

ters the Presidential libraries, which preserve, describe, and provide reference service on Presidential papers and other donated historical materials, and exhibit historical documents and museum items. The Office of the Federal Register files, makes available for public inspection, and publishes in the daily *Federal Register* Presidential proclamations and Executive orders, Federal administrative regulations, and orders and notices having general applicability and legal effect; it also publishes the *Code of Federal Regulations*, the *United States Government Organization Manual*, the *Public Papers of the Presidents of the United States*, and the *United States Statutes at Large*. The Office of the Executive Director plans, programs, and budgets administrative and technical services; operates the library; and administers printed and microfilm publication programs. Microfilm copies of the laws, administrative regulations, and related documents published by the Office of the Federal Register are in this record group, but the original documents submitted for publication in the *Federal Register* are among general records of the U.S. Government (see RG 11).

There are 516 cubic feet of records dated between 1927 and 1970 in this record group.

RECORDS OF THE OFFICE OF THE ARCHIVIST. 1934-59.
248 lin. ft.

These consist primarily of correspondence and subject files, 1934-59, and memorandums and official circulars, 1935-50. There are also quarterly and annual reports, 1935-57; budget estimates, 1935-51; selected planning and control case files, 1943-59, with a subject index; minutes and other records relating to participation in agency and interagency committees, 1934-51; files on the Franklin D. Roosevelt Presidential Library, 1937-47; articles and addresses by NARS staff members, 1935-50; and a record set of National Archives forms, procedural issuances, and organization charts, 1935-59.

RECORDS OF DISCONTINUED OFFICES AND DIVISIONS. 1935-62.
236 lin. ft.

These consist of reports, memorandums, and correspondence of the Executive Officer, 1935-42; general records of the administrative secretary and of the Legislative Records and General Records Divisions, 1935-62; files of the Director of Archival Service, 1935-41, and of the Director of the Division of Reference and the Records Control Office, 1936-51, including working papers relating to the World War II records project, 1948-51; records of the

Division of Accessions, consisting chiefly of original reports prepared by deputy examiners, 1935-36, and copies of State archival legislation and other records accumulated by the Works Progress Administration survey of Federal archives, 1935-43; general files of the Classification, 1935-40, and Cataloging, 1935-41, Divisions; records of the Photographic Records Office and predecessor units, 1935-59; and records of the Division of Research, consisting primarily of working papers and a manuscript copy of "The Archives of the United States: A Documentary History, 1774-1934," compiled in 1938.

There are also reports, correspondence, and other records of the Director of Research and Records Description and the Program Adviser, 1941-47; files of the Director of Archival Management, consisting primarily of planning and control case files, 1946-59, and records relating to the Inter-American Seminar, 1961; records of the Management Office, 1945-50; and files of the Records Officer, relating primarily to central files operations, 1941-50.

RECORDS OF THE OFFICE OF RECORDS MANAGEMENT. 1950-64.
32 lin. ft.

Records of this Office and its predecessor, the Division of Records Management, consist principally of policy correspondence and general administrative files for records center operations, 1950-60; reference material and survey files relating to technical assistance given Federal agencies, 1950-60; and a record set of numbered memorandums sent to NARS regional directors, 1951-64.

MISCELLANEOUS RECORDS.
1935-70. 62 lin. ft. and 186 rolls of microfilm.

Included are completed disposal transaction files, 1935-52, inherited by the Records Appraisal Division; and microfilm copies of laws, administrative regulations, and related documents (with indexes) published daily in the *Federal Register*, 1936-70.

CARTOGRAPHIC AND AUDIOVISUAL RECORDS. 1927-66. 2,100 items.

Cartographic records, 1937-54 (125 items), consist of maps compiled or annotated in the Cartographic Branch to show Federal mapping and exploration activities and to index or illustrate information about NARS holdings and projects.

Photographs (1,931 items) of the National Archives Building under construction and upon completion; archival activities in the building; and records storage conditions in Federal, State, and foreign government buildings, 1932-45. Also photographs from "Engraved and Lithographed Portraits of Abraham Lincoln" by Winfred Porter Truesdell, 1933, and of the Capitol and other Federal buildings, 1951-63.

Motion pictures (17 reels) of the first meeting of the National Archives Council, June 10, 1936; tests conducted at the National Bureau of Standards on burning characteristics of nitrate motion picture film, 1936-38; ceremonies at the National Archives Building opening the exhibit of the Japanese surrender documents, 1945; historical documents in the Library of Congress and the transfer of the Declaration of Independence and the Constitution from the Library to the National Archives Building, 1952; the luncheon meeting of the National Historical Publications Commission, June 17, 1958; the film "Your National Archives," 1953; and the 1958 voyage of the U.S.S. *Skate* under the North Pole.

Sound recordings (27 items) of speeches and ceremonies relating to activities of the National Archives and Records Service, including the opening of the Freedom Train exhibit, 1949; the enshrinement of the Declaration of Independence and the Constitution in the exhibition hall, 1952; an interview with Wayne C. Grover conducted by Linton Wells for the radio program "Report to the People," 1966; and the proceedings of the National Historical Publications Commission luncheon meeting of June 17, 1958. Also recordings of Charles A. Lindbergh's reception in Washington, D.C., and his address to the National Press Club, 1927; Adlai E. Stevenson's acceptance speech at the Democratic National Convention, 1952; state of the Union messages by Presidents Eisenhower, 1960, and Kennedy, 1961; the space flight of Comdr. Alan Shepard, 1961; President Kennedy's address to the United Nations, September 25, 1961; and the sound of an atomic bomb explosion.

Microfilm Publications: NARS printed publications, including finding aids; the daily *Federal Register; Territorial Papers of the United States;* and records supplementary to those published in the Wisconsin volumes of the *Territorial Papers* have been included in the microfilm publication program. For a complete listing see the current *List of National Archives Microfilm Publications.*

RECORDS OF THE PROPERTY MANAGEMENT AND DISPOSAL SERVICE (GENERAL SERVICES ADMINISTRATION) (RECORD GROUP 291)

The Property Management and Disposal Service, established July 29, 1966, by the Administrator of General Services, assumed functions formerly assigned to the Defense Materials Service and the Utilization and Disposal

Service. The Property Management and Disposal Service acquires, stores, and manages inventories of strategic and critical materials for U.S. military and industrial requirements during national emergencies; supports Department of Defense and Department of Health, Education, and Welfare civil defense emergency programs and the Department of Defense national industrial equipment reserve program; aids in expanding production of industrial raw materials; provides technical assistance to Department of Agriculture barter programs; administers the lead-zinc sta-

bilization program; and promotes maximum utilization of Federal personal and real property and disposes of surplus property through donations, sales, and other authorized methods.

There is less than 1 cubic foot of records dated ca. 1957 in this record group.

AUDIOVISUAL RECORDS. ca. 1957. 1 reel.

A film on processing nickel ore at the Defense Materials Service's Nicaro project in Cuba.

RECORDS OF THE INDIAN CLAIMS COMMISSION (RECORD GROUP 279)

The Indian Claims Commission was created by an act of August 13, 1946, to hear and determine claims against the United States on behalf of any tribe, band, or other identifiable group of American Indians residing in the United States. The Commission consists of a chief commissioner and four associate commissioners appointed by the President. Hearings may be conducted by one or more commissioners and may be held anywhere in the United States. The act establishing the Commission provided that it should receive claims for a period of only 5 years after the date of approval of the act, and that all such claims must be heard and decided within a further 5-year period. In 1956 this period was extended to April 10, 1962; in 1961, to April 10, 1967; and in 1967, to April 10, 1972.

There are 130 cubic feet of records dated between 1947 and 1967 in this record group.

CLOSED DOCKETED CASE FILES. 1947-67. 197 lin. ft.

Each case file includes some or all of the following documents: original, amended, and supplementary petitions; motions; briefs; transcripts of hearings; powers of attorney; findings; opinions of the Commission; and appeals. A case file may also include a wide range of materials furnished as evidence by both plaintiff and defendant, such as cartographic and photographic material, reports from the General Accounting Office, special surveys of land values, anthropological and ethnological reports, documentary publications, published histories of Indian tribes and the regions they inhabited, magazine articles, doctoral dissertations, and excerpts from annual reports of the Secretary of War, the Secretary of the Interior, and the Commissioner of Indian Affairs.

RECORDS OF THE INTERSTATE COMMERCE COMMISSION
(RECORD GROUP 134)

The Interstate Commerce Commission was created as an independent agency by an act of February 4, 1887, to regulate in the public interest common carriers engaged in transportation, interstate commerce, and foreign commerce to the extent that it takes place within the United States. Subsequent legislation strengthened the authority and extended the jurisdiction of the Commission. It is now responsible for promoting safe, adequate, economical, and efficient service on all modes of transportation subject to its authority; encouraging the establishment and maintenance of reasonable charges for transportation services, without unjust discriminations or unfair competitive practices; requiring carriers and freight forwarders to file and publish rates, rules, and regulations concerning interstate traffic; and fostering the development, coordination, and preservation of a national transportation system adequate for the postal service, the national defense, and U.S. commerce.

There are 5,930 cubic feet of records dated between 1887 and 1942 in this record group.

GENERAL RECORDS. 1887-1942. 634 lin. ft. and 1,348 rolls of microfilm.

General files of the Operating Division, including correspondence of the Chairman, commissioners, secretary, and the Operating Division, 1887-1906, with an index; letters sent to the White House, Members of Congress, heads of Federal agencies, State Governors, and business leaders, 1887-1942; microfilm copies (1,348 rolls) of annual reports of carriers, containing data on corporate structure, finance, and activities, 1888-1914; and canceled passenger rate schedules, 1887-1935.

CASE FILES. 1887-1934. 5,456 lin. ft. (in WNRC).

Case files of controversies between carriers and shippers and of cases instituted by the Commission, including pleadings, transcripts of testimonies, exhibits, and reports, 1887-1924; concerning investigation and suspension of carrier tariffs, including petitions for suspension of new rates, exhibits, transcripts of hearings, reports, and briefs, 1910-34; concerning Commission action on carrier requests for permission to issue bonds, make loans, effect consolidations, and engage in other financial operations, April-November 1920; and containing records filed under an act of March 1, 1913, relating to initial valuation of common carrier property, 1916-27.

CARTOGRAPHIC RECORDS. 1900-1941. 683 items.

These consist primarily of maps relating to the railroad industry and prepared by the Bureau of Formal Cases, 1900-1934, the Bureau of Finance, 1910-41, and the Valuation Division, 1913-38.

Microfilm Publication: *Annual Reports by Common Carriers to the Interstate Commerce Commission, 1888-1914*, T913, 1,348 rolls.

RECORDS OF THE
NATIONAL AERONAUTICS AND SPACE ADMINISTRATION
(RECORD GROUP 255)

The National Aeronautics and Space Administration (NASA) was preceded by the National Advisory Committee for Aeronautics, created by an act of

March 3, 1915. The principal activities of the Committee were the scientific study of flight and aeronautical research and experiment. Committee membership included the Chairman of the Research and Development Board of the Department of Defense and representatives from the Departments of the Air Force and Navy, Civil Aeronautics Authority, Smithsonian Institution, U.S. Weather Bureau, and the National Bureau of Standards. The Committee was terminated by the act of July 29, 1958, that created NASA and transferred to it Committee functions and records.

There are 133 cubic feet of records dated between 1914 and 1965 in this record group.

RECORDS OF THE NATIONAL ADVISORY COMMITTEE FOR AERONAUTICS. 1914-58. 69 lin. ft.

Included are segments of general decimal correspondence and subject files, 1915-58; reports and correspondence relating to careers of Committee members ("Biography File"), 1915-58; office file of Walter T. Bonney, assistant to the secretary, 1917-58; miscellaneous technical reports, 1914-26; transcripts of speeches by Committee members and by John F. Victory, Executive Secretary of the Committee, 1935-58; and a card file of former officials and other persons concerned with aeronautics. There are also records relating to field installations, including correspondence, inspection reports, historical notes, press releases, and newspaper clippings relating to aeronautical laboratories, high-speed flight stations, and activities of the Committee's Western Coordination Office and the Wallops Island Station, Va., 1916-58; and records of the Paris Office, including reports of the technical assistant in Europe relating to European aviation, and miscellaneous records, 1918-51.

AUDIOVISUAL RECORDS. 1917-65. 23,416 items.

Photographs made or collected by NASA and the Committee, relating to aerodynamics, aircraft powerplants, materials and construction, types of aircraft and structures, operating problems and navigation, research facilities and projects, and rocket experiments, 1917-61; of testing, launching, and tracking the first U. S. satellite by Project Vanguard, 1956-59; of charts used in lectures and other presentations; and of the lunar surface made by Rangers VII and VIII, 1964-65.

RECORDS OF THE NATIONAL ACADEMY OF SCIENCES (RECORD GROUP 189)

The National Academy of Sciences was established by an act of March 3, 1863, to investigate and report on scientific or artistic subjects at the request of any Federal agency. In 1916, at the request of the President, the Academy organized the National Research Council to coordinate the scientific resources of the country in the interests of national defense. The Council has been continued to promote research in the mathematical, physical, and biological sciences, and the application of these sciences to engineering, agriculture, medicine, and other useful arts. A quasi-official body of prominent scientists, the Council functions through conferences, technical committees, and surveys. It sponsors research organizations and scientific publications, and administers funds for research projects. Its administrative work is financed from a Carnegie Corporation endowment and from other special funds. Research relating to World War II activities were financed through contracts with the Office of Scientific Research and Development and other Government agencies.

There are 64 cubic feet of records dated between 1900 and 1961 in this record group.

RECORDS. 1900-1961. 77 lin. ft.

These consist of reports and related correspondence, 1917-21, of the Washington office of the National Research Information Committee from its Paris, Rome, and London offices concerning aviation, munitions, ordnance, equipment, and other military and naval technical matters; papers, 1900-1945, of Robert E. Horton, a hydraulics engineer, left to the American Geophysical Union, a component of the National Research Council, and relating primarily to snow surveys, studies of irrigation, soil conservation, and water levels (a list of these studies is available); maps (12 items) used by the National Research Council in its World War I studies of mapping; maps (17 items) of the United States, relating to agriculture, mining, and manufacturing, 1930-37; an incomplete set of maps (74 items) prepared for the *National Atlas of the United States*, a project sponsored by the National Research Council, 1954-58; and photographs (151 items) of the activity of Paricutin Volcano, Michoacan, Mexico, 1943-45.

RECORDS OF THE NATIONAL LABOR RELATIONS BOARD
(RECORD GROUP 25)

The present National Labor Relations Board (NLRB) was created by the National Labor Relations Act (the Wagner Act) of July 5, 1935. It was preceded by two earlier boards, the first of which, the National Labor Board (NLB), was established August 5, 1933, by the President to adjust industrial disputes arising from the interpretation and application of the President's Reemployment Agreement or any approved code of fair competition under the National Industrial Recovery Act. The NLB was replaced by the first National Labor Relations Board, established by authority of a public resolution of June 19, 1934. Both these Boards utilized a system of regional boards to deal with labor controversies in the field; and both regional and national boards engaged in the settlement of labor disputes, enforced collective-bargaining requirements, and conducted elections for employee representatives. After the National Industrial Recovery Act was declared unconstitutional on May 27, 1935, the first National Labor Relations Board virtually ceased to function.

The Wagner Act affirmed the right of employees to organize and designate representatives for collective-bargaining purposes. The second NLRB was authorized to determine the unit of employees appropriate for bargaining, conduct secret elections for employee representatives, and require employers to end specified unfair labor practices frustrating collective bargaining in industries other than the railroads, and, after 1936, the airlines. The War Labor Disputes Act of June 25, 1943 (the Smith-Connally Act), authorized the Board to hold strike vote elections in labor disputes that seriously threatened to interrupt war production. The Labor Management Relations Act of 1947 (the

Taft-Hartley Act), as amended, defined additional labor practices forbidden to organized labor and restricted the Board to a primarily judicial and policy-making role. NLRB operations, particularly administrative procedures, were further modified by the Labor-Management Reporting and Disclosure Act of 1959 (the Landrum-Griffin Act). The first National Labor Relations Board continued many cases and enforced decisions of the NLB.

See Lewis L. Lorwin and Arthur Wubnig, *Labor Relations Boards* (1935); William H. Spencer, *Collective Bargaining Under Section 7(a) of the National Industrial Recovery Act* (Chicago, 1935); Joseph Rosenfarb, *The National Labor Policy and How It Works* (New York, 1940); D. O. Bowman, *Public Control of Labor Relations: A Study of the National Labor Relations Board* (New York, 1942); and the *Decisions* of the National Labor Board (1934) and *Decisions and Orders* of the National Labor Relations Board (issued annually since 1936).

There are 5,140 cubic feet of records dated between 1933 and 1959 in this record group.

HEADQUARTERS RECORDS OF THE NATIONAL LABOR BOARD. 1933-35. 56 lin. ft.

The first National Labor Relations Board, in continuing cases and enforcing decisions of the NLB, often changed the numbers of NLB case files to conform to its own filing system, which usually makes the use of indexes, case files, transcripts, exhibits, and correspondence files of both Boards necessary to locate all records relating to a particular labor dispute. Many NLB headquarters and regional board records were maintained in a continuous series. The records comprise case files, with briefs, exhibits, transcripts of hearings, and indexes, 1933-35 (in WNRC); correspondence and related records concerning such matters as Board and regional board cases and complaints, 1933-35; original signed decisions of the Board and records of the Chairman, technical advisor to the Board, General Counsel,

and executive director and executive officer, 1933-34; and monthly statistical summaries of regional board cases, January-July 1934.

RECORDS OF THE FIRST NATIONAL LABOR RELATIONS BOARD. 1933-36. 90 lin. ft.

These consist of case files (see above for discussion of cases begun by the NLB), with briefs, transcripts of hearings, exhibits, and indexes, 1933-35 (in WNRC); and reports, memorandums, correspondence, press releases, and other records relating to headquarters and regional board cases, complaints of unfair labor practices, decisions, administrative procedures, mediators, examiners, and regional board operations, 1933-36. There are also records of the Board Chairman about organization and personnel of regional boards, of Board members about the organization and functions of regional boards and industrial relations boards created under National Recovery Administration codes, and of the director of research and staff members of the Research Department about election studies conducted by boards during labor disputes, 1934-35.

REGIONAL RECORDS OF THE NATIONAL LABOR BOARD AND THE FIRST NATIONAL LABOR RELATIONS BOARD. 1933-38. 240 lin. ft.

NLB regional labor boards were established at Boston, New York, Buffalo, Philadelphia, Newark, Pittsburgh, Atlanta, New Orleans, Cleveland (with a subboard at Toledo), Detroit, Chicago, Indianapolis, Minneapolis, St. Louis, Kansas City, San Antonio, Los Angeles, San Francisco, and Seattle. The first NLRB maintained part of the NLB regional board organization, but it created new boards for Region V (Baltimore), Region IX (Cincinnati), Region XIII (Ft. Worth), and Region XIV (Denver). The Newark board was abolished, and its jurisdiction was divided between Region II (New York) and Region IV (Philadelphia), the latter of which also acquired its records; the Pittsburgh board was made a branch office of Region IV; the Toledo subboard and the Detroit board were made branch offices of Region VIII (Cleveland); the Indianapolis board was made a branch office of Region X (Chicago), and a new branch office of that region was established at Milwaukee; the Kansas City board was made a branch office of Region XII (St. Louis); and the San Antonio board was abolished, and its jurisdiction and records were divided between Region VII (New Orleans) and Region XIII. Records, as late as 1938, of regional boards established by the second NLRB are to be found among records of some regional boards of the NLB and the first NLRB. Records of regional boards and branches include case files (see above for discussion of cases begun by the NLB), transcripts, and exhibits (in WNRC). Most also include general subject files consisting of memorandums, issuances, correspondence, reports, statistical data, and other records relating to administration, board cases, operations, and relations with headquarters and other regional boards. Some boards arranged administrative and operational records into categories of correspondence, decisions, issuances, press releases, narrative and statistical case reports, and press clippings. Records for several boards include minutes of meetings. Most regional board records include docket books or indexes (in WNRC) to case files, and, in some instances, indexes to correspondence files.

RECORDS OF THE SECOND NATIONAL LABOR RELATIONS BOARD. 1935-59. 5,728 lin. ft.

There are headquarters and regional case records (5,681 lin. ft. in WNRC), including Wagner Act case files, with transcripts, dockets, and exhibits, 1935-

48 (documenting all unfair labor practices and representation cases heard and adjusted at the Board's headquarters and a 10 to 12 percent sample of those at regional offices); War Labor Disputes Act strike-vote case files, with dockets, 1943-45; Taft-Hartley Act case files, with transcripts and exhibits, 1947-59 (documenting a 1 to 3 percent yearly sample of the various categories of unfair labor practice and collective-bargaining representation cases); union authorization cases that were closed after formal action or appealed to the Board, 1947-51; and union-shop deauthorization cases, 1947-59.

Other records of administrative units of the Board include records relating to an action of the Federal Power Commission, 1936; records of the Office of the Secretary, including reports and correspondence about regional offices, cases, and personnel, 1935-40; and a file of the Administrative Division, concerning procedures of the Files and Mails Section (later the Files and Dockets Section), 1938-41. There are Legal Division records, consisting of correspondence, case reports, and transcripts of meetings of the legal staff in the Office of General Counsel, 1935-44; Litigation Section records, comprising the senior litigation attorney's files and records relating to NLRB cases in Federal court litigations, 1935-42; and Review Section files, 1935-39. Also included are press releases of the Division of Information, 1935-42.

The House of Representatives Special Committee To Investigate the National Labor Relations Board (the Smith Committee) was created by a House resolution of July 2, 1939, to investigate the administration of the National Labor Relations Act. As a result of this investigation amendments to the act were recommended and organizational changes were made in the NLRB. The records comprise files documenting NLRB operations brought together by the General Counsel's Office and the Legal Division for the use of the Board and the Committee during the investigation. Included are records of the Office of the General Counsel, comprising letters sent about the investigation, general files containing data and reports prepared for the investigation, and related correspondence, 1939-41; questionnaires containing information about union activities and membership of Board personnel and transcripts of Smith Committee hearings on exhibits received into evidence, 1940; minutes of NLRB executive meetings, 1936-39; testimonies concerning amendments to the Wagner Act presented before hearings of the Senate Committee on Education and Labor, 1939; news clippings about the Wagner Act and the NLRB, 1937-39; and lists of and documents from NLRB files taken by the Smith Committee, correspondence with the Attorney General's Committee on Administrative Procedures, and the latter Committee's monograph on the NLRB, 1939-40. Records of the Assistant General Counsel, consisting of regional directors' reports about the effects of NLRB decisions on labor relations, excerpts from speeches and articles prepared as exhibits, and lists of and receipts for NLRB case files and other records that were sent to the Smith Committee, 1939-40; exhibits prepared for the NLRB Chairman's testimony before the Smith Committee, 1940; and miscellaneous transcripts of Smith Committee proceedings, news clippings, and information regarding cases in litigation, 1934-40. Records of attorneys

assisting the General Counsel consist of records that concern Board policies, operations, and personnel, and cases prepared for Board members testifying before the Smith Committee. There are also reports, statistical charts, and memorandums of the Technical Service Division's chief economist and the Case Statistics Section about Board cases.

SPECIFIC RESTRICTIONS

I. *Records*: All documents in the Wagner Act case files and the Taft-Hartley Act case files other than formal documents that are a matter of official record.

   Restrictions: No one may examine these records or be given information from them or copies of them except by permission of the National Labor Relations Board under procedure specified in section 102.117 (c) of the Board's rules and regulations (32 Fed. Reg. 9551).

   Specified by: National Labor Relations Board.

II. *Records*: Records of the National Labor Relations Board relating to the operations of the House of Representatives Special Committee To Investigate the National Labor Relations Board (the Smith Committee).

   Restrictions: No one may examine these records or be given information from them or copies of them except by permission of the National Labor Relations Board.

   Specified by: National Labor Relations Board.

RECORDS OF THE NATIONAL MEDIATION BOARD
(RECORD GROUP 13)

The National Mediation Board was created by the amended Railway Labor Act of June 21, 1934, to mediate railroad labor disputes. This function evolved

from an act of October 1, 1888, that authorized the President to establish temporary commissions to investigate and report on railroad labor controversies and provided for voluntary arbitration of disputes between carriers engaged in interstate commerce and their employees. In 1894 the President appointed the U.S. Strike Commission to investigate the Pullman strike. Under the Erdman Act of June 1, 1898, responsibility for mediation was assigned jointly to the Chairman of the Interstate Commerce Commission and the Commissioner of Labor, who were known in their mediatory capacity as the Board of Arbitration, Interstate Commerce Controversies. The mediatory function was more specifically defined in the Newlands Act of July 15, 1913, which created the U.S. Board of Mediation and Conciliation. This Board was not officially abolished until 1926, but most of its jurisdiction was transferred in 1918 to the U.S. Railroad Administration and was assumed by the Railroad Labor Board in 1920. The Railroad Labor Board—representing management, labor, and the public—was created by the Transportation Act of February 28, 1920. It was superseded, under the terms of the Railway Labor Act of May 20, 1926, by the Board of Mediation, which was superseded by the present National Mediation Board.

The jurisdiction and functions of the National Mediation Board were expanded beyond those of its predecessors to cover air as well as rail carriers and to include the settlement of collective-bargaining representation disputes. The National Railroad Adjustment Board—which for the most part operates independently from the National Mediation Board in adjudicating grievances and disputes related to the interpretation and application of collective-bargaining agreements—was also created by the 1934 act.

From 1920 to 1934 secondary adjustment boards, permitted by law but formed by agreements between single carriers or groups of carriers and their employees, were created to handle minor grievances.

Since 1926 the President has appointed, under section 10 of the Railway Labor Act, emergency boards to investigate and make recommendations for the settlement of disputes, unresolved by mediation, that threatened serious interruption of interstate commerce through imminent strike action. To supplement section 10 procedures during the war period, the National Railway Labor Panel was created by an Executive order of May 22, 1942; from it railroad emergency boards were selected to investigate and recommend settlements to the President. In 1943 the Panel was given the additional responsibility of administering rail and airline wage and salary stabilization under the wartime economic stabilization program. The Panel was terminated by an Executive order of August 11, 1947.

There are 1,261 cubic feet of records dated between 1887 and 1962 in this record group.

RECORDS OF PREDECESSOR BOARDS AND COMMISSIONS. 1887-1934. 810 lin. ft.

Included are records of the U.S. Strike Commission, consisting of letters sent by Carroll D. Wright, Commissioner of Labor and Chairman of the Commission, 1894-96.

The Board of Arbitration, Interstate Commerce Controversies, consisting of case files (in WNRC), 1899 and 1907-13, that contain correspondence regarding disputes and the selection of arbitrators, transcripts of testimony, hearing exhibits and briefs, mediators' notes and reports, awards, and press clippings; correspondence about railroad labor disputes not acted on by the Board, 1908-13; an index of qualified arbitrators; correspondence of Commissioner of Labor Charles P. Neill, concerning his work as a mediator, legislation regarding arbitration of railroad labor disputes, and statistical data about railroad employment, wages, and labor disputes, 1909–13; railroad wage schedules, 1911–12; and press clippings and other reference material relating to railroad labor disputes and legislation, 1907–13.

The U.S. Board of Mediation and Conciliation, including decisions, interpretations, and correspondence of the Chairman, Judge Martin A. Knapp, some of which relate to cases under the Erdman Act, 1912–18. Files of Judge William L. Chambers, a Board Commissioner, relating to labor disputes and legislation affecting the Board and railroad labor, 1913–20; records concerning his work as an arbitrator, 1910–18; and speeches and working papers, 1887–1920. Records of the Office of the Secretary, consisting of general files documenting policies and operations, 1913–20, with related indexes; case files, 1913–21, and related indexes (in WNRC); and records concerning the 8-hour-day controversy in 1916, the Adamson Act, and other legislation affecting railroads and railroad labor. Records of the disbursing officer, consisting of files relating to budget estimates and disbursements, accounts, correspondence, and excerpts from Board minutes concerning organizational and personnel matters, 1913–20.

The Railroad Labor Board, 1920–26, including minutes of executive sessions, with related indexes; files of Board members; the central files of the Board maintained in the Office of the Secretary and documenting activities and functions of the Board, its committees, and administrative units; records of the Office of the Assistant Secretary, including files on administrative and fiscal matters and Board decisions in several series, with supporting materials and indexes; records of the Docket Department, comprising the Board's cases (in WNRC), with supporting files of correspondence, exhibits, related indexes (in WNRC), and registers; and records of the Statistical Department, consisting of adminis-

trative files and statistical reports, charts, and tables, with related working papers, correspondence, questionnaires, and reference material regarding studies and surveys of wages, working rules and conditions, cost of living, changes in rates of pay and in earnings and purchasing power of railroad workers, railroad revenues and expenses, effects of Board decisions, and the voting record of Board members.

The Board of Mediation, 1926–34, including minutes of executive sessions, correspondence of the Chairman, and correspondence of Board member Oscar B. Colquitt and records relating to cases in which he acted as mediator, 1930–34. Records of the Office of the Secretary, consisting of general and correspondence files relating to the activities; administration; and wage, representation, grievance, and miscellaneous cases (in WNRC) of the Board, with supporting files of reports, exhibits, transcripts of proceedings, awards, opinions, correspondence, indexes, and registers. Records of the Division of Administration, consisting of press digests and files concerning organizational, personnel, and fiscal matters. Records of Technical Divisions A, B, and C, which handled disputes involving clerical, yard and maintenance, and operating personnel, respectively, including case files and digests, studies, records of staff members, correspondence, and statistical data on cases handled by the Board.

RECORDS OF THE NATIONAL MEDIATION BOARD. 1934–60.
679 lin. ft. (in WNRC).

Mediation ("A" cases) and arbitration case files, 1934–60, concerning disputes between rail, express, and air carriers and employees on pay rates, working conditions, and rules; representation case files ("R" cases), 1934–59, regarding disputes about bargaining representatives; and emergency board case files, 1934–60, relating to disputes that could not be adjusted under provisions of the Railway Labor Act and that were referred to emergency boards established by the President.

RECORDS OF THE NATIONAL RAILWAY LABOR PANEL. 1942-47. 71 lin. ft.

Subject files of successive Chairmen, 1942-47; case files, 1942-47 (in WNRC); and records from the Office of the Assistant to the Chairman, concerned principally with applications for wage and salary stabilization and adjustments for railroad and airline employees, 1943-47.

RECORDS OF THE RAILROAD MARINE WORKERS COMMISSION AND THE RAILROAD LIGHTER CAPTAINS COMMISSION. 1962. 2 lin. ft.

By Executive orders on March 24 and June 12, 1961, the Railroad Marine Workers Commission and the Railroad Lighter Captains Commission were created to assist in settling disputes in the New York Harbor area that had not been successfully adjusted by the National Mediation Board and Presidential emergency boards. The records for each commission consist of reports containing findings and recommendations to the President, transcripts of public hearings, and carrier and union exhibits, 1962.

SPECIFIC RESTRICTIONS

Records: Mediation ("A" cases) and representation ("R" cases) case files of the National Mediation Board.

Restrictions: These records may not be examined by or copies of or information from them furnished to any person except by permission of the National Mediation Board.

Specified by: National Mediation Board.

RECORDS OF THE NATIONAL SCIENCE FOUNDATION (RECORD GROUP 307)

The National Science Foundation was established by an act of May 10, 1950, to promote basic research and education in the sciences and the most effective use of scientific manpower by initiating and supporting research, coordinating programs and improving techniques for the dissemination of scientific information, evaluating and coordinating governmental and nongovernmental scientific research programs, and maintaining a clearinghouse for scientific and technical personnel information.

There are 2 cubic feet of records dated between 1956 and 1958 in this record group.

RECORDS. 1956-58. 2 lin. ft.

Records of the President's Committee on Scientists and Engineers, established by the President April 3, 1956, and terminated December 31, 1958, consist of summaries of meetings about the training, use, and availability of scientific personnel, 1956-57; press releases, including copies of speeches, 1956-58; and publications issued by the Foundation and private sources about training and using scientific personnel, 1956-58.

RECORDS OF THE PANAMA CANAL
(RECORD GROUP 185)

The Panama Canal—the name of the organization that maintained and operated the canal, including government of the Canal Zone from 1914 to 1950—had its beginning in 1895 in the Nicaragua Canal Board appointed by the President to study the feasibility of completing the Nicaragua Ship Canal begun by the Maritime Canal Co. of Nicaragua. From 1897 to 1899 the Nicaragua Canal Commission made further studies. On March 3, 1899, Congress authorized the President to investigate the Panamanian as well as the Nicaraguan route for a canal. The first Isthmian Canal Commission, appointed June 10, 1899, by President McKinley, reported in favor of the Panama route and recommended the purchase of the property of the French Compagnie Nouvelle du Canal de Panama, which had been organized in 1894 and had taken over the property of the earlier Compagnie Universelle du Canal Interoceanique, headed by Ferdinand de Lesseps. An act of June 28, 1902, authorized the purchase of the property and records of the French company following the ratification of a treaty with Panama and created a second Isthmian Canal Commission. Under the supervision of the Secretary of War, the Commission directed construction work and governed the Canal Zone. After several reorganizations the Commission was abolished in 1914, and its functions and records were transferred to the permanent organization, the Panama Canal. An act of September 26, 1950, changed the name of the organization to the Canal Zone Government and limited its functions to maintaining civil government. Operation and maintenance of the canal was assigned to the Panama Canal Company, which replaced the Panama Railroad Company organized in 1849 to construct and operate a railroad across the isthmus.

There are 446 cubic feet of records (in WNRC except for nontextual records) dated between 1849 and 1957 in this record group.

RECORDS. 1849-1938. 396 lin. ft.

There are general records of the two French companies, 1879-1904; a few records of the Nicaragua Canal Board, 1895; reports, correspondence, press clippings, estimates, field notes of surveys, and hydrographic and meteorologic records of the Nicaragua Canal Commission, 1897-99, and the Washington office, and the Nicaragua, Panama, and Darien routes of the first Isthmian Canal Commission, 1899-1902; correspondence and periodic narrative and statistical reports of the second Isthmian Canal Commission, 1904-14; and minutes and legal and fiscal documents of the Panama Railroad Company, 1849-1938.

CARTOGRAPHIC AND AUDIOVISUAL RECORDS.
1881-1957. 19,242 items.

Cartographic records (9,215 items) consist of maps, plans, cross sections, and profiles prepared during preliminary surveys of proposed sea-level routes in Nicaragua and Panama; detailed working maps and plans relating to the excavation and construction of the Panama Canal, 1881-1913; and maps of the Canal Zone, 1921-57.

Photographs (10,027 items) primarily document the construction, operation, and history of the canal, 1881-1940.

See Richard W. Giroux, comp., and Garry D. Ryan, rev., *Preliminary Inventory of the Textual Records of the Panama Canal*, PI 153 (1963); and James B. Rhoads, comp., *Preliminary Inventory of the Cartographic Records of the Panama Canal*, PI 91 (1956).

RECORDS OF THE SECURITIES AND EXCHANGE COMMISSION (RECORD GROUP 266)

The Securities and Exchange Commission was established by the Securities Exchange Act of June 6, 1934. It administered the Securities Act of 1933 and later became responsible for administering the Public Utility Holding Company Act of 1935, the Trust Indenture Act of 1939, and the Investment Company and the Investment Advisers Act of 1940, all of which were intended to protect public and investor interests against malpractices in the securities and financial markets. The Commission investigates complaints or other evidence of securities violations and takes appropriate administrative action or refers the facts to the Attorney General, enforces sanctions against companies and persons guilty of such violations as securities frauds and manipulations, receives and holds open for public inspection registration statements on all securities publicly offered for sale in interstate commerce or through the mails and annual reports from all companies whose securities are listed on national exchanges, makes special studies in the investment field, renders advisory services to courts in reorganization proceedings for bankrupt corporations, and participates in formulating and executing foreign economic and financial programs of the Government.

There are 836 cubic feet of records (in WNRC) dated between 1933 and 1943 in this record group.

RECORDS. 1933–43. 1,050 lin. ft.

Registration dossiers, with an index to names of registrants, concerning administration of the Securities Act of 1933, as amended. Documents include registration statements and amendments; reports of offering price; prospectuses; orders, findings, and opinions issued by the Commission; transcripts of hearings; papers filed under Commission rules; periodic financial reports; and correspondence.

SPECIFIC RESTRICTIONS

Records: Records relating to the administration of the Securities Act of 1933, as amended, consisting of correspondence files and records relating to private hearings that bear the tertiary file numbers -3 (correspondence) and -5 (investigations), respectively.

Restrictions: No one may examine these records or obtain information from them or copies of them except the records officer of the Commission, who is authorized to withdraw the files on official loan.

Specified by: Securities and Exchange Commission.

RECORDS OF THE SELECTIVE SERVICE SYSTEM, 1940– (RECORD GROUP 147)

The Selective Service System was established by an Executive order of September 23, 1940, under the Selective Training and Service Act of September 16, 1940, to provide an orderly, just, and democratic method of obtaining men for military and naval service. The System operated through a Director and national headquarters, regional offices, State headquarters, medical advisory boards, registrant advisory boards, boards of appeal, and local boards. Through the local boards the System registered, classified, and selected for induction male citizens and aliens subject to service. Except between December 5, 1942, and December 5, 1943, when it was under the jurisdiction of the War Manpower Commission, the System was responsible to the President.

On March 31, 1947, when legislation authorizing selective service expired, the Office of Selective Service Records was established to liquidate the System and preserve and provide service on its records. The Selective Service System was reconstituted by an act of June 24, 1948, and remains in operation.

There are 1,417 cubic feet of records (in WNRC) dated between 1940 and 1948, with a few dated as late as 1953, in this record group.

RECORDS. 1940-48. 1,785 lin. ft. and 805 rolls of microfilm.

Most of the records are of the national headquarters. They include central files of the Selective Service System, 1940-47, and of the Office of Selective Service Records, 1947-48; records concerning personnel and men released from active duty; records, chiefly microfilm copies (11 rolls), of the three national lotteries held in 1940, 1941, and 1942 to determine registrant classification order; case files and other records concerning conscientious objectors (including 297 rolls of microfilm); and case files and related records, chiefly microfilm copies (246 rolls), of appeals to the President. There are also directives and other issuances (including 2 rolls of microfilm) of national and State headquarters, narrative and statistical reports, studies, lists of certain deferred and exempted persons, sample forms, and newspaper clippings. The only field office records are microfilm copies (249 rolls) of records concerning registrants of two local boards in the District of Columbia, samples of minute books of local and appeal boards, and bulletins and circulars of the Massachusetts State Headquarters.

See Richard G. Wood, comp., *Preliminary Inventory of the Records of the Selective Service System, 1940-47*, PI 27 (1951).

SPECIFIC RESTRICTIONS

I. *Records*: Records pertaining to registrants who appealed to the President.

   Restrictions: No one except appropriate personnel of the Selective Service System may have access to these records until they are 50 years old.

   Specified by: Director of Selective Service.

II. *Records*: Records pertaining to all other registrants.

   Restrictions: Except as hereinafter provided, no information in a registrant's file pertaining to his earnings or income as a civilian, dependency status, physical or mental condition, previous court record, or previous military service shall be disclosed.

   All records, or information from them, pertaining to a registrant will be furnished to him or to an agent having the registrant's written authorization. All records or information from them necessary for the performance of official duties will be furnished employees and officials of the Selective Service System and other officials of the Federal Government, State governments, and quasi-governmental organizations, such as the American Red Cross.

   All records may be made available for bona fide research that does not involve the use of individual names in connection with the classes of information described as restricted.

   Specified by: Director of Selective Service.

RECORDS OF THE SMALL BUSINESS ADMINISTRATION
(RECORD GROUP 309)

The Small Business Administration (SBA), an independent agency, was established by the Small Business Act of July 30, 1953. Under provisions of that act and Executive Order 10504 of December 1, 1953, the powers and responsibilities of the terminated Small Defense Plants Administration, including liquidation activities and the administration of its prime contracts, were transferred to the SBA. SBA functions were expanded by the Small Business Investment Act of August 21, 1958, and the Secretary of Commerce, in accordance with the Area Redevelopment Act of May 1, 1961, delegated to the SBA some responsibilities and functions for the area redevelopment program. The purposes of the SBA are to counsel, assist, and protect the interests of small businesses; ensure that a fair proportion of Government purchases and contracts are placed with small businesses; make loans to small businesses and investment companies, victims of floods or other catastrophes, and State and local development companies; license and regulate small business investment companies; and assist small business owners in improving managerial skills.

There are 17 cubic feet of records dated between 1951 and 1955 in this record group.

RECORDS. 1951-55. 20 lin. ft.

These include records of the Small Defense Plants Administration, 1951-53, consisting of correspondence relating to organization and management, appropriations, prime contracts and contract procurements, loans and other fiscal operations, production and management assistance, and personnel; sample case files relating to tax amortization, materials and equipment, contract procurement, certificates of competency, loans, and joint determination; and records of Director of Contract Procurement Charles H. Swisher, relating primarily to the ammunition program. Also included are records of the SBA, consisting of sample case files relating to applications for business loans that were declined, canceled, or withdrawn, 1954-55.

SPECIFIC RESTRICTIONS

Records: Small Defense Plants Administration and Small Business Administration sample case files relating to applications for loans.

Restrictions: No one other than employees of the Federal Government on official business may examine these records or be given information from them or copies of them except by permission of an authorized official of the SBA.

Specified by: Administrator of the Small Business Administration.

RECORDS OF THE SMITHSONIAN INSTITUTION
(RECORD GROUP 106)

The Smithsonian Institution was created by an act of August 10, 1846, under terms of the will of James Smithson of London, as an establishment for the "increase and diffusion of knowledge among men." The Institution performs fundamental research; publishes the results of studies, explorations, and investigations; preserves for study and reference millions of scientific, cultural, · and historical items; maintains exhibits of the arts, American history, aeronautics and space exploration, technology, and natural history; participates in the international exchange of learned publications; and engages in national and international cooperative research and training programs. The Institution is governed by a Board of Regents, consisting of the Vice President, the Chief Justice, three members each from the U.S. Senate and House of Representatives, and six other American citizens appointed by joint resolution of Congress. The Secretary of the Institution is its executive officer and director of activities.

Under general or immediate direction of the Institution are the U.S. National Museum, consisting of the Museum of Natural History (including the former Bureau of American Ethnology) and Museum of History and Technology; Astrophysical Laboratory; Radiation Biology Laboratory; Smithsonian Tropical Research Institute; National Zoological Park; National Air and Space Museum; National Armed Forces Museum Advisory Board; National Collection of Fine Arts; Freer Gallery of Art; National Portrait Gallery; Jospeh H. Hirshhorn Museum and Sculpture Garden; National Gallery of Art; John F. Kennedy Center for the Performing Arts; International Exchange Service; and Science Information Exchange.

Records of the Meteorological Division of the Institution, 1845-73, including some material relating to other than meteorological activities, are among records of the Weather Bureau (see RG 27). Records relating to the Institution's early interest in developing fisheries are among records of the Fish and Wildlife Service (see RG 22).

See Webster P. True, *The First Hundred Years of the Smithsonian Institution, 1846-1946* (1946).

There are 72 cubic feet of records dated between 1871 and 1952 in this record group.

RECORDS. 1891-1952. 7 lin. ft.

These consist of personnel files, 1892-1952, and correspondence of Hugh McCormick Smith, U.S. Fish Commission staff member, 1891-1903, and U.S. Commissioner of Fisheries, 1903-22.

CARTOGRAPHIC AND AUDIOVISUAL RECORDS. 1871-1950. 4,128 items.

Cartographic records (7 items) include isothermal maps showing mean temperatures in the United States for 1874; maps relating to the Cherokee Indian Nation in 1884; a map of the floral areas of Washington in 1906; a map prepared by J. W. Powell for the Seventh Annual Report of the Bureau of American Ethnology, showing the distribution of the American Indian linguistic stock in North America and Greenland; and a map of South America, showing the distribution of Indian tribal and linguistic groups in 1950.

Still pictures, 1871-1918 (3,650 items), consist of photographs of the Bureau of American Ethnology, 1871-1907, including American Indian chiefs and villages; Indians, Mormons, the petrified forest, and ranch life in the Arizona Territory; delegations to Washington, D.C.; western Indians and geological formations, made by the Geographical Surveys West of the One Hundredth Meridian, 1871-74; watercolor sketches of Indian pueblos and cave dwellings, by Matilda Cope Stevenson, 1882; fish and other marine life; foreign customs and cultures, and historic places in the British Isles, Europe, and the Pacific Islands; the River Clyde, Scotland, and rural Philadelphia, ca. 1900; the Canal Zone and construction of the Panama Canal; and World War I battle scenes taken in Belgium and France.

Motion pictures (49 reels) consist of films from the Bureau of American Ethnology, illustrating the preparation of an anthropological exhibit at the Smithsonian; archaeological explorations and diggings in New Mexico, Arizona, Tennessee, Colorado, Yucatan, and Honduras, 1931-41; the making of an intertribal sign language dictionary of the American Indians of the Great Plains, and the theory, history, and practice of the sign language, ca. 1930-31. Films of the Washington zoo; National Gallery of Art films on the history of the planning and development of Washington, D.C., 1929 and 1949; and National Museum films on the history of flight, 1903-27, important events in the life of Charles A. Lindbergh, and a glider exhibition and contest.

Sound recordings (422 items) from the Bureau of American Ethnology of songs and linguistic material in Indian languages, including Aleut, Mission, Chumash, and Creek, with some translations, 1912, 1914, and 1930-41; and recordings of the radio series "The World is Yours," broadcast for the Smithsonian Institution by the U.S. Office of Education, 1936-41.

RECORDS OF THE TENNESSEE VALLEY AUTHORITY
(RECORD GROUP 142)

The Tennessee Valley Authority (TVA) is a corporation created by an act of May 18, 1933, to conduct a unified program of resource conservation, development, and use; speed the economic development of the Tennessee Valley region; and advance its national defense capabilities. All functions of the Authority are vested in its three-member Board of Directors, appointed by the President and reporting directly to him. The General Manager, TVA's principal administrative officer, reports to the Board of Directors.

TVA operates the Tennessee River control system, investigates the need for and feasibility of additional river control projects, assists State and local governments in reducing local flood problems, and, with cooperating agencies, encourages use of navigable waterways. At a national laboratory at Muscle Shoals, Ala., TVA develops new and improved fertilizers. With other agencies it conducts research and development programs in forestry, fish and game conservation, watershed protection, health services, and economic development of the Tennessee Valley tributary areas.

There are 10 cubic feet of cartographic and audiovisual records dated between 1933 and 1956 in this record group. No textual records have been accessioned.

CARTOGRAPHIC AND AUDIOVISUAL RECORDS. 1933-56. 3,754 items.

Maps of the Southeastern United States and of the Tennessee Valley, including general, planimetric, and specialized maps showing hydrography, climatic patterns, minerals, forests, crops, landownership, flood control projects, transportation and communication systems, and various types of demographic and social data.

Photographs (2,000 items) of the Tennessee Valley and vicinity, showing soil erosion, taverns, mills, homes, barns, bridges, waterfalls, national and State parks, roads and trails, and dams.

RECORDS OF THE
UNITED STATES CIVIL SERVICE COMMISSION
(RECORD GROUP 146)

The U.S. Civil Service Commission, created by an act of January 16, 1883, replaced a Civil Service Commission that had originated under an act of March 3, 1871, as the Advisory Board of the Civil Service. The Commission was authorized to establish a merit system under which selections for Government-service appointments would be based on applicants' demonstrated relative fitness. Additional legislation, including Reorganization Plan No. 5 of 1949, and Executive orders have clarified and broadened the authority of the Commission. Its activities now include examining applicants for Federal positions; supplying personnel officials with qualified candidates' names; establishing standards for reinstating, promoting, and transferring Federal employees; conducting investigations to enforce Civil Service laws and regulations; studying the administration of the Government security program and conducting national agency checks and inquiries concerning that program; and administering the statutory provisions and Civil Service regulations that restrict Federal employee political activity, the Veterans Preference Act of 1944, the Classification Act of 1949, the Government Employees Incentive Awards Act, and the Civil Service Retirement Act.

There are 109 cubic feet of records dated between 1871 and 1946 in this record group.

RECORDS. 1871–1946. 131 lin. ft.

These consist of minutes of the (Grant) Civil Service Commission and its predecessor, 1871–75, the Civil Service commissioners, 1886–1901 and 1917–18,

and the Boards of Civil Service Examiners for Port Huron, Mich., 1883–97, and the customhouse, New York City, May-October 1898; letters sent by the Commission, 1883–97, and by its offices, 1883–1919; correspondence of the Commission, 1884–1906, and its offices, 1898–1914; Executive orders that changed Civil Service rules, 1883–1901; position allocation appeal dossiers of the Personnel Classification Division, 1923–38; records of an interagency committee that recommended improvements in Federal retirement and personnel reporting systems, 1942–46; and the motion picture film "Won Through Merit," ca. 1921.

SPECIFIC RESTRICTIONS

Records: Position allocation appeal dossiers.

Restrictions: All requests for information about specific individuals will be referred for determination of action thereon to the Chairman of the Civil Service Commission or a member of his staff authorized to act for him. Determination of action on all other requests will be made by the Archivist . . . subject to the specific requirement that each person seeking information from these records will obligate himself not to reveal the names of individuals as obtained from them without the written approval of the Chairman of the Civil Service Commission or a member of his staff authorized to act for him.

Specified by: U.S. Civil Service Commission.

RECORDS OF THE
UNITED STATES INFORMATION AGENCY
(RECORD GROUP 306)

The U.S. Information Agency (USIA) was established by Reorganization Plan No. 8 and Executive Order 10477 of August 1, 1953. It carries out international information activities under the United States Information and Educational Exchange Act of 1948, as amended, and international activities under the United States Mutual Educational and Cultural Exchange Act of 1961, as amended. The purpose of the USIA is to help achieve U.S. foreign policy objectives by influencing public attitudes in other nations and by advising the President, his representatives abroad, and various departments and agencies on the implications of foreign opinion for present and contemplated U.S. policies, programs, and official statements. The media services of the USIA are the Broadcasting Service (Voice of America), which produces and broadcasts radio programs in English and other languages; the Information Center Service, which promotes distribution of American books, operates an exhibits program, supports the teaching of English in foreign countries, and otherwise assists information centers; the Motion Picture and Television Service, which provides motion pictures and television films and tapes for foreign viewing; and the Press and Publications Service, which produces a wide variety of editorial material for placement in foreign publications. The USIA offices abroad (the U.S. Information Service), under supervision of chiefs of diplomatic missions, conduct public information, public relations, and cultural activities for U.S. Government agencies to inform or influence foreign public opinion.

There are 1,091 cubic feet of records (including 5 cu. ft. in JFKL) dated between 1900 and 1965 in this record group.

RECORDS. 1963. 5 lin. ft. (in JFKL).

These consist of condolence books, telegrams received and drafts of telegrams sent, memorandums, messages, and drafts of replies to condolences from heads of state regarding the death of President Kennedy.

AUDIOVISUAL RECORDS.
1900-1965. 664,393 items.

Photographs, 1900-1961 (663,998 items), consist of the photographic file of the Paris Bureau of *The New York Times*, 1900-1950, covering a broad range of subjects, including worldwide coverage of sports, festivities, industries, institutions, and fashions; the Paris Exposition of 1900; World War I; French troops and maneuvers between wars; the Paris riots of 1934; the Saar Plebiscite, 1935; the Russo-Finnish War, 1939-40; the opening phases of World War II and activities of Allied and Axis Armed Forces; the liberation and Allied occupation of Europe; and postwar international meetings, treaties, and conferences, including organization of the United Nations. There are also photographs from the International Press Service "hold file" used in its news activities and for the production of displays, picture stories, and posters, and to illustrate press releases, 1948-57; relating to activities of prominent persons, the American Council on Education, industry, conservation, the merchant marine, the North African campaign in World War II, and the role of women in war, 1948-61; and of overseas installations and activities of the Information Center Service, 1948-54.

Motion pictures, 1954-57 (8 reels), relate to the peacetime uses of atomic energy and the second inauguration of President Dwight D. Eisenhower, and also document the Agency's activities.

Sound recordings, 1950-65 (387 items), made by or for the Voice of America for overseas release, consist of dramatizations, reports, speeches, and interviews designed to promote better understanding of the United States. They relate to rural America, labor, farming, education, scientific development, economics, the role of women, travel, immigrants in America, conservation, politics, food inspection, public health, charitable and service organizations, literature, foreign students in the United States, communications media, world food production, world health, the establishment of the Constitution and the concept of individual freedom, the sesquicentennial of the birth of President Abraham Lincoln, and the Korean action. Included are programs from the "Washington Interview," "The Puerto Rican Story," "The Jeffersonian Heritage," "Document: Deep South," "Atoms for Power," "New World of Atomic Energy," "Indian Country," "The Great Lakes," and the "New Horizons in Science" series.

RECORDS OF THE UNITED STATES TARIFF COMMISSION
(RECORD GROUP 81)

The U.S. Tariff Commission was created by an act of September 8, 1916, which also provided for the transfer to the Commission of all records and functions of its predecessors, the Tariff Board and the Cost of Production Division of the Bureau of Foreign and Domestic Commerce. Commission functions include investigation of problems of customs administration; domestic and foreign tariff regulations, industries, and manufacturing costs; questions relating to commercial treaties; unfair competition in the import trade; and foreign discrimination against American trade. It cooperates with other agencies in implementing reciprocal trade and agricultural programs.

There are 153 cubic feet of records dated between 1909 and 1944 in this record group.

RECORDS OF THE TARIFF BOARD. 1909-12. 23 lin. ft.

These consist of reports of meetings and hearings, correspondence relating to Board organization, and general correspondence, 1909-12; and records relating to investigations of foreign tariff laws and tariff discrimination, 1909-10, and to Board cost-of-production studies, 1910-12.

RECORDS OF THE COST OF PRODUCTION DIVISION OF THE BUREAU OF FOREIGN AND DOMESTIC COMMERCE. 1915-16. 2 lin. ft.

These consist of working papers and studies relating to business activities, foreign commerce, tariffs, and administrative activities.

RECORDS OF THE U.S. TARIFF COMMISSION. 1917-44. 128 lin. ft. and 167 rolls of microfilm.

There are general correspondence files relating to administration, 1921-39; microfilm copies of general correspondence (104 rolls), 1917-44, reports and correspondence of European agents and personal correspondence of Chairman F. W. Taussig (23 rolls), 1919-35, and statistical reports (40 rolls), 1930-38; questionnaires, statistical tables, and correspondence relating to a study of free ports, 1917-19; and records relating to surveys of the production of various commodities and investigations of the Commission, 1918-40. Also included are a published outline map of Mexico and Central America, 1943, and maps showing legal limits of U.S. territorial waters, 1930 (27 items).

SPECIFIC RESTRICTIONS

I. *Records*: Records in the general files of the Tariff Board and the U. S. Tariff Commission that contain information on trade secrets and processes.

Restrictions: "It shall be unlawful for any member of the Commission, . . . or any other officer or employee of the United States, to divulge, or to make known in any manner whatever not provided for by law, to any person, the trade secrets or processes of any person, firm, . . . or association embraced in any examination or investigation conducted by the Commission, . . ." (39 Stat. 798 and 46 Stat. 701).

Specified by: Congress of the United States.

II. *Records*: Records in the general files of the U.S. Tariff Commission that are marked "Confidential."

Restrictions: These records may not be examined by or copies of or information from them furnished to any person except as designated by the Tariff Commission.

Specified by: U.S. Tariff Commission.

RECORDS OF THE VETERANS ADMINISTRATION
(RECORD GROUP 15)

The present Veterans Administration (VA) is the result of policies and programs that date back to the American Revolution. The First Congress enacted legislation in 1789 to continue pensions provided in acts of the Continental Congress, and as early as 1792 the War Department was concerned with pension matters. Congress controlled the actual allowance of Revolutionary War claims until 1803, when this responsibility was delegated to the Secretary of War. Naval pensions were paid from a fund created in 1799 and administered until 1832 by a commission composed of the Secretaries of War, Navy, and Treasury, and from 1832 to 1840 by the Secretary of the Navy alone. The Secretary of the Treasury administered an act of 1828 granting pensions to Revolutionary War veterans until 1835 when its administration was transferred to the War Department, where Congress, in 1833, had made provision for the appointment of a Commissioner of Pensions. After 1840 his duties were placed under the direction of the Secretaries of War and Navy. The office of the Commissioner was transferred to the Department of the Interior in 1849. Later the office became the Bureau of Pensions.

An act of August 9, 1921, created the Veterans' Bureau (soon renamed the U.S. Veterans' Bureau) in which were consolidated the Bureau of War Risk Insurance (established in 1914) from the Treasury Department, the Rehabilitation Division of the Federal Board for Vocational Education (established in 1918), and activities of the Public Health Service concerning World War I veterans. An Executive order of July 20, 1930, created the Veterans Administration by merging the Bureau of Pensions, the U.S. Veterans' Bureau, the National Home for Disabled Volunteer Soldiers (incorporated in 1866), and functions of the Office of the Surgeon General concerned with providing artificial limbs and other appliances to veterans. Domiciliary facilities developed by the National Home for Disabled Volunteer Soldiers were continued as the Homes Service.

The VA is an independent Federal agency, under an Administrator for Veterans Affairs. It administers laws relating to benefits and relief for veterans and is responsible for extending relief to dependents of disabled or deceased veterans.

See John William Oliver, *History of Civil War Military Pensions, 1861-1885* (Madison, 1917); William H. Glasson, *Federal Military Pensions in the United States* (New York, 1918); and Gustavus A. Weber and Lawrence F. Schmeckebier, *The Veterans' Administration: Its History, Activities and Organization* (1934).

There are 76,203 cubic feet of records dated between 1773 and 1964 in this record group.

ADMINISTRATIVE AND LEGAL RECORDS. 1826-1964. 2,285 lin. ft. (in WNRC).

Administrative records consist of order books of the Secretary of the Interior, Commissioner of Pensions, and other pension officials; collections and digests of pension decisions and indexes; decisions by the Secretary of the Interior on pension appeals, 1849-96; a register of appeals; reviews; legal opinions; and indexes. Fragmentary personnel records consist of miscellaneous correspondence, memorandums, reports, and registers for periods between 1884 and 1930; records of examining surgeons consist of lists, memorandums, correspondence, instructions, and other records for periods between 1903 and 1931.

Other records dated between 1826 and 1941 include correspondence, registers of letters, pension materials, bounty land correspondence, reports, tables, record books, lists, scrapbooks, statistical charts, and collections of publications. There is an index for Civil War military hospitals, 1882, and guides and records for certain hospitals.

Records relating to the Civilian Conservation Corps (CCC), 1933-41, consist of regulations and instructions relating to the selection of a veterans contingent of the CCC.

Legal records of the Office of the Solicitor of the Veterans Administration and predecessor units of the Bureau of Pensions and the Veterans' Bureau consist primarily of case files of investigations handled by those offices, 1862-1933, relative to charges of malfeasance against individual attorneys, agents, notaries, and other persons. An estimated 60,000 cards show the status of attorneys, firms, subagents, and organizations admitted to prosecute claims for the Bureau of Pensions, the Veterans' Bureau, or the VA, 1862-1933. Other legal records include synopses of cases, indexes, digests, and court proceedings, 1882-1924; and title papers and office case files, 1940-64.

WAR RISK INSURANCE RECORDS. 1914-34. 313 lin. ft.

The Bureau of War Risk Insurance was established in the Department of the Treasury September 2, 1914, to insure American vessels and cargoes. On June 12, 1917, an amendment provided for the insurance of officers and members of the crew of vessels in the American Merchant Marine against loss of life, injury, or detention resulting from the hazards of war. Additional functions authorized on October 6, 1917, included the issuance of insurance to World War I personnel against disability or death. In order to provide insurance to men outside the United States, a temporary administrative organization was formed in Paris in November 1917, and on January 7, 1918, a War Risk Section was established in the Line of Communication, American Expeditionary Forces. The Bureau also administered the provisions of article 4 of the Civil Relief Act, approved March 8, 1918, for the protection of life insurance policies of members of the Armed Forces against lapse because of nonpayment of premiums. The Bureau was abolished and its functions and records were transferred to the Veterans' Bureau on August 9, 1921. All accounts with insurers concerned with "civil relief" protection of life insurance were terminated by June 30, 1924. Records of World War I veterans relating to war risk insurance benefits are also among the records of the Bureau of War Risk Litigation (see RG 190), among which are files created by the Bureau of War Risk Insurance of the Treasury Department, the Veterans' Bureau, and the Veterans Administration dating from 1919 that were inherited and continued by the Bureau of War Risk Litigation when it was established in the Department of Justice in 1933.

The records consist of general correspondence of the Director and Assistant Director, 1914-31, and the Advisory Board, 1914-21; administrative correspondence of the Allotment and Allowance Division, 1918-34; records of the Marine, Seamen's, and Civil Relief Sections, 1914-22; correspondence and other records of the Insurance Division of the Veterans' Bureau, 1914-17; administrative and claims files of the War Risk Section, Line of Communications, American Expeditionary Forces, 1917-24; and some records relating to claims brought before the Mixed Claims Commission, United States and Germany. The "diary" of the Paris office is with records of the American Expeditionary Forces (see RG 120).

VOCATIONAL-REHABILITATION RECORDS. 1918-28. 2,265 lin. ft. (in WNRC).

The program for the vocational rehabilitation of disabled veterans of World War I, administered from 1918 to 1921 by the Federal Board for Vocational Education and by the Veterans' Bureau until 1928, was carried out by the Rehabilitation Division. The records consist of training-center files, trainee record cards, sample regional office training case files, district and regional files, and files of correspondence with educational institutions, hospitals, private business organizations, welfare and veterans organizations, and field, medical, placement, and other Division officers. Also included are bulletins, general orders, regulations and field orders, and numerous small files of correspondence and reports.

RECORDS RELATING TO PENSION AND BOUNTY LAND CLAIMS. 1773-1942. 64,250 lin. ft. and 2,811 rolls of microfilm.

These records include many originally accumulated in the War, Treasury, Navy, and Interior Departments, all of which at one time had the function of adjudicating claims for pensions and bounty lands. They include correspondence of the Commissioner of Pensions and his predecessors from 1800 to 1866; correspondence relating to claims filed under special congressional acts of 1828, 1832, and 1853; and letters sent by the Commissioners of the Navy Pension Fund, 1800-1809 and 1813-16.

Pension application files cover service in the Revolution, the War of 1812, the Mexican, Civil, Spanish-American, and Indian Wars, and other military operations to 1917. Revolutionary War service case files consist of pension and bounty land applications filed between 1800 and 1900, claims for half-pay-for-life and pensions filed between 1800 and 1859, and disapproved applications. War of 1812 service case files consist of pension and bounty land applications filed between 1812 and 1910. Mexican War service case files consist of applications filed between 1847 and 1930, approved and disapproved applications filed between 1887 and 1926, and approved and disapproved applications by dependents and widows. Miscellaneous applications for the period before 1861 include files based on service between 1783 and 1861 and submitted between 1800 and 1930, case files of bounty land applications for the period 1812 to 1855, and claims by Indians for the period 1812 to 1855. For case files based on service before 1865 there is a card register of application and certificate numbers.

With the exception of certain limited series, the Civil War and Spanish-American War pension applications are filed together. These records consist of approved and disapproved pension applications based on service chiefly in these two wars filed between 1861 and 1934 and covering both Army and Navy service after 1910. Pension applications of widows and dependents consist of approved and disapproved applications. Naval files consist of approved and disapproved pension applications of Navy veterans submitted between the years 1861 and 1910. Case files of pension applications of widows and dependents consist of approved and disapproved claims. There are microfilm indexes (2,811 rolls) to most of these case files, and a card index of names of remarried widows.

Pension application files for service in the Indian wars cover the period from 1892 to 1926. These files consist of veterans', widows', and dependents' approved and disapproved pension applications. There are case files of pension applications arising out of new claims filed after 1934 for service from 1817 to 1917 and 1921 to 1940 (exclusive of the Revolution, the War of 1812, and World War I), with indexes, 1861-1942. There are also bounty land records that consist of an incomplete list of bounty land applications (filed ca. 1800-1900), registers of bounty land claims filed and warrants issued from 1800 to 1912, and stubs and duplicates of bounty land warrant and scrip certificates, 1803-97.

Other records consist of Navy Department claims, correspondence, and accounts relating to naval and privateer

service pensions from 1800 to 1900; War Department miscellaneous correspondence, reports, and records for the years 1812 to 1913; scrapbooks, 1773-1919; administrative orders, pension board decisions, and other records relating to bounty land warrants from 1813 to 1875; and registers, 1865-1900.

Individual case files contain birth, marriage, and death records, copies of military records, medical histories, personal histories of dependents, affidavits and testimonials, correspondence, examiners' reports, and decisions of adjudicating agencies. Many of these accompanying papers are of earlier or later date than the dates of applications.

FINANCIAL RECORDS. 1805-1933. 2,639 lin. ft.

These records consist of pension agency payment books, 1805-1909, with a card index; pension payment rolls of Army veterans, their widows and dependents for the years 1857-76, pension rolls of Navy veterans and their dependents, 1860-76, ledgers of pension accounts for the years 1890-1921, appropriation accounts for the years 1891-1908, and pension payment cards, 1907-33.

Also included are many pension applications, certificates, and lists and registers of pensioners, most of which are registers of pension certificates issued to Army and Navy veterans between 1816 and 1914 and to widows and other dependents between 1862 and 1914; lists of veterans and dependents pensioned under laws enacted between 1818 and 1853; and registers of applications by veterans who served after March 4, 1861, with similar registers for dependents.

RECORDS RELATING TO VETERANS' HOMES. 1866-1938. 237 lin. ft.

Legislation of 1865, 1866, and 1873 established a National Home for Disabled Volunteer Soldiers. There were 10 branch homes and a sanitarium (all administered by a Board of Managers) by 1930 when they were transferred to the Veterans Administration to be operated by its Homes Service. There are records of the homes at Dayton, Ohio, 1867-1935; Danville, Ill., 1898-1934; Togus, Maine, 1866-1934; Marion, Ind., 1890-1931; Johnson City, Tenn., 1903-34; Milwaukee, Wis., 1867-1934; Sawtelle, Calif., 1888-1933; Roseburg, Oreg., 1894-1937; Hampton, Va., 1871-1938; and Leavenworth, Kans., 1885-1934. There are also records of the Battle Mountain Sanitarium in Hot Springs, S. Dak., 1907-34; and the home for soldiers and sailors at Bath, N.Y., a State home that passed into Federal hands in 1932. The records include registers of members, with indexes; sample case files of members; and proceedings, correspondence, memorandums, reports, and other administrative records of the councils of administration or governors of the branch homes.

1890 CENSUS SCHEDULES ENUMERATING UNION CIVIL WAR VETERANS. 1890. 23 lin. ft.

The act of March 1, 1889, authorizing the 11th decennial census, provided for a special enumeration of Union survivors or their widows, and legislation of 1894 directed that the resulting schedules be transferred to the Commissioner of Pensions. These records are arranged alphabetically by State and thereunder by county. The schedules for the first half of the alphabet were destroyed by fire; those that remain are for States from Kentucky through Wyoming. These schedules list Civil War Union veterans of all services, or their widows, residing in the United States on June 1, 1890. Each veteran is recorded by name, residence, rank, company, regiment or Navy vessel, dates of service, and any incurred disability.

RECORDS RELATING TO ISSUANCE OF PROSTHETIC APPLIANCES. 1862-1935. 291 lin. ft. (in WNRC).

The first provision for supplying disabled veterans with prosthetic appliances was made by an act of July 16, 1862. Legislation in 1872 and 1879 extended this service to trusses. A cash commutation was available to veterans in lieu of such appliances until legislation in 1933 and 1944 ended the practice. The Surgeon General of the Army administered this function until December 1, 1930, when it was transferred with related records to the VA. Most extensive are the case files relating to applications for prosthetic appliances or commutation in lieu thereof, 1862-1933, including applications, correspondence, pension certificates, medical reports, and other records. There are also record books and registers of claims for prosthetic and other appliances and their issuance; and correspondence relating to approved and disapproved applications, 1875-1935.

AUDIOVISUAL RECORDS. 1861-1960. 1,704 items.

Still pictures (1,677 items) include photographs of Commissioners of Pensions, 1861-1925; photographs relating to the rehabilitation program of the Federal Board for Vocational Education, 1918-28, and VA rehabilitation activities, 1945-60; photographs of VA facilities and construction projects, including plans and architectural drawings for some hospitals, 1932-60; photographs of the Pension Building, 1883-85, and a Liberty Loan mass meeting in Washington, D.C., 1917; and a color lithograph of the Volunteer Refreshment Saloon in Philadelphia, ca. 1860.

There are motion pictures (27 reels) showing the work of the Bureau of War Risk Insurance, 1919, the organization of the VA in 1946, and educational, financial, medical, and rehabilitation services.

See Thayer M. Boardman, Myra R. Trever, and Louise W. Southwick, comps., *Preliminary Inventory of the Administrative Records of the Bureau of Pensions and the Pension Service*, PI 55 (1953).

Microfilm Publications: For a complete listing see the current *List of National Archives Microfilm Publications*.

SPECIFIC RESTRICTIONS

Records: Claims records based on service terminated less than 75 years ago.

Restrictions: No disclosure shall be made from these records of any information that would be detrimental to the veteran or prejudicial, so far as may be apparent, to the interests of any living person or to the interests of the Government. No confidential communications among them, including medical evidence, summaries and recommendations of inspectors or field examiners, and reports relating to criminal charges and investigations or to evidence obtained in cases involving departments, bureaus, or other agencies, shall be made available to the general public. No statement regarding military service shall be supplied from them except for service as claimed by the veteran.

Specified by: Administrator of Veterans Affairs.

DISCONTINUED INDEPENDENT AGENCIES

From World War I to 1933

RECORDS OF THE ALLIED PURCHASING COMMISSION
(RECORD GROUP 113)

Under an act of April 24, 1917, arrangements were made between the Secretary of the Treasury and representatives of France, Great Britain, Russia, Belgium, Serbia, Italy, and the National Czechoslovak Council for the establishment of credits and the purchase of supplies by nations at war with the Central Powers. By agreements with France, Great Britain, and Russia in August 1917, the Allied Purchasing Commission, consisting of three members, was established to handle applications to purchase supplies in the United States. The Commission members were also members of the War Industries Board (see RG 61). The Commission met with representatives of the Allied Governments and officials of the War Industries Board, the War Trade Board, and the Treasury Department to discuss requirements, priorities, prices, and supply and transportation problems. When agreements were terminated by mutual consent in December 1918, the Chairman of the Commission resigned, and some of its personnel and all of its records were transferred to the Treasury Department. The last report on Commission business was completed in May 1919.

There are 14 cubic feet of records dated between 1917 and 1919, with a few as early as 1914, in this record group.

RECORDS. 1917-19. 17 lin. ft.

These consist of minutes, with indexes and historical summaries of operations and procedures; correspondence; summaries of applications approved and canceled; lists, tabulations, and statements of contracts let, completed, or canceled; consolidated statements by the Inter-Ally Council on War Purchases and Finance of orders placed and requirements estimated; a register of orders and applications, with indexes by country and commodity; schedules of expenditures from U.S. Government credits, relating to purchases by Allied war missions; and a statement and general summary relating to Russian contracts.

See *Preliminary Inventory of the War Industries Board Records*, PI 1 (1941).

RECORDS OF THE CAPITAL ISSUES COMMITTEE
(RECORD GROUP 158)

A Capital Issues Committee of three members was created within the Federal Reserve Board in January 1918 to prevent, through voluntary regulation, the diversion of capital to unessential projects. In May 1918 it was replaced by a new Capital Issues Committee of seven members appointed by the President under authority of the War Finance Corporation Act of April 5, 1918. This Committee was authorized to determine whether proposed security issues were compatible with the national interest. Much of the work of the Committee was decentralized and assigned to subcommittees in each Federal Reserve district. The Committee suspended its activities on December 31, 1918. A Presidential proclamation of August 30, 1919, directed the Committee to terminate its affairs and to transfer its records to the Federal Trade Commission.

There are 124 cubic feet of records (in WNRC) dated between 1918 and 1919 in this record group.

RECORDS. 1918-19. 149 lin. ft.

Records of the Washington office, including minutes; office files of Charles S. Hamlin, Chairman and fiscal agent; correspondence and an accompanying

index; applications for security issue permits; decisions on applications; and bulletins and other issuances. There are also minutes, correspondence, and other records of the field offices at Atlanta, Chicago, Kansas City, New York, Philadelphia, Richmond, St. Louis, and San Francisco. (Records of the San Francisco subcommittee, except the minutes, are in the University of Washington Library, Seattle, Wash. There are no records of the Boston and Minneapolis subcommittees.)

RECORDS OF THE COUNCIL OF NATIONAL DEFENSE
(RECORD GROUP 62)

The Council of National Defense was established August 29, 1916, to coordinate resources and industries for national security and welfare. It was the first large emergency agency of World War I and the parent agency of most of the other special war agencies. The Council, which consisted of six Cabinet members—the Secretaries of War, the Navy, the Interior, Agriculture, Commerce, and Labor—and was assisted by an Advisory Commission, directed investigations and made recommendations concerning mobilization of resources for defense and sought to create conditions that would permit immediate concentration and utilization of resources in time of need. Originally a research and planning agency, it later assumed some administrative responsibilities. Early in 1917 the Council and its Advisory Commission organized numerous boards, sections, committees, and subcommittees, many of which developed into or were replaced by more permanent organizations. Much of the work of the Council was gradually centralized in the War Industries Board (see RG 61), which became a separate administrative agency on May 28, 1918. The Council then became concerned mainly with stimulating civilian morale, coordinating the

work of some 164,000 State and local defense councils and 18,000 women's committees, and studying problems of postwar readjustment and reconstruction.

The Council's activities were suspended June 30, 1921, and its records were placed in the custody of the War Department. It was reactivated briefly during World War II, but there are no records of the Council for that period in this record group. The Council still has a legal existence, but it is inactive.

Papers, 1940-42 (8 lin. ft.), of the Office of the Secretary of the Advisory Commission to the Council of National Defense are in FDRL.

See Council of National Defense, *Annual Reports* (1917-20).

There are 385 cubic feet of records (in WNRC) dated between 1916 and 1921, with some dated as early as 1914 and as late as 1937, in this record group.

RECORDS. 1916-21. 462 lin. ft.

Minutes, correspondence, periodic and special reports, memorandums, bulletins, circulars, tables, lists, press releases, newspaper clippings, publications, abstract record cards, and indexes relating to the general administration and functions of the Council and its Advisory Commission and to the work of subordinate units. These include the Commercial Economy Board; Committees on Coal Production, Labor, Supplies, and Women's Defense Work; Files and Records Division (postwar); General Medical Board; General Munitions Board; Highways Transport Committee; Medicine and Sanitation Committee; Munitions Standards Board; Reconstruction Research Division; State Councils Section and its successor, the Field Division; and Statistics Division. There are also records of the War Department as custodian of the Council's records.

See *Preliminary Inventory of the Council of National Defense Records, 1916-1921*, PI 2 (1942).

RECORDS OF THE FEDERAL FUEL DISTRIBUTOR
(RECORD GROUP 89)

The office of the Federal Fuel Distributor was created by an act of September 22, 1922, "to assure an adequate supply and an equitable distribution of coal and other fuel . . . and for the further purpose of assisting in carrying into effect the orders of the Interstate Commerce Commission." The Federal Fuel Distributor assumed the functions of the President's Fuel Distribution Committee, which had been appointed in July 1922 during a period of strikes to establish voluntary price agreements for coal and to help administer an Interstate Commerce Commission (ICC) order establishing coal transportation priorities for public institutions, railways, public utilities, and vital industries. The Federal Fuel Distributor was to determine whether a shortage of fuel existed; fuel sources, markets, and distribution facilities; normal and current fuel prices and whether current prices were reasonable; and the nature and location of fuel consumers and which of them should receive transportation and distribution priority. The organization of the office provided for an administrative committee, advisory committees on industry and transportation, and 17 district committees that primarily allocated coal priority orders under ICC authority. The office worked closely with the Secretary of Commerce, the ICC, and the U.S. Coal Commission. It was terminated by statutory limitation September 21, 1923.

See Federal Fuel Distributor, *Final Report* (1923).

There are 57 cubic feet of records (in WNRC) dated between 1922 and 1923 in this record group.

RECORDS OF THE PRESIDENT'S FUEL DISTRIBUTION COMMITTEE. Aug.-Sept. 1922.
12 lin. ft.

These records include Committee correspondence, with an index, and some press releases; and correspondence of the Committee's district representatives at Birmingham, Ala.; Louisville, Ky.; Knoxville, Tenn.; Norton, Va.; and Bluefield, Fairmont, Huntington, and Thurmond, W. Va.

RECORDS OF THE FEDERAL FUEL DISTRIBUTOR. 1922-23.
54 lin. ft.

Included are correspondence of the Federal Fuel Distributor with the States and Federal agencies and officials, and of Secretary of Commerce Hoover with trade associations; correspondence and related reports of the Advisory Committee on Industry; reference files including printed and processed material on the coal industry, strikes, and other coal-related matters; appointments, oaths of office, releases, and memorandums concerning employees; and correspondence of district representatives at Bluefield, W. Va., Columbus, Ohio, and St. Louis, Mo.

RECORDS OF THE NATIONAL WAR LABOR BOARD
(WORLD WAR I)
(RECORD GROUP 2)

The National War Labor Board, composed of representatives from labor, management, and the general public, was appointed March 29, 1918, by the Secretary of Labor in his capacity as War Labor Administrator to arbitrate, mediate, and conciliate labor disputes that might interfere with the effective conduct of the war. The Board was formally dissolved August 12, 1919.

There are 136 cubic feet of records dated between 1918 and 1919 in this record group.

RECORDS. 1918-19. 163 lin. ft.

These consist of minutes; case files (in WNRC); transcripts of hearings (in WNRC); records, with an index, relating to cases, including registers, resumes, digests, hearing schedules, examiners' reports, findings and awards, arbitrators' opinions, appeals, interpretations, correspondence, rulings, briefs, questionnaires, nominating petitions, and election ballots and results; files of staff members; a general subject file; correspondence, with an index; administrative and fiscal records; and newspaper clippings.

See Herbert Fine, comp., *Preliminary Inventory of the Records of the National War Labor Board*, PI 5 (1943).

RECORDS OF THE
RECONSTRUCTION FINANCE CORPORATION
(RECORD GROUP 234)

The Reconstruction Finance Corporation (RFC) was created by an act of January 22, 1932, to extend aid during the depression to agriculture, commerce, and industry by direct loans to banks, other credit agencies, and, with approval of the Interstate Commerce Commission, to railroads or receivers of railroads. Subsequent legislation authorized the RFC to purchase capital stock of banks and insurance companies; make loans to businesses and other classes of borrowers; and, with the advent of World War II, acquire strategic and critical materials, provide financing for plant conversion and construction, and undertake many other activities involved in the war effort.

The RFC was headed by a Board of Directors with a Chairman of the Board, an Executive Committee, a Secretary, and a Treasurer. In May 1951 an Administrator replaced the Board of Directors. It operated through its Washington office, loan agencies in 33 cities, subsidiary corporations, the Federal Reserve banks, and special representatives in Hawaii, Puerto Rico, and the Virgin Islands. The following subsidiaries were established: Defense Homes Corporation, Defense Plant Corporation, Defense Supplies Corporation, Disaster Loan Corporation, Federal National Mortgage Association, Metals Reserve Company, Pacific Development Corporation, Petroleum Reserve Corporation, Regional Agricultural Credit Corporations (which were transferred to the Farm Credit Administration in 1933), Rubber Development Corporation, Rubber Reserve Company, RFC Mortgage Company, U.S. Commercial Company, War Assets Corporation, and War Damage Corporation. In addition the RFC acquired the assets of the Electric Home and Farm Authority and the Lafayette Building Corporation. The subsidiaries were dissolved and liquidated by the RFC or were transferred to other Federal agencies when the RFC was terminated.

The RFC functioned as an independent agency except when it was under jurisdiction of the Federal Loan Agency (April 25, 1939–February 24, 1942, and February 24, 1945–June 30, 1947) and the Department of Commerce (February 24, 1942–February 24, 1945). The RFC was originally established for 10 years, but amendments to the original act extended this to June 30, 1948, and again to June 30, 1956. The RFC Liquidation Act terminated the Corporation's lending powers on September 28, 1953, although the RFC continued until June 30, 1954. Thereafter, the Secretary of the Treasury assumed all powers, duties, and authority previously held by the RFC Administrator. The RFC was finally abolished on June 30, 1957.

In 1954 certain RFC functions were assigned to appropriate agencies for liquidation. Foreign loans were assigned to the Export-Import Bank of Washington; loans to victims of floods or other catastrophes, to the Small Business Administration; and mortgages held by the RFC, to the Federal National Mortgage Association. In 1957 RFC's remaining functions were transferred as follows: loans and contracts with States, municipalities, and other public bodies for drainage and irrigation projects, to the Housing and Home Finance Agency; affairs of the Smaller War Plants Corporation and of the RFC Price Adjustment Board, to the General Services Administration; loans to business enterprises, to the Small Business Administration; and all remaining functions, including loans to railroads, financial institutions, and insurance companies, and affairs of the War Damage Corporation, to the Department of the Treasury. RFC disposition of synthetic rubber production facilities, which had been assigned to the Rubber Producing Facilities Disposal Commission, and tin smelting facilities was transferred to the Federal Facilities Corporation (FFC) in 1954. The FFC was placed under the direction of the Administrator of General Services in 1957, and its functions were transferred to the Administrator by the act in 1961 that abolished the FFC.

There are 4,187 cubic feet of records dated between 1932 and 1961 in this record group.

RECORDS OF THE OFFICE OF THE SECRETARY OF THE RFC. 1932-57. 667 lin. ft.

These consist of minutes of the Board of Directors and the Executive Committee, 1932-51, the RFC Administrator, 1951-54, and the assistant to the Secretary of the Treasury, 1954-57, with related exhibits, reports, documents, and transcripts of congressional hearings, reports to the Congress, and other records relating to RFC legislation, 1932-54; official seals, charters and bylaws, and organizational charts of the RFC and subsidiary corporations, 1932-54; transcripts of proceedings of the Board of Directors with representatives of banks, insurance companies, trust companies, railroads, and local government agencies, 1932-35; administrative subject files, general correspondence, and separate files of correspondence with Government agencies, the White House, and the Bureau of the Budget, 1932-57; administrative manuals, instructional issuances, bulletins, and circulars, 1932-57; resolutions regarding delegations of authority, with indexes, 1932-55; administrative histories of RFC wartime programs, 1943-54; speeches and diaries of RFC officials,

1932-54; records relating to a financial survey of airlines, 1947-50; correspondence relating to the 1944 Servicemen's Readjustment Act, 1944-53; minutes and other records relating to meetings of the Claims Review Committee of the Office of Loans, 1950-54, the Committee on Operations, 1936, the Office of Production Review Committee, 1949-51, the Advisory Loan Committee of the Atlanta Loan Agency, 1932-53, the Central Advisory Committee of the Boston Loan Agency, 1944-53, and the Midwest Disaster Loan Committee, 1951; financial and statistical reports, 1948-54; and press releases and forms, 1932-57.

RECORDS OF THE RFC LEGAL DIVISION. 1933-59. 18 lin. ft.

Included are legal opinions of the General Counsel, with indexes, 1934-57; correspondence and other records relating to investments in preferred stock of banks and trust companies, 1933-40; reports of litigation authorized by the Board of Directors, 1936-50; and files of the deputy assistant general counsel in charge of litigation and liquidation, 1947-59.

RECORDS OF THE OFFICE OF THE CONTROLLER-TREASURER OF THE RFC. 1932-57. 1,465 lin. ft.

Included are a general file, 1932-57; reports to the Congress, reports on lending activities, and RFC and subsidiaries financial statements, 1932-57; records relating to the 1934 Gold Reserve Act, 1933-36; private accounting firms' audit reports, 1932-46; agreements, legal documents, and correspondence relating to RFC establishment and organization, and loans, notes, and other RFC financial arrangements, 1932-54; and management project records, 1946-52. There are also files of the assistant treasurer, 1933-54; Examining Division case files (in WNRC) relating to declined, canceled, and paid loans, 1932-46; indexes to loan case files of the RFC and RFC

Mortgage Company, 1932-57; records relating to RFC emergency relief funds made available to the States, 1932-34; Statistical and Economic Division records consisting of a general file, 1932-44, and reports on general loans, RFC investments in preferred stock, capital notes, debentures, loans to industries and businesses, and loans for national defense, 1932-47; and reports and surveys of the Industrial Analysis Branch, 1948-53.

RECORDS OF THE RFC RAILROAD DIVISION. 1932-57. 657 lin. ft.

These consist of a general file, 1932-53; files of Division officials, 1932-57; case files relating to paid, canceled, and withdrawn railroad loans, 1932-57 (in WNRC); legal staff files, 1932-57; court dockets and briefs relating to reorganization proceedings, 1932-56 (in WNRC); Federal Emergency Administration of Public Works railroad loan case files, 1933-35; records of loans, notes issued for loans, and collateral pledged, 1940-51; Accounting Division railroad loan records, 1932-55; data relating to financial conditions of railroads, 1932-53; and financial reports submitted by railroads to the Interstate Commerce Commission, 1938-54.

RECORDS OF THE RFC PRICE ADJUSTMENT BOARD. 1942-54. 48 lin. ft.

These comprise minutes, with related indexes, 1943-48; regulations and issuances, 1942-50; reports, 1944-46; general records, 1943-54; orders and correspondence relating to liability for excessive profits under the Renegotiation Act, 1943-54; case files relating to the right of the Board to apply the Renegotiation Act retroactively, 1944-51; renegotiation agreements, 1943-48; war contract renegotiation agreements of

RFC subsidiaries, 1944-49; renegotiation agreements by other agencies, 1943-49; letters discharging firms from excessive profits claims, 1945-48; memorandums of the secretary, 1943-49; and miscellaneous financial records, 1945-48.

OTHER RECORDS OF THE RFC. 1932-53. 24 lin. ft.

Included are Deposit Liquidation Board general records, 1932-43; Office of War Activity Liquidation records of meetings of the Plant Liquidation Division Review Committee and of the Contract and Commodity Claims Committee, 1948-50; Loan Policy Board minutes, 1951-53; Federal Loan Agency general correspondence file, 1939-45, and administrative subject file, 1939-45, and directives, 1939-49; general correspondence and general subject files of the Secretary of Commerce, 1942-44; and minutes of the RFC Supervising Committee for Settlement of Terminated War Contracts, June-October 1944, and of the RFC Contract Settlement Committee, 1944-45.

RECORDS RELATING TO REGIONAL AGRICULTURAL CREDIT CORPORATIONS. 1932-33. 1 lin. in.

Twelve corporations were established in 1932 by the RFC in Federal land bank districts to make loans for agriculture and livestock production. They were transferred to the Farm Credit Administration in 1933. The records consist of summary histories of principal and branch offices in each district, including information about district officers, and bulletins.

RECORDS OF THE RFC MORTGAGE COMPANY. 1935-48. 60 lin. ft.

This Company was incorporated March 14, 1935, by RFC officials, and the RFC purchased its capital stock. Its function was to assist in the reestablishment of a normal mortgage market. The records include minutes, with indexes and memorandums, 1935-48; and organizational material, correspondence with the Federal Housing Administration, interoffice memorandums relating to policies and procedures for loans on real estate mortgages, bulletins and circular letters, periodic financial statements, statistical reports on loans, and newspaper clippings.

RECORDS OF THE FEDERAL NATIONAL MORTGAGE ASSOCIATION. 1938-50. 2 lin. ft.

The Federal National Mortgage Association (FNMA) was originally chartered as the National Mortgage Association of Washington on February 10, 1938, to provide a secondary market for mortgages insured by the Federal Housing Administration. It was made a subsidiary of the RFC, and the name was changed to the Federal National Mortgage Association on April 5, 1938. The FNMA was transferred to the Housing and Home Finance Agency in 1950. The records consist of legal and financial documents, reports, correspondence, interoffice memorandums, charts, bulletins, and resolutions of the Board of Directors relating to organization, policy, operations, and procedure.

RECORDS OF THE DISASTER LOAN CORPORATION. 1937-45. 49 lin. ft.

Created by an act of February 11, 1937, to meet a flood emergency in the Ohio-Mississippi Valley, the Disaster Loan Corporation (DLC) was empowered to make loans to relieve conditions brought about by natural catastrophes. It was dissolved on June 30, 1945, and its operations, functions, and records were transferred to the RFC. The records comprise minutes, with related memorandums and indexes, 1937-45; and reports, bulletins, resolutions of the RFC Board of Directors and the DLC

Managing Director, forms, and press clippings relating to DLC organization, administration, and operations.

RECORDS OF THE METALS RESERVE COMPANY. 1940-53. 74 lin. ft.

The Metals Reserve Company (MRC) was organized June 28, 1940, to procure, stockpile, and dispose of metals and minerals defined as strategic and critical and to pay subsidies to producers of such materials. The MRC was dissolved and merged with the RFC July 1, 1945, after which the liquidation of MRC assets and liabilities was taken over by the RFC Office of Metals Reserve. The records include minutes, with an index, 1940-45; reports, memorandums, and other records relating to MRC activities, 1940-53; records relating to the premium price plan, which provided for incentive payments to domestic producers of copper, lead, and zinc for exceeding production quotas and exploratory projects, 1942-50; and contracts, agreements, audit reports, and other financial records, with related correspondence, 1940-49.

RECORDS OF THE DEFENSE PLANT CORPORATION. 1940-60. 815 lin. ft.

The Defense Plant Corporation (DPC) was organized on August 22, 1940, to finance and supervise construction and equipping of industrial facilities operated, for the most part, by private concerns sponsored by Federal agencies administering defense and war programs. It was dissolved July 1, 1945, and its functions, assets, and liabilities were merged with the RFC. The RFC Office of Defense Plants was established to liquidate DPC assets. The records consist of minutes, with accompanying supporting documents and an index, 1940-45; reports, correspondence, memorandums, and resolutions relating to DPC operations, 1940-51; engineer reports ("Plancor" files) regarding plant facili-

ties, 1942-50 (in WNRC); final accountability reports, 1942-50 (in WNRC); correspondence with sponsoring agencies, relating to the leasing of equipment and property to defense plants ("take out letters"), 1941-46 (in WNRC); correspondence and agreements concerning additional funds from DPC for plant facilities ("Green Light" letters), 1941-45 (in WNRC); correspondence relating to canceled projects, 1941-45; files relating to leasing machinery and equipment to small defense plants ("SWAPCO'S"), 1942-46 (in WNRC); construction and acquisition contracts, 1942-46 (in WNRC); Office of Defense Plants and General Services Administration files relating to liquidation of DPC assets ("Rentra" files), 1944-60; and correspondence and agreements relating to machine and cutting tool emergency production, 1948-49.

RECORDS OF THE DEFENSE SUPPLIES CORPORATION. 1940-49. 198 lin. ft.

Organized August 29, 1940, the Defense Supplies Corporation (DSC) financed or administered programs for stockpiling strategic and critical materials and paying subsidies to relieve inflationary pressures and promote domestic production of strategic and critical materials. It also financed or administered some projects that had no direct relationship to RFC activities. When DSC was dissolved July 1, 1945, its functions were transferred to the RFC, which established the Office of Defense Supplies to administer those projects that related to the reconversion program. The records include minutes, with accompanying supporting documents and an index, 1940-45; resolutions of the Board of Directors, memorandums, instructions, directives, legal documents, financial statements, reports, correspondence, statistical data, accounts, and audit reports relating to

DSC organization, administration, operations, and the commodity procurement program, 1940–49; records of the Division of American Republics Aviation, relating to commercial aviation development in South American countries and elimination of Axis influence on Latin American aviation, 1941–46; and reports, memorandums, legal opinions and decisions, studies, correspondence, statistical data, payment claims, regulations, and audit reports relating to the subsidy payments program, 1942–49.

RECORDS OF THE DEFENSE HOMES CORPORATION. 1940–49. 62 lin. ft.

The Defense Homes Corporation (DHC) was created October 23, 1940, to alleviate a housing shortage for defense workers. In cooperation with the Office of the National Housing Administrator, the DHC built housing facilities that could be economically rented to defense workers. On February 24, 1942, the DHC was transferred to the Federal Public Housing Authority of the National Housing Agency. Liquidation of the DHC began in 1945, and its assets were transferred in 1948 to the RFC for final liquidation. These records include minutes, with accompanying supporting documents and a card index, 1940–48; reports, orders, issuances, instructions, correspondence, and forms, 1940–49; defense housing project construction and management files, 1941–47; and records of the General Counsel and the Treasurer, 1941–48.

RECORDS OF THE WAR DAMAGE CORPORATION. 1941–59. 139 lin. ft.

The War Insurance Corporation, established December 13, 1941, was renamed the War Damage Corporation (WDC) on March 27, 1942. Its purpose was to provide property owners in the United States and its territories and possessions with reasonable insurance protection against loss or damage to property as a result of enemy attack or of U.S. military action in resisting attack. Established insurance companies acted as WDC agents in receiving applications, issuing policies, and handling the program. Its charter extended only until January 22, 1947, and no policies were issued after March 15, 1946. All policies expired April 1, 1947, and WDC assets were liquidated before June 30, 1949. WDC stock was transferred to the Secretary of the Treasury and was not canceled until suits against the WDC had been settled. The records include minutes, with an index, 1941–59; records of the Secretary, 1941–49, the Treasurer, 1942–47, and the Chief Auditor, 1943–49; records relating to compensation claims for war damages, 1942–51; correspondence with agents, 1942–49; agents' correspondence with field offices and insurance brokers, 1942–44; records of the WDC Seattle office, 1942–46; war damage insurance applications and policies, 1942–43; and instructions, regulations, and periodic financial statements, 1942–44.

RECORDS OF THE U.S. COMMERCIAL COMPANY. 1940–57. 181 lin. ft.

Created March 26, 1942, to conduct joint preclusive and preemptive purchasing operations with England and to share their cost, the U.S. Commercial Company (USCC) developed and purchased foreign strategic commodities for import. In 1943 the USCC was transferred to the Foreign Economic Administration (FEA), which supervised all U.S. foreign procurement agencies. When the FEA was dissolved in 1945, the USCC was returned to the RFC, where it was terminated June 30, 1948. Liquidation of its activities was completed by the Liquidation Division of the RFC Office of Loans, and the USCC was dissolved June 20, 1957. The records include minutes, with accompanying supporting documents and an index, 1942-57; records of the Board of Directors, 1942-46; minutes, resolutions, agreements, directives, reports, memorandums, correspondence, and surveys relating to USCC policies, organization, administration, and operations, 1942-48; administrative issuances of the Board of Economic Warfare and the Foreign Economic Administration, 1942-45; records relating to preclusive buying operations and the administration of the Preclusive Operations Division, 1942-47; records relating to sources of commodities, 1941-45; records of the Metals and Minerals Division, 1942-45; records relating to a survey of foreign mineral resources, 1940-45, and to production and procurement of cinchona, 1942-45, balsa, 1942-44, and mahogany, 1942-44; records relating to recruitment of foreign personnel by USCC, 1942-45, and USCC activities in Latin America, 1942-45, Turkey, 1943-48, India, 1944-45, Germany, 1944-47, France, 1945-46, and Pacific islands, 1945-47; Anglo-American Economic Committee records relating to the negotiation of a war trade agreement with Portugal, 1942-44; budget estimates, 1944-46; and financial records, 1942-45.

RECORDS OF THE WAR ASSETS CORPORATION. 1943-48. 2 lin. ft.

The Petroleum Reserves Corporation (PRC), predecessor of the War Assets Corporation, was created June 30, 1943, to acquire ownership of, or interest in, foreign reserves of crude petroleum. On July 15, 1943, the PRC was transferred to the Office of Economic Warfare, which in September was consolidated into the Foreign Economic Administration. The PRC did not accomplish its primary purpose; no basis was found for successful negotiations, and it became virtually inactive. In 1945 the PRC was returned to the RFC, its name changed to War Assets Corporation (WAC), and its function changed to disposing of surplus property. In March 1946 WAC functions were transferred to the War Assets Administration, and on June 30, 1946, the WAC was dissolved. The records consist of minutes of the PRC, 1943-44, and of the WRC, 1945-46, legal documents, resolutions, correspondence, memorandums, financial records, and issuances relating to PRC and WAC organization, administration, and operations, 1943-44; and records relating to an Arabian American Oil Co. reimbursement claim for construction expenditures on an oil refinery in Saudi Arabia, 1944-48.

RECORDS OF THE RUBBER RESERVE COMPANY AND ITS SUCCESSORS. 1937-56. 167 lin. ft. and 13 rolls of microfilm.

The Rubber Reserve Company (RRC) was organized June 28, 1940, to purchase and distribute natural and synthetic rubber and rubber scrap to meet both military and civilian requirements. The RRC coordinated plans for Government-owned plants that were built and operated for the synthetic rubber program and entered into agreements with universities and private research organizations to conduct research in the development of synthetic rubber. The RRC was dissolved July 1, 1945, and its functions, assets, and liabilities were merged with those of RFC. The Office of Rubber Reserve was established within the RFC to continue or conclude RRC activities. The Office of Rubber Reserve was succeeded in 1951 by the Synthetic Rubber Division, which became, in 1952, the Office of Synthetic Rubber. Under the terms of the Rubber Producing Facilities Disposal Act of 1953, the Government's synthetic rubber facilities were sold to private industry, and on June 30, 1954, the synthetic rubber program was transferred from the RFC to the Federal Facilities Corporation.

The records include minutes of the RRC, with an index, 1940-45, the Buying Committee, 1940-42, the Rubber

Research Board, 1943-44, and the Butadiene Producers Technical Committee,
with related supporting documents,
1944-45; summary minutes of the
Research and Development Advisory
Group, 1944-53, digests of meetings of
the Research and Development Management Committee, 1946-47, summaries of
proceedings of the Rubber Research
Board, 1944, and minutes of the Polymer
Development Committee, with related
supporting documents, 1944-54; legal
documents, memorandums, administrative manuals, correspondence, statistical
data, budgetary records, and audit
reports relating to the organization,
administration, and operations of the
RRC and successors, 1940-55; memorandums of the secretary, 1940-48; records
of the Research Compounding Branch,
1943-44, and of the Copolymer Development Branch, Office of the Rubber
Director, 1942-44; records relating to
Government-equipped rubber plants
(Plancors), 1943-44; reports and accounting records relating to butadiene plants,
1942-44; technical reports, with an
index, 1943-54; research contracts and
authorizations, 1942-48; records of the
International Rubber Regulation Committee, 1940-44; microfilm copies (13
rolls) of German reports on synthetic
rubber, 1937-45; records of the Research
and Development Division, 1943-52, and
the Polymer Research Branch, 1949-55;
and files of officials, 1948-56.

RECORDS OF THE RUBBER DEVELOPMENT CORPORATION. 1940-47. 73 lin. ft.

The Rubber Development Corporation (RDC) was created February 16,
1943, from the Pacific Development
Company, Inc., to develop and acquire
foreign sources for natural rubber and
related products (formerly a function of
the RRC). In July 1943 the RDC was
transferred to the Office of Economic
Warfare, and in September 1943 to the
Foreign Economic Administration. In

September 1945 the RDC was returned
to the RFC, where it remained until its
charter expired June 30, 1947. Included
are a few records of the Pacific Development Company, 1940-43; minutes of
RDC meetings, with related records and
index, 1943-47; legal documents, administrative records, reports, correspondence, memorandums, studies, and financial records relating to RDC
organization, administration, policies,
and operations, 1942-47; reports and correspondence relating to rubber production in Latin American and African
countries, 1942-47; agreements between
the RDC and rubber-producing countries for procurement and development
of crude rubber, 1942-44; Interagency
Policy Committee on Rubber (the Batt
Committee) records, 1945-46; records
relating to committees concerned with
rubber conservation, development, and
production, 1942-46; and records relating to the history and organization of
the rubber program, 1943-47.

RECORDS OF THE RUBBER PRODUCING FACILITIES DISPOSAL COMMISSION. 1953-56. 9 lin. ft.

This Commission was organized
November 10, 1953, to transfer to private industry the Government's synthetic rubber-producing facilities. On September 24, 1956, this responsibility was
transferred from the Commission to the
Federal Facilities Corporation. The
records consist of minutes of the Commission, 1953-56; brochures issued in
1953, containing information about each
Government-owned synthetic rubber
plant or facility offered for sale to the
public; agreements and other records
relating to rubber-producing plants; and
reports, contracts, technical papers, correspondence, and memorandums relating to Commission administration and
operations, 1953-56.

RECORDS OF THE FEDERAL FACILITIES CORPORATION. 1941–61. 68 lin. ft. and 41 rolls of microfilm.

The Federal Facilities Corporation (FFC) was created June 30, 1954, to administer RFC tin and synthetic rubber programs. In June 1955 the Research and Development Division of the Office of Synthetic Rubber, and part of its staff, was transferred to the National Science Foundation. In 1956 the FFC succeeded the Rubber Producing Facilities Disposal Commission in matters relating to the disposal of Government-owned synthetic rubber plants. On June 30, 1957, liquidation of the synthetic rubber program became the responsibility of the Administrator of General Services, who succeeded the Secretary of the Treasury as head of FFC. An act of August 30, 1961, dissolved the FFC and gave responsibility for any remaining functions to the Administrator of General Services. The records include FFC minutes, with accompanying supporting documents, 1954–61, and minutes of committees, 1942–52; legal and administrative records, reports, and memorandums relating to FFC organization, administration, policies, and operations, 1942–52; records of the Director, Office of Synthetic Rubber, 1945–56; Polymer Development Branch reports, 1943–55; microfilm copies (41 rolls) of records of the RFC Office of Rubber Reserve and the FFC Office of Synthetic Rubber, relating to research programs, 1941–53; reports, studies, and issuances relating to synthetic rubber development, 1943–55; records of the Office of the Controller-Treasurer, 1954–56; and audit reports relating to plants producing synthetic rubber, 1942–55.

RECORDS OF THE ELECTRIC HOME AND FARM AUTHORITY. 1934–42. 46 lin. ft.

The Electric Home and Farm Authority (EHFA) was created June 16, 1933, to finance installment sales of electric and gas equipment and appliances to families of moderate income. First made an agency of the National Industrial Recovery Administration and later placed under the Tennessee Valley Authority, in August 1935 it was incorporated under the laws of the District of Columbia and transferred to the RFC. On October 13, 1942, EHFA assets were transferred to the RFC for liquidation. The records, 1934–42, consist of minutes; legal documents, annual reports, correspondence, memorandums, reports, financial statements, transcripts of testimony at congressional hearings, press releases, and newspaper clippings relating to EHFA administration and operations; a "dealer file," including applications from and correspondence with merchandisers of electrical appliances; a "manufacturer file," including correspondence with manufacturers of electrical appliances, relating to proposed EHFA financial arrangements; a "utility file," including correspondence with utility companies regarding the collection and billing of funds due EHFA from purchasers of appliances; contracts with utility companies, with an index; correspondence with banks; and accounts.

RECORDS OF THE LAFAYETTE BUILDING CORPORATION. 1938–49. 8 lin. ft.

This Corporation was organized September 30, 1938, to acquire land in Washington, D.C., and erect a building to be used for RFC central offices. After construction was completed Corporation assets were acquired by the RFC Mortgage Company, and the Corporation was dissolved July 1, 1941. The records include minutes, 1938–41; legal documents and correspondence relating to organization and financing of the Corporation and construction of the Lafayette Building, 1938–49; correspondence of Treasurer Robert F. McCord, 1939–41;

Thompson-Starrett Co. construction expense vouchers, 1938–41; and construction specifications and blueprints, 1938–39.

CARTOGRAPHIC AND AUDIOVISUAL RECORDS. 1932–50. 4,018 items.

Cartographic records include charts and maps (2,777 items) prepared by the RFC Railroad Division, showing the corporate structure, property ownership, and related railroad studies for about 125 railroads, 1934–50; maps (259 items) of parts of Brazil, Colombia, and Peru, showing rubber production and transportation facilities, prepared or collected by divisions of the Rubber Development Corporation, 1943–44; and maps, plans, and related field notebooks (36 items) from surveys of airport sites in Brazil, prepared by the Division of American Republics Aviation of the Defense Supplies Corporation, 1943–44.

Audiovisual records consist of photographs (917 items) relating to activities of the Rubber Development Corporation in Brazil, 1943–44, and the Reconstruction Finance Corporation Board of Directors, 1932 and 1938. There are also motion pictures (29 reels) relating to a U.S. Commercial Company survey of the economy, geography, and sociology of the Micronesian islands, 1945–47; of Guatemalan cinchona plantations, natives, and countryside, taken in connection with activities of the U.S. Commercial Company in developing sources of quinine, 1943–44; and of Brazilian plantations, natives, cities, and countryside, made in connection with activities of the Rubber Development Corporation, 1943–44.

SPECIFIC RESTRICTIONS

I. *Records*: Records of the Reconstruction Finance Corporation, relating to the airline survey, 1947–50.

Restrictions: No one may examine these records or be given information from them or copies of them except by permission of the President of the United States or his authorized representative.

Specified by: General Counsel, General Services Administration.

II. *Records*: Records of the Metals Reserve Company and the Reconstruction Finance Corporation, relating to the processing of vanadium ore.

Restrictions: Only those employees of the Atomic Energy Commission who are approved by the Security Officer of the Commission or those employees of the General Services Administration approved by its Administrator may examine these records or be given information from them or copies of them.

Specified by: General Counsel, General Services Administration.

III. *Records*: Minutes of the Reconstruction Finance Corporation dated later than June 30, 1945, its agreements with private firms, records of the Lafayette Building Corporation, case files relating to applications for financial assistance to insurance companies and financial institutions, records maintained by officials of the Railroad Division of the Reconstruction Finance Corporation, directives of the Administrator of the Federal Loan Agency, and records relating to railroad loans identified by the following folder titles: File No. 2—Correspondence; File No. 6—RFC and ICC Memorandums; File No. 9—Working Papers of RFC Railroad Examiners; and File No. 10—Salaries of Borrowers' Officers.

Restrictions: No one except employees of the Federal Government on official business may examine these records or be given information from them or copies of them without the permission of the Director, Office of Defense Lending, Department of the Treasury. This provision, however, does not restrict the release of information about the identity of a borrower, the amount and purpose of a loan, and the dates on which the loan was approved.

Specified by: Director, Office of Defense Lending.

IV. *Records*: Records of the Reconstruction Finance Corporation consisting of case files and other records that relate to business loan applications and business loans approved (except the business loans described in Schedule A attached to Reorganization Plan No. 1 of 1957) and that contain financial information or data concerning an applicant or an obligor and information about the operations, style of work, or apparatus of private firms.

Restrictions: No one except employees of the Federal Government on official business may examine these records or be given information from them or copies of them without the permission of the Administrator, Small Business Administration, or his authorized representative. This provision, however, does not restrict the release of information about the identity of a borrower, the amount and purpose of a loan, and the dates on which the loan was approved.

Specified by: General Counsel, Small Business Administration.

V. *Records*: All records of the Defense Supplies Corporation, Metals Reserve Company (except records relating to the processing of vanadium ore), Pacific Development Corporation, U.S. Commercial Company, Petroleum Reserve Corporation, and the Rubber Development Corporation; minutes and related indexes of the Defense Plant Corporation, RFC Price Adjustment Board, Rubber Reserve Company, Federal Facilities Corporation, and the Rubber Producing Facilities Disposal Commission; records of the Defense Plant Corporation, showing the schedule for machine tool production; and drawings of a copolymer plant, prepared by the Federal Facilities Corporation.

Restrictions: No one except employees of the Federal Government on official business may examine these records or be given information from them or copies of them without the permission of the Administrator, General Services Administration, or his authorized representative.

Specified by: General Counsel, General Services Administration.

RECORDS OF THE UNITED STATES COAL COMMISSION
(RECORD GROUP 68)

The U.S. Coal Commission was created by an act of September 22, 1922, to aid Congress in framing legislation by gathering data regarding interstate commerce in coal and the coal industry. The Commission expired by statutory limitation on September 22, 1923, after conducting a broad investigation of the coal industry and its problems. An Executive order of September 13, 1923, authorized the Director of the Geological Survey to perform any necessary administrative duties to terminate the work of the Commission and placed its records in the custody of the Secretary of the Interior. Most of the records of the Commission were lost in March 1936.

See Edward E. Hunt et al., *What the Coal Commission Found* (Baltimore, 1925); and U.S. Coal Commission, *Report* (1925).

There are 164 cubic feet of records (in WNRC) dated between 1922 and 1927 in this record group.

RECORDS. 1922-27. 247 lin. ft.

These include records of the office of one commissioner, George Otis Smith, who was also Director of the Geological Survey, and of the Office of the Executive Secretary of the Commission, including minutes, administrative records, correspondence, reports, and working papers.

Investigative records include reports, correspondence, memorandums, completed questionnaires, schedules, statistical tables, and field notes. Records of labor investigations relate to living conditions, cost of living and retail prices, earnings and wage rates, and labor relations. Records of economic investigations concern wholesaling and retailing costs, production costs, investment, and profits. Records of engineering investigations relate to production, storage, transportation, and distribution of anthracite and bituminous coal.

RECORDS OF THE
UNITED STATES FOOD ADMINISTRATION
(RECORD GROUP 4)

The U.S. Food Administration was created by an Executive order of August 10, 1917, to assure the supply, distribution, and conservation of foods; facilitate their movement and prevent monopolies and hoarding; and maintain governmental control over foods chiefly by means of voluntary agreements and a licensing system. It assumed jurisdiction over commodities when they reached commercial channels. The Food Administration was assisted by a number of boards and committees, including the interdepartmental Food Purchase Board and the Sugar Distributing Committee. To enable the Administrator to buy and sell grain and sugar and their products, two subsidiaries, the Food Administration Grain Corporation (see RG 5) and the U.S. Sugar Equalization Board, Inc. (see RG 6), were organized.

After November 11, 1918, rules and regulations of the Food Administration were revoked, and its organization was gradually dismantled. On November 21, 1919, Administration functions regarding wheat and its products were transferred to the Chief of the Cereal Division, who was also President of the U.S. Grain Corporation (successor to the Food Administration Grain Corporation) and U.S. Wheat Director; powers relating to other foods were transferred to the Attorney General.

An Executive order of August 21, 1920, terminated all branches of the Food Administration still in existence, and its records, with a few exceptions, were placed in the custody of the reorganized U. S. Grain Corporation. In 1927 these records were transferred to the Department of Commerce.

See William C. Mullendore, *History of the United States Food Administration, 1917–1919* (Stanford University, 1941), prepared in 1921 as the final report of the Administration.

There are 2,995 cubic feet of records (in WNRC except for nontextual records) dated between 1917 and 1920 in this record group.

RECORDS OF THE CENTRAL OFFICE. 1917–20. 2,210 lin. ft.

The central office underwent frequent reorganizations. After the first few months each organizational unit kept its own records, but a master file of outgoing letters and telegrams was maintained. Divisions whose basic records have been preserved include the Home Conservation, States Administration, Cereal, Educational, Legal, Meat, Statistical, Canned Foods, Accounting, Distribution, Coordination of Purchase, Sugar, Transportation, Perishable Foods, Marine Transportation, License, Cottonseed, Collateral Commodities, Fats and Oils, Hotels and Restaurants, Enforcement, Wholesale and Retail, Staple Groceries, and Baking Divisions. The records include minutes, reports, correspondence, memorandums, agreements, license approvals, procedural material, hearings, legal documents, tables, graphs, data files, and press releases and clippings. Personal files of the U.S. Food Administrator are in the Hoover Institution on War, Revolution, and Peace at Stanford University.

RECORDS OF THE STATE FOOD ADMINISTRATIONS. 1917–19. 1,305 lin. ft.

Federal food administrators were appointed for every State, Alaska, Hawaii, Puerto Rico, the District of Columbia, the New York City area, Philadelphia County, and St. Louis. These administrators usually appointed county and often district, city, and town administrators. State offices, as they finally developed, tended to be organized like the Washington, D.C., office. Prices were controlled mainly through local price interpreting committees, which prepared and published fair price lists. The State offices closed in 1919. There are records of all State food administrations except for Delaware and Florida, usually consisting chiefly of correspondence of the administrator and some of the divisions. There are also records of some county administrations.

RECORDS OF THE MILLING DIVISION. 1917–18. 179 lin. ft.

The Milling Division originated as a Milling Committee composed of nine members of the milling industry and appointed June 27, 1917, to work out a plan of voluntary control over the wheat-milling industry. In August the Committee and its office staff became the Milling Division of the Food Administration. The central office of the Division was in New York City, where close cooperation was maintained with the Food Administration Grain Corporation. Throughout the winter of 1917–18 a large office organization, operating through a number of departments and nine regional offices, administered the distribution of the 1917 wheat crop under voluntary agreements signed with millers. A different plan of control was developed for administering the 1918 crop, and in July the Division was reduced in size and designated as the Milling Section of the newly established Cereal Division.

Records include a central file of correspondence with mills and general correspondence with divisional offices and the Washington office of the Food Administration. There are also reports, correspondence, and other records of divisional departments and regional offices.

RECORDS OF THE SUGAR DISTRIBUTING COMMITTEE. 1917–19. 8 lin. ft.

The Sugar Distributing Committee was appointed September 21, 1917, by the U.S. Food Administrator to distribute the beet sugar crop under agreements between the Food Administrator and producers. It was reappointed September 30, 1918, to allocate the beet sugar crop of that season. The executive offices of the Committee were at Chicago, and it had five distributing district offices. The Committee was terminated October 15, 1919. Its records include minutes and correspondence of the treasurer and the traffic and office manager.

RECORDS OF THE FOOD PURCHASE BOARD. 1917-19.
10 lin. ft.

The Food Purchase Board was an interdepartmental agency formed in December 1917 to represent the Army and Navy in their relations with the Coordination of Purchase Division of the Food Administration. It was formally authorized by a Presidential proclamation of May 8, 1918, to consist of representatives of the Secretaries of War and the Navy, the Federal Trade Commission, and the Food Administration. It operated as a conference or clearing committee to consider the needs of the Armed Forces in relation to other needs and market conditions and to determine purchasing policy for each food commodity. Its last meeting took place in December 1918, and its records were closed in February 1919. The records include minutes, recommendations of the Board and the Food Administration, and correspondence.

CARTOGRAPHIC AND AUDIOVISUAL RECORDS. 1912-20.
3,563 items.

Cartographic records, 1912-20 (11 items), consist of maps relating to the production and consumption of food products in the United States and Europe, European transportation, and the political and military situation in Europe.

Audiovisual records consist of still pictures, 1917-20 (3,550 items), including photographs, lantern slides, posters, and notices relating to or used in activities of the Food Administration, conservation campaigns, food conservation in other countries, and other wartime activities; and motion pictures, 1917-18 (2 reels), consisting of a film on wartime farming in France, animated cartoons about the need to conserve food, and films of Food Administrator Herbert Hoover and congressional supporters of the Food Control Act.

See *Preliminary Inventory of the Records of the United States Food Administration, 1917-1920, Pt. 1, The Headquarters Organization*, PI 3 (1943).

RECORDS OF THE
UNITED STATES FUEL ADMINISTRATION
(RECORD GROUP 67)

The U.S. Fuel Administration was established as an emergency agency by an Executive order of August 23, 1917. Its Administrator had authority to regulate the production, distribution, and consumption of coal, coke, natural gas, and fuel products of petroleum, including the powers to grant licenses, determine and fix reasonable prices for those commodities, prescribe rules for the conduct of business, and take over and operate fuel plants and businesses. Although the Administration was formally discontinued on June 30, 1919, the act under which it functioned was not repealed, and a threatened coal famine during the bituminous coal strike of 1919 resulted in a brief revival of the agency from

October 26 to December 13, 1919, when the Fuel Administrator resigned.

See U.S. Fuel Administration, *Final Report* (1919-21); and Don B. Cook, *Records Problems and Policies in the Dismantling of the United States Fuel Administration*, National Archives Records Administration Circular 6 (1944).

There are 943 cubic feet of records (in WNRC except for nontextual records) dated between 1917 and 1920 in this record group.

RECORDS OF THE EXECUTIVE OFFICE. 1917-19. 44 lin. ft.

Included are records of Administrator Harry A. Garfield, Assistant Administrator Cyrus Garnsey, Jr., the Executive Secretary and historian, the Anthracite Committee, and the advisor on retail coal; the technical advisor's correspondence; and the Chief Counsel's office files.

RECORDS OF THE ADMINISTRATIVE DIVISION. 1917-19. 520 lin. ft.

These consist of the Director's general correspondence, the general solicitor's office files, and records of the Mine Track Bureau and the Bureaus of State Organizations, Prices, Production, the Business Manager, Conservation, Education, Traffic and Transportation, Investigation, and Labor.

RECORDS OF THE DISTRIBUTION DIVISION. 1917-19. 480 lin. ft.

In cooperation with the War Industries Board and the U.S. Railroad Administration, this Division controlled distribution of coal and coke; allocated coal and coke supplies to the Army, railroads, and certain war industries; and arranged the routing of shipments. The records include correspondence of the Director and the Bureau of Bituminous Coal and Coke, and records of the Bureaus of State Distribution, Gas Plants, and Anthracite Coal.

RECORDS OF THE OIL DIVISION. 1917-19. 150 lin. ft.

This Division, created in January 1918, stimulated the production and conservation of crude petroleum and its products, supervised the transportation and allocation of oil, and assisted the oil industry in organizing to effectively contribute to the war effort. These records consist of central files; records of the Office of the General Director and the Office assistant, the oil director for the Pacific coast, the Inter-Allied Petroleum Conference, and the Bureaus of Law, Statistics, Production, Technology, Engineering, Oil Well Supplies, Pipe Lines, Refining, Prices and Licenses, Oil Conservation, Domestic Consumption, Traffic and Transportation, and Lubricants and Foreign Requirements; and correspondence of the Advisory Committee on Natural Gas.

RECORDS OF THE U.S. BITUMINOUS COAL COMMISSION. 1919-20. 3 lin. ft.

Created by the President on December 19, 1919, to investigate and adjust differences between miners and operators involved in the bituminous coal strike of 1919, this Commission submitted its report on March 10, 1920. An Executive order of March 24, 1920, authorized the Commission's dissolution. Included are drafts of the Commission agent; transcripts of proceedings; administrative records; correspondence and reports, with briefs and related data presented by miners and operators; petitions and decisions; and press releases.

AUDIOVISUAL RECORDS. ca. 1918. 55 items.

Included are a panoramic photograph and other photographs of Fuel Administration directors, staff, advisors, buildings, and offices; and panoramas of the West Virginia Coal and Coke Co.'s installations at Coalton and Bower, the Hitchman Coal and Coke Co.'s installa-tion at Wheeling, and an unidentified coal and coke community.

RECORDS OF THE UNITED STATES GRAIN CORPORATION (RECORD GROUP 5)

The U.S. Grain Corporation was orga-nized July 1, 1919, from the Food Administration Grain Corporation, an agency of the U.S. Food Administration (see RG 4) created in 1917. It had a cen-tral office in New York City, 14 zone offices throughout the country, and, in 1919, offices in European cities. Its main functions were to regulate grain trade by purchasing, storing, and selling grain and grain products and, in cooperation with the War Trade Board, to control grain imports and exports. Its work was affiliated with that of the Milling, Coor-dination of Purchase, Cereal, and Enforcement Divisions of the Food Administration. Before 1919 the U.S. Food Administrator was Chairman of the Board of Directors of the Grain Cor-poration, and the Chief of the Cereal Division of the Food Administration was President of the Grain Corporation. In 1919 the President of the Grain Corpora-tion was appointed to also serve as U.S. Wheat Director. In 1918-19 the Corpora-tion was purchasing agent for the Com-mission for Relief in Belgium, in 1919 it was fiscal and purchasing agent for the American Relief Administration, and in 1921-22 it was fiscal agent for the Purchasing Commission for Russian Relief. The Corporation had been in the process of liquidation for several years when it was abolished by an Executive order of December 31, 1927.

Some materials of the Wheat Director and of Grain Corporation officials, and most of the papers of the American Relief Administration and the Commis-sion for Relief in Belgium, are in the Hoover Institution on War, Revolution, and Peace at Stanford University; addi-tional materials of the American Relief Administration and the Commission for Relief in Belgium are in the Herbert Hoover Presidential Library, West Branch, Iowa.

There are 198 cubic feet of records (in WNRC except for nontextual records) dated between 1917 and 1932 in this record group.

RECORDS OF THE HEADQUARTERS ORGANIZATION. 1917-32. 158 lin. ft.

Included are general correspondence, 1917-19, and correspondence with zone agents, 1917-19; and records of the pres-ident, vice presidents, secretary, treas-urer, comptroller, office manager, finan-cial units, several commodity departments, offices of crop experts, the Grain Threshing Division, the Bureau of Information, and the Statistical, Trans-portation, and European Departments. There are also records of the Corpora-tion in dissolution, 1919-28, and of the Department of Commerce as custodian of the Corporation's records, 1928-32. The records include minutes, reports, circular letters, correspondence, memo-randums, bulletins, tables, graphs, press clippings, and ledgers and other account-ing records. There are also manuscript and annotated maps (18 items) showing famine areas and depicting relief activi-ties of the American Relief Administra-tion, 1918-19.

RECORDS OF ZONE AGENCIES. 1917-20. 16 lin. ft.

The Corporation divided the United States into 14 grain zones with a vice president in charge of each zone and offices in the important grain terminal and seaboard markets. Records of the

New York Agency are with headquarters records. There are accounting records and/or records of the vice president—including minutes, correspondence, circulars, memorandums, bulletins, vouchers, and receipts—for Baltimore, Buffalo, Galveston, Kansas City, Minneapolis, New Orleans, Omaha, Philadelphia, St. Louis, and San Francisco.

RECORDS OF EUROPEAN OFFICES. 1918-21. 35 lin. ft.

The London office of the Corporation was organized in January 1919 as European headquarters to supervise movement of American relief ships in European waters and to act as fiscal agent for the American Relief Administration. It was closed in September, and part of its staff was moved to New York for the conclusion of the work. There are records of the office both at London and New York; of Grain Corporation and American Relief Administration offices at Copenhagen, Danzig, Gravosa, Hamburg, Rotterdam, and Paris; and of missions to Finland, the Baltic States, Poland, the old Austro-Hungarian Empire and Serbia, Southern Europe (the Near East), and Rumania. The records include minutes, correspondence, accounting records, and photographs.

RECORDS OF THE UNITED STATES WHEAT DIRECTOR. 1919-20. 19 lin. ft.

The position of U.S. Wheat Director was established by an Executive order of May 14, 1919, to carry out price guarantees on the 1919 wheat crop. The President of the Grain Corporation was appointed to the office with certain of the functions and powers of the Food Administrator and use of Grain Corporation personnel and facilities to perform his duties. The work of the Wheat Director was terminated by an Executive order of August 21, 1920, and his records were placed in the custody of the Corporation. They include reports, correspondence, memorandums, personnel records, and records concerning enforcement.

RECORDS OF THE UNITED STATES HOUSING CORPORATION (RECORD GROUP 3)

The U.S. Housing Corporation (USHC) was incorporated July 8, 1918, to provide housing, local transportation, and other community facilities for industrial workers. Incorporated in New York and Pennsylvania, the USHC acted as executive agent for the Bureau of Industrial Housing and Transportation, established in the Department of Labor February 12, 1918, to carry on work begun by the Council of National Defense. The USHC Division of Surveys and Statistics conducted general surveys of industrial communities for the Joint Board on Industrial Surveys of the War Industries Board. The USHC also planned and contracted construction projects to provide housing and other facilities to war workers for the Commission on Living Conditions of War Workers. Construction activities were completed in 1919, and thereafter the USHC was concerned with the operation and sale of properties and the liquidation of other assets. The USHC was transferred in 1937 from the Labor Department to the Procurement Division of the Treasury Department, in 1939 to the newly created Public Buildings Administration of the Federal Works Agency, and in 1942 to the Federal Home Loan Bank Administration of the National Housing Agency (now the

Federal Home Loan Board, an independent agency). Liquidation was assigned to the Home Owners' Loan Corporation, itself subject to liquidation by the Home Loan Bank Board. Dissolution of the USHC of Pennsylvania was effective February 28, 1951; of the USHC of New York, November 30, 1948. Final termination of the USHC and all claims against it, however, was contingent on the filing of a final certificate of termination after a 3-year waiting period. Therefore, termination was not accomplished until July 17, 1952.

There are 444 cubic feet of records dated between 1917 and 1952 in this record group.

CENTRAL OFFICE RECORDS.
1917-52. 443 lin. ft.

Records of predecessor and related agencies consist primarily of questionnaires and correspondence of the Section on Housing and the Housing Committee, 1917-18; general records of the Commission on Living Conditions, including minutes, reports, and studies on housing in the United States and other countries, 1918-19; and Department of Labor records, relating to housing and the Housing Corporation, 1917-35 and 1937.

Records of USHC officials comprise records of Presidents Leroy K. Sherman, 1919-20, and Robert Watson, 1918-27; records relating to a Senate investigation of the USHC, 1918-20, including general and project records and divisional reports; minutes and correspondence relating to reports to the Congress, 1919-20; records maintained by the Office of Vice President, including a subject file of Vice President Irving E. Macomber, 1919-20; pamphlets, newspaper clippings, housing legislation, and other material accumulated by the Reference Library, 1917-19; records of the Office of the Secretary, consisting chiefly of minutes of the Board of Directors of the USHC of New York, 1918-52, and of Pennsylvania, 1918-33 and 1941-50;

records of the Office of the Treasurer, consisting of journal entries and supporting fiscal documents and correspondence relating to payments made, 1918-35; records maintained by the executive secretary, including memorandums and forms relating to project activities, 1918-19; and records of the Office of General Manager, 1918-19.

Divisional records consist of Fiscal Division periodic financial statements, correspondence, and ledgers, ca. 1918-40; Legal Division general records and contracts, 1917-24; a general subject file, 1917-20, with index of the Service Division; project file No. 1368 for the seven pines project, 1918-19; applications for USHC employment, 1918-19; records relating to USHC liquidation plans, 1919-22; general records of the Homes Registration and Information Division, 1918-19; reports and correspondence relating to housing needs, 1918; records of the Homes Registration and Information Division and of the Home Registration Section, including the office file of the Division manager, reports, a reference file, correspondence with field agents and committees, and records relating to rent profiteering, 1918-19; general records relating to publicity, 1918-19; records of the Committee on Requisitioned Houses, including reports and other records of conferences on the Washington, D.C., housing situation and on commandeering houses, 1918-19; questionnaires, exhibits, reports, and correspondence relating to industrial and housing surveys accumulated by the Surveys and Statistics Division, 1918; records of the Transportation and Municipal Loans Division, including a subject file, 1918-22; "project books" relating to transportation and Norfolk ferries, 1918-24; correspondence, agreements, and other records relating to contracts for payments in lieu of local taxes, 1918-24; records of the Real Estate Division, consisting chiefly of miscellaneous correspondence and a reference file of the Division manager, 1918-23; general records, publicity material, and a subject file of the "Own Your Own Home" Section, 1917-19; an office file of the specialist of the Building Loan Section, 1919; and Architectural Division records, including blueprint copies of plans of standard type buildings, 1918.

There are also investigative reports, memorandums, and other records of the assistant to the manager of the Town Planning Division, 1919; correspondence, memorandums, and reports of the Chief Engineer of the Engineering Division, 1918-19; records of the Construction Division, including reports, correspondence, and instructions of the manager and assistant manager, 1918-19; a card file relating to construction companies, 1918; a general subject file of the chief cost engineer, 1918-19; Engineering-Construction Division records, including consolidated files of construction projects and of tracings, 1918-20; records of the Requirements Division, consisting primarily of applications from private builders for industrial housing construction permits in critical areas, and correspondence relating to housing construction with private capital, 1918; general correspondence and a subject file of the Industrial Relations Division, 1918-19; records of the Operating Division, including a general subject file, 1918-20; correspondence, reports, and other documents relating to the operation of projects, 1918-20; general records of the Insurance Division, 1918-20; records of the Adjustment Committee, consisting primarily of minutes, 1918-21; correspondence and reports relating to contractor claims adjustment, 1918-20; report of the Adjustment Committee, 1919-20; correspondence and a subject file of the custodian of salvaged properties, 1919-20; records of the Legal and Real Estate Division, consisting primarily of reports, memorandums, and correspondence concerning Division activities, 1918-42; and general records

relating to Glenwood, 1918-29, Norfolk district, 1918-40, Philadelphia, 1918-42, Rock Island district, 1918-42, Vallejo, 1918-39, and Watertown, 1918-41, properties.

Records relating to USHC transfer of functions or liquidation consist of records of Public Buildings Service officials, relating to liquidation of the Housing Corporation, 1937-42; reports, correspondence, and other records of the Federal Home Loan Bank Administration, relating to liquidation of the USHC, 1942-50; records of the Home Owners' Loan Corporation (HOLC), including general records of the Auditing Department, 1942-50, and of the Comptroller, 1942-46; the Treasurer's schedules of disbursements and vouchers, 1943-45; Legal Department subject file and project records, 1942-50; New Brunswick property records, 1920-44; and the Property Management Division dockets, 1941-45, and the office file, 1942-45, of Stanley Baughman, HOLC Deputy General Manager in Charge of Property Management and a member of the USHC Board of Directors.

FIELD OFFICE RECORDS. 1918-30. 25 lin. ft.

These comprise records of the Transportation and Municipal Loans Division, consisting of reports, correspondence, and other records of the New York City Branch Office, 1918-19; reports, correspondence, blueprints, and newspaper clippings accumulated by the consulting engineer, 1918; an office file of the project manager for the Norfolk ferries, 1918-19; records of the Town Planning Division, consisting of correspondence and other records, 1918-19, relating to town planning in Erie, Pa.; records of the Washington Division of the U.S. Homes Registration Service, 1918-19; correspondence and other records relating to housing needs, 1918, and rooming houses and commandeered houses, 1918–19, in Washington, D.C.; and records of the Government Hotels, a Washington housing project also known as the Washington Dormitories and the Washington Residence Halls, including general records, miscellaneous correspondence, and ledgers relating to the operation of the project, 1919-30.

CARTOGRAPHIC AND AUDIOVISUAL RECORDS. 1918-20. 2,565 items.

Cartographic records (567 items) include maps and plans of project areas, showing boundaries, street patterns, property ownership, housing types, industrial sites, and transportation systems; and maps and plans prepared by the Town Planning Division of parts of certain cities showing USHC properties.

Audiovisual records (1,998 items) include photographs and architectural drawings of grading plans, street layouts, maps, house plans, housing construction in all stages, finished projects, and bad housing conditions; and posters used in promotional campaigns. Included is a photographic album entitled "Progress Report of the Transportation Division," 1918. There are also photographs of dining facilities at a factory at Saint Etienne, Loire, France, and architectural drawings of French rural dwellings.

See Katherine H. Davidson, comp., *Preliminary Inventory of the Records of the United States Housing Corporation*, PI 140 (1962).

RECORDS OF THE UNITED STATES RAILROAD ADMINISTRATION (RECORD GROUP 14)

Under authority of the Army Appropriation Act of August 29, 1916, President Wilson took full control of railroads and certain allied activities on December 28, 1917. Later proclamations extended Federal control to specified steamship lines, canals, and the American Express Company. Control was exercised through the Director General of Railroads and the U.S. Railroad Administration (USRA), which was organized into eight main divisions and seven regional offices. Federal managers were in charge of the most important groups of railroads. Government operation continued, except on short lines that were released, until March 1, 1920, when it was ended by the Transportation Act of 1920. Thereafter the Director General's staff was concerned chiefly with liquidation and final settlement of USRA affairs. Most of these activities were completed by 1927, but a skeleton force functioned until 1937. Necessary clerical duties were performed by the Treasury Department, and in 1939 the remaining functions of the Director General were transferred to the Secretary of the Treasury.

There are 1,353 cubic feet of records dated between 1917 and 1945 in this record group.

RECORDS OF THE OFFICE OF THE DIRECTOR GENERAL. 1917-35. 371 lin. ft.

These include minutes, general files of correspondence and an index (in WNRC), memorandums, and related records on all phases of USRA activities; records used in making settlements with carriers, including reports, inventories, accounts, statements, correspondence, and working papers; correspondence and issuances relating to the appointment of the Director General; records of agreements and contracts; general orders, circulars, and other issuances; fiscal records; correspondence of the Secretary of the Treasury in his capacity as Director General of Railroads and as liquidator of the USRA; and indexes.

RECORDS OF THE BOARD OF RAILROAD WAGES AND WORKING CONDITIONS. 1918–20. 32 lin. ft.

In January 1918 the Director General appointed the Railroad Wage Commission to study wages and working conditions. The Commission's recommendations were incorporated in a general order of May 25, 1918, which created the Board of Railroad Wages and Working Conditions, composed of representatives of management and labor, to hear and investigate complaints and disputes. The Board was abolished in 1920. Its records include transcripts and digests of proceedings at hearings, docketed case files and related records concerning recommendations, and compilations of reports, data, and working papers.

RECORDS OF THE DIVISION OF LAW. 1918–45. 614 lin. ft.

This Division, headed by the General Counsel until 1921 and thereafter by the General Solicitor, existed from 1918 to 1933. Its unfinished business was concluded by the Assistant Director General. The Division had general supervision over all legal activities of the carriers under Federal control, the preparation of contracts with the carriers, and the settlement of claims. Most of this work was done in the field. The records include general files (in WNRC); Executive orders and Presidential proclamations; office files of the General Counsel, general solicitors, special counsels, and the Chairman of the Committee on Compensation and Contracts; files of cases against the Director General brought to court under the Transportation Act of 1920, with an index, 1923–30; correspondence and other records relating to litigation and claims, including those of

France aginst the USRA; correspondence of the director of the Southern District; records of the regional counsel of the Southeastern Region; dockets and orders of the Interstate Commerce Commission involving suits against the Director General; financial records; and indexes.

RECORDS OF THE DIVISION OF OPERATION. 1918–20. 61 lin. ft.

First named the Division of Transportation, this unit was organized in February 1918 to control and coordinate the operations of all railroads and water carriers under the Director General. It cooperated with the Division of Labor in reviewing disputes between managers and employees. On January 14, 1919, an Automatic Train Control Committee was created in the Division to study automatic train-control devices being adopted. The Division was discontinued March 1, 1920. The records include general files of the Director and Assistant Director, cases and reports relating to labor problems, related indexes, and records of the Automatic Train Control Committee.

RECORDS OF THE DIVISION OF LABOR. 1917–23. 286 lin. ft.

The Division was created February 9, 1918. Later that year three separate railway boards of adjustment were established within the Division to review disputes involving specific unions or crafts representing organized workers. An assistant director was appointed to handle disputes involving unorganized workers, and a Women's Service Section was established. The Division was abolished March 1, 1920, and thereafter labor matters were handled in the Office of the Director General. The railway boards of adjustment functioned until 1921. The records include a general file and index; files of the Director and assistant directors; correspondence and memorandums; case files; decisions and agreements, with some copies of agreements between railroads and unions dating back to 1917; a general file of the Women's Service Section; records of Railway Board of Adjustment 1, consisting of correspondence and case files; records of Railway Board of Adjustment 2, consisting of minutes, administrative records, docketed case files and indexes, decisions, and other records relating to its cases; and records of Railway Board of Adjustment 3, consisting of administrative files, correspondence files relating to various types of railroad employees, and docketed case files and indexes.

RECORDS OF THE OFFICE OF THE COMPTROLLER. 1918–36. 110 lin. ft.

The Division of Accounting, separated in 1919 from the former Division of Public Service and Accounting, was abolished in January 1920 and succeeded by the Office of the Comptroller, which functioned until 1937. The records include a general file and index, correspondence, and records relating to final settlement accounts and agreements.

RECORDS OF THE DIVISION OF TRAFFIC. 1918–20. 3 lin. ft.

This Division, created Febrary 9, 1918, supervised both freight and passenger traffic and directed its work toward economy and simplification of railroad operations and the correction of freight rate inequities. It was abolished March 1, 1920, and its functions were transferred to the Division of Liquidation Claims and later to the Division of Law. The records consist of correspondence relating to freight rates governing exports and imports and the assumption and relinquishment of Federal control of railroads.

RECORDS OF THE DIVISION OF PURCHASES, FOREST PRODUCTS SECTION. 1918–20. 1 lin. ft.

The Division of Finance and Purchasing, created February 9, 1918, was divided into separate Divisions of Finance and Purchases on March 5, 1919. The Division of Purchases coordinated the purchase of certain types of railroad supplies and equipment through regional committees. Its records are those of the Forest Products Section, relating to the production and procurement of crossties.

RECORDS OF THE UNITED STATES SHIPPING BOARD (RECORD GROUP 32)

The U.S. Shipping Board, established by the Shipping Act of 1916, was formally organized January 30, 1917, to regulate carriers by water and develop a naval auxiliary and merchant marine. On April 16, 1917, the Board established the U.S. Shipping Board Emergency Fleet Corporation (known after 1927 as the U.S. Shipping Board Merchant Fleet Corporation) to procure, construct, charter, equip, man, operate, and dispose of merchant vessels for the Board. Under the Merchant Marine Act of 1920 and subsequent legislation the Board was given additional responsibilities. Its duties included regulating rates charged in waterborne interstate commerce, trade practices, the transfer of ships from American registry, and insurance matters; investigating adequacy of port and water transportation facilities; subsidizing private construction of ships; and determining the steamship lines necessary for U.S. commerce and the characteristics of vessels to be operated on those lines. The Board was abolished by

Executive Order 6166 of June 10, 1933, and its functions, including those with respect to the Corporation, were administered through the U.S. Shipping Board Bureau in the Department of Commerce until that Bureau and the Corporation were abolished by the Merchant Marine Act of 1936 (see RG 178).

See U.S. Shipping Board, *The Shipping Act and Merchant Marine Act* (1920); William C. Mattox, *Building the Emergency Fleet* (Cleveland, 1920); and Edward N. Hurley, *The New Merchant Marine* (New York, 1920), and *Bridge to France* (Philadelphia, 1927).

There are 6,502 cubic feet of records dated between 1914 and 1938 in this record group.

RECORDS OF THE SHIPPING BOARD AND THE SHIPPING BOARD BUREAU. 1917–36.
4,301 lin. ft.

Records that document Federal maritime policies and reflect Shipping Board activities include official minutes of the Board, 1917–33, and of the Bureau Advisory Committee and special committees, 1933–35; verbatim reports of Board meetings, 1917–35, with supplementary reports, memorandums, and indexes; correspondence files (2,329 lin. ft.), 1917–36, with indexes; records of the Office of the Historian, 1918–20; office files of commissioners and other officials; Personnel Division records; orders relating to vessel documentation, shipping rates, and claims, 1917–36; Information Bureau records, 1918–19; and reports concerning maritime policy and Board conferences, 1919–27.

Records relating to port and harbor facilities, 1917–30, include those about World War I activities of the Port and Harbor Facilities Commission; records, chiefly correspondence, for the period after December 1, 1919, concerning cooperative activities between the Shipping Board and the War Department Board of Engineers for Rivers and Harbors; wartime data on port facilities furnished by mayors, chambers of commerce, port engineers, and others; reports of a mission that studied port and harbor facilities in England and France, 1918; reports on the facilities at foreign ports, 1929–30; blueprints, maps, and statistical tables and charts; news releases and newspaper clippings; and records of the Inter-Regional Traffic Committee of the U.S. Railroad Administration, functions of which were absorbed by the Port and Harbor Facilities Commission.

Planning and statistical records, 1917–36, created or gathered by the Division of Planning and Statistics, 1917–19, and the Bureau of Research, 1922–36 (which also inherited Field Information Division records, 1921–22), include reports, correspondence, memorandums, charts, tables, and notes containing statistical data about ships, shipping, trade routes, foreign discrimination and unfair competition, commercial and economic aspects of port development, status and relations of shipping companies, preferential treaties, tax-exemption plans, and conversion of vessels from steam to diesel propulsion.

Records relating to industrial relations, 1917–22, consist of records of the Marine and Dock Industrial Relations Division, 1917–22, which handled labor problems with seamen, longshoremen, and harbor craft workers, concerning wages, hours, labor conditions, disputes, and collective-bargaining negotiations between shipowners and labor unions; and records of two independent agencies associated with the Shipping Board—the National Adjustment Commission, 1917–20, which governed longshoremen's wages, hours, and working conditions, and the New York Harbor Wage Adjustment Board, 1917–19, which had jurisdiction over harbor craft workers at that port.

Records concerning claims and legal matters, 1917–35, include files of the General Counsel for the Shipping Board and the Fleet Corporation, 1925–33, and officials of the Legal Department, 1918–33; records relating to cases brought to litigation, 1918–33; files of the Admiralty Divisions at New York, 1919–20, and Washington, 1921–33; records concerning contracts for vessel construction and operation, 1919–33, congressional investigation of the Shipping Board, 1924–25, legislation, 1921–35, and codification of navigation laws, 1920–29; ocean mail contract records, 1928–35, including records of or relating to the Interdepartmental Subcommittee on Ocean-Mail Contracts, 1929–33; and records of Board and Bureau committees regarding the Special Senate Committee Investigating Ocean-Mail Contracts, 1933–35.

Records of the Bureau of Regulations, 1917–36, consist of general correspondence and reference material relating to freight and tariff rates. There are Bureau of Finance legal documents, including building, insurance, and operating contracts; mortgages; leases; and bills and contracts for the sale of vessels, docks, wharves, equipment, real estate, and housing facilities, 1917–36. There are also Bureau records relating to joint financial accounts, managing agents' agreements, lump-sum contracts, and trade studies, 1928–36.

RECORDS OF THE EMERGENCY (MERCHANT) FLEET CORPORATION. 1917–38.
6,952 lin. ft.

Records of the Board of Trustees and staff officers include legal documents relating to the establishment of the Corporation and official minutes of Board proceedings. The Office of the General Comptroller originated in September 1919 and centralized first the auditing and accounting functions of the Corporation, later those of the combined Shipping Board Bureau and Merchant Fleet Corporation, and finally those of the U.S. Maritime Commission. The Office was abolished in November 1936, and its duties delegated to the Commis-

sion's Division of Finance. The records, 1917–36, include general correspondence, correspondence regarding financial transactions with shipbuilding companies and steamship lines, and financial and statistical reports of the Corporation.

The Ship Protection Committee, appointed in May 1917 to consider methods of protecting merchant ships from torpedoes, received and considered citizens' suggestions and cooperated with the Naval Consulting Board. The records consist of general correspondence, with indexes, 1917–21.

Records of claims organizations concerning investigation, negotiation, and settlement of claims arising from cancellation of ship construction contracts and contract adjustments after World War I, functions of which were consolidated in a Department of Claims in February 1922, include files of the Cancellations, Claims, and Contracts Board and the Requisition Claims Committee, 1919–20; the Construction Claims Board, 1919–21; Claims Commission, 1921–22; Committee on Settlement and Adjustment, 1922; Committee on Wage Reimbursement, 1920–24; and Department of Claims, 1918–36.

The records, 1918–26, of the Investigations Department—created in 1920 and given the functions and records of the Construction Organization's Plant Protection Section relating to intelligence investigations—concern subversive activities, thefts, smuggling, and claims investigations.

The American Marine Standards Committee was an independent agency functioning from 1923 until 1938 to promote standardization and simplification of equipment used in ship construction and operation. It was closely associated first with the Construction Organization and later with the Shipping Board Bureau. The records consist of committee reports on specific equipment and correspondence, 1923–38.

RECORDS OF THE CONSTRUCTION ORGANIZATION, FLEET CORPORATION. 1917-28.
2,047 lin. ft.

The Construction Organization of the Fleet Corporation acquisitioned and built vessels, drydocks, shipyards, and housing and transportation facilities. Created in 1917, it was headed by the general manager of the Corporation, but in April 1918 the Corporation's director general was given responsibility for supervising the Organization. After the Armistice, production was curtailed, and in February 1926 the Organization was discontinued.

Office files of principal construction executives, 1917-20, include a few records maintained in the offices of Charles Piez, Charles M. Schwab, John L. Ackerson, H. E. Frick, and F. P. Baldwin.

General files, 1917-26, also contain records relating to the activities of prominent officials, including G. W. Goethals, and to such elements of the construction program as administration, shipyards and plants, ships, shipbuilding, finance and accounting, supplies, labor affairs, harbors, and inland water routes. Card indexes to correspondents and subjects accompany these files.

Records concerning relations with congressional committees, 1918-20, include a general information file, a group of documents known as "Ackerson's Story for Congress," and other records of or about the Senate Committee on Commerce, the House Committee on Merchant Marine and Fisheries, and a select investigating committee (Walsh Committee) of the House.

Administrative records, 1917-20, include correspondence, reports, and other records accumulated by the Office of Vice President for Administration; reports and other records concerning financial relations with companies; records relating to plant protection; and correspondence, organization charts, and other records accumulated by the Organization and Efficiency Committee.

Records of the Ship Construction Division, 1917-21, consist of files of the Technical Section, including specifications for ships, contracts for building ships and installing machinery, records relating to ship protection (especially to the otter gear, also known as paravane), and tracings of vessel plans, 1917-20; Steel Ship Section, including correspondence of officials and administrative units and records relating to standard practices in constructing and camouflaging vessels, 1917-19; Concrete Ship Section, consisting of reports, notes, correspondence, memorandums, drawings, and blueprints relating to building, testing, and performance of concrete ships, 1917-21; Wood Ship Section, consisting of records similar to those of the Concrete Ship Section but about wooden ships, 1917-21; and Records (Statistical) Section, including reports, correspondence, speeches, statistical documents showing progress of the construction program, design drawings of vessels, and general files relating to contracts, types of ship construction, shipyards, labor, and fiscal matters, 1917-21.

Records of the Shipyard Plants Division, 1917-28, include reports, correspondence, memorandums, statistical material, shipyard location maps, construction plans for shipways and buildings, and records relating to fire protection, plant protection, health and sanitation, the transportation of labor, housing, dredging, drydocks, and marine railways. Records of the Passenger Transportation and Housing Division, 1917-26, include correspondence, reports, and statistical material concerning programs to provide housing for shipyard workers and to facilitate their transportation to and from work. Records of the Supply and Sales Division, 1918-20, relate to plant production capacities, equipment standardization, and the Youngstown, Ohio, district office. Records of the Fir Production Board, 1917-19, an independent agency associated with the Construction Organization that handled procurement and shipment of fir lumber for war industries, consist primarily of reports, correspondence, and circulars of offices in Portland, Oreg., and Seattle, Wash.

The records of Construction Organization representatives, 1917-22, at the shipyards of the American International Shipbuilding Corp. at Hog Island, Pa., the Merchant Shipbuilding Corp. at Bristol, Pa., and the Submarine Boat Corp. at Newark, N.J., 1917-22, relate to construction, launching, and trials of fabricated ships. Included with the records of the Hog Island Yard are reports of a private management engineering firm, the Egstrom-Holt Co., that contain detailed analyses of the procedures and operations of the yard. Records of the Construction Organization district and foreign offices, 1917-22, consist primarily of managers' reports and general personnel records of the district offices; and correspondence, contracts, specifications, inspectors' reports, progress charts, and statistical and accounting records of the special representative in Japan and China regarding vessels built in those countries for the Fleet Corporation. Records of the Legal Division, 1917-20, consist of correspondence, reports, and memorandums relating chiefly to legal aspects of ship construction, procurement of materials, foreign contracts, shipping patents, claims, insurance, contract cancellations, and construction of shipyard plants, facilities, and housing. Records of the Contract Division, 1918-20, relate to contract negotiations for construction of vessels, machinery and equipment, and to inspection and investigation of companies.

There are records, chiefly reports, correspondence, memorandums, transcripts of hearings, and statistical data, 1917-19, of the Industrial Relations Division,

which adjusted labor disputes, trained shipyard workers and instructors, established and enforced wage scales, supervised safety and sanitary standards, and prevented unfair labor practices to maintain an adequate labor supply; and of the Shipbuilding Labor Adjustment Board (also known as the Macy Board), an independent agency established by agreement of the Fleet Corporation, the Navy Department, the American Federation of Labor, and shipbuilders to regulate hours, wages, and labor conditions in the shipbuilding industry.

RECORDS OF THE OPERATIONS ORGANIZATION. 1917-36.
4,099 lin. ft.

The Operations Organization consisted of administrative units of the Fleet Corporation that supervised and controlled operation of Shipping Board merchant vessels. General records, 1917-36, include the official minutes of the Committee of Operations, 1918-20; general records of the Division of Operations, containing information on vessels owned, operated, or requisitioned by the Shipping Board, and data on daily shipping operations, 1917-36 (the major part falling within the period 1917-20); subject correspondence of the Chartering Committee, which controlled operations of American vessels under 2,500 tons and neutral shipping in American foreign trade from September 1917 to March 1919 by granting charters and fixing charter rates, 1917-19; correspondence of the Shipping Control Committee, which allocated vessels to cargoes and routes and controlled the discharge of American tonnage, 1918-19; records relating to vessel personnel; and records relating to other Organization units.

Records of the Contact Division, 1917-32—which interpreted managing and operating agreements and performed for the Fleet Corporation the duties of a chartering department, including delivery of vessels purchased, chartered, or sold—relate to charters, agreements, and contracts of affreightment. Records of the Maintenance and Repair Division, 1919-31, consist of general correspondence, blueprints, and charts relating to maintenance and repair of vessels controlled by the Fleet Corporation. Records of the Purchases and Supplies Division, 1920-36, consist of general correspondence relating to procurement of fuel and bunker and steward supplies for Fleet Corporation vessels. Records of the Traffic Department, 1918-36, relate to such Department functions as allocating and assigning vessels, establishing and publishing freight rates and tariffs, investigating claims related to cargoes, securing cargoes and mail contracts, and booking passengers on vessels owned by the Shipping Board, and contain information on shipping companies, trade routes, and ship operator conferences.

Records of the Advertising Department, 1920-32, relate to publicity arrangements for the sale of Shipping Board vessels and surplus property, the sale of cargo and passenger space on vessels still owned and/or operated by the Board, and procurement of vessel operators. Records of the Ship Sales Division, 1919-36, relate to such functions as negotiations for the disposal of Board vessels, supervision of the laid-up (reserve) fleet of vessels, the ship-scrapping program, and the disposal of marine railways and drydocks, and contain information about the appraisal of individual ships and preservation techniques for idle vessels.

Records of the Insurance Division—which administered the fund for insuring vessels, cargoes, and freight, and for "protection and indemnity" risks, such as accidents to seamen and passengers, loss or damage to cargoes from improper stowage or rough passage, and losses due to fines for violations of customs and port rules—include correspondence and case files, 1918-36.

Records of the Statistical Department, 1918-34, include reports, correspondence, memorandums, and statistical charts relating to the movements and operating costs of vessels under jurisdiction of the Fleet Corporation. Records of the Operations district offices, 1917-36, relate primarily to vessel personnel and operations, including New York office records dated before 1923 about the operations of the entire fleet and the Cleveland special agent's correspondence about transfer of vessels from the Great Lakes area to the Atlantic coast. Records of foreign offices maintained by the Operations Organization to promote U.S. shipping activities, 1919-32, relate chiefly to ship movements, freight rates and traffic, stevedoring, labor conditions, cargo delays, claims, vessel repair, port facilities, and bunkering. Records of the European Headquarters Office at London include information about requisitioning foreign vessels, European and Russian relief, immigration, emigration, and passenger and cargo solicitation. Records of the United States Lines, a steamship company owned and operated by the Shipping Board, 1921-29, include New York office correspondence about revenues, expenses, and office organization; photographs of company vessels and publicity scenes; London office publicity releases and other records relating chiefly to passenger solicitation and restrictions, immigration policies, and rates; and Paris office correspondence relating to the first voyage of the rebuilt SS *Leviathan* in 1923, other passenger vessels owned by the company, and office organization.

CARTOGRAPHIC AND AUDIOVISUAL RECORDS. 1914-31. 40,149 items.

Cartographic records (249 items) comprise maps relating to U.S. shipping routes, 1914-31; plans of harbors in England and Scotland, prepared by the Port and Harbor Facilities Commission, 1917-18; and charts of U.S. harbors, ports, and coastal areas, annotated by the Division of Shipyard Plants to show harbor activities, 1917-19.

Audiovisual records include photographs (39,900 items) of shipyards, shipbuilding activities, merchant marine training and apprenticeship, and housing project construction, 1917-20; ships of the United States Lines, 1925-28; fuel oil installations at Honolulu, 1920; illustrations for *The Merchant Marine Bulletin*, 1920-30; the fender system of the James River Bridge; and storage and condition of Government records, ca. 1919.

See Forrest R. Holdcamper, comp., *Preliminary Inventory of the Records of the United States Shipping Board*, PI 97 (1956).

RECORDS OF THE UNITED STATES SUGAR EQUALIZATION BOARD, INC. (RECORD GROUP 6)

The U.S. Sugar Equalization Board was established as a Government-owned corporation in July 1918. The Board was an agency of the U.S. Food Administration, and the Food Administrator was Chairman of its Board of Directors (see RG 4). The principal functions of the Board were to buy and distribute the 1918-19 crop of Cuban sugar and to stimulate U.S. production by equalizing prices of domestic and imported sugars. In the fall of 1918 the War Trade Board and the Food Administration agreed that all coffee should be imported through the Sugar Equalization Board. The Board was assisted by a number of committees and commissions, including the International Sugar Committee, Cuban Export Committee, American Refiners Committee, Joint Commission on West Indies Transportation, and Sugar Distributing Committee. It operated through a 1918 agreement with the Cuban Government and Cuban producers and a contract with American refiners. To reduce home consumption of sugar, the Board, in cooperation with the central and State offices of the Food Administration, established throughout the country a certificate system of sugar distribution, which was abandoned December 1, 1918.

A Presidential proclamation of November 21, 1919, transferred to the Attorney General the Food Administrator's responsibilities regarding sugar licensing, hoarding, profiteering, and unfair practices. On December 31, 1919, the contract with American refiners expired, and the Board's control over the sugar industry ended. Liquidation began in 1920, and the Board was terminated July 14, 1926. The Board's records were transferred first to the U.S. Grain Corporation and, in 1927, to the Department of Commerce.

There are 60 cubic feet of records (in WNRC) dated between 1917 and 1923 in this record group.

RECORDS. 1917-23. 52 lin. ft.

These include Board minutes and general correspondence; records of the President, secretary, General Counsel, and other officials; reports and other records of the Statistical Department; minutes of the Sugar Distributing Committee and the Cuban Export Committee; minutes, correspondence, and other records of the American Refiners Committee and of the International Sugar Committee; records of the Joint Commission on West Indies Transportation; records concerning claim settlements; and reports and correspondence on liquidation of the Board.

RECORDS OF THE WAR FINANCE CORPORATION
(RECORD GROUP 154)

The War Finance Corporation was created by an act of April 5, 1918, to give financial support to industries essential to the war effort and to banking institutions that aided such industries. After the Armistice the Corporation's activities were extended to assist in the transition to peacetime. In the spring of 1919 it financed railroads still under Government control and made loans to American exporters; in 1921 it made advances for agricultural purposes to financial institutions and to cooperative marketing associations. To facilitate the handling of agricultural loans, it established agricultural loan agencies in farming areas and cooperated with several livestock loan companies. The Corporation began terminating its activities on January 1, 1925, and an act of March 1, 1929, assigned to the Secretary of the Treasury the liquidation of its assets. The Corporation was abolished on July 1, 1939, with the termination of its business to be completed by December 31, 1939.

Duplicate copies of minutes of the Corporation, 1921-31, are in the Hoover Institution on War, Revolution, and Peace at Stanford University. Correspondence of the Secretary of the Treasury with or concerning the Corporation, 1918-32, is among records of the Department of the Treasury (see RG 56).

See Secretary of the Treasury, *Liquidation of the War Finance Corporation* (1943); and Woodbury Willoughby, *The Capital Issues Committee and War Finance Corporation* (Baltimore, 1934).

There are 627 cubic feet of records dated between 1918 and 1939 in this record group.

RECORDS. 1918-39. 752 lin. ft.

Headquarters records consist chiefly of minutes of the Board of Directors and of the Liquidation Committee, 1918-34, with related indexes; administrative records and correspondence, 1918-39, including sample completed loan applications of banks, trust companies, railroads, public utilities, livestock loan companies, exporters, and agricultural cooperatives; correspondence with agricultural loan agencies and Federal Reserve banks, relating to the purchase and sale of liberty and other bonds; and ledgers and cash accounts, 1918-31. Also a few field records of agricultural loan agencies at Atlanta, Boise, Chicago, Dallas, Denver, Helena, Minneapolis, Omaha, and Santa Fe, consisting chiefly of minutes and fiscal records, 1918-31.

RECORDS OF THE WAR INDUSTRIES BOARD
(RECORD GROUP 61)

The War Industries Board was established by the Council of National Defense on July 28, 1917, to act as a clearinghouse for the war industry needs of the Government. The Council's committees on industries and materials were reorganized and made subordinate to the Board, and at various times other units of the Council were attached to the Board. On March 4, 1918, the President enlarged the functions of the Board and appointed Bernard M. Baruch as its

Chairman. It became an independent agency by Executive order on May 28, 1918.

The Board analyzed the industrial requirements and capabilities of the United States and of the Allies, issued "clearances" on Government orders before they were placed with contractors, determined priorities in production and delivery of commodities, arranged price-fixing agreements for certain raw materials, encouraged conservation of existing facilities and resources and the development of new ones, and supervised Allied purchasing in the United States. The complex organization of the Board included a Price-Fixing Committee, a variety of divisions, and a large number of "commodity sections" that gathered information and performed other duties regarding specific commodities and industries.

An Executive order of December 31, 1918, provided for dissolution of the Board; liquidation was completed July 22, 1919, and most of the Board's records were placed in the custody of the Council of National Defense. In 1921 these records were transferred to the War Department. Records of the Board's Domestic Wool Section are among records of the Bureau of Agricultural Economics (see RG 83).

See War Industries Board, *Outline of the Board's Origin, Functions, and Organization* (1918).

There are 872 cubic feet of records (in WNRC) dated between 1917 and 1919, with a few dated as early as 1916 and as late as 1933, in this record group.

RECORDS. 1917-19. 1,046 lin. ft.

Included are minutes, rulings, reports, studies, memorandums, questionnaires, compilations and statistical tabulations of data, forms, charts, printed and processed publications, press releases, cablegrams, photographs, and indexes. Some of the records are arranged by organizational unit, including those of the offices of the Chairman and Vice Chairman, the Price-Fixing Committee, and certain divisions and sections. During the years 1919-23, however, most of the records were reorganized into consolidated files. These include administrative records and a large volume of technical or commodity records arranged alphabetically by subject. Records concerning particular subjects were assembled in other consolidated files for the use of Senate committees, the Department of Justice, and the Army Industrial College.

See the Council of National Defense, *Fourth Annual Report* (1920), pp. 74-91; and *Preliminary Inventory of the War Industries Board Records*, PI 1 (1941).

RECORDS OF THE WAR LABOR POLICIES BOARD (RECORD GROUP 1)

In January 1918 the President appointed the Secretary of Labor as War Labor Administrator, and the Secretary in turn appointed an Advisory Council to help deal with labor problems involving war production. On the recommendation of the Council, the War Labor Policies Board was established May 13, 1918, by the War Labor Administrator to standardize labor policies of Government agencies. The agencies represent-

ed on the Board were the Departments of Labor, War, Navy, and Agriculture; the War Industries and U.S. Shipping Boards; the Emergency Fleet Corporation; the Railroad, Food, and Fuel Administrations; and the Committee on Public Information.

The Board formulated uniform policies for war labor administration, promoted better housing conditions for warworkers, and, after the Armistice, considered proposals for canceling Government contracts and for demobilization. It also made studies of domestic and foreign wartime labor conditions and of labor policies relating to immediate postwar conditions in the United States. The Board was discontinued in March 1919.

There are 12 cubic feet of records dated between 1918 and 1919 in this record group.

RECORDS. 1918-19. 14 lin. ft.

Minutes of the Board and its committees, 1918-19; correspondence of the Chairman and the Executive Secretary, 1918-19; correspondence of business and reconstruction advisers, June-December 1918; correspondence with Governors and State labor officials, 1918-19; and bulletins, newspaper clippings, and daily digests of articles and editorials concerning war labor policies and Board activities, 1918-19.

See Mary Walton Livingston and Leo Pascal, comps., *Preliminary Inventory of the War Labor Policies Board Records*, PI 4 (1943).

RECORDS OF THE WAR TRADE BOARD
(RECORD GROUP 182)

The War Trade Board, established by Executive order on October 12, 1917, replaced the Exports Council and the Division of Export Licenses of the Bureau of Foreign and Domestic Commerce, both established June 22, 1917, and the Exports Administrative Board, established August 21, 1917, as successor to the Export Licenses Division. The War Trade Board licensed exports and imports, rationed supplies to neutrals, and conserved commodities and shipping facilities for American and Allied use. It sought to keep strategic goods out of enemy hands and prevent the use of enemy credit and financial holdings in the United States. Agencies represented on the Board were the State, Treasury, Agriculture, and Commerce Departments and the Food Administration, Shipping Board, and War Industries Board. The War Trade Board worked through an Executive Office, an Information Division, a Contraband Committee, and the Bureaus of Administration, Branches and Customs, Enemy Trade, Exports, Foreign Agents and Reports, Imports, Research and Statistics, Transportation, and War Trade Intelligence.

A subsidiary corporation known as the Russian Bureau, Inc., was formed in November 1918. The Board began relaxing its controls after the end of the war, and on June 30, 1919, its remaining functions were transferred to the War Trade Board Section of the Department of State, which continued a limited operation until May 27, 1921.

See War Trade Board, *Report* (1920).

There are 722 cubic feet of records (all in WNRC except for one motion picture) dated between 1917 and 1921, with some dated as late as 1935, in this record group.

RECORDS. 1917-21. 1,530 lin. ft.

Records are those of the War Trade Board and its predecessors, 1917-19, the Russian Bureau, Inc., 1918-20, and the War Trade Board Section of the Department of State, 1917-21 (with a few dated as late as 1935). They include minutes, resolutions, rules and regulations, instructions, correspondence, cablegrams, memorandums, reports and studies, trade agreements, export lists, license applications, copies of licenses, statistical tables and charts, indexes and digest record cards, appropriation ledgers, and a motion picture of the War Trade Board Building, Board members, and Board employees. There are also minutes of the Superior Blockade and Supreme Economic Councils; Supreme Blockade, Allied Blockade, and British Contraband Committees; and various interallied trade committees.

See Alexander P. Mavro, comp., *Preliminary Inventory of the Records of the War Trade Board*, PI 100 (1957).

From 1933 to 1950

RECORDS OF THE AMERICAN COMMISSION FOR THE PROTECTION AND SALVAGE OF ARTISTIC AND HISTORIC MONUMENTS IN WAR AREAS
(RECORD GROUP 239)

Establishment of the American Commission for the Protection and Salvage of Artistic and Historic Monuments in War Areas was approved by the President on June 23, 1943, and announced by the Secretary of State on August 20, 1943. Its chairman was Supreme Court Justice Owen J. Roberts. The Commission cooperated with the U.S. Army in protecting cultural treasures, gathered information about war damage to such treasures, and compiled data on cultural property appropriated by the Axis Powers and encouraged its restitution. The Commission was assisted by the private American Defense-Harvard Group and the American Council of Learned Societies' Committee on the Protection of Cultural Treasures in War Areas, which turned over its research files to the Commission. The Commission was terminated June 30, 1946, and its remaining functions, chiefly involving restitution of art objects, were taken over by the Department of State.

There are 46 cubic feet of records dated between 1943 and 1946 in this record group.

RECORDS. 1943-46. 57 lin. ft. and 23 rolls of microfilm.

These consist of minutes; letters of application and recommendation; records of Commissioner Sachs, consisting chiefly of correspondence; general correspondence; fiscal records; lists and handbooks concerning cultural institutions in Europe; Allied military government records, including final reports of the Mediterranean and European Theaters of Operations, drawn from the "Analytical File" (on microfilm); reports of the Art Looting Investigation Unit, including some reports of the Office of Strategic Services and the Strategic Services Unit; and special reports from various sources.

CARTOGRAPHIC AND AUDIOVISUAL RECORDS. 1943-46. 1,831 items.

A major wartime activity of the Commission was the compilation of maps showing locations of areas or sites in enemy or enemy-occupied areas that were to be spared destruction, if possible. Base maps of provinces, regions, and sites were acquired; and tissue overlays were made on which numbers were placed indicating such areas or sites. Photocopies were then made of the base maps and accompanying overlays. Lists identifying each site or area shown were also prepared. The records, 1943-46 (1,489 items), consist of a set of instructions for the preparation of maps, lists of maps prepared, and a set of these photoprocessed maps and accompanying identification lists. In a few instances a base map with a manuscript overlay substitutes for a photocopy. The records relate to Albania, Austria, Belgium, Bulgaria, Corsica, Czechoslovakia, Dalmatia, Denmark, France, Germany, Hungary, Indochina, Italy, Japan, Java, Korea, the Netherlands, Norway, the Philippine Islands, Rumania, Sardinia, Sicily, and Yugoslavia, and are arranged by continent, thereunder alphabetically by name of country, and thereunder alphabetically by name of city or province.

Audiovisual records consist of photographs, 1943-46 (342 items), of monuments and buildings in Frankfurt, Germany, and aerial photographs of cities in Italy, Spain, and Burma.

RECORDS OF THE BOARD OF INVESTIGATION AND RESEARCH—TRANSPORTATION
(RECORD GROUP 198)

The Board of Investigation and Research was established by the Transportation Act of September 18, 1940. The Board was directed to investigate the relative economy and efficiency of carriers in transportation services and the extent to which carriers were aided by public funds and taxed by each level of government. Its conclusions and recommendations were to be reported to the President and the Congress. The Board held its first meeting in August 1941; however, appropriations for a research staff were not made available until December, and work was not begun until 1942. The Board's tenure, originally fixed at 2 years, was extended by Presidential Proclamation 2559 of June 26, 1944, until September 18, 1944.

The Board's investigations were conducted through research groups functioning under a secretary in charge of research and later under a research director. The research groups were organized into divisions and further subdivided into sections. Most research was conducted by the Economy and Fitness Research Group. Other groups were concerned with international freight rates, public aids, and taxation. The Board's Legal Division conducted several investigations, notably on transportation and storage activities of Federal agencies and on the legal and administrative aspects of Government control of transportation, in addition to its regular duties. Facilitative functions of the Board were performed by an Administrative Division. The Board also undertook specific studies at the request of war agencies and congressional committees concerned with transportation problems, and coordinated its activities with those of the Office of Defense Transportation.

There are 59 cubic feet of records dated between 1941 and 1944 in this record group.

RECORDS. 1941-44. 71 lin. ft.

These consist of minutes; a central file containing correspondence, memorandums, charts, and reports on the administration, organization, and operation of the Board; files of the Chairman and Board members, including general correspondence, drafts of studies and reports, exhibits referred to in Board minutes, and transcripts, briefs, and exhibits relating to Board hearings; records of research groups, including office files of secretaries in charge of research, research directors, and directors of divisions and sections; reports and studies prepared by the Board; and records of the Administrative Division, consisting of office files of the senior administrative officer and miscellaneous records of the Personnel Section.

See Leo Pascal, comp., *Preliminary Inventory of the Records of the Board of Investigation and Research—Transportation*, PI 19 (1949).

RECORDS OF THE BOARD OF WAR COMMUNICATIONS (RECORD GROUP 259)

The Defense Communications Board was established by an Executive order of September 24, 1940, and was renamed the Board of War Communications in 1942. The Board was directed to plan the most efficient use and control of the Nation's radio, telephone, telegraph, and cable communications to meet the needs of the Armed Forces, Government agencies, industry and commerce, and other civilian activities. After U.S. entry into World War II, the President delegated to the Board authority to control the use of radio and wire communications, direct the closing of such stations and facilities when necessary, and establish priorities for communications essential to national defense. The Board—consisting of representatives of the State, Treasury, War, and Navy Departments; the Federal Communications Commission (FCC); and the Coast Guard—functioned through a coordinating committee, five advisory committees, and 13 special planning committees. It had no appropriation or staff of its own, but used FCC and other Government agency personnel as well as employees of private communications concerns. The Board was terminated February 24, 1947, and its property and records were transferred to the FCC for liquidation. This record group also includes records of the Interdepartmental Advisory Committee on Hemisphere Communications, which, though not a formal part of the Board, performed functions similar to those of its advisory committees.

There are 74 cubic feet of records dated between 1930 and 1947 in this record group.

RECORDS OF THE BOARD OF WAR COMMUNICATIONS. 1940-47. 51 lin. ft.

These records comprise general subject files consisting of reports and correspondence relating to functions, policies, and procedures, 1940-47; minutes, with related summaries and agenda, 1940-46; orders, issuances, releases, and publications, 1940-47; minutes, reports, and correspondence relating to the coordinating committee, the advisory committees (including the Law Committee, 1940-46, the Cable Committee, 1941-45, and the Telegraph Committee, 1940-46), and special planning committees, 1940-46; a card file containing information on committee members, 1941-46; "company files" consisting of correspondence with private companies and organizations, labor unions, and Government agencies, 1940-46; citizenship data on employees of international broadcasting stations, 1942-44; and "amateur files" containing correspondence on control of amateur radio stations, 1941-42.

RECORDS OF THE
INTERDEPARTMENTAL
ADVISORY COMMITTEE ON
HEMISPHERE
COMMUNICATIONS. 1930–47.
28 lin. ft.

This Committee was established in 1941 to provide information, advice, and assistance in formulating and executing an inter-American communications program. The records include proceedings, memorandums, and reports, 1942–45;

records on Latin American and international communications, 1930-45, and relating to U.S. and foreign communications companies, 1932–45; photostatic copies of printed works on the history of the telephone and telegraph in Brazil, Chile, and Colombia; and compilations of laws, regulations, decrees, and administrative orders governing foreign operation of radios, telegraphs, and telephones.

RECORDS OF THE CIVILIAN CONSERVATION CORPS
(RECORD GROUP 35)

The Civilian Conservation Corps (CCC) was created by an act of June 28, 1937, to succeed the Emergency Conservation Work that had been established by Executive order in 1933. In 1939 the CCC became part of the Federal Security Agency. An appropriation act of July 2, 1942, provided for the termination of the CCC not later than June 30, 1943. The CCC and its predecessor provided employment and vocational training for unemployed youths and, to a limited extent, war veterans and Indians through conservation and natural resources development work. Enrollees were selected chiefly by State welfare agencies, with some participation by the Department of Labor and the Veterans Administration. The War Department assembled the enrollees; provided transportation to camps, housing, food, and medical services; and was in general charge of camp finances and operations. Work performed by the camps was planned and supervised by certain technical agencies, principally the Forest Service, the Soil Conservation Service, the Bureau of Plant Industry, the Bureau of Entomology and Plant Quarantine, and the National Park Service.

See John A. Salmond, *The CCC, 1933-42; A New Deal Case Study* (Durham, N.C., 1967).

There are 732 cubic feet of records dated between 1933 and 1948 in this record group.

GENERAL RECORDS OF THE
CCC. 1933–43. 432 lin. ft. and 193
rolls of microfilm.

These include general correspondence, 1933–43, in several series, relating to administration, investigation, complaints, cooperation, annual reports, budget and finance, supplies and equipment, and regulations (419 lin. ft.); a reference file concerning CCC organization and work, with emphasis on the role of the Forest Service in CCC activities, 1933–42; minutes of the Advisory Council, 1933–42; manuals of cooperating bureaus, 1939; microfilm copies (193 rolls) of progress reports, 1933–42; camp directories, 1933–42; organization charts, 1941–42; *Happy Days*, the CCC weekly newspaper, 1933–40; and correspondence and resolutions relating to memorials for Robert Fechner, first CCC Director, 1940–41.

DIVISIONAL RECORDS. 1933–43.
457 lin. ft.

These are primarily records of the Division of Investigations, consisting of camp inspection reports and correspondence, 1933-42; the Safety Division, consisting chiefly of correspondence, and accident reports, 1933-42, reports of proceedings of boards of officers, which investigated circumstances surrounding deaths of enrollees, 1937-40, and official reports of injury, 1937-40; the Division of Planning and Public Relations, consisting of correspondence, pictographs, articles and speeches, clippings, and publications concerning the CCC, 1933-42, and a general information file on conservation work in various States, 1933-42; the Division of Research and Statistics, consisting chiefly of correspondence, 1933-42, records relating to legislation, 1937-42, monthly station and strength reports prepared by the War Department giving location and strength of CCC work companies and projects, 1940-42, reports by company commanders showing company strength and other information, 1941, and reports on educational activities, 1936-40; the Division of Selection, consisting of selection reports, several series of correspondence, a selection policy file relating to CCC enrollees, 1933-42, and State procedural manuals and letters of instruction to local selection agents, 1938-42; and the Automotive and Priorities Division, consisting of correspondence, 1938-43.

RECORDS OF THE CCC LIQUIDATION UNIT. 1942-48.
34 lin. ft.

Records of the director include earlier material accumulated in the process of liquidation and later records of the Federal Security Agency and the Department of Health, Education, and Welfare. They are primarily reports, regulations, correspondence, and other records concerning terminal operations of the CCC and National Youth Administration and the disposition of their property.

AUDIOVISUAL RECORDS. 1933-43.
10,852 items.

Photographs, 1933-43 (10,850 items), of the office of the Director of the CCC and camp facilities; activities in the nine army corps areas and individual companies; of conservation work, civilian defense training, academic and vocational programs, sightseeing in Washington, D.C., and religious services for CCC personnel and local residents; black enrollees; dams and recreation facilities begun in the TVA area; and totem poles restored by Indian enrollees in the Tongass National Forest, Alaska. Motion pictures, ca. 1934 (2 reels), illustrate CCC work in erosion control and activities in a CCC camp.

See Harold T. Pinkett, "Records in the National Archives Relating to the Civilian Conservation Corps," *Social Science Review* (March 1948); and Pinkett, comp., *Preliminary Inventory of the Records of the Civilian Conservation Corps*, PI 11 (1948).

RECORDS OF THE COMMITTEE FOR CONGESTED PRODUCTION AREAS (RECORD GROUP 212)

The Committee for Congested Production Areas was established in the Executive Office of the President by Executive Order 9327 of April 7, 1943, to coordinate Federal, State, and local governmental activities in congested production areas, especially with regard to plant and site availability, local labor supply, and transportation, housing, social service, recreational, and commercial facilities. It designated critical areas and prescribed binding policies and programs for Federal agencies involved. The Committee Chairman was the Director of the Bureau of the Budget, and its six other members were officials of the War and Navy Departments, War Production Board, Federal Works Agency, War Manpower Commission, and National Housing Agency. An act of June 28, 1944, continued the Committee until December 31, 1944, and provided for its liquidation between January 1 and June 30, 1945.

There are 56 cubic feet of records dated between 1943 and 1945 in this record group.

RECORDS. 1943–45. 68 lin. ft.

Included are central files containing resumes of Committee meetings, minutes of meetings between Washington staff members and area representatives and of agency meetings; general correspondence; procedural and organizational records; records relating to the operations of area offices; reference files of newspaper clippings and congressional publications; records of the Analysis Section, consisting of narrative reports to the Chairman, status reports, and census population studies relating to congested areas; project files maintained by the Liaison Officers Section; and miscellaneous personnel and budget records of the Administrative Section.

See Leo Pascal and Jeanne McDonald, comps., *Preliminary Inventory of the Records of the Committee for Congested Production Areas*, PI 128 (1960); and Elaine C. Bennett, comp., for the Committee on Negro Studies of the American Council of Learned Societies, *Calendar of Negro-Related Documents in the Records of the Committee for Congested Production Areas in the National Archives* (1949).

RECORDS OF THE
COMMITTEE ON FAIR EMPLOYMENT PRACTICE
(RECORD GROUP 228)

The first Committee on Fair Employment Practice was established in the Office of Production Management (OPM) by Executive Order 8802 of June 25, 1941. The Committee was assigned to the War Production Board when that agency succeeded the OPM and was transferred to the War Manpower Commission in 1942. Executive Order 9346 of May 27, 1943, abolished that Committee and created a new Committee on Fair Employment Practice in the Office for Emergency Management. The National War Agencies Appropriation Act of 1946 provided funds for the second Committee until June 30, 1946, and the Committee terminated its business on June 28 when it issued its final report to the President. The Committee formulated and interpreted policies to combat racial and religious discrimina-

tion in employment; received, investigated, and adjusted complaints of such discrimination; and assisted Government agencies, employers, and labor unions with problems of discrimination.

There are 200 cubic feet of records dated between 1940 and 1946 in this record group.

RECORDS OF THE OFFICE OF THE CHAIRMAN. 1940–46. 30 lin. ft.

These consist of summary minutes, action summaries, agenda, and a documents file relating to Committee meetings; correspondence sent by the Chairman and other headquarters officials; and office files of Malcolm Ross, 1940–46, who served as Chairman from October 1943 to its termination, and of Max Berking, assistant to the Chairman, 1944–45.

RECORDS OF THE OFFICE OF THE DEPUTY CHAIRMAN. 1941-45. 3 lin. ft.

These consist of correspondence sent, 1942-45, by George M. Johnson, Deputy Chairman from October 1943 to February 1946, and his office files, 1941-45.

RECORDS OF THE OFFICE OF THE EXECUTIVE SECRETARY. 1941-43. 2 lin. ft.

These consist of correspondence sent, including identical letters to heads of Federal agencies requesting information about Federal employment of blacks.

RECORDS OF THE LEGAL DIVISION. 1941-46. 31 lin. ft.

This Division prepared for and conducted hearings and rendered general counsel services for the agency. After a 1943 reorganization, the Deputy Chairman of the Committee served as Director of the Legal Division and was the General Counsel. The records consist of general files of George M. Johnson, 1941-45, Division Director from November 1941 to February 1946; files of hearing examiners Emanuel H. Bloch and Maceo W. Hubbard (who also served as Acting Division Director from April 1945 to January 1946); records of several trial attorneys; records relating to hearings; and indexes to cases, opinions, interpretations, agreements, and policies.

RECORDS OF THE DIVISION OF BUDGET AND ADMINISTRATIVE MANAGEMENT. 1941-46. 77 lin. ft.

This Division was responsible for budgetary, fiscal, personnel, and administrative services and for supervising the Mail and File Unit, which maintained the Central files. The records consist of the central files, including transcripts of Committee meetings, summaries of conference proceedings, reports, correspondence, legal opinions, accounting records, and miscellaneous issuances of the Committee and other Government agencies.

RECORDS OF THE DIVISION OF REVIEW AND ANALYSIS. 1941-46. 44 lin. ft.

This Division was created in 1943 when the function of reviewing compliance with provisions of Executive orders establishing governmental policies on fair employment practices was transferred to the regional offices. The Division developed statistical analyses of case data used in preparing reports and recommendations; assembled, analyzed, and coordinated information compiled by other agencies concerning the utilization of minority group labor; developed staff training materials; and made studies of race relations and tensions in industry. The records include general files of John A. Davis, 1941-46, Division Director from August 1943 to May 1946, and of Marjorie M. Lawson, 1942-45, Assistant Division Director; and files of consultant Wilford C. Leland, Jr., of the clerk-stenographer, and of compliance analysts. There are also reference files containing published material relating to industrial, labor, and minority problems; studies; reports; synopses of books and articles by the staff; and speeches and statements of Committee officials, other Government officials, and members of private organizations. Also included are drafts and working papers relating to the first published Committee report, reports and statistical data relating to cases, a file about racially disturbed areas, and issuances relating to the Production Readjustment Committee.

RECORDS OF THE INFORMATION OFFICE. 1941-46. 16 lin. ft.

This Office, which was attached to the Office of the Chairman, was abolished in July 1945, and its functions were transferred to the Division of Review and Analysis. The records consist of files of the information officer, 1943-45, press releases, 1941-45, weekly news digests, 1943-45, and newspaper clippings, 1943-46. There are also sound recordings (4 items) of the radio script for "Weapons for Victory," 1946.

RECORDS OF THE DIVISION OF FIELD OPERATIONS. 1941-46. 39 lin. ft.

Cases were processed by a headquarters staff of examiners until 1943 when this Division was created to administer a system of regional offices, establish procedures for adjusting complaints, and negotiate formalized operating relationships with other Government agencies. The records include general files of the Division Director Will Maslow and his successors, 1943-45; of Assistant and Associate Directors, 1941-46; and of senior field representatives, 1941-46. There are also correspondence, memorandums, instructions, notices, case records referred to headquarters for settlement, weekly reports of field activities, and indexes to case files and to related records.

RECORDS OF THE REGIONAL OFFICES. 1941-46. 140 lin. ft.

The first Committee employed field investigators, but the second Committee established regional offices to handle the initial investigation of complaints and to make adjustments when possible. The field organization, at maximum strength, comprised 13 regional and 5 subregional offices. The records consist of case files, with indexes, including active cases involving unsettled complaints not dismissed for lack of merit (Region VII case files in FRC Atlanta), closed cases (Region VII case files in FRC Atlanta), settled or dismissed for lack of merit, nondocketable cases dismissed for lack of Committee jurisdiction or lack of essential information (Region VII case files in FRC Atlanta), and predocketed cases involving complaints in Region II (New York) that were investigated before being docketed. There are also general records and correspondence relating to complaints in Region II; fiscal records for Region III (Philadelphia); general records of Regions IV (Washington, D.C.) and V (Cleveland), with a general file of the Cincinnati office; general records and correspondence of Region VI (Chicago); and general records of Regions VII (in FRC Atlanta), IX (Kansas City and St. Louis), and XII (San Francisco and Los Angeles).

See Charles Zaid, comp., *Preliminary Inventory of the Records of the Committee on Fair Employment Practice*, PI 147 (1962).

RECORDS OF THE
FEDERAL COORDINATOR OF TRANSPORTATION
(RECORD GROUP 133)

The Federal Coordinator of Transportation was authorized by the Emergency Railroad Transportation Act of June 16, 1933, to relieve the existing national emergency in interstate railroad transportation and to safeguard and maintain an adequate national transportation system by investigating railroad labor conditions and assisting the railroad industry reduce duplicate services and facilities, eliminate practices impairing net earnings, and accomplish financial reorganization. The Federal Coordinator, appointed by the President, created a field organization composed of Eastern, Western, and Southern Regions, with headquarters in New York, Chicago, and Atlanta, respectively. In each region a coordinating committee of carrier representatives was established and advisory committees representing railroad labor and other railroad organizations were appointed. In the headquarters organization several operating sections—Research, Transportation and Service, Labor Relations, Property and Equipment, and Car Pooling—were established to make comprehensive studies. The office of Federal Coordinator was terminated June 16, 1936.

There are 879 cubic feet of records dated between 1930 and 1937 in this record group.

GENERAL RECORDS OF THE COORDINATOR'S OFFICE. 1933-36. 113 lin. ft.

Included are a subject-classified file consisting of reports, studies, correspondence, memorandums, telegrams, and other records concerning the organization, jurisdiction, functions, and activities of Coordinator Joseph B. Eastman's office and its relationship to other Government agencies, 1933-36, with a card index; printed and processed copies of reports on the transportation industry, 1933-36; press releases, 1933-35; and assessment cards showing the amount to be contributed by each carrier for operation of the Coordinator's Office, 1933-36.

RECORDS OF THE MECHANICAL ADVISORY COMMITTEE. 1934-36. 8 lin. ft.

The Committee was appointed to appraise mechanical railroad equipment and to make recommendations for future requirements. The records consist of minutes; reports; office files of Chairman of the Committee L. K. Sillcox, 1934-36; and correspondence and memorandums concerning Committee programs and assignments, 1934-36.

RECORDS OF THE GENERAL COUNSEL. 1933-36. 2 lin. ft.

Originally part of the Office of Executive and Legal Assistant, the Office of General Counsel became a separate unit in 1934. The counsel was in charge of all litigation and drafting and presenting to congressional committees proposed legislation. Included is a series of subject-classified reports, correspondence, memorandums, and legal opinions on matters affecting the railroad industry.

RECORDS OF THE EXECUTIVE AND TRAFFIC ASSISTANT. 1933-36. 12 lin. ft.

This official assisted in regulating allowances to shippers and charges for subsidiary services, which had been duties of the Office of Executive and Legal Assistant until it was abolished in 1934. The records consist of a series of subject-classified reports, correspondence, memorandums, statistics, and reference material of the executive and traffic assistant, 1933-36.

RECORDS OF THE EXECUTIVE ASSISTANT. 1933-36. 1 lin. ft.

This official acted as office manager for the agency. His records relate to appointments, transfers, resignations, and other personnel matters.

RECORDS OF THE RESEARCH SECTION. 1932-37. 20 lin. ft.

Originally designated the Section of Legislative Research, this unit studied the need for legislation to improve the regulation of motor, water, and air carriers; the extent of transportation subsidies; and foreign transportation conditions and regulations. Included are the office file of the Director relating to State laws, bills, and regulations relating to public utilities, and work papers on research projects, 1933-35; reports, correspondence, memorandums, and notes maintained by the research assistant, 1933-36; completed questionnaires, correspondence, and other records relating to surveys of water transportation of freight, 1933, interroad accounts, 1934, and grain elevators, 1933-35; and records relating to Federal and State legislation and regulatory activities affecting the transportation industry, 1932-37.

RECORDS OF THE RESEARCH STAFF ON RAILROAD CONSOLIDATION. 1933-34.
12 lin. ft.

The Federal Coordinator, aided by advisory committees and railroad representatives, collected data for analyzing plans to consolidate the Nation's railroads, chiefly the plan developed by Frederick H. Prince. The records include correspondence, telegrams, memorandums, progress reports, and copies, exhibits, statistics, and analyses of the "Prince plan," 1933-34; office files of William B. Poland, who headed the study of the "Prince plan," 1933; and reports, correspondence, and reference material maintained by the Southern Advisory Committee on Railroad Consolidation, 1933.

RECORDS OF THE TRANSPORTATION SERVICE SECTION. 1933-36. 43 lin. ft.

This Section investigated transportation service, recommended methods for its improvement, and surveyed types of railroad service. The records consist of subject-classified reports, correspondence, memorandums, and reference material relating to Section activities, 1933-36; a list of U.S. corporations owning fleets of 10 or more vehicles, 1933; correspondence, statistics, and other records on highway freight service, 1934-35; correspondence and questionnaires relating to the work of the Shippers' Advisory Committee, 1933; work materials, statistical data, and other records of surveys of carload traffic, 1933-35; transport by motor trucks and pipelines, 1934-35, passenger traffic, 1933-34, bus traffic, 1934, and merchandise traffic, 1933-35; and records relating to containers used in handling freight traffic, 1933-34.

RECORDS OF THE SECTION OF LABOR RELATIONS. 1933-36.
44 lin. ft.

This section investigated the stability of railroad employment and ways to improve labor conditions and its relations with management, and assisted the Federal Coordinator to enforce restrictions on management in employee relations. The records include reports, correspondence, memorandums, reference material, and other records relating to Section work, 1933-36; memorandums, reports, press releases, and reference material maintained by Adjudicator with the Railroad Retirement Board Tedford E. Schoonover, 1933-36; copies of legislative bills affecting the transportation industry, 1934-36; correspondence with railroad employees and labor organizations, relating to employment conditions and disputes with carriers, 1933-34; reports, correspondence, replies to a questionnaire, exhibits, and other records relating to an investigation of company unions and charges of railroad resistance to the organization of independent unions among railroad employees, 1933-35; correspondence, forms, instructions, and working papers relating to Section inquiries and surveys, 1933-36; and reports, correspondence, worksheets, and rosters relating to employment aspects of proposed consolidations of terminal facilities, 1934-35.

RECORDS OF THE SECTION OF PROPERTY AND EQUIPMENT.
1930-36. 44 lin. ft.

This Section, originally the Section of Purchases, was concerned with promoting economy in procurement by standardizing equipment and simplifying purchasing methods, with problems of storage and waste disposal, and with investigating new materials and procedures. Its records consist chiefly of subject-classified files relating to operational problems, such as centralized purchasing and simplification and standardization of equipment, and to Section activities, 1930–36; correspondence and statistics concerning costs and estimated economies of proposed shop facilities consolidation, 1934–36; reports and correspondence concerning the use of diesel equipment in European countries, 1934–36; correspondence and descriptive literature relating to highway freight equipment, 1935; reports, correspondence, questionnaires, statistical data, and work materials relating to operations of railroad stores departments, 1934–36; reference files on standardization and simplification of railway equipment and the use of freight containers, 1933–36; records relating to surveys and studies of handling and preparing scrap material, 1934–35, and of motive power equipment, 1935; and subject-classified files of the assistant director and other officials, 1934–36.

RECORDS OF THE SECTION OF CAR POOLING. 1933–36. 8 lin. ft.

This Section investigated equipment pooling, use, and maintenance. The records consist primarily of reports, correspondence, statistics, surveys, and reference material relating to the development of car pooling plans, movement of freight cars, and disposition of worn and obsolete equipment, 1933–36.

RECORDS OF THE SECTION OF REGIONAL COORDINATION. 1933–36. 40 lin. ft.

This Section investigated operating and management economies on a local level, such as joint use of particular terminal facilities or elimination of wasteful routing. The records include correspond-

ence and related records concerning economy in regional coordination projects and meetings of regional directors, 1933–36; correspondence with the Eastern Regional Coordinating Committee and the Eastern Regional Director, and reports relating mainly to studies of proposed coordination of transport facilities and services, 1934–35; subject-classified files of the Director of the Section, 1933–36; reports relating to proposed consolidations of shop facilities, 1935–36; and reports and correspondence relating to activities in the Southern Region, 1934–36.

RECORDS OF REGIONAL OFFICES. 1933–36. 59 lin. ft.

Included are records of the Eastern Regional Office, consisting of case files, with indexes, relating to consolidation and coordination projects, 1933–36, general correspondence, 1933–36, coordination and consolidation reports, 1934–35, and a subject-classified file of the eastern traffic assistant, 1933–36; records of the Southern Regional Office, including subject-classified central files, 1933–36, office file of the regional director, 1933–35, and case files and reports relating to proposed consolidation projects, 1935–36; and records of the Western Regional Office, comprising office files of the assistant regional director, 1933–35, records relating to consolidation of terminal facilities studies, 1933–36, reports on coordination projects, 1934–35, data on leases of railroad-owned warehouse and storage space, and a subject-classified file of the western traffic assistant, 1933–36.

CARTOGRAPHIC RECORDS. 1932–36. 87 items.

Maps showing time zones, railroad lines, bus and truck routes, and trade areas in the United States.

RECORDS OF THE
FOREIGN BROADCAST INTELLIGENCE SERVICE
(RECORD GROUP 262)

The Foreign Broadcast Intelligence Service (FBIS), originally called the Foreign Broadcast Monitoring Service, was established in the Federal Communications Commission in February 1941 to record, translate, and analyze foreign broadcast programs and to report on them to interested Government agencies. Monitoring stations intercepted broadcasts of foreign news, intelligence, or propaganda emanating from belligerent, occupied, and neutral countries. At the monitoring stations recordings, transcripts, and translations of selected broadcasts were made and teletyped, cabled, or mailed to Washington headquarters where they were edited and significant parts (occasionally full texts) teletyped to concerned Government war agencies. Special analyses and daily and weekly summaries were also prepared at headquarters and distributed to appropriate agencies and officials. The FBIS was transferred to the War Department in December 1945 and placed under the Military Intelligence Division of the General Staff. On August 5, 1946, it was tranferred to the Central Intelligence Group of the National Intelligence Authority, where it was renamed the Foreign Broadcast Information Service on November 1, 1946, and the Foreign Broadcast Information Branch on December 31, 1946. This record group comprises only records created by the FBIS and its predecessors. Records created after December 31, 1946, by the Foreign Broadcast Information Branch (later Division) are among the records of the Central Intelligence Agency (see RG 263).

There are 512 cubic feet of records dated between 1940 and 1947 in this record group.

CENTRAL FILES. 1940-47.
647 lin. ft.

These include reports, correspondence, and memorandums relating to the organization, functions, and activities of the FBIS, 1941-46; English translations of monitored foreign broadcasts, 1940-46 (in WNRC), with indexes; records of incoming wires, including London cables of partial or full texts of broadcasts from Europe and Africa, 1942-43; partial or full texts of broadcasts from the Far East and the Soviet Union, and Latin American broadcasts, September 12-December 12, 1942; and records of outgoing wires, consisting of those sent principally to Government agencies concerned with war propaganda, 1941-46 (in WNRC). Also included are daily reports of foreign radio broadcasts, 1941-45; daily reports of the Far Eastern, Latin American, and European sections, 1941-46; weekly reviews of official foreign broadcasts, 1941-44; radio reports on the Far East, 1942-45; and program schedules of foreign broadcasts, 1942-47.

RECORDS OF THE OFFICE OF THE DIRECTOR. 1941-46. 10 lin. ft.

These comprise the reading file and miscellaneous correspondence of Director Harold N. Graves, Jr., 1941-43, letters prepared by FBIS officials for the signature of the Chairman of the Federal Communications Commission, 1941-45, correspondence relating to monitoring operations in North Africa, 1942-43, correspondence with field installations, 1946, and personnel records, 1941-44.

RECORDS OF THE OFFICE OF THE CHIEF EDITOR. 1945. 1 lin. ft.

The records consist of directives, memorandums, teletype messages, and correspondence.

RECORDS OF DIVISIONS. 1941-45. 27 lin. ft.

Records of the Analysis Division consist primarily of reports, correspondence, and memorandums, 1941-44; reports and transcripts concerning subjects such as the Casablanca Conference and Axis war aims, 1941-44; and records relating to the distribution of reports, 1941-44. Records of the Monitoring Division include reports, memorandums, guidebooks, correspondence with field installations, and personnel correspondence and memorandums, 1944-45. Records of the News and Intelligence Division consist chiefly of reports, correspondence, and memorandums relating to the operations of the Division, 1944; records of the Director, 1942-44; and office files, 1941-45, relating chiefly to the organization, administration, and operations of field installations. Records of the Distribution Division consist chiefly of correspondence, memorandums, and cables exchanged with field offices, 1944-45. Records of the Broadcast Recording Unit, successor to the Engineering Division, consist of reports, memorandums, and survey and fiscal records, 1941-44.

RECORDS OF FIELD OFFICES. 1942-45. 1 lin. ft.

Included are general correspondence and administrative records documenting most of the functions and activities of the San Francisco office, 1942-45; and administrative records of the Kingsville, Tex., office, relating to monitoring operations, supplies, and personnel, 1942-44.

AUDIOVISUAL RECORDS. 1940-47. 608 items.

These are recordings of foreign broadcasts in English, German, Japanese, and other languages monitored by the FBIS, including broadcasts by Ezra Pound from Italy, October 2, 1941-July 24, 1943; speeches by Adolph Hitler, Joseph Goebbels, Joachim von Ribbentrop, Benito Mussolini, Marshal Henri Petain, Pierre Laval, and others; broadcasts by American citizens over German radio, including Fred Kaltenback, Douglas Chandler, and Edward Delaney; broadcasts from Japan or Japanese-held territory, including news reports and commentary by "Tokyo Rose" (Iva Toguri D'Aquino); also speeches by Presidents Roosevelt and Truman, King George VI, and other Allied leaders.

See Walter W. Weinstein, comp., *Preliminary Inventory of the Records of the Foreign Broadcast Intelligence Service*, PI 115 (1959).

RECORDS OF THE FOREIGN ECONOMIC ADMINISTRATION (RECORD GROUP 169)

The Foreign Economic Administration (FEA) was established within the Office for Emergency Management by an Executive order of September 25, 1943, to centralize responsibilities relating to foreign economic affairs. It exercised control over commercial exports and imports and other aspects of foreign economic affairs, and was responsible for related economic analysis and intelligence work. To it were transferred the Office of Economic Warfare, Office of Lend-Lease Administration, Office of Foreign Relief and Rehabilitation Operations, and foreign economic operations of the Office of Foreign Economic Coordination of the Department of State. An Executive order of October 6, 1943, transferred to the FEA the foreign procurement activities of the War Food Administration and the Commodity Credit Corporation. The FEA was terminated by an Executive order of September 27, 1945, and its functions redistributed among the Departments of State, Commerce, and Agriculture, and the Reconstruction Finance Corporation. There are separate records of most of its predecessors, but there was much interfiling of records by the successor organizations.

There are 2,066 cubic feet of records (in WNRC except for nontextual records) dated between 1939 and 1947, with a few as late as 1952, in this record group.

RECORDS OF THE OFFICE OF LEND-LEASE ADMINISTRATION AND ITS PREDECESSORS. 1939-44. 288 lin. ft.

On December 6, 1939, the President established the Interdepartmental Committee for Coordination of Foreign and Domestic Military Purchases, commonly known as the President's Liaison Committee, to represent the Government in matters relating to military or naval purchases made in the United States by foreign governments. The President dissolved the Committee on April 14, 1941, after the Lend-Lease Act was passed. On May 2 he established the Division of Defense Aid Reports in the Office for Emergency Management to administer the act. The Division was abolished in October 1941, and its functions, personnel, and records were transferred to the new Office of Lend-Lease Administration.

Records of the President's Liaison Committee include an office file of the Chairman, correspondence concerning British Purchasing Mission orders and negotiations, reports and correspondence concerning Latin American purchase negotiations, and foreign priority request case files. There are no separate records of the Division of Defense Aid Reports. Combined records of the Office of Lend-Lease Administration and its predecessors include some central files, but most were maintained by individual units. Records of the Offices of the Administrator, Deputy Administrators, and General Counsel; of the Offices of Foreign Liaison and Operations; and of the Division of Finance and Statistics and subordinate units include agenda and minutes of committee meetings, correspondence, memorandums, reports and studies, statistical tabulations, applications for materials, and other records arranged for the most part in general, subject, or geographic files. Other records of the Administration are interfiled with those of the FEA.

RECORDS OF THE BOARD OF ECONOMIC WARFARE AND ITS PREDECESSORS. 1940-43. 201 lin. ft.

An export control program under the supervision of an Administrator of Export Control and the Department of State was authorized by the Congress on July 2, 1940, to license export of certain materials. The Economic Defense Board was established by an Executive order of July 30, 1941, to protect and strengthen the international economic relations of the United States in the interest of national defense. The Board functioned chiefly in an advisory coordinating and factfinding capacity until September 15, 1941, when it assumed responsibility for the export control program. On December 17, 1941, the name of the Board was changed to Board of Economic Warfare. An Executive order of April 13, 1942, gave the Board a large measure of control over imports. It was terminated July 15, 1943, and replaced by the Office of Economic Warfare. This Office, which also took over control of certain corporations from the Reconstruction Finance Corporation, existed only until the FEA was established.

Many of the records of the Board of Economic Warfare and the earlier Economic Defense Board and Office of the Administrator of Export Control are in a central subject classified file, 1940-42. For the same period there are separate records relating to specific countries and an addressee file of letters sent. Other records include minutes of the Policy Committee of the Office of the Administrator of Export Control, office files of officials, and records of the Office of the General Counsel, the Information Division, and branches of the Office of Exports. Most records dated after June 1942 are with those of the FEA.

RECORDS OF THE OFFICE OF FOREIGN RELIEF AND REHABILITATION OPERATIONS. 1942-44. 90 lin. ft.

This Office was established in the Department of State on December 4, 1942, for the relief of war victims in territories occupied by Allied armies. It continued to operate until the establishment of the FEA. Most of its separate records were assembled by the historian of the Office, with some material dated before 1942 and after 1944. There are also interoffice memorandums, a general subject file, and letters sent.

RECORDS OF THE FEA. 1940-47, with a few as late as 1952. 1,797 lin. ft.

The FEA developed a complicated organization, and most of its records were kept by individual organizational units. Records of the Office of the Administrator include general and historical records, Office of the General Counsel and Office of Economic Programs (whose staffs of advisers assisted in preparing policies and programs) records, statistical and financial records, and a large collection of newspaper clip-

pings concerning export controls. The Bureau of Supplies was responsible for procurement abroad, export licensing, and certain other activities; it was organized to a considerable extent in relation to classes of commodities. The Bureau of Areas, concerned with programs in various areas of the world, was organized on a geographical basis. Both Bureaus had numerous branches, divisions, sections, and other units that maintained their own records. There are also some records of one of the FEA's subsidiary corporations, Cargoes, Inc., concerning construction of experimental vessels.

Records of FEA units include numerous general or central files (usually arranged by subject) and case, geographic (or country), commodity, and historical files containing agenda and minutes, correspondence, memorandums, reports, historical monographs and studies, administrative issuances, applications, lend-lease agreements and requisitions, charts, ledgers, registers, press releases and clippings, and statistical and reference material.

OTHER RECORDS. 1939-47. 56 lin. ft.

These are records of W. Averell Harriman's mission to London, the Mission for Economic Affairs in London that followed, 1941-44, and Harriman's special mission to the U.S.S.R., 1941-42. There are also a "History of Lend-Lease," completed by the Department of State, and supporting documents, 1939-47.

CARTOGRAPHIC AND AUDIOVISUAL RECORDS. 1942-45. 2,270 items.

Cartographic records consist of maps, 1942-45 (42 items), compiled and produced by the FEA and its predecessors, showing economic subjects, such as the distribution of minerals, cereals, forest industries, and trade routes for certain countries and the world.

Audiovisual records include photographs, 1943-45 (2,220 items), of procurement and development of agricultural and mineral commodities, cinchona production in Guatemala, and forestry plantations from the air. Also filmstrips, n.d. (8 reels), of unidentified places and people.

See H. Stephen Helton, comp., *Preliminary Inventory of the Records of the Foreign Economic Administration*, PI 29 (1951).

SPECIFIC RESTRICTIONS

Records: All records less than 30 years old.

Restrictions: These records may be used only with the permission of the Department of State.

Specified by: Department of State.

RECORDS OF THE MARITIME LABOR BOARD
(RECORD GROUP 157)

The Maritime Labor Board was established by an amendment of June 23, 1938, to the Merchant Marine Act of 1936 to strengthen the development of the American merchant marine by improving labor relations in the maritime industry. Created as an independent agency, the three-member Board was to encourage collective bargaining in the settlement of labor disputes, provide mediation and arbitration services to the maritime industry in labor disputes, maintain files of collective bargaining agreements, and recommend to the President and the Congress a permanent Federal policy in maritime labor relations. An act of June 23, 1941, continued the Board for 1 year, but only as a research agency. The Board thereupon dismissed its mediators and referred pending cases to the Conciliation Service of the National Defense Mediation Board. The Maritime Labor Board ceased operations in February 1942 after exhausting its appropriated funds.

See Maritime Labor Board, *Report to the President and to the Congress* (1940), and *Supplemental Report* (1942).

There are 77 cubic feet of records dated between 1938 and 1942 in this record group.

RECORDS. 1938-42. 92 lin. ft.

A classified file, including Board minutes, administrative records, reports and studies, correspondence, research material, collective bargaining agreements, and mediation case files; a reading file of outgoing correspondence, interoffice memorandums, and records of telephone conversations and conferences of Board members; a "specimen" agreement file of sample collective bargaining agreements; questionnaires on earnings of seamen; and a reference file.

See Caroline W. Hiatt and Salvatore D. Nerboso, comps., *Preliminary Inventory of the Records of the Maritime Labor Board*, PI 20 (1949).

RECORDS OF THE
NATIONAL RECOVERY ADMINISTRATION
(RECORD GROUP 9)

The National Recovery Administration (NRA) was created by an Executive order of June 16, 1933, under authority of the National Industrial Recovery Act.

Its purpose was to rehabilitate industry and trade in the United States, expand employment, and improve labor conditions. Special codes of fair competition were drafted under its supervision to govern industries and trades, and a "blanket code," the President's reemployment agreement, was offered for voluntary acceptance by employers pending the approval of specific codes. On May 27, 1935, all mandatory codes were declared unconstitutional by the U.S. Supreme Court. After this decision NRA activities were confined to promoting industrial cooperation and preparing a series of economic studies. On January 1, 1936, the NRA was terminated, and most of its divisions were transferred to the Department of Commerce for liquidation by April 1. The study program was transferred to the Committee of Industrial Analysis, assisted by a Division of Industrial Economics established in the Department of Commerce. Promotion of industrial cooperation remained under the direction of the Coordinator for Industrial Cooperation. The Committee of Industrial Analysis and its adjunct division terminated their work in February 1937. The Office of the Coordinator for Industrial Cooperation ceased to function June 30, 1937.

See Charles L. Dearing et al., *The ABC of the NRA* (1934); and Leverett S. Lyon et al., *The National Recovery Administration* (1935).

There are 5,186 cubic feet of records dated between 1927 and 1937 in this record group.

GENERAL RECORDS OF THE NRA. 1933-37. 4,241 lin. ft. and 186 rolls of microfilm.

These comprise records of the National Industrial Recovery Board, consisting principally of general subject files maintained by Chairmen S. Clay Williams and Donald R. Richberg, reports on activities of NRA divisions, and office files of the Executive Secretary and of several Board members, 1934-35; records of the Office of the Coordinator for Industrial Cooperation, consisting of a subject file and an office file of the technical assistant, 1935-37; and records maintained by

the Code Record Unit, filed in the process of drafting fair competition codes, 1933-35 (in WNRC), and microfilm copies (186 rolls) of codes and related records of each codified industry, 1933-36. Also included are records maintained by the General Files Unit, consisting of subject-classified files, 1933-35; consolidated files on 757 industries and trades governed by approved codes, 1933-36 (2,200 lin. ft.); files on approximately 1,800 industries and trades whose proposed codes were never approved, 1933-36 (in WNRC); administrative files, 1933-36; congressional correspondence and records maintained by NRA members of code authorities, 1934-35; graphic materials, 1933-36; special research and planning reports on the economy made by the Research Planning Division, 1933-35, and statistical material prepared by the Division of Review, 1935-36; and miscellaneous reports and records, 1933-37. Records maintained by the Library Unit consist of transcripts of hearings relating to proposed codes, code modifications and violations, and labor disputes, 1933-35; housekeeping records consist of reports on mail received and fiscal and accounting records, 1933-36.

DIVISION RECORDS. 1929-37. 1,068 lin. ft.

These comprise records of the Legal Division—which acted in an advisory capacity for code development, administration, and compliance and enforcement—and include office files and related records of the General Counsel and other officials, 1933-35; central files of the Division, 1933-35; records of the Enforcement Department, including docketed litigation case files (in WNRC) and docket books, 1934-35; reports and records concerning restitution of funds, 1935-37; records of the Federal Trade Commission Section, consisting primarily of requests for investigation and reports, 1933-35; affidavits of the Economic and Procedural Section, 1934-35; files of State relations attorneys concerned with State adoption of the model State recovery bill, 1933-35; and general correspondence of the Legal Research Section, 1933-36.

Records of the State Relations Division consist of a subject file containing a compilation of State recovery acts, a complaints file that is mostly correspondence with State officials regarding alleged code violations, and a State legislation file, 1933-36.

Compliance Division records include closed case files, 1933-35; correspondence, 1933-35; reports and correspondence from field offices, 1934-35; rulings and interpretations of code provisions, 1933-34; records relating to local compliance boards, 1933-35; reports and correspondence relating to the W. P. Robert Committee investigation, 1935; reports from field offices on public attitude toward NRA programs, 1933-35; files of Division officials, ca. 1933-35; records of the Contributions Section, consisting primarily of letters from business firms protesting code authority assessments and correspondence with code authorities regarding nonpayment of contributions by delinquent firms, 1934-35; records of the Coordinating Branch, including interoffice correspondence, 1934-35, general case records, 1933-35, memorandums containing analyses of complaints, 1934-35, and records containing analyses of alleged violations, 1933-34; files of the Office of the Assistant Administrator for Field Administration, ca. 1933-35; and records of the Office of the Director of Compliance and Enforcement, consisting principally of files of the Director and other officials, and reports, correspondence, and memorandums relating to publicity and compliance and complaint activities, 1933-35.

Government Contracts Division records include office instructions, staff memorandums, and other administrative records, 1934-36; general correspondence, 1933-35; closed case files, 1934-35; office files, 1933-35; correspondence and other records relating to the Government contracts survey, 1935; and records relating to field activities in conducting the survey of Government contracts, 1935-36.

Review Division records consist primarily of memorandums concerning the review of proposed codes and summaries of code documents, 1933-35, and memorandums and other records of the Rulings and Policy Sections, 1934-35.

Public Relations Division records consist principally of general records, 1933-35; correspondence of the Chief of the Public Relations Bureau, 1933; general correspondence of the special assistant, 1934; correspondence with chambers of commerce, 1933; questionnaires showing public opinion, 1934; poems and slogans, 1933-34; daily press digests, releases, and clippings, 1933-36 (in WNRC); and records of the Insignia and Women's Sections, 1933-35.

Research and Planning Division records, 1933-35, are those of the Director and of the chief statistician; and records maintained by the Statistics, Economic Advisory, and Import Sections and other sections.

The Division of Review, established June 15, 1935, inherited most of the functions and personnel and some of the records of the terminated Review Division and Research and Planning Division. Its records include files of the Director, 1934-36; weekly reports, 1935-36; code histories for industries under approved codes and histories of industries for which codes were proposed but never approved, 1935-36; records maintained by the nine sections in the Division, including statistical materials maintained by the Industries Studies Section relating to the automotive industry, 1929-35, and records of the Tariff Unit maintained by the Foreign Trade Studies Section, 1933–35.

The industry divisions, which increased from four in October 1933 to 12 in March 1935, were the Amusements, Basic Materials, Chemical, Construction, Distribution, Equipment, Food, Graphic Arts, Manufacturing, Public Agencies, Public Utilities, and Textile Divisions. Their records consist primarily of reading files, correspondence, and a few reports. Most records of these divisions were incorporated in the series of consolidated files of industries and trades governed by approved codes and of industries and trades for which proposed codes were never approved. The series of consolidated files are part of the general records of the NRA described above.

The Trade Association Division was created October 26, 1933, to assist in establishing and strengthening industrial and trade associations, advise NRA administrators on plans for code authority activity, and recommend to the NRA organization and performance standards applicable to associations and code authorities. Its records consist of completed questionnaires, 1934–35, containing information on the general activities of trade associations and their organization, finances, and relationships with the NRA and code authorities.

The Division of Industrial Economics, established in 1936, completed the 130 code histories unfinished by the Division of Review and compiled the series of staff studies used by the Committee of Industrial Analysis in its general report on the NRA. The Division's records comprise drafts of staff studies, 1936–37, and miscellaneous records, consisting of excerpts from newspapers, magazines, and books and other reference material, 1935–37.

RECORDS OF BOARDS AND COMMITTEES. 1933–37. 171 lin. ft.

The President's Reemployment Agreement Policy Board was established August 7, 1933, to report on petitions to substitute provisions of proposed codes for certain paragraphs of the President's Reemployment Agreement and to correlate NRA policies. Its records consist of petitions and other records that show the nature of the proposed substitutions, give information about the petitioning industry, and indicate approval or disapproval of proposed substitutions, August-October 1933.

The Labor, Industrial, and Consumers' Advisory Boards were created by authority of the President's statement of June 16, 1933, outlining policies of the NRA. To resolve differences of opinion among the Boards an advisory council, consisting of three members from each Board and a chairman, was established on May 21, 1934. The records consist primarily of memorandums, 1934–35, and subject files, 1933–35, of the Advisory Council; subject files, 1934–35, correspondence of Chairman Leo Wolman, 1933–34, and office files of Labor Advisory Board members, 1933–35; general correspondence of the Industrial Advisory Board, 1933–36; and memorandums, 1933–35, and the office file of the special adviser to the Consumers' Advisory Board, 1935.

Industrial Appeals Board records include correspondence of the Executive Secretary, 1934–35, and records relating to cases presented to the Board, 1935.

National Recovery Review Board records consist chiefly of correspondence, 1933–34, between the Board and non-Government organizations regarding complaints against codes, the attitude of operators of small businesses toward the NRA, and suggestions for improving relations between the NRA and industry.

Homework Committee records consist chiefly of correspondence, memorandums, reports, and other papers, 1934–35, on industrial homework and exceptions to its prohibitions under NRA codes, child labor, and safety standards.

Apprenticeship Committee records consist primarily of correspondence of its Executive Secretary, 1934, with Committee members and persons involved in State, city, school, industrial, and commercial vocational training programs.

Automobile Labor Board records include employee complaints of discriminatory practices in discharging and rehiring workers, 1934–35, and records relating to Board hearings and decisions and employee representation and elections, 1934–35.

The Bituminous Coal Labor Boards comprised five boards established in the coal-producing areas of the United States. The records include Board correspondence, subject files, and case files for Divisions I (North and South), II, and V, ca. 1933–35.

National Steel Labor Relations Board records consist of case files, correspondence, and administrative records, 1934–35.

Cotton Textile National Industrial Relations Board and Textile National Industrial Relations Board records consist of general records and records relating to employee complaints in the textile industry, 1933–34.

Textile Labor Relations Board records consist primarily of case files of correspondence, reports, exhibits, and other records relating to labor disturbances in the textile industry, 1933–37.

RECORDS OF CODE
AUTHORITIES. 1927–35. 149 lin. ft.

Each code of fair competition provided for a code authority selected by members of the participating industry. The functions of code authorities were to perform certain administrative and enforcement tasks required by the codes. There was, however, little uniformity in the organization and functions of the 757 code authorities organized during the NRA's existence. Codes were usually sponsored by existing trade or industrial associations. After the invalidation of the codes by the Supreme Court, most records of code authorities went to the sponsoring trade and industrial associations, although some went to the NRA and later to the National Archives. These comprise the files of 18 code authorities and fragmentary records of several others, including general records and case files of the Code Authority for the Artificial Flower and Feather Industry, 1933–35; general records of the Fabric Auto Equipment Division, the Mattress Cover Division, and the Quilting Division of the Code Authority for the Light Sewing Industry, Except Garments, 1933–35; miscellaneous records of the Code Authority for the Porcelain Breakfast Furniture Assembling Industry, 1934–35; questionnaires of the National Retail Drug Code Authority, 1934; general records of the Central Code Authority for the Retail Farm Equipment Trade, 1934–35; records of the Code Authority for the Retail Solid Fuels Industry, 1934–35; general records, case files, and price lists of the Code Authority for the Rock Crusher Industry, 1933–35; records of the National Code Authority for the Trucking Industry, consisting of central files of the American Highway Truck Association, 1932–33, central files of American Trucking Associations, Inc., 1933–35, records maintained by the Secretary of the American Trucking Association, 1927–35, correspondence and docketed case files, 1934–35, and reporting forms and questionnaires, 1934–35; general correspondence, subject file, and docketed case files of the Pennsylvania State Code Authority for the Trucking Industry, 1934–35; payroll reports of the Undergarment and Negligee Code Authority, 1934–35; miscellaneous records of the Divisional Code Authority for the Upholstery and Decorative Fabrics Trade, 1934–35; and miscellaneous records of the Virginia Lumber and

Building Supply Dealers Association, 1933-35.

RECORDS OF REGIONAL AND TERRITORIAL OFFICES. 1933-36. 230 lin. ft.

A system of nine regions was established December 28, 1934. Each regional office, with the exception of the one for New York, had jurisdiction over several States. Regional office records usually include a general subject file, correspondence, files of key officials, legal records, reports, some undocketed case files, and general records and case files of the Regional Compliance Council, ca. 1933-36 (those for Region IV are in FRC Atlanta). Region V records include docketed case files relating to code violations, 1935.

Territorial offices to administer NRA programs were established in Puerto Rico, Hawaii, and Alaska. For Puerto Rico there are general records, 1933-36; office files of the Deputy Administrator, 1933-35; radiograms and press releases, 1933-36; records relating to the formulation of codes for Puerto Rican industries, 1933-35; records relating to

needlework, 1934-36, and baking, 1934-35, industries; forms containing information on Puerto Rican industries, 1935; and case files and legal records, 1934-35. Records for Hawaii include correspondence, memorandums, reports, resolutions of local committees, histories of codes for industries in Hawaii, and press releases, 1934-35. Records for Alaska relate chiefly to the establishment and local application of industrial codes, 1934-35.

CARTOGRAPHIC RECORDS. 1933-36. 238 items.

These consist of maps showing code authority areas, code authority divisions within industries, trade areas, transportation facilities, individual industries, code compliance, and industrial productivity.

See Homer L. Calkin, Meyer H. Fishbein, and Leo Pascal, comps., *Preliminary Inventory of the Records of the National Recovery Administration,* PI 44 (1952); and Calkin and Fishbein, comps., *Select List of Documents in the Records of the National Recovery Administration,* SL 12 (1954).

Microfilm Publications: *Document Series of the National Recovery Administration, 1933-1936,* M213, 186 rolls, DP; and *NRA* Blue Eagle *Weekly Newspaper, 1934-1935,* T692, 1 roll.

RECORDS OF THE NATIONAL WAR LABOR BOARD (WORLD WAR II) (RECORD GROUP 202)

The National War Labor Board (NWLB) was established in the Office for Emergency Management (OEM) by an Executive order of January 12, 1942, to succeed duties of the National Defense Mediation Board (NDMB), created by an Executive order of March 19, 1941. The NWLB was to act as final arbiter of wartime labor disputes and to pass on adjustments in certain wages and salaries. It established 12 regional war labor boards and a territorial war labor board for Hawaii. It also created

for key industries commissions and panels authorized to settle all but the most important dispute and wage stabilization cases. The NWLB was given statutory recognition by the War Labor Disputes Act of June 25, 1943. An Executive order of September 19, 1945, transferred the NWLB to the Department of Labor. The NWLB was terminated by an Executive order of December 31, 1945, which established the National Wage Stablization Board (NWSB) with all powers, functions, and responsibilities of the NWLB relating to stabilization of wages and salaries as well as limited functions relating to settlement of disputes. The NWSB was terminated by an Executive order of December 12, 1946.

There are 3,535 cubic feet of records dated between 1941 and 1947 in this record group.

RECORDS OF THE NDMB. 1941–43. 23 lin. ft.

These include verbatim transcripts of executive sessions, 1941–42; dispute case files, 1941–43 (in WNRC); transcripts of hearings in dispute cases, 1941–42 (in WNRC); findings, recommendations, and agreements in dispute cases, 1941–42; indexes to dispute case files, 1941–42; and office files of the Vice Chairman of the NDMB, 1941–42.

RECORDS OF THE NWLB. 1941–47. 4,220 lin. ft.

These are headquarters case records that include dispute case files, indexes, and transcripts of hearings, 1942–45 (in WNRC); indexes to NDMB and NWLB dispute case files, 1941–45; voluntary wage and salary adjustment case files, 1942–45 (in WNRC); national jurisdiction case files, 1942–45 (in WNRC); transcripts of hearings in national jurisdiction dispute cases, 1942–45 (in WNRC); NWLB and NWSB enforcement case files, 1943–47 (in WNRC); and noncompliance case files, 1942–45 (in WNRC). Other headquarters records include transcripts of NWLB executive sessions, memorandums, resolutions, and general orders, 1942–45; files of the Chairman, Vice Chairman, and members representing the public, 1941–45; files of Board members and executive assistants representing labor, 1942–45; committee minutes, reports, and other records, 1941–45; records of the Office of the Executive Director, comprising staff and field memorandums, activity reports, and correspondence, 1942–46,

and Historical Section subject files and related records, 1942–45; Legal Division general records, 1942–46, records relating to civil cases, 1944–45, and chronological files, 1942–47; general records and office files of key officials of the Office of the General Counsel, 1942–45; Division of Public Information general records, correspondence, reports, transcripts of conferences and hearings, press releases, and newspaper clippings, 1941–45; central files for NWLB and general records of the Division of Administrative Management, 1942–45; Disputes Division Director's files, 1942–45, and Strike Section records, 1942–45; and Wage Stabilization Division Director's office files, 1942–45, and files of the Program Appraisal Branch and its administrative units, the Research Statistics and Regional Operations Sub-Branches, and the Policy Analysis, Board Action Reference, Wage Reference, and Delegated Authorities Review Sections, 1942–45.

Regional case records include dispute case files, 1942–45 (in WNRC), selected voluntary wage and salary adjustment case files, 1942–45 (in WNRC), NWLB and NWSB enforcement case files, 1943–47 (in WNRC), and related indexes. Other regional records include a lengthy historical and policy documentation file, 1943–45, selected from files of regional offices to document the organization, policies, procedures, and operations of regional boards; an index to occupation wage-rate survey reports, 1943–45; and regional war labor board records. Organization of the regional boards was similar to that of the national board, and their records are similar to those described for the administrative units of the national board. They include records of the regional boards for Regions 1, 4–8, 10, and 12; Information Divisions for Regions 1, 7, 8, and 10–12; Administrative Management Divisions for Regions 1–3, 6–8, 11, and 12; Wage Stabilization Divisions for Regions 1–3, 6–8, and 11;

Disputes Division for Regions 2, 3, 6, and 7; and Legal Divisions for Regions 3, 6, and 12. There are also records of the Enforcement Division and of the Research and Statistics Section for Region 7. There are no separately maintained records for Region 9.

Case records (in WNRC) of commissions and panels consist of cases assigned to special industry commissions and panels for settlement, including dispute case files, 1942–46; voluntary wage and salary adjustment case files, 1942–46; and enforcement case files, 1943–46. Other records of commissions and panels, maintained separately for each commission or panel, usually comprise general records, historical and policy documentation files, reports, and miscellaneous records, ca. 1942–45. Included are records of the West Coast Lumber, Nonferrous Metals, Detroit Tool and Die, Trucking, Shipbuilding, Daily Newspaper Printing and Publishing, National Telephone, Meat Packing, Steel, and Textile Commissions; the West Coast Aircraft Committee; the War Shipping Panel; and the National Airframe Panel.

RECORDS OF THE NWSB. 1943–47. 444 lin. ft.

Headquarters case records consist of voluntary wage and salary adjustment case files, 1945–46 (in WNRC), case files for voluntary wage and salary adjustment cases relating to general wage approvals, 1946 (in WNRC), case files for voluntary cases submitted by the War Department Wage Coordination Board, 1946 (in WNRC), and related indexes. Other headquarters records include Office of the Board transcripts of executive sessions, 1946–47, case analysis memorandums, 1946, office files of Board members representing the public, 1945–47, and records of labor and industry members of NWLB and NWSB, 1942–47; general files, reports, and correspondence of the Office of the Execu-

tive Director, 1943–47; correspondence and records relating to regional enforcement activities, and office files of staff members of the Legal Division, 1943–46; general records and press releases of the Division of Public Information, 1945–47; NWLB and NWSB forms, and operations and administrative manuals of the Division of Administrative Management, 1943–46; and records of the Case Analysis and Program Appraisal Division, including files of its Wage and Board Action Reference Section, 1945–46.

Regional case records consist primarily of voluntary wage and salary adjustment case files, 1945–46 (in WNRC), voluntary wage and salary adjustment case files handled by the West Coast Lumber Commission, 1942–46 (in WNRC), and related indexes. Organization of regional wage stabilization boards was similar to that of the administrative organization of the national board, and their records are similar. They comprise general records and files of the Offices of the Regional Boards for Regions 1, 3-6, 8, and 10-12; Legal Divisions for Regions 1, 6, 8, and 12; Information Divisions for Regions 1, 3-5, and 8; Wage Stablization Divisions for Regions 1-12; and Administrative Management Divisions for Regions 6 and 8. Files of the West Coast Lumber Commission are also included in the records of Region 12.

See Estelle Rebec, comp., *Preliminary Inventory of the Records of the National War Labor Board (World War II)*, PI 78 (1955); and Rebec, Arthur Hecht, and Paul Flynn, comps., *Lists of Wage Stablization Cases Acted on by the Headquarters Office of the National War Labor Board, 1942–45*, SL 10 (1953).

SPECIFIC RESTRICTIONS

I. *Records*: Transcripts of Executive Sessions of the National Defense Mediation Board, National War Labor Board, and National Wage Stabilization Board.

Restrictions: No one may examine these records or be given information from them or copies of them except by permission of the Records Officer of the Department of Labor.

Specified by: Department of Labor.

II. *Records*: All documents in National Defense Mediation Board, National War Labor Board, and National Wage Stabilization Board voluntary wage and salary adjustment, dispute, and enforcement case files other than those of a public record character (rulings; directive orders; decisions; company wage rates as approved, modified,

or denied by the Board even though not specifically set forth in the ruling, directive order, or decision issued in the case; panel and hearing officer reports; and public hearings transcripts and exhibits).

Restrictions: No one other than representatives of agencies of the Federal Government may examine these records or be given information from them or copies of them except by permission of the Records Officer of the Department of Labor.

Specified by: Department of Labor.

RECORDS OF THE NATIONAL YOUTH ADMINISTRATION
(RECORD GROUP 119)

The National Youth Administration (NYA) was established within the Works Progress (later the Work Projects) Administration (WPA) by an Executive order of June 26, 1935. In 1939 the NYA was transferred to the Federal Security Agency and in 1942 to the War Manpower Commission. An act of July 12, 1943, directed liquidation of the NYA not later than January 1, 1944, but the agency remained in existence until the end of 1944 with liquidation responsibilities assumed by the Federal Security Agency.

The NYA conducted two major programs for needy young people between the ages of 16 and 24: an out-of-school work program, which provided employment and vocational training on public industrial, manual, construction, professional, and clerical projects to unemployed youth who had left school; and a student work program, which furnished part-time employment on projects devised by school authorities to high school, college, and graduate students who otherwise would have been

unable to continue their education. After December 1941 both programs were reoriented to serve the needs of national defense—particularly the out-of-school work program, which in 1942 became the war production training program. The NYA was headed by an administrator, who determined basic policies with the assistance of a national advisory committee designated by the President. Operations in the field were directed by a network of regional, State, and area offices assisted at each level by advisory committees.

There are 993 cubic feet of records dated between 1934 and 1944 in this record group.

RECORDS OF THE NATIONAL ADVISORY COMMITTEE. 1935-42. 28 lin. ft.

Included are proceedings, correspondence, and reference files maintained by the Chairman, 1935-42; records of the Office of the Director, consisting chiefly of a report and a general correspondence file, 1935-42; a State file of correspondence, advisory committees' reports, forms, and membership data, 1937-42; local advisory committees' form and narrative reports, 1937-41; and card lists of members of advisory committees.

RECORDS OF THE OFFICE OF THE ADMINISTRATOR. 1935-43. 310 lin. ft.

These include correspondence, reference files, and related records maintained by the Administrator and other officials, including the general office file of the Deputy Administrator, 1939-43; the personal and desk file of Special Assistant to the Executive Director Cary J. Randolph, 1935-36; correspondence and reference file of George Sanford Holmes as regional representative of Region 2, 1938-40; file of Karl E. Jensen, senior administrative assistant, chiefly concerning potential or actual NYA projects and activities in research, cultural, and technical fields, 1936-41; budget and personnel correspondence of the Deputy Executive Director, 1935-38; letters sent by officials in the NYA central office, 1935-40; miscellaneous alphabetic-name correspondence, 1935-41; administrative reports received from NYA State offices, 1935-38; data file on youth movements, programs, and conditions abroad, 1935-39; dossiers on NYA projects reviewed by the Coordinating Committee, 1936-37; and working and data files of an NYA history project, 1935-43.

RECORDS OF THE DIVISIONS. 1934-44. 635 lin. ft.

Records of the Division of Finance and Statistics consist chiefly of correspondence and accounting records maintained by the Director, 1935-41; numeric-subject classified file on NYA budgets and appropriations, 1939-42, and general budget data file, 1934-44, maintained by the Budget Section; and related fiscal records of other accounting and statistical analysis units in the Division.

Records of the Division of Student Work include the general subject file of the Director, 1936-43, correspondence of the Director with field advisers on industrial training, 1939-41, data files on secondary school and college work councils, 1940-43, affidavits of eligibility of colleges and graduate schools to participate in the NYA college-aid programs, 1935-39, descriptions of student-aid work projects, 1937-42, and background material for a history of the student work program, 1935-43.

Records of the Division of Youth Personnel consist of records of the Director, including administrative, reference, and correspondence files, 1935-42; field inspection reports, 1939-43; periodic and narrative reports concerning junior placement in the States, 1936-39; divisional and other NYA correspondence concerning the work of youth personnel in the regions, 1941-43; and letters received by the NYA and other Federal agencies on NYA training and trainees, 1941-42.

Records of the Division of Work Projects consist of correspondence and related records of the Director and other Division officials, including letters sent to State youth directors concerning projects, 1937-38; correspondence of the Director with State administrators on defense training activities, 1941-42; miscellaneous correspondence of the Director, 1940-43; personal and desk files of the Assistant Director, 1934-39; and records of Staff and Line Sections of the Division, including a classified file of technical and scientific reference materials and an office file of the Chief of the Technical Information Section, 1938-40; case files of the Project Planning and Control Section, including project application case files, 1935-41; tracings and copies of plans for NYA buildings, 1937-43, accumulated by the Construction Maintenance Section; shop training blueprints maintained by the Shop Operations Section, 1940-43; general administrative correspondence of the Assistant Chief of the Mechanical Shops Section, concerning operation of the NYA mechanical shops, 1940-42; and the subject file of the Resident Center Section, 1939-43.

Records of the Division of Reports and Records include statistical data on approved applicants for NYA student aid, 1937-38. Records of the Division of Community Organization consist of correspondence of the Director with youth organizations, 1935-37.

OTHER CENTRAL OFFICE RECORDS. 1935-43. 130 lin. ft.

Records of the Personnel Office include notices of NYA job vacancies, 1940-41, and notes of applicants interviews, 1935-38. Records of the Office of Information include correspondence of the Director and other officials, 1938-42; alphabetic subject-name files, 1936-42; NYA policy and procedural releases, 1939-42; case histories, mainly "success stories" and endorsements of NYA by beneficiaries of its services, 1937-42; press releases, 1935-42 (with gaps); and radio scripts, 1936-42. Records of the Health Office consist principally of correspondence of the Director with regional offices, 1942, and with State administrators and other State NYA officials, 1940-42; and reports concerning State NYA health programs, 1941-42.

Records of the Office of Negro Affairs consist chiefly of the general subject file of the Director, 1936-41, correspondence and reports on black conferences, 1935-41, and reports of State directors of Negro Affairs, 1936-39. Records of the chief architect include tracings and processed copies of plans for NYA buildings, 1937-41. Records of the music director include correspondence concerning administration of the NYA music program, 1940-41. Other records include correspondence relating to educational camps for unemployed young women, ca. 1935-37, NYA file of processed and printed materials, 1935-42, and final reports of State offices, 1943.

RECORDS OF REGIONAL OFFICES. 1935-43. 25 lin. ft.

Included are fragmentary correspondence of regional directors of "old" NYA Regions 1, 2, and 3, which corresponded to the WPA regional organization, 1935-42; and correspondence of regional youth administrators of "new" NYA Regions 3, 8, and 12, which corresponded to the regional organization of the War Manpower Commission, ca. 1939-43.

AUDIOVISUAL RECORDS. 1935-43. 20,975 items.

Still pictures (20,900 items) include photographs of job training and student aid programs and recreational activities, some arranged by general subject and some by State; lantern slides for a lecture on NYA achievements; and photographs to illustrate projected publications on NYA history.

Motion pictures (56 reels) illustrate the activities of the NYA, including work and student programs, recreational activities, programs for blacks, and resident centers; dramatize problems of unemployed youth and assistance given them by NYA; and show the visit of the King and Queen of England to Washington, D.C., 1939, and the inauguration of Franklin D. Roosevelt, 1941.

Sound recordings (19 items) include a discussion by NYA personnel on the Passamaquoddy Tidal Power Development, a radio drama about young persons assisted by NYA, and the dedication ceremonies of the NYA exhibit at the New York World's Fair, June 3, 1939.

RECORDS OF THE OFFICE OF THE BITUMINOUS COAL CONSUMERS' COUNSEL
(RECORD GROUP 223)

An office of Consumers' Counsel of the National Bituminous Coal Commission was established in the Department of the Interior by the Bituminous Coal Conservation Act of August 30, 1935, and reestablished by the Bituminous Coal Act of April 26, 1937, for the second National Bituminous Coal Commission. The Counsel, who functioned independently of the Commissions, represented the interest of the coal-consuming public in proceedings before the Commissions and conducted investigations to protect that interest. On behalf of coal producers, distributors, and consumers, he initiated and prosecuted complaints before the Interstate Commerce Commission with respect to rates, charges, tariffs, and practices relating to the transportation of coal. Reorganization Plan No. II of 1939 abolished the office of Consumers' Counsel and transferred its functions to the Office of the Solicitor in the Department of the Interior where they were administered by a Consumers' Counsel Division. An act of April 11, 1941, established the Office of the Bituminous Coal Consumers' Counsel as an independent agency and transferred to it the Division's functions. With the expiration August 24, 1943, of congressional authorization, the Office was terminated.

There are 403 cubic feet of records (in WNRC except for nontextual records) dated between 1935 and 1943 in this record group.

RECORDS. 1935-43. 684 lin. ft.

The records of the Office and its predecessors include correspondence and general subject files; procedural records; such records concerning cases as orders, notices, reports on hearings, briefs, motions, petitions, exhibits, and transcripts of hearings; price schedules; reports and studies; office files; and reference material. Also motion picture films (2 reels) entitled "Coal for Victory" and "Know Your Coal."

SPECIFIC RESTRICTIONS

Records: Records containing "information obtained from a producer disclosing costs of production or sales realization."

Restrictions: "No information obtained from a producer disclosing costs of production or sales realization shall be made public without the consent of the producer from whom the same shall have been obtained, except where such disclosure is made in evidence in any hearing before the Commission or any court and except that such information may be compiled in composite form in such manner as shall not be injurious to the interests of any producer and, as so compiled, may be published by the Commission." (50 Stat. 88).

Specified by: Congress of the United States.

RECORDS OF THE OFFICE OF CENSORSHIP
(RECORD GROUP 216)

Immediately after the President's declaration of a state of national emergency on September 2, 1939, the military services began planning for wartime censorship of international communications. Censorship operations were carried on by the War and Navy Departments from the time the United

States entered the war to March 15, 1942, when the Army and Navy personnel engaged in these operations were formally transferred to the Office of Censorship.

The Office of Censorship was established by an Executive order of December 19, 1941, to censor all communications passing between the United States and any foreign country or between foreign countries by means of transportation that touched U.S. territory. The Executive order also created the Censorship Policy Board to advise on policy and coordination and the Censorship Operating Board to arrange for other Government agencies to use information acquired through censorship. Voluntary censorship of information concerning the war effort by the domestic press and radio was initiated by the Director. After Germany's surrender the activities of the Office were greatly curtailed; they were terminated by an Executive order of September 28, 1945.

See Office of Censorship, *A Report on the Office of Censorship* (1945).

There are 539 cubic feet of records dated between 1939 and 1945 in this record group.

RECORDS. 1939–45. 657 lin. ft.

These consist of minutes, including those of the Censorship Policy and the Censorship Operating Boards; reports of divisions and field stations; directives; instructions; correspondence; memorandums; manuals; handbooks; press releases; confidential material; a history of the Office compiled by its Historical Section; and an illustrated lecture on the Office's history.

Also included are intelligence records; records created by the War and Navy Departments relating to the planning, organization, and early operation of postal and cable censorship, respectively; records maintained by the

Administrative, Postal, Cable, and Press Divisions; shortwave watch logs and a card record of foreign-language broadcasts monitored by the Broadcasting Division; records of the postal censorship station at San Juan, P.R.; and budget records.

See Henry T. Ulasek, comp., *Preliminary Inventory of the Records of the Office of Censorship*, PI 54 (1953).

SPECIFIC RESTRICTIONS

I. *Records*: All intelligence and security records of the Office of Censorship except the "History of the Technical Operations Division."

Restrictions: These records are under seal and may not be examined by anyone for any purpose without the permission of the President of the United States.

Specified by: President of the United States.

II. *Records*: The "History of the Technical Operations Division" and all other records of the Office of Censorship not covered by restriction I for this record group that contain information concerning techniques and methods of censorship or information that would, if released, invade the right of privacy of individuals or firms.

Restrictions: These records shall not be made available to the general public, and their use shall be restricted to those agencies of the Federal Government having a legitimate interest in the information they contain.

Specified by: Office of Emergency Planning in conformity with policies stipulated by the former Office of Censorship.

RECORDS OF THE OFFICE OF CIVILIAN DEFENSE
(RECORD GROUP 171)

The Office of Civilian Defense (OCD) was established in the Office for Emergency Management by an Executive order of May 20, 1941, to coordinate Federal, State, and local defense relationships regarding the protection of civilians during air raids and other emergencies, and to facilitate civilian participation in war programs. It took over the functions and records of the Division of State and Local Cooperation of the Advisory Commission to the Council of National Defense. Fiscal, budgetary, and personnel responsibilities for the OCD were handled by the Division of Central Administrative Services of the Office for Emergency Management until 1942 when these responsibilities, with minor exceptions, were transferred to the OCD. The nine regional offices that coordinated the work of State and local defense organizations were closed June 30, 1944, and an Executive order of June 4, 1945, terminated the OCD.

There are 606 cubic feet of records (in WNRC except for nontextual records) dated between 1939 and 1945 in this record group.

RECORDS. 1940-45. 861 lin. ft.

There are some records of the Division of State and Local Cooperation of the Council of National Defense. OCD records are those of the national headquarters, including central files, records of the Director's office, and records of the Administrative, Federal-State Cooperation, Industrial Protection, Labor, Legal, Medical, Protection Services, Public Counsel, and Report Analysis and Statistics Divisions; the Library; and the Reports and Awards Office. Records of Region IX, with headquarters in San Francisco and serving eight Far Western States, include records of the office of the regional director, of organizational units similar to those of the national office, and of sector offices.

See Office of Civilian Defense, *Inventory of the Records of the Office of Civilian Defense* (1945).

CARTOGRAPHIC AND AUDIOVISUAL RECORDS. 1939-45. 5,290 items.

Cartographic records, 1941-45 (533 items), consist of maps of the United States, showing administrative offices and regional and local civil defense boundaries and groups; and maps prepared by the Ninth Civilian Defense Region (Washington, Oregon, and California), relating to civilian defense facilities and activities.

Audiovisual records consist of still pictures, 1940-44 (4,500 items), including photographs of bombs, bomb tests, camouflage materials, camouflaged industrial installations, and OCD personnel, and illustrating such civilian defense activity as fire prevention, drills, rescue operations, defense against and injuries caused by poison gas attack, and air raid instruction; aerial photographs of industrial and residential areas, relating to camouflage studies; and drawings of camouflage plans. Filmstrips, 1941-45 (11 items), illustrating lectures in the air raid warden training program. Motion pictures, 1941-45 (46 reels), used in training civilian defense workers and relating to mobilization, rescue, firefighting and prevention, child care, defense against poison gas attack, smoke concealment, air raid defense operations, and equipment and its use; promoting victory gardens and food conservation; and of London under aerial attack. Sound recordings, 1939-45 (200 items), of radio broadcasts of speeches, discussions, and dramas promoting participation in the civilian defense program and explaining the operation of all its phases.

Included are broadcasts by the OCD, the Office of War Information, the National Safety Council, the Commerce and Industry Association of New York, the YMCA, the U.S. Army, the Burns and Allen show, and the Vic and Sade show; and a series relating to civil defense in England.

RECORDS OF THE
OFFICE OF COMMUNITY WAR SERVICES
(RECORD GROUP 215)

The Office of Community War Services (OCWS) was established in the Federal Security Agency by an Executive order of April 29, 1943, to succeed the Office of Defense Health and Welfare Services (ODHWS). The latter had been established in the Office for Emergency Management under an Executive order of September 3, 1941, to supersede the Office of the Coordinator of Health, Welfare, and Related Defense Activities, which had originated in the designation by the Council of National Defense on November 28, 1940, of the Federal Security Administrator as coordinator of all health, medical, welfare, nutrition, recreation, and related fields of activity affecting national defense. The functions and records of the ODHWS Procurement and Assignment Service were transferred to the War Manpower Commission in 1942 (see RG 211); those of its Nutrition Division were delegated to the Food Distribution Administration in 1943 (see RG 136). In the field, regional directors of the Social Security Board served as regional directors for OCWS and its predecessors, and as chairmen of regional advisory councils. The OCWS was discontinued June 30, 1946, except for the Recreation Division, which existed until June 30, 1947. The work of liquidating the OCWS was carried out by the Federal Security Agency's Deputy Commissioner for Special Services between July 1947 and May 1948. OCWS records include those of two closely related organizations: the Health and Medical Committee, established by the Council of National Defense on September 19, 1940, and the Committee on Physical Fitness, which originated under ODHWS and was separately established in the Federal Security Agency by an Executive order of April 29, 1943.

There are 237 cubic feet of records dated between 1940 and 1948 in this record group.

HEADQUARTERS RECORDS.
1940-48. 331 lin. ft.

General records, 1940-47, comprise a small documentation file and subject-classified central files (209 lin. ft.) in which the central files of the OCWS, its predecessors, and the Health and Medical Committee and the Committee on Physical Fitness were integrated. Records, 1941-45, of the Office of the Director include general files; correspondence and other records relating to critical areas, agency programs, and relationships with the Federal Security Agency; records relating to the Joint Committee on Evacuation; and a reading file and budgetary records of the Office of the Executive Officer.

Records of the Recreation Division, 1941-48, include records of the Director's office; general and regional files; the Associate Director's files; records relating to juvenile delinquency, youth centers, and "living war memorials"; reports and surveys; dockets for wartime public works recreational projects; records concerning postwar plans; general, regional, and foreign correspondence files; and a motion picture entitled "When Work Is Done." Records of the Social Protection Division, 1941–46, include minutes; general, subject, and regional files; and statistical materials, reports, studies, and publications. Records of the Day Care Division, 1941–46, consist of general files and records of grants to States. Field Operations Division records include a reading file, April-June 1941, of the Director of the Program Operations Branch, the predecessor of the Division; policy and information issuances; regional and conference files; community reports; records documenting reporting procedures; and records relating to ODHWS and OCWS relationships with the War Manpower Commission. There are also minutes and general records of the Family Security Committee, 1941–42; and records of the Health and Medical Committee, consisting of general files, 1940-43, and records that relate to recruiting nurses and regional advisory councils, 1941-42.

REGIONAL RECORDS. 1941-46.
9 lin. ft.

These consist of general records of Region II, 1941-46; records relating to the Willow Run, Mich., area, April-July 1943; and office files of the OCWS director for the Caribbean area, relating to venereal disease control, recreation facilities for U.S. Armed Forces in Brazil, and welfare services for the Virgin Islands.

See Estelle Rebec, comp., *Preliminary Inventory of the Records of the Office of Community War Services*, PI 132 (1960).

RECORDS OF THE OFFICE OF CONTRACT SETTLEMENT (RECORD GROUP 246)

The Office of Contract Settlement was established by the Contract Settlement Act of July 1, 1944, to continue the work of the Joint Contract Termination Board of the Office of War Mobilization (see RG 250). The act also provided for the Contract Settlement Advisory Board, composed of officials of major contracting agencies, to advise the Director of Contract Settlement, and for the Appeal Board, appointed by him, to hear appeals from war contractors on decisions of contracting agencies. An act of October 3, 1944, placed the Office of Contract Settlement and the two boards in the Office of War Mobilization and Reconversion. An Executive order of December 12, 1946, transferred to the Treasury Department the boards and the functions and records of the Office and gave the authority of the Director of Contract Settlement to the Secretary of the Treasury. The Federal Property and Administrative Services Act of 1949 transferred the boards and contract settlement functions to the General Services Administration (GSA). Both the Treasury Department and the GSA maintained a small Office of Contract Settlement to continue the remaining work. The Appeal Board was terminated January 13, 1953, ending active contract settlement activities.

The Office of Contract Settlement established policies and coordinated operations of Federal agencies engaged in settling terminated war contracts. It prescribed uniform standards and procedures for issuing termination notices, handling claims, and negotiating final settlements. Regulations of the Office covered such matters as interim financing of war plants, removal of Government-owned equipment from war plants, protection of the claims of subcontractors, microfilming and destruction of war contractor records, and retention of records by contracting agencies. The Office was assisted by several technical committees, composed of representatives of contracting agencies, that studied and made recommendations on such matters as terminations, plant clearance, interim financing, training, public information, property and plant accounting, and legal questions.

See Office of Contract Settlements, *A History of War Contract Terminations and Settlements* (1947).

There are 130 cubic feet of records (in WNRC) dated between 1941 and 1955 in this record group.

RECORDS OF THE JOINT CONTRACT TERMINATION BOARD. 1943-44. 6 lin. ft.

The Board, composed of representatives of Federal agencies interested in terminations of war contracts, was established November 12, 1943, by the Director of the Office of War Mobilization and placed under the Advisory Unit for War and Post-War Adjustment Policies. Its policies were expressed in Office of War Mobilization directives. General correspondence of the Board and the Advisory Unit is with the correspondence of the Office of Contract Settlement. Separate records of the Board include its minutes and those of its subcommittees; reports, correspondence,

and other records of the Board Chairman; correspondence of the secretary; and correspondence, memorandums, and other records of a consultant to the Board.

RECORDS OF THE OFFICE OF CONTRACT SETTLEMENT. 1941-55. 142 lin. ft.

Included are general correspondence, 1943-47; records of the Office of the Director, 1944-47, including minutes and other records of the Contract Settlement Advisory Board, of which the Director served as Chairman, and reports and correspondence of the Director; reports, correspondence, and other records of the Office of the Deputy Director, the Office of the General Counsel, and the Accounting, Interim Financing, Progress and Statistics, Property and Plant Clearance, and Public Information Divisions, 1943-46; case files of the Appeals Board, 1945-53; and records concerning termination and settlement of war contracts inherited and created by the Treasury Department and the GSA, 1941-55.

RECORDS OF THE OFFICE OF DEFENSE TRANSPORTATION (RECORD GROUP 219)

The Office of Defense Transportation (ODT), successor to the Transportation Division of the Advisory Commission to the Council of National Defense, was established in the Office for Emergency Management on December 18, 1941, with responsibility for assuring "maximum utilization of the domestic transportation facilities . . . for the successful prosecution of the war." The ODT was authorized to coordinate activities of Federal agencies and private transportation groups in adjusting domestic transportation systems to the necessi-

ties of war, determine the adequacy of transport facilities and act to provide necessary additional facilities, coordinate and direct traffic movement to prevent congestion, coordinate domestic traffic movements with ocean shipping in conjunction with the U.S. Maritime Commission and other agencies, determine storage and warehouse requirements, represent the defense interest of the Government in rate matters, and recommend emergency legislation affecting domestic transportation. The ODT was also authorized to limit and regulate domestic use of transportation facilities; advise and assist Federal, State, and local agencies and private organizations in providing transportation service for personnel essential to the military and civilian war effort; review and approve Federal contracts and arrangements involving local passenger transportation to war plants and establishments; operate transportation properties seized by the Government; and act in matters relating to airline needs of materials and manpower. Postwar ODT activities were restricted mainly to alleviating serious freight car shortages in cooperation with the Civilian Production Administration and the Interstate Commerce Commission, operating under Government seizure in 1946 certain tugboat properties and railroads because of labor troubles, handling unsettled claims and other legal problems arising from Federal management of seized transportation firms (particularly in the trucking industry), and gradually liquidating its business. The ODT was terminated July 1, 1949, and the Interstate Commerce Commission completed the liquidation of its affairs.

There are 1,095 cubic feet of records dated between 1934 and 1952 in this record group.

RECORDS OF THE OFFICE OF THE DIRECTOR. 1940-49. 231 lin. ft.

These comprise the general file of the Advisory Commission to the Council of National Defense, 1940-41; the Director's reading and historical files, ca. 1941-49; reports, correspondence, and memorandums, 1942-49; general records of the Deputy Director, 1941-44; reading file of the Executive Officer, 1941-47; memorandums and correspondence relating to organization and staffing of the Washington and field offices, 1942-44; budget records, ca. 1943-49; minutes, regional attorneys' reports, general orders, memorandums, and correspondence of the General Counsel, 1941-49;

and reports and correspondence relating to railroad and trucking companies seized by the Government, 1942-45.

RECORDS OF TRANSPORT DEPARTMENTS. 1942-49. 585 lin. ft.

Included are records of the Highway Transport Department, consisting of minutes of meetings with Government agencies, 1942-44; correspondence and other records maintained by the Executive Assistant, ca. 1942-45; and Division of Equipment and Research reports, correspondence, and memorandums, ca. 1942-45, correspondence with motor carriers and field offices, reports of equipment needs for various cities, and correspondence on taxicab requirements, 1942-45. Records of the Railway Transport Department, including reports, correspondence, and memorandums, 1942-45; and reports, correspondence, and other records of departmental sections, 1942-49. Records of the Waterway Transport Department, consisting of reports, correspondence, and memorandums, 1942-45; and correspondence with water carriers and the War Production Board, 1942-45. Records of the Liquid Transport Department, consisting primarily of records relating to the transportation of petroleum and petroleum products, 1942-45, correspondence and related records of the adviser on State barriers, 1942-45, correspondence of the Pipeline Division with major pipeline companies, 1942-45, and correspondence of the Tank Truck Division and the Tank Car Service Section, 1942-45.

RECORDS OF DIVISIONS. 1940-49. 162 lin. ft.

These include records of the Division of Puerto Rican Transport, consisting of general correspondence of the Director with the regional director in Puerto Rico, ca. 1942-45, reports on the conservation and utilization of Puerto Rican transportation facilities, ca. 1942-45, and executive orders and correspondence about U.S. Government administration and operation of the American Railroad Company of Puerto Rico, 1943–44; the Information Division, consisting of correspondence, photographs, press releases, and clippings, 1942–45; the Division of Transport Personnel, including orders, reports, correspondence, and memorandums, ca. 1942–46; the Division of Materials and Equipment, consisting of reports, correspondence, and memorandums with railroads and other transportation companies, 1942–49; the Division of Rates, consisting principally of correspondence with Government agencies and private carriers about rate problems and rate legislation before the Congress, 1942–45; the Division of Storage, including its correspondence, 1942–45, and the correspondence of the Merchandise Warehouse Section, 1940–46; and the Manpower and Materials Division, consisting primarily of classified general files, statistical reports, and correspondence, ca. 1946–49.

RECORDS OF ODT FIELD OFFICES. 1942–46. 191 lin. ft.

These include case files of the New York attorney of the Office of the General Counsel, 1944–45; correspondence of the southern and western regional offices of the Railway Transport Division, 1942–46; correspondence of the New York, Houston, San Francisco, and Los Angeles offices of the Liquid Transport Department, 1942–46; correspondence of the New York, San Francisco, Seattle (in FRC Seattle), and New Orleans offices of the Waterway Transport Department, 1942–45; and general files of port offices of the Division of Storage, 1942–45.

RECORDS OF THE MOTOR CARRIER CLAIMS COMMISSION. 1946–52. 9 lin. ft.

This Commission was established to adjudicate claims against the United States by 103 midwestern motor carriers for losses and damages resulting from ODT seizure and control or operation of their properties in 1944 and 1945. The records consist chiefly of minutes, 1949–52, correspondence and administrative subject files, 1949–52, a reading file, 1950–52, and records relating to the legislative history of the Commission, 1946–52.

CARTOGRAPHIC RECORDS. 1934–44. 7 items.

Included are maps relating to railroad lines, properties, and terminal facilities, 1934–44; a schematic diagram and flow chart showing pipelines and the flow of oil in the northeastern part of the United States; and diagrammatic maps showing shipments of bituminous coal on the Great Lakes and the St. Lawrence River, 1941.

RECORDS OF THE OFFICE FOR EMERGENCY MANAGEMENT (RECORD GROUP 214)

The Office for Emergency Management (OEM) was established in the Executive Office of the President by an administrative order of May 25, 1940 (in accordance with Executive Order 8248 of September 8, 1939), to assist the President in clearing information on defense measures and to maintain liaison with national defense agencies. An administrative order of January 7, 1941, which transferred responsibility for coordinating the national defense program from the National Defense Advisory Commission to the OEM, made the

OEM responsible for keeping the President informed about emergency activities of Government agencies, assembling and analyzing information concerning additional measures, and assisting in the preparation of recommendations for legislation. The order placed the Council of National Defense and the Advisory Commission to the Council under OEM coordination. By Executive Order 9182 of June 13, 1942, OEM information functions were divided among the Office of War Information (see RG 208) and other agencies.

The OEM was directed by an administrative assistant to the President, later known as the Liaison Officer for Emergency Management. On November 3, 1943, the President accepted the resignation of the Liaison Officer and appointed no successor, thereby terminating OEM liaison functions. The OEM Division of Central Administrative Services—which had been established in 1941 to provide a budgeting, accounting, and fiscal control system for the Office and its agencies—continued to operate, with diminishing responsibilities, until November 30, 1944.

Among the agencies established in or coordinated by the OEM were the Committee on Fair Employment Practice, Foreign Economic Administration, National War Labor Board, Office of Alien Property Custodian, Office of Civilian Defense, Office of the Coordinator of Inter-American Affairs, Office of Defense Transportation, Office of Economic Stabilization, Office of Scientific Research and Development, Office of War Information, War Manpower Commission, War Production Board, and War Shipping Administration. The OEM served primarily as a framework within which most civilian war agencies functioned. Although the framework remained, no agencies operated within it after World War II.

There are 79 cubic feet of records (in WNRC) dated between 1940 and 1944 in this record group.

RECORDS. 1940–44. 99 lin. ft.

The records of the Liaison Office, 1941–43, include records concerning the creation, organization, and functions of the OEM; reports prepared by Government agencies; minutes of the Board of Economic Warfare and the Committee on War Information; and memorandums and correspondence. Records of the Office of the Director of the Division of Central Administrative Services include administrative memorandums, 1941; correspondence with Government agencies and regional offices, 1941–44, records of the Field Operations Office, 1942–43, and records of the Assistant Secretary to the Advisory Commission to the Council of National Defense, 1940–42. Records, 1941–44, of the Office of the Executive Assistant to the Director and its predecessor, the Budget Office, include general records, correspondence with constituent agencies, transcripts of budget hearings, survey reports, procedural and other releases, and records of the Management Analysis and Planning Section. There are also case files and other records of the Investigations Office, 1942–44, and records of the General Supply and General Services Divisions, 1940–44.

See Henry T. Ulasek, comp., *Preliminary Inventory of the Records of the Office for Emergency Management,* PI 92 (1956).

RECORDS OF THE
OFFICE OF INTER-AMERICAN AFFAIRS
(RECORD GROUP 229)

The Office for Coordination of Commercial and Cultural Relations Between the American Republics was established in the Office for Emergency Management on August 16, 1940. It was replaced by the Office of the Coordinator of Inter-American Affairs, created in 1941 to serve as the coordination center for cultural and commercial relations with other American republics. The Office worked closely with the Department of State to plan and conduct programs relating to commerce and economics, the arts and sciences, education and travel, and radio, press, and cinema. It also established nonprofit Government corporations to implement programs.

In April 1942 many economic responsibilities of the Office were delegated to the Board of Economic Warfare (later the Foreign Economic Administration), and in the same year some of its long-range cultural activities were transferred to the Department of State. The name of the Office was changed in March 1945 to the Office of Inter-American Affairs. Informational activities were transferred in August 1945 to the Department of State. An Executive order in April 1946 terminated the Office and transferred its remaining functions and responsibilities, including its corporations, to the Department of State where it functioned until 1953 as the Institute of Inter-American Affairs.

There are 540 cubic feet of records (in WNRC except for nontextual records) dated between 1940 and 1951 in this record group.

GENERAL RECORDS AND RECORDS OF THE COORDINATOR'S IMMEDIATE OFFICE. 1940-49. 41 lin. ft.

Included are minutes, reports, correspondence, memorandums, a history of the Office prepared in 1946, and records of the Office of the General Counsel.

RECORDS CONCERNING PROGRAM AREAS. 1940-51. 536 lin. ft.

These records were created by Office departments and divisions and by coordination committees composed of U.S. citizens living in Latin American countries. They relate to programs of health and sanitation, food supply, emergency rehabilitation, economic development, advertisement, transportation, information, and education; and they include reports, minutes, correspondence, memorandums, project authorizations and case files, plans and blueprints, charts, statistical data, maps, newspaper clippings, publications, and scripts of radio broadcasts to Latin America.

RECORDS RELATING TO INTERNAL ADMINISTRATION. 1940-46. 17 lin. ft.

These consist of records of the Office's Department of Administration and its Personnel and Service Operations Divisions, including correspondence with coordination committees and field personnel, weekly reports of divisions, project authorizations, and correspondence and memorandums relating to operational services.

RECORDS OF SUBSIDIARY CORPORATIONS. 1942-46. 79 lin. ft.

These include letters and memorandums sent by the Institute of Inter-American Affairs, 1943-45; and records of the Institute of Inter-American Transportation, including correspondence and reports from the Washington and Mexico City offices of the U.S. Railway Mission in Mexico, the major project of the Institute, 1942–46.

AUDIOVISUAL RECORDS. 1941–45. 148 items.

These include still pictures (79 items), consisting of original paintings, drawings, sketches, and cartoons relating to inter-American cooperation; American war production; and assistance given by the United States to Latin American countries in improving agriculture and public health.

Motion pictures (45 reels) consist of films dealing with the peoples and cultures of Latin America, inter-American cooperation, Latin American minerals and archaeological treasures, a study of an ancient Inca city, and war activities of the United States.

Sound recordings (24 items) consist of recordings in Spanish and Portuguese of broadcasts to Latin America about life in the United States and American ideals, institutions, and war efforts and peace aims.

See H. Stephen Helton, comp., *Preliminary Inventory of the Records of the Office of Inter-American Affairs*, PI 41 (1952).

RECORDS OF THE OFFICE OF PRICE ADMINISTRATION
(RECORD GROUP 188)

The Office of Price Administration (OPA) originated in the Price Stabilization and Consumer Protection Divisions of the Advisory Commission to the Council of National Defense (NDAC) on May 29, 1940, and in their successor, the Office of Price Administration and Civilian Supply (OPACS), created in April 1941 and redesignated the Office of Price Administration by an Executive order of August 28, 1941, which transferred its civilian supply functions to the Office of Production Management (see RG 179). The OPA was given statutory recognition as an independent agency by the Emergency Price Control Act of January 30, 1942. To stabilize prices and rents, the OPA established maximum prices for commodities (except agricultural commodities actually controlled by the Secretary of Agriculture) and maximum rents in defense areas, rationed scarce essential commodities, and authorized subsidies for production of some of those commodities. Most of the price and rationing controls were lifted between August 1945 and November 1946.

An Executive order of December 12, 1946, transferred the functions of the Financial Reporting Division to the Federal Trade Commission and consolidated the OPA with other wartime agencies to form the Office of Temporary Controls. The Sugar Control Extension Act of March 31, 1947, transferred responsibility for sugar controls to the Department of Agriculture. Two Executive orders of April 23, 1947, provided for the termination of the Office of Temporary Controls according to a schedule that transferred to the Department of Agriculture price control over rice, to the Reconstruction Finance Corporation OPA functions relating to food subsidies, to the Office of the Housing Expediter rent control, to the Attorney General litigation functions arising from violations of price regulations, and to the Department of Commerce all functions not otherwise disposed of— mainly those of liquidation.

There are 8,860 cubic feet of records dated between 1940 and 1949 in this record group.

GENERAL RECORDS. 1940–43.
74 lin. ft.

These consist of the general report and reading files of the Defense Finance Section, Price Stabilization Division, 1940–42; administrative records, including minutes, reports, correspondence, speeches, requisitions, and orders of the Price Stabilization Division, 1940–43; letters from the general public and Government officials, and newspaper clippings concerning the Administrator's policies, 1941–42; reports, correspondence, tables, newspaper clippings, and circulars relating to the production, stockpiling, and costs of commodities, 1941–42; correspondence on commodities and services subject to the April 28, 1942, General Maximum Price Regulation, March–September 1942; and minutes, correspondence, and other records relating to price and procedural regulations.

RECORDS OF THE OFFICE OF THE ADMINISTRATOR. 1942–47.
79 lin. ft.

This Office directed and supervised all activities of the agency, determined overall policies, and determined organization. The Administrator was an ex officio member of the Supply Priorities and Allocations Board and later of the War Production Board and the Economic Stabilization Board. The records consist of office files of the Administrator, 1941–46, correspondence and other records of Deputy Administrators, 1943–47, and office files of assistants to the Administrator, 1943–47. Administrative correspondence includes letters from the general public expressing opinions of OPA policies, 1943–46.

RECORDS OF THE OFFICE OF ADMINISTRATIVE HEARINGS.
1943–47. 132 lin. ft.

This Office was responsible for hearing, determining, and reviewing OPA administrative proceedings. The records consist of selected national office sus-pension order case files involving appeals of decisions made by regional hearing commissions on violations of OPA regulations, 1943–46; selected regional suspension order case files consisting of notices of hearings, specifications of charges, transcripts of hearings, decisions, and motions to amend and modify decisions; regional suspension orders, 1943–47, with an alphabetical index; instructions, reports, briefs, and correspondence relating to opinions and procedures of the Office of Administrative Hearings, 1943; and monthly reports on personnel and workload submitted by chief hearing commissioners, 1943–47.

RECORDS OF THE OFFICE OF CONGRESSIONAL INFORMATION.
1941–47. 117 lin. ft.

Included are records of the congressional adviser to the Administrator and Chief of the Congressional Correspondence Section, 1944–47, transcripts and digests of proceedings at congressional committee hearings, 1941–47, and correspondence with Members of Congress about complaints and with congressional committees on proposed legislation.

RECORDS OF BOARDS AND COMMITTEES. 1940–47. 55 lin. ft.

Included are minutes of the Price Decontrol Board, regional administrators, the Automotive Conservation Committee, and control analysts, 1940–46; minutes and transcripts of press conferences, 1941–45; transcripts of meetings and conferences of national and field offices, 1943–45; and proceedings of regional hearings concerning suspension orders, 1943–47.

PROGRESS REPORTS OF THE OPA, ITS PREDECESSORS, AND ITS DIVISIONS. 1940–47. 15 lin. ft.

Included are weekly progress reports of the NDAC, 1940–41, the OPACS, May–September 1941, and OPA divisions, branches, and sections on administration, rent control, and enforcement of policies and regulations, 1941-43; drafts and published copies of OPA quarterly progress reports to the Congress, 1942-47; weekly reports submitted to the Deputy Administrator by the Administrative Services, Budget and Planning, Personnel, Credit Policy, and Price Board Management Offices, and the Committee on Economic Demobilization, 1943-46; weekly and monthly progress reports of regional administrators and district directors, concerning food supply, rationing, price control, "black" and "brown" market operations, and rent control, 1941-45; weekly progress reports of regional directors and attorneys at Baltimore, Kansas City, and Philadelphia, January-May 1942; and monthly legal narrative reports from area rent directors and rent attorneys, concerning rent control in Alabama, Florida, Georgia, North and South Carolina, Tennessee, Virginia, Mississippi, and Minnesota, 1942-46.

RECORDS OF THE OFFICE OF THE AGRICULTURAL RELATIONS ADVISER. 1944-46. 4 lin. ft.

Established in December 1943 to develop among farmers an understanding of the OPA program and to advise the Administrator on agricultural policy, this Office was terminated in October 1946. Its records include general correspondence with the OPA Administrator, Members of Congress, and Federal agencies, relating to meat control, subsidies, decontrol, vocational training, and the agricultural extension service; correspondence on commodity prices; correspondence with and reports of regional offices concerning field programs; and form letters, instructional issuances sent to the field, and speeches and issuances, including copies of the "Agricultural Situation Summary," "The National Farm Federation News," the "Washington Farm Letter," and weekly letters published by farm commodity organizations.

RECORDS OF THE OFFICE OF CONSUMER RELATIONS ADVISER. 1941-47. 3 lin. ft.

Functions of the Consumer Protection Division (inherited from the NDAC) were absorbed in 1942 by the OPA Information Department. In 1944, however, the Office of Consumer Relations Adviser was established in the Office of the Administrator to coordinate a program of consumer participation through national and district consumer advisory committees. The records include minutes of the consumer advisory national committee, 1943-46; committee memorandums relating to organization, functions, and personnel, 1941-47; national committee press releases, 1943-46; and Decontrol Board issuances, 1945-47. Records of the Office of Consumer Relations Adviser consist of memorandums sent to the Administrator and other OPA officials, consumer advisory committees, and consumer organization leaders, 1943-47; weekly, monthly, and quarterly narrative reports of the Office, 1945; and minutes of the Consumer Leader Conference of October 10, 1945. Records of regional and district consumer relations advisers consist of regional and district committee correspondence, 1944-47; regional committee minutes, 1945-46; and lists of district consumer committee chairmen and programs of their committees, 1944-46.

RECORDS OF THE OFFICE OF CREDIT POLICY ADVISER. 1941-46. 5 lin. ft.

This staff office, established in the Office of the Administrator December 19, 1942, cleared credit policy questions and recommended action by the OPA or other Federal agencies to ease inflationary pressure. The director acted as the OPA alternate on the consultative committee on consumer credit control, which operated under the general supervision of the Board of Governors of the Federal Reserve System. The Office was terminated in 1946. The records consist of correspondence concerning OPA credit policies, 1942-43; drafts and interpretations of Regulation W and its amendments applying to credit, and correspondence and reports regarding enforcement, 1941-46; reports and related correspondence concerning retail credit, loan credit (including credit unions, life insurance policy loans, and finance companies), and consumer credit control, with material relating to commercial credit, gold release, credit control in Great Britain and Canada, inflation, installment purchases of war bonds, reconversion, and taxes; memorandums and reports on special commodities, 1941-43, and cash credit prices, 1942-46; and statistical records, including charts of consumer loans, reports of family expenditures, outstanding balances on new automobiles, and amount of Treasury savings bonds purchased.

RECORDS OF THE OFFICE OF INDUSTRY ADVISORY COMMITTEES. 1941-47. 139 lin. ft.

The Industry Council, made up of leading businessmen, assisted the Administrator in obtaining information about industry organization and business practices and helped the commodity branches select industry advisory committees for consultation before price regulations were issued. Most of the Council's duties were taken over by the Office of Industry Advisory Committees late in 1943. This Office assisted in establishing and staffing the more than 700 industry advisory committees provided for by the Price Control Act or by the OPA itself. Included are records of the Industry Council, consisting of reports, correspondence, and memorandums, 1941-43, and correspondence of or relating to personnel of the Council or the OPA and to industries, 1941-43;

records of the Office of Industry Advisory Committees, consisting of reports, correspondence, and memorandums on the need for more industry advisory committees, relations of OPA with business and industry, meetings with the OPA staff, and transcripts of office meetings, 1944-47; weekly progress reports, staff reports on committee meetings, and lists of industry advisory committees, 1941-46, and their members, 1942-46; and minutes of industry advisory committees, 1941-47.

RECORDS OF THE OFFICE OF LABOR RELATIONS ADVISER. 1942-46. 26 lin. ft.

On June 30, 1942, the Administrator established the Labor Office and the Labor Policy Committee. The Office served as his liaison with organized labor and with other Federal agencies on questions affecting labor. The name of the Office was changed in 1944 to Office of Labor Relations Adviser. Liaison officers followed up field grievances or queries on the intent of price and rationing regulations. The Labor Policy Committee, composed of representatives of the AFL, the CIO, and the Railroad Brotherhoods, recommended major policies in price, rent, and rationing programs, and assisted in establishing volunteer district labor advisory committees and in appointing members of labor organizations to local war price and rationing boards. The records consist of correspondence of the Director of the Labor Office, relating to wage policy, price, and rent control; records documenting Labor Policy Committee activities; office files of aides to the labor relations adviser; and minutes, correspondence, and related records of regional, State, and local labor advisory committees.

RECORDS OF THE DIVISION OF RESEARCH. 1940-47. 179 lin. ft.

This Division was established late in 1941 under the direction of the OPA economic adviser. It conducted economic and financial research and analyses required by the economic adviser, and other research for the Administrator and staff or for public information programs. On September 17, 1946, the Division was assigned responsibility for reviewing and tabulating economic data that had been collected by the OPA and publishing the tabulations. The records consist of correspondence, orders, and reports of the Division. Also included are reports, memorandums, related correspondence, and press releases of the Economic Section of the Consumer Division, Council of National Defense, concerning domestic and international monetary problems and policies and the effect of the defense program on domestic consumption.

RECORDS OF THE OFFICE OF THE GENERAL COUNSEL. 1941-47. 134 lin. ft.

Created in 1941, the Legal Division (at that time designated "Department") was abolished in September 1943, its staff assigned to legal divisions set up in the program departments, and its enforcement functions transferred to a new and separate Enforcement Department. Thereafter the Office of General Counsel advised the Administrator on legal matters, represented the OPA in legal matters not delegated to other counsel, established standards for the agency's legal staffs, and directed review boards. The boards, established in 1944, were appointed by the Administrator to hear protests against the validity of price and rent actions before such actions should be brought before the Emergency Court of Appeals. Attached to the Office of the General Counsel was the Internal Intelligence Division, which was responsible for investigating all charges of corruption or misconduct against agency employees. Included are records relating to legislation, subsidies, enforcement, and decontrol; general legal reports and memorandums, opinions, interpretations, and correspondence, 1941-47; associate general counsel case files of cases tried by the Emergency Court of Appeals, 1942-47; reports, briefs, and memorandums relating to petitions filed by transportation and public utility companies requesting increases in rates and fares, 1941-44; protest files relating to cases heard by review boards; and records relating to persons investigated by the Internal Intelligence Branch and its predecessor units.

RECORDS OF THE OFFICE OF RACIAL RELATIONS ADVISER. 1942-47. 3 lin. ft.

This Office was established in 1943 to encourage participation of minority racial groups in OPA programs and recommend appropriate action to responsible agency officers. Functions of the Office were transferred in 1944 to other units of the agency, but the special assistant to the Administrator on racial relations was retained in the Administrator's Office. The name of the staff office was restored in September 1946, but in November it was changed to Office of Minority Group Adviser. The records consist of reports and correspondence relating to the employment of blacks in the OPA and other Federal agencies, and minutes of meetings with minority groups protesting discrimination in employment practices, housing, and rationing.

RECORDS OF THE OFFICE OF VETERANS' RELATIONS ADVISER. 1945-47. 3 lin. ft.

In 1945 veterans' relations advisers were appointed in the eight regional offices to assist veterans in readjusting to civilian economic life and enlist the support of veterans, veteran organizations, and members of the Armed Forces in making the OPA program effective. The program was discontinued January 30, 1947. The records consist largely of general correspondence relating to the price, rationing, and rent programs as they affected veterans; and correspondence with veteran organizations.

ADMINISTRATIVE RECORDS OF REGIONAL AND DISTRICT OFFICES. 1940–47. 241 lin. ft. (including 72 lin. ft. of Region IV records in FRC Atlanta).

There were eight regional offices for the continental United States and a varying number of district offices. Each regional office included administrative service, budget and finance, accounting, enforcement, price, rent, rationing, and information divisions, with functions analogous to those of their departmental counterparts at headquarters. The regional administrator was responsible for general administration, but technical divisions (accounting, price, rationing, enforcement, rent, and information) were responsible for their activity to the corresponding program departments in Washington. The staff of a typical district office consisted of a director, an attorney, and district price, rationing, consumer relations, and rent representatives. The district director supervised general administration and each representative was responsible for his program activity to the corresponding official in the next level of authority—to State officers until early 1943 and thereafter to regional executives. Regional office administrative records include minutes, narrative reports, budget statements, data on public reactions, and records of labor, agricultural, and race relations. The administrative records of district offices generally parallel those of the regional offices and include minutes, budget and personnel data, field instructions, and district office histories.

RECORDS OF ADMINISTRATIVE MANAGEMENT OFFICES. 1941–47. 305 lin. ft.

Functions of budget, administrative services, and personnel were assigned in 1942 to the Office of General Services, which was divided in November 1942 into the Professional Services Department (comprising the Research, Accounting, Standards, and Transportation and Public Utilities Divisions) and the Administrative Management Department (comprising the Budget and Finance, Personnel, Business Services— later the Office of Administrative Service—and Organization and Planning Divisions, and the Offices of Statistical Standards and Local Board Operations). The Professional Services Department was abolished in 1943. The Administrative Management Department continued until 1945 when its main subdivisions became separate offices under the Deputy Administrator. The records consist of general records of the Administrative Management Department, 1941–47, relating to organization, budgets, procedures, and personnel, and including a master set of the agency's "News Letters" to the field, various series of operating manuals and procedural issuances, and samples of all forms used by the OPA; correspondence, reports, and related records of the Office of Administrative Service, 1943–47; records of the Historical Branch (known as the Policy Analysis Branch after January 1947), 1941–47, consisting of miscellaneous documents relating to the history of the OPA and numerous draft histories of the OPA and predecessor agencies (listed in section 10 of *OPA Bibliography, 1940–47*); records of the Professional Services Department, 1941–43, consisting of reports, correspondence, and memorandums on administrative subjects; and records of the Office of Personnel, 1941–47, consisting of correspondence of the Director, position descriptions, and training program material.

RECORDS OF THE OFFICE OF THE OPA SECRETARY. 1941–47. 532 lin. ft. (in WNRC).

This Office, which was established within the Office of Budget and Planning (formerly separate divisions in the Administrative Management Department), was composed of the Secretary, recording secretary, Editorial and Reference Section, and Statistical Review Section. The Secretary supervised the Office; reviewed and issued all official documents; received, docketed, and routed protests and petitions; analyzed public reporting forms and surveys; and advised operating units of regulations concerning publication, distribution, and use of forms and surveys. The recording secretary reviewed official documents for style, form, and conformity to OPA policy and procedures, and determined for each official document its issue and effective dates. The records consist of price regulations, with supporting justification statements and orders of the Administrator exempting specific companies from certain provisions of the regulations, 1941–47; letter orders issued under various price regulations, approving or denying requests for price increases, 1945–47; petitions for amendment of regulations, 1942–46; protest case files, 1942–47; exception orders issued by regional administrators and district directors, 1946; and headquarters and regional card indexes to the orders and protests.

RECORDS OF THE OFFICE OF PRICE BOARD MANAGEMENT. 1941–46. 67 lin. ft.

This Office, established on May 17, 1946, was the last of a succession of headquarters offices that began in December 1941 with the Field Operations Division. The Office and its predecessors, which were usually linked with other administrative-management units of the OPA, were primarily responsible for coordinating the activities of local price and rationing boards. It acted through regional and district offices to control operations, facilities, staffing, location, and other management phases of local board operation. The Office was abolished November 1, 1946. The records include administrative files of the Director of the short-lived Field Operations Division, 1941–42; correspondence and reports of the Field Organization Branch of the Organization Planning Division, 1942–43; and headquarters and regional manuals and bulletins, regional office narrative reports, reports of the director and his staff, correspondence and other records relating to price-panel activities, and data on volunteer programs, workload, and organization, 1943–46.

REGIONAL PRICE BOARD MANAGEMENT RECORDS. 1942–46. 111 lin. ft. (including 10 lin. ft. of Region IV records in FRC Atlanta).

The records of the regional price-board management divisions for Regions I–VIII contain data on board organizations, statistical reports, and minutes of committees and panels. Also included are official correspondence and memorandums, local board histories, instruction material, conference notes, field bulletins, addresses of local boards, and lists of chairmen and board members.

RECORDS OF THE ACCOUNTING DEPARTMENT. 1940–47. 1,844 lin. ft.

The accounting function of OPA originated in the Advisory Commission to the Council of National Defense as an adjunct to the Price Division. After several reorganizations it became late in 1944 an operating department comprising Divisions of Consumer Products

Accounting, Industrial Accounting, Services Accounting and Audits, Financial Reporting, and Field Accounting. The operations divisions made accounting examinations, audits, analyses, and investigations for the Price, Rent, and Enforcement Departments; studied the costs and profits of individual concerns and reported their findings as the basis for action on hardship cases, requests for exemption, and protests; and performed other technical accounting services delegated to them by the Administrator. The Financial Reporting Division collected and analyzed financial data concerning representative industrial and commercial concerns subject to OPA regulations. The Field Accounting Division coordinated accounting activities of the national and field offices. The records of the Department consist of the office files of the Deputy Administrator for Accounting and his predecessor, the Director of Accounting, 1940-47; records of the Director of the Services Accounting and Audits Division, 1943-47; accountants' reports of enforcement investigations of common and contract carriers, 1943-46; records of the Director of the Industrial Accounting Division, 1941-47; records of commodity branches of the Consumer Products Accounting and the Industrial Accounting Divisions, including general industry surveys and individual company studies of consumer durable goods, food, textiles, leather, apparel, chemicals, rubber, lumber, machinery, iron and steel, and paper; corporation financial reports and related correspondence of the Financial Reporting Division, 1941-46 (including 600 lin. ft. in WNRC); weekly progress field reports and administrative correspondence of the Director of the Field Accounting Division, 1941-47; and correspondence with national and district offices, minutes and transcripts of staff meetings, records of company investigations, case and survey files, and progress reports of the field accounting divisions,

Regions I-VIII (including 86 lin. ft. of Region IV records in FRC Atlanta).

RECORDS OF THE ENFORCEMENT DEPARTMENT. 1941-47. 430 lin. ft. (including 13 lin. ft. of Region IV records in FRC Atlanta).

A division in the Legal Department became the Enforcement Department on September 14, 1943, with responsibility for planning, directing, and executing enforcement activities. It was composed of the Office of the Deputy Administrator for Enforcement; operating divisions for specific groups of commodities or services, such as the Food, the Apparel and Industrial Materials, the Fuel and Consumer Goods, the Rent and Services, and the Rent and Durable Goods Enforcement Divisions; the Litigation Division; and the Division of Special Investigations. The operating divisions, through their commodity branches, developed enforcement programs and instructions to field staffs regarding violations and the imposition of sanctions, and advised the Price and Rent Departments on regulations and orders. The Litigation Division assisted the Deputy Administrator for Enforcement in litigation policy and in liaison with the Department of Justice. The Division of Special Investigations investigated violations of price regulations in commodity fields where strong enforcement action was of great importance to the price program. The records of this Department consist of periodic reports of all national and field enforcement offices and divisions, 1941-47; manuals, specifications, and instructions; forms; statements of policy and procedure; records relating to enforcement activities of war price and rationing boards, 1943-46; interagency and regional correspondence of several administrative units; and a sample of enforcement cases illustrating types of OPA sanctions, 1943-47.

RECORDS OF THE INFORMATION DEPARTMENT. 1940-47. 139 lin. ft. (including 3 lin. ft. of Region IV records in FRC Atlanta).

In cooperation with the operating divisions this Department formulated and performed OPA public information and educational policies. It consisted of the Office of the Deputy Administrator for Information and the Field, Program Planning, Editorial, and Community Service Divisions. The Deputy Administrator for Information was responsible for information programs disseminated to the general public and to the trade. The records include correspondence of the Deputy Administrator with other OPA departments and Government agencies, OPA regional offices, and business, press, and other associations; information and procedure issuances, 1940-47; transcripts of the OPA Administrator's press conferences; radio scripts prepared by the OPA; newspaper clippings and transcripts of radio broadcasts; and correspondence, reports, and press releases of regional offices.

RECORDS OF THE PRICE DEPARTMENT. 1940-47. 4,865 lin. ft. (including 213 lin. ft. of Region IV records in FRC Atlanta).

The Price Department prepared and issued maximum price regulations and provided technical supervision over the price program in the field. A General Maximum Price Regulation was promulgated April 28, 1942, but special regulations were also issued for many commodities or classes of commodities during the period when price controls were in effect. In 1943 the Department adopted a plan of community price ceilings fixed for particular communities by the district offices of the agency. The Department was composed of the Office of the Deputy Administrator for Price; the Price Legal Division, the Standard Division, and the Price Decontrol Division; and the Consumer Goods, Food, Indus-

trial, Building and Construction, and Transportation, Services, and Fuels Price Divisions. The operating divisions, covering specific groups of commodities or commodity areas, drafted and administered price regulations for commodities and services within their jurisdictions. The records of the Department include Department and regional price division progress reports, 1940-47, and the office files of assistants to the Deputy Administrator; records of the Associate General Counsel in charge of the Price Legal Division, 1940-46; records of the operating divisions, consisting of files on each maximum price regulation and price schedule issued, protests, petitions for their amendment, hardship case files, and files for transportation cases brought before the Interstate Commerce Commission and State regulatory commissions; and records of the field price divisions, Regions I-VIII.

RECORDS OF THE RATIONING DEPARTMENT. 1940-47. 840 lin. ft. (including 39 lin. ft. of Region IV records in FRC Atlanta).

The Rationing Division, established March 3, 1942, became a department on September 1, 1942. After one of the supply agencies (War Production Board, Petroleum Administration for War, or War Food Administration) had determined that a commodity should be rationed and had fixed the aggregate allocation of the commodity for civilian use, the Rationing Department planned an equitable distribution and administered such plans through field representatives and local boards. The Department was composed of the Office of the Deputy Administrator for Rationing, the Rationing Legal and Ration Currency Control Divisions, and a number of operating divisions. The records include those of the Office of the Deputy Administrator for Rationing, 1940-46; the Rationing Legal Division, relating to general legal problems of the Department and specific problems of appeals, interpretations, administrative exceptions, and requests for changes in the programs, 1942-45; of the Ration Currency Control Division, relating to accounting methods for ration currency, OPA's issuance of such currency, ration banking, issuance centers, tokens, and verification centers, 1942-47; records of the operating divisions, arranged under specific commodities and consisting of materials relating to the background of the particular program, program planning, ration eligibility, industrial relations, appeals, inventory audit and control, and field surveys; records of the field rationing divisions, Regions I-VIII; and records of 16 war price and rationing boards, retained to document the operation of the rationing programs at local level, 1942-45.

REGION IX (TERRITORIAL) RECORDS. 1941-47. 127 lin. ft.

Between November 1941 and February 1942 the OPA had created 11 regional offices within the United States. The number of regional offices was reduced to eight on May 7, 1942, and a ninth region, with its main office in Washington, D.C., was set up to supervise OPA district offices in the territories and possessions. The district offices of Region IX were located in Alaska, Hawaii, the Panama Canal Zone, Puerto Rico, and the Virgin Islands. The records include those of the regional administrator, consisting of correspondence with field personnel, histories of regional and district OPA offices, transcripts of trade advisory committee meetings, and reports of regional operating divisions, 1942-47; records of the accounting divisions of the Hawaii, 1942-46, and Puerto Rico, 1941-46, offices; records of the price divisions of the Alaska, Hawaii, Puerto Rico, and Virgin Islands offices;

and records of local price boards in Alaska, Hawaii, Puerto Rico, and the Virgin Islands, 1943-46.

RECORDS OF THE OFFICE OF THE DIVISION OF LIQUIDATION, DEPARTMENT OF COMMERCE. 1941-49. 140 lin. ft.

This Division was established in the Office of the Secretary, Department of Commerce, on June 1, 1947, as the successor to the OPA Office of Temporary Controls, to liquidate the industrial alcohol audit and pricing programs and the adjudication of pending protest cases. The records include those concerning ethyl alcohol protest cases, 1941-48, filed by distillers; correspondence, reports, and work papers relating to the development and administration of price regulations for alcohols and solvents, 1942-49; and records of the Alcohol Price Section, relating to price policies for acids, anhydrides, antifreeze, charcoal, industrial alcohol, and molasses for distillers, 1941-48.

AUDIOVISUAL RECORDS. 1941-47. 2,449 items.

Still pictures, 1941-47 (2,232 items), include photographs of OPA activities and officials and relate to the necessity of price controls and rationing. There are also posters used in promoting compliance with regulations.

Motion pictures, 1943-46 (15 reels)—created to enlist the cooperation of the public in OPA programs—concern the necessity for price controls and rationing both during and immediately following the war, explain the role of the consumer in enforcement of the regulations, and warn of the inflationary results of participation in the black market.

Sound recordings, 1941-46 (202 items), of radio broadcasts concerning the importance and necessity of price controls and rationing and enforcement of the regulations, and consisting of news commentaries, dramatizations, panel discussions, speeches, and interviews featuring prominent persons, including Chester Bowles, Robert S. Kerr, Donald M. Nelson, Leon Henderson, Harold L. Ickes, Harry S. Truman, Robert A. Taft, Paul Porter, and Fiorello H. La Guardia. Included are broadcasts of "Neighborhood Call," "Hasten the Day," "OPA Weekly Report," "A Hundred Million Questions," and "You Can't Do Business With Hitler." There is also a recording of a congressional debate on the extension of price controls beyond the end of the war.

See Meyer H. Fishbein and Elaine C. Bennett, comps., *Preliminary Inventory of the Records of the Accounting Department of the Office of Price Administration*, PI 32 (1951); Fishbein, Walter W. Weinstein, and Albert W. Winthrop, comps., *Preliminary Inventory of the Records of the Price Department of the Office of Price Administration*, PI 95 (1956); Fishbein et al., comps., *Preliminary Inventory of the Records of the Rationing Department of the Office of Price Administration*, PI 102 (1958); Betty R. Bucher, comp., *Preliminary Inventory of the Records of the Information Department of the Office of Price Administration*, PI 119 (1959); and Fishbein and Bucher, comps., *Preliminary Inventory of the Records of the Enforcement Department of the Office of Price Administration*, PI 120 (1959).

Microfilm Publication: *Studies and Reports of the Office of Price Administration*, M164, 2 rolls.

SPECIFIC RESTRICTIONS

Records: Records containing industrial information obtained by the OPA that was deemed confidential by the Administrator or with reference to which request for confidential treatment was made by the person furnishing such information.

Restrictions: Such information may not be published or disclosed in any way to the public or to another Federal agency with the following statutory exceptions: (a) this restriction should not be construed to "prohibit the publication or disclosure of studies, graphs, charts, or other documents of like general character wherein individual statistics or the source thereof is not disclosed or identified directly or indirectly"; (b) this restriction should not "prevent the furnishing in confidence to the War Department, the Navy Department, or the Maritime Commission, such data and information as may be requested by them for use in the performance of their official duties"; and (c) that this restriction should not prevent the release of information "to any other Federal agency," provided the persons who supplied the information consent to its release to such agency, or provided such agency has authority supported by provisions of legal penalties to collect the same information itself.

Specified by: Congress of the United States.

RECORDS OF THE OFFICE OF SCIENTIFIC RESEARCH AND DEVELOPMENT (RECORD GROUP 227)

The Office of Scientific Research and Development (OSRD) was created June 28, 1941, within the Office for Emergency Management to ensure adequate provision for research in scientific and medical problems relating to national defense. A center for the mobilization of scientific personnel and resources, the OSRD coordinated, aided, and supplemented research activities of the War and Navy Departments and other Federal agencies. It entered into contracts and agreements with individuals, educational and scientific institutions (including the National Academy of Sciences and the National Research Council), industrial organizations, and other agencies for studies, experimental investigations, and reports. It was also given responsibility for similar contracts entered into before its establishment by the National Defense Research Committee (NDRC) and the Health and Medical Committee—created by order of the Council of National Defense on June 27 and September 19, 1940, respectively—and by the Federal Security Administrator in his capacity as coordinator of health, medical, and related activities as authorized by the Council of National Defense. The OSRD was terminated December 31, 1947, and its business was transferred for completion to the National Military Establishment.

There are 2,965 cubic feet of records dated between 1940 and 1947 in this record group.

RECORDS OF THE CHAIRMAN, NDRC, AND OF THE DIRECTOR, OSRD. 1940-47. 100 lin. ft.

Included are minutes of the NDRC, 1940-45; administrative and other reports, 1940-46; records of Vannevar Bush, Chairman of the NDRC, 1940-41, and Director of the OSRD, 1941-47, and of J. B. Conant, Chairman of the NDRC, 1941-46, consisting of correspondence, memorandums, and informal reports on agency projects, 1940-47; correspondence relating to reports to the President, 1941-46; a draft of a short agency history, histories of various divisions of the NDRC, and office memorandums and circulars of the NDRC and the OSRD, 1943-46; general correspondence and technical reports of Section "T," concerning research on proximity fuses, 1942-44; Office of Scientific Personnel correspondence with contractors, 1943-46; Committee on Publications correspondence, memorandums, and reports,

1944-47; and Committee on Sensory Devices correspondence, minutes, reports, and memorandums relating to aids for the blind, 1944-46.

RECORDS OF THE ADMINISTRATIVE OFFICE. 1940-47. 1,150 lin. ft. and 487 rolls of microfilm.

These consist of reports (including some from other Government agencies and from foreign governments), circulars, orders relating to general policies and activities of OSRD subdivisions, memorandums, and correspondence, 1940-47; outgoing correspondence and memorandums of the OSRD, NDRC, and Committee on Medical Research (CMR), 1940-47; contract records of the Budget and Finance Office, 1940-47, with an index (in WNRC); Project Control Section correspondence relating to project assignments to particular panels, committees, and divisions of the NDRC and CMR, 1941-47; OSRD and NDRC published histories and monographs, 1945-47; CMR published reports and collected reprints, 1941-47; NDRC published summary technical reports, 1946-47; microfilm copies (487 rolls) of summary technical reports for all divisions, panels, and committees of the NDRC, including laboratory reports, 1941-47; bimonthly and final project reports of NDRC divisions, panels, and committees, 1940-47; reports of contractors, containing information on all technical scientific work of the NDRC and OSRD, 1940-47, with an index; and files of the Legal Division, 1941-47. Records of the Patent Division include correspondence relating to patent clearance of contracts, 1941-47, to inventions reported by the NDRC and the CMR, 1941-47, and to the Government radar patent program, 1942-44; and an inventors file containing the names of inventors and detailed descriptions of their inventions, 1941-47.

RECORDS OF THE NATIONAL DEFENSE RESEARCH COMMITTEE. 1940-47. 1,178 lin. ft.

Office files of civilian officials, such as Richard C. Tolman, Frank B. Jewett, and Karl T. Compton, 1940-47; and records of technical divisions, panels, and units of NDRC, including, for the Office of the Chairman of the NDRC and of the Engineering and Transition Office, general records, divisional correspondence, and blueprints and drawings of the Washington, D.C., Office, 1942-46; and general records and divisional correspondence of the California Office, 1944-45. Records of Technical Divisions 1 through 19, of Division "B," and of various panels and committees, consisting primarily of reports, office files of division officials, correspondence, contract records, and project files relating to research on ballistics and weapons performance (Divisions 1 and 2); special projectiles and rocket ordnance (Division 3); ordnance accessories, including proximity fuses (Division 4); guided missiles (Division 5); subsurface warfare, including devices for detection from aircraft and surface craft (Division 6); fire control, including development of airborne, landbased, and shipborne rangefinders, gunsights, and directors (Division 7); high explosives and propellants (Division 8); chemical warfare (Division 9); absorbents and aerosols (Division 10); chemical engineering, including development of incendiary bombs (Division 11); transportation development, including amphibious vehicles (Division 12); electrical communication, including study of direction finders and speech scrambling and decoding (Division 13); microwave radar (Division 14); radio coordination, principally the study of electronic countermeasures (Division 15); optics and techniques of camouflage (Division 16); miscellaneous problems in physics not handled by other divisions and ranging from detection of landmines to studies of the human ear (Division 17); war metallurgy (Division 18); and miscellaneous weapons, including development of instruments for sabotage and espionage (Division 19).

Also similar records of the Applied Mathematics Panel, which furnished mathematical advice to all NDRC divisions, carried out requested mathematical analyses, and acted as a consultant; the Applied Psychology Panel, which devised selection and classification tests, developed training methods, and improved the design of equipment; the Committee on Propagation, which conducted scientific investigation of the propagation of electromagnetic waves through the lower atmosphere under varying conditions; and the Tropical Deterioration Administrative Committee, which studied organisms producing tropical deterioration and its effect on textiles, optical instruments, and photographic and electrical equipment.

RECORDS OF THE COMMITTEE ON MEDICAL RESEARCH. 1940-46. 83 lin. ft.

Included are minutes of the CMR, 1941-46; office files of Hans Clarke, Chairman of the Penicillin Committee, 1943-45; contracts, contract terminations, correspondence, and other records relating to contracts, 1941-46; records, consisting primarily of minutes, reports, correspondence, and memorandums of subcommittee meetings relating to CMR administration and medical research, 1940-46; minutes and reports of the Board for the Coordination of Malarial Studies, 1943-46; and correspondence of the New York Records Section, 1944-46.

RECORDS OF THE LIAISON OFFICE. 1940-46. 128 lin. ft.

Included are reports, memorandums, and correspondence concerning exchange of information with foreign countries, the Army and Navy, and other Government agencies, and relating to operations of the Liaison Office, 1941–46; correspondence on the exchange of technical information, 1940–46; travel files containing reports, diaries, and correspondence, 1941–46; lend-lease files, consisting of correspondence, requisitions, and shipment receipts relating to radar equipment sent to Great Britain under the lend-lease program, 1942–45; records of the London Mission, consisting of reports and correspondence, a general subject file, and drafts of the history of the mission, 1941–46; and general records, including a history, relating to the commercial radar exchange agreement, 1942–45.

RECORDS OF THE OFFICE OF FIELD SERVICE. 1943–46. 29 lin. ft.

Administrative records, consisting of correspondence, memorandums, and reports relating to contracts, employment, budget and finance, and travel, 1943–46; reports by the Service, concerning various projects undertaken in the field at the request of the Army and Navy, 1943–45; manuscript histories and project summaries of the Office of Field Service, 1943–46; project files, 1943–46; correspondence relating to liaison activities, 1943–46; correspondence, reports, and memorandums of H. K. Stephenson, head of the Southwest Pacific Research Section, 1944–45; and correspondence, reports, and memorandums relating to amphibious warfare, radar, weapons, rockets, and communications in the Pacific Ocean area, 1944–45.

AUDIOVISUAL RECORDS. 1943–44. 1,703 items.

Photographs (1,500 items) relating to the development of amphibious vehicles. Motion picture films (203 reels) submitted by several divisions to illustrate reports on the development of high explosives and rocket propellants; insecticides and protective chemicals for clothing and equipment; aerosols, gas mask absorbents, filters, and smokescreens; incendiary devices and hydraulic fluids; and amphibious vehicles.

RECORDS OF THE OFFICE OF WAR INFORMATION
(RECORD GROUP 208)

The Office of War Information (OWI) was established in the Office for Emergency Management (OEM) by Executive Order 9182 of June 13, 1942, to coordinate the Government's war information program. It assumed the coordinating functions and related records of the OEM Division of Information and functions and records of the Office of Government Reports (and predecessor agencies dating from 1933), the Office of Facts and Figures, and the Office of the Coordinator of Information units concerned with foreign propaganda activities. The OWI formulated and carried out programs to disseminate information in the United States and abroad about the progress of the war and Government policies, activities, and objectives. Duties of the OWI included coordinating informational activities of other Government agencies, issuing necessary directives for accurate and consistent Government information, reviewing and approving proposed motion pictures and radio programs sponsored by Federal agencies, and maintaining liaisons between the Government and the radio and motion picture industries and United Nations (UN) information offices. Foreign propaganda activities were originally divided between the Office of Strategic Services (see RG 226) and the OWI, but the OWI was directed by an Executive order of March 9, 1943, to conduct all activities relating to U.S. propaganda abroad except in Latin America. The OWI was terminated December 31, 1945, by Executive order. OWI overseas operations were transferred to the Department of State; its domestic operations were performed by the Bureau of the Budget until December 12, 1946, when they were assigned to the reconstituted Office of Government Reports (see RG 44).

Many records of the OWI Overseas Operations Branch are still maintained by the Department of State.

There are 4,630 cubic feet of records dated between 1941 and 1948, with some dated as early as 1926, in this record group.

GENERAL RECORDS OF THE OWI. 1941-45. 84 lin. ft. (in WNRC).

Included are records of the OEM Division of Information, 1941-42, established to provide a centralized information service for constituent OEM agencies; and general and divisional records of the Office of Facts and Figures, October 1941-June 1942, created to facilitate dissemination of information to American citizens about the progress of defense policies and activities. Other records of OWI predecessors have been incorporated with records of corresponding OWI units.

Also included are minutes, reports, memorandums, and correspondence of the Office of the Director, OWI, 1942-45; minutes of the War Information Board, 1943-44; records of the Historian, including those of the Director of the Overseas Operations Branch and other materials accumulated to prepare a history of the OWI, 1941-45; and records of the Security Office and the interdepartmental Security Advisory Board, both of which coordinated practices concerning security-classified information, and of the Procedures Section of the Management Planning Division, 1942-45.

RECORDS OF THE DOMESTIC OPERATIONS BRANCH. 1933-46, with some records as early as 1926. 3,114 lin. ft. (in WNRC).

This Branch disseminated war information within the continental United States and coordinated war information programs of Federal agencies. The records—among which are many inherited from the Office of Government Reports, the Office of Facts and Figures, and the OEM Division of Information—include office files of the Office of the Director of the Branch, 1942-45; letters sent by the Executive Director, 1942-45; and records of the Office of the Assistant Director, 1942-45, relating chiefly to clearance of speeches, publications, and other issuances by Government officials. There are also records of the Office of the Director of War Programs and its predecessors, which coordinated war information programs, 1941-45.

Deputy directors of the Branch were responsible for fields of war information and maintained liaison with other agencies in those fields. There are records, 1942-45, of the Deputy Directors for Economic Stabilization, War Finance, and Taxation; Food, Gasoline, and Rationing; Military Information; Labor and Civilian Welfare; Pacific Operations; and Production and Manpower.

Branch bureaus and subordinate units were usually organized according to communication media. Records, generally dated 1941-46 but with some as early as 1926, of the following bureaus and their predecessors—Radio, News, Foreign News, Graphics, Motion Pictures, Book and Magazine, and Field Operations—relate to disseminating information by way of radio through Government-sponsored programs and spot announcements, distributing information to the press, advertising outdoors and on transportation facilities, producing and distributing motion pictures, and promoting propaganda through books and magazines. Included are minutes, administrative issuances, correspondence, memorandums, reports and survey forms, abstracts, summaries, other analyses of propaganda programs and materials, scripts for radio programs and announcements, press releases, scripts for motion pictures, film catalogs, pamphlets, booklets, other publications, and background and reference materials. There are also clippings of interest to or concerning the Government taken from several hundred newspapers throughout the country and press intelligence bulletins, which serve as daily indexes to the clippings, 1933–42; and reports and survey forms, digests, abstracts, summaries, and other analyses of propaganda programs and materials.

RECORDS OF THE OVERSEAS OPERATIONS BRANCH. 1941–46. 1,157 lin. ft. (in WNRC).

The main predecessor of this Branch was the Foreign Information Service of the Office of the Coordinator of Information. In active military zones Branch agents cooperated with military organizations in psychological warfare. The Branch established outposts in more than 20 neutral and Allied nations and provided State Department missions with materials for distribution in areas where there were no Branch representatives. Principal offices were in Washington, New York, and San Francisco; there were operating bureaus for communication facilities, intelligence, the support of field offices, and propaganda media.

There are records of the Information Liaison Office and the Office of Policy Coordination; records of the Bureau of Overseas Intelligence, including reports on Japanese morale of the Foreign Morale Analysis Division, 1944–45, central intelligence records, and information files about various foreign countries; cables, letters, and reports from OWI outposts of the Office of Communica-

tions Control, which coordinated and controlled the classification, processing, and distribution of communications; cables of the Communication Facilities Bureau, which operated a worldwide information and propaganda network; and records of the Outpost Service Bureau, chiefly relating to labeling goods shipped abroad and other special activities promoting U.S. propaganda.

The New York Office processed news and produced materials chiefly for Europeans and Africans. Records of the Office include agenda and minutes of a review board, general files, reports and other analyses, newspapers, news clippings, news stories cabled to posts, press releases, feature stories, and publications intended for overseas distribution.

The San Francisco Office, which had branches in Los Angeles and Denver, was responsible for propaganda activities in the Pacific area. Included are records of the Office of Control, 1943–45, and of other organizational units and officials. There are also intelligence reports, reports of monitored Japanese broadcasts, information files, scripts and program sheets for radio programs, and reviews and analyses of motion pictures.

AUDIOVISUAL RECORDS. 1931–48. 207,875 items.

Motion pictures (660 reels), including informational and propaganda films, 1941–45, concerning such homefront activities as farming, conservation, industry, housing, education, manpower needs, war bond drives, the roles of women and blacks in the war effort, and Japanese relocation; urging citizens to prevent inflation and to safeguard military information; illustrating benefits to the working man of the Social Security system; relating to the lend-lease program, military training, fighting fronts in all theaters, and other aspects of the conflict; depicting Allied civilians, customs, and contributions to the war effort; and illustrating the Axis conduct of the war, military strength, and ambitions. Also a film narrated in Chinese of the memorial service at Chungking for President Franklin D. Roosevelt, 1945; "United News" and other newsreels sponsored by the OWI, usually narrated in English but sometimes in Portuguese, Arabic, French, Chinese, Afrikaans, and Japanese, 1941-45; "Fox Movietone News," 1931-44; "News of the Day," 1937-43; "French Libre Actualites" (Free French newsreels) and "Indian News," made in India, 1945; "Russian News," made in Russia, 1942-45; and "War Pictorial News," produced in England, 1943.

Still pictures (206,100 items) consist of photographs, 1941-45, illustrating women's fashions, transportation, industrial and governmental roles of blacks, and other scientific, artistic, and industrial progress in the United States; Allied and Axis war prisoners, wounded soldiers, political and military leaders, and military operations, including Free French military training, supply methods, the Battle of the Bulge, the liberation of France and Italy, and the German surrender; German concentration camps; President Roosevelt's funeral; V-E and V-J Day celebrations; a Chinese translation of the UN Charter; the Statute of the International Court of Justice; and OWI overseas outposts. Photographs of the Inter-American Conference at Mexico City, 1944-45, the UN Conference on International Organization, 1945, and foreign dignitaries' postwar visits to the United States, 1945-48. Also posters, streamers, stickers, handbills, and placards promoting conservation, war bonds, increased production, and the protection of military information, 1941-45; undated watercolors, woodcuts, sketches, etchings, and photographs of architecture, portraits of prominent Americans, domestic activities, and other aspects of American culture from 1776 to 1945; photographs of illustrations published in *U.S.A., Photo*

Review, Factual History, and *Victory*, 1943-46; and a file of *Victory* magazines in English and other languages, 1943-45, and newspaper clippings, 1933-45.

Sound recordings (1,115 items), comprise recordings from radio broadcasts, 1941-46, of or concerning the war effort on the homefront; the Allies and their contributions to the war; the Axis and its conduct of the war; the defeat of Italy, Germany, and Japan; speeches of Presidents Roosevelt and Truman, Winston Churchill, and other prominent persons; relating to visits of world leaders to the United States; international conferences (including Casablanca, 1942, Dumbarton Oaks, 1944, Yalta, 1945, and the UN Conference on International Organization and Charter-signing ceremonies, 1945); the lend-lease program; U.S. aid to smaller nations; reciprocal trade agreements; International Red Cross activities; the death of President Roosevelt; atom bomb tests; the opening session of the UN General Assembly and Security Council; functions of the International Bank for Reconstruction and Development, the International Monetary Fund, the World Health Organization, the UN Relief and Rehabilitation Administration, and the UN Educational, Scientific, and Cultural Organization; and the music of many countries. Overseas broadcasts include "Uncle Sam Speaks," "Voice of Freedom," "You Can't Do Business With Hitler," "We Fight Back," and a series broadcast to the Japanese by Captain Zacharias. Domestic broadcasts include "This Is Our Enemy," "Soldiers of Production," "Three-Thirds of a Nation," "Neighborhood Call," "Hasten the Day," "Victory Front," and commercial daytime serials.

See Emma B. Haas, Anne Harris, and Thomas W. Ray, comps., *List of Photographs Made by the Office of War Information at the United Nations Conference on International Organization, San Francisco*, 1945, SL 11 (1953); and H. Stephen Helton, comp., *Preliminary Inventory of the Records of the Office of War Information*, PI 56 (1953).

SPECIFIC RESTRICTIONS

Records: Records of the Office of the Director, Office of War Information, and of the Historian, 1941-45; of the Foreign Morale Analysis Division, Bureau of Overseas Intelligence, 1944- 45; and of the Office of Control, San Francisco, 1943-45.

Restrictions: These records may be used only with the permission of the Department of State.

Specified by: Department of State.

RECORDS OF THE OFFICE OF WAR MOBILIZATION AND RECONVERSION (RECORD GROUP 250)

The Office of War Mobilization and Reconversion (OWMR) was established October 3, 1944, with an Advisory Board, as successor to the Office of War Mobilization that had been established in 1943. OWMR was to develop programs and policies for efficient use of the Nation's natural and industrial resources, for maintenance and stabilization of the civilian economy, and for adjustment of the economy to military requirements and subsequent transition to peacetime conditions; to unify Federal activity concerned with production, procurement, distribution, and transportation of supplies and materials; and to develop programs and policies essential to an orderly transition from war to peace. The OWMR was given supervisory authority over the Office of Contract Settlement (see RG 246); the Surplus War Property Administration and its successor, the Surplus Property Board (see RG 270); and the Retraining and Reemployment Administration (see RG 244). In 1946 the OWMR and its Advisory Board were transferred to the Office of Temporary Controls. The Board completed its work in February 1947, and on June 1, 1947, the OWMR was transferred to the Department of Commerce for liquidation.

See Herman Miles Somers, *Presidential Agency, the Office of War Mobilization and Reconversion* (Cambridge, 1950).

There are 189 cubic feet of records dated between 1942 and 1947 in this record group.

RECORDS OF THE OFFICE OF WAR MOBILIZATION.
May-Dec. 1943. 8 lin. ft.

These comprise a general classified file primarily of reports, memorandums, correspondence, and other records of the Office of War Mobilization and the War Mobilization Committee, May-December 1943; outgoing correspondence of Director James F. Byrnes and other staff members, May-December 1943; and minutes of the War Department Procurement Review Board, July 7-30, 1943.

RECORDS OF THE OFFICE OF WAR MOBILIZATION AND RECONVERSION. 1942-47.
174 lin. ft.

Included are a general classified file of reports, memorandums, correspondence, and other records, 1944-46; outgoing correspondence, 1944-46; and indexes to incoming correspondence, 1945-46.

Records of the Office of the Director consist of a partially indexed general classified file in two segments, May 1943-May 1945 and May 1945-December 1946, relating to coordination of war mobilization and reconversion problems and programs; a legislative file, 1945-46, concerning export and import controls, subsidies, standby plants, the Renegotiation Act, the First and Second War Power Acts, and consolidation of war agencies; and records of the Special Assistant on Procurement and Cutback Determinations and of other officials, 1945-46.

Also included are records of the Office of the Deputy Director for War Programs, including reports and working papers, 1945, records relating to manpower and employment, 1944-46, and a subject file maintained by the special assistant to the Director, including reports and correspondence on military requirements and postwar readjustment problems, 1944-45; and records of the Office of the Deputy Director for Agriculture, relating primarily to food supplies, 1942-45.

Records of the Office of the Deputy Director for Reconversion include reports and correspondence of Deputy Director Robert R. Nathan, 1945; reports and correspondence on construction problems, 1944-47, and War Production Board records relating to war housing, 1942-45, maintained by the Construction Division; a general classified file of Harold Stein of the Foreign Operations and Stockpiling Division, 1945-47; correspondence, memorandums, and other records of the Division of Manpower and Veterans Affairs, relating to manpower and employment problems, 1945-47; general records of the Reconversion Programming Division, 1945-47; and office files of Chief of the Science Division James R. Newman, 1945-46.

Records of the Office of the Deputy Director for Information and Reports include reports, correspondence, and other records, 1945-47; reports, speeches, and press releases of the Reports and General Information Division, 1945-47; and the general file of the Chief of the Media Programming Division, 1945-47.

There are also records of the Office of the Commissioner for War Mobilization and Reconversion, Office of Temporary Controls, including records of the Advisory Board comprising minutes, 1944-47, resolutions and correspond-

ence, 1945-47, and general correspondence relating to studies and surveys of the Guaranteed Wage Study, 1945-47; a general classified file and an incomplete manuscript of OWMR history, 1946-47; records of Assistant to the President John R. Steelman, including a general classified file, 1946-47; and records of the Committee on Carbon Black, the Committee to Coordinate the Export of Civilian Supplies, the Policy Committee on Rubber, and the Reconversion Working Committee, including transcripts of meetings, reports, and correspondence, ca. 1944-46.

RECORDS OF THE OFFICE OF ECONOMIC STABILIZATION. 1942-47. 61 lin. ft.

The Office of Economic Stabilization (OES) was created in the Office for Emergency Management October 3, 1942. When OES was abolished in 1945, its functions were transferred to OWMR. In 1946 OES was reestablished as a separate agency, but later in the year it became a unit under OWMR. The records include general correspondence, 1942-43; reports, correspondence, and related records concerning the stabilization program, 1942-46; correspondence on price stabilization, 1942-46, and on price control and subsidies, 1946-47; and miscellaneous correspondence, 1943-46. Also records of the Director's Office, consisting principally of the general files of Stabilization Director William H. Davis and Stabilization Administrator John C. Collet, 1945-46, and Director Chester Bowles, 1943-46; correspondence relating to decontrols, housing and building materials, food problems, and textiles and clothing, 1946; OES directives, 1944-46; and press releases and other issuances, 1942-46. There are also records of the General Counsel's

Office, consisting primarily of correspondence on stabilization policy, 1945-46, wage-price case files, 1943-46, and compliance and seizure case files, 1944-46; and minutes, correspondence, and

related records of the Board of Economic Stabilization, 1942-46.

See Homer L. Calkin, comp., *Preliminary Inventory of the Records of the Office of War Mobilization and Reconversion*, PI 25 (1951).

RECORDS OF THE
PETROLEUM ADMINISTRATION FOR WAR
(RECORD GROUP 253)

The Office of Petroleum Coordinator for National Defense (later designated "for War") was established by a Presidential letter dated May 28, 1941, to the Secretary of the Interior. An Executive order of December 2, 1942, abolished this agency and transferred its personnel, records, property, and funds to the Petroleum Administration for War (PAW), created by the same order. The Secretary of the Interior, who had been Petroleum Coordinator, served as Administrator of PAW, but it remained independent.

PAW was responsible for wartime conservation and development of petroleum products in all areas under U.S. jurisdiction and directed the petroleum industry to guarantee an adequate supply of its products for military and other essential uses. It served as claimant agency for the industry under the controlled materials plan and distributed critical materials allotted to it, recommended what amounts of petroleum products should go toward meeting military and other requirements, determined the quantity of petroleum products available for civilian use, made surveys of and recommended petroleum prices, directed the shipment and receipt of petroleum products and regulated the operation of pipelines, conducted and promoted research to produce petroleum components for synthetic rubber, and collaborated with other Federal agencies to determine policies relating to foreign petroleum activities.

In addition to its Washington headquarters, PAW had district offices in New York, Chicago, Houston, Denver, and Los Angeles. The Petroleum Industry War Council, composed of leaders from all branches of the industry, and the Foreign Operations Committee, consisting of representatives of American oil companies operating abroad, were established to advise PAW on domestic and foreign petroleum matters. The interagency Petroleum Board, Foreign Petroleum Committee, Petroleum Supply and Distribution Committee, and Petroleum Requirements Committee were created to coordinate the Government's wartime petroleum program. PAW was terminated by Executive order on May 8, 1946.

See Petroleum Administration for War, *A History of the Petroleum Administration for War, 1941-1945*, edited by John W. Frey and H. Chandler (1946).

There are 2,192 cubic feet of records dated between 1941 and 1946 in this record group.

RECORDS. 1941-46. 2,811 lin. ft.

These consist of all field and headquarters records of PAW and its predecessor, 1941-46, including reports, memorandums, and correspondence; complete sets of orders, recommendations, and directives; circulars; reports; policy correspondence, procedural data, and press releases concerning the operation and effect of PAW and War Production Board restrictions on use of petroleum and other critical materials; reports and correspondence relating to construction, maintenance, and operation of production, refining, and distribution facilities in the United States and abroad; minutes and reports prepared by or for the agency on the quantity of petroleum produced and shipped; technical reports by industry committees and research laboratories on methods of producing and refining petroleum; and materials assembled in compiling a published history of the agency.

CARTOGRAPHIC RECORDS.
1942-46. 1,135 items.

These consist of maps of areas throughout the world, showing oil pipelines and other conveying facilities, oil production volumes, and export and import volumes; and graphs comparing U.S. and world petroleum resources.

RECORDS OF THE
PHILIPPINE WAR DAMAGE COMMISSION
(RECORD GROUP 268)

The Philippine War Damage Commission was created by the Philippine Rehabilitation Act of April 30, 1946, to receive, adjudicate, and pay private and public claims for World War II property damage or destruction in the islands. The organization of the Commission, which changed with work requirements and emphasis, was composed for the greater part of its existence of three commissioners who decided claims not settled by the Board of Review, formulated policies and procedures for paying claims, and made all major decisions involving policies, procedures, appeals, and personnel. The Secretary of the Commission prepared reports and agenda for meetings and served as Chief Executive Officer of the Commission and as Chairman of the Staff Policy and Planning Committee, which recommended policies and procedures to the Commission. The Board of Review reviewed all claims and settled those not exceeding a specified amount. The Commission completed adjudicating claims on March 31, 1951, 1 month before the date provided by the act for its termination.

See *Reports* of the Philippine War Damage Commission, 1946-51.

There are 16 cubic feet of records dated between 1945 and 1951 in this record group.

RECORDS. 1945-51. 19 lin. ft.

Included are Commission minutes, 1946-51, and its official seal; records of the Secretary, consisting of agenda for Commission meetings, transcripts of conferences, correspondence with Philippine and U.S. Government agencies and with claimants, minutes of the Board of Review, and progress reports of Commission bureaus, 1946-51; records of the Office of Information, consisting of press releases, speeches, public notices and advertisements, and newspaper clippings of rehabilitated buildings, Commission buildings, and personnel, 1946-51; and the Appraisal Division's valuation handbook and tables of values for use in appraising articles for which claims were made. There are also photographs, 1945-51 (1,100 items), taken before and after reconstruction of schools, waterworks, hospitals, Government buildings, tenement houses, and the School of Art and Trade and other buildings at the Philippine University damaged by war or typhoons.

RECORDS OF THE PRICE DECONTROL BOARD
(RECORD GROUP 251)

The Price Decontrol Board was established by an act of July 25, 1946. Its functions were to determine whether price controls should be reimposed after August 20, 1946, on grain, livestock, cottonseed, soybeans, and milk and on food or feed products made from these commodities; to pass on proposals made by the Price Administrator or the Secretary of Agriculture for reimposing controls on other commodities; and to review, on appeal, petitions for decontrol of commodities denied by the Price Administrator or the Secretary of Agriculture. From August 12 to August 15 the Board held public hearings on prices of commodities specifically named in the act; on August 20 it announced its decision to reimpose all such controls except those on dairy products and grain or grain products. In November 1946 the Price Administrator decontrolled all commodities except rice and sugar, and the following month the Price Decontrol Board transferred its remaining administrative affairs and records to the Treasury Department for liquidation.

There are 9 cubic feet of records dated between 1946 and 1947 in this record group.

RECORDS. 1946-47. 11 lin. ft.

Minutes of Board meetings, September 1946-January 1947; transcripts of hearings, August 1946; briefs and statements of industry associations, State agencies, labor organizations, and other interested groups, 1946; correspondence maintained by the Board secretary, 1946; correspondence, reports, and other records relating to price control of dairy products, 1946; memorandums, reports, charts, and statistical data from other Government agencies, 1946; a file relating to commodities under consideration by the Board, 1946; and telegrams received, press releases, and a history of the Board, 1946-47.

See James J. Fleischmann and Victor Gondos, Jr., comps., *Preliminary Inventory of the Records of the Price Decontrol Board*, PI 46 (1952).

RECORDS OF THE PRISON INDUSTRIES REORGANIZATION ADMINISTRATION
(RECORD GROUP 209)

The Prison Industries Reorganization Administration, established by Executive Order 7194 of September 26, 1935, was responsible for studying industrial operations and markets for products of State and District of Columbia penal and correctional institutions, minimizing competition between such products and those of private industry, recommending loans or grants to implement the program, and administering the program once approved by the President. The Administration, assisted by an advisory board, had no administrative connection with the Federal prison system. From June 30, 1938, to September 30, 1940, when its activities ceased, the Administration operated with funds provided by the Public Works Administration.

Records about open-market competition for prison-made products are also contained in the Public Agencies Division files among records of the National Recovery Administration (see RG 9); records concerning the control of industrial operations in Federal penal and correctional institutions by the Superintendent of Prisons before 1930, by the Bureau of Prisons, 1930–34, and by the Federal Prison Industries, Inc., 1934–43, are among records of the Bureau of Prisons (see RG 129).

There are 45 cubic feet of records dated between 1935 and 1940 in this record group.

RECORDS. 1935–40. 54 lin. ft.

Included are records of advisory board member Gustav Peck, the Assistant Executive Director, the Chief Clerk, the Legal Section, and a statistician; general correspondence; statistical reports from State institutions on consumption of food, clothing, and other supplies; Library Division reference materials; drafts of reports and publications; correspondence and reports relating to road construction and farm, forestry, and industrial work for prisoners; records of a survey of District of Columbia penal institutions, including 676 case histories; and architectural blueprints of penal institutions.

RECORDS OF THE PUBLIC WORKS ADMINISTRATION
(RECORD GROUP 135)

The Public Works Administration (PWA), established originally as the Federal Emergency Administration of Public Works by the National Industrial Recovery Act of June 16, 1933, was to prepare and help construct and finance a comprehensive public works program. The agency administered a large field organization and established boards, committees, corporations, and divisions to carry out special functions. In 1939 the PWA became a part of the Federal Works Agency (see RG 162), and in 1943 PWA powers and functions were transferred for liquidation to the Office of the Federal Works Administrator.

Most of the general classified correspondence before 1941 and some divisional records were inadvertently destroyed in 1943. Extant records of PWA boards, committees, and divisions are also in the following record groups: National Planning Board and the Mississippi Valley Committee in Records of the National Resources Planning Board (RG 187); Housing Division in Records of the Public Housing Administration (RG 196); and National Power Policy Committee in Records of the Office of the Secretary of the Interior (RG 48), which also includes materials relating to allotments, appropriations, the Power

Division, the Housing Division, and Harold L. Ickes' efforts in public works. The records of the Bureau of Indian Affairs (see RG 75) include records of PWA projects sponsored by the Bureau.

See Harold L. Ickes, *Accomplishments of the Federal Emergency Administration of Public Works, 1933-36* (1936).

There are 284 cubic feet of records dated between 1933 and 1945, with some dated as late as 1948, in this record group.

GENERAL RECORDS OF THE PWA. 1933-43. 63 lin. ft.

These consist primarily of general classified files (arranged for the most part by decimal classification systems), 1933-40 and 1941-43; minutes and reports of conferences; policy and general administrative records, including administrative orders, special orders, and other procedural issuances, 1933-42; press releases, bulletins, and processed copies of speeches and public statements of Harold L. Ickes, 1934-39, in his dual role as Secretary of the Interior and Federal Emergency Administrator of Public Works; records relating to the Special Board for Public Works, 1933-35; and copies of some decisions rendered by the Board of Labor Review, 1934-36.

RECORDS OF THE PROJECTS CONTROL DIVISION. 1933-47. 108 lin. ft. and 8,856 rolls of microfilm.

The Projects Control Division established policy on priorities, handled applications, maintained project records, and prepared reports and statistics relating to Federal and non-Federal projects and resolutions affecting allotment actions. The records include administrative files of the Director and the Assistant

Director, correspondence and related material concerning reclamation and other projects, status reports on non-Federal projects, and subject files, 1933-40. There are also justification data files, "change" letters, and "transfer" letters relating to allotment and reallocation of Federal project funds, 1933-43; and publications and statistical and research material created by the Division of Economics and Statistics, which was later merged with the Projects Control Division.

Also included are microfilm copies (8,856 rolls) of docket files for non-Federal projects, 1933-47, and related indexes; and contracts, memorandums, correspondence, and related records of the Washington National Airport project, 1934-41.

RECORDS OF THE ENGINEERING DIVISION. 1935-40. 5 lin. ft.

The Engineering Division, established in 1933 to handle engineering and architectural aspects of all PWA projects, assumed the powers and functions of the Inspection Division in 1937 and remained in existence until 1942. Its records include orders and memorandums issued by the Division, correspondence and related records concerning equipment and materials used on PWA projects, and correspondence relating to non-Federal projects.

RECORDS OF THE DIVISION OF INVESTIGATION. 1933-48. 95 lin. ft. and 824 rolls of microfilm.

This Division was established by the Federal Emergency Administrator of Public Works to provide information on the manner in which agency functions were being executed. It remained in existence until 1941 when all its functions, records, equipment, and supplies (except those directly relating to personnel of the PWA) were transferred to the Federal Works Agency. Records of the Division include case files relating to personnel investigations, 1933–41; microfilm copies (824 rolls) of records relating to investigations of Federal and non-Federal PWA projects, 1933–45, and a related index; and records not microfilmed relating to eight additional investigations, 1938–48, to the investigation of the Engineering Division, 1934, and investigations in the Virgin Islands, 1934–36.

RECORDS OF THE ACCOUNTING DIVISION. 1933–41. 8 lin. ft.

The Accounting Division was established in 1934 to supervise accounting functions relating to non-Federal projects, slum clearance projects, and administrative expenditures. It was organized regionally under a supervising officer known as the district project auditor. The records include classified files, 1938–41, correspondence relating to non-Federal projects, memorandums, and procedural and miscellaneous issuances.

RECORDS OF OTHER DIVISIONS. 1933–41. 5 lin. ft.

Included are the surviving records of the Inspection Division, consisting of three series of orders; of the Legal Division, including memorandums and orders, digests of decisions affecting the Division, special legal opinions, and bulletins; and of other divisions, consisting of orders, memorandums, copies of correspondence, processed volumes, blueprints, and lists of projects.

CARTOGRAPHIC AND AUDIOVISUAL RECORDS. 1933–40. 15,505 items.

Included are maps of the United States, showing PWA project locations, 1936; the Mississippi Drainage Basin, 1934; and national forests, flood control, drainage stations, fire control, and soil conservation districts in Florida, 1940.

Audiovisual records consist of photographs (15,500 items) of complete and incomplete PWA projects in the 48 States, the District of Columbia, Alaska, Hawaii, and Puerto Rico, including a photographic report to the President entitled "Survey of the Architecture of Completed Projects of the Public Works Administration."

See L. Evans Walker, comp., *Preliminary Inventory of the Records of the Public Works Administration*, PI 125 (1960).

RECORDS OF THE RETRAINING AND REEMPLOYMENT ADMINISTRATION (RECORD GROUP 244)

The Retraining and Reemployment Administration was established February 24, 1944, in the Office of War Mobilization. The Administration was transferred to the Office of War Mobilization and Reconversion (see RG 250) in October 1944, to the Department of Labor in September 1945, and was terminated June 30, 1947. The Administration was responsible for general supervision and direction of Federal activity (except of the Veterans Administration) concerned with retraining and reemployment of persons discharged or released from the armed services or other warwork, including vocational training, resumption of interrupted education, and rehabilitation for the wounded and disabled.

There are 84 cubic feet of records (in WNRC) dated between 1944 and 1947 in this record group.

RECORDS. 1944-47. 107 lin. ft.

These include transcripts of policy board and advisory council meetings; correspondence, arranged by subject; a reading file; and bulletins, pamphlets, and catalogs issued by organizations that aided veterans.

See Thayer M. Boardman, comp., *Preliminary Inventory of the Records of the Retraining and Reemployment Administration*, PI 28 (1951).

RECORDS OF THE
SHIPBUILDING STABILIZATION COMMITTEE
(RECORD GROUP 254)

The Shipbuilding Stabilization Committee was originally established in the National Defense Advisory Commission on November 27, 1940; it was transferred to the Office of Production Management on January 7, 1941, to the War Production Board (WPB) on January 24, 1942, to the Civilian Production Administration (which succeeded the WPB in November 1945), and to the Department of Labor on November 15, 1945. Composed of representatives of labor, shipbuilding management, the Navy Department, and the Maritime Commission, the Committee's objective was to create an employment stabilization program in the shipbuilding industry to achieve maximum war production. To achieve this objective it sponsored the development of uniform voluntary agreements by Government, management, and labor specifying basic wage rates and working conditions for each of the Nation's major shipbuilding zones—Atlantic, Pacific, Gulf, and Great Lakes areas. The Committee assumed responsibility for the administration, interpretation, and enforcement of these agreements. An Executive order of October 3, 1942, which provided that wage changes could be effected only through the National War Labor Board, canceled the power of the Committee to rule on wage adjustments. The Committee, however, continued to perform all functions not inconsistent with the order and administered the zone standards agreements until after World War

II. In the fall of 1947 the organizations represented on the Committee voted unanimously to terminate the zone standards agreements. A letter of December 19, 1947, from the Secretary of Labor to leading members of the Committee announcing this decision in effect dissolved the Committee, although no formal action was taken.

There are 53 cubic feet of records dated between 1940 and 1947 in this record group.

RECORDS. 1940-47. 64 lin. ft.

The records consist of a subject-classified central file (53 lin. ft.) that covers all aspects of Committee policy, programs, operations, and organization, with an index to incoming correspondence; letters, memorandums, and telegrams sent by the Chairman, Deputy Chairman, and staff aides; general office records relating to construction programs and manpower requirements in the shipbuilding industry, stabilization policy developments, conferences, labor relations, production, working conditions in British shipyards, and Committee procedural and budgetary matters; orders, rulings, and other issuances of the National War Labor Board's Shipbuilding Commission; records of the Chairman, accumulated through his participation in other war industry stabilization activities as Chief of the WPB's Stabilization Branch and its successor, the Shipbuilding Stabilization Board, relating to wage and labor relations stabilization developments in the Douglas fir, railroad, tool and die, and Pacific coast airframe industries; and reference material consisting of published issuances of the Committee and other Federal agencies, relating to economic trends, the manpower situation, and labor conditions in war industries.

See Leo Pascal, comp., *Preliminary Inventory of the Records of the Shipbuilding Stabilization Committee*, PI 121 (1959).

RECORDS OF THE SMALLER WAR PLANTS CORPORATION (RECORD GROUP 240)

The Smaller War Plants Corporation (SWPC) was created by an act of June 11, 1942, to promote effective utilization of small businesses producing war material and essential civilian supplies. The Corporation made loans to small concerns; purchased plants, equipment, and supplies, which it sold or leased to small concerns; made procurement contracts with Government agencies and distributed them among small businesses; facilitated the settlement of contract termination claims of small contractors; and administered preferences in the disposal of surplus property to small businesses and veterans. A Board of Directors, appointed by the Chairman of the War Production Board, established policies for the Corporation and selected a Chairman, who also served as the Corporation's Executive Director (later General Manager) and also as Deputy Chairman of the War Production Board in charge of the smaller War Plants Division—a unit that provided administrative services for the Corporation until early 1943. After that date the Corporation operated as an autonomous unit having a separate administrative organization, although it reported through the Chairman of the War Production Board. An Executive order of December 27, 1945, provided for dissolution of the Corporation on January 28, 1946, and the transfer of its lending functions to the Reconstruction Finance Corporation (see RG 234), its functions in obtaining priorities on surplus property to the War Assets Corporation, and all other functions—along with its field offices—to the Department of Commerce. The functions transferred to the Department of Commerce were combined with those of the Small Business Division of the Bureau of Foreign and Domestic Commerce (see RG 151) to form the Office of Small Business. The functions transferred to the Reconstruction Finance Corporation were abolished in 1947.

There are 278 cubic feet of records dated between 1940 and 1948 in this record group.

RECORDS OF THE CENTRAL OFFICE. 1941-47. 306 lin. ft.

Included are records of the Board of Directors, consisting primarily of minutes, 1942-46, records of Clerk of the Board Marion T. Woodruff, 1943-45, records of several Board officials, 1942-46, and SWPC general files, 1943-46.

Records of the Chairman of the Board of Directors include correspondence and memorandums relating to policy and legal matters, 1943-46; correspondence and other records of Chairman Maury Maverick, 1943-46; records of Acting Chairman Albert M. Carter, 1942-45, and of Lawrence F. Arnold, 1945-46; and reports, correspondence, and memorandums of Secretary Jesse Robison, 1943–46.

Records of the Chairman and General Manager of the Corporation consist primarily of records of the Office of Special Consultants, including files of William J. Bray, 1943, Louis C. Reynolds, 1943–45, Coronado Walter Fowler, 1942–45, Luther B. Gulick, 1944–45, and others; correspondence reflecting the attitude of small businesses toward the SWPC, 1943–44; histories of the SWPC, 1945; and the general file and related records of the Office of Engineering Advisers, 1943–44. Also records of the Office of the General Counsel, including correspondence, memorandums, reports, and agenda maintained by Joseph W. Kaufman and other officials, 1944–47; and of the Office of Comptroller, including records of R. F. Nachtrieb, 1944–45. There are also records of the Office of Administrative Finance and Management, consisting of correspondence, memorandums, and reports, 1943–46; directives, forms, and other SWPC issuances, 1942–45; personnel records and investigative reports, 1942–45; Washington Office correspondence with regional offices, 1942–46; and a central file maintained by the Business Services Division, 1942–46.

Records of the Office of Reports include correspondence, memorandums, and reports of the Director's office, 1944–46; reports and other records accumulated by Director John M. Blair, 1944–46; correspondence and memorandums relating to statistical matters and reporting, 1943–45; miscellaneous reports, 1941–46; correspondence and related records of Head of the Research and Statistical Section Frank A. Hanna, 1942–43; general records of the Chief of the Planning and Research Branch, 1943–44; correspondence and statistical and narrative reports maintained by Kenneth C. Beede of the Operating Analysis Branch, 1942–46; and records relating to the submission of bimonthly reports to the President and to the Congress, 1942–46. Records of the Office of Information consist principally of correspondence, memorandums, and reports of Director Paul H. Jordan, 1945–46. Records of the Office of Reconversion include studies and correspondence of Senior Economist Siegfried S. Hirsch, relating to industrial development corporations, 1944–45; company case files documenting procurement requests for materials and related services, 1943–46; and correspondence, memorandums, and other records maintained by officials of the Agency Contract, the Labor Policy, the Surplus Property, and the Contract Settlement Divisions, 1943–46.

Records of the Loan Bureau include memorandums, reports, and time studies of Assistant Chief Loan Agent Carroll A. Gunderson, 1943–44; miscellaneous records of the Chief, 1943–45; loan management reports, correspondence, and memorandums, 1944–46; and correspondence and other records of officials of the Loan Management Division, 1943–46.

Records of the Operations Bureau consist primarily of reports and correspondence, 1943–45, and of records of the following offices and divisions: Office of the Chief of Operations, including correspondence and other records of Jesse French, 1944, M. Rea Paul, 1943–46, Kennard Weddell, 1944–46, and other Division officials, and correspondence relating to surplus property, 1945–46; Contract Division, 1943–45; Pooling Section, including case files and reports, 1942–46; Lumber Section, consisting of inspection reports of lumber mills, progress reports of field activities and other general records, 1945–46, and miscellaneous records relating to lumber activities, 1943–45; Maritime Division, including memorandums and correspondence of the Maritime Staff, 1942–45, records of Division Chief William E. Flanagan, including correspondence and reports, 1943–46, procurement and award reports and correspondence, 1943-45, and correspondence with regional offices, 1943-44; Procurement Division, including records of Acting Director Eugene F. Kinnaird, 1944-45, and correspondence, memorandums, and reports of Chief of the Army Branch George J. Hoeflich, relating to procurements from the War Department and to operations of the Branch, 1943-46; Production Service Division, consisting of files of Jacob Levin, 1943-46, and other officials, 1942-45, and miscellaneous records, 1942-45; and the Technical Advisory Service, including a subject file, 1944-45, reports on industrial problems, 1943-46, and publications, 1945.

Field Bureau records consist mainly of correspondence of the Chief, 1943-44; correspondence with field offices, 1944-45; field letters and memorandums, 1943-45; and minutes, agenda, and other general records, 1943-46.

RECORDS OF THE OFFICE OF SMALL BUSINESS. 1940-48.
15 lin. ft.

Included are reports on services rendered to small business, 1946-47; general records, 1946-48, of Publications Officer Frank C. Cross, and a speech file and other publicity material, 1940-47; miscellaneous records of John E. Saunders of the Office of the General Counsel, 1943-48; records of Acting Chief of the Finance and Tax Division Warren F. Hickernell, 1946; correspondence, memorandums, and letters of the Business Counseling Division, 1944-46; correspondence, reports, and general records of the Management Division, 1942-47; and memorandums, correspondence, and reports maintained by Maj. Carroll W. Dunning, Harry E. Pontius, and other Industrial Production Division officials, 1946-48, and Division records, 1947-48.

RECORDS OF FIELD OFFICES.
1943-46. 3 lin. ft.

Reports of the San Francisco Regional Office, 1943-44, correspondence of the Baltimore Area Office, 1944-46, and miscellaneous records of certain area and regional offices, 1943-46.

See Katherine H. Davidson, comp., *Preliminary Inventory of the Records of the Smaller War Plants Corporation*, PI 160 (1964).

RECORDS OF THE UNITED STATES MARITIME COMMISSION (RECORD GROUP 178)

The U.S. Maritime Commission was created as an independent agency by the Merchant Marine Act of June 29, 1936, to further develop and maintain a merchant marine for the promotion of U.S. commerce and defense. It was authorized to regulate U.S. ocean commerce, supervise freight and terminal facilities, and administer Government funds to construct and operate commercial ships.

The Commission was the successor agency of the U.S. Shipping Board (see RG 32) and the U.S. Shipping Board Bureau of the Department of Commerce. It also took over the property and records of the U.S. Shipping Board Emergency Fleet Corporation, known as the U.S. Shipping Board Merchant Fleet Corporation after 1927. When the War Shipping Administration was established in 1942 (see RG 248), it took over many functions of the Commission, including the operation of the merchant marine; the shipbuilding activity remained under the Commission. These functions were returned to the Commission after September 1, 1946.

The Commission was abolished on May 24, 1950, and its functions were transferred to the Department of Commerce where they were assigned to the Federal Maritime Board (see RG 358) and the Maritime Administration (see RG 357).

See Fredrick C. Lane, *Ships for Victory* (Baltimore, 1951).

There are 6,487 cubic feet of records dated between 1917 and 1950 in this record group.

GENERAL RECORDS. 1936-50. 182 lin. ft.

These consist of minutes, with exhibits and indexes, 1936-50; actions, orders, and memorandums, with indexes, of the Chairman, General Manager, and Executive Panel, 1947-50; and orders for the transfer of vessels to foreign registry, the transfer and surrender of vessel documents, and the approval of vessel charters, 1936-50. Records of Commissioners Henry A. Wiley, 1936-40, Edward C. Moran, Jr., 1937-41, John M. Carmody, 1941-46, and Howard L. Vickerey, 1942-46, relating to trade routes, subsidies, labor problems, personnel recruitment and training, and shipbuilding; and of special assistants to the commissioners, 1937-45, relating to shipbuilding, subsidies, inland waterways, and shipyard labor. Reference files of Executive Director S. Duvall Schell, 1940-46.

Records of the General Counsel's Office, 1936-48, relating to legislation, statistical data, costs of foreign labor and material, and insurance. Records of the Public Information Office, 1936-47, consisting of press releases, speeches, and correspondence concerning censorship, merchant marine casualties, Liberty ships, and accounts of incidents involving merchant vessels and personnel. Records of the Historian's Office, 1944-47, including correspondence of Fredrick C. Lane, the historian, and reports of interviews with Commission officials.

RECORDS OF THE DIVISION OF REGULATIONS. 1917-48. 311 lin. ft.

Included are a correspondence file; records relating to "conference" agreements among shipping companies in certain geographical areas and concerning rates and commodities, including inactive agreements, 1920-40 (in WNRC), and records of inactive freight-rate "conference" agreements (in WNRC); formal (in WNRC) and investigative dockets pertaining to tariffs and rebates; and periodical reports of the Division.

RECORDS OF THE DIVISION OF OPERATIONS. 1917-41. 4,242 lin. ft.

These comprise a collection of merchant ship logs and indexes (4,158 lin. ft. in WNRC), vessel movement cards, and service records of shipboard personnel relating to vessels owned or operated by the U.S. Shipping Board Merchant Fleet Corporation and the U.S. Maritime Commission.

RECORDS OF OTHER ADMINISTRATIVE UNITS. 1918-49. 3,047 lin. ft.

Included are records of the Finance Division, 1921-43, relating to contracts for construction and insurance, and reports of the Division; the East Coast Director for Construction, 1942-46; the Surplus Property Division, 1945-47, relating to the disposal of materials and facilities and the distribution of surplus materials through the Lend-Lease Act; the Production Division, 1940-47, relating to shipyard facilities, construction problems, and labor relations (in WNRC); and the Division of Research and Statistics, 1918-49, consisting of statistics of U.S. waterborne commerce and of Cargo, Mail, and Passenger Reports and Vessel Utilization Reports, or the equivalent (in WNRC), for privately owned vessels carrying non-Goverment cargoes.

CARTOGRAPHIC AND AUDIOVISUAL RECORDS. 1924-50. 203 items.

Included is a published map of the world showing ports of call, trade routes, and statistics of U.S. foreign trade, 1940.

Motion pictures, 1924-45 (75 reels), illustrating recruiting, training, and other activities of the Commission at training schools and stations, a convalescent center, and aboard sailing vessels and steamships, 1938-44; the history of the merchant marine from Revolutionary times through World War II; peacetime shipping and passenger service on the Great Lakes and at sea; rescue work; and convoy duties to and from theaters of operations in World War II. There are films showing the construction of all types of merchant vessels during World War II; showing President Franklin D. Roosevelt, Henry J. Kaiser, and others at ship launchings; and relating to the repair and renovation of ships for the Victory Fleet and to the manufacture of material for World War II. Also films of Richard E. Byrd and Clarence Chamberlin during an early airmail flight from the deck of a ship, 1928; the work of the Coast Guard in keeping shipping lanes open, 1929; and British coastal fortifications, 1940.

Sound recordings, 1941-45 (127 items), of radio broadcasts of "Information Please," "It's Maritime," "For This We Fight," "Heroes of the Merchant Marine," "Men at Sea," "Fibber McGee and Molly," "Sing Along," "Deeds Without Words," and similar programs concerning the work of the Commission and the merchant marine in the war effort. Included are dramatizations of the history of the merchant marine, including the arrival of the *Franklin* at Nagasaki, 1799, the voyage of the *Margaret* from Salem to Nagasaki in 1801, the beginning of American and Canadian shipping on the Great Lakes, and the life of Herman Melville; speeches; interviews; panel discussions; news commentaries; and award presentations. Participants in these broadcasts included President Franklin D. Roosevelt, Commission members, Carl Sandburg, Edward R. Murrow, and other prominent individuals.

SPECIFIC RESTRICTIONS

I. *Records*: Minutes of the Commission and related exhibits, 1936-50.

Restrictions: No one, other than employees of the Federal Government in their official capacity, may examine these records or be given information from them or copies of them except with the permission of both the Secretary of the Federal Maritime Commission and the Secretary of the Maritime Administration of the Department of Commerce, or their authorized representatives.

Specified by: Federal Maritime Commission and the Maritime Administration.

II. *Records*: Formal and investigative dockets, agreements, and correspondence of the Division of Regulation relating to the regulation of freight and tariff rates and other activities of the Division.

Restrictions: No one, other than employees of the Federal Government in their official capacity, may examine these records or be given information from them or copies of them except with the permission of the Secretary of the Federal Maritime Commission or his authorized representatives.

Specified by: Federal Maritime Commission.

III. *Records*: Cargo, Mail, and Passenger Reports and Vessel Utilization Reports, or the equivalent, for privately owned vessels carrying non-Government cargoes, 1918-48.

Restrictions: No one, other than employees of the Federal Government in their official capacity, may examine these records or be given information from them or copies of them except with the permission of the company filing the report, or the Chief, Division of Trade Studies, Maritime Administration, or his authorized representatives.

Specified by: Maritime Administration.

RECORDS OF THE
UNITED STATES WAR BALLOT COMMISSION
(RECORD GROUP 230)

The U.S. War Ballot Commission was created April 1, 1944, to facilitate absentee voting by members of the Armed Forces and merchant marine in wartime elections. Its members were the Secretaries of War and the Navy and the Administrator of the War Shipping Administration, and its chief functions were to furnish members of the Armed Forces with official information regarding elections, including dates and lists of candidates; prepare and issue servicemen's applications for State absentee ballots; and issue supplementary Federal war ballots for States authorizing their use. Both the Commission and authorization for supplementary Federal war ballots were terminated by an act of April 19, 1946.

See War Ballot Commission, *Report to Congress*, S. Doc. 6, 77th Cong., 1st sess. (1945).

There are 6 cubic feet of records (in WNRC) dated between 1944 and 1946 in this record group.

RECORDS. 1944-46. 7 lin. ft.

These consist of a general file, arranged by subject, including minutes, reports, correspondence, memorandums, schedules and tables, lists of candidates, sample ballot forms, and newspaper clippings; correspondence with State secretaries of state and Governors; letters sent; correspondence relating to printing and delivery of war ballots and envelopes; a mail log; and copies of State voting laws.

See Robert W. Krauskopf, comp., *Preliminary Inventory of the Records of the United States War Ballot Commission*, PI 24 (1951).

RECORDS OF THE WAR ASSETS ADMINISTRATION
(RECORD GROUP 270)

The War Assets Administration (WAA) was established in the Office for Emergency Management by Executive order on March 25, 1946. Its immediate predecessors were the Surplus Property Administration, created in 1945, and the War Assets Corporation, created in 1946. The chief WAA function was the disposal of surplus consumer, capital, and producer goods; industrial and maritime real property; and airports and aircraft located in the United States and its territories. The WAA was abolished by an act of June 30, 1949, and its functions were transferred to the newly created General Services Administration for liquidation.

There are 29 cubic feet of records dated between 1945 and 1949 in this record group.

RECORDS. 1945–49. 20 lin. ft.

These consist chiefly of operating manuals, general and special orders, administrative letters, bulletins, circulars, and memorandums.

AUDIOVISUAL RECORDS. 1946–49. 2,800 items.

Photographs illustrating WAA activities, arranged alphabetically by subject, and of real estate assets, arranged by plant contract number.

RECORDS OF THE WAR MANPOWER COMMISSION (RECORD GROUP 211)

The War Manpower Commission (WMC) was established within the Office for Emergency Management by an Executive order of April 18, 1942, which transferred to the WMC the Civil Service Commission's National Roster of Scientific and Specialized Personnel, the Office of Procurement and Assignment of the Office of Defense Health and Welfare Services, and the labor supply functions of the Labor Division of the War Production Board. Within a short period the Committee on Fair Employment Practice, the U.S. Employment Service, the Apprentice Training Service, the Training Within Industry Service, the National Youth Administration, and the Selective Service System were all transferred to the WMC. On March 6, 1943, the Review Committee on Deferment of Government Employees was established within the WMC to pass on draft deferment requests; that same year the Committee on Fair Employment Practice was replaced by an independent committee, the National Youth Administration was transferred to the Federal Security Agency for liquidation, and the Selective Service System was made a separate agency.

The WMC recruited labor for war and essential civilian industries, trained labor for jobs essential to the war effort, analyzed manpower utilization practices to increase labor efficiency, and accumulated national labor market information. The WMC worked through a headquar-

ters office, regional and State offices (which planned and supervised work), and area offices and local U.S. Employment Service offices (which handled operations). An Executive order of September 19, 1945, terminated the WMC and transferred its functions (except those of the Procurement and Assignment Service) to the U.S. Employment Service, reconstituted by a Labor Department order. The procurement and Assignment Service was attached to the Federal Security Agency.

There are 1,212 cubic feet of records dated between 1940 and 1947 in this record group.

GENERAL RECORDS OF THE COMMISSION. 1942–45. 3 lin. ft.

Representatives of the Departments of War, Navy, Agriculture, and Labor; the Federal Security Administration; War Production Board; Selective Service; and U.S. Civil Service Commission, with the Federal Security Administrator as Chairman, made up the Commission. The records consist of minutes, May 6 and 13, 1942; summary minutes of, agenda for, and documents to be considered at meetings, 1942–45; and railroad labor contracts for transportation and employment of unskilled Mexican labor, 1943–45.

RECORDS OF THE CHAIRMAN. 1942–45. 18 lin. ft.

Included are correspondence with Government agencies, unions, and the general public, 1943–45; Government officials and Members of Congress, 1942–45; and WMC regional directors, 1944. Also speeches, radio addresses, interviews, and statements of Chairman McNutt and other WMC officials, 1942–45.

RECORDS OF THE OFFICE OF THE VICE CHAIRMAN (LABOR RELATIONS). 1943–45. 7 lin. ft.

These consist chiefly of correspondence and miscellaneous publications concerning manpower requirements, women workers, job stabilization programs, reemployment of veterans, and reconversion to a peacetime economy, 1943–45.

RECORDS OF THE MANAGEMENT-LABOR POLICY COMMITTEE (MLPC). 1942–46. 35 lin. ft.

Originally consisting of 12 members equally divided between management and labor, the membership of the MLPC was changed by a reorganization in 1943 to nine, equally divided between management, labor, and agriculture. The MLPC was assisted in 1945 by an advisory committee of 10 industrialists to the management members. Management-labor committees were usually established in WMC regional and area offices.

Records of the Executive Secretary include minutes of national committee meetings and summary minutes of regional, State, and area committee meetings, with indexes, 1942–45; field unit administrative reports, 1945; national committee appeals case files, 1943–45; and motions and resolutions, reports, correspondence, employment stabilization plans, statistical issuances, and press releases, 1942–46.

Records of the Office of the Executive Assistant to Management Members and of the Office of the Executive Assistant to Labor Members consist of corre-

spondence with management members of the national and regional committees, 1943–45, and with unions, WMC regional and area directors, other Government agencies, Members of Congress, and the general public.

RECORDS OF THE WOMEN'S ADVISORY COMMITTEE. 1942–45. 11 lin. ft.

Composed of a chairman and 12 members representing labor, management, and the general public, the Committee was established on August 31, 1942. It considered major WMC policy regarding women in war industry by conducting studies and making recommendations about recruiting, training, and wages of women; employment of youth under 18 years of age; and employment in industry of women with young children.

The records include minutes and agenda for meetings, 1942–45; speeches and radio addresses by the Chairman, 1943–45; reports, statements, and news releases issued by the Committee, and issuances originating in other agencies relating to the employment of women in industry, 1942–45; and correspondence of the Chairman and the Executive Secretary, 1942–45.

RECORDS OF THE REVIEW COMMITTEE ON DEFERMENT OF GOVERNMENT EMPLOYEES. 1942–47. 65 lin. ft.

This Committee was established to centralize procedures for draft deferments of Federal employees. Deferments had been made by Department heads according to guidelines set forth by a Presidential committee until July 1942 when deferments were made on recommendations of the Civil Service Commission (CSC) to the Selective Service System and, later, to the WMC Chairman. The recommendations of the President's Committee on Deferment of Federal Employees, appointed December 15, 1942, led to the establishment of the Review Committee on Deferment of Government Employees within the WMC. The Committee was transferred to the Labor Department when the WMC was terminated in 1945 and to the Office of War Mobilization and Reconversion in 1946. After the Selective Training and Service Act of 1940 expired in March 1947, the Committee no longer made deferment rulings; its operations were discontinued in May 1947.

The records include files of the CSC Committee on Occupational Deferment, consisting of correspondence and other records submitted by Federal agencies seeking deferment of key personnel, 1942; files of the President's Committee on Deferment of Federal Employees, consisting of records used in preparing its report to the President in February 1943, and agency emergency deferment requests submitted to the President, 1942-43; and records of the Review Committee on Deferment of Government Employees, consisting of reports, memorandums, issuances, agency reports on selective service status of employees, lists of key positions, correspondence, and employee deferment case files, 1943-47.

RECORDS OF THE OFFICES OF THE DEPUTY CHAIRMAN AND THE EXECUTIVE DIRECTOR.
1942-46. 24 lin. ft.

These offices were established as separate units on May 5, 1942, consolidated on June 16, 1943, and separated again on February 5, 1945. The Deputy Chairman represented the Commission in its relations with other agencies and served on the Management-Labor Policy and Women's Advisory Committees and on the Washington Policy Group Joint Program Information Committee, established in March 1945. The Executive Director was a member of the Production Executive Committee of the War Production Board, established in December 1942. The Deputy Chairman and

Executive Director served as Chairman of the National Manpower Priorities Committee, established by the WMC Chairman in June 1944.

The records include files of the Office of the Executive Director, consisting of minutes and agenda for staff meetings and regional directors conferences, 1942-45; summary minutes, reports, correspondence, and issuances of the Production Executive Committee and its field units, 1943-45; records of the consolidated and separate Offices of the Deputy Chairman and the Executive Director, consisting of correspondence, memorandums, reports, minutes, and related materials, 1943-45; summary minutes of the National Manpower Priorities Committee and its field units, 1944-45; and records of the Office of the Deputy Chairman, consisting of correspondence with regional directors, 1943-45, and records relating to the Joint Program Information Committees, 1945.

RECORDS OF THE OFFICE OF THE VICE CHAIRMAN AND CHIEF, EXECUTIVE SERVICES.
1942-45. 1 lin. ft.

The Office reviewed new projects, maintained progress control on investigations, prepared analyses and reports, and conducted liaison with the War Department for the Chairman. The records consist of reports, correspondence, interoffice memorandums, summary minutes of staff conferences, and issuances of the WMC and other agencies, 1942-45.

RECORDS OF THE OFFICE OF THE DIRECTOR OF OPERATIONS.
1942-43. 1 lin. ft.

This Office, under the Executive Director, directed and supervised operating subdivisions, including the field establishment. Its functions were transferred in 1942 to the Office of the Executive Director and were exercised by the Deputy Executive Director. Included are summary minutes and agenda of staff meetings, June-December 1942; weekly progress reports, October-December 1942; correspondence relating to labor piracy complaints, 1942–43; and records relating to the War Production Board's Committee on Concentration of Production, of which the Director of Operations was a member, 1942–43.

RECORDS OF THE OFFICE OF THE DEPUTY EXECUTIVE DIRECTOR. 1942–45. 7 lin. ft.

The records include summary minutes of staff meetings, March-July 1944; organization and operation manuals and headquarters and field staff memorandums and instructions, 1942–45; materials relating to a survey of unemployment compensation claims, April 1944; and files of the assistant to the Deputy Executive Director, 1943–44.

RECORDS OF THE OFFICE OF THE ASSISTANT EXECUTIVE DIRECTOR FOR FIELD SERVICE. 1942–45. 16 lin. ft.

The Office of the Assistant Executive Director for Field Management, established in January 1943 (changed to Field Service late in 1943), was a combination of the functions of the Field Management Division of the U.S. Employment Service and the field duties of the WMC Director of Operations. The records include office files of assistant executive directors for field service, 1943–45; office files of the special assistant, 1942–45; reports of regional directors, 1942–45; and field service publications, 1943–45.

RECORDS OF THE OFFICE OF THE ASSISTANT EXECUTIVE DIRECTOR FOR PROGRAM DEVELOPMENT. 1942–45. 16 lin. ft.

The Assistant Executive Director for Program Development coordinated all WMC policy and program-development activities and supervised the work of the Reports and Analysis, Information, and Legal Services. The records consist of office files of the Assistant Executive Director for Program Development, 1942–45, periodic reports of regional activities, 1942–44, office files of Assistant to the Director Julius J. Joseph, 1942–43, staff memorandums, 1942–43, and files of the Planning Committee and the Planning Board, 1943–45.

RECORDS OF THE ESSENTIAL ACTIVITIES COMMITTEE. 1942–45. 14 lin. ft.

This Committee developed from the Interdepartmental Committee on Essential Activities, established in July 1942, and was attached to the Office of the Assistant Executive Director for Program Development. Committee membership during most of its existence consisted of one representative of the War, Navy, and Agriculture Departments, the WMC, the War Production Board, and the Bureau of Selective Service. The Committee reviewed and kept current lists of essential activities, essential occupations by activity, and critical occupations.

Records include summary minutes and agenda, 1942–45; memorandums to members and regional directors, 1943–45; correspondence, 1942–45; an exhibits file of materials submitted with requests for inclusion in the List of Essential Activities, 1942–45; and case files relating to applications for the designation of local trades, services, and industries as essential.

RECORDS OF THE REPORTS AND ANALYSIS SERVICE. 1939–46. 105 lin. ft.

Records of the Office of the Chief of the Service consist of a reading file, some periodical progress reports, and staff memorandums, 1941–44. Records of the Reports Division consist of statistical charts, 1943–44, and monthly operating reports prepared by WMC local, area, and State offices, 1943–45. Records of the Analysis Division include records of the Area Section, relating to war housing, 1942–44; industry labor market reports of the Industry Section, 1942–44; files of the Chief of the Special Studies Section, 1942–44, and issuances concerning employment trends and cutbacks in war industries, 1942–45; Foreign Labor Market Section source materials on foreign labor, 1939–44, and manpower reports, 1940–44; and Historical Analysis Section records collected from WMC units and other agencies, 1940–46, draft chapters of the unpublished WMC history of labor mobilization for war production, recruiting campaign records, excerpts from WMC field reports, 1944–46, and newspaper clippings and excerpts relating to manpower, 1939–42.

RECORDS OF THE INFORMATION SERVICE. 1942–45. 90 lin. ft.

Included are records of the Office of the Director, consisting of minutes, communications with regional directors, correspondence, reference files of publications relating to labor market developments, and office files of assistants to the Director; records of the News Division, consisting of WMC press releases and other issuances, with guides, and office files of a staff information specialist; records of the Program Division, consisting of office files of officials who served as managers of publicity campaigns for manpower programs or as information specialists, and collections of human interest stories and radio broadcast scripts; records of the Field Division, consisting of office files of officials and staff members, working papers relating to and copies of publicity materials distributed to field offices, reference files of publications, and instructions to and reports from regional offices; and records of the Special Serv-

ices Office, consisting of information materials submitted for clearance.

RECORDS OF THE LEGAL SERVICE. 1942–45. 36 lin. ft.

The records include a general file, 1942–45, of reports, drafts of proposed legislation, memorandums, correspondence, and publications concerning functions and operations of the Service; office files of general counsels, 1942–44; regional attorneys' monthly activity reports, 1942–45; records relating to procedural matters and special problems of several WMC agencies, 1942–45; and reference files on legislation and WMC policies, programs, procedures, and operations, 1942–45.

RECORDS OF THE ASSISTANT EXECUTIVE DIRECTOR FOR BUSINESS MANAGEMENT. 1941–45. 127 lin. ft.

The Office of the Assistant Executive Director for Business Management was established early in 1943 to recentralize WMC administrative functions, originally placed with an administrative service in the Office of the Executive Director, but dispersed in December 1942 with the appointment of a special assistant executive director for personnel management and the creation of a budget and administrative planning service. The records include files of the Office of the Director, consisting of minutes and agenda of meetings, reports, correspondence, budget estimates, job descriptions, and administrative and procedural issuances, 1944–45. Files of the Budget and Finance Service, 1941–45, consisting of correspondence, budget estimates and justifications, organization charts, and lists of position titles. Records of the Personnel Service, 1942–45, consisting of reports and correspondence of the Director. Records of the Administrative Service, consisting of WMC central files, 1942–45, arranged by year and thereunder according to a subject-numeric filing scheme, with indexes; outgoing correspondence of the WMC Chairman and WMC offices; and administrative manuals, publications, and issuances.

RECORDS OF THE BUREAU OF PLACEMENT. 1939-46. 68 lin. ft.

This Bureau, established in December 1942, included the Industrial and Agricultural Employment Division, which had absorbed most of the headquarters functions of the USES; the Minority Groups Service; the National Roster of Scientific and Specialized Personnel; and the Procurement and Assignment Service. Later, other divisions were created within the Bureau or transferred to it. In 1945 the Bureau of Placement was largely disbanded. The National Roster of Scientific and Specialized Personnel and units of the Industrial Allocation Division dealing with labor transfer and foreign workers were transferred to the Office of Operations, and the Procurement and Assignment Service and the Veterans' Employment Service became independent offices directly responsible to the WMC Executive Director. Remaining Bureau of Placement units became the Division of Employment Office Standards and Methods. When the WMC was terminated, most of the functions of the former Bureau of Placement were absorbed by the USES, which was transferred to the Department of Labor.

General records, 1943-46, include reports, correspondence, and press releases concerning Legal Service and Bureau of Placement appraisals of State and regional office employment stabilization plans, 1943-45; records concerning employment of prisoners of war, 1944-46; publications of the National Roster of Scientific and Specialized Personnel, describing specialized work in various professions; workbooks, discussion outlines, and instructors guidebooks issued by the USES and the Bureau of Placement; and letters sent by the Director of the Bureau. Records of the Employment Office Service Division, formerly the Industrial and Agricultural Employment Division, include USES instructional bulletins for administering and operating field offices, 1942-43; and office files of the Chief of the Field Service, Ohio State Employment Service, 1939-42.

Records of the Industrial Allocation Division (43 lin. ft.) include a general file of minutes and agenda of meetings, reports, correspondence, and publications relating to the organization and functions of the Division, 1943-45; records of the Office of the Chief, relating to the manpower situation in certain industries and companies, 1943-45; records of the Industry Section, consisting of office files of several staff members who served as industrial employment specialists, 1943-45; files relating to manpower and production in the steel, 1944-45, forge and foundry, 1943-45, mining, 1943-45, and cotton textile, 1943-45, industries; office files of the Foreign Labor Section representative in Mexico, 1943-46; Recruitment and Transportation Section correspondence, reports, and other records concerning the transportation of foreign workers, labor recruitment efforts for railroads and shipyards, and interregional labor recruitment, 1944-45; and copies of USES form "Request for Clearance" submitted to local USES offices by employers, 1941-43.

Records of the Rural Industries Division (19 lin. ft.) include office files of the Chief of the USES Farm Placement Service, 1940-43; general records of the USES Farm Placement Service, 1939-43, consisting of agricultural reports of State USES offices, reports and studies prepared by the Agricultural Extension Service, correspondence, reports on field trips, agenda for meetings, and summaries of conference proceedings; and farm labor market reports, 1941-43.

RECORDS OF THE PROCUREMENT AND ASSIGNMENT SERVICE. 1941–46. 76 lin. ft.

This Service, established in the Office of Defense Health and Welfare in 1941, was transferred to the WMC on April 18, 1942. The directing board helped develop policies and programs for recruiting physicians, dentists, veterinarians, sanitary engineers, and nurses for the Armed Forces; allocating such personnel for the civilian population; and appraising such personnel for proper placement. When the WMC was terminated the Service was transferred to the Federal Security Agency, where it continued until 1946. The records include minutes and agenda of meetings and conferences, 1941–46; reports, correspondence, budget estimates, press releases, and lists of Medical Corps appointments, 1941–46; field correspondence, 1942–46, and reports, 1944–45; processed forms, form letters, directives, and instructions used by the Service, and statistical data relating to the training, recruitment, and classification of nurses, 1944–45; a card index to members in State and local committees and files of the Executive Officer, 1942–45; and records of the Field Service Section, 1942–45.

RECORDS OF THE BUREAU OF MANPOWER UTILIZATION. 1936–45. 21 lin. ft.

This Bureau was established in January 1943 to develop programs and policies for maximum use of manpower by industry, agriculture, and the Government. Included are records of the Office of the Director, 1942–45, consisting of minutes of meetings; reports; correspondence; newspaper clippings; press releases; copies of congressional bills and acts; issuances of the Bureau, the WMC, and other Government agencies; and records relating to conferences and meetings. Records of the Industrial Division (formerly Division of Industrial Consultants), 1943–45, consist of manpower utilization survey reports on companies having Government war contracts, and instructions to regional manpower directors. Records of the Division of Occupational Analysis and Manning Tables (formerly a part of USES), 1936–45, include publications and issuances containing interviewing aids, job descriptions, industry manning tables, and job analysis manuals. Records of the Industry Associations Committee (formerly Special Industrial Division), 1943–45, consist of minutes, reports, correspondence, manpower utilization case histories, and press releases relating to the Bureau's contacts with trade associations.

RECORDS OF THE BUREAU OF TRAINING. 1939–45. 123 lin. ft.

Established in November 1942 to consolidate and coordinate WMC training functions with those transferred from the Federal Security Agency under an Executive order of September 17, 1942, the Bureau included the National Youth Administration, the Apprentice Training Service, the Training Within Industry Service, and the defense training units of the Office of Education. The Bureau developed procedures and standards and assisted field offices in training matters.

Records of the Office of the Director include records of the Office of the Director of Defense Training, Federal Security Agency, relating to defense training courses, 1941–42; letters sent relating mainly to surveys of occupational and training needs and training projects in operation, 1942–43; and issuances and publications, 1943–45, prepared by the Bureau of Training and its constituent and affiliated agencies. Records of the Professional and Technical Training Division include a fragmentary file of correspondence, memorandums, and reports on problems of youth and defense training, and war emergency training facilities and services, 1939-43; the *Handbook of Operations* issued by the Bureau of Training on April 30, 1943, containing organization charts, copies of Executive orders, statements of functions and relationships, position descriptions, and copies of instructional and procedural memorandums; and miscellaneous issuances, 1940-43, relating mainly to training for war production and to occupation classification.

The Training Within Industry Service was established in August 1940 under the Advisory Commission to the Council of National Defense. It was later transferred to the Labor Division of the Office of Production Management (OPM) and to the War Production Board. In April 1942 it was transferred to the Federal Security Agency and in the following September to the WMC. The records (119 lin. ft.) comprise a subject-classified general file relating to the policies, organizations, and procedures of the Service, 1940-45; outgoing correspondence, 1942-43; files relating to field office organization and operations, 1940-45; records of the principal training specialist, 1941-45; and files of the Office of the Director, 1940-45. Files of the Office of the Associate Director, 1940-45, consist of records used to prepare the final report of the Service, *The Training Within Industry Report*; records documenting the training programs developed by the Service, including job instruction, methods, and relations programs; supervisory selection bulletins; the Red Cross home nursing course; records relating to meetings and conferences, 1940-45; information exchanges with foreign governments, organizations, and individuals, relating to training programs, 1941-45; policy and procedural issuances to headquarters and field offices, 1941-45; publications, 1941-45; and speeches, articles, radio scripts, and other publicity material, 1940-45. The records of the Service also include assistant directors' general

correspondence, program development reports, and records relating to the OPM Labor Supply Committee, 1941-45; correspondence of the Office of Labor Consultant, 1941-45; and Administrative Service budget estimates and justifications, records relating to "without compensation" personnel, and job descriptions, 1942-45.

RECORDS OF REGIONAL OFFICES. 1942-45. 543 lin. ft. (including 102 lin. ft. of records for WMC Region VII in FRC Atlanta).

Twelve WMC regional offices were established in July 1942, and a territorial office was established later in Honolulu. Each office was headed by a regional manpower director appointed by the WMC Chairman. Supervised successively by the Director of Operations, the Executive Director, and the Deputy Executive Director, the regional manpower directors coordinated all WMC activities in the field. Basic operations were the responsibilities, respectively, of the Placement, Manpower Utilization, and Training Divisions. The staff services were the counterpart of headquarters services. Typical regional records, 1942-45, include regional and State office publications and issuances; regional central files, consisting of agenda and minutes of meetings of State and area directors, of regional and State office staffs, of interagency conferences at regional or State levels, and of joint meetings of WMC manpower priorities committees and War Production Board production urgency committees; progress reports submitted by regional directors to the Executive Director and by the regional office division heads to the regional directors; reports, divisional correspondence and subject files, organizational materials consisting of handbooks and manuals, administrative and procedural issuances, lists of positions, and organization charts; records relating to "essential" and "locally needed" activities, to housing contruction, and to applications for civilian-type production; reports, tabulations, and compilations pertaining to the labor market; appeal case records arising from employment stabilization programs; press releases, speeches, newspaper clippings, and radio scripts; training material for regional and State office staffs; State office field supervisors' narrative monthly and annual reports analyzing the operations of local USES offices; records relating to agricultural labor and rural industry; manpower utilization surveys and case histories; and records relating to manning tables and to WMC training programs.

RECORDS OF THE WAR PRODUCTION BOARD
(RECORD GROUP 179)

The War Production Board (WPB) was established in the Office for Emergency Management by an Executive order of January 16, 1942, which transferred to it the functions of the Supply Priorities and Allocations Board and the Office of Production Management (both established in 1941). Certain units of the Advisory Commission to the Council of National Defense had been transferred to the Office of Production Management in 1941. The function of the WPB was to exercise general direction over the war procurement and production programs of all Federal departments and agencies. The WPB was terminated November 3, 1945, and its remaining functions and powers were transferred to the Civilian Production Administration (CPA), which, in turn, was consolidated with other agencies in 1946 to form the Office of Temporary Controls. An Executive order of April 23, 1947, provided for the termination of the Office and transferred the functions of the former CPA to the Department of Commerce for liquidation.

There are 1,750 cubic feet of records dated between 1940 and 1947 in this record group.

RECORDS OF THE WAR PRODUCTION BOARD. 1940-47. 1,640 lin. ft.

These consist of minutes of the Advisory Commission to the Council of National Defense, 1940-41, the Emergency Facilities Committee of the Advisory Commission to the Council of National Defense, 1940-41, the Supply Priorities and Allocations Board, 1941-42, the Council of the Office of Production Management, 1941-42, the War Production Board, 1942-45, the WPB Planning Committee, 1942-43, the Production Executive Committee, 1943-44, the Requirements Committee, 1942-45, the Committee on Conservation in Construction, 1943-44, and the CPA Priorities Policy Committee, 1946-47. Also a "policy documentation file," comprising selected records from the files of organizational units of the WPB and its predecessor and successor agencies, brought together to document the growth and development of policies, functions, and administration of agencies responsible for controlling scarce and critical materials and commodities and for mobilizing national industrial resources for war. A subject index accompanies the file. There are also a "select document file" of records selected from units of the CPA and its predecessor agencies for inclusion in the "policy documentation file," but not interfiled when the CPA was discontinued; a "related materials file" or "mobilization planning file" relating to the mobilization of industry during the war, with subject indexes; and files of the Office of Industry Advisory Committees, 1942-47. Also included are orders and regulations, 1941–47; reports, special studies, and reference files; applications for certificates of necessity, nonreimbursement, and protection; records of the WPB Appeals Board, 1942–47, including case files and summary card records; correspondence of the Office of General Counsel, 1941–46; WPB manpower survey reports and budget estimates, 1943–44; an office procedures file, 1942–46; records regarding protection of defense plants and railroad bridges and tunnels, 1942–47; and press releases, 1940–47.

RECORDS OF THE COMBINED RAW MATERIALS BOARD. 1942–46. 158 lin. ft.

Following the attack on Pearl Harbor, meetings were held between interested agencies of the United Kingdom and the United States concerned with coordinating control of raw materials at the international level, and a joint public statement of January 26, 1942, announced the creation of the Combined Raw Materials Board (CRMB). The CRMB was to plan the best and fastest method of developing, expanding, and using raw materials controlled by the two countries; formulate plans and make recommendations to their respective agencies; and collaborate with other United Nations members to ensure effective deployment of raw materials. The CRMB held its final meeting in December 1945.

The records consist of minutes, decisions and recommendations, reports, general correspondence, cables, and publications; agenda, minutes, and decisions of the Advisory Operating Committee and the Committee on Fertilizer, 1942–45; records of the Office of the Executive Secretary relating chiefly to liberated areas, 1942–45; and correspondence of staff officers and analysts, 1942–46.

RECORDS OF THE COMBINED PRODUCTION AND RESOURCES BOARD. 1942–47. 221 lin. ft.

The Combined Production and Resources Board (CPRB) was established in June 1942 by a memorandum dated June 9, 1942, from President Roosevelt to Donald Nelson of the WPB "to complete the organization for the most effective use of the combined resources of the United States and the United Kingdom for the prosecution of the War." The United States and the United Kingdom were represented on the CPRB by the Chairman of the WPB and the Minister of Production, respectively.

On November 10, 1942, by agreement of President Roosevelt and the Prime Ministers of Great Britain and Canada, the CPRB was expanded to include a Canadian member. India and France became members of the CPRB Textile Committee, but did not have representation on the CPRB itself; the U.S.S.R. was never included. The CPRB was terminated December 31, 1945, and five international committees were constituted to allocate commodities still in short supply. These committees, which became operative January 1, 1946, were the Combined Rubber Committee, the Combined Coal Committee, the Combined Textile Committee, the Combined Tin Committee, and the Combined Hides, Skins, and Leather Committee.

The records consist of agenda for meetings, minutes, directives, issuances, general correspondence, and a master file of cables received and sent, 1942–45; records relating to the allocation of materials to liberated areas and to programs conducted by the Combined Civil Affairs Committee and the United Nations Relief and Rehabilitation Administration, 1944–45; and records of the Executive Officer, 1944–45, the CPRB Registry, 1942–45, the statistical officer, 1943–45, the public relations officer, 1944–45, the director of research and statistics, 1943–45, and the Office of the

Special Assistant, 1942–45. Also included are minutes, agenda, and other records of committee meetings, 1942–45; and the final report, minutes, and correspondence of the Conference on the Unification of Engineering Standards, 1943–45. Other records include general correspondence of the office of William L. Batt, U.S. deputy member of the CPRB, 1940–46; and records of the postwar international commodity committees, 1945–47.

CARTOGRAPHIC AND AUDIOVISUAL RECORDS. 1940–45. 1,740 items.

Maps (2 items) of the United States, overprinted to show locations of munitions plants, June and October 1941; and a map of the United States, showing regional boundaries of the WPB, 1942.

Pictorial records, 1942–45 (1,602 items), consist of original posters used in production drives initiated by the WPB, and lantern slides used in training staff members and industrial employees engaged in war production.

Motion pictures, 1940–44 (15 reels), produced to stimulate war production,

and showing military action in several theaters, Allied and Axis military and political leaders, and the manufacture, transportation, repair, and destruction of war materiel. There are also films showing good telephone manners.

Sound recordings, 1942–45 (120 items), of radio broadcasts, consisting of dramatizations, speeches, interviews, and entertainment featuring, among others, Eleanor Roosevelt, Donald M. Nelson, Joseph C. Grew, Frank Knox, Leon Henderson, and a number of writers, actors, and actresses. Included are broadcasts of "Men, Machines and Victory," "You Can't Do Business With Hitler," and "Fibber McGee and Molly." There are also records used in training mail and messenger service personnel, secretaries, and switchboard operators.

Microfilm Publications: *Press Releases of the Advisory Commission to the Council of National Defense, June 3, 1940-January 15, 1941*, M185, 1 roll, DP; *Progress Reports of the Advisory Commission to the Council of National Defense, July 24, 1940-May 28, 1941*, M186, 1 roll, DP; and *Numbered Document File of the Advisory Commission to the Council of National Defense, 1940-1941*, M187, 2 rolls, DP.

RECORDS OF THE WAR RELOCATION AUTHORITY
(RECORD GROUP 210)

The War Relocation Authority (WRA) was established in the Office for Emergency Management by Executive Order 9102 of March 18, 1942, to provide for the removal, relocation, maintenance, and supervision of persons excluded from strategic military zones. Initial assembling of evacuees had been undertaken by the Wartime Civil Control Administration (WCCA), organized March 11, 1942, by the Army's Western Defense Command. Although the primary function of the WRA was to assist persons of Japanese ancestry who had been evacuated from the west coast by

military order, the agency was also responsible for the relocation of other persons, particularly German and Italian aliens excluded from sensitive military areas. Approximately 110,000 persons of Japanese ancestry were resettled in 10 relocation centers, where a variety of economic activities for self-support were maintained. Regional offices provided field supervision in establishing, staffing, and supplying the relocation centers, and district offices aided evacuees who worked or resided outside relocation centers. The WRA was transferred in February 1944 to the Department of the Interior. In June 1944 the President directed the WRA to operate, under policies formulated by the War Refugee Board (WRB), a shelter at Fort Ontario, Oswego, N.Y., for European refugees. In June 1945 responsibility for administration of the refugee shelter was transferred to the Interior Department. In December 1944 the west coast general exclusion order was revoked, and the Supreme Court ruled certain of the detention features of the relocation program unconstitutional. Thereafter the WRA largely engaged in the resettlement of evacuees. The agency was terminated by Executive Order 9742 of June 25, 1946, and responsibility for the liquidation of its affairs was assigned to the War Agency Liquidation Unit of the Department of the Interior.

There are 2,990 cubic feet of records dated between 1941 and 1947 in this record group.

HEADQUARTERS RECORDS.
1941-47. 3,458 lin. ft.

WRA headquarters comprised the offices of the Director and the Solicitor, and the Administrative Management, Reports, Relocation Planning, Relocation, Operations, Community Management, and War Refugee Divisions. The records consist of general and topical final reports, 1946; and basic documentation material, 1941-46 (from the files of headquarters divisions and field units), including minutes, reports, correspondence, memorandums, surveys, statistical materials, administrative and informational issuances, budgetary materials, forms, radio scripts, newspaper clippings, and histories. They relate to resettlement of evacuees; attitudes of evacuees, refugees, and the general public to WRA installations and programs; the establishment and operation of field units and offices; and activities and conditions in assembly centers (operated by the WCCA), relocation centers, area relocation offices, and the Fort Ontario emergency refugee shelter. There are

also serial sets of WRA issuances, 1942-45, and nonserial WRA issuances, 1942-46; reference files of issuances of other agencies of the Federal Government, State and local governments, and private institutions, organizations, and individuals, 1942-46; magazine articles, with indexes, 1942-46; newsletters relating to Japanese-American evacuees, 1942-46; and Japanese-American newspapers, 1942-47.

General files consist of subject-classified files relating to WRA organization, functions, policies, procedures, and operations, 1942-46. Evacuee and "excludee" case files, 1942-46 (in WNRC), include personal history, health, property, occupation, leave, and school records, and related correspondence from files of field offices, relocation centers, and the Statistics Section of the Relocation Planning Division; IBM punch cards ("locator index"), 1942-46, of summary personal data about individual evacuees; an index, 1942-46, with data about evacuees under WRA jurisdiction who were confined to institutions; lists of evacuees transferred from or assigned to the Tule Lake segregation center, 1943-44; and individual exclusion case files, 1942-45, containing personal history data, material documenting property disposition and WRA assistance grants, copies of exclusion orders and notices of suspension of such orders, and related administrative reports and correspondence about persons other than those of Japanese descent excluded from military areas.

Other records include statistical reports on the population of relocation centers and the refugee shelter, 1942-46; the WRA administrative manual stating policies and procedures for WRA activities, with an index to revisions; supplementary handbooks; operations and administrative forms used by WRA; headquarters account control ledgers, 1943-46; and job descriptions of WRA headquarters and field positions, 1942-46.

FIELD RECORDS. 1942-46.
344 lin. ft.

Records of regional and field assistant directors' offices, San Francisco, consist of subject-classified general files and a file of outgoing correspondence, 1942, subject-classified general files of the field assistant director, 1942-46, and press digests, April-December 1942 and July 1944-January 1946.

Records of the Evacuee Property Division consist of subject-classified general files, 1942-45; inventory cards containing such information about evacuee-owned real property as type of use, identification of legal owner, location, size, structures, assessed value, and legal description; and inventories of property confiscated from evacuees and stored by WRA, 1944.

Records of relocation offices, 1943-46, comprise subject-classified general files, consolidated after WRA's termination.

Records of relocation centers consist of subject-classified general files for each of the 10 centers, 1942-46, cards for evacuees containing data about members of family units, 1942-46, final accountability rosters of evacuees, 1944-46, internal security case reports with related indexes, 1942-46, drawings and specifications, 1942-44, and fixed property inventories, 1942-47.

Records of the emergency refugee shelter, Fort Ontario, Oswego, N.Y., consist of subject-classified general files, 1944-46; and refugee case files, 1944-46, including, for individual refugees, applications for admission to the shelter, identification charts, photographs, biographical data, social case studies, health reports and employment data with related correspondence, interrogation reports, and supplementary information.

RECORDS OF OTHER AGENCIES.
1942-47. 2 lin. ft. and 60 rolls of microfilm.

Records of the Wartime Civil Control Administration consist of microfilm copies of voluntary evacuee change-of-residence cards, 1942; a master index of evacuees, containing personal data about individuals, 1942-43; social data registration forms, summary tabulations, and vital statistics, 1942; and photostatic copies of WCCA-WRA lists of persons transferred from assembly centers to relocation centers, 1942. Records of the War Refugee Board include correspondence, reports, statements, Executive orders, and publicity material documenting the origin of the program for establishment of emergency refugee shelters in the United States and the policies governing the Fort Ontario shelter, 1944-45. Records of the War Agency Liquidation Unit of the Interior Department consist of files relating to a study of the resettlement of evacuees and office files of the director of the study, 1946-47.

AUDIOVISUAL RECORDS. 1942-45.
12,632 items.

There are photographs (12,600 items) of Japanese property before evacuation; WRA evacuation activities; housing, vocation, education, and recreation facilities at relocation centers; and the emergency refugee shelter for displaced Europeans at Fort Ontario, Oswego, N.Y. There are also motion pictures (4 reels) of WRA activities and the training and accomplishments of nisei soldiers in World War II, and sound recordings (28 items) of radio broadcasts concerning WRA activities and accomplishments of nisei soldiers.

See Estelle Rebec and Martin Rogin, comps., *Preliminary Inventory of the Records of the War Relocation Authority*, PI 77 (1955).

RECORDS OF THE WAR SHIPPING ADMINISTRATION
(RECORD GROUP 248)

The War Shipping Administration (WSA) was established in the Office for Emergency Management by Executive Order 9054 of February 7, 1942, to cooperate with other Government agencies in ensuring the most effective utilization of U.S. shipping. The personnel, records, and duties of the U.S. Maritime Commission relating to purchase, charter, requisition, insurance, maintenance, operation, and use of U.S. ocean vessels (except those of the Navy, Army, Coast Guard, and Office of Defense Transportation) were transferred to the Administration. On July 11, 1942, duties regarding the training of officers and crews for the merchant fleet, which had been transferred from the Commission to the Coast Guard in February 1942, were also transferred to the WSA. The Administration was terminated, and its functions and records were transferred to the Commission by an act of July 8, 1946 (effective September 1, 1946).

There are 280 cubic feet of records dated between 1941 and 1950 in this record group.

RECORDS OF THE OFFICE OF THE ADMINISTRATOR. 1941–47.
60 lin. ft.

Included are "actions" of the Administrator, consisting of administrative and operative issuances, supporting correspondence, drafts of regulations and charters, and exhibits, 1942–46, with indexes and summaries; records of Coordinator of Ship Defense Installations Vice Adm. A. P. Fairfield, containing reports, correspondence, memorandums, and other materials about the arming of merchant vessels, the Admiral's activities as Chairman of the Merchant Marine Medal Awards Committee, and the development of antisubmarine, antitorpedo, antimine, and antiaircraft devices, 1941–47.

RECORDS OF THE OFFICE OF THE DEPUTY ADMINISTRATOR FOR VESSEL UTILIZATION, PLANNING, AND POLICIES.
1941–46. 233 lin. ft.

This Office directed the use and operation of all merchant vessels under WSA jurisdiction. The records include reports, correspondence, memorandums, and statistical studies of Deputy Administrators Lewis W. Douglas, 1942–44, and Granville Conway, 1944–46, and of special or executive assistants to the Deputy Administrator, including Fred Searls, 1942–43, George Talmage, Jr., 1942–43, Maxwell Brandwen, 1942–44, Frank J. Mahoney, 1944–45, and Julius J. Rosenberg, 1945–46.

"Documents" of the Combined Shipping Adjustment Board, consisting of statistical and information studies prepared for the Board by the WSA and the British Ministry of War Transport, 1942–43.

Records of the Office of the Assistant Deputy Administrator for Ship Control include records of the Division of Allocations and Assignments, relating to coordination of vessel movements, port facilities, and cargo requirements, 1941–46; monthly shipping summaries produced by the Division of Statistics and Research, 1944–46; correspondence of the Division of Ship Requirements, with minutes of board and committee meetings and Office of Naval Intelligence reports about ship and cargo requirements, 1942–45; and records of the Division of Cargo Requirements, consisting of correspondence of Director C. C. Abbott and reports and statistical studies of commodity requirements used as a basis for vessel assignments, 1942–43.

Records of the Office of the Assistant Deputy Administrator for Ship Operations, 1941–46, consist of files of the Division of Traffic, relating to the Persian Gulf shipping area; records of the Division of Foreign Charters and Ship Warrants, which include materials about the issuance of ship warrants and the administration of the Ship Warrants Act; and files of Director John W. Mann, relating to the Rates Appeals Committee and the Ship Warrants Subcommittee of the United Maritime Authority Planning Committee.

Records of the Office for the Russian Shipping Area, relating to development of Soviet and East European shipping programs, 1941–46.

RECORDS OF THE DEPUTY ADMINISTRATOR FOR LABOR RELATIONS, MANNING, TRAINING, AND RECRUITMENT. 1941–50. 2 lin. ft.

These consist of decisions and memorandums of the Maritime War Emergency Board on maritime labor disputes concerning hazardous duty, 1941–50, and minutes of the Executive Committee of the United Seamen's Service, Inc., created by the WSA to provide merchant marine personnel with recreational, medical, educational, religious, and personal services, 1942–44.

RECORDS OF THE MARITIME WAR EMERGENCY BOARD. 1942–50. 2 lin. in.

The Maritime War Emergency Board, which was appointed by the President on December 19, 1941, regulated war risk insurance on maritime personnel,

their bonuses for voyages in dangerous areas, their bonuses and wages when their vessels were captured or lost, and their reimbursement for loss of personal effects. The agency was formally abolished September 1, 1950.

The records consist of two bound volumes: *Maritime War Emergency Board Decisions, Clarifications, and Amendments* (Vol. 1) (1942-50), and *Maritime War Emergency Board Weekly Bulletins 1-50* (Vol. 2) (1942-45). (These evidently were bound by WSA as consecutive volumes.) Attached to the former are single copies of two publications, *Questions and Answers on the Second Seamen's War Risk Policy As Amended* (issued by the WSA and the MWEB, n.d.) and *Crew War Risk Insurance (World War II and After)* (issued by the Maritime Administration, 1957).

See Allen M. Ross, comp., *Preliminary Inventory of the Records of the War Shipping Administration,* PI 30 (1951).

SPECIFIC RESTRICTIONS
Records: Maritime War Emergency Board Decisions, Clarifications, and Amendments, 1942-50, and Maritime War Emergency Board Weekly Bulletins, 1942-45.
Restrictions: These records may not be examined by or copies of or information from them furnished to any person except by permission of the Maritime Administration.

Specified by: Maritime Administration.

RECORDS OF THE WORK PROJECTS ADMINISTRATION (RECORD GROUP 69)

The Work Projects Administration (known as the Works Progress Administration until July 1, 1939) was established May 6, 1935, with responsibility for the Government's work-relief program. It succeeded the Federal Emer-

gency Relief Administration (FERA) and the Civil Works Administration (CWA), both established in 1933. On July 1, 1939, the WPA was made part of the Federal Works Agency (see RG 162) and the National Youth Administration was separated from the WPA and placed in the Federal Security Agency (see RG 119). When the WPA was officially abolished June 30, 1943, the Division for Liquidation of the Work Projects Administration was set up in the Federal Works Agency and functioned until June 30, 1944.

The WPA operated at four organizational levels—the central administration at Washington, regional offices, State administrations, and district offices. Except for certain federally sponsored projects, State and local governments helped finance and supervise WPA work projects. Because of the close administrative and chronological relationship between the three Federal relief agencies and because of numerous changes in their organization, some of the records described below are interrelated and overlapping.

See Edward A. Williams, *Federal Aid for Relief* (New York, 1939); A. W. MacMahon, J. D. Millett, and Gladys Ogden, *The Administration of Federal Work Relief* (Chicago, 1941); and Donald S. Howard, *The WPA and Federal Relief Policy* (New York, 1943).

There are 4,637 cubic feet of records dated between 1933 and 1945 in this record group.

CENTRAL FILES OF CWA, FERA, AND WPA. 1933-44. 1,576 lin. ft.

These are organized similarly into "State" and "general subject" series. Administrative reports and correspondence relating to a program within a single State or territory are filed under the name of that State or territory and thereunder according to a subject classification. Correspondence relating to operation of the relief program as a whole or in more than one State is filed by subject in the "general subject" series.

CWA central files, 1933-34, include general correspondence concerning appeals for employment, commendations, demolition and housing projects, employment of blacks, program policy,

and rules and regulations; and correspondence with various Federal departments, agencies, and private organizations. Correspondence for each State or territory is filed under six general headings.

FERA central files, 1933-36, include the "old general subject" series relating to the FERA program, 1933-35; the "new general subject" series (a decimal classification plan adopted in 1935, which included most "old general subject" classifications and some additional ones, among them the Florida hurricane disaster of 1935); and some separately filed records relating to the history of the Federal relief program, 1935. Also included is correspondence with State administrators, maintained as a continuous "State" series from March 1933. When the decimal classification scheme was adopted in 1935, most of the earlier records were interfiled with the later classified "State" correspondence. Minutes of State relief agencies and inquiries concerning chattel mortgages and rural relief, found only in the earlier material, are filed at the end of the classified files for each State or territory.

WPA central files, 1935-44, were organized according to a decimal classification plan. Since this same plan was used by the Federal Works Agency Division for the Liquidation of the WPA, its central files constitute part of the WPA central files. These files document all WPA functions and contain material relevant to divisional records. In general, records in the "general subject" series reflect the attitude of the Washington office staff on the type of project or program, while records in the "State" series relate to specific projects. Filed separately are final State reports of the women's, professional, and service projects that were removed from the "State" series; final narrative reports on the operation and accomplishments of the overall WPA program in each State; and a selection from the former "index" to the WPA central files, 1935-38, consisting of extra copies of letters sent to certain prominent individuals, agencies, and organizations.

MICROFILM COPIES OF CENTRAL OFFICE AND STATE FERA, CWA, AND WPA RECORDS. 1933-45. ca. 15,980 rolls.

Included are project files, statistical data, financial and accounting records, Presidential letters, and miscellaneous records of various offices and divisions, with card indexes to some project files and miscellaneous indexes to central office and State files. Also included are records relating to the WPA scrap collection program, 1940-43; copyright records of Federal Writers' Project publications, 1935-40, and correspondence concerning royalty payments on the publication *A Guide to Alaska, Last American Frontier*, 1939-45; records relating to the allocation of WPA works of art, 1937-43; reports on the emergency education program, 1933-37, and the college student aid program, 1934-35; and statistical reports and correspondence on the rural rehabilitation program, 1934-37, and certain rural rehabilitation colonies, 1933-40, including the Matanuska Valley colony in Alaska, 1935-39.

RECORDS OF THE FERA DIVISION OF SELF-HELP COOPERATIVES. 1933-37. 46 lin. ft.

The Federal Emergency Relief Act of 1933 attempted to aid cooperatives by authorizing grants to States to facilitate the "barter of goods and services." The records of the Division consist of monthly progress, financial, and field reports; correspondence; and records about cooperatives. This Division maintained all its records apart from the central files.

RECORDS OF THE FERA TRANSIENT DIVISION. 1933-36. 27 lin. ft.

The Transient Division was established to supervise grants to States for the relief of indigent persons who could not qualify under State laws requiring that only residents could be recipients of relief. Most of the administrative correspondence of the Division was placed in the central files. The separately maintained records consist largely of periodic statistical reports, surveys of camp facilities, and policy records on establishment of work camps and the WPA reorganization of the transient program.

RECORDS OF THE FERA SECTIONAL ECONOMIC RESEARCH PROJECT. 1934-37. 13 lin. ft.

Included are administrative records and some research material created in studies of the United States by economic sections under the "four phases of sectional economy—industrial, agricultural, political, and social."

RECORDS OF THE FERA WORK DIVISION. 1934-36. 12 lin. ft.

These include procedural bulletins for specific work projects and reports and correspondence concerning a rural electrification survey, engineering and construction projects, the drought relief and subsistence garden programs, and the mattress-making project of the Women's Section.

RECORDS OF THE FERA AND WPA EMERGENCY EDUCATION PROGRAM. 1933-39. 113 lin. ft.

This program supervised State and local projects for adult education in arts and crafts, vocational training, parent education, and child care; conducted classes in black and workers education and in literacy; assisted in operating nursery and rural schools; and supervised the college student aid program. The records consist of Washington office reports, memorandums, correspondence, and some teaching material. Records of this program after 1939 were incorporated in the WPA central files.

RECORDS OF WPA FEDERAL
PROJECT NO. 1. 1935-42. 792 lin. ft.

The Federal arts program was approved as WPA-sponsored Federal Project No. 1 on September 12, 1935, to provide employment for qualified artists, musicians, actors, and authors on local relief rolls. It superseded all art projects operating under FERA or WPA State administrations and consisted of the Federal Art, Music, Theater, and Writers' Projects, including the Historical Records Survey until October 1936 when the Survey was made an independent unit. Federal Project No. 1 was terminated June 30, 1939. With the exception of the Federal Theater Project, which was abolished in July 1939, the arts programs continued as State projects.

The records of Federal Project No. 1 include statistical summaries of project employment and costs and procedural records as well as records of the following individual projects: (1) The Federal Art Project. 1935-40. Included are correspondence with State and regional offices; field trip reports; periodic progress reports for New York City, New York State, and New Jersey; and miscellaneous records relating to National Art Week, community art centers, and the "Index of American Design." (2) The Federal Music Project. 1935-40. These consist of correspondence; narrative, statistical, and miscellaneous reports on the general program and its sponsorship; and newspaper clippings. (3) The Federal Theater Project. 1935-39. Included are records of Washington and New York City national offices, the National Service Bureau in New York, regional service bureaus, and State offices. They consist of correspondence, including files of the national director; narrative and statistical reports on productions; newspaper clippings, press releases, and other publicity; research material, monographs, and histories of the theater; and playscripts, play catalogs, and produc-

tion bulletins. (4) The Federal Writers' Project. 1935-44. These consist of Washington office administrative files; field trip reports; editorial correspondence and reports; publication contracts; regional office files from southern California and New England; and a few edited manuscripts, with related research material and correspondence. (5) Records of the Historical Records Survey (HRS). 1935-42. Included are reports from regional and field supervisors, general and editorial correspondence, manuals, and an incomplete set of HRS publications. Most of the records concern the inspection, listing, and inventorying of archival and other materials in libraries, historical societies, city and county offices, churches, and other non-Federal depositories. There are some that concern the Survey of Federal Archives, the American Imprints Inventory, and national defense work undertaken after 1940.

OTHER RECORDS OF THE
DIVISION OF PROFESSIONAL
AND SERVICE PROJECTS. 1935-43.
941 lin. ft.

This unit was known successively as the Division of Professional and Service Projects, 1935-41, the Division of Community Service Programs, 1941-42, and the Service Division, 1942-43. Its general function was to supervise federally sponsored "white collar" work relief projects. The records consist of narrative reports submitted by State offices, 1935-39; scrapbooks of "This Work Pays Your Community Week" exhibits submitted by State offices, 1940-41; final reports on national operations and accomplishments of service projects, 1942-43; and records for the following projects: (1) The Survey of Federal Archives. 1935-43. These comprise reports; copies of a form giving location, volume, title, dates, and other information concerning records surveyed; correspondence; unpublished manuscripts; instructional materials; records of several regional offices; and a set of published inventories. (2) The Research and Records Projects. 1935-42. The work of this unit did not differ greatly from that of the Division of Statistics, but the Research and Records Projects unit was concerned only with sponsored projects rather than with research within or for the WPA. The records consist of project application files, general administrative correspondence, reports and unpublished studies, procedural material, statistical data, and copies of publications and final project reports. In most cases research and unpublished materials assembled by projects were retained by their sponsors. (3) Miscellaneous projects. 1935-43. Included are administrative correspondence and procedural manuals of library service and newspaper-indexing projects; and records of a Library of Congress project to inventory and arrange records of WPA arts projects, the workers service program, and a project to teach Spanish to members of the Army Air Forces.

RECORDS OF THE WPA DIVISION OF STATISTICS. 1935-43. 101 lin. ft.

This Division—known also as the Division of Social Research; the Division of Research, Statistics, and Finance; and the Division of Research, Records, and Statistics—was responsible for assembling and analyzing statistical information for WPA use. The records include general administrative correspondence, statistical tabulations, and materials used at appropriation hearings.

RECORDS OF THE WPA NATIONAL RESEARCH PROJECT. 1935-42. 61 lin. ft.

The National Research Project on Reemployment and Recent Changes in Industrial Techniques analyzed and augmented existing information with field surveys to determine "the extent of recent changes in industrial techniques and to evaluate the effects of these changes on the volume of employment and unemployment." Most of its records were turned over to the Bureaus of Labor Statistics and of Agricultural Economics. Included here are reports, memorandums, and correspondence relating to the organization and administration of the project and its relations with other Government agencies and private institutions.

RECORDS OF THE WPA DIVISION OF INFORMATION. 1934-42. 381 lin. ft.

Included are interoffice memorandums, speeches and publicity material, community improvement appraisal committee reports, correspondence, newspaper and magazine clippings concerning the national WPA program, and radio scripts. There are also records relating to CWA final State reports, FERA expenditures, and CWA and FERA projects.

RECORDS OF THE WPA DIVISION OF ENGINEERING AND CONSTRUCTION. 1935-44. 72 lin. ft.

This Division was responsible for planning and supervising construction projects for highways, airports, dams, and sanitation works. The records consist of central classified files, administrative files, and project files, including those on airways and airports.

RECORDS OF THE PUBLIC WORK RESERVE PROJECT. 1941-42. 60 lin. ft.

The project secured prospectuses of projects planned by Federal, State, and local agencies for postwar operation and made selective preliminary studies of proposed projects. The records include correspondence, the office file of the consultant on planning, construction project summaries, individual project prospectuses, and code files. There are also records relating to 6-year plans in the States, the planning of defense and war projects, the scrap collection program, and service projects.

RECORDS OF THE WPA DIVISION OF INVESTIGATION. 1934–43. 767 lin. ft.

These consist primarily of investigation reports on fraud, defalcations, the misappropriation of funds, inefficiency, and disloyalty. They include FERA, CWA, and WPA investigation case files, Division Reference and Office of Deputy Commissioner case files, and FBI investigative reports, with indexes, miscellaneous correspondence, interoffice memorandums, and field reports.

RECORDS OF THE WPA DIVISION OF FINANCE. 1935-43. 113 lin. ft.

Included are correspondence relating to the general supply fund and "restitution files" relating to recovery of misappropriated funds.

MISCELLANEOUS FERA AND WPA DIVISIONAL AND PROJECT RECORDS. 1934-43. 367 lin. ft.

Included are records of the social service training program, 1934-36, and the Divisions of Adjustment, 1934-35, Supply, 1940-43, Safety, 1934-41, Employment, 1935-36, Training and Reemployment, 1940-43, and Records and Microphotography, 1937-43. There are also reports and miscellaneous records of the recreation program, 1934-43, and entry slips of the bibliography of territories and island possessions.

OTHER CWA, FERA, AND WPA RECORDS. 1933-43. 534 lin. ft.

Often fragmentary and sometimes duplicated in the central files, these include records of the Office of the FERA Assistant Administrator, 1934-36, relating to general policy, wages and hours, worker classifications, self-help cooperatives, "white-collar" projects,

and WPA organization; records of the Office of the WPA Commissioner (formerly Administrator), 1935-41, including fragmentary correspondence and memorandums of policy, and Presidential letters allocating funds for WPA projects, 1939-41; and records of the Director of the Administrative Budget Section of the Division of Management, 1940-43. A record set of procedural publications includes the WPA *Manual of Rules and Regulations* and project manuals, memorandums, telegrams, circular letters, copies of speeches, minutes of FERA-WPA conferences, technical publications, and some CWA, FERA, and WPA research publications. The records also include the Federal Works Agency collection of WPA publications, project reports, and reference materials.

There are also WPA organizational charts, 1935-42; outgoing correspondence with prominent individuals and organizations, 1935-38; samples of FERA and WPA complaint correspondence, 1933-36; records of the liaison officer for the WPA Oklahoma State administration, 1937-39; and records of the Operations, Statistical, and Employment Divisions for Region 1, relating to the District of Columbia, Delaware, and Maryland.

CARTOGRAPHIC AND AUDIOVISUAL RECORDS. 1931-43. 122,266 items.

Cartographic records, 1933-41 (133 items), include FERA maps showing major types of economic activity by county; maps relating to the distribution of Federal funds, airport and landing field projects, and WPA work districts; and maps and reports relating to FERA and WPA projects in Iowa and New York, and real property surveys in Georgia.

Still pictures, 1931-43 (121,610 items), include photographs relating to activities of the central office; the Federal Emergency Relief Administration; the

Work Division; the Divisions of Engineering and Construction, Information, and Statistics; the central office of the service projects; State offices; the Federal Music, Theater, Art, and Writers' Projects; the Survey of Federal Archives; the National Research Project; and the Public Roads, Public Works, and Federal Housing Administrations.

Motion pictures, 1931-39 (105 reels), produced or distributed by the Motion Picture Record Division or its successors, relate to WPA activities and National Youth Administration and Civilian Conservation Corps activities.

Sound recordings, 1936-43 (418 items), are of performances by Federal Music Project groups, many with intermission talks by prominent persons about WPA work; and recordings of radio broadcasts by the Federal Theater Project. There are also recordings of special radio programs sponsored by the Democratic National Committee in support of New Deal programs; Department of the Treasury radio programs urging the purchase of U.S. savings bonds; a drama produced by the Resettlement Administration; a Department of Agriculture program on conservation; and a program about the White House made by the National Broadcasting Company for the Federal Housing Administration.

See Katherine H. Davidson, comp., *Preliminary Inventory of the Records of the Federal Writers' Project, Work Projects Administration, 1935-44,* PI 57 (1953).

Microfilm Publications: *Index to Reference Cards for WPA Project Files, 1935-1937,* T935, 79 rolls; *Index to Reference Cards for WPA Project Files, 1938,* T936, 15 rolls; and *Index to Reference Cards for WPA Project Files, 1939-1942,* T937, 19 rolls.

NATIONAL ARCHIVES COLLECTION OF WORLD WAR II WAR CRIMES RECORDS
(RECORD GROUP 238)

The Moscow Declaration, signed by representatives of the United States, Great Britain, and the Soviet Union on November 1, 1943, provided that major war criminals were to be punished in accordance with the joint decisions of the Allied Governments. On May 2, 1945, President Truman appointed Robert H. Jackson, an Associate Justice of the U.S. Supreme Court, as the representative and Chief of Counsel for the United States in preparing and prosecuting cases against major Axis war criminals. An agreement signed by Justice Jackson and representatives of the French, British, and Soviet Governments on August 8, 1945, established the International Military Tribunal. On October 18, 1945, the chief counsels of the Allied Governments submitted to the tribunal an indictment charging 24 German nationals with conspiring to wage aggressive war, breaching international peace, violating rules of warfare, and committing wholesale crimes against humanity. From September 30 to October 1, 1946, the tribunal delivered judgments. Justice Jackson resigned October 7, 1946, as Chief of Counsel for the United States.

President Truman had provided in January 1946 that the Office of Military Government for Germany, United States, would handle remaining trials of Nazi war criminals. On October 18, 1946, Gen. Joseph T. McNarney established U.S. military tribunals at Nuremberg, with supporting administrative units. Between 1946 and 1949 the tribunals heard 12 trials; under Brig. Gen. Telford Taylor the Office of the Chief of Counsel for War Crimes, which was formally inactivated June 20, 1949, handled the legal work.

In the Far East Gen. Douglas MacArthur, as Supreme Commander for the Allied Powers (SCAP), established on January 19, 1946, the International Military Tribunal for the Far East to try persons charged with war crimes. On February 15, 1946, MacArthur appointed nine members to the tribunal from nominations submitted by nations accepting the Japanese surrender, India, and the Commonwealth of the Philippines. Preparation of the Allied case was assigned to SCAP's International Prosecution Section (see RG 331) under Chief of Counsel Joseph B. Keenan. The tribunal sat from April 29, 1946, until November 1948 when it delivered judgments and pronounced sentences.

See Brig. Gen. Telford Taylor, *Final Report to the Secretary of the Army on the Nuremberg War Crimes Trials Under Control Council Law No. 10* (1949); *Trials of War Criminals Before the Nuremberg Military Tribunals* (15 vols., 1949-53); and Eugene Davidson, *The Trial of the Germans: Nuremberg, 1945-46* (New York, 1966).

There are 1,614 cubic feet of records dated between 1900 and 1950 in this record group.

RECORDS OF THE OFFICE OF THE U.S. CHIEF OF COUNSEL FOR THE PROSECUTION OF AXIS CRIMINALITY. 1933-46. 401 lin. ft. and 107 rolls of microfilm.

These consist of documentary evidence and reference files, staff evidence analysis forms, transcripts of proceedings of the International Military Tribunal, pretrial interrogations, and U.S. trial briefs and document books, 1945-46; defense documents and American, Soviet, British, and French exhibits, 1933-46; transcripts of hearings in defense of organizations, May-August 1946; State Department despatches, 1933-44; copies of the diaries of Hans Frank, kept while Governor General of Poland (partly on microfilm), 1939-45, and Joseph Goebbels (on microfilm), 1942-43; microfilm copies (107 rolls) of the diaries and correspondence of Gen. Alfred Jodl, 1937-45, and the death books of the Mauthausen Concentration Camp, 1939-45; copies of the Four Power Agreement, the Charter of the International Military Tribunal, and opening addresses of Justice Jackson and the other three chief counsels, 1945; and defense arguments, defendants' final pleas and statements, and judgments of the tribunal, 1946.

RECORDS OF TRIALS BY U.S. MILITARY TRIBUNALS, NUREMBERG ("SUBSEQUENT PROCEEDINGS"). 1946-49.
770 lin. ft.

The individuals tried before these tribunals were Field Marshals Wilhelm List and Wilhelm von Leeb; Luftwaffe Gen. Erhard Milch; SS officers Oswald Pohl, Ulrich Greifelt, and Otto Ohlendorf; civilian officials Karl Brandt and Josef Altstoetter; diplomat Ernst von Weizsaecker; and businessmen Alfried Krupp von Bohlen, Friedrich Flick, and Carl Krauch.

Trial records consist of transcripts and minutes in English and German of tribunal proceedings, prosecution and defense exhibits and documents, and court records (orders, motions, lists of documents and witnesses, instructions, counsel statements and arguments, legal briefs, pleas, judgments, and clemency petitions); and administrative records consisting of trial enabling documents, procedural correspondence, memorandums, reports, transcripts of executive and joint sessions, tribunal orders, correspondence relating to the 12 cases, daily bulletins of the Office of the Chief of Counsel for War Crimes, and registers of transcripts of proceedings and the documents and exhibits used as evidence.

RECORDS OF THE OFFICE OF THE CHIEF OF COUNSEL FOR WAR CRIMES. 1933–49. 524 lin. ft. and 38 rolls of microfilm.

The Chief of Counsel's records consist of correspondence and reports of the Office, 1945–49; reports, interrogations, and other records concerning war crimes from Allied military agencies, 1945–48; indexes of prosecution and defense exhibits; and Public Information Office records, 1945–47.

The Executive Counsel's records (352 lin. ft.), 1933–49, include press releases, notes, articles, and statistics of the Economics Division, and reports, lists, and other records of the Apprehension and Locator Branch, Evidence Division, 1945–47; documents maintained by the Document Control Branch (partly on 38 rolls of microfilm), Evidence Division, concerning Reich ministries, German business, the German Army, the SS, and other aspects of the Nazi era, 1933–45; the office file, 1945–47, and staff evidence analysis records, 1945–48, of the Document Control Branch; interrogations of defendants and witnesses and related summaries and reports, 1945–48, and correspondence, 1945–47, of the Interrogation Branch, Evidence Division; reports, correspondence, and memorandums of the Military, the Ministries, and the SS Divisions, 1945–47; and correspondence, statements, lists, interrogation reports, affidavits, and memorandums of trial teams 1, 2, and 3, and the Dresdner Bank trial team, 1945–47.

Executive Office records consist of administrative correspondence of the Publications Division, including reports, memorandums and bulletins, and other records that relate to publishing trial documents and testimonies, 1943–49; charts of German economic and political organizations, 1933–45; and records of the Nuremberg Military Post, including internee personnel records, 1945–48, passes for personnel of the Office of the Chief of Counsel, 1946–47, and correspondence, memorandums, and other records of the 6850th Internal Security Detachment, 1945–49.

Berlin Branch records consist of administrative correspondence, memorandums, and other general records, and the reports, correspondence, and related records of its Economics, Ministries, and SS Divisions, 1946–48; and the collected documents, 1933–45, and staff evidence analysis forms, 1945–48, of the Document Control Branch of the Evidence Division.

RECORDS OF THE ADVISORY BOARD ON CLEMENCY FOR WAR CRIMINALS. 1947–50. 9 lin. ft.

This Board was established in the Office of the U.S. High Commissioner for Germany. The records include reports, correspondence, and petitions for clemency.

RECORDS OF THE OFFICE OF THE U.S. COMMISSIONER, UNITED NATIONS WAR CRIMES COMMISSION. 1943–48. 6 lin. ft.

This 17-member Commission was established at London in October 1943 to prosecute Axis war criminals. It was dissolved in 1948. The records include minutes, reports, and memorandums, 1943–46; correspondence, 1944–48; and issuances, 1945–46.

RECORDS OF THE INTERNATIONAL MILITARY TRIBUNAL FOR THE FAR EAST. 1900–1948. 149 lin. ft. and 62 rolls of microfilm.

Included are the partially indexed transcripts of its proceedings, miscellaneous records, the court journal, and such indexed documents comprising the court docket as indictments, motions, opinions, judgments, and dissents (partly on microfilm), 1946–48; court exhibits, with registers, and rejected exhibits and defense documents with indexes (partly on microfilm), 1900–1945; and a review of the sentences by General MacArthur, 1948.

AUDIOVISUAL RECORDS. 1921–49. 7,108 items.

Included are photographs (5,022 items) of the courtrooms, judges, prosecution and defense counsels, defendants, witnesses, and prisons connected with the International Military Tribunal, 1945–46; the U.S. military tribunals at Nuremberg, 1946–49; the International Military Tribunal for the Far East, 1946–48; and exhibits for the prosecution, consisting of photographs of Nazi destruction in the Warsaw ghetto, other Nazi activities in Poland, 1939–41, and Nazi activities at the Krupp works, 1933–41.

Motion pictures (76 reels) used as evidence at the war crimes trials of Axis leaders before the International Military Tribunal and the International Military Tribunal for the Far East consist of films of concentration camps taken by American and Russian forces as they advanced through Germany, 1945; a Japanese film entitled "Japan in Time of Emergency"; and German films that document the Nazi rise to power, 1921–44, the entry of Germany into Austria, 1938, the political and industrial activities of the Krupp family and company officials, 1930–40, the construction of the No. 1 Hermann Goering steel plant, 1939–41, and the Nazi Supreme Court trial of the plotters against Hitler, 1944.

Also included are sound recordings (2,010 items) of the entire proceedings of the International Military Tribunal, November 20, 1945-October 1, 1946; of a Stalag (a German prison camp for noncommissioned officers and privates) conference, introduced as evidence before that tribunal, May 22, 1944; and of speeches by Himmler.

See Fred G. Halley, comp., *Preliminary Inventory of the Records of the United States Counsel for the Prosecution of Axis Criminality*, PI 21 (1949).

Microfilm Publications: For a complete listing see the current *List of National Archives Microfilm Publications*.

Since 1950

RECORDS OF THE COMMITTEE ON GOVERNMENT CONTRACT COMPLIANCE
(RECORD GROUP 325)

The Committee on Government Contract Compliance, established by an Executive order of December 3, 1951, was composed of representatives of industry, labor, the general public, and several Government agencies, including the Departments of Defense and Labor, the Atomic Energy Commission, the General Services Administration, and the Defense Materials Procurement Agency. The purpose of the Committee was to improve ways of obtaining compliance with nondiscrimination provisions of Federal contracts. The Committee became inactive after publication of its final report in January 1953 and was officially abolished by an Executive order of August 13, 1953, which established the Government Contract Committee and transferred to it all property and records of the former committee.

See *Equal Economic Opportunity: A Report by the President's Committee on Government Contract Compliance* (1953).

There are 10 cubic feet of records dated between 1952 and 1953 in this record group.

RECORDS. 1952-53. 12 lin. ft.

These comprise reports; records relating to Committee meetings, hearings on training and apprenticeship practices of Federal agencies, and hearings with State and municipal antidiscrimination commissions and private voluntary organizations; administrative files; correspondence; staff research material and working papers; reference files; files relating to complaints of discrimination; issuances and publicity materials; and personnel files. Some miscellaneous records of the President's Committee on Government Contracts are also included.

GENERAL RECORDS OF THE ECONOMIC STABILIZATION AGENCY (RECORD GROUP 296)

The Economic Stabilization Agency (ESA) was established by an Executive order of September 9, 1950, to control inflation and maintain national economic stability in accordance with the Defense Production Act of 1950. The ESA was authorized to plan and develop price and wage stabilization policies and create necessary organization for their administration; inform the public, agriculture, industry, and labor about the need for stabilization; consult with Government officials responsible for procurement, production, manpower, rent control, and fiscal, credit, and monetary policies; and establish price ceilings and stabilize wages and salaries where necessary. The ESA Administrator, appointed by the President, had supervisory responsibility and policy direction over activities of the Office of Price Stabilization, the Wage Stabilization Board, the Salary Stabilization Board, the Office of Rent Stabilization, the Railroad and Airline Wage Board, and the National Enforcement Commission—all constituent organizations under the ESA. Wage and salary controls were suspended by an Executive order of February 6, 1953, and ESA's remaining controls were terminated April 30, 1953, in accordance with an amendment to the Defense Production Act. An Executive order of August 14, 1953, designated the Director of the Office of Defense Mobilization as ex officio Administrator of the ESA to liquidate its Affairs by October 31. Functions of the National Enforcement Commission and other enforcement and investigative functions under title IV of the Defense Production Act were transferred to the Attorney General by an Executive order of October 14, 1953; and functions of conducting administrative proceedings and liquidating fiscal affairs were transferred to the Director of the Office of Defense Mobilization and to the Secretary of the Treasury, respectively, effective November 1, 1953.

There are 83 cubic feet of records dated between 1950 and 1953 in this record group.

RECORDS OF THE OFFICE OF THE ADMINISTRATOR. 1951-53. 47 lin. ft.

The records consist of reports, orders, issuances, memorandums, and correspondence relating to the policies, organization, and activities of the Office, 1951-53; outgoing correspondence, 1951-53; security-classified records relating to the economic situation and standards for decontrol, 1951-53; abstracts of significant letters and memorandums sent and received by Administrator Eric A.

Johnston, 1951; subject files of Administrators Roger L. Putnam, 1951-52, and Michael V. DiSalle, 1953; and correspondence of Assistant to the Administrator Kenneth Clark, 1951.

RECORDS OF THE OFFICE OF THE GENERAL COUNSEL. 1951-53. 20 lin. ft.

These consist of reports, correspondence, memorandums, and other records, 1951-53; subject files of associate general counsels, 1951-53, relating to the steel strike of 1952, decontrol of wages and prices in 1952, and legislative plans for 1953; memorandums and reports of the consultant, 1951; records of the Committee on Compliance Policy, 1951-53; and a processed manual issued by the Litigation Branch, Office of Rent Stabilization, for use by its attorneys, 1952.

RECORDS OF THE OPERATIONS OFFICE. 1950-53. 26 lin. ft.

These include the subject file of the Assistant Administrator (Operations), 1951-53; sets of general and administrative orders maintained by the Deputy Assistant Administrator, 1951-52; records of the budget adviser, 1950-53, consisting of estimates, tabulations, and reports relating to financial requirements of the ESA and its constituent agencies for fiscal years 1951-54; security-classified reports compiled by the Reports and Secretariat Section for the Administrator, 1950-53; administrative histories of the ESA during the successive administrations of Alan Valentine and Eric A. Johnston, and related correspondence, 1951-53; and specimen samples of forms used, 1951-53.

AUDIOVISUAL RECORDS. 1951-53. 39 items.

These consist of recordings of a speech by Michael V. DiSalle, 1951; of a Reconstruction Finance Corporation conference, 1952; and of administrative hearings concerning personnel matters of the ESA, 1953.

See Charles Zaid, comp., *Preliminary Inventory of the General Records of the Economic Stabilization Agency*, PI 129 (1960).

GENERAL RECORDS OF THE FEDERAL WORKS AGENCY (RECORD GROUP 162)

The Federal Works Agency was created by the President's Reorganization Plan No. I of July 1, 1939, which transferred to it the Public Buildings Administration (see RG 121), the Public Roads Administration (see RG 30), the Public Works Administration (see RG 135), the Work Projects Administration (see RG 69), and the U.S. Housing Authority (this latter agency was transferred in 1942 to the Federal Public Housing Authority of the National Housing Agency (see RG 196). An Executive order of July 6, 1939, placed the Federal Fire Council under the jurisdiction of the Federal Works Agency. On December 21, 1944, a Bureau of Community Facilities was established within the Agency to administer loans and grants relating to wartime public works and service programs. The Federal Works Agency was abolished by an act of June 30, 1949, and its functions were transferred to the General Services Administration.

There are 151 cubic feet of records dated between 1930 and 1950 in this record group.

RECORDS. 1930-50. 181 lin. ft.

Included are operating manuals, general and special orders, and administrative regulations; correspondence and copies of speeches of Administrators John M. Carmody, 1939-41, and Gen. Philip B. Fleming, 1942-49, including two sound recordings by Carmody on defense housing, 1941; a central correspondence file, 1941-49; records of the General Counsel, 1939-46, and of the Executive Officer, 1939-47; records of the war public works program, 1941-49; project summary lists, 1942-43, and individual project files, 1936-44; employee and project investigative files, 1936-49; records relating to the organization of the General Services Administration, 1949-50; and records of the Federal Fire Council, 1930-44, including correspondence, 1931-41, fire reports, 1930-44, and surveys and reports of standing committees, 1931-41. There are also 4,300 photographs of the activities of the Federal Works Agency (arranged by subject), of the Public Buildings Administration, 1939-43, and of the Division of War Public Works, 1942-44.

Microfilm Publication: *Checklist of Historical Records Survey Publications, April 1943*, T1028, 1 roll.

RECORDS OF THE OFFICE OF PRICE STABILIZATION
(RECORD GROUP 295)

The Office of Price Stabilization (OPS) was established within the Economic Stabilization Agency on January 24, 1951, with the Director of Price Stabilization, appointed by the President on November 30, 1950, as its head. Major units within the OPS, which was authorized to obtain voluntary compliance with measures to stabilize prices and to establish and administer price regulations, were the Offices of the Director, Chief Counsel, Economic Policy, Management, Public Information, Price Operations, Enforcement, Accounting, and Field Operations. The OPS, assisted by industry advisory committees, functioned through 14 regional and about 90 district offices in principal cities of the United States, its territories and possessions. Price regulation, authorized by title IV of the Defense Production Act, began January 26, 1951. All prices were decontrolled in a series of actions beginning February 6 and ending March 17, 1953; title IV expired April 30, 1953. The OPS was engaged in liquidation activities until June 30, 1953, when residual functions reverted to the Economic Stabilization Agency.

There are 404 cubic feet of records dated between 1950 and 1953 in this record group.

RECORDS. 1950-53. 485 lin. ft.

Records of the Office of the Director consist of minutes of policy committees, publications, organizational charts, correspondence, and memorandums, 1950-53; a general subject file, 1950-53 (with index); and letters, telegrams, and circulars sent to regional and field offices, 1951-53. Records of the Office of Price Operations include reports relating chiefly to activities of regional and district offices, 1951-53. Records of the Office of Enforcement include subject files, 1951-53, with a related index; district office enforcement case files, 1951-53; selected national office and regional office enforcement case files, 1951-53; reports on enforcement activities, 1951, and of inspection of district offices, 1951-52; and correspondence and other records relating to district offices, 1951-53. Records of the Office of the Boards of Review include docketed protest case files, 1951-53. There are also minutes and correspondence of the policy committees, 1951-53. Records of the Budget and Finance Division relate to the preparation of the OPS budget, 1950-53, and selected compromise settlement case files, 1951-53. Other records consist of narrative reports relating to the history of the OPS, 1953, and OPS publications and issuances, 1950-53.

AUDIOVISUAL RECORDS. 1950-53. 47 items.

These are sound recordings of radio talks, interviews, dramas, spot announcements, and music featuring Tighe Woods, Eric Johnston, Michael V. DiSalle, Roger Putnam, and several prominent entertainers.

Microfilm Publication: *Defense History Program Studies Prepared During the Korean War Period*, T460, 3 rolls.

SPECIFIC RESTRICTIONS
Records: Records containing personal

and industrial information obtained in confidence under the provisions of section 705 of the Defense Production Act of 1950, as amended, and not made public before April 30, 1953.

Restrictions: Such information may not be published or disclosed to the public or to another Federal agency except the Congress or any duly authorized committee thereof, the Department of Justice in the performance of its functions, and the successors to the Economic Stabilization Agency, unless the President determines that withholding the information is contrary to the interest of the national defense.

Specified by: Congress of the United States in the Defense Production Act Amendments of 1953 (67 Stat. 131).

RECORDS OF THE
WAGE AND SALARY STABILIZATION BOARDS
OF THE ECONOMIC STABILIZATION AGENCY
(RECORD GROUP 293)

The Wage Stabilization Board (WSB), a tripartite body equally representing labor, industry, and the public, was created as a constituent agency of the Economic Stabilization Agency (ESA) by Executive Order 10161 of September 9, 1950, under authority of the Defense Production Act of 1950, to control wages and salaries during the Korean war emergency period. An Executive order of April 21, 1951, reestablished the Board with power to assist the President in settling industrial disputes. In July 1952 the Board was reconstituted under legislative authority and stripped of its functions in the area of labor disputes. To aid its programs it established the Construction Industry Stabilization Commission and the National Enforce-

ment Commission. In 1952 the latter was made an ESA constituent agency, and its functions were transferred in 1953 to the Office of Defense Mobilization and the Attorney General.

The WSB had full control over wage and salary stabilization functions until the ESA Administrator created the Salary Stabilization Board in May 1951 and vested in it authority over administrative, executive, and professional salaries, and created the Railroad and Airline Wage Board in September 1951 to determine the wage and salary stabilization program for employees subject to the Railway Labor Act. Wage controls were suspended February 6, 1953, and the Boards were terminated April 30, 1953.

There are 3 cubic feet of records dated between 1950 and 1953 in this record group.

RECORDS. 1950–53. 4 lin. ft.

These consist of histories of the ESA and of the wage and salary stabilization programs; terminal reports and histories of the Wage Stabilization Board, the Salary Stabilization Board, the Railroad and Airline Wage Board, the Construction Industry Stabilization Commission, and WSB regional offices; and case files of proceedings against firms violating Board regulations that were referred to the National Enforcement Commission, with statements, findings, and determinations.

SPECIFIC RESTRICTIONS

Records: Case files of the National Enforcement Commission, 1951-53.

Restrictions: These records may be made available only to the Congress or any duly authorized committee thereof, the Department of Justice in performance of its functions, and successors to the Economic Stabilization Agency, unless the President determines that withholding the records would be contrary to the interest of the national defense.

Specified by: Congress of the United States in the Defense Production Act Amendments of 1953 (67 Stat. 131).

PART V

RECORDS OF OR RELATING TO OTHER GOVERNMENTS

DISTRICT OF COLUMBIA

RECORDS OF THE
GOVERNMENT OF THE DISTRICT OF COLUMBIA
(RECORD GROUP 351)

The District of Columbia, created by acts of July 16, 1790, and March 3, 1791, from lands ceded by Virginia and Maryland, was permanently established as the seat of government in 1800. In 1846 the Congress returned to Virginia its part, including both the city and county of Alexandria.

The Constitution of the United States gave the Congress power to legislate for the capital of the United States, and the first District of Columbia government was established under an act of May 3, 1802, which provided for a mayor, appointed by the President, and a city council, elected by District residents. That charter was modified by later acts and in 1871 was revoked. The Congress then established a territorial form of District government composed of a governor, a board of public works, and a legislative assembly consisting of a council and a house of delegates. The governor, board members, and council members were appointed by the President by and with the advice and consent of the Senate; house members were elected by District residents. In 1874 three commissioners were appointed by the President to govern the District. An act of June 11, 1878, authorized the President to appoint the Board of Commissioners, which was composed of two civilian residents of Washington and a member of the U.S. Army Corps of Engineers holding a rank not lower than that of captain. Those District commissioners, who had authority over all the usual activities of a municipal government, prepared annual estimates of District expenditures and submitted them to the Congress through the Bureau of the Budget. Reorganization Plan No. 3 of 1967 provided for the Commissioner of the District of Columbia and the District of Columbia Council composed of a chairman, a vice chairman, and seven other members, all appointed by the President with the advice and consent of the Senate.

There are 454 cubic feet of records dated between 1792 and 1967 in this record group.

GENERAL AND LAND RECORDS OF THE GOVERNMENT OF THE DISTRICT OF COLUMBIA.
1792-1967. 286 lin. ft.

General records include tax and assessment records, 1824-98; records relating to the issuance of licenses, 1819-79, and stocks and bonds, 1820-77; laws of the legislative assembly, 1871-74; minutes and orders of the Board of Commissioners, 1874-1952; records of the Treasurer's Office, 1871-81; a real estate directory, 1874; journals and ledgers,

1819-80; letters sent by the Office of the Mayor, 1857-63; annual reports, 1874-1941; records of the Office of the Superintendent of Property, Bureau of Public Works, and of the Office of the Comptroller, 1820-81; and a collection of photographs (33 items) of the Engineer Commissioners of the District of Columbia, 1873-1967.

The records that relate to land consist of deedbooks (200 lin. ft.) to real property in the District, 1792-1869 (in WNRC).

RECORDS OF THE DISTRICT OF COLUMBIA POLICE DEPARTMENT. 1851-79. 9 lin. ft.

Records include reports concerning cases, 1851-78; registers of oaths, 1862-79, and of letters received, 1877-78; orders, 1862-63; a property book, 1861-75; daily precinct returns, 1861-78; and case files (in WNRC) of police personnel appointed in the District, 1862-1900 (some dated as late as 1950). Missing from these materials are all records containing information about President Lincoln's assassination and the arrest and detention of the assassins.

RECORDS OF THE GOVERNMENT OF WASHINGTON COUNTY.
1819-79. 4 lin. ft.

Included are real property taxbooks, 1854-79, levy court proceedings, 1819-63, and a register of tax lien certificates, 1871-77.

RECORDS OF THE GEORGETOWN CITY GOVERNMENT. 1800-1879.
9 lin. ft.

These consist of tax and assessment records, 1800-1879, journals and ledgers, 1801-73, ordinances, 1803-71, a daybook, 1800-1807, and a list of municipal jobs, 1878.

RECORDS OF THE WASHINGTON CANAL COMPANY. 1810-71.
1 lin. ft.

Included are a minute book, 1810-34; proceedings of the Joint Committee on the Canal Fund, 1830-34; a ledger, 1857-58; statements of interest due, 1835-38; and Canal Commission records, consisting of the act creating the Commission, a list of bids, 1870, and minutes of meetings, 1870-71.

Microfilm Publications: *Records of the City of Georgetown (D.C.), 1800-1879*, M605, 49 rolls, DP; and *Proceedings of the Board of Commissioners for the District of Columbia, 1791-1802*, T69, 1 roll.

RECORDS OF THE NATIONAL CAPITAL HOUSING AUTHORITY (RECORD GROUP 302)

The National Capital Housing Authority, the public housing agency for the District of Columbia, was established as the Alley Dwelling Authority by Executive Order 6868 of October 9, 1934, in accordance with the District of Columbia Alley Dwelling Act of June 12, 1934. It was given its present name in 1943, the Commissioner of the District of Columbia was designated the National Capital Housing Authority in 1968, and the functions of the Authority were delegated to the Commissioner's assistant.

Originally the Authority reclaimed District of Columbia slums in squares containing inhabited alleys, but 1938 amendments to the Alley Dwelling Act enabled the Authority to provide low-rent housing for low-income families under the auspices of the U.S. Housing Authority and in accordance with the U.S. Housing Act of 1937, as amended. The wartime objective of the Authority was to provide housing for war workers under the Lanham Act and other legislation. When slum reclamation in the District was resumed after the war it was made the responsibility of the District of Columbia Redevelopment Land Agency. At present the chief function of the Authority is to assure an adequate supply of proper dwellings for low-income families at rents commensurate with their income.

There are 18 cubic feet of records dated between 1934 and 1951 in this record group.

RECORDS. 1934-51. 23 lin. ft.

Included are reports, correspondence, speeches, statements, lectures, and other records of John Ihlder, Executive Director and Secretary of the Alley

Dwelling and the National Capital Housing Authorities, 1935-45. Also records maintained by the Central Files Unit, consisting mainly of reports, correspondence, and general records concerning the organization, administration, and activities of the Authority, 1935-49; correspondence with municipal housing and welfare organizations and housing surveys, 1935-51; interagency correspondence, 1934-47; records relating to the low-rent housing program, including financial statements, contracts, and applications for fund allotments, 1941-51; and reports, correspondence, memorandums, and other records of the Office of the Director of Management, relating to housing management, 1945-51.

RECORDS OF THE
NATIONAL CAPITAL PLANNING COMMISSION
(RECORD GROUP 328)

The National Capital Planning Commission was created by an act of July 19, 1952, and succeeded the National Capital Park Commission, established in 1924, and its successor, the National Capital Park and Planning Commission, established in 1926. Created as the central planning agency for the Federal and District of Columbia Governments, the National Capital Planning Commission is to plan the development and redevelopment of the National Capital and the conservation of its natural and historical features. The 12-member Commission is composed of officials of the Federal and District Governments and private citizens. Commission duties are to prepare, adopt, and amend a comprehensive plan for the National Capital and make recommendations to the appropriate development agencies; review the development programs of the Federal and District Governments for the National Capital region; administer, in conjunction with the District of Columbia Commissioners, the permanent system-of-

highways plan; perform planning, coordinating, and administrative functions related to zoning, public works, urban redevelopment, public housing, and public buildings; acquire land for the development of District park, parkway, and playground systems; and perform duties prescribed in section 6 of the District of Columbia Redevelopment Act of 1945.

There are 183 cubic feet of records dated between 1791 and 1962 in this record group.

GENERAL RECORDS. 1924-60.
190 lin. ft.

These include minutes, 1930-55; general subject and land acquisition records, 1924-58; planning records, 1924-57; project files, 1930-54; office files of Director John Nolen, Jr., 1926-58, and Chairman Frederic A. Delano, 1932-47; reports and clippings on projects considered by the Commission, 1929-50; records relating to the comprehensive plan for the National Capital, 1950; special Commission studies on Commission projects, 1926-29; and announcements, 1926-60.

CARTOGRAPHIC AND AUDIOVISUAL RECORDS.
1791-1962. 6,562 items.

Cartographic records (3,890 items) include maps and plans of the District of Columbia, relating to schools, municipal and Federal buildings, parks, bridges, monuments, military posts, and highway systems, 1791-1962. Also aerial photographs of a parked-car survey in the District of Columbia, 1930, and in the District and vicinity, 1932; and of flood conditions along the Potomac and Anacostia Rivers, 1936, and in parts of Virginia and Maryland near the District, 1950 and 1956.

Still pictures (2,660 items) include a heraldic cartoon, drawings of the Chesapeake and Ohio Canal and the Washington Monument, a diagram of subsurface conditions at the Washington Monument, and photographs of European and U.S. parks and of Federal and other buildings, monuments, bridges, parks, the zoo, the George Washington Canal, highway systems, land use, planning, and slums in or around Washington, D.C., 1873-1942; a group portrait of the Supreme Court Justices, ca. 1916; and display photographs of the Grand Coulee Dam project, 1934-36.

Sound recordings (12 items) of Commission proceedings, March-April and May 22, 1953.

RECORDS OF THE
OFFICE OF PUBLIC BUILDINGS AND GROUNDS
(RECORD GROUP 42)

The Office of Public Buildings and Grounds had its origin in 1791 when the Board of Commissioners for the District of Columbia was appointed to plan and construct a capital city. In 1800 the Capital was moved from Philadelphia to Washington, D.C., and in 1802 the Board was abolished. Part of its functions and its records were inherited successively by the Superintendent of the City of Washington, 1802-17, the Commissioner of Public Buildings, 1816-67 (after 1849 in the Department of the Interior), and the Office of Public Buildings and Grounds under the Chief of Engineers in the Department of War, 1867-1925. The functions of the Office of Public Buildings and Grounds and of the Office of the Superintendent of the State, War, and Navy Building (created in 1883 as an independent agency to maintain the building) were transferred in 1925 to the newly established Office of Public Build-

ings and Public Parks of the National Capital. This Office or its predecessors acquired the records of temporary agencies established to erect buildings or monuments in the District. The Office was abolished in 1933. Its functions concerning public buildings in the District of Columbia are now vested in the Public Buildings Service (see RG 121); those concerning public grounds and parks are the responsibility of the National Park Service (see RG 79).

There are 434 cubic feet of records dated between 1771 and 1951 in this record group.

RECORDS OF THE BOARD OF COMMISSIONERS FOR THE DISTRICT OF COLUMBIA. 1791-1802, with some dated as late as 1823. 10 lin. ft.

These include minutes, 1791-1802, with an index; photostats of Pierre

Charles L'Enfant's letters and of letters received from Presidents (originals are in the Library of Congress); other letters received, with an index; and letters sent, 1791-1802, with an index. Land records include deeds of trust from proprietors of the land chosen as the site for the city of Washington to the trustees appointed by the President, 1791-ca. 1823; other deeds and agreements relating to lands in Carrollsburgh and Hamburgh and to the property of James Greenleaf, Robert Morris, and John Nicholson; division sheets, assignments, and other records for squares (city blocks) 1-1149 and reservations 1, 9, 13, and 29, 1791-1802; records about the division of squares, 1796-1800; a register of squares, ca. 1798-1801; and records relating to public lot sales, 1796-1802. Fiscal records include ledgers, journals, contracts, and miscellaneous accounts.

RECORDS OF THE SUPERINTENDENT OF THE CITY OF WASHINGTON. 1802-17. 1 lin. ft.

These include letters received, with an index, 1802-17; deeds and agreements relating to original proprietors' property, including statements and final settlements, ca. 1804-7, of proprietors' land accounts; records that relate to the division of squares in Washington, including a list of squares, ca. 1804; and ledgers, journals, and other fiscal records, 1802-17.

RECORDS OF THE COMMISSIONERS TO SUPERVISE THE REPAIR OR REBUILDING OF THE PUBLIC BUILDINGS. 1815-16. 1 lin. ft.

A special commission was appointed by President Madison in 1815 to supervise repairing and rebuilding public buildings in Washington damaged during the War of 1812; its records include minutes, letters received and sent, and miscellaneous fiscal records.

RECORDS OF THE COMMISSIONER OF PUBLIC BUILDINGS. 1799-1867. 26 lin. ft.

Included are the Commissioner's journal, 1816-20 and 1824-ca. 1851; letters received and sent, 1816-67, with indexes; building plans; rough plats and drawings of Capitol Square, levels near the White House, and other squares and reservations, 1799-ca. 1836; deeds, agreements, and other records relating to the land of original proprietors, including James Greenleaf, Robert Morris, and John Nicholson, and to property bought or donated by the United States for the District of Columbia; and miscellaneous fiscal and personal records of Commissioner Benjamin B. French, including a cashbook, 1862, in which bounties given to enlisted soldiers were recorded.

RECORDS OF THE OFFICE OF PUBLIC BUILDINGS AND GROUNDS. 1867-1935. 126 lin. ft.

Included are letters received, 1871-1906, with indexes and registers; letters sent, 1867 and 1877-89, with an index; the personal and semiofficial correspondence of Col. A. F. Rockwell, the officer in charge, 1881-85, and Col. Charles S. Bromwell, 1904-9; general correspondence, 1907-25, with indexes; and annual reports, 1885-97, 1899, 1900, and 1902.

Fiscal records of the officer in charge, including ledgers and other expenditure statements about constructing and repairing Long Bridge, 1868, and the highway bridge, 1901-7, over the Potomac; and Col. Theodore A. Bingham's fiscal records relating to the Washington aqueduct, 1898-99.

Inventories of public property in and about the White House, 1869 and 1875; Abby Gunn Baker's catalog of the White House Presidential china collection, ca. 1921; letters received, 1898-1917, letters sent, 1898-1902, and a diary or scrapbook, 1902-16, relating to official functions at the White House; programs of White House receptions and dinners, 1898-1909; and records about constructing, remodeling, and maintaining the White House and White House Office Building, 1877-1907.

Other records relating to bridge, public building, statue, and memorial construction, including proposals and specifications for Chain Bridge, 1872-75; correspondence and other records relating to Thomas Jefferson's grave, 1882-95, the monument at President Washington's birthplace (Wakefield, Va.), 1883-1930, and a monument at President Washington's Newburgh, N.Y., headquarters, 1882-1902; and records concerning Meridian Hill Park, 1921-35, and the American Red Cross Building, 1929-34.

Land records include deeds and agreements that relate to original proprietors' property and to property bought or donated by the United States for the District of Columbia; and records of the U.S. Surveyor and Custodian of Old Records, including his reports, 1882-97, a platbook of Washington, 1874, a platbook of Georgetown, 1883, and a list of the lots in Washington sold by the Government and the squares and lots assigned to the original proprietors, 1900.

RECORDS OF THE OFFICE OF PUBLIC BUILDINGS AND PUBLIC PARKS OF THE NATIONAL CAPITAL. ca. 1900-1933. 51 lin. ft.

Included are the Director's general and personnel orders, 1925-32, classified general correspondence, 1925-28, and a reference file concerning buildings, parks, memorials, and Office history, ca. 1900-1933.

RECORDS OF THE OFFICE OF THE SUPERINTENDENT OF THE STATE, WAR, AND NAVY BUILDING. 1871-1925. 128 lin. ft.

Records of the Officer in Charge of Construction include annual, 1878-87,

and monthly, 1871-88, reports; letters sent, 1871-88, with an index; letters received, 1875-88, with indexes and a register; and fiscal records, 1873-74. The Superintendent's records include monthly, 1883-85, and quarterly, 1895-1913, reports; letters received, 1877-1909, and sent, 1883-1909; general correspondence, 1910-25, with an index; and fiscal records including appropriation ledgers, 1883-1906 and 1909-24.

RECORDS OF THE ROCK CREEK PARK COMMISSION AND THE BOARD OF CONTROL OF ROCK CREEK PARK. 1890-1918. 3 lin. ft.

An act of September 27, 1890, created the Rock Creek Park Commission to acquire land for Rock Creek Park in Washington. In 1918 its responsibilities were transferred to the Office of Public Buildings and Grounds. These records include Commission and Board of Control proceedings, letters received, land acquisition records, and records of the assistant engineer in charge of Rock Creek Park.

RECORDS OF THE ROCK CREEK AND POTOMAC PARKWAY COMMISSION. 1913-33. 9 lin. ft.

This Commission, established by an act of March 4, 1913, acquired land for a parkway connecting the Rock Creek, Zoological, and Potomac Parks. Included are general records of the executive and disbursing officer, 1923-33, land acquisition records, 1913-ca. 1930, accounts, 1915-26, and reference material concerning the Chesapeake and Ohio Canal, 1926-30.

RECORDS OF THE WASHINGTON NATIONAL MONUMENT SOCIETY. 1833-1951. 28 lin. ft.

In 1848 the Congress authorized the Washington National Monument Society, organized by Washington citizens in 1833, to erect the Washington Monument on public grounds. The task was transferred to the Joint Commission for the Completion of the Washington Monument, appointed by the Congress in 1876 and dissolved in 1888. The records include proceedings of the Society, 1833-1934, with gaps, and of the Board of Managers, 1834-58; organizational and administrative records of the Society, 1833-87; fragmentary general and miscellaneous letters received, 1835-1925; letters sent, 1858-83 and 1889-95; letters received by the Society, 1879-1907; correspondence, 1923-44; drawings, designs, plans, and photographs of the monument, 1836-1934; records relating to the "Pope's Stone" and other memorial stones donated for the monument, ca. 1833-85; proceedings and letters received and sent, 1876-88, of the Joint Commission for the Completion of the Washington Monument, and proceedings, 1879-84, and letters received and sent, 1879-88, of its Building Committee; proceedings, 1884-85, and a report published by congressional order, 1885, of the Joint Commission on the Dedication of the Monument; records concerning the construction of the monument, 1879-89; and records of the custodian of the monument concerning its maintenance, 1884-1922.

RECORDS OF STATUE AND MEMORIAL COMMISSIONS. 1889-1941. 71 lin. ft.

Included are records of the Arlington Memorial Amphitheater, Arlington Memorial Bridge, Barry Statue, Columbus Memorial, Grant Memorial, Hancock Memorial, John Paul Jones Statue, Kosciuszko Statue, Lincoln Memorial, Logan Statue, Longfellow Statue, McClellan Statue, Meade Memorial, Pulaski Statue, Sheridan Statue, Sherman Statue, Witherspoon Statue, Memorial to Women of the Civil War, and Memorial to Women of the World War (I) Commissions,

including minutes, correspondence of commission secretaries and executive and disbursing officers, scale drawings, samples of marble and other stone, work and time reports, fiscal records, and records concerning monument dedications.

CARTOGRAPHIC AND AUDIOVISUAL RECORDS. 1771-1934. 1,073 items.

Cartographic records (152 items) include maps and plans of Washington showing wards, public reservations, street patterns, property valuations, the Executive Mansion, the Capitol grounds, wharves, and Federal office buildings, 1771-1919; plats of Washington showing Water Street, water lots, and wharfing plans, 1793-1835; Nicholas King's manuscript plats of Washington, 1803; and copies of P. C. L'Enfant's, Ellicott's, and Dermott's maps of the District of Columbia, with a history of each map, 1791-95.

Audiovisual records, 1860-1934 (921 items), consist of photographs of memorials, monuments, parks, and buildings, including the Arlington Memorial, Woodrow Wilson, and 14th Street Bridges; White House reconstruction, 1927; the Navy Department Building, 1884; the State, War, and Navy Building, 1907-12; the Washington Monument, 1860-1934; the construction of the Lincoln Memorial; and the Grant Memorial Commission and its monument. There are also photographs of maps of European areas, ca. 1918, and of the Pasadena Stadium.

Microfilm Publication: *Records of the District of Columbia Commissioners and of the Offices Concerned With Public Buildings, 1791-1867*, M371, 27 rolls, DP.

RECORDS OF THE
RENT COMMISSION
OF THE DISTRICT OF COLUMBIA
(RECORD GROUP 132)

The Rent Commission of the District of Columbia was created by an act of October 22, 1919, as an emergency agency with authority to fix fair and reasonable rentals for dwellings, apartments, hotels, and business properties in the District of Columbia; prescribe standard forms of leases; and recover, through actions in municipal court, rents collected in excess of amounts fixed by the Commission. The establishing act provided for terminating the Commission on October 22, 1921, but subsequent statutes extended its life to May 22, 1925. After that date prosecution of pending cases was vested in the Attorney General and was handled at his direction by the U.S. attorney for the District of Columbia. By June 1928 all rent actions had been resolved and the records were transferred to the Department of Justice. Case papers filed in appeals to the Supreme Court of the District of Columbia, 1925-28, are among the records of district courts of the United States (see RG 21.)

There are 7 cubic feet of records dated between 1920 and 1925 in this record group.

RECORDS. 1920-25. 8 lin. ft.

These consist chiefly of minutes, 1923-25, a final report, 1925, general correspondence, 1920-25, and copies of records relating to cases taken to the Court of Appeals and to the Supreme Court of the District of Columbia, 1923-24.

OTHER GOVERNMENTS

WAR DEPARTMENT COLLECTION OF
CONFEDERATE RECORDS
(RECORD GROUP 109)

The War Department Collection of Confederate Records consists of records of the Confederate States of America acquired by capture or surrender at the close of the Civil War and those later acquired by donation or purchase. On July 21, 1865, the Secretary of War established a unit in the Adjutant General's Office for the collection, safekeeping, and publication of the "rebel archives." The records were used in protecting the U.S. Government against claims arising from the war, in establishing pension claims, and for historical purposes. After many changes both in location and custody, the records were placed in the Organization Records Section of the Old Records Division of the Adjutant General's Office, from which they were transferred to the National Archives. Certain Federal records relating to Confederate soldiers, maintained with the Confederate records and in part interfiled with them, are included in this record group. Also included are records created by the custodians of the records.

See Dallas Irvine, "The Fate of Confederate Archives," *American Historical Review*, 44: 823-841 (July 1939); Irvine, "The Archive Office of the War Department; Repository of Captured Confederate Archives," *Military Affairs*, 1: 93-111 (Spring 1946); and Carl L. Lokke, "The Captured Confederate Archives Under Francis Lieber," *American Archivist*, 9: 277-319 (October 1946).

There are 5,730 cubic feet of records dated between 1860 and 1867 in this record group.

COLLECTED BOUND RECORDS OF EXECUTIVE, LEGISLATIVE, AND JUDICIAL OFFICES. 1860-65. 275 lin. ft.

In 1881 the first of the 129 volumes of *The War of the Rebellion: A Compilation of the Official Records of the Union and Confederate Armies* was published. To facilitate this publication and to make the records more usable for researches regarding claimants and pension applications, the offices having custody of the Confederate archives classified the bound volumes roughly according to provenance into subgroups designated "chapters," the volumes numbered serially in each chapter. The volumes consist of diverse records of varying importance, such as letters, telegrams, and endorsements sent; registers of letters received; orders, circulars, regulations, and other issuances; records of appointments, promotions, discharges, and other personnel actions; account books; and records of receipts, requisitions, and inventories of supplies.

The chapters into which the volumes were classified are I, Adjutant and Inspector General's Department; II, Military Commands; III, Engineer Department; IV, Ordnance Department; V, Quartermaster Department; VI, Medical Department; VII, Legislative Records; VIII, Miscellaneous Records; IX, Office of the Secretary of War; X, Treasury Department; XI, Post Office Department; and XII, Judiciary.

UNBOUND CORRESPONDENCE, PAPERS, AND REPORTS. 1861–65. 670 lin. ft.

Most of the records are those of the Confederate War Department and consist of reports, letters, and telegrams. received chiefly by the Offices of the Secretary of War, the Adjutant and Inspector General, the Quartermaster General, and territorial commands and armies. Other records include inspection and battle reports, orders and circulars, and a collection of officers' papers. There are some records of other executive departments, such as Treasury Department returns relating to the war tax, and also documents relating to vessels owned or chartered by the Navy Department. In addition there are South Carolina District Court sequestration case files and some legislative records, including bills and resolutions, messages from the President, and rough journal notes.

Much correspondence relating to particular officers or enlisted men was removed from the letters received and other series and filed in the compiled military service records. Original documents selected for publication in the *War of the Rebellion: A Compilation of the Official Records of the Union and Confederate Armies* were placed in a "publication file," arranged in the order in which the documents were published.

CONFEDERATE ARMY ROLLS AND RETURNS. 1861–65. 1,000 lin. ft.

Most of the muster rolls, payrolls, and returns of the Confederate Army are for organizations connected with a Con-

federate State. There are similar rolls and returns for organizations raised directly by the Confederate Government and not identified with a State. The rolls list name, rank, age, date of joining for duty, and similar information for persons mustered into the service, and are supplemented by clothing, commutation, extra-duty, and hospital rolls and casualty lists. Information relating to the military service and medical treatment of individual soldiers contained in the rolls was abstracted on cards and placed in the compiled military service records.

CONFEDERATE PAYROLLS. 1861–65. 120 lin. ft.

These consist of receipts of payment for civilian labor, with the name of employing officer, place of employment, name and occupation of employee, period of service, and rate and amount of pay on each roll; and slave payrolls with similar information and name of owner, with his or his attorney's signature for receipt of wages.

COMPILED MILITARY SERVICE RECORDS. 1861–65. 13,500 lin. ft.

These records and their name indexes were compiled by the War Department beginning in 1903. They consist of a jacket-envelope for each Confederate soldier labeled with his name, rank, and unit in which he served. The jacket-envelope typically contains card abstracts of entries relating to the soldier as found in original muster rolls, returns, rosters, payrolls, appointment books, hospital rolls and registers, Union prison registers and rolls, parole lists, inspection reports, and similar records; and the originals of any papers relating to the particular soldier.

The series of compiled service records for soldiers is arranged in three subseries filed in jacket-envelopes. The first includes men who served in organizations connected with one of the Confederate States. The second includes men who served in organizations raised directly by the Confederate Government and not identified with any one State. The third is for general and staff officers and nonregimental enlisted men. There is also a series consisting of card abstracts and personal papers accumulated by the War Department to be interfiled with the regular series of compiled service records. There are three similar, but very small, series of compiled service records for naval and marine personnel.

DOCUMENTS RELATING TO CONFEDERATE CITIZENS OR BUSINESS FIRMS. 1861-65. 1,240 lin. ft.

These documents relate to Confederate citizens, railroads, newspapers, and companies doing business with the Confederate Government. The file was compiled by the U.S. War Department and contains original documents, with cross-references to other compiled records and to the bound records. Most of the material was originally included in money accounts of Confederate quartermasters, commissaries, and other disbursing officers that had been settled or were in the process of being settled by the Confederate Treasury Department.

UNITED STATES RECORDS RELATING TO CONFEDERATES. 1861-67. 900 lin. ft.

These consist of prisoner-of-war records, chiefly of Union prisons in which Confederate soldiers were confined, and include prison registers and rolls, records of arrivals, commitments, transfers, deaths, paroles, and prisoners desiring to take oaths of allegiance to the United States (information from many of these records was abstracted on cards and placed in the compiled military service records); and Union provost marshals' records relating to such matters as charges, arrests, and detentions of persons suspected of aiding or spying for the enemy or violating military orders, persons claiming compensation for property used or seized by Union military authorities, and persons requesting passes to cross the lines into the Confederacy or permits to visit persons in prisons.

See Elizabeth Bethel, comp., *Preliminary Inventory of the War Department Collection of Confederate Records*, PI 101 (1957).

Microfilm Publications: Numerous series of these records are available as microfilm publications. Among them are the letters and telegrams sent and received by the Confederate Secretary of War, the Adjutant and Inspector General, and Quartermaster Generals; and the compiled service records of Confederate soldiers and related indexes, selected records relating to Confederate prisoners of war, and papers relating to civilians and business firms. For a complete listing see the current *List of National Archives Microfilm Publications*.

TREASURY DEPARTMENT COLLECTION OF CONFEDERATE RECORDS (RECORD GROUP 365)

Although most Confederate treasury records that came into the possession of the U.S. Government passed into and remained in the custody of the War Department (see RG 109), some were acquired by the Treasury Department through special agents appointed to regulate commerce in areas recaptured by Federal forces and to superintend captured and abandoned Confederate property. These records were supplemented by purchases in 1872 and 1873 and the transfer of a small quantity of records from the War Department. This collection comprises records of the central office of the Treasury Department, records of local officials of the Treasury and Justice Departments and of State governments, records of the War Department's Trans-Mississippi Department cotton bureaus, and records of the U.S. Treasury Department relating mainly to attempts after the war to secure Confederate property abroad. Indexes prepared after the records were acquired by the U.S. Treasury Department are included.

The Confederate Treasury Department was established February 21, 1861, by an act of the Confederate Congress. Its internal structure, patterned after that of the Federal Treasury, included Offices of the Secretary of the Treasury, Assistant Secretary, Treasurer, Comptroller, First, Second, and Third Auditors, Register, Commissioner of Taxes, and Deposit; and the Produce Loan, Treasury Note, and Lighthouse Bureaus. Department field officers included assistant treasurers; collectors of customs; superintendents of the mints; tax officials; employees of the Produce Loan, Treasury Note, and Lighthouse Bureaus; and agents assigned to the Trans-Mississippi Department cotton bureaus. Duties of these officers were the receipt and disbursement of public funds; sale and distribution of bonds and stocks; purchase and transportation of cotton and other supplies; printing of treasury notes, stocks, and bonds; collection of taxes and customs; and maintenance of lighthouses and lightships.

There are 102 cubic feet of records dated between 1861 and 1865 in this record group.

RECORDS. 1861-65. 122 lin. ft.

Central office records include letters received and sent by the Office of the Secretary of the Treasury and financial and accounting records relating to loans, expenses of Members of the House of Representatives, naval and army accounts, military claims, diplomatic accounts, post office accounts, and customs and internal taxes. Field records relate to cotton transactions, produce loans, loan certificates, and customs, including cargo manifests. For the southern district of Georgia and the eastern district of Texas there are district court records relating to sequestered property; there are also admiralty and criminal case files for the latter court.

Records of the Trans-Mississippi Department Headquarters Office of the Cotton Bureau and the cotton bureau at Houston include cotton transactions and related correspondence. Records relating to the Federal Government's attempts to obtain title to Confederate property abroad include correspondence relating to foreign loans, including the Erlanger loan, and to the construction of ships.

See Carmelita S. Ryan, comp., *Preliminary Inventory of the Treasury Department Collection of Confederate Records*, PI 169 (1967); and Beers, *Confederate Guide* (1968).

Microfilm Publications: *Letters Received by the Confederate Secretary of the Treasury, 1861-1865*, M499, 57 rolls, DP; and *Letters Sent by the Confederate Secretary of the Treasury, 1861-1865*, M500, 1 roll, DP.

RECORDS OF FORMER RUSSIAN AGENCIES
(RECORD GROUP 261)

This collective record group consists of records of certain agencies of the Imperial Russian Government that later came into the possession of the Department of State.

The Russian-American Company was

created July 8, 1799, by Czar Paul I and was granted de facto political authority and a monopoly of trade in Russia's North American possessions, including Alaska. The Company was administered by a board of directors in St. Petersburg, while control of affairs in Alaska was in the hands of governors general appointed by the directors. Local headquarters were established at Sitka in 1799, but an Indian revolt in 1802 drove out the Russians. In 1804 the Company retook Sitka, built a strong fort, and used it as a central office until 1867 when Alaska was purchased by the United States.

A second body of records orginated in consulates maintained by the Imperial Russian Government in the United States and Canada that were closed on different dates in the 1920's. A third group is the records of the Russian Supply Committee, organized in 1915 with central offices in New York, which coordinated and supervised the purchase of supplies for military purposes during World War I.

On the Russian-American Company see Hubert H. Bancroft, *History of Alaska* (San Francisco, 1886); and S. B. Okun, *The Russian-American Company* (Cambridge, Mass., 1951).

There are 679 cubic feet of records dated between 1802 and 1922 in this record group.

RECORDS OF THE RUSSIAN-AMERICAN COMPANY. 1802 and 1817-67. 23 lin. ft.

Under the convention by which Russia ceded Alaska to the United States, concluded March 30, 1867, "any Government archives, papers, and documents relative to the territory and dominion aforesaid, which may now be existing there," were transferred to the United States. Consisting of 92 volumes, almost entirely in Russian longhand, they include: letters sent, 1818-67, to the board of directors in St. Petersburg and to subordinate local settlements, relating to native tribes, the Hudson Bay Company, fur prices, transportation, food and supplies, farming and animal husbandry, and vital statistics; letters received, April 18, 1802, and 1817-66, from the board of directors, relating to fur, trade, fisheries, native tribes, boundaries, and the Russian Orthodox Church (the Department of State prepared a calendar for these letters); logs of Company ships, 1850-67, on their voyages to California, Siberia, China, the Hawaiian Islands, and Russia; and journals of explorations of Lt. Lavrentii A. Zagoskin, 1842-44, into the lower Yukon basin and the southwestern mainland of Alaska, and of Capt. N. Arkhimandritov, June-August 1860 and July-August 1864, on Kodiak Island, Norton Sound, and the Pribilof Islands.

RECORDS OF RUSSIAN CONSULATES. 1862-1922. 165 lin. ft. (in WNRC).

Included are records of consulates at New York, Philadelphia, Washington, Chicago, San Francisco, Portland, Seattle, Honolulu, Montreal, and Vancouver.

RECORDS OF THE RUSSIAN SUPPLY COMMITTEE. 1914-22. 603 lin. ft. (in WNRC).

These consist of correspondence with commercial firms and U.S. Government agencies, reports, and accounting and other records.

Microfilm Publication: *Records of the Russian-American Company, 1802-1867*, M11, 77 rolls.

RECORDS OF THE GOVERNMENT OF THE VIRGIN ISLANDS
(RECORD GROUP 55)

The Danish West Indies (consisting of three main islands—St. Thomas, settled by the Danes in 1672, St. John, occupied in 1717, and St. Croix, purchased from the French in 1733—and many smaller, uninhabited islands) were administered by the Danish West India and Guinea Co. until they became Danish royal colonies in 1754. Except for a few months in 1801 and for the period 1807-15, when England held them, these islands remained under Danish rule until the United States purchased them in 1917. They were renamed the Virgin Islands of the United States and placed under the jurisdiction of the Navy Department. In 1931 they were transferred to the jurisdiction of the Interior Department (see RG 126). A Governor appointed by the President heads the local administration of the islands.

Danish records relating to the cession or the rights and property of the inhabitants of the islands were transferred to the United States by the treaty of cession and are in this record group. Some records of the Danish administration of the islands are in the Rigsarkivet and in Danish provincial archives. Other records of the islands, chiefly relating to land titles, are in the Bancroft Library at the University of California. Remaining in the Virgin Islands are all extant land records from 1754 to the present time. The Library of Congress has transcripts relating to the Danish West Indies, 1653-1790, that were made from records in the Danish archives and other depositories.

There are 1,670 cubic feet of records dated between 1672 and 1950 in this record group.

RECORDS OF THE GOVERNMENT OF THE DANISH WEST INDIES. 1672-1917. 1,147 lin. ft.

Most of these records are in Danish. Administrative records include the Governor's orders issued at St. Thomas, 1672-1840, and St. Croix, 1733-1862; the daybook of Johan Lorentz, the Vice Commandant at St. Thomas, 1694-97; Governor Clausen's letters to foreign officials, 1774-84; Governor von Schol-

ten's letter books, 1834-53; Governor Helweg-Larsen's official records, 1916; drafts of letters to Denmark, 1778-1831; letters to Denmark or to island officials transmitting instructions from Denmark, 1874-1917; correspondence with consular officials in St. Thomas, 1839-1916; protocols and other records of the sanitary, poor, health, quarantine, hospital, road, and other quasi-executive governmental commissions in St. Thomas and St. Croix, 1853-1917; general ledgers for St. Thomas, 1816-1908, and St. Croix, 1741-1850; duplicate accounts of the St. Thomas colonial treasury, 1829-1916; tax lists for St. Thomas, 1823-54, and St. Croix, 1743-1850; lists of the King's Negroes, 1820-33; reports about slaves appraised value, 1846-52, and sugar exported from St. Croix, 1835-92; a record book of government-owned sugar plantations, 1835-88; records relating to the insurrections of 1848 and 1878; correspondence and reports concerning education, 1876-1917; and miscellaneous administrative records, 1855-1917.

Legislative records include proceedings of the St. Croix Burgher Council, 1767-80, and of colonial councils, 1852-1917.

Judicial and police records from St. Thomas include an upper court protocol, 1794-98; town court cases, 1860-1917; police journals and protocols, 1853-1917; and police correspondence, 1852-1917. Judicial and police records from St. Croix include public notices, contracts, and petitions, 1771-1818; annual reports of the town court, 1879-1908; police court cases, 1852-1912; police journals and protocols, 1844-1917; and police reports, 1869-1914. There are also police journals and protocols, 1892-1917, and correspondence, 1915-17, from St. John.

Military records include reports and rolls of the royal military force at St. Thomas, 1802-86, and military letter books from St. Croix, 1854-81. There are also correspondence and other records relating to St. Thomas Harbor, 1854–1917.

RECORDS OF THE GOVERNMENT OF THE VIRGIN ISLANDS OF THE UNITED STATES. 1917–50. 190 lin. ft.

Records of the Office of Governor and of the Government Secretary, including annual reports of the Governor and subordinate offices, 1917–49; orders and proclamations issued by the Governor, 1917–43; executive officials' miscellaneous correspondence, 1920–50; general files concerning island government, 1917–43, and radiograms sent and received, 1917–49; records relating to relief and rehabilitation programs of the Civil Works Administration, 1933–34, Federal Emergency Relief Administration and National Industrial Recovery Act, 1933–37, Public Works Administration, 1933–38, Virgin Islands Emergency Relief Administration, 1935–36, and Work Projects Administration, 1938–44; St. Croix homestead agreements, 1933–39, and contracts, 1933–41; records concerning the establishment of the Virgin Islands Company, 1934–36; records relating to budgetary and other fiscal matters of the central administration, 1920–41; records concerning the budgets for St. Thomas, St. John, and St. Croix, 1921–42; correspondence concerning passports, 1917–43; registration certificates and correspondence relating to trademarks and patents, 1918–33; and inventories of property and furnishings, chiefly for executive mansions, 1940–49.

General files of an office successively known as the Office of the Despatching Secretary, the Lieutenant Governor, and the Administrator for St. Croix, 1917–40.

Fragmentary records of departments and officials, including the Aide for Public Welfare, 1923–30; Director of the Department of Agriculture, Commerce, and Labor, 1925–31; Commissioner of Finance, 1927–46; and Director of Community Activities, 1931. Fragmentary records of emergency or special offices, consisting of correspondence of the Food Commission, 1917–20; records of the supervisor of the Civilian Conservation Corps, Virgin Islands, 1939–43; correspondence of the Council for Defense, Municipality of St. Thomas and St. John, 1941–42, and of the manager of the Bluebeard Castle Hotel at St. Thomas, 1935–37.

AUDIOVISUAL RECORDS. 1934–41. 300 items.

Photographs of projects sponsored by the Civil Works Administration, the Public Works Administration, the Work Projects Administration, the Civilian Conservation Corps, and governmental units in the Virgin Islands to improve housing, public buildings, parks, and roads in the islands.

See Donn Hooker, comp., *Preliminary Inventory of the Records of the Government of the Virgin Islands of the United States*, PI 126 (1960).

Microfilm Publications: *Records of the Danish Government of the Virgin Islands*, T39, 22 rolls; and *Records Relating to the Danish West Indies, 1672–1860, Received From the Danish National Archives*, T952, 19 rolls.

RECORDS OF THE SPANISH GOVERNORS OF PUERTO RICO (RECORD GROUP 186)

By the Treaty of Paris of December 10, 1898, Spain ceded Puerto Rico to the United States. The cession included Spanish rights to the official archives and records on the islands, which the United States agreed to preserve and make available for use. After visiting Puerto Rico the superintendent of the

Manuscript Department of the Library of Congress recommended to American military authorities the transfer of part of the records of the Spanish period to the Library of Congress. Cayetano Coll y Toste, a Puerto Rican scholar, was put in charge of selecting material for the transfer, which was made between June 13, 1899, and March 6, 1900. Important administrative records were later returned to Puerto Rico. These records were received by the Quartermaster Department at San Juan from the transport *McClellan* on April 8, 1901. Most of them were destroyed in 1926 by fire in the Archivo Historico at San Juan. The fragmentary correspondence and related executive records received or created by the Spanish Governors of Puerto Rico remaining in the United States were first placed in the Library of Congress; they were transferred to the National Archives in 1943. A joint resolution of August 21, 1957, authorized the return of the Puerto Rican archives in the National Archives to the Commonwealth of Puerto Rico.

There are 134 cubic feet of records dated between 1754 and 1899 in this record group.

RECORDS RELATING TO POLITICAL AND CIVIL AFFAIRS. 1754-1899. 61 lin. ft.

These records, concerning the activities of the Gobierno Politico, include royal orders, census records, consular correspondence, and records that relate to elections, foreigners, publications, and the Rebelion de Lares. Also included is the Coll y Toste inventory, compiled in 1899 at the time of the transfer of the records to the Library of Congress. It lists the contents of the 2,246 legajos (bundles) included in the transfer.

RECORDS RELATING TO FISCAL AFFAIRS. 1782-1896. 12 lin. ft.

These relate to matters such as budgets, contraband, counterfeiting, debts, fines, and public expenditures, and include correspondence signed by Alejandro Ramirez, the Puerto Rican official who planned and established a fiscal system for the island, 1813-16, and financial reports.

RECORDS RELATING TO MILITARY AFFAIRS. 1761-1890. 15 lin. ft.

These records concern such topics as artillery, cavalry, defense, deserters, fortifications, military conduct and decorations, other military affairs, and the Presidio of La Puntilla.

RECORDS RELATING TO NAVAL AFFAIRS. 1782-1891. 4 lin. ft.

Included are correspondence and other records concerning appointments, lighthouses, naval matters, shipwrecks, and Commodore David Porter, USN, who conducted a campaign to suppress piracy in Caribbean waters, landed troops in Fajardo, P.R., and allegedly committed hostile acts on Spanish soil, 1823-25.

RECORDS RELATING TO ECCLESIASTICAL AFFAIRS. 1782-1897. 3 lin. ft.

Included are records relating to such matters as appointments of priests, church statistics, the Convent of San Francisco, pastoral visits, and tithes.

RECORDS FROM GOVERNMENT AGENCIES. 1796-1897. 31 lin. ft.

These consist of correspondence and other records received by the Governor's Office from government agencies, including those concerned with public health, public works, and postal delivery.

RECORDS FROM MUNICIPALITIES. 1765-1898. 76 lin. ft.

Included are letters received by the Governor's Office from mayors and other public officials of approximately 75 towns in Puerto Rico, accompanied by resolutions of town councils, tax lists, proposed budgets, lists of inhabitants, and reports on the number of persons vaccinated and on other topics.

Microfilm Publications: *Expediente Sobre la Rebelion de Lares (Case File on the Rebellion of Lares)*, *1868-1869*, T1120, 6 rolls; *Registro Central de Esclavos (Slave Schedules)*, *1872*, T1121, 8 rolls; and *Reales Ordenes, 1792-1793, y Reales Ordenes y Decretos, 1767-1854 (Royal Orders and Decrees)*, T1122, 1 roll.

NATIONAL ARCHIVES COLLECTION OF FOREIGN RECORDS SEIZED, 1941- (RECORD GROUP 242)

During and after World War II and the Korean war many seized records were sent to the United States. Seized German records that had no security restrictions were returned to the Federal Republic of Germany after historically valuable parts were microfilmed by the National Archives in cooperation with the American Historical Association. This record group consists of such records that have been separately maintained and that have not been assimilated into the National Archives Collection of World War II War Crimes Records, Record Group 238, or several other record groups. The collection was augmented by microfilm of seized records accessioned from the Department of State, the U.S. Naval History Division, and other sources as described below; in fact, the majority of these records are microfilm copies and photoprints.

See Air University Human Resources Research Institute, *Guide to Captured German Documents* (Maxwell Air Force Base, 1952), and National Archives and Records Service, *Supplement to the Guide to Captured German Documents* (1959); National Archives and Records Service, *Guides to German Records Microfilmed at Alexandria, Va.*, 1- (1958-), and *Guide to Records of the Italian Armed Forces* (1967); American Historical Association Committee for the Study of War Documents, *A Catalog of Files and Microfilms of the German Foreign Ministry Archives, 1867-1920* (1959); and Department of State and Hoover Institution, *A Catalog of Files and Microfilms of the German Foreign Ministry Archives, 1920-45* (1962).

There are 4,600 cubic feet of records dated between 1679 and 1952 in this record group.

RECORDS OF THE GERMAN FOREIGN MINISTRY AND THE REICH CHANCELLERY.
1833-1945. 5,795 rolls of microfilm.

The German Foreign Ministry in 1939 consisted of the Office of the Foreign Ministry, Office of the State Secretary, Head of the Foreign Organization in the Foreign Ministry, Office of the State Secretary for Special Duties, Office of the Ambassador for Special Duties, Political and Legal Departments, and Departments of Protocol, Personnel and Administration, Economic Policy, Cultural Policy, News Service and Press, and Information. While Foreign Ministry organization remained almost unchanged between 1867 and 1919, in 1920 and again in 1936 major reorganizations occurred. The records consist of selected diplomatic documents of the German Foreign Ministry, 1833-1945 (mostly dated after 1914), and papers of Gustav Stresemann, 1887-1930, Friedrich von Holstein, 1883-1909, and other German diplomats, 1833-1927.

Records of the Old and New Reich Chancelleries, 1919-45, which were evacuated to Whaddon Hall, England, with unrelated records of the Foreign Ministry, include Old Chancellery records consisting of protocols of cabinet meetings, cabinet files on foreign and military affairs, and records relating to such domestic matters as policing political activities and relations with Prussia, Bavaria, and other State or Provincial governments; and records of relations with churches and on racial policies.

RECORDS OF THE REICH MINISTRY OF ECONOMICS. 1914–45. 8 lin. ft. (in WNRC) and 156 rolls of microfilm.

The Reichswirtschaftsministerium, established in 1919 to succeed the Reich Economics Office, was unified with its Prussian counterpart in 1934 as the Reich and Prussian Ministry of Economics. After annexation of Austria in 1938 the name was changed to Reich Ministry of Economics. The records consist of correspondence and other files concerning operations of the Ministry and its offices, including the Reich Office for Soil Exploration, personnel matters, the economy, employment of prisoners of war, security in war plants, and industrial planning, production, and distribution.

RECORDS OF THE REICH MINISTRY FOR PUBLIC ENLIGHTENMENT AND PROPAGANDA. 1928–45. 133 rolls of microfilm.

The Reichsministerium fuer Volksaufklaerung und Propaganda, which prepared Nazi propaganda and was the censorship authority for Germany, was established in 1933 to publicize the national reconstruction program and Reich domestic and foreign policies, and to disseminate news. The records consist of correspondence and other records concerning personnel, administration, and budgetary matters; organization, operation, and censorship of theatrical, musical, broadcasting, and publishing industries; professional and technical training schools; and jurisdiction of courts.

RECORDS OF THE REICH AIR MINISTRY. 1912–45. 526 rolls of microfilm.

Although set up in 1933, as successor to the Office of Reich Commissioner for Aviation, to deal with civil and military aviation, the Reichsluftfahrtministerium was concerned mostly with Air Force matters. The records are those of the Ministry and affiliated organizations—including the German Academy for Aeronautical Research—and aircraft manufacturing firms, relating to aeronautical research, aircraft production and maintenance, mobilization of the aircraft industry, contracts, labor (including forced labor), aviation clubs, and general administration.

RECORDS OF THE REICH MINISTRY FOR ARMAMENTS AND WAR PRODUCTION. 1925–45. 193 rolls of microfilm.

The Reichsministerium fuer Ruestung und Kriegsproduktion was established in March 1940, and Fritz Todt, who headed the "Organisation Todt," was its first minister. The functions of the Office of War Economy and Armaments of the German Armed Forces High Command were absorbed by the Ministry in February 1943, and it was renamed the Reich Ministry for Armaments and War Production in September 1943. Records include those of the Ministry, the subordinate Augsburg Armament Command, and the "Organisation Todt," comprising Reich Minister Albert Speer's correspondence with other officials and industrial firms. Other records relate to war production, planning, and quotas; allocation of raw materials, fuel, machinery, plants, and labor; use of foreign workers and prisoners of war; transportation; air raid damage; industrial security; and personnel and administration.

RECORDS OF THE REICH COMMISSIONER FOR THE STRENGTHENING OF GERMANDOM. 1939-45. 20 rolls of microfilm.

The Office of the Reichskommissar fuer die Festigung des deutschen Volkstums was established in 1939 under Himmler as Commissioner to repatriate ethnic Germans from the Baltic countries. Later it resettled ethnic Germans from Rumania, the Soviet Union, and Tyrol. The records, which include some orders, circulars, and other administrative records, relate to resettlement in Germany of ethnic Germans from occupied territories and to confiscated land and estates.

RECORDS OF THE PLENIPOTENTIARY FOR HIGH FREQUENCY RESEARCH. 1930-45. 45 lin. ft. (in WNRC) and 153 rolls of microfilm.

The Bevollmaechtigter fuer Hochfrequenzforschung was instituted to coordinate German research and development in high frequency techniques and related fields and to keep informed of developments in other countries. The records consist of minutes (in WNRC), English-language extracts of reports from individuals and State and private technological institutions, and reports concerning radio, television, radar, navigation, and communications.

RECORDS OF THE REICH MINISTRY FOR THE OCCUPIED EASTERN TERRITORIES. 1924-45. 152 rolls of microfilm.

The Reichsministerium fuer die besetzten Ostgebiete, established July 17, 1941, succeeded the Defense Economy Staff East. Three subordinate Reich commissioners were appointed to direct the administration of the Ostland (Estonia, Latvia, and Lithuania), the Ukraine, and White Ruthenia. The majority of these records, 1941-45, relate to activities of the Ministry and its subordinate Reichskommissariat Ostland, chiefly the exploitation of resources and workers in occupied eastern territories, treatment of Jews and eastern partisans, land reform, and the status of church and clergy under German occupation. Also included are records of the Einsatzstab Reichsleiter Rosenberg (Task Force Reich Leader [Alfred] Rosenberg), which was engaged in cultural spoliation throughout occupied Europe during the same period, and records pertaining to Rosenberg's function as Hitler's appointee for the supervision of the entire intellectual and ideological schooling and education of the Nazi Party, 1935-43.

RECORDS OF THE OFFICE OF THE GENERAL PLENIPOTENTIARY FOR THE SERBIAN ECONOMY. 1941-45. 89 rolls of microfilm.

The office of Generalbevollmaechtigter fuer die Wirtschaft in Serbien was established in 1941 to meet goals of the Reich 4-year plan by exploiting the Balkan areas. The records consist of reports, contracts, appraisals, and other records concerning economic conditions in Serbia, confiscating real property and businesses of Jews, administering estates, legal status of seized assets, and the appointment of German administrators.

RECORDS OF OTHER REICH MINISTRIES AND OFFICES. 1919-45. 23 rolls of microfilm.

These include fragmentary records of the Reichsjustizministerium (Reich Ministry of Justice) on administering prisons and transferring prisoners to the Gestapo or to concentration camps, 1926-45; Reichsfinanzministerium (Reich Ministry of Finance), relating to taxation, social security, war loans, and expenditures, 1924-45; Reichsarbeitsministerium (Reich Ministry of Labor), on economic and political conditions and economic exploitation of occupied territories, conscript labor, and persecution of Jews, 1941–42; Reichsministerium des Innern (Reich Ministry of the Interior), relating to police regulations and budgetary and personnel matters, 1932–44; Reichsministerium fuer Ernaehrung und Landwirtschaft (Reich Ministry for Food and Agriculture), 1919–45; Reichsforschungsrat (Reich Research Council), relating to research and production of war materials, 1934–45; Reichsamt fuer Wetterdienst (Reich Weather Bureau), relating to weather in the Soviet Union, 1941–42; and the Generalinspektor fuer das deutsche Strassenwesen (General Inspector for German Roads), relating to construction of the Autobahn, provisions for air raid shelters, evacuation of agencies close to the front, and administration and personnel, 1936–45.

RECORDS OF THE REICH LEADER OF THE SS AND CHIEF OF THE GERMAN POLICE.
1922–45. 16 lin. ft. and 1,746 rolls of microfilm.

The protean office of the Reichsfuehrer SS und Chef der deutschen Polizei had its modest beginnings in the Stabswache (Headquarters Guard), which was founded in March 1923 (to protect Hitler, party functionaries, and the Nazi Party itself), renamed Stosstrupp Hitler (Hitler's Shock Troop) in May 1923, and reorganized as the Schutzstaffel/SS (Security Force) in 1925. After Heinrich Himmler was appointed Reich leader in 1929, SS functions were expanded to include control of SS Verfuegungstruppe (SS Special Employment Troops), which formed the nucleus of the Waffen SS (Armed SS), established in 1940, and the Totenkopf Verbaende (Death's Head Formations), which furnished guards and administrative personnel for concentration camps. Between 1933 and 1936, Himmler

expanded his initial government assignment as Chief of Bavarian State Police to the same position in all German States, culminating in his appointment as Chief of German Police. In the process, he achieved a combination of existing government agencies (uniformed police, civilian police, political police) and party organization (security services). During the war the SS, through the SS Wirtschafts-Verwaltungshauptamt, also operated industrial enterprises, such as the Deutsche Wirtschaftsbetriebe G.m.b.H., established in 1940 as a holding company. Labor was supplied mainly by concentration camp inmates. As microfilmed, the records are a conglomeration of the central files for all of Himmler's variegated activities; substantial but incomplete files of central, regional, and local police; and incomplete records of the security service's domestic and intelligence activities as well as general and personnel records of the SS and the SA (Sturmabteilung), records of military operations of the Armed-SS, records relating to combat activities of the police (including the Gestapo), security measures, procuring raw materials, resettling Germans and non-Germans, race policies, persecution of Jews, Nazi ideology and philosophy, church affairs, organization, administration, military and political training, antipartisan and partisan warfare, medical experiments, dossiers on persons, business correspondence of the Deutsche Wirtschaftsbetriebe, and lists of concentration camp inmates.

RECORDS OF HEADQUARTERS, GERMAN ARMED FORCES HIGH COMMAND. 1914–45. 2 lin. ft. and 1,524 rolls of microfilm.

The Oberkommando der Wehrmacht/ OKW was created by the Fuehrer on February 4, 1938, to replace the Reich War Ministry. Subordinate to it were the Army, Navy, and Air Force High Commands. The Chief of the Armed Forces High Command, Gen. (later Field

Marshal) Wilhelm Keitel, was subordinate only to Hitler. There are general records relating to overall activities and operations of the Reich War Ministry, 1925-44, particularly during World War II; the Supreme Commander of the Armed Forces, 1933-45; the Chief of the Armed Forces High Command and the Armed Forces Operations Staff, 1936-45; the Organization Branch, 1941-45; the Foreign and Counterintelligence Office, 1928-45; the Military Economics and Armament Office, 1931-45; the Armed Forces adjutant at Hitler's headquarters, 1938-45; and other offices, 1914-45.

RECORDS OF HEADQUARTERS, GERMAN AIR FORCE HIGH COMMAND. 1925-47. 51 lin. ft. and 709 rolls of microfilm.

The Oberkommando der Luftwaffe/OKL was established March 1935 to direct the German Air Force. The records include general records of the Oberbefehlshaber der Luftwaffe (Commander in Chief), Hermann Goering, 1939-43, the Chief of the Air General Staff, 1940-45, the Air Force Operations Staff, 1941-45, the Intelligence Branch, 1938-42, the Office of the Director of Technical Armaments and the Air Force Personnel Office, 1939-45, the Academy for Aeronautical Research, 1928-44, the Office of the Director for Awards and Disciplinary Matters, 1940-44, Luftflotten-Kommandos (German Air Force operational organizations), 1938-45, and other offices, 1927-45. Research materials of the German Air Force in World War II, assembled by Brig. Gen. Herhudt von Rohden, head of the Historical Division, General Staff, relating to the official history of the German Air Force and including records of the Air Force High Command; the Reich Air Ministry, 1925-39; operational commands, intelligence units, and experiment stations, 1936-45; the Central Planning Committee of the Reich Ministry for Arma-

ments and War Production, 1940-44; and German aircraft firms, 1930-45. Technical and aeronautical publications and press reports, 1933-45, and portions of a German Air Force history prepared by von Rohden's staff, 1946-47.

RECORDS OF GERMAN AIR FORCE COMMANDS. 1932-45. 202 lin. ft. and 196 rolls of microfilm.

Germany and its territories were divided into Luftgau-Kommandos (Air Force commands) for such administrative purposes as recruitment and training of Air Force personnel, operation of Air Force signal units, defense against air attacks, and furnishing supplies to flying units. These records include records of German antiaircraft units on shooting down American, British, and Russian aircraft, and correspondence and reports of the German Air Force Mission in Rumania. General records relate to operations and administration of flying units, personnel files of German Air Force officials, and reports (in WNRC) covering American and British airmen held prisoners of war.

RECORDS OF HEADQUARTERS, GERMAN NAVY HIGH COMMAND. 1850-1945. 4,172 rolls of microfilm.

The Oberkommando der Kriegsmarine/OKM directed overall planning and operations of the German Navy. The Navy, which had been restricted by the Treaty of Versailles, was proclaimed one of the three major components of the Wehrmacht by the National Defense Act of May 1935. The designation of Reichsmarine (Reich Navy) was changed to Kriegsmarine (War Navy) and the former Chef der Marineleitung (Chief of Naval Operations) assumed the title of Oberbefehlshaber der Kriegsmarine (Commander in Chief of the War Navy). These are general records of the War Historical Division of the German Naval Staff, Prussian Navy, Imperial German Navy, Reich Navy, and War Navy, and of subordinate commands, 1850-1945; and fragmentary records of the German Navy High Command, 1936-45.

RECORDS OF HEADQUARTERS, GERMAN ARMY HIGH COMMAND. 1862-1945. 18 lin. ft. and 2,356 rolls of microfilm.

The Oberkommando des Heeres/ OKH, headed by the Oberbefehlshaber des Heeres (Commander in Chief), directed overall planning and operations of the German Army. Commanders in Chief during World War II were Gen. (later Field Marshal) Walther von Brauchitsch, 1938-41, and Hitler, 1941-45. There are general records, order-of-battle cards, Army registers, tables of organization, personnel files, service regulations, and records of the Office of the Commander in Chief of the Army, 1921-40; the Chief of the Army General Staff, 1937-45; the Operations Branch and the Ordnance Stores Inspectorate, 1939-45; the Organization Branch, 1920-45; the Foreign Armies branches, 1918-45; the Chief of Transportation, 1896-1945; the Mapping and Survey Branch, 1928-44; the Quartermaster General, the General Army Directorate, and the Chief Army Medical Inspector, 1938-45; the Chief Infantry Officer, 1931-45; the Chief Engineer and Fortifications Officer, 1924-45; the Chief of Army Equipment and Commander of the Replacement Army, 1936-45; the Army Ordnance Office, 1925-45; the Inspector General of Armored Troops, 1933-45; the Army Personnel Office, 1914-45; the Chief of Army Archives, 1862-1945; and other offices, 1894-1945.

RECORDS OF GERMAN ARMY AREAS. 1880-1945. 4 lin. ft. and 563 rolls of microfilm.

The Wehrkreis (Army area) constituted the basic military subdivision of Germany and its incorporated territories. It resembled a pre-World War II U.S. corps area but had the added function of conscripting replacements for corps and divisions stationed therein. These records consist of personnel files, war journals, and general records covering especially the 1930's and early 1940's, and include information about political, economic, and social developments in Germany during the Nazi era; German Army indoctrination; defense against subversion, espionage, and sabotage; border protection; supply; and prisoners of war.

RECORDS OF THE GERMAN ARMY FIELD COMMANDS. 1936-45. 6,883 rolls of microfilm.

These consist of records of Heeresgruppen (army groups), Armee-oberkommandos (armies), corps, divisions, occupation authorities, and operations of other military units, including enemy units.

RECORDS FROM THE HEERESARCHIV. 1679-1947. 169 rolls of microfilm.

These records consist of the relatively few documents evacuated from the Heeresarchiv at Potsdam before its destruction in April 1945 and include private and official correspondence and other records of Hermann von Boyen, 1771-1848; August Wilhelm, Duke of Braunschweig-Bevern, 1715-81; Friedrich Wilhelm III of Prussia, 1770-1840; Count August Neithardt von Gneisenau, 1760-1831; Gen. Wilhelm Groener, 1867-1939; Helmuth Carl Bernhard von Moltke, 1800-1891; Hermann Ritter Mertz von Quirnheim, 1866-1947; Albrecht von Roon, 1803-79; Gerhard Johann David von Scharnhorst, 1775-1813; Heinrich Scheuch, 1864-1946; Alfred von Schlieffen, 1883-1913; Hans Friedrich Leopold von Seeckt, 1866-1936; and Hans Karl von Winterfeldt, 1707-57. There are also miscellaneous records, 1860-1945, about war mobilizations in 1866, 1870, and 1914; German military documents, 1679-1935, used in a permanent exhibit; and documents, 1716-1935, used in a special exhibit to exalt the military tradition in Germany.

RECORDS OF THE NATIONAL SOCIALIST GERMAN WORKERS' PARTY. 1915-45. 2,126 rolls of microfilm.

The Deutsche Arbeiter Partei (German Workers' Party) was founded at Munich in January 1919. Hitler soon gained control of the small organization and renamed it the Nationalsozialistische Deutsche Arbeiterpartei (National Socialist German Workers' Party, or Nazi Party). Abolished and banned after the unsuccessful Munich Putsch of November 1923, the Nazi Party was revived legally in 1925, by 1932 had become the strongest political party in Germany, and after Hitler was appointed Reich Chancellor in January 1933 quickly was made the sole legal party in the totalitarian state. The records consist of general records of party units and affiliated organizations, and relate to such subjects as administration, personnel, indoctrination, party discipline, the resettlement of ethnic Germans, race policies, foreign labor recruitment, and party operations at the national, regional, and local levels.

RECORDS OF AXIS CULTURAL AND RESEARCH INSTITUTIONS. 1914-45. 551 rolls of microfilm.

These consist of records of the Institut fuer Deutsche Ostarbeit (Institute for German Work in the East), established at Cracow in 1940 to research the history and culture of Poland and other eastern areas and to increase German influence there, 1940-45; Akademie fuer Deutsches Recht (Academy for German Law), founded in 1933 to help draft a new German code of justice and to work with Reich authorities in enacting laws to promote national socialism, 1933-45;

Deutsche Akademie Muenchen (German Academy Munich), founded at Munich in 1925 to support research in German culture and promote world interest in German language and culture, 1925-45; miscellaneous documents of the German Armed Forces High Command, Army High Command, Air Force High Command, Army Area XII, and Armed SS, 1936-45; German Foreign Office, Reich Air Ministry, Reich Ministry of Economics, Reich Postal Telegraph Office at Bad Gastein, and municipal court at Hamburg, 1935-45; private and semiofficial associations, 1930-45; private individuals, 1914-41; Japanese and Manchurian Embassies, Legations, and consular offices, 1934-45; Italian governmental agencies, 1938-42; and German, Japanese, and Manchurian industrial and export companies engaged in transactions with Germany, Japan, and other Far Eastern countries, 1924-45.

OTHER RECORDS OF EMBASSIES AND CONSULATES. 1919-45. 78 rolls of microfilm.

These are records of the German consulates in Tsingtao and Hankow, China, and Yokohama, Japan; the Japanese Legation in Vienna, Embassy and military attaches in Berlin, and consulates in Leipzig and Hamburg; and the Manchurian Legation in Rome.

RECORDS OF PRIVATE GERMAN ENTERPRISES AND INDIVIDUALS. 1914-45. 5 lin. ft. (in WNRC) and 632 rolls of microfilm.

These consist of general records of private German firms, 1920-45, and papers of Walter Luetgebrune, a noted German lawyer involved in political cases during the Weimar period, 1916-33; Theo Morell, personal physician to Hitler, 1929-45; and Karl Haushofer, a geopolitician and personal friend of Rudolf Hess, 1914-44.

LIBRARY OF GERMAN MICROFILMS ("ML COLLECTION"). 1870-1945. 1,079 rolls of microfilm.

This collection consists of records of the Reich Ministry of Economics; Reich Defense Council; Military Security Office, Bremen; Armed Forces Academy; Quartermaster General and Foreign Armies East Branch of the Army High Command; Air Force Operations Staff Intelligence Branch; and the 20th Mountain Army Operations Branch. Also Hitler's orders; medical reports on Hitler; records of the July 1944 plot against Hitler; German Army manuals, personnel records, and indexes to military identification tags; intelligence reports on the Russian Army postal system, Soviet airborne troops, and industrial development; Russian propaganda leaflets; German casualty statistics for World War II; records about the German military surrender; descriptions of Helgoland fortifications; lists of American prisoners of war and soldiers buried in cemeteries in Germany; lists of members of the Nazi Party outside Germany; reports on foreign iron and coal industries; the periodical *Das Archiv*, 1934 and 1936-45; Albert Speer's personal papers, 1942-45; papers of Wilhelm Groener, 1870-1938; diaries of Joseph Goebbels, 1942-43, Gen. Erwin Lahousen, 1941-43, and Hans Frank, 1940-44; and records of the firms of Krupp and Wilhelm Schmidding.

Records in Italian, 1938-44, including the Italian Foreign Minister's reports; congratulatory letters to Marshal Pietro Badoglio on becoming Commander in Chief of the Italian Army; a card file on Italian military personnel; and data on powerplants in Sicily, Italian and Albanian beaches, and Italian gun specifications.

CAPTURED GERMAN DOCUMENTS FILMED AT THE BERLIN DOCUMENT CENTER. 1,031 rolls of microfilm.

These are nonbiographic records of Nazi Party offices, associations, and supervised organizations; private papers of some Nazi leaders; and records of some Reich ministries, government agencies, and industrial corporations and persons.

OTHER GERMAN RECORDS. 1881-1946. 174 lin. ft. and 678 rolls of microfilm.

The miscellaneous German records collection (40 lin. ft. and 445 rolls of microfilm), 1892-1945, includes letters to Hitler from Nazi Party members, court proceedings of Hitler's 1924 trial by the State of Bavaria, minutes of Hitler's meetings with his military leaders, and records relating to the governmental structure of the Third Reich; political, social, military, and economic developments in Germany and other countries; international law; the organization and function of German military agencies; mobilization preparedness; manpower; personnel administration; training; personal papers of officials and officers; records relating to antitank, desert, partisan, and winter warfare; combat training in the Soviet Army; construction of the Siegfried Line (Westwall) and other defenses; activities of "Organization Todt"; international and national air traffic regulations; civil defense measures; administration of military installations; transportation; claims against Germany for air raid losses; the July 1944 plot against Hitler; the Office of the Reich Commissioner for the Restoration of Austria to Germany; records of the Anti-Comintern; and records (in WNRC) relating to prisoners of war.

The records include field and technical manuals of the German Army, Air Force, Navy, SS, Waffen-SS, and Reich Labor Service, containing administrative, operational, training, and maintenance regulations, 1910-45. Included also are deck logs of the North German Lloyd steamer *Europa* (subsequently the U.S.S.*Europa*), 1930-45; correspondence of Herbert von Bismarck-Schoen-hausen, 1881-83; Hitler's engagement book, August 14-December 24, 1943; an undated book in typescript, concerning Germany and the world situation some 50 years hence; Eva Braun's diary, February 6-May 28, 1935; Hitler's marriage certificate and private and political wills, and Martin Bormann's letter to Admiral Karl Doenitz transmitting Hitler's political will, April 29, 1945, with English translations; and Secretary of War Robert P. Patterson's letter to President Truman transmitting Hitler's wills and related documents, March 19, 1946.

RECORDS OF THE ALL-UNION COMMUNIST PARTY, SMOLENSK DISTRICT. 1917-41. 28 lin. ft.

These consist of records captured by German forces in 1941 and seized by U.S. forces in 1945, including reports, directives, press clippings, personnel records, and official and unofficial correspondence between individuals and between Communist Party organizations and agencies.

RECORDS OF THE SOVIET PURCHASING COMMISSION AT PRAGUE. 1936-41. 49 lin. ft. (in WNRC).

This Commission was established in 1936 by the People's Commissariat for Foreign Trade of the Soviet Union to handle business between Moscow and Czechoslovakian industry. These records, in German, Czech, and Russian, comprise business correspondence on the purchase of machinery from the Skoda Works and other Czech firms; export orders, export and import permits, and shipping documents; records concerning manufacturing standards, administration, and finance; and photographs, blueprints, and technical drawings.

MISCELLANEOUS RUSSIAN RECORDS. 1870-1947. 146 lin. ft. and 6 rolls of microfilm.

These comprise reports, publications,

correspondence, and other documents concerning industrial economy, political organization, scientific research, and military forces of the Soviet Union (in WNRC); and records about prominent Soviet citizens.

POLISH RECORDS. 1887-1939. 30 lin. ft. (in WNRC).

These records, captured by the Germans during World War II and recaptured by American forces in 1945, consist of geodetic journals and survey notebooks of the Military Geographical Institute, Ministry of Communications, and the Ministry of Public Utilities, 1929-39; geological books, periodicals, and maps published by the Academy of Science Commission on Physiography at Cracow, 1887-1908; archeological books and periodicals published by the National Archeological Museum at Warsaw, 1926-38; statistical books and periodicals published by the Central Statistical Office of Poland, 1931-38; and miscellaneous publications on Polish history and literature.

MISCELLANEOUS RECORDS. 1815-1945. 93 lin. ft. (in WNRC).

These consist of military and civilian books, periodicals, newspapers, and official and technical publications of Bulgarian, Chinese, Czechoslovakian, Danish, Dutch, English, Estonian, Finnish, French, Greek, Hebrew, Hungarian, Japanese, Latvian, Lithuanian, Norwegian, Portuguese, Rumanian, Spanish, Swedish, Swiss, Turkish, and Yugoslavian origin or language.

ITALIAN RECORDS. 1922-43. 1 lin. ft. and 825 rolls of microfilm.

These records were captured by German forces after surrender of the Italian Government to Allied forces in 1943 and recaptured by U.S. forces in 1945. Included are records of the Comando Supremo (High Command) that comprise correspondence and messages to and from Benito Mussolini, Pietro Badoglio, and Vittorio Ambrosio; reports of conferences with Hitler and Field Marshal Albert Kesselring, the German commander in Italy; mobilization schedules; order-of-battle charts; organizational tables; operation plans; situation and strength reports; intelligence reports and summaries; supply surveys; Italian Air Force operation reports; and maps of fronts and occupied areas.

Records of the Army General Staff and field forces include war journals; papers on guerrilla warfare in Slovenia, Croatia, and Montenegro; reports and plans on field fortifications; records of military governments and civil affairs; records concerning liaison with German troops, mostly of the Armed Forces Headquarters in Slovenia-Dalmatia; records of army corps headquarters and territorial commands, relating to mapping and surveying, construction of roads and field fortifications, and mobilization; records of the 5th and 6th Armies, concerning territorial defense measures; activity reports of the 8th Army (formerly the Italian Expeditionary Force in Russia), relating to logistics and engineering on the Russian front; and Italian Air Force and Army manuals, records of combat units, and Navy records captured by U.S. forces in North Africa and Sicily during 1942 and 1943. Also personal files of Mussolini and official records of such Italian Government agencies as the Foreign Office and the Ministry of Culture, 1922-40; the Ciano "Lisbon Papers," 1938-40; and the Ciano "Rose Garden Papers," 1938-43.

JAPANESE RECORDS. 1928-47. 366 rolls of microfilm.

These records are studies on aeronautics, aviation medicine, and electronics of the Aeronautical Research Institute, Imperial University, Tokyo, mostly in Japanese, but with some in English and German, 1928-44; Japanese military, economic, political, and other records, including records of the Japanese Army and Navy High Commands; tables of organization of Japanese Armed Forces; situation reports on Japanese World War II campaigns; Japanese Army and Navy orders and reports to the Emperor; mobilization, naval afteraction, and casualty reports; lists of Japanese vessels surviving the war; records on war material production and national economic strength; stenographic records of the Diet; reports on Japanese political activities; plans for negotiations with the Soviets and a report on the Soviet entry into World War II, 1937-47; and Japanese newspapers and private papers of individuals.

RECORDS SEIZED BY U.S. MILITARY FORCES IN KOREA. 1921-52. 1,206 lin. ft. (in WNRC).

Included are administrative and personnel files, bulletins, books, periodicals, and newspapers—mostly in the Russian and Korean languages but some in Bulgarian, Chinese, English, French, German, Hungarian, Italian, and Polish—on aeronautics, agriculture, classical and modern literature, construction projects, economics, engineering, geography, industry, mathematics, medicine, motion pictures, navigation, politics, propaganda, and sociology, chiefly in the Soviet Union and North Korea; the Chinese People's Volunteer Army in Korea; the history and activities of the Communist Party; Korean-Russian trade; life in the Soviet Union and Soviet satellites; North Korean courts; the North Korean Army; and the United Nations forces in Korea.

CARTOGRAPHIC RECORDS. 1934-45. ca 30,000 items.

These comprise German Army maps showing the daily military situation in operations on all fronts during World

War II; air reconnaissance maps of the eastern front; maps showing disposition of Red army units; military atlases; miscellaneous German operation maps of World War II; situation maps prepared by the Soviets, showing their army operations on the eastern front; unmarked maps of Europe; and road, railroad, and weather maps, 1939–45. Also German Air Force target maps from World War II; German Air Force Staff Photographic Branch maps; Russian maps from captured German World War II records; and descriptive texts, charts, and photographs published by the German Navy High Command, covering strategic coastal waters, British shipping, Siberian ice conditions, and the organization of the French, British, and American Navies.

AUDIOVISUAL RECORDS. 1913–50. 327,372 items.

Photographs (323,797 items) of World War I events, ca. 1916; the collection "Greater Germany in World History," 1940–42; photographs published during World War II in the Spanish-language magazine *Revista Alemana;* German military operations and personnel, 1930–45; Axis leaders and activities; the Heinrich Hoffmann Collection, relating to Nazi activities, the Spanish Civil War, and the 1936 Olympic games at Berlin, 1919–44; and photograph albums of Eva Braun, 1913–44, and Joachim von Ribbentrop, 1934–42. Also photographs and slides (10,800 items) of prominent citizens, bridges, waterways, cities, farms, industrial plants, and terrain in the Soviet Union.

Motion pictures (1,024 reels) consist of German documentaries and newsreels of World War I, Paul von Hindenburg,

the 1936 Olympic riding competition, the history of the Nazi Party, and World War II, including films of Eva Braun and Hitler, ca. 1939–40; Italian documentaries and newsreels of World War II; Japanese documentaries and newsreels, 1932–44; French (Vichy) newsreels, 1944; Russian films on the death of Lenin, 1924, the fall of Berlin and the meeting of Russian and other Allied troops at the Elbe, anti-Americanism, North Korea and the 38th parallel in 1950, Hungary, and American prisoners of war at Pyongyang; and American films showing civilian victims of military brutality, 1942, and the escape of American prisoners of war from the Philippine island of Palawan.

Sound recordings, 1925–44 (1,551 items), collected by war crimes investigators, including speeches by Hitler, Joseph Goebbels, Hermann Goering, Albert Speer, and other Nazis; propaganda recorded by Fascists in Italy; and speeches by Mussolini, Count Ciano, and other Italian leaders.

Note: Some of the material in this record group (whether available on microfilm or in its original form) is of private origin. The fact of its seizure does not necessarily divest the original owners of literary property rights in them. Anyone who publishes them in whole or in part without permission of the original owners or their heirs may be held liable for infringement of such literary property rights.

Microfilm roll numbers prefixed by the letter "R" designate rolls reproducing privileged material. Such rolls are not for sale but are open to examination in the National Archives Building under the restriction that no reproductions may be made.

PART VI

OTHER HOLDINGS

GIFT COLLECTIONS

NATIONAL ARCHIVES COLLECTION OF RECORDS OF INAUGURAL COMMITTEES (RECORD GROUP 274)

Inaugural committees, chairmen of which have been appointed by the President-elect since 1948, are organized into several staff offices and special committees to stage traditional public ceremonies in Washington, D.C., to honor the newly elected President and Vice President. The committees also provide accommodations for guests; compile guest lists; arrange for newspaper, radio, and television coverage of inaugural activities; and sell souvenirs. The Federal and the District of Columbia Governments provide aid and facilities to the committees. Preinaugural committees, first appointed in 1956, and inaugural planning committees, first appointed in 1960, procure office space and make other preliminary arrangements for the inaugural committees.

The location of early inaugural committee records is largely unknown, but records relating to early inaugurations are in the Library of Congress, the District of Columbia Public Library, Georgetown University, the Smithsonian Institution, and the Art and Reference Library of the Office of the Architect of the Capitol. Related records in the National Archives are among records of the U.S. Coast Guard (see RG 26), records of the Office of Public Buildings and Grounds (see RG 42), National Archives gift collection (see RG 200), and records of the Adjutant General's Office, 1917– (see RG 407).

There are 102 cubic feet of records dated between 1932 and 1965 in this record group.

RECORDS OF THE 1933, 1937, 1941, AND 1945 INAUGURAL COMMITTEES. 1932–45. 1 lin. ft.

Fragmentary records of the Grandstand Ticket Committees, 1933, 1937, and 1941 Inaugural Committees; and of the Medal Committee, 1945 Inaugural Committee.

RECORDS OF THE 1949 INAUGURAL COMMITTEE. 1948–49. 24 lin. ft.

These consist of records of General Chairman Melvin Hildreth, including reports made to or by the General Chairman, the Executive Secretary, the Archivist, the Publicity Office, the Budget and Audit Control Office, and the Agriculture, Concessions, General Services, Government Liaison and Ticket Sales, Grandstand Construction, Grandstand Sales, Hospitality and Housing, Inaugural Ball, Insurance, Legal and Legislative, Medals, Medal Sales, Parade and Special Events, Reception for Governors and Distinguished Guests, State Groups, Transportation (Domestic), Transportation and Information, and Veterans' Committees.

RECORDS OF THE 1953 INAUGURAL COMMITTEE. 1952–53. 11 lin. ft.

These are records of Chairman Joseph C. McGarraghy, including reports made to or by the Chairman, the assistant to the Chairman, the Executive Secretary, the director of publicity, and the Audit, Concessions, Decorations, Festival, General Services, Hospitality, Inaugural Ball, Law and Legislation, Medal Distribution, Medical Aid, Parade, Program, Transportation, and Young Republican Activities Committees.

RECORDS OF THE 1957 INAUGURAL COMMITTEE. 1956–57. 16 lin. ft.

These consist of records of General Chairman Robert V. Fleming, including reports made to or by the General Chairman, the Executive Secretary, the director of public relations and publicity, and the Ball, General Services, Inaugural Stands, Insurance, Official Hostesses and Hospitality, Parade, Parade Tickets, Reception for Governors and Distinguished Guests, Religious Observance, Transportation, and Young Republicans Participation Committees.

RECORDS OF THE 1961 INAUGURAL COMMITTEE. 1960–61. 28 lin. ft.

Included are the final reports of the 1960 Pre-Inaugural Committee and Inaugural Planning Committee, and records of General Chairman Edward H. Foley, including reports made to or by the General Chairman, the Executive Director, and the Armed Forces Participation, Armed Forces Public Relations, Ball, Budget, Concessions, Decorations, Finance, General Services, Grandstand, Official Hospitality and Reception for Distinguished Ladies, Housing, Insurance, Parade, Publicity, Public Safety, Reception for Governors and Special Distinguished Guests, Religious Observance, Veterans' Participation, and Young Democratic Festivities Committees.

RECORDS OF THE 1965 INAUGURAL COMMITTEE. 1964–67. 30 lin. ft.

These consist of records of Chairman Dale Miller, including reports made to or by the Chairman, the Executive Director, and the Ball, Citizens for Johnson-Humphrey, Concert, Concessions, General Services, Governors' Reception, Grandstand, Hospitality, Housing, Parade, Program and Book, Publicity, Public Safety, Transportation, Volunteer Participation, and Young Democratic Festivities Committees.

AUDIOVISUAL RECORDS. 1949–65. 11 items.

These include a motion picture (1 reel) "1965 Inaugural Preview"; and sound recordings (10 items) of committee meetings, interviews with committee members, and press conferences relating to plans for the inaugurals of Presidents Truman and Kennedy, 1949 and 1961.

See Hardee Allen, comp., *Preliminary Inventory of the Records of Inaugural Committees*, PI 131 (1960); Marion M. Johnson, comp., *Preliminary Inventory of the Records of the 1961 Inaugural Committee*, PI 162 (1964); E. Daniel Potts, comp., *List of Motion Pictures and Sound Recordings Relating to Presidential Inaugurations*, SL 16 (1960); and Library of Congress, *Presidential Inaugurations, A Selected List of References* (3d ed. rev., 1969).

NATIONAL ARCHIVES GIFT COLLECTION (RECORD GROUP 200)

This record group includes gifts of personal papers, historical manuscripts, and cartographic and audiovisual materials donated to the National Archives and Records Service. Although these materials are not official records of the

U.S. Government, the National Archives Act of June 18, 1934, authorized their acceptance as gifts if they related to and illustrated historical activities of the United States. The Federal Property and Administrative Services Act of 1949, as amended (44 U.S.C., section 2107 (2)), which superseded the 1934 act, authorized the acceptance from private sources of such gifts that are appropriate for preservation by the Government as evidence of its organization, functions, policies, decisions, procedures, and transactions. The materials allocated to this record group have been donated by a wide range of business and cultural organizations and institutions and by many individuals.

There are 1,995 cubic feet of records dated between 1837 and 1967 in this record group.

PERSONAL PAPERS AND HISTORICAL MANUSCRIPTS. 1837-1960. 459 lin. ft.

These gift collections range in size from more than 100 cubic feet to single documents. They are so numerous and varied as to preclude description of each donation in a general work of this type. Lists and descriptions of all gift items are available, however, at the National Archives Building. Among the materials are the following: *Johnston Avery Papers*, relating to his service as Chief of the Enforcement Section, Decartelization Branch, U.S. Office of Military Government in Germany, 1944-52 (6 lin. ft.); *The Brainard Collection*, 1881-1918, consisting of the journal and related papers of David Legge Brainard, created primarily during his service with the Lady Franklin Bay Expedition (1 lin. ft.); *Leslie R. Groves Letters*, written as Army chaplain from Cuba, the Philippines, and China, 1898-1901 (5 lin. in.); *Herbert James Hagerman Papers*, relating to his service as a Federal commissioner to various southwestern Indian tribes and as a member of

the Pueblo Lands Board, 1906-60, chiefly 1923-35 (6 lin. ft.); *Maj. Gen. James G. Harbord Papers*, chiefly relating to his military career during World War I, 1917-18 (3 lin. in.); *Ethan Allen Hitchcock Papers*, chiefly correspondence and newspaper clippings documenting the history of the Department of the Interior, Hitchcock's service as Secretary of the Interior, 1898-1907, and his earlier business and political activities, 1835-1907 (33 lin. ft.); *Jacob H. Hollander Papers*, relating to a report he prepared on the foreign debts of the Dominican Republic, 1900-1915 (4 lin. ft); *Mark Jefferson Diary*, a one-volume typescript copy of the original kept while in Paris as a member of the American Commission To Negotiate Peace, 1918-19; and *Arthur W. Macmahon Collection*, consisting primarily of personal interviews with several hundred Federal administrators in and outside of Washington, accumulated by Professor Macmahon after having been commissioned by the Social Science Research Council to "capture and record" the nationwide administrative evolution of the Federal work relief program, 1935-37 (40 lin. ft.).

See Arthur W. Macmahon et al., *The Administration of Federal Work Relief* (Chicago, 1941).

Also included are: *David M. Matteson Papers*, relating to his service as Historian of the U.S. Constitution Sesquicentennial Commission, 1933-40 (1 lin. ft.); *Gen. John J. Pershing Collection*, chiefly documents, correspondence, operations reports, and other materials relating to the Mexican Punitive Expedition, World War I, and the immediate postwar years, 1917-30 (12 lin. ft.); *Lt. Col. Benjamin Pritchard Diary and Papers*, 65 items relating to the capture of Jefferson Davis and Pritchard's role in escorting him to Fortress Monroe, Va., 1862-68; *Edwin M. Stanton Collection*, about 70 items of personal and family interest, 1854-70; *Robert J. Walker Let-*

ters, photocopies chiefly of letters sent and received, 1845-49, while Secretary of the Treasury, 1837-68 (2 lin. ft.); *John J. Young Papers,* about 50 items, including 18 sketches by engraver Young, relating to the Pacific Railroad Surveys, 1855-73; and *Sir Henry S. Wellcome Papers* (in FRC Seattle), relating chiefly to the Metlakahtla Indians of Alaksa and including photographs, maps, plats, plans, and drawings of the Metlakahtla colony and of Alaska, 1856-1936 (105 lin. ft.).

See Elmer W. Lindgard, comp., *Preliminary Inventory of the Sir Henry S. Wellcome Papers in the Federal Records Center, Seattle, Washington,* PI 150 (1963).

CARTOGRAPHIC AND RELATED RECORDS. 1861-1930. 185 items and 24 rolls of aerial film.

Maps from the Papers of George Scott Stewart, Jr., relating to World War I operations in France; from the Papers of Col. W. H. Paine, relating to Civil War operations in Maryland, Pennsylvania, and Virginia; and from the Papers of Gen. W. C. Brown, chiefly concerning operations against Indians in the West, 1865-1900. Also aerial film containing 1,658 negatives of Adm. Richard E. Byrd's 1928-30 antarctic expedition.

STILL PICTURES AND OTHER PICTORIAL MATERIALS. 1858-1964. 14,008 items.

Civil War

Photographs, artworks, and photocopies of artworks of Lincoln; Union Gens. U. S. Grant, Philip H. Sheridan, Gordon Granger, and George A. Custer; Confederate Gen. George E. Pickett; and battlefields, fortifications, campsites, events, and military units—both Union and Confederate, 1861-65. Also watercolor sketches of camps and fortifications and of the activities of soldiers by William McIlvaine, 1863-64, and engravings from Robert Tomes' history of the Civil War, 1880.

Spanish-American War

Photographs of U.S. troops in Florida and Cuba; Col. William Jennings Bryan; Capt. Charles D. Sigsbee of the U.S.S. *Maine;* and Philippine Insurrection troops and activities in the Philippine Islands, and Gen. Emilio Aguinaldo.

World War I

Photographs of battlefields, towns, and damaged areas in France and Germany, 1915-19; of the women's training camp at Chevy Chase, Md.; and relating to the history of the 29th Division, 1917-19. Also a lithograph of the declaration of war between the United States and Germany signed by U.S. Congressmen; lithographs by Lucien Jones, official artist with the French forces, 1914-16; and American posters.

World War II

Photographs of the German advance through Poland, 1939, the construction and launchings of American merchant ships, 1939-48, campaigns in Alsace and south Germany, 1945, and the U.S.S. *West Point* with returning troops aboard.

Presidential Photographs

Photographs and photographs of artworks relating to activities of Presidents Abraham Lincoln and his family and concerning his assassination and the capture of John Wilkes Booth; U. S. Grant and his second inaugural; Rutherford B. Hayes and Mrs. Hayes; James A. Garfield; Theodore Roosevelt; William Howard Taft as Governor of the Philippines, 1900, and signing the Arizona Statehood Proclamation, 1912; Woodrow Wilson and his 1913 inaugural and at the first airmail flight, 1918; Herbert C. Hoover; Franklin D. Roosevelt as a young man and his activities as President, 1933-39; Dwight D. Eisenhower and his family, 1903-52; John F. Kennedy at the opening of the Kennedy Highway, 1963; and Vice President and Mrs. Lyndon B. Johnson in 1962.

Photographs of Prominent Individuals

Photographs and photographs of art-works of prominent persons, including Supreme Court Justices, Cabinet members, political and military leaders, civil rights workers, writers, and artists; and of members of political committees, Government commissions, Indian delegations, and the armed services, 1858-1964.

Photographs of Buildings and Sites

Photographs of Washington, D.C., and vicinity, 1859-1943, including the Department of Agriculture Building, 1868, the construction of the Capitol dome, the Treasury Building, and Walter Reed Hospital; of the 1958 Post Office dedication at Little Rock, Ark.; of San Francisco and Yosemite, Calif., 1900; of the New Orleans Mint, n.d.; of Boston, Lexington, and Plymouth, Mass., 1930; of Ortonville, Minn., 1880; of Pittsburgh and Gettysburg, Pa., 1929, and a drawing of the Philadelphia Mint, ca. 1910; of New York City, 1900; of a lighthouse of Charlotte, N.C., ca. 1890; of places in Alaska, 1870-1910; of the Georgetown mining region in Colorado Territory, n.d.; of Hawaii and the Philippine Islands, 1900-1911; of Panama and the construction of the canal, 1911-16; of the weighing station at the customhouse at St. Croix, West Indies, n.d.; and of various places in France and England, 1919-27.

Miscellaneous Photographs

Photographs relating to the Korean Punitive Expedition under the command of Commodore C. R. Perry Rodgers, 1871; made by John Hillers for the Powell survey, 1870-78; of Army Engineer activities, 1900-1920; of the Rainbow Bridge discovery expedition, 1909; of Theodore Roosevelt's 1912 campaign train at Baldwin, Kans.; relating to the history of aircraft, 1900-1945; and of the wreckage of the dirigible *Shenandoah* (ZR-1), 1925. Photographs, postal cards,

illustrations from magazines, watercolors, and woodcuts illustrating the Lady Franklin Bay expedition, 1881-84; and of survivors of the expedition and their families, of other associates of David Legge Brainard, and of prominent arctic explorers, 1884-1931. Also included are photographs and X-rays relating to the autopsy of President Kennedy (257 items), 1963, consisting of black and white negatives and prints; color negatives, transparencies, and prints; and X-ray negatives and prints.

MOTION PICTURES. 1896-1969. 8,502 reels.

Newsreels. 1919-67. Chiefly unbroken series of Paramount News, October 1941-March 1957, Movietone News, January 1957-October 1963, and News of the Day, October 1963-December 1967. Also newsreels produced by Movietone, Pathe, Fox, International, Paramount, and Telenews, covering selected news items and including the Big Four at the Peace Conference in Paris, 1919; the Navy's transatlantic flight from the Azores to Lisbon, 1919; activities of Presidents Coolidge, Franklin D. Roosevelt, Truman, and Eisenhower; the 1924 Republican National Convention; events leading to and occurring during World War II; and the 1959 swearing-in ceremonies of Alaska's Senators and Hawaii's Congressmen.

The March of Time. 1939-51. Documentary films relating to U.S. history, culture, social problems, science, education, mental health, and international problems; to Government agencies, such as the FBI, the Secret Service, and the Post Office Department; to wartime and postwar activities of private institutions, such as the American Red Cross; and to the effect of World War II on one small American town.

World War I Films. 1917-19. Included are films made behind the German lines by Jacob Berkowitz; the Official War Review series on land and air battles, maneuvers, and training, which were distributed by the Films Division of the Committee on Public Information; the National Aeronautics Committee's film of the celebration of Air Memorial Day, 1919; a documentary produced in 1956 by the National Broadcasting Co. entitled "The Great War"; and a large quantity of film collected by the Columbia Broadcasting Co. from worldwide sources in the production of a documentary entitled "World War I."

World War II Films. 1940-45. Films produced by Warner Bros. Pictures, Inc., Paramount Pictures, Inc., and Columbia Pictures, Inc., under the technical supervision of the armed services; and several films distributed by the War Activities Committee of the Motion Picture Industry, concerning activities of the Army, the Army Air Corps, the Navy, the Marine Corps, and the Coast Guard, including officer training programs and homefront aspects of the war effort. Also documentaries compiled from newsreels, one of events leading up to the war entitled "The World in Flames," and one by Paramount concerning resettlement of Jewish refugees in the Dominican Republic; a re-release by the National Film Board of Canada of a World War I Charlie Chaplin film promoting the sale of war bonds; pictures of German air raids on London, presented by the British Library of Information; a Finnish Relief Fund film about the Russo-Finnish War; films relating to the training of Dutch troops in exile and to the liberation of Greece; a collection of German newsreels covering the early stages of the war, presented by Lt. William F. Rope; and a film of the ceremonies at the opening of the exhibit at the National Archives Building of the German surrender documents.

Ford Collection. 1914-56. 2,500 reels. This collection, presented by the Ford Motor Co., includes the "Ford Animated Weekly," 1914-21, consisting of short news features, productions about cities, and general interest items; the "Ford Educational Weekly" and the "Ford Educational Library," 1916-25, consisting of short features and unedited film on agriculture, civics and citizenship, industrial geography, regional geography, history, nature study, recreation and sports, sanitation and health, and technical subjects; the "Ford News," a series of newsreels shown at Detroit area theaters during 1934; and films with information on agriculture and conservation, charity, drama, education, geography, news, and sports and recreation.

There are films of the personal, social, and philanthropic activities of the Ford family and of personal projects of Henry Ford, including the *Dearborn Independent* newspaper, the Ford farm, and the Henry Ford Museum and Greenfield Village. A significant part of the collection illustrates the activities of the Ford Motor Co., including domestic and foreign branches, 1928-54; nonmanufacturing activities, 1914-54, and plants and the major manufacturing activities, 1906-56; and war-related activities during both World Wars and the Korean action. Also several films made by producers other than the Ford Motion Picture Laboratories and not produced for the Ford Motor Co., including advertisements for companies other than Ford, cartoons, early comedies by Edison, dramas, documentaries, newsreels, personal films, propaganda, public service features, technical features, and travelogs.

See Mayfield Bray, *Guide to the Ford Film Collection in the National Archives* (1970).

Harmon Collection. 1930-51. 1,400 reels. A gift of the Harmon Foundation, this collection consists of educational films on many aspects of the history and accomplishments of minority cultures in the United States and the cultures of Asia, Africa, and other developing areas.

League of Nations Collection. 1920-46. 56 reels. Films of the first and last meetings of the League; meetings and activities concerning such problems as the Greco-Bulgar Incident, 1925, the Sino-Japanese conflict, 1932, and the Italo-Ethiopian conflict, 1936; health and disarmament conferences; and League delegates and officials.

Other Educational and Documentary Films. 1915-69. These include a series by Eastman Teaching Films, Inc., 1927-35, on history, geography, industry, conservation, recreation, agriculture, and sports; two series produced by Warner Bros. Pictures, Inc., 1934-35, entitled "See America First" and "Our Own United States," concerning our history and industry, occupations, recreation, scenery, and ethnic groups; a series, "The Washington Parade," by Columbia Pictures, Inc., on scenes and activities at various Federal agencies, chiefly at Washington, D.C.; a Columbia Broadcasting System series, "Eyewitness to History," 1950-60, with pictorial resumes of President Eisenhower's trips abroad, Nikita Khrushchev's visit to the United States in 1959 and his visit to France in 1960, and Charles de Gaulle's visit to the United States in 1960; and a TV series, "Longines Chronoscope," about public affairs, with important persons participating in panel discussions and interviews, 1951-55. Also documentaries, dramas, and television news specials and stock footage received from individuals, motion picture companies, and other organizations on American history; political parties; the administrations of Presidents Coolidge, Franklin D. Roosevelt, Eisenhower, and Kennedy; the career of Vice President Spiro T. Agnew; the funeral services for John Foster Dulles and Adm. William F. Halsey in 1959; the development of motion picture equipment, radio broadcasting, the telephone, aviation, atomic energy, and space flight from the experiments in the 1920's and 1930's of Robert H. Goddard to the 1962 orbital flight of Col. John H. Glenn; on Donald MacMillan's

expedition to Greenland, 1925; on Sir Ernest Shackleton's 1922 antarctic expedition, Adm. Richard E. Byrd's 1927 transatlantic flight and his antarctic expeditions of 1926, 1928-30, 1933-35, and 1947-48, and Lincoln Ellsworth's 1936 antarctic expedition; of a congressional visit in 1915 to the Philippines and Hawaii; on the 1947 Texas City disaster; on activities of the American Red Cross and the National 4-H Club Foundation; and on other topics as diverse as poverty in the Tennessee hill country, the integration of Atlanta, Ga., the charting of ocean winds, and social problems ranging from venereal diseases to the need for city planning.

There are also films relating to events and conditions outside the United States and its territories, including life in East Africa in 1924; the eruption of Paricutin in Mexico in 1943; communism in Russia and Cuba; nazism in Germany; the history of Austria from the Hapsburgs to the end of World War II; the National Archives of India; "La Vie de Ho Chi Minh," a biography up to 1963, made by the North Vietnam Government, with soundtrack in Vietnamese; and the state funeral of Sir Winston Churchill in 1965.

Historical Commercial Film Productions. 1896-1943. Prints of motion picture productions presented to the National Archives as having historical or research interest incidental to the dramatic presentation. Among these are two collections presented by Thomas Armat, consisting of penny-in-the-slot and nickelodeon shows produced by the Edison, Pathe, Melies, and Urban companies, 1896-1910; "The New York Hat," 1912, and "Birth of a Nation," 1916, both produced by D. W. Griffith; Selznick International Pictures' "Gone With the Wind"; Paramount Pictures' "The Biscuit Eater"; Warner Brothers' "Mission to Moscow" and an edited version of "Black Legion"; and Theatre-on-Film, Inc.'s "Journey to Jerusalem." Also eight films ("The Man I Married," "Man

Hunt," "They Dare Not Love," "Night Train," "Confessions of a Nazi Spy," "Dispatch from Reuter's," "Underground," and "Foreign Correspondent") studied by the subcommittee of the Senate Interstate Commerce Committee that investigated alleged dissemination of war propaganda before U.S. entry into World War II.

SOUND RECORDINGS. 1892–1966. 1,618 items.

Speeches, Interviews, and Panel Discussions

Included are recordings of speeches of Presidents Franklin D. Roosevelt, Truman, and Eisenhower; and speeches and parts of speeches of Presidents Cleveland, Theodore Roosevelt, Taft, Wilson, Harding, Coolidge, and Kennedy, 1892–1961. Also recordings of speeches, interviews, and panel discussions by a large number of prominent persons, including Thomas A. Edison, Adm. Robert E. Peary, Amelia Earhart, Will Rogers, Norman Thomas, Henry A. Wallace, Cordell Hull, Sumner Welles, Alben W. Barkley, Adlai E. Stevenson, Gen. Douglas MacArthur, Eleanor Roosevelt, Sara Delano Roosevelt, Wendell Willkie, Winston Churchill, King George VI of Great Britain, Mme. Chiang Kaishek, Mahatma Gandhi, and a number of Senators and Representatives; and well-known singers, actors, writers, religious leaders, World War I heroes, and combat airmen of World War II.

Radio and Special Events Recordings

Included are recordings of radio coverage of the *Hindenburg* disaster, 1937; the day of September 21, 1939, including the President's neutrality message delivered before Congress; the 24 hours after the attack on Pearl Harbor on December 7, 1941; the first 36 hours of the Allied invasion of Europe, June 6, 1944; the 3 days following the death of President Roosevelt, April 12, 1945; V-J Day; the signings of the German and Japanese surrender documents; highlights of the Nuremberg trial; the Nuremberg executions; and the 1960 Democratic and Republican National Conventions. Also recordings relating to National Defense Day, 1924; the sesquicentennial celebration of the Constitution, 1936; the centennial celebration of the American patent system, 1936; the laying of the cornerstone of the Roosevelt Library, 1939; and the Inter-Asia Relations Conference at New Delhi, 1947.

Other Recordings

Included are recordings of British refugee children in the United States broadcasting Christmas greetings in 1941 to their parents in England; the sound of an atomic test at Yucca Flats, Nev., 1953; hearings of the Special Senate Committee on the Communication Satellite bill, 1962; relating to activities of the National Tuberculosis Association, 1939–44; and promoting the Junior League baseball program of the American Legion, 1946. Also recordings of dramas including eight Shakespearean plays and a biography of Matthew Fontaine Maury; of a concert presented by the American Society of Composers and Publishers, September 24, 1940; of "Wing of Expectation," an opera in three acts based on the life of Mary Todd Lincoln, libretto and music by Kenneth Wright, 1965; from a series of talking books prepared by the American Foundation for the Blind; comparing the speech patterns of various parts of the United States; concerning the history of political conventions; and from Edward R. Murrow's "I Can Hear It Now" series.

SPECIFIC RESTRICTIONS

Records: X-rays and photographs relating to the autopsy of President John F. Kennedy.

Restrictions: Access to these materials is limited to persons authorized to act for a committee of Congress, a Presidential commission, or any other agency of the Federal Government having authority to investigate matters relating to the assassination of President Kennedy; and recognized experts in the field of pathology or related areas of science or technology for serious purposes relevant to the investigation of matters relating to the death of President Kennedy. The

determination of whether such an expert has suitable qualifications and serious purposes will be made by the Kennedy family representative.

Specified by: Archivist of the United States in conformity with the letter agreement between the Administrator of General Services and the Kennedy family representative dated October 29, 1966.

NATIONAL ARCHIVES GIFT COLLECTION OF MATERIALS RELATING TO POLAR REGIONS (RECORD GROUP 401)

Under authority of acts of September 5, 1950, and July 12, 1952, amending the Federal Property and Administrative Services Act of 1949, the National Archives accepts donated historical materials of prominent explorers and scientists and private firms relating to U.S. activities in the Arctic and Antarctic.

There are 514 cubic feet of records dated between 1865 and 1968 in this record group.

RECORDS. 1865-1968. 500 lin. ft.

Included are *Adm. Robert E. Peary Papers*, ca. 1865-1945, consisting of field notebooks, manuscripts for publication, correspondence, maps (ca. 150 items), and drawings and photographs (ca. 3,000 items) created by him or relating especially to his arctic explorations and his service in Central America (175 lin ft.); *Mrs. Marie Peary Kuhne Papers*, ca. 1920-66, including correspondence and memorabilia of Admiral Peary's daughter (7 lin. ft.); *Paul A. Siple Papers*, 1905-65, including expedition journals, scientific notes, scientific and other writings, correspondence, publications relating to polar regions, cartographic mate-

rial (ca. 150 items), photographs and sketches (ca. 5,000 items), motion pictures (15 reels), and sound recordings (20 items) of an antarctic explorer, geographer, and member of Adm. Richard E. Byrd's and other polar expeditions (150 lin. ft.); *Mrs. Paul A. Siple Papers*, 1926-68, including correspondence, college notebooks, biological notes and sketches, and photographs (2 lin. ft. and ca. 25 items); *Carl R. Eklund Papers*, 1935-62, consisting of journals, manuscripts of publications, scientific notes, field notebooks, correspondence, cartographic material (5 items), and photographs of an antarctic explorer, zoologist, member of the U.S. Antarctic Service, and station scientific leader at Wilkes Station, 1957-58 (5 lin, ft.); *Stevenson Corey Papers*, 1931-36, including diaries, journals, correspondence, supply lists, memorabilia, and photographs of a member of the 1933-35 Byrd Antarctic Expedition (2 lin. ft.); *Alton A. Lindsey Papers*, 1933-52, including journals, notebooks, research notes, correspondence, maps (5 items), photographs (ca. 2,000 items), motion pictures (2 reels), and sound recordings (2 items) of a biologist with the 1933-35 Byrd Antarctic

Expedition and the 1951 Purdue-Canadian Permafrost Expedition (4 lin. ft.); *Capt. Harold E. Saunders Papers*, 1928-60, including manuscripts, research notes, correspondence, maps (ca. 250 items), and photographs (ca. 5,000 items) relating to the Byrd Antarctic Expeditions, 1928-30 and 1933-35, the U.S. Antarctic Service, 1939-41, and the Advisory Committee on Antarctic Names, 1945-61, of an associate of Byrd and a pioneer in aerial photographic maps (10 lin. ft.); *James E. Mooney Papers*, 1930-68, including reports, manuscript speeches and articles for publication, correspondence, memorandums, drafts, photographs (ca. 50 items), motion pictures (12 reels), and a sound recording of another Byrd associate and Deputy U.S. Antarctic Projects Officer, 1959-65 (15 lin. ft.); and *Herbert G. Dorsey Papers*, 1939-41, consisting of meteorological data from East Base and Plateau Station, Antarctica, 1939-41.

Also *Maj. Palle Mogensen Papers*, 1954-58, including reports, observation notes, correspondence, and photographs (ca. 1,000 items) relating to his service in Greenland, 1954-55, as commander of the U.S. Army-Navy trail team to Byrd Station for Little America, 1956-57, and as station scientific leader of the Amundsen-Scott (South Pole) Station, 1957-58 (1 lin. ft.); *George E. Tyson Papers*, 1871-1909, consisting of journals, notebooks, correspondence, and family memorabilia of a member of the U.S.S. *Polaris* arctic expedition, 1871-73, under Charles Francis Hall (5 lin. ft.); *Mrs. Evelyn Stefansson Nef Papers*, 1913-39, including correspondence of Vilhjalmur Stefansson, notebooks, publications, newsclippings, and photographs (5 items) relating to the Arctic (7 lin. ft.); *Robert W. Wood Collection*, 1929, consisting of correspondence, newsclippings, sketches by Eskimos, photographs (ca. 45 items), and a motion picture relating to the flight of the "'Untin' Bowler" from Chicago to Ungava Bay, July 1929, collected by a journalist with the *Chicago Tribune; Col. Charles J. Hubbard Papers*, 1931-54, consisting of reports, biographical material, photographs (ca. 150 items), correspondence, and publications of a pioneer arctic pilot (9 lin. ft.); *John A. Pope Papers*, 1927, consisting of a journal and photographs (ca. 100 items) taken while aboard the *Morrissey* off the Foxe Peninsula; *Paul Sullivan Papers*, 1919-58, including notes, manuscript maps (ca. 50 items), and photographs (ca. 50 items) relating to the research, compilation, and printing of *The Dynamic North, Canadian North*, and *Meteorology of the Arctic* (3 lin. ft.); *Duncan Stewart VII Papers*, 1920-69, including a diary, correspondence, publications on polar regions, a motion picture, and scrapbooks on the rescue of two pilots in 1928, of a geologist and authority on the geology and petrography of Antarctica (14 lin. ft.); *Russell W. Porter Papers*, 1890-1940, including diaries and journals, field notebooks, correspondence, newsclippings, memorabilia, photographs and paintings, pastels, watercolors, and pencil sketches (ca. 250 items) to illustrate the unpublished manuscript of his autobiography "Arctic Fever," of an explorer, leader of three expeditions to Greenland, and member of the Baldwin-Ziegler, 1901-2, and Fiala-Ziegler, 1903-5, expeditions to Franz Josef Land and two Frederick A. Cook expeditions, 1894 and 1906 (8 lin. ft.); *Dayton Brown Papers*, 1946, including 32 oil paintings of the Arctic (8 lin. ft.); and *Herman R. Friis Papers*, 1920-70, including diaries, journals, and maps (ca. 175 items) relating to service on antarctic and other expeditions, correspondence, lecture manuscripts, research notes in historical geography and cartography, publications, photographs (ca. 5,000 items), and sound recordings (4 items) of a cartographer, geographer, archivist, and Director of the Center for Polar Archives (75 lin. ft.).

SPECIFIC RESTRICTIONS

Nearly all of these donated historical materials have restrictions of various kinds. Most of these generally require only that the searcher have the written approval of the donor of the papers to examine, take notes, quote, reproduce, or publish them.

APPENDIX A

PUBLIC USE OF RECORDS, DONATED HISTORICAL MATERIALS, . . . IN THE NATIONAL ARCHIVES AND RECORDS SERVICE

(41 CFR PART 105–61)

§ 105–61.000 Scope of part.

This part prescribes rules and procedures governing the public use of records and donated historical materials that have been transferred to the National Archives and Records Service, GSA, but does not apply to current operating records of the Service. . . .

§ 105–61.001 Definitions.

The following definitions are established for terms used in this part.

§ 105–61.001–1 Records.

"Records" means only records that have been transferred to the National Archives and Records Service, in accordance with 44 U.S.C. 2103, 3103; namely, archives and Federal records center records, as those terms are defined in this § 105–61.001. The term "records" does not include current operating records of the National Archives and Records Service, the public availability of which is governed by Part 105–60, or donated historical materials, as defined and considered in this part.

§ 105–61.001–2 Archives.

"Archives" means official records that have been determined by GSA

to have sufficient historical or other value to warrant their continued preservation by the U.S. Government, and have been accepted for deposit with the National Archives of the United States.

*   *   *   *   *   *   *

§ 105–61.001–4 Donated historical materials.

"Donated historical materials" means books, correspondence, documents, papers, pamphlets, magnetic tapes, pictures, photographs, plats, maps, films, motion pictures, sound recordings, and other documental media having historical or commemorative value accepted by GSA from a source other than an agency of the U.S. Government.

§ 105–61.001–5 Director.

"Director" means the head of a Presidential library, the head of an Office of the National Archives division, branch, or unit responsible for servicing records, or the head of a Reference Service Branch or an Archives Branch in a Federal records center.
[34 F.R. 200, Jan. 7, 1969]

§ 105–61.001–6 Researcher.

"Researcher" means a person who has applied for access to

records or donated historical materials, in accordance with § 105-61.101-3, and who has been issued a researcher identification card.

Subpart 105–61.1 — Public Use of Archives . . .

§ 105–61.101 Availability of records.

§ 105–61.101–1 General.

(a) Researchers will normally use records in designated research rooms only.

(b) Original records will not normally be made available when microfilm copies are available.

(c) Persons seeking information that is published and readily available will normally be referred to a public library.

(d) Records will not be furnished to a researcher under the age of 16 years unless he is accompanied by an adult researcher who agrees, in writing, to be present when the records are used and to be responsible for compliance with the research room rules set forth in § 105-61.103.

§ 105–61.101–2 Location of records and hours of use.

(a) A prospective researcher should first ascertain the location of the records desired. Inquiries may be addressed to the Archivist of the United States, Washington, DC 20408.

(b) The locations and hours of duty (expressed in local time) of depositories administered by the National Archives and Records Service are shown in § 105-61.4801.

(c) Except for Federal holidays and other times specified by the Archivist, records will be made available according to the schedule set forth in § 105-61.4801.

(d) In addition to the times specified in § 105-61.4801, records may be made available at such other times as authorized by a director.

§ 105–61.101–3 Application procedures.

(a) Applicants shall apply in person at the depository that has custody of the records sought and shall furnish, on a form provided for the purpose, information necessary for registration and for determining which records will be made available. Applicants shall furnish proper identification and, if applying for access to large quantities of records or to records that are especially fragile or valuable, shall upon request furnish a letter of reference or introduction.

(b) In advance of applying for the use of records, a prospective researcher is encouraged to determine from the appropriate depository whether the records are available and whether their volume is sufficient to warrant a personal visit in lieu of reproduction.

(c) In addition to the procedures prescribed in this § 105-61.101-3, researchers desiring to apply for the use of archives that contain defense-classified information shall follow procedures prescribed in § 105-61.104.

[33 F.R. 4885, Mar. 22, 1968, as amended at 34 F.R. 200, Jan. 7, 1969]

§ 105–61.101–4 Researcher identification card.

A researcher identification card will be issued to each person whose application is approved. The card will be valid for the use of records at only the depository where it was issued, and for a period of not more than 1 year, but it may be renewed upon application. Cards are not transferable and shall be produced when requested by a guard or research room attendant.

§ 105–61.102 Restrictions and appeals.

§ 105–61.102–1 Restrictions.

The use of records is subject to any restrictions specified in writing by the agency from which the records were transferred and to restrictions set forth by the Archivist of the United States in pertinent restriction statements. . . .

§ 105–61.102–2 Denials and appeals.

Denials of use of records, except those made in the normal course of reference service, shall be made by the Deputy Archivist of the United States, in accordance with § 105–60.403, and any resulting appeals shall be made and conducted in accord with § 105–60.404.

§ 105–61.103 Research room rules.

§ 105–61.103–1 Registration.

Researchers shall register each day they enter a research room, furnishing the information specified on the registration form.

§ 105–61.103–2 Researcher's responsibility for records.

The research room attendant may limit the quantity of records to be delivered at one time to a researcher. When requested, researchers shall acknowledge receipt of records by signature. A researcher is responsible for all records delivered to him until he returns them. When a researcher has completed his use of records, he shall return them to the research room attendant. When requested, researchers shall return records as much as 10 minutes before closing time. Before leaving a research room, even for a short period of time, a researcher shall notify the research room attendant and place all records in their proper containers.

§ 105–61.103–3 Prevention of damage to records.

The researcher shall exercise all possible care to prevent damage to records. Records shall not be used at a desk where there is a container of liquid or where a fountain pen is being used. Records shall not be leaned on, written on, folded anew, traced, fastened with paper clips or rubber bands, or handled in any way likely to cause damage. The use of records of exceptional value or in fragile condition shall be subject to any conditions specified by the research room attendant.

§ 105–61.103–4 Removal or mutilation of records.

Researchers shall not remove records from a research room. The unlawful removal or mutilation of records is forbidden by law and is punishable by fine or imprisonment or both (18 U.S.C. 2071). When so requested, researchers shall check parcels and luggage before entering a research room; and upon leaving, a researcher shall, if so requested, present for examination any brief-case, notebook, package, envelope, book, or other article that could contain records.

§ 105–61.103–5   Conduct.

Researchers are subject to the provisions of Subpart 101–19.3, Conduct on Federal Property. Eating in a research room is prohibited. Smoking is prohibited except in designated smoking areas. Loud talking and other activities likely to disturb other researchers are also prohibited. Persons desiring to use typewriters, sound recording devices, or photocopying equipment shall work in areas designated by the research room attendant.

§ 105–61.103–6   Keeping records in order.

A researcher must keep unbound records in the order in which they are delivered to him. Records appearing to be in disorder should not be rearranged by a researcher, but should be referred to the research room attendant. Normally, a researcher will not be allowed to remove records from more than one container at a time.

§ 105–61.104   Access to national security information.

Public access to national security information and materials is governed by Executive Order 11652 of March 8, 1972 (37 F.R. 5209, March 10, 1972), and by the National Security Council Directive of May 17, 1972 (37 F.R. 10053, May 19, 1972).

*   *   *   *   *   *   *

§ 105–61.105   Copying services.

The copying of records will normally be done by personnel of the National Archives and Records Service with equipment belonging to the Service. With the permission of a director, researchers may use their own copying equipment. Permission will be based on the director's determination that such use will not harm the records or disrupt reference activities. Equipment will be used under the supervision of personnel of the Service.

§ 105–61.106   Information services.
§ 105–61.106–1   About records.

Upon request, overall information pertaining to holdings or about specific records will be furnished, provided that the time required to furnish the information is not excessive, and provided that the information is not restricted (see § 105–61.102). When so specified by a director, requests shall be made on prescribed forms.

§ 105–61.106–2   From records.

Normally, information contained in the records will be furnished in the form of photocopies of the records, subject to the provisions of §105–61.105. The National Archives and Records Service will certify facts and make administrative determinations on the basis of archives . . . when appropriate officials of other agencies have authorized GSA to do so. Such certifications and determinations shall be authenticated by the seal of GSA, the National Archives of the United

States, or the transferring agency, as appropriate.

[34 F.R. 19979, Dec. 20, 1969]

§ 105–61.107 Authentication of copies.

The responsible director, or any of his superiors, and the Director of the Federal Register are authorized to authenticate and attest copies of records.

§ 105–61.108 Fees.

Fees charged for the reproduction, certification, and authentication of records must be paid in advance, except when the appropriate director approves a request for handling them on an accounts receivable basis. Fees may be paid in cash or by check or money order made payable to GSA. Remittances from outside the United States should be made by international money order or check drawn in U.S. dollars on a bank in the United States or one of its territories or possessions.

* * * * * * *

Subpart 105–61.2 — Public Use of Donated Historical Materials

§ 105–61.201 General.

The use of donated historical materials (as defined in § 105–61.001–4) is governed by the provisions of Subpart 105–61.1, except that § 105–61.202 shall apply in lieu of § 105–61.102.

§ 105–61.202 Restrictions.

The public use of donated historical materials is subject to the following restrictions:

(a) Use is subject to all conditions specified by the donor or transferor of such materials or by the Archivist of the United States. (Researchers are encouraged to confer with directors on any question of literary property right.)

(b) Use must relate to a study requiring the unique resources of the depository.

[33 F.R. 4885, Mar. 22, 1968, as amended at 34 F.R. 19979, Dec. 20, 1969; 35 F.R. 18737, Dec. 10, 1970]

* * * * * * *

§ 105–61.4801 Location of records and hours of use.

This section relates to § 105–61.101–2.

(a) The Archives Building, Eighth and Pennsylvania Avenue NW., Washington, DC 20408.

Hours: For the Central Research Room and Microfilm Research Room, 8:45 a.m. to 10 p.m., Monday through Friday, and 8:45 a.m. to 5 p.m. on Saturday. For other research rooms, 8:45 a.m. to 5 p.m., Monday through Friday. Records to be used on Friday after 5 p.m. or on Saturday must be requested by 3 p.m. Friday. Records to be used after 5 p.m., Monday through Thursday, must be requested by 4 p.m. of the day on which they are to be used.

(b) [Reserved]

(c) Presidential libraries, as follows:

(1) Herbert Hoover Library, South Downey Street, West Branch, IA 52358.

Hours: 9 a.m. to 5 p.m., Monday through Friday.

(2) Franklin D. Roosevelt Library, Albany Post Road, Hyde Park, NY 12538.

Hours: 9 a.m. to 5 p.m., Monday through Friday.

(3) Harry S. Truman Library, Highway 24 at Delaware Street, Independence, MO 64050.

Hours: 9 a.m. to 5 p.m., Monday through Friday.

(4) Dwight D. Eisenhower Library, South East Fourth Street, Abilene, KS 67410.

Hours: 9 a.m. to 5 p.m., Monday through Friday.

(5) John F. Kennedy Library, 380 Trapelo Road, Waltham, MA 02154.

Hours: 8:30 a.m. to 5 p.m., Monday through Friday.

(6) Lyndon B. Johnson Library, 2313 Red River, Austin, TX 78705.

Hours: 9 a.m. to 5 p.m., Monday through Friday.

(d) [Reserved]

(e) Washington National Records Center, 4205 Suitland Road, Suitland, MD.

Mailing address: General Services Administration, Washington National Records Center, Washington, DC 20409.

Hours: 8 a.m. to 4:30 p.m., Monday through Friday.

(f) National Personnel Records Center (military personnel records), 9700 Page Boulevard, St. Louis, MO 63132.

Hours: 7:30 a.m. to 4 p.m., Monday through Friday.

(g) National Personnel Records Center (civilian personnel records), 111 Winnebago Street, St. Louis, MO 63118.

Hours: 7:30 a.m. to 4 p.m., Monday through Friday.

(h) Regional Federal records centers, as follows:

(1) 380 Trapelo Road, Waltham, MA 02154.

Hours: 8:20 a.m. to 4:50 p.m., Monday through Friday.

(2) 641 Washington Street, New York, NY 10014.

Hours: 8:30 a.m. to 5 p.m., Monday through Friday.

(3) 5000 Wissahickon Avenue, Philadelphia, PA 19144.

Hours: 8:30 a.m. to 5 p.m., Monday through Friday.

(4) Naval Supply Depot, Building 308, Mechanicsburg, PA 17055.

Hours: 7:30 a.m. to 4:30 p.m., Monday through Friday.

(5) 1557 St. Joseph Avenue, East Point, GA 30044.

Hours: 8 a.m. to 4:30 p.m., Monday through Friday.

(6) 7201 South Leamington Avenue, Chicago, IL 60638.

Hours: 8 a.m. to 4:30 p.m., Monday through Friday.

(7) 2400 West Dorothy Lane, Dayton, OH 45439.

Hours: 8 a.m. to 4:30 p.m., Monday through Friday.

(8) 2306 East Bannister Road, Kansas City, MO 64131.

Hours: 8 a.m. to 4:30 p.m., Monday through Friday.

(9) 4900 Hemphill Street, Fort Worth, TX 76115.

Hours: 8 a.m. to 4:30 p.m., Monday through Friday.

(10) Building 48, Denver Federal Center, Denver, CO 80225.

Hours: 8 a.m. to 4:30 p.m., Monday through Friday.

(11) Building 1, 100 Harrison Street, San Francisco, CA 94105.

Hours: 8 a.m. to 4:30 p.m., Monday through Friday.

(12) 4747 Eastern Avenue, Bell, CA 90201.

Hours: 7:30 a.m. to 4 p.m., Monday through Friday.

(13) 6125 Sand Point Way, Seattle, WA 98115.

Hours: 8 a.m. to 4:30 p.m., Monday through Friday.

[36 F.R. 25408, Dec. 31, 1971]

APPENDIX B

SUGGESTIONS FOR CITING RECORDS IN THE NATIONAL ARCHIVES OF THE UNITED STATES

The National Archives and Records Service is frequently asked to provide recommendations regarding information to be included in footnotes or other references to records among its holdings. The following suggestions should serve this purpose and their use will also enable our staff more readily to locate records that have been cited.

Sequence of Elements in Citation

The most convenient citation for archives is one similar to that used for personal papers and other historical manuscripts. Full identification of most unpublished material usually requires giving the title and date of the item, series title (if applicable), name of the collection, and the name of the depository. Except for placing the cited item first, there is no general agreement on the sequence of the remaining elements in the citation. Publishers, professional journals, and graduate faculties all prescribe their own style. Whatever sequence is adopted, however, should be used consistently throughout the same work.

Full Identification of Archival Material

Because of the greater complexity and more formal structure of archival material, additional elements may be needed in citations not only to fully identify an item, but also to indicate its relative location within a given record group. The record group is a unit of control for records based upon their administrative origin, and, for citation purpose, is comparable to a collection or an organized body of personal papers. The elements that may be necessary for full identification of archival material, depending upon its complexity, include:

(Item)
Charles G. Hewett to Aubrey Williams, December 28, 1936,
(File Unit)
File "Adm. Reports, October thru December 30," Maine,
(Series Title)
Administrative Reports Received from N.Y.A. State Officers, 1935–38,
(Subgroups)
Records of the Deputy Executive Director and Deputy Administrator, Office of the Administrator,
(Record Group Title and Number)
Records of the National Youth Administration, Record Group 119,
(Depository)
National Archives Building.

In the above example, all of the elements before record group title and number indicate how the agency received or created and where it filed the record. The final two elements have been added by the archival depository for control and retrieval purposes.

An example of the method of identifying and indicating the hierarchical location of an originating office through subgroups would be, for example, "Metals Section, Mineral Deposits Branch, Geologic Division," which is part of Records of the Geological Survey, Record Group 57. Subsequent citations of items from the records of the Metals Section could omit the hierarchical location information; i.e., "Mineral Deposits Branch, Geologic Division." The first time records from another originating office are cited, however, the names of the successive administrative units in the hierarchy of which that office is a part should be given.

Basic Elements in Citation

Because of the great variety and complexity of some archival material, there are no convenient models that would be applicable to all records. The minimum initial citation, however, should consist of the item, file unit or subseries (i.e., volume, with title and page numbers, if applicable; or file or folder, with title or other designation), series title, subgroup(s) or originating office (including the hierarchy of administrative units of which that office is a part, if applicable), record group title and number, and name of depository. These are the elements necessary to identify adequately most archival material, and the above order of entry is that adopted by the National Archives and Records Service for its own publications. If in doubt regarding a particular citation, the researcher should confer with an archivist to determine what elements may be necessary to identify adequately specific records being cited. Because it is sometimes necessary to move records from one type of container to another and to rebox records, box or other container numbers should not be included in citations.

Unless the file unit or series is arranged chronologically, it is usually necessary to show exact file location of the document cited, as illustrated by the italicized symbols in the examples below, which also show some of the various orders in which the necessary elements of the citation may be entered, as determined by individual editors:

Commissioner of Indian Affairs to Chu-he-sa-da, January 12, 1883, *Letter Book 106, pp. 127-128*, Letters Sent, Land Division, Records of the Bureau of Indian Affairs, Record Group 75, National Archives Building.

Military Attache Report, National Archives Building, Records of the War Department General and Special Staffs, Record Group 165, *File 2657-I-281/120*.

Dispatch No. 1988, James G. Bailey to Philander C. Knox, December 25, 1909, *Case 13367/54, Vol. 941*, Numerical File, National Archives Building, General Records of the Department of State, Record Group 59.

Suggested Short Form
Following Initial Citation

Following the initial citation, the author may save space in citing items from the same record group by using the symbol RG and the record group number in place of the full record group title; i.e., "RG 59," rather than "General Records of the Department of State, Record Group 59." When an item is first cited from a different record group, however, the full record group title and the new record group number should be given. The author may also save space by including at the end of the first citation to records in the National Archives Building a statement to the effect that "hereafter records in the National Archives Building are indicated by use of the symbol NA." With the development of regional archives and Presidential libraries, parts of the same record group may be located in several different depositories. It is therefore essential that the depository be indicated with each citation.

In addition to the National Archives Building, archival depositories currently administered by the National Archives and Records Service include the General Archives Division, Washington National Records Center, Suitland, Md. (for which the suggested location reference for use in subsequent citations is WNRC), and the 11 archives branches in Federal records centers located throughout the country. The suggested location reference for each of these is the symbol FRC with the name of the city in which the records center is located; e.g., FRC Atlanta and FRC San Francisco. Suggested location references for Presidential libraries are in the style "Franklin D. Roosevelt Library, Hyde Park, N.Y., hereafter cited as FDRL."

Citing Enclosures and Records
in Combined Files

In citing enclosures record items that have been brought forward in a file or otherwise combined, it is necessary to specify the document with which the enclosure was received or filed, or, in the case of records consolidations, to indicate the file unit with which the document has been combined:

Special Order 156, Dept. of Dakota, October 14, 1869, enclosed in Maj. Gen. A. Baird to the Adjutant General's Office, November 1, 1869, File 793B1869, Letters Received, Main Series, RG 94, NA.

Bvt. Lt. Col. John S. Billings to the Adjutant General's Office, October 31, 1869, File 787B1869, filed with William A. Richardson to the Acting Secretary of War, September 10, 1869, File 294T1869, Letters Received, Main Series, RG 94, NA.

Citation of Microfilm Publications

Citations to records reproduced in National Archives microfilm publications should provide, in general, the same information as suggested above, but with sufficient additional information to identify the particular publication as well as roll and frame numbers, if applicable:

C. A. Ruffee to the Acting Commissioner of Indian Affairs, December 2, 1867, File R202–1867 Sisseton, Letters Received, 1824–80, Records of the Bureau of Indian Affairs, Record Group 75, National Archives Microfilm Publication M234, roll 824, frames 23–27.

Particularly in the case of records reproduced in microfilm publications, as well as in some other cases, the control and retrieval information imposed by the National Archives and Records Service is sufficiently precise that subsequent citations may be greatly simplified. The location of another document in the same series of "Letters Received" could be identified, after an explanatory note, as briefly as "M234, 824/29–31." Such a citation would give the exact location on film of the document: M234 is the number of the National Archives microfilm publication covering Letters Received, 1824–80, Records of the Bureau of Indian Affairs, Record Group 75, so this symbol can substitute in subsequent citations for this information. The symbols "824/29–31" indicate the roll and frame numbers containing the document.

Some microfilm publications, particularly those of foreign records seized during World War II, involve such peculiarities of identification that largely individualized suggested systems of citation have been developed for them. Since July 1970, National Archives and Records Service finding aids to microfilm publications reproducing captured German and related records have contained suggestions to assist researchers in preparing citations to such records. Staff members upon request will assist researchers in preparing citations to other complicated bodies of material.

Citing Cartographic and Audiovisual Records

The informational elements suggested above for the citation of textual records are also applicable to cartographic and audiovisual records, although this kind of material usually requires only the item, series title, record group title and number, and name of depository. When citations of cartographic and audiovisual material occur in credit lines rather than in footnotes, the identification of a photograph or map should include the agency of origin (usually given in the record group title), the identifying number on the back of the print or map, and the fact that the photograph or map is in the National Archives Building. Adequate citations for credit purposes would include:

Signal Corps No. 111–RB–5242 in National Archives Building (hereafter NA).

U.S. Information Agency No. 306–NT–38790V in NA.

Office of the Chief of Engineers Map N.2–19 in NA.

General Land Office Local Office Plat in NA.

APPENDIX C

LIST OF RECORD GROUPS ARRANGED BY RECORD GROUP NUMBER

Omitted from this list are all record groups for which no records have been accessioned as part of the National Archives of the United States, as well as record groups that have been canceled. In the few instances where it has been necessary to cancel record groups, the records that had been or were to be allocated to them have been reallocated to other record groups.

		Page
1	Records of the War Labor Policies Board	609
2	Records of the National War Labor Board (World War I)	580
3	Records of the United States Housing Corporation	596
4	Records of the United States Food Administration	591
5	Records of the United States Grain Corporation	595
6	Records of the United States Sugar Equalization Board, Inc.	607
7	Records of the Bureau of Entomology and Plant Quarantine	453
8	Records of the Bureau of Agricultural Engineering	447
9	Records of the National Recovery Administration	626
10	Records of the National Commission on Law Observance and Enforcement	63
11	General Records of the United States Government	41
12	Records of the Office of Education	505
13	Records of the National Mediation Board	558
14	Records of the United States Railroad Administration	599
15	Records of the Veterans Administration	571
16	Records of the Office of the Secretary of Agriculture	423
17	Records of the Bureau of Animal Industry	445
18	Records of the Army Air Forces	324
19	Records of the Bureau of Ships	305
20	Records of the Office of the Special Adviser to the President on Foreign Trade	126
21	Records of District Courts of the United States	72
22	Records of the Fish and Wildlife Service	394
23	Records of the Coast and Geodetic Survey	470
24	Records of the Bureau of Naval Personnel	310
25	Records of the National Labor Relations Board	555
26	Records of the United States Coast Guard	522
27	Records of the Weather Bureau	476
28	Records of the Post Office Department	358
29	Records of the Bureau of the Census	465
30	Records of the Bureau of Public Roads	525

Page

31 Records of the Federal Housing Administration...................... 515
32 Records of the United States Shipping Board...................... 601
33 Records of the Federal Extension Service...................... 432
34 Records of the Federal Deposit Insurance Corporation.............. 537
35 Records of the Civilian Conservation Corps...................... 614
36 Records of the Bureau of Customs...................... 168
37 Records of the Hydrographic Office...................... 313
38 Records of the Office of the Chief of Naval Operations.............. 296
39 Records of the Bureau of Accounts (Treasury)...................... 165
40 General Records of the Department of Commerce...................... 464
41 Records of the Bureau of Marine Inspection and Navigation...... 480
42 Records of the Office of Public Buildings and Grounds.............. 714
43 Records of International Conferences, Commissions, and Exposi-
    tions...................... 146
44 Records of the Office of Government Reports...................... 124
45 Naval Records Collection of the Office of Naval Records and
    Library...................... 293
46 Records of the United States Senate...................... 49
47 Records of the Social Security Administration...................... 510
48 Records of the Office of the Secretary of the Interior.............. 364
49 Records of the Bureau of Land Management...................... 371
50 Records of the Treasurer of the United States...................... 157
51 Records of the Bureau of the Budget...................... 96
52 Records of the Bureau of Medicine and Surgery...................... 301
53 Records of the Bureau of the Public Debt...................... 162
54 Records of the Bureau of Plant Industry, Soils, and Agricultural
    Engineering...................... 450
55 Records of the Government of the Virgin Islands...................... 723
56 General Records of the Department of the Treasury.................. 152
57 Records of the Geological Survey...................... 389
58 Records of the Internal Revenue Service...................... 177
59 General Records of the Department of State...................... 131
60 General Records of the Department of Justice...................... 336
61 Records of the War Industries Board...................... 608
62 Records of the Council of National Defense...................... 578
63 Records of the Committee on Public Information...................... 119
64 Records of the National Archives and Records Service.............. 549
65 Records of the Federal Bureau of Investigation...................... 348
66 Records of the Commission of Fine Arts...................... 531
67 Records of the United States Fuel Administration...................... 593
68 Records of the United States Coal Commission...................... 590
69 Records of the Work Projects Administration...................... 693
70 Records of the Bureau of Mines...................... 407
71 Records of the Bureau of Yards and Docks...................... 309

Page

72 Records of the Bureau of Aeronautics.................................... 318
73 Records of the President's Organization on Unemployment
   Relief.. 120
74 Records of the Bureau of Ordnance.. 302
75 Records of the Bureau of Indian Affairs.................................... 377
76 Records of Boundary and Claims Commissions and Arbitrations.. 143
77 Records of the Office of the Chief of Engineers......................... 236
78 Records of the Naval Observatory.. 315
79 Records of the National Park Service.. 397
80 General Records of the Department of the Navy......................... 291
81 Records of the United States Tariff Commission......................... 570
82 Records of the Federal Reserve System.................................... 542
83 Records of the Bureau of Agricultural Economics...................... 455
84 Records of the Foreign Service Posts of the Department of
   State... 140
85 Records of the Immigration and Naturalization Service............. 345
86 Records of the Women's Bureau.. 494
87 Records of the United States Secret Service............................. 176
88 Records of the Food and Drug Administration........................... 507
89 Records of the Federal Fuel Distributor.................................... 579
90 Records of the Public Health Service.. 502
91 Records of the Inland Waterways Corporation........................... 488
92 Records of the Office of the Quartermaster General.................... 245
93 War Department Collection of Revolutionary War Records........ 37
94 Records of the Adjutant General's Office, 1780's–1917................. 230
95 Records of the Forest Service... 426
96 Records of the Farmers Home Administration........................... 442
97 Records of the Bureau of Agricultural and Industrial Chemistry.. 449
98 Records of United States Army Commands, 1784–1821............... 271
99 Records of the Office of the Paymaster General......................... 250
100 Records of the Bureau of Labor Standards.............................. 495
101 Records of the Office of the Comptroller of the Currency........... 159
102 Records of the Children's Bureau... 510
103 Records of the Farm Credit Administration.............................. 533
104 Records of the Bureau of the Mint.. 172
105 Records of the Bureau of Refugees, Freedmen, and Abandoned
    Lands... 263
106 Records of the Smithsonian Institution.................................... 565
107 Records of the Office of the Secretary of War........................... 207
108 Records of the Headquarters of the Army................................. 214
109 War Department Collection of Confederate Records.................. 719
110 Records of the Provost Marshal General's Bureau (Civil War)... 256
111 Records of the Office of the Chief Signal Officer....................... 254

Page

112 Records of the Office of the Surgeon General (Army)................. 250
113 Records of the Allied Purchasing Commission........................... 577
114 Records of the Soil Conservation Service................................. 437
115 Records of the Bureau of Reclamation.................................... 406
117 Records of the American Battle Monuments Commission........... 529
118 Records of United States Attorneys and Marshals.................... 343
119 Records of the National Youth Administration......................... 634
120 Records of the American Expeditionary Forces (World War I), 1917–23... 283
121 Records of the Public Buildings Service.................................. 545
122 Records of the Federal Trade Commission............................... 542
123 Records of the United States Court of Claims.......................... 90
124 Records of the Surplus Marketing Administration..................... 458
125 Records of the Office of the Judge Advocate General (Navy)...... 317
126 Records of the Office of Territories....................................... 403
127 Records of the United States Marine Corps............................. 300
128 Records of Joint Committees of Congress................................ 54
129 Records of the Bureau of Prisons... 349
130 Records of the White House Office... 95
131 Records of the Office of Alien Property.................................. 354
132 Records of the Rent Commission of the District of Columbia...... 718
133 Records of the Federal Coordinator of Transportation............... 618
134 Records of the Interstate Commerce Commission...................... 553
135 Records of the Public Works Administration............................. 669
136 Records of the Agricultural Marketing Service......................... 460
137 Records of the Federal Supply Service.................................... 548
138 Records of the Federal Power Commission............................... 541
139 Records of the Dominican Customs Receivership...................... 282
140 Records of the Military Government of Cuba............................ 280
141 Records of the Military Government of Veracruz....................... 283
142 Records of the Tennessee Valley Authority.............................. 567
143 Records of the Bureau of Supplies and Accounts (Navy)............ 308
144 Records of the Temporary National Economic Committee.......... 62
145 Records of the Agricultural Stabilization and Conservation Service... 435
146 Records of the United States Civil Service Commission.............. 568
147 Records of the Selective Service System, 1940–....................... 563
148 Records of Minor Congressional Commissions........................... 61
149 Records of the Government Printing Office............................... 57
150 Records of the National Bituminous Coal Commission, 1935–36... 417
151 Records of the Bureau of Foreign and Domestic Commerce........ 486
152 Records of the Bureau of Dairy Industry................................ 447
153 Records of the Office of the Judge Advocate General (Army)...... 258

Page

154 Records of the War Finance Corporation...................................... 608
155 Records of the Wage and Hour and Public Contracts Divisions... 496
156 Records of the Office of the Chief of Ordnance.......................... 242
157 Records of the Maritime Labor Board....................................... 626
158 Records of the Capital Issues Committee................................... 577
159 Records of the Office of the Inspector General........................... 241
160 Records of Headquarters Army Service Forces.......................... 228
161 Records of the Commodity Credit Corporation.......................... 434
162 General Records of the Federal Works Agency.......................... 704
163 Records of the Selective Service System (World War I).............. 265
164 Records of the Office of Experiment Stations............................ 446
165 Records of the War Department General and Special Staffs........ 216
166 Records of the Foreign Agricultural Service............................. 430
167 Records of the National Bureau of Standards........................... 474
168 Records of the National Guard Bureau.................................... 264
169 Records of the Foreign Economic Administration...................... 623
170 Records of the Bureau of Narcotics and Dangerous Drugs......... 350
171 Records of the Office of Civilian Defense................................. 639
172 Records of the United States Commerce Court.......................... 92
173 Records of the Federal Communications Commission................. 535
174 General Records of the Department of Labor............................ 491
175 Records of the Chemical Warfare Service................................. 266
176 Records of the Bureau of Human Nutrition and Home
      Economics... 458
177 Records of the Chiefs of Arms.. 225
178 Records of the United States Maritime Commission................... 675
179 Records of the War Production Board..................................... 687
180 Records of the Commodity Exchange Authority......................... 432
181 Records of Naval Districts and Shore Establishments................ 320
182 Records of the War Trade Board.. 610
183 Records of the Bureau of Employment Security........................ 498
185 Records of the Panama Canal... 562
186 Records of the Spanish Governors of Puerto Rico...................... 725
187 Records of the National Resources Planning Board.................... 122
188 Records of the Office of Price Administration........................... 647
189 Records of the National Academy of Sciences........................... 554
190 Records of the Bureau of War Risk Litigation........................... 356
191 Records of the War Department Claims Board.......................... 223
192 Records of the Office of the Commissary General of Subsistence... 252
193 Records of the Commissioner of Railroads............................... 411
194 Records of the War Minerals Relief Commission........................ 414
195 Records of the Federal Home Loan Bank System....................... 538
196 Records of the Public Housing Administration.......................... 519

Page

197 Records of the Civil Aeronautics Board.................................... 530
198 Records of the Board of Investigation and Research—Trans-
        portation... 612
199 Records of the Provisional Government of Cuba......................... 281
200 National Archives Gift Collection.. 742
202 Records of the National War Labor Board (World War II).......... 631
203 Records of the Office of the Chief of Finance (Army)................. 252
204 Records of the Office of the Pardon Attorney........................... 344
205 Records of the Court of Claims Section (Justice)....................... 351
206 Records of the Solicitor of the Treasury................................... 352
207 General Records of the Department of Housing and Urban
        Development.. 513
208 Records of the Office of War Information................................. 660
209 Records of the Prison Industries Reorganization Administration. 668
210 Records of the War Relocation Authority................................. 689
211 Records of the War Manpower Commission............................. 679
212 Records of the Committee for Congested Production Areas........ 615
213 Records of the Foreign Claims Section (War)........................... 224
214 Records of the Office for Emergency Management..................... 644
215 Records of the Office of Community War Services...................... 640
216 Records of the Office of Censorship.. 637
217 Records of the United States General Accounting Office............ 57
218 Records of the United States Joint Chiefs of Staff.................... 188
219 Records of the Office of Defense Transportation....................... 642
220 Records of Presidential Committees, Commissions, and Boards... 102
221 Records of the Rural Electrification Administration................... 440
222 Records of the Bituminous Coal Division................................. 418
223 Records of the Office of the Bituminous Coal Consumers' Counsel. 637
224 Records of the Office of Labor (War Food Administration).......... 459
225 Records of Joint Army and Navy Boards and Committees.......... 200
226 Records of the Office of Strategic Services............................... 204
227 Records of the Office of Scientific Research and Development..... 657
228 Records of the Committee on Fair Employment Practice........... 616
229 Records of the Office of Inter-American Affairs........................ 646
230 Records of the United States War Ballot Commission............... 678
231 Records of the United States Soldiers' Home........................... 289
232 Records of the Petroleum Administrative Board........................ 415
233 Records of the United States House of Representatives............. 51
234 Records of the Reconstruction Finance Corporation.................. 580
235 General Records of the Department of Health, Education, and
        Welfare... 501
236 Records of the Wage Adjustment Board................................... 497
237 Records of the Federal Aviation Administration........................ 527

Page

238 National Archives Collection of World War II War Crimes
    Records... 699
239 Records of the American Commission for the Protection and Sal-
    vage of Artistic and Historic Monuments in War Areas........... 611
240 Records of the Smaller War Plants Corporation......................... 673
241 Records of the Patent Office.. 469
242 National Archives Collection of Foreign Records Seized, 1941-.... 727
243 Records of the United States Strategic Bombing Survey............ 206
244 Records of the Retraining and Reemployment Administration..... 671
245 Records of the Solid Fuels Adminstration for War...................... 419
246 Records of the Office of Contract Settlement.............................. 641
247 Records of the Office of the Chief of Chaplains.......................... 266
248 Records of the War Shipping Administration............................... 692
249 Records of the Commissary General of Prisoners........................ 253
250 Records of the Office of War Mobilization and Reconversion......... 664
251 Records of the Price Decontrol Board....................................... 668
252 Records of the Office of the Housing Expediter.......................... 517
253 Records of the Petroleum Administration for War........................ 666
254 Records of the Shipbuilding Stabilization Committee.................. 672
255 Records of the National Aeronautics and Space Administration... 553
256 Records of the American Commission To Negotiate Peace......... 148
257 Records of the Bureau of Labor Statistics.................................. 493
258 Records of the Federal Crop Insurance Corporation..................... 441
259 Records of the Board of War Communications............................. 613
260 Records of United States Occupation Headquarters, World War II 197
261 Records of Former Russian Agencies... 722
262 Records of the Foreign Broadcast Intelligence Service............... 622
263 Records of the Central Intelligence Agency................................ 101
264 Records of the Commissions on Organization of the Executive
    Branch of the Government... 64
265 Records of the Office of Foreign Assets Control.......................... 180
266 Records of the Securities and Exchange Commission.................. 563
267 Records of the Supreme Court of the United States.................... 69
268 Records of the Philippine War Damage Commission.................... 667
269 General Records of the General Services Administration........... 544
270 Records of the War Assets Administration.................................. 678
272 Records of the President's Commission on the Assassination of
    President Kennedy.. 128
274 National Archives Collection of Records of Inaugural Com-
    mittees.. 741
275 Records of the Export-Import Bank of the United States........... 532
276 Records of the United States Courts of Appeals......................... 71
277 Records of the National Production Authority............................ 489

Page

279 Records of the Indian Claims Commission.................................. 552
280 Records of the Federal Mediation and Conciliation Service........ 540
282 Records of the National Advisory Commission on Civil Disorders... 129
283 Records of the National Commission on the Causes and Prevention of Violence.. 127
284 Records of the Government of American Samoa......................... 409
286 Records of the Agency for International Development.............. 142
291 Records of the Property Management and Disposal Service
 (General Services Administration).. 551
293 Records of the Wage and Salary Stabilization Boards of the Economic Stabilization Agency.. 706
294 Records of the Federal National Mortgage Association.............. 516
295 Records of the Office of Price Stabilization............................. 705
296 General Records of the Economic Stabilization Agency.............. 703
302 Records of the National Capital Housing Authority................... 712
304 Records of the Office of Civil and Defense Mobilization.............. 269
306 Records of the United States Information Agency...................... 569
307 Records of the National Science Foundation............................. 561
309 Records of the Small Business Administration........................... 565
310 Records of the Agricultural Research Service............................ 443
313 Records of Naval Operating Forces....................................... 323
314 Records of the Farmer Cooperative Service............................... 444
315 Records of the Federal Interagency River Basin Committee...... 420
318 Records of the Bureau of Engraving and Printing...................... 175
319 Records of the Army Staff.. 220
323 Records of the Puerto Rico Reconstruction Administration........ 416
324 Records of the Office of Geography....................................... 421
325 Records of the Committee on Government Contract Compliance... 702
327 Records of the Defense Electric Power Administration.............. 422
328 Records of the National Capital Planning Commission.............. 713
330 Records of the Office of the Secretary of Defense...................... 182
331 Records of Allied Operational and Occupation Headquarters,
 World War II.. 191
332 Records of United States Theaters of War, World War II............ 196
333 Records of International Military Agencies............................... 195
334 Records of Interservice Agencies.. 201
335 Records of the Office of the Secretary of the Army..................... 212
337 Records of Headquarters Army Ground Forces.......................... 227
338 Records of United States Army Commands, 1942– 278
340 Records of the Office of the Secretary of the Air Force.............. 329
341 Records of Headquarters United States Air Force...................... 331
342 Records of United States Air Force Commands, Activities, and
 Organizations.. 333
348 Records of the Alaskan Territorial Government......................... 412

Page

349 Records of Joint Commands... 199
350 Records of the Bureau of Insular Affairs................................. 413
351 Records of the Government of the District of Columbia.............. 711
353 Records of Interdepartmental and Intradepartmental Committees (State Department)... 149
354 Records of the Economic Research Service............................ 444
357 Records of the Maritime Administration................................ 478
358 Records of the Federal Maritime Commission.......................... 539
359 Records of the Office of Science and Technology...................... 101
360 Records of the Continental and Confederation Congresses and the Constitutional Convention.. 29
364 Records of the Office of the Special Representative for Trade Negotiations... 100
365 Treasury Department Collection of Confederate Records........... 721
366 Records of Civil War Special Agencies of the Treasury Department... 179
370 Records of the Environmental Science Services Administration... 479
374 Records of the Defense Atomic Support Agency........................ 189
387 Records of the Southwestern Power Administration.................. 411
389 Records of the Office of the Provost Marshal General, 1941–....... 267
391 Records of United States Regular Army Mobile Units, 1821– 1942.. 271
392 Records of United States Army Coast Artillery Districts and Defenses, 1901–42.. 275
393 Records of United States Army Continental Commands, 1821– 1920.. 273
394 Records of United States Army Continental Commands, 1920– 42.. 274
395 Records of United States Army Overseas Operations and Commands, 1898–1942.. 276
401 National Archives Gift Collection of Materials Relating to Polar Regions.. 749
404 Records of the United States Military Academy....................... 288
405 Records of the United States Naval Academy.......................... 321
407 Records of the Adjutant General's Office, 1917– 234
409 Records of the Public Land Law Review Commission................. 65

INDEX

It should be noted that the index is limited to organizational units, names, and functions or broad subjects mentioned in the text of the Guide. It is not intended and cannot serve as a general subject guide to the specific content of records in the National Archives of the United States.

Record group titles are indexed as separate entries and are set in bold type and capitalized.

Dates following prepositions are set in roman type; when not preceded by prepositions, they are italicized to distinguish them from page numbers.

An italic *and* is used between two cross-references and before the last cross-reference in a series. General cross-references, such as *See also names of specific tribes,* are also italicized.

The following abbreviations are used:

s.r. — sound recording(s)
m.p. — motion picture(s)
s.p. — still picture(s) or photograph(s)

A

"A" Awards program, 462
Aandahl, Fred G., 367
Abatement cases, 546
Abbe, Cleveland, 478
Abbott, C.C., 692
Aberdeen Proving Ground, 245
Absentee voting, 678
Absorbents, 659
Academic Board, Naval Academy, U.S., 322
Accidents
　Air, 530
　Child, 510
　Industrial, 493
　Mining, 407, 408
Accounting, 57, 58, 59, 60, 97, 152, 167
Accounting Policy and Financial Procedures, Committee on, 221
Accounts, Bureau of (Treasury), 162, 362

ACCOUNTS, BUREAU OF (TREASURY) (RG 39), 165-167
Accounts, Commissioner of, Treasury, 166
Accounts, Division of, Department of Justice, 342
Accounts and Deposits, Commissioner of, 165
Accounts and Deposits, Office of the Commissioner of, 165
Accounts or Claims, Committee of, 30
Acetphenetidine, 509
Acids, 656
Ackerson, John L., 604
Actors, 696, 748
Adams, John, 33, 35, 84
Adams, John Q., 36
Adamson Act, 560
Addiction. *See* Narcotics and Dangerous Drugs, Bureau of (RG 170)
Adjutant and Inspector General, 230
　Confederate, 719, 720, 721

Adjutant General, 192, 194, 227, 228, 231, 232, 234, 241, 258, 264, 280, 284, 290
Adjutant General, Department of, 215, 230
Adjutant General, Office of the, 200, 207, 208, 211, 253, 254, 257, 263, 264, 265, 283, 284, 719, 741
Adjutant General of the Continental Army, 37, 230
ADJUTANT GENERAL'S OFFICE, 1780'S-1917 (RG 94), 230-234
ADJUTANT GENERAL'S OFFICE, 1917- (RG 407), 234-236
Administrative Procedure, Attorney General's Committee on, 341, 558
Administrators, Advisory Committee on, 104-105
Admiralty, Board of, 31, 34
Admiralty cases, 69, 72-90, 317, 318, 722
Adriatic Base Command, 280
Advanced Research Projects Agency, 186
Advertising
    False, 359, 543
    Programs, 646
Advisory Commission to the Council of National Defense, 105, 643, 653, 686
    See also National Defense Advisory Commission
Advisory Committee for the National Archives Building, 137, 547
Advisory Committee on Education, 104
Advisory Committee on Education by Radio, 506
Advisory Committee on Fiscal Relations Between the United States and the District of Columbia, 98, 99
Advisory Committee on Geographic Names, 421
Advisory Committee on Industry, 579
Advisory Committee on Service Pay, 183
Advisory Committee on Social Scientists and Economists, 104-105
Advisory Committee on Specialized Engineering Fields, 104-105
Advisory Committee to the Secretary of Labor, 98
Advisory Committee to the Treasury on Fine Arts, 547
Advisory committees. See also committees under subject name
Advisory Law Commission, 281
Advisory Operating Committee, 688
Aerodynamics, 554
Aerology. See Naval Observatory
Aeronautical Board, 202, 217
Aeronautical Chart and Information Center, 333, 334
Aeronautical Chart Service, 327
Aeronautical charts, 315, 472, 474, 480
Aeronautical Division, Office of the Chief Signal Officer, 324
Aeronautical Research, German Academy for, 728, 731

Aeronautical Research Institute, Tokyo, 736
Aeronautics, 187, 202, 262, 334, 371, 528, 553, 554, 566, 746
    Civil, 211, 527, 528, 530, 554
    Korean, 736
    Russian, 736
    See also Aviation
AERONAUTICS, BUREAU OF (RG 72), 318-320
Aeronautics, National Advisory Committee for, 553, 554
Aerosols, 659, 660
Aerospace Defense Command, 333
Aerospace Research, Office of, 334
Aerospace technology, 335
Afghanistan, U.S. assistance to, 143
Africa, 205, 233, 295, 328, 337, 370, 569, 746
    See also East Africa and North Africa
Age Discrimination in Employment Act of 1967, 496
Agents
    County agricultural, 433
    Diplomatic, 35, 132
    Disbursing, 166
    Naval, 294, 295
    See also Special agents
Agnew, Spiro T., 747
Agricultural Adjustment Act, 424, 435, 441, 459
Agricultural Adjustment Administration, 424, 426, 435, 436, 455, 458, 459, 461
Agricultural Adjustment Agency, 435
AGRICULTURAL AND INDUSTRIAL CHEMISTRY, BUREAU OF (RG 97), 449-450
Agricultural Appropriation Act, 453, 507
Agricultural attaches, 431
Agricultural Chemistry and Engineering, Bureau of, 448, 449, 450, 451
Agricultural Commission to Europe, 445
Agricultural commodities, 431, 449, 459, 460, 461, 488, 626, 647
    Marketing, 431, 458
    Production, 405, 423, 425, 431, 435, 457, 458
Agricultural Credits Act of 1923, 160
Agricultural Defense Relations, Office of, 425
Agricultural Economics, Bureau of, 431, 438, 444, 460, 609, 697
AGRICULTURAL ECONOMICS, BUREAU OF (RG 83), 455-458
Agricultural engineering, 446, 452
    See also Plant Industry, Soils, and Agricultural Engineering, Bureau of
Agricultural Engineering, Bureau of, 438, 449, 526
AGRICULTURAL ENGINEERING, BUREAU OF (RG 8), 447-448

Agricultural Extension Service, 649, 684
Agricultural Geography of Europe and the Near East, 431
Agricultural Geography of the Philippine Islands, A Graphic Summary, 431
Agricultural Labor Administration, 459, 460
Agricultural Marketing Administration, 432, 459, 460, 461
Agricultural Marketing Service, 444, 445, 455, 459
AGRICULTURAL MARKETING SERVICE (RG 136), 460-463
Agricultural Relations Adviser, Office of the, 649
Agricultural Research Administration, 443, 446, 450
Agricultural Research Center, Beltsville, Md., 443
Agricultural Research Service, 444, 445, 446, 447, 449, 451, 453, 455, 458
AGRICULTURAL RESEARCH SERVICE (RG 310), 443
Agricultural Science Register, 446
Agricultural Section, Patent Office, 450, 453
"Agricultural Situation Summary," 649
AGRICULTURAL STABILIZATION AND CONSERVATION SERVICE (RG 145), 435-436
Agricultural Trade Development and Assistance Act of 1954, 142
Agricultural War Relations, Office for, 425
Agriculture, 64, 108, 119, 147, 365, 370, 406, 407, 416, 425, 426, 433, 439, 458, 493, 495, 554, 555, 580, 608, 652, 665, 680, 685, 703, 725, 746, 747
Censuses of, 467, 468, 469
Colleges, 236, 372, 373, 433, 434, 446
Credit corporations, 160, 533, 534, 580, 583
Extension services, 434, 444, 446, 448
Foreign, 198, 414, 430-431, 736
Grading services, 460
Indian, 381, 382, 383, 388
Machinery, 270, 490
Marketing, 423, 455
Policies, 423, 431, 436, 457, 649
Societies, 423
Statistics of, 426, 460
Surpluses, 459
Surveys, 375
Technology, 451
War-related, 458
Waste utilization, 450
See also Commodity Credit Corporation; Commodity Exchange Authority (RG 180); Farms and farming; Federal Crop Insurance Corporation; *and* Plant Industry, Soils, and Agricultural Engineering, Bureau of

Agriculture, Commissioner of, 423, 445
Agriculture, Department of, 103, 105, 365, 371, 394, 397, 400, 420, 423, 424, 426, 430, 431, 432, 433, 434, 435, 437, 440, 441, 442, 443, 444, 445, 446, 447, 449, 450, 451, 453, 455, 457, 458, 459, 460, 476, 507, 526, 533, 552, 609, 610, 624, 647, 679, 682, 699
Building, 745
War Board, 436
Agriculture, International Institute of, 147, 431
Agriculture, Office of the Secretary of, 431
AGRICULTURE, OFFICE OF THE SECRETARY OF (RG 16), 423-426
Agriculture, Secretary of, 99, 104, 423, 424, 425, 431, 432, 433, 434, 435, 437, 443, 444, 447, 448, 449, 451, 460, 461, 508, 525, 526, 541, 578, 647, 668
Agriculture, Solicitor of the Department of, 508
Agriculture and Forestry, Senate Committee on, 508
Aguinaldo, Emilio, 744
Aid for Information, Office of, 298
Ainsworth, Fred C., 37
Air, Office of the Assistant Secretary of War for, 211
Air attache, 332
Air Board, 330, 326
Air carriers, 530, 559, 560, 619
Air Commerce, Bureau of, 527, 528, 530
Air Coordinating Committee, 182, 330, 332
Air Corps, 324, 325, 326, 328, 334
Air Corps, Chief of the, 325
Air Corps, Office of the Chief of the, 325, 326
Air Corps Act of 1926, 211, 324
Air Corps Library, 326
Air Defense Division, Supreme Headquarters Allied Expeditionary Forces, 192
Air Division, 324
Air Force, 108, 113, 186, 187, 191, 196, 203, 204, 236, 290, 324, 326, 327, 329, 330, 331, 332
Bases, 192, 332, 333, 334
Civilian personnel, 327
Training, 333, 334
See also Army Air Forces *and* Joint Commands (RG 349)
Air Force, Assistant Chief of Staff, Intelligence, 331
Air Force, Assistant Chief of Staff, Reserve Forces, 331
Air Force, Assistant Chief of Staff, Studies and Analysis, 331
Air Force, Chief, Operations Analysis, 331
Air Force, Comptroller of the, 331, 332
Air Force, Department of, 195, 204, 207, 264, 305, 324, 329, 330, 554
Air Force, General Headquarters, 324, 325

Air Force, German, 728, 731, 734, 737
AIR FORCE, HEADQUARTERS U.S.
      (RG 341), 331-333
Air Force, Italian, 736
Air Force, Office of the Secretary of
      the, 211
AIR FORCE, OFFICE OF THE
      SECRETARY OF THE (RG 340),
      329-330
Air Force, Office of the Under
      Secretary of the, 329
Air Force, Secretary of the, 269, 331,
      329
Air Force, Under Secretary of the, 329
Air Force Academy, 332, 334
Air Force Accounting and Finance
      Center, 334
Air Force Chief of Staff, 188, 264
Air Force Combat Command, 324, 325
Air Force Commands, 327
AIR FORCE COMMANDS,
      ACTIVITIES, AND
      ORGANIZATIONS, U.S.
      (RG 342), 333-335
Air Force Contract Adjustment Board, 329
Air Force Council, 331
Air Force Data Systems Design Center, 334
"Air Force Elgin Jewel Bearing Project,"
      186
Air Force Headquarters Command, 333
Air Force Operations Staff, German, 731
Air Force Overseas Command, 334
Air Force Postal Service, 331
Air Force Printing Board, 329
Air Force Reserve, 329, 334
Air Force Reserve Policy, Air Staff
      Committee on, 331
Air Force Security Courier Service, 331
Air Forces Southern Command, 334
Air General Staff, German, 731
Air Mail, Bureau of, 527, 530
Air Memorial Day, 1919, 746
Air National Guard of the United
      States, 264
Air races, 256, 293, 334
Air raids, 639
   Against Germany, 728, 730, 734
   German, 746
Air Reserve Personnel Center, 334
Air routes, 524, 527, 528
Air Service, Army, 235, 256, 261, 284,
      324, 326, 327, 397
Air Service Advisory Board, 327
Air Service Claims Board, 327
Air Service Control Board, 327
Air Service Library, 326
Air Service Section, War Department
      Claims Board, 224
Air shows, 334
Air Staff, Supreme Headquarters Allied
      Expeditionary Forces, 192
Air Staff Intelligence, Office of the
      Assistant Chief of, 327

Air stations, naval, 58, 293, 310, 319,
      320, 321
Air Systems Command, 319
Air Technical Intelligence Center, 332
Air traffic control, 527, 734
Air Training Command, 333
Air Transport Command, 328
Air University, 192, 333, 334
Airbases, 211, 319, 328, 334
Aircraft, 58, 168, 182, 183, 185, 187,
      188, 299, 301, 302, 313, 315, 319,
      320, 324, 326, 327, 328, 332, 333,
      340, 554, 633, 659, 728, 731
   Disposal of, 678
   History of, 745
   Naval, 321
   See also Air carriers; Airplanes;
      Airships; Blimps; Helicopters;
      and Jets
Aircraft Board, 326
Aircraft Division, 319
Aircraft Production, Bureau of,
      324, 325, 326
Aircraft Production Board, 270,
      324, 325, 326
Aircraft Warning Service Section, 255
Airfields, 211, 293, 327, 328, 333,
      505, 528
Airframe industries, 673
Airlines, 528, 530, 582, 643
   Employees, 561
   Industry, 555
   Wages, 559, 703, 707
Airmail service, 334, 360, 362
   Contracts, 352, 359
   Routes, 360, 362
Airplanes, 245, 293, 299, 304, 319,
      324, 325, 328, 360, 362
   Amphibious, 320
   Development of, 334
   Flying boats, 293
   German, 335
   Naval, 293, 320
Airports, 362, 527, 528, 548, 670, 678,
      697, 698
Airships, 304, 319, 320
Airstrips, 327
Airways, 527, 528
Airways Modernization Board, 527
Akademie fuer Deutsches Recht, 733
Akron, 320
Alabama, 134, 341, 344, 372, 394
Alabama (C.S.S.), 158, 164, 166
Alaska, 46, 61, 117, 119, 134, 145, 168,
      172, 213, 233, 237, 255, 276, 307,
      328, 367, 370, 377, 383, 393, 394,
      395, 396, 397, 404, 405, 412, 450,
      477, 478, 523, 615, 631, 695,
      744, 745
   Admission to Union, 412
   Development of, 369
   Experiment stations in, 446
   Explorations of, 723

Homestead laws, 412
Native tribes, 377, 386, 723
Reservations in, 376
Surveys in, 373, 473
U.S. District of, 412
Alaska Communication System, 255
Alaska Defense Command, 280
Alaska Division, 377, 383, 505
Alaska Fur Seal Service, 394
Alaska Mental Health Enabling Act of
    1956, 412
Alaska Patrol, 524
Alaska Radio Expedition, 307
Alaska Railroad, 370, 404, 405
Alaska Railroad and River Service, 119
Alaska Reindeer Service, 383
Alaska Road Commission, 404
Alaska-Yukon-Pacific Exposition, 154,
    209, 365, 433
Alaskan Agricultural Fair, 370
Alaskan Air Command, 334
Alaskan Command, 200
Alaskan Fisheries, Division of, 394
Alaskan Fur Seal Fisheries, Bureau of, 464
ALASKAN TERRITORIAL
    GOVERNMENT (RG 348), 412
Albania, 193, 612, 734
Albatross (schooner), 396, 397
"Alberttypes," 403
Albright, Horace M., 398
Alcan Highway, 526
Alcatraz, Calif., 235
Alcohol
    Beverages, 177, 178, 461, 509
    Industrial, 106, 178, 656
    International conferences on, 146
Aleut Indians, 567
Alexander, Archibald S., 213
Alexander, W.D., 473
Alexandria, Va., 711
Alexandria County, Va., 75
Algiers, 164, 205
Alien Property, Office of, 180, 371
ALIEN PROPERTY, OFFICE OF
    (RG 131), 354-356
Alien Property Bureau, 354
Alien Property Custodian, 155,
    165, 340, 354, 355
Alien Property Custodian, Office of,
    354, 355, 645
Alien Property Division, Department
    of Justice, 354
Alien Registration Act of 1940, 347
Aliens, 72, 83, 279, 345, 346, 564, 689
    Departure permits for, 136
    Deportation of, 344, 345
    Drafted, 137
    Enemy, 136, 137, 235, 280, 347
    Internees, 268
    Registration of, 336, 410
All-Volunteer Armed Force,
    President's Commission on
    an, 119

Allegiance, oaths of, 33
Allen, George E., 99
Alley Dwelling Authority, 712, 713
Alliance (U.S.S.), 296
Alliance for Progress, 142
Allied Blockade Committee, 611
Allied Commission/Allied Military
    Government (Italy), 193
Allied Control Authority, 197, 198
Allied Council for Japan, 194
Allied Expeditionary Air Force, 192
Allied Expeditionary Forces, 189, 192, 195
Allied Force Headquarters, 193
Allied Military Government, British-United
    States Zone, Free Territory of
    Trieste, 193-194
Allied Military Government for
    Venezia Giulia, 193
Allied military governments, 193-194,
    212, 256, 577, 611
Allied Naval Commander, Expeditionary
    Force, 192
ALLIED OPERATIONAL AND
    OCCUPATION HEADQUARTERS,
    WORLD WAR II (RG 331),
    191-195
ALLIED PURCHASING
    COMMISSION (RG 113), 577
Allied Screening Commission (Italy), 193
Allies
    World War I, 138, 220
    World War II, 256, 299, 328, 569,
        609, 623, 662, 663, 699, 737,
        748
Allotments, Advisory Committee on, 125
Allotments, Indian, 367
Alsace, World War II campaigns, 744
ALSOS, 217
Altstoetter, Josef, 700
Alum, 509
Aluminum, 270, 391, 409
Alvin Field, Colo., 528
Ambassadors, 46, 69, 140
    See also Diplomatic service
Ambassadors, Conference of, 148
Ambrosio, Vittorio, 736
"America Honors Her Dead" (m.p.), 530
American Air Almanac, 315
American and Mexican Joint
    Commission, 147
*American Armies and Battlefields
    in Europe*, 529
American Banknote Co., 164
American Base Depot in France,
    243-244
AMERICAN BATTLE MONUMENTS
    COMMISSION (RG 117),
    529-530
*American Battlefields in Europe,
    A Guide to the*, 529
American Bird Banding Association, 396
American Colonization Society, 295

AMERICAN COMMISSION FOR THE
PROTECTION AND SALVAGE
OF ARTISTIC AND HISTORIC
MONUMENTS IN WAR AREAS
(RG 239), 611-612
American Commission To Negotiate
Peace, 146, 148, 287, 288, 743
American Council of Learned
Societies' Committee on the
Protection of Cultural Treasures
in War Areas, 611
American Council on Education, 569
American Defense-Harvard Group, 611
American Education Week, 506
*American Ephemeris and Nautical
Almanac*, 315, 316
American Ethnology, Bureau of, 566,
567
American Expeditionary Forces,
220, 225, 235, 236, 255, 256,
260, 276, 277, 284, 286, 288, 301,
529, 572, 573

AMERICAN EXPEDITIONARY
FORCES (WORLD WAR I),
1917-23 (RG 120), 283-288
American Express Company, 599
American Farm Bureau Federations,
434
American Federation of Labor,
498, 605, 650
American Foundation for the Blind, 748
American Geophysical Union,
393, 555
American Historical Association, 727
American Homecroft Society, 407
American Imprints Inventory, 696
American International Shipbuilding
Corp., 605
American Knights, Order of, 259
American Legion, 503, 748
American Marine Standards
Committee, 603
American Military Missions, 286, 287
American Mutoscope and Biograph
Co. *v.* Sigmund Lubin, 86
American Nautical Almanac, 315
American Ordnance Co., 245
American Polish Relief Expedition, 286
American Printing House for the
Blind, 501
American Prisoner of War Information
Bureau, 268
American Protective League, 348
American Railroad Company of
Puerto Rico, 644
American Red Cross, 201, 284, 745, 747
Building, 716
American Refiners Committee,
607, 608
American Relief Administration,
595, 596
American Republics, 142, 149

American Republics, Committee of
Executive Departments and
Independent Agencies To
Consider the Question of
Cooperation With the, 150
American Republics, Committee on
Cooperation With the, 150
American Republics,
Interdepartmental Committee
on Cooperation With the, 150
American Republics, Office for
Coordination of Commercial and
Cultural Relations Between the,
646
American Republics Allocations
Board, 201
American Revolution. *See*
Revolutionary War
American Samoa, 308, 404
AMERICAN SAMOA, GOVERNMENT
OF (RG 284), 409-410
American Society of Composers
and Publishers, 748
American States, International
Conferences of, 146
American Statistical Association, 98
American University Experiment
Station, 408
American War Production Mission
in China, 106
Americanization programs, 346, 506
Ames, Iowa, 439
Amity and Commerce, Joint
Commissioners for the
Formation of Treaties of, 33
Ammonia, synthetic, 452
Ammunition, 223, 245, 303, 308,
523, 565
Trains, 285
Amnesty
Civil War, 137
Utah cases, 345
Amphibious operations, 328, 525
Bases, 321
Forces, 300
Amundsen-Scott (South Pole)
Station, 750
Amusement industry, 629
Anacostia River, 714
Anchorage, Alaska, 117
Anchorages, 471
Anderson, Marian, 371
Anderson, Robert, 153
Anderson, Tom, 127
Anderson Memorial, 371
Andrew, Israel, 156
Andrews, Frank, 326
Angel Island immigration station, 347
Anglo-American Economic
Committee, 586
Anhydrides, 656
Animal and Poultry Husbandry
Research Branch, 445

Animal Disease and Parasite Research
    Branch, 445
Animal Disease Eradication Branch,
    445
Animal farming, 434
Animal husbandry, 445, 723
Animal Industry, Bureau of,
    447, 463
ANIMAL INDUSTRY, BUREAU OF
    (RG 17), 445
Animal Inspection and Quarantine
    Branch, 445
Animals, 247
    Diseases of, 445
    Fur-bearing, 396, 523
Annapolis, Md., 316, 321
Annapolis convention, 31
Annual Report of the Commissioner
    of Indian Affairs, 384
Antarctic, 314, 323, 394
    Expeditions and explorations,
        334, 744, 747, 749-750
    See also Expeditions, polar
Antarctic Names, Advisory
    Committee on, 750
Antarctic Service, 404, 749-750
Antarctic Service Expedition, 405
Anthracite Coal, Bureau of, 594
Anthracite Coal Strike Commission, 493
Anthracite Committee, 594
Anthropology, 552
Anti-Aircraft Service, 284
Anti-Americanism, 737
Anti-Comintern, 734
Antiaircraft
    Devices, 245, 692
    German units, 731
Antiaircraft Command, 226
Antidiscrimination commissions, 703
Antietam Battlefield Commission, 247
Antifreeze, 656
Antimine devices, 692
Antisubmarine devices, 692
Antitorpedo devices, 692
Antitrust Act of 1890, 338
Antitrust laws, 339, 344
Apache Indians, 388
Apalachicola Indians, 380
Apothecaries, 302
Appalachia, 429, 503, 526
Appeal Board, Office of Contract
    Settlement, 641, 642
Appeal Section, War Department
    Claims Board, 224
APPEALS, UNITED STATES
    COURTS OF (RG 276),
    71-72
Appleby, Paul H., 424
Apples, 442
Appointments, Presidential, 46, 364
Apportionment, 467
Appraisal Section, War Department
    Claims Board, 224

Appraisers, Board of, 224
Appraisers, Board of General, 83
Apprentice Training Service,
    679, 685
Apprentices, naval, 310, 311, 312
Apprenticeship
    Indentures of, 76
    Practices, Federal agencies, 703
Apprenticeship Committee, 630
Arabian American Oil Co., 586
Arapaho Indians, 388
Arbitration, 143-146, 560
    Labor, 540, 559, 580
    See also Maritime Labor Board
        (RG 157)
Arbitration, Interstate Commerce
    Controversies, Board of, 559
Archaeology, 567
    Latin American, 647
Archangel, 286
Architect of the Capitol, Office
    of the, 741
Architects, Advisory Committee
    on, 104
Architecture, 532, 636, 670
    Foreign, 532
    International conferences on, 146
    See also Supervising Architect,
        Office of the
Archives
    Annamese, 136
    German, 198
    Puerto Rican, 725, 726
    "Rebel," 719
    Spanish, of East and West Florida,
        374
    See also India, National Archives
        of, *and* National Archives and
        Records Service
Archives, Committee on, 149
Archives, Survey of Federal, 696, 699
Archivist of the United States, 549
Archivo General de la Nación, 282
Archivo Histórico, 726
Arctic, 317
    Expeditions and exploration, 747,
        749-750
    See also Expeditions, polar
Arctic, Desert, and Tropic
    Information Center, 334
"Arctic Fever," 750
Area Redevelopment Act of
    1961, 565
Areal Geology, Section of, 391
Areas, Bureau of, Foreign Economic
    Administration, 625
Argentina, 137, 145, 457
"Argentine Blue Book," 137
Argonne Cemetery, 531
Arica. *See* Tacna-Arica arbitration
Ariel (U.S.S.), 296
Arizona, 134, 344, 404, 409, 430
Arizona Statehood Proclamation, 744

Arizona Territory, 566
Arkansas, 328, 372, 531, 745
Arkansas Centennial Coin, 531
Arkansas River Compact Administration,
    392
Arkansas River Compact Commission,
    392
Arkansas-White-Red River Basins
    Interagency Committee, 421
Arkhimandritov, N., 723
Arlington County, Va., 75
Arlington Memorial Amphitheater
    Commission, 717
Arlington Memorial Bridge, 403, 531
    Commission, 402, 717
Armaments and War Production,
    Reich Ministry for, 728, 731
Armat, Thomas, 747
Armed Forces, 116, 183, 184, 185, 187,
    188, 212, 222, 529, 593, 641,
    652, 678, 685, 742
  Air demonstrations, 185
  American Republics, 150
  Communications, 613
  Joint training, 188
  Unification, 330, 331
  See also Armed services and
      Arms, Chiefs of (RG 177)
Armed Forces Academy, German, 734
Armed Forces-Atomic Energy
    Commission Panel on Radiological
    Warfare, 190
Armed Forces Courier Service, 202
Armed Forces Day, 185, 214
Armed Forces Disciplinary Control Board,
    202
Armed Forces Epidemiological Board,
    203
Armed Forces Information and
    Education, Office of, 184
Armed Forces Medical Advisory
    Committee, 182, 187
Armed Forces Medical Library, 203
Armed Forces Medical Policy
    Council, 187
Armed Forces Radiobiology Research
    Institute, 189
Armed Forces Special Weapons
    Project, 189, 190
Armed Service Renegotiation
    Board, 212
Armed services, 108, 201, 212, 217,
    267, 671, 745, 746
  See also Armed Forces
Armed Services Board of Contract
    Appeals, 214
Armed Services Disciplinary Control
    Board, 203
Armed Services Medical Regulating
    Office, 203
Armed Services Personnel Board, 184
Armed Services Petroleum Board,
    188, 203

Armed Services Textile and Apparel
    Procurement Agency, 203
Armee-oberkommandos, 732
Armenia, 313
Armistice, 119, 196, 265, 283, 284,
    287, 313, 604, 608
Armistice Agreement of 1953, 189
Armor Factory Board, 304
Armor Plate, Special Board on, 304
Armorplate, 245
Arms. See Munitions
ARMS, CHIEFS OF (RG 177),
    225-226
Army, 33, 108, 113, 154, 184, 186, 191,
    194, 196, 197, 201, 210, 217, 222,
    223, 232, 233, 237, 241, 245, 246,
    249, 255, 277, 281, 284, 286, 290,
    295, 300, 412, 503, 527, 574, 593,
    594, 611, 640, 659, 660, 675, 692,
    746
  Accounts, 59
  Camps, 228, 234, 241, 256, 273, 275,
      277, 505
  Civilian personnel, 213, 214, 221, 222
  Corps, 273, 274, 276, 277
  Disciplinary facilities, 234, 235
  Field establishments, 271, 276
  General Headquarters, 227, 274, 325
  Insignia, 532
  Installations, 217, 219, 229, 234, 241,
      267
  Investigations, 241, 242
  Overseas commands, 196
  Posts, 34, 228, 234, 240, 273, 275, 277
  Service organizations, 236, 267
  Supplies, 38, 39, 213, 221, 223, 230,
      244, 245, 246, 247, 249
  Territorial departments, 196-197
  Training, 194, 203, 212, 214, 221,
      222, 227, 228, 230, 234, 256,
      278
  See also American Expeditionary
      Forces (World War I),
      1917-23 (RG 120); Defense,
      Office of the Secretary of;
      Finance, Office of the Chief of
      (Army) (RG 203); Joint
      Commands (RG 349); National
      Guard Bureau (RG 168);
      Paymaster General, Office of
      the (RG 99); Schools, military;
      and Selective Service System
Army, Assistant Secretary of the,
    213, 214
Army, British, 286
Army, Commander in Chief of the, 34
Army, Commanding General of the,
    214, 215, 241
Army, Comptroller of the, 221, 253
Army, Department of the, 195, 203, 204,
    207, 212, 213, 216, 231, 234, 235,
    242, 252, 254, 260, 264, 267,
    289, 305, 329, 445

Army, Department of the, Special
    Staff, 241
Army, General in Chief of the, 288
Army, General of the, 208
Army, German, 217, 279, 701, 730,
    732, 734, 736
ARMY, HEADQUARTERS OF THE
    (RG 108), 214-215
Army, Italian, 734, 736
Army, Office of the Assistant Secretary
    of the, 213
Army, Office of the Comptroller of
    the, 221, 253
Army, Office of the Secretary of the,
    208
ARMY, OFFICE OF THE SECRETARY
    OF THE (RG 335), 212-214
Army, Office of the Under Secretary
    of the, 213
Army, Regular. See Regular Army
Army, Russian, 734
Army, Secretary of the, 182, 203,
    212, 213, 220, 258, 267, 269,
    288
Army, Under Secretary of the, 213
Army, Volunteer. See Volunteer Army
Army Accounts, Commissioner for,
    34
Army Accounts for the United States,
    Commissioner of, 163
Army Administration Officer Training
    Schools, 236
Army Advisory Board on Government-
    Furnished Property, 214
Army Air Corps, 319, 327, 746
Army-Air Force Postal Service
    Headquarters, 236
Army-Air Force Wage Board, 214
Army Air Forces, 211, 229, 278, 330,
    333, 334, 472, 697
    Headquarters, 325, 326, 331
    Installations, 326
    Women in, 334
Army Air Forces, Chief of the, 324
    325
Army Air Forces, Commanding
    General of the, 326, 327
Army Air Forces Foreign Service
    Concentration Command, 327
ARMY AIR FORCES (RG 18),
    324-328
Army Air Forces Scientific Advisory
    Board, 326
Army-Air Forces Security
    Service, 202
Army Air Service, 327, 334
Army Air Support Center, 228
Army and Navy Helium Board, 319
Army and Navy Maneuvers, Board
    of Arbitration for, 295
Army and Navy Munitions
    Board, 269, 292
Army Appropriation Act, 1916, 599

Army Audit Agency, 221
Army bizone European recovery
    program, 213
Army Civilian Legal Personnel
    Committee, 214
ARMY COAST ARTILLERY
    DISTRICTS AND DEFENSES,
    U.S., 1901-42 (RG 392),
    275-276
Army Combat Developments
    Command, 246
Army commands, 202, 207,
    228, 273, 280, 720
ARMY COMMANDS, U.S.,
    1784-1821 (RG 98), 271
ARMY COMMANDS, U.S.,
    1942- (RG 338), 278-280
Army continental commands, 280
ARMY CONTINENTAL
    COMMANDS, U.S., 1821-1920
    (RG 393), 273-274
ARMY CONTINENTAL COMMANDS,
    U.S., 1920-42 (RG 394),
    274-275
Army Engineer School, 288
Army Engineers, Board of, 406
Army Equipment Board, 243
Army Equipment Policy Panel, 228
Army Exchange System, 213
Army Field Commands, 280
Army Field Forces, Office of the
    Chief of, 227, 228
Army Forces in the British Isles,
    Headquarters U.S., 278
Army Forces (U.S.), Central
    Pacific Area, 279
Army Forces (U.S.), Korea, 280
Army Forces (U.S.), Middle
    Pacific, 279
Army Forces (U.S.), Pacific
    Ocean Area, 279
Army Forces (U.S.), South
    Pacific, 279
Army General Service School, 227
Army Ground Forces, 278
    Combat Arms, 227
Army Ground Forces, Commanding
    General, 226
ARMY GROUND FORCES,
    HEADQUARTERS (RG 337),
    227-228
Army Ground Forces (U.S.),
    Pacific, 279
Army in the Field, Headquarters
    of the, 214-215
Army Industrial College, 203,
    204, 609
Army Installations Board, 214
Army List and Directory, 231
Army-McCarthy hearings, 213
Army Map Service, 240
Army Materiel Command, 242,
    246

Army Medical Corps, 251
Army Medical Department, 250
Army Medical Department Field
    Installations, 251
Army Medical Examining Boards, 251
Army Medical Library, 203
Army Medical Specialist Corps, 250
Army National Guard of the United
    States, 227, 264
Army-Navy football games, 256
Army-Navy Petroleum Board, 203
Army-Navy Trail Party of Operation
    Deep Freeze II, 323
Army Nurse Corps, 250, 251
Army of Occupation, 225
Army Operations Deputy, 222
Army Ordnance Corps, 245
Army Organization Act of 1950, 212
ARMY OVERSEAS OPERATIONS
    AND COMMANDS, U.S.,
    1898-1942 (RG 395),
    276-278
Army Pearl Harbor Board, 211
Army Postal Service, 236
Army Price Adjustment Board,
    212, 214
Army Publication Board, 235
Army Register, 231
Army reorganization act of
    1920, 324
Army Reserves, 224, 251, 256
Army Retiring Board, 212
Army Security Center, 203
Army Service Corps, 285
Army Service Forces, 227, 231, 234,
    252, 254, 258, 264, 266, 267,
    274, 278
Army Service Forces, Chief of
    Staff, 229
Army Service Forces, Commanding
    General, 229
Army Service Forces, Headquarters,
    236
ARMY SERVICE FORCES,
    HEADQUARTERS (RG 160),
    228-230
Army Special Service School, 227
Army Special Staff, 234, 267
Army Specialist Corps, 210
ARMY STAFF (RG 319), 220-224
Army Topographical Engineers,
    Corps of, 237
Army Transport Service, 248
Army War College, 218, 219, 226, 287
Army Welfare Board, 214
Army's Western Defense Command, 689
Arnold, H.H., 325, 326, 327
Arnold, Laurence F., 673
Arsenals, 244, 245
Art, 193, 262, 455, 532, 546, 547,
    663, 695, 696, 744
    Federal projects, 531, 547, 695,
        696, 697, 699

Galleries, 547, 566, 567
German, 198, 356
Grants-in-aid for, 496
Objects, war damage to, 611
Polish, 198
Art Looting Investigation Unit, 611
Articles of Confederation, 29, 30,
    31, 32, 35, 138, 291
Artillery, 226, 242, 245, 271,
    272, 273, 275, 276, 284, 285
Puerto Rican, 726
See also Coast artillery *and* Field
    artillery
Artillery, Chief of, 225, 226
Artillery Ammunition Board, 243
Artillery Corps, 225, 275
Artists, 531, 547, 696, 745
Asbestos, 409
Ashburton, Lord, 145
Asia, 139, 746
    See also Southeast Asia
Asiatic Squadron, 323
Assassinations, 127
    Presidential, 75, 76, 176, 259, 712
    See also President's Commission
        on the Assassination of
        President Kennedy (RG 272)
Assay commissions and offices,
    173, 174, 175
Assets
    American-owned abroad, 138, 180, 181
    Foreign-owned, 180, 181, 354
    Frozen, 180
Astronomy, 314, 315, 316, 475
    See also Naval Observatory
Astrophysical Laboratory, 566
Asylums, 290, 295, 310, 466
Atlanta, Ga., 343, 747
Atlanta Loan Agency, 582
Atlanta (U.S.S.), 365
Atlantic Coast Communications
    Superintendent, Office
    of the, 297
Atlas of World Maps, 230
*Atlas To Accompany the Official
    Records of the Union and
    Confederate Armies*, 233
Atomic bombs, 206, 239, 256,
    271, 328
    Tests, 190, 334, 663, 748
Atomic energy, 102, 182, 190, 332,
    333, 371, 569, 570, 747
Atomic Energy, Joint
    Committee on, 54
Atomic Energy Act of 1946, 54
Atomic Energy Commission,
    189, 190, 589, 702
Atomic Energy Program, Military
    Liaison Committee on the
    Development of the, 183
Atomic weapons. *See* Defense
    Atomic Support Agency
"Atoms for Power" (s.r.), 570

Attorney General, 92, 116, 164, 259, 318, 336, 337, 338, 341, 342, 343, 345, 348, 349, 351, 352, 353, 381, 469, 563, 591, 607, 647, 703, 706, 718

Attorney General, Assistant, 340, 351, 355, 356, 364, 366

Attorney General, Assistant, Office of the, 368

Attorney General, Office of the, 344, 345

American Samoa, 410

Attorney General, Special Executive Assistant to the, 342

Attorney in Charge of Pardons, Office of, 344

Attorneys, 79, 336, 337, 338, 339, 345, 353, 354

ATTORNEYS AND MARSHALS, U.S. (RG 118), 343-344

Auctions, 178

Auditor for the State and Other Departments, Office of the, 60

Auditor for the Treasury Department, Office of the, 59

Auditor for the War Department, 59

Auditor of Railroad Accounts, Office of, 411

Augsburg Armament Command, 728

August Wilhelm, 732

Augusta (cruiser), 323

Australia, 194, 431

Austria, 113, 114, 144, 193, 198, 214, 279, 612, 702, 728, 734, 747

Occupation of, 150, 197, 198

Restitution of property in, 198

Austria, Allied Commission for, 197, 198

Austria, American Zone of, 197, 198

Austria, Headquarters, U.S. Forces in, 197, 279

Austria, U.S. High Commissioner for, 197

Austro-Hungarian Empire, American Relief Administration missions to, 596

Autobahn, 730

Autogiros, 334, 360

Automatic Train Control Committee, 600

Automobiles, 270

Industry, 409, 628, 630

See also Public Roads, Bureau of

Automotive Conservation Committee, 648

Auxiliary Naval Force, 323

Avery, Johnston, 743

Aviation, 55, 107, 108, 195, 207, 211, 227, 233, 293, 304, 318, 319, 324, 327, 328, 330, 525, 527, 528, 530, 555, 747

Civil, 329, 332, 522, 527, 530

European, 554, 728

History of, 256, 334, 567, 677

Latin American, 585, 589

Military, 58, 202, 212, 293, 318, 319, 320, 321, 325

Transoceanic, 522, 745, 747

See also Aeronautics *and* National Aeronautics and Space Administration (RG 255)

Aviation Petroleum Allocations Committee, 195

Awards, Board of, 154, 548

Awards and decorations

Army, 246

Civilian, 212, 568

Awards to Civil Employees, Board on, 292

Axis Criminality, U.S. Chief of Counsel for the Prosecution of, 700

Axis Powers, 205, 256, 569, 611, 623, 662-663

Atrocities, 107, 328, 334, 700

Leaders, 206, 663, 689, 702, 737

Propaganda, 220

Research institutions, 733

War criminals, 701

Azores Islands, 477

B

Bache, Alexander Dallas, 471

Bache, Richard, 31

Badoglio, Pietro, 734, 736

Baird, Julian B., 153

Baker, Abby Gunn, 715

Baker, Lafayette C., 257

Baker, Newton D., 236

Baking industry, 631

Balance of payments, 464

Baldwin, F.P., 604

Baldwin, Henry, 70

Baldwin-Ziegler expedition, 750

Balkan Front, 288

Balkan States, 138, 205

German exploitation of, 729

Military Headquarters, 193

Ballard, E., 473

Ballentine, A.A., 153

Ballinger-Pinchot controversy, 427

Ballistics, 303, 334, 335, 659

Balloons, 293, 319, 320, 324, 334

Balsa, 586

Baltic States, 729

American Relief Administration mission to, 596

Bancroft Library, 724

"Bank holiday," 160

Bank of the United States, 164, 336

Bankers Joint Stock Land Bank, 534

Bankhead-Jones Act of 1935, 446

Banknotes, 158, 159, 160, 161, 164

Bankruptcy, 69, 73-90, 338, 339,
    341, 563
  National acts, 72, 79, 80, 82,
      83, 85, 86, 88, 89
Bankruptcy Administration,
    Committee on, 341
Banks and banking, 33, 152, 155, 159,
    160, 161, 163, 164, 173, 336,
    338, 353, 355, 381, 434, 537,
    538, 580, 582, 588, 598, 608,
    663, 701
  Depository, 159
  Dividends, 178
  Export-Import, 126, 532-533, 581
  Federal Home Loan, 513, 538, 539,
      596, 597, 598
  Federal Reserve, 157, 158, 162,
      542, 580, 608
  German, 198
  Investment, 62
  Japanese-owned, 160
  Land, 533, 534, 535, 583
  National, 158, 159, 160, 166,
      167, 537, 542
  Nonnational, 160
  State, 155, 159, 160, 538, 542
Bankson's Journal, 41
Barbary States, 33, 35, 164
  Pirates, 295
Barclay, Thomas, 33, 163, 166
Barges, 310, 488, 489
Baring, Alexander, 145
Barkley, Alben W., 748
Barley, 442
Barns, 567
Barry Statue Commission, 717
Bartelt, Edward F., 153
Barter programs, 552
Baruch, Bernard, 97, 105, 608, 609
Base Defense Section, Navy, 299
Base Maintenance Division,
    Navy, 299
Batt, William L., 689
Batt Committee, 587
Battelle Memorial Institute, 111
Battle of New Orleans Sesquicentennial
    Celebration Commission, 402
Battlefields, 393, 400, 529
  Civil War, 398, 744
  World War I, 530, 744
Battleground National Cemetery, 401
Baughman, Stanley, 598
Bauxite, 391
Bavaria, 728, 730, 734
Beach Erosion Board, 239, 240
Beacon sites, 528
Beaman, E.O., 394
Beans, 442, 451
Bear (Coast Guard cutter), 523, 524
Beaumarchais, Pierre Augustin
    Caron de, 33
Beavers, 397
Bedford Springs, Pa., 312

Bee culture, 454
Beede, Kenneth C., 674
Beetle, white fringe, 454
Beets, sugar, 442, 443, 449, 453,
    593
Belgium, 192, 198, 236, 362,
    566, 612
  Military cemeteries in, 529
  War damage in, 206, 313
Belgium, Commission for Relief
    in, 595
Belknap, William, 37
Bell, Daniel W., 99
Beltsville, Md., 452
Bennett, Elmer F., 367
Bennett, Floyd, 334
Bennett, Hugh H., 437
Benson, Ezra Taft, 424
Bering Sea, 395
Bering Sea Claims Commission
    of 1896-97, 145
Bering Sea Patrol, 524
Bering Sea Squadron, 323
Berking, Max, 616
Berkowitz, Jacob, 745
Berlin, 287, 737
  Airlift, 334
  1899 Treaty of, 409
  Surrender at, 188
Berlin Document Center, 734
Bertillon criminal identification
    cards, 348
Bessel Friedrich Wilhelm, 472
Best, Robert, 343
Bethlehem Steel Corp., 243
Better Housing Division, 125
Beverages, 508
  Alcoholic, 177, 461
Bevollmaechtigter fuer
    Hochfrequenzforschung, 729
Bi-Partisan Treason, 127
Big Four, 745
Bikini, Army Ground Group at, 190
Bikini Scientific Resurvey Group, 190
Bill of Rights, 30, 41, 507
Billings case. See Mooney-Billings case
Bingham, Theodore A., 715
Bingham, William, 33
Biological sciences, 554
Biological Survey, 426
Biological Survey, Bureau of,
    370, 394, 396, 399
Biophysical Laboratory, 451
Bipartite Board, 197
Bipartite Control Office, 197, 198
Birds, 394, 396, 397
Birdseye, Claude H., 392
"Birth of a Nation" (m.p.), 747
Birth rate, 510
Birth records, 141, 574
"Biscuit Eater, The" (m.p.), 747
Bismarck-Schoenhausen,
    Herbert von, 735

Bituminous coal, 106, 408, 417,
    418, 419, 630, 637, 644
Bituminous Coal Act of 1937,
    418, 637
Bituminous Coal and Coke,
    Bureau of, 594
Bituminous Coal Commission,
    U.S., 594
    See also National Bituminous
        Coal Commission
Bituminous Coal Conservation Act
    of 1935, 417, 418, 637
Bituminous Coal Consumers'
    Counsel, Office of the, 417
BITUMINOUS COAL CONSUMERS'
    COUNSEL, OFFICE OF THE
    (RG 223), 637
Bituminous Coal Division, 420
BITUMINOUS COAL DIVISION
    (RG 222) 418-419
Bituminous Coal Labor Board, 417
Black Hawk War, 388
"Black Legion" (m.p.), 747
Black market, 649, 656
    Japanese, 335
Blackfoot Indians, 388
Blacks, 178, 264, 636, 663
    Colonization, 365
    Education, 506, 695
    Employment of, 617, 651, 694
    In war effort, 211, 232, 256, 263, 662
    Newspapers, 185
    Return to Africa, 337
    Small businesses, 464
Blair, John M., 674
Blaisdell, Thomas C., 123
Blake (SS), 473
Blast, effects on equipment, 191
Blennerhasset, Harman, 85
Blighted Areas and Slums,
    Committee on, 475
Blimps, 293
Blind, aid to the, 466, 501, 511, 658, 748
    See also Health, Education, and
        Welfare, Department of
Bliss, Tasker H., 288
Blister Rust Control Division,
    Forest Service, 453
Bloch, Emanuel H., 617
Blood programs, 187
Bloomfield, Joseph, 36
Bluebeard Castle Hotel, 404, 725
Boats. See Ships and Vessels
Boggs, S.W., 136
Bohlen, Alfried Krupp von, 700
Bolivia, 138, 145
"Bolling Agreement," 262
Bolshevik. See German-Bolshevik
    cooperation
Bombing raids, 192, 206, 220, 299,
    328, 334
Bombs, 303, 332, 639
    Aerial, 245, 397

Incendiary, 206, 659
Shelters, 245
    See also Atomic bombs and Defense
        Atomic Support Agency
Bonds, 33, 60, 160, 162, 166,
    175, 176, 178, 381, 411, 553
    Confederate, 722
    Defense, 156
    District of Columbia, 157
    Liberty, 165, 288, 608
    Nonintercourse, 170
    Philippine, 157
    Puerto Rican, 157
    Railroad, 159, 163
    Savings, 156, 650, 699
    Ship, 34
    Surety, 167
    Victory, 156
    War, 299, 650, 662, 663, 746
Bonhomme Richard (U.S.S.), 296
Bonney, Walter T., 554
Bookbinding, 57
Bookkeeping and Warrants,
    Division of, 165
Books, nautical, 316
Booth, John Wilkes, 744
Bormann, Martin, 735
Boston, Mass., 745
    British garrison at, 70
    Harbor, 471
    Navy yard, 295, 305
Boston Loan Agency, 582
Botany, 430, 452, 523
Bottomry, bills of, 83
Boudinot, Elias, 32
Boulder Dam, 368
Boundaries
    Alaskan, 134, 145, 723
    District of Columbia, 370
    Indian land, 376
    Political, 299, 333
    States, 34, 372
    Surveys, 237, 366
    U.S., 143, 144, 145, 241, 426
BOUNDARY AND CLAIMS
    COMMISSIONS AND
    ARBITRATIONS (RG 76),
    143-146
Bounties, 91, 169, 257, 263, 351
    Claims, 59
    Enlistment, 715
    Fishing, 170
Bounty and Claims Division, 232
Bounty lands, 59, 163, 207, 247,
    365, 380, 572, 573, 574
    Applications, 573, 574
Bower, W. Va., 595
Bowers, T. S., 215
Bowles, Chester, 657, 665
Bowman Act, 52, 91
Boxer Rebellion, 276
Boxing matches, 89
Boy Scouts, 397

Boyen, Hermann von, 732
Boys clubs, 433
Brady, Matthew B., 75, 255
"Brady's Album Gallery," 501
Brainard, David Legge, 743, 745
Brainard Collection, 743
Brandt, Karl, 700
Brandwen, Maxwell, 692
Brauchitsch, Walther von, 732
Braun, Eva, 735, 737
Bray, William J., 674
Brazil, 139, 145, 150, 196, 391,
    589, 614
Brazilian International Exposition, 154
Breakwaters, 310
Brearley, David, 36, 37
Breech-Loading Rifles Board, 304
Brewing industry, 461
Briar, John, 415
Bridgeport, Conn., 53
Bridges, 237, 240, 288, 310, 402, 407,
    527, 567, 607, 715, 745
    Construction, 428, 716
    District of Columbia, 403, 531, 714, 717
    Railroad, 688
Briggs, Lyman J., 475
Britain. See Great Britain
British Air Ministry, 279
British-American Joint Patent
    Interchange Committee,
    147, 149
British Claims, Commission for
    Adjustment of, 259, 262
British Contraband Committee, 611
British Expeditionary Forces, 287
British.Guiana, 145
British Intelligence Objectives
    Subcommittee, 197
British Isles, 278, 328, 566
British Library of Information, 746
British North American Colonies, 156
British Purchasing Mission, 624
Broadcast Bureau, Federal
    Communications Commission,
    536
Broadcasting networks and stations,
    535, 536, 746, 747
    See also Communications; Foreign
        Broadcast Intelligence Service
        (RG 262); and Radio,
        broadcasts
Broadcasting Service, U.S.
    Information Agency, 569
Broadsides, 36
Brokers, misuse of funds by, 432
Bromwell, Charles S., 715
Brooke, John R., 280
Brown, Dayton, 750
Brown, H. "Rap," 127
Brown, Major General, 54
Brown, W.C., 744
Brown market, 649
Brussels World's Fair, 139

Bryan, William Jennings,
    135, 744
Bryce Canyon National Park, 402
Budget, Bureau of the, 58, 112, 123,
    166, 183, 371, 548, 581, 616,
    661, 711
BUDGET, BUREAU OF THE
    (RG 51), 96-100
Budget Advisory Committee, 229
Budget and Accounting Act of
    1921, 57, 152
Buell, Herbert L., 237
Builders Iron Foundry, 245
Building and Construction Trades
    Department, American
    Federation of Labor, 498
Building and loan associations, 160
Building construction, 365, 398,
    475, 516, 544
    Materials, 514, 515, 517, 518, 665
Buildings
    District of Columbia, 714
    Federal, 364, 545, 547, 548, 714
    Public, 402, 545, 546, 547, 548
    See also Public Buildings and
        Grounds, Office of
Buildings Management, Branch of, 545
Bulama arbitration, 145
Bulgaria, 612
Bulge, Battle of the, 663
Bulletin of the Bureau of Standards,
    475
Bullion, 173, 174, 175
Bundy, Harvey H., 239
Bunkering, 606
Buoys, light, 525
Burgher Council, St. Croix, 724
Burgman, Herbert J., 343
Burials, 247, 248
Burma, 195, 612
Burma Theater. See China-Burma-India
    Theater
Burnett, Edmund C., 36
Burnett, H. L., 259
Burns and Allen show, 640
Burnside, Ambrose E., 208
Burr, Aaron, 85, 89
Burr, David, 362
Bush, Vannevar, 658
Business, 543, 650
    Censuses of, 466, 467, 468
    Cycles, 475
    Leaders, 553
    Loans, 563, 580, 581, 582, 673
    Management, 565
    Schedules, 467, 468
    Small, 188, 270, 464, 486, 489,
        490, 565, 581, 629, 673,
        674, 675
    Trends, 122
Business and Defense Services
    Administration, 489
Business Methods, Committee on, 509

Business Organization, Committee on, 65
Butadiene plants, 587
Byrd, Richard E., 334, 677, 744, 749-750
Byrd Expedition, 405
Byrd Station, Antarctica, 750
Byrnes, James F., 664

C

Cabinet, U.S., 46, 133, 138, 156, 548, 745
Cabinet Food Committee, 426
Caddo Indians, 388
Cadets
  Air, 528
  Military Academy, 288, 289
  Naval Academy, 321, 322
Cairo, Egypt, 205
Cairo Conference, 256
California, 50, 134, 247, 299, 328, 336, 344, 380, 430, 598, 717, 723, 745
  Rancho period, 374
California Land Claims Commissioners, Board of, 374
California Pacific International Exposition, 154
California War Board, 436
Caliver, Ambrose, 506
Cammerer, Arno B., 398
Camouflage, 288, 306, 639, 659
Camp A.A. Humphreys, Va., 237
Camp John Hay, P.I., 277
Camp Kenedy, Tex., 138
Camp Kilmer, N.J., 113
Camp Roosevelt, 403
Campanella, Roy, 114
Campbell Commission. See Davis-Holt-Campbell Commission
Camps
  Army, 228, 234, 241, 256, 273, 275, 277, 505
  Civilian Conservation Corps, 400, 425, 430, 439, 547, 614, 615
  Concentration, 328, 334, 663, 702, 729, 730
  Migratory labor, 442, 443
  Women's training, 744
  Work, 695
Canada, 33, 145, 147, 156, 220, 241, 392, 395, 476, 650, 677, 750
  Prime Minister of, 688
Canada, National Film Board of, 746
Canadian-Alaskan boundary, 134
Canadian North, 750
Canadian-United States border, 145
Canal Commission, 712
Canal Fund, Joint Committee on the, 712

Canal Zone. See Panama Canal Zone
Canals, 154, 178, 238, 239, 240, 372, 374, 376, 401, 402, 407, 474, 562, 599, 712, 714, 716
  Routes, 137
Cancellation Board (Navy), 318
Cancer, 504, 505
Candy, 509
Cannons, 303
Cape Cod, Mass., 471
Cape Fear, N.C., 471
Cape Hatteras, N.C., 471
Capias, writs of, 83, 89
Capital, U.S., 164, 713, 714
CAPITAL ISSUES COMMITTEE (RG 158), 577-578
Capitol, U.S., 238, 366, 370, 551, 717
  Buildings and grounds, 364
  Dome, 745
Capitol Square, 715
Capriles, Miguel A. de, 339
Carbines, 215
Carbon Black, Committee on, 665
Carbon monoxide, 409
Carborundum, 409
Career Management Group, 222
Cargoes, 572, 625, 692
  Manifests, 169, 170
Caribbean, U.S. Army, 280
Caribbean area, 328, 404
"Carl Mackley houses," 520
Carlisle Indian Industrial School, 387, 388
Carmichael, William, 33, 35
Carmody, John L., 440
Carmody, John M., 676, 705
Carnegie Corporation, 554-555
Carnegie Institution of Washington, 474
Caroline Islands, 299
Carpenter, Donald F., 187
Carpenter-Whitney expedition, 370
Carpooling, 619, 621
Carr, E.W., 410
Carriages, 178
Carriers, 560, 600, 612, 619, 620, 644
  Common, 535, 536, 539, 553, 654
  Interstate, 553
  Motor, 619, 621, 643, 644
  Railroad, 599
  Water, 600, 601
Carrollsburgh, 715
Carter, Albert M., 673
Carter, Oberlin M., 237
Cartography, 480, 742, 744, 749-750
Cartoons, 746
Casablanca Conference, 623, 663

Cass, Millard, 491
Catalogue of Manuscript Books, 29
Cathcart, James L., 375
Cattle, 379, 445, 447, 459
CAUSES AND PREVENTION OF
    VIOLENCE, NATIONAL
    COMMISSION ON THE
    (RG 283), 127-128
Caustic Poison Act, 507
Cavalry, 215, 272, 285
    Puerto Rican, 726
Cavalry, Chief of, 225, 226
Cavalry, Office of the Chief of,
    215, 226
Cavalry Equipment Board, 243
Cavalry School, 226
Cement, 409, 416
Cemeterial Division, 248
Cemeteries, 241, 247, 249, 288,
    376, 531, 734
    National, 213, 397, 400, 401,
        529
    U.S., in Europe, 255, 529
Censor, Chief Military, 217
Censorship, 676
    German, 728
    Motion picture, 298
    Voluntary press, 119
CENSORSHIP, OFFICE OF
    (RG 216), 637-638
Censorship Board, 358
Censorship Operating Board, 638
Censorship Policy Board, 638
Census, 54, 88, 133, 135, 281,
    344, 364, 365, 467, 468,
    469, 616
    American Samoan, 410
    Decennial, 465, 466, 575
    Indian, 380, 389, 468
    Nonpopulation schedules,
        468, 469
    Puerto Rican, 414
    Security classification, 467
    Special schedules, 467
    Special State, 469
    See also Population
Census, Bureau of the, 364, 486
CENSUS, BUREAU OF THE
    (RG 29), 465-469
Census, Superintendent of the, 465
Census Advisory Committee, 466
Center Market, Washington, D.C.,
    456
Central America, 137, 138, 147,
    301, 314, 571, 749
    Conferences on, 146
    Vital statistics of, 468
Central Defense Command, 279
Central Deferment Board, 212
Central Housing Committee,
    513, 538
Central Intelligence Agency,
    128, 203, 222

CENTRAL INTELLIGENCE
    AGENCY (RG 263), 101
Central Intelligence Group,
    101, 222
Central Map Reproduction
    Plant, 240
Central Pacific Railroad,
    158, 412
Central Patent Section, War
    Department, 261, 262
Central Powers, 220, 543
Central Statistical Boards,
    96, 98, 457
Central Statistical Clearing
    House, 97
Central Statistical Committee,
    96, 97
Central Statistical Office of Poland,
    735
Century of Progress Building, 532
Cereal, 591, 592, 595, 625
Certificate of Merit, 96
Certiorari, writs of, 70, 91
Chain Bridge, 716
Chamberlain Indian School, 387
Chamberlain-Kahn Act, 503
Chamberlin, Clarence, 677
Chambers, Williams L., 560
Chancery, 74, 75, 76, 78, 80,
    85, 88, 89, 90
Chandler, Douglas, 343, 623
Chapels and churches, 267, 346,
    530, 730
Chaplains, Chief of
    Air Force, 331
    American Expeditionary
        Forces, 284
CHAPLAINS, OFFICE OF THE
    CHIEF OF (RG 247),
    266-267
Chaplains Division, Navy,
    312, 313
Chaplin, Charlie, 746
Chapman, Oscar L., 367
Charcoal, 656
Charitable organizations,
    570, 746
    See also Pennsylvania Board
        of Public Charities
Charlotte, N.C., 745
Chart Board, Coast and
    Geodetic Survey, 472
Chart Publication,
    Committee on, 472
Charters, foreign, 693
Charts and Instruments,
    Depot of, 313, 315, 316, 477
Chaumont, Le Ray de, 35
Chef der Marineleitung, 731
Chemical Corps Patent Agency, 266
Chemical Engineering Research
    Division, 450
Chemical warfare, 236, 266, 285, 659

Chemical Warfare School, 266
Chemical Warfare Section, War
    Department Claims
    Board, 224
Chemical Warfare Service, 408
CHEMICAL WARFARE
    SERVICE (RG 175), 266
Chemical Warfare Service,
    Chief of, 229
Chemicals, 408, 490, 509, 654
    Industry, 356, 629
    Research, 389, 391, 449, 450
Chemie, I.G., Industries, 198
Chemistry, Bureau of, 449, 463,
    507, 508, 509
Chemistry, Division of, 449
Chemistry and Soils, Bureau of,
    437, 438, 448, 449, 451,
    452
Chemnyco, Inc., 356
Cherokee, Old Settler, 384
Cherokee freedmen, 384
Cherokee Indians, 91, 232, 377,
    380, 383, 389, 566
    Eastern, Guion Miller
        enrollment of, 91
Cherokee Strip, 376
Chesapeake and Ohio Canal,
    401, 402, 714, 716
Chesapeake and Ohio Canal,
    Commissioner of the, 401
Chesapeake and Ohio Canal
    Company, 401, 402
Chesapeake Bay, 279, 397
Cheyenne Indians, 388
Chiang Kai-shek, 335
Chiang Kai-shek, Mme., 748
Chicago, Ill., 127, 750
    Commodities market, 432
Chicago Century of Progress
    Building, 532
Chicago Harbor, Office of
    Public Works, 238
Chicago Police Department, 127
Chicago Road, 238
Chicago Tribune, 750
Chicago World's Fair Centennial
    Celebration, 154
Chickasaw Indians, 375, 380
Chief Accountant, Office of
    the, Federal Communications
    Commission, 536
Chief Clerk, Office of the, 153
Chief Clerk and Superintendent, 154
Chief Clerk and Superintendent,
    Office of the, 153
Chief Disbursing Clerk, 209
Chief Disbursing Clerk, Office
    of the, 209
Chief Engineer, 236, 237, 288, 381
Chief Engineer, Office of the, 381
Chief Examiner, Department of Justice,
    342, 348

Chief Inspector, Bureau of the, 362
Chief Justice, U.S., 69, 70, 164, 566
Chief Naval Constructor, 295
Chief of Staff
    Air Force, 331
    Army, 188, 211, 215, 216, 218, 220,
        222, 225, 229, 231, 234, 252,
        264, 266, 267, 268, 274, 275,
        278, 284
Chief of Staff (Army), Office of
    the, 194, 216, 227, 228, 252
Chief of Staff Supreme Allied
    Command, 192
Chief Scientist, Air Force, 331
Chief Signal Officer, 229, 254, 255,
    285, 286, 289, 324
Chief Signal Officer, Office of the,
    324, 325, 327, 476, 478
CHIEF SIGNAL OFFICER, OFFICE
    OF THE (RG 111), 254-256
Chief Surgeon, American Forces in
    France, 286
Chief Surgeon, European Theater of
    Operations, Office of the, 197
Chiefs of Police, International
    Association of, 348
Child Health and Protection,
    White House Conference
    on, 458
Children
    Health and welfare, 504, 505,
        510, 511, 639, 695
    Labor, 41, 371, 495, 496, 510, 630
Children and Youth, White House
    Conference on, 116
Children's Bureau, 511
CHILDREN'S BUREAU (RG 102), 510
Chile, 145, 299, 457, 614
China, 106, 139, 168, 180, 195, 205,
    233, 255, 262, 299, 301, 328,
    344, 346, 351, 423, 523, 605,
    723, 743
    Aid program, 222
    Communist forces of, 196
    Japanese invasion of, 256
    Officer training, 217
    U.S. troops in, 276, 277, 301
China-Burma-India Theater, 197, 280
China Relief Expedition, 241, 255,
    276, 277, 278
China Theater Command, U.S., 106
China Theater of Operations, 205
Chinese Exclusion Acts, 346
Chinese exclusion laws, 345
Chinese People's Volunteer Army
    in Korea, 736
Chinese Training Center, 197
Chinese War Production Board, 106
Chippewa Commission of 1889, 386
Chippewa Halfbreed Scrip, 373
Chippewa Indians, 375, 380, 386
Chiwiwi, Marie, 370
Choctaw freedmen, 380

Choctaw Indians, 380
Choctaw Net Proceeds Case, 380
Choctaw Scrip, 373
Christian Commission, U.S., 233
Christy, Howard Chandler, 165
Chrome, 414
Chromite deposits, 391
Chronograph tapes and sheets, 316
Chumash Indians, 567
Chungking, 663
Churchill, Winston, 195, 335,
    663, 747, 748
Ciano, Galeazzo, 736, 737
Cinchona, 586, 589, 626
Circuit Court, U.S., for the
    District of Columbia, 75, 76
Circuit courts, 69, 72-90, 338,
    339, 352, 480
    Central States, 92
Circuit courts of appeals, 69,
    261, 339
Cities, 118, 207, 514
    See also names of individual
    cities
Citizens, protection of U.S., 132
Citizens for Johnson-Humphrey, 742
Citizenship, 347, 373, 746
    Education, 346, 347
    Proof of, 484
City of Washington, Superintendent
    of the, 714
City planning, 475, 747
Civil Aeronautics Act of
    1938, 527, 530
Civil Aeronautics Administration,
    527, 528
Civil Aeronautics Administration
    War Training Service, 528
Civil Aeronautics Authority,
    527, 528, 530, 554
Civil Aeronautics Board, 527
CIVIL AERONAUTICS BOARD
    (RG 197), 530
Civil Affairs, Office of, 273
Civil Affairs and Military
    Government, Office of
    the Chief of, 221
CIVIL AND DEFENSE
    MOBILIZATION, OFFICE
    OF (RG 304), 269-271
Civil cases, 72, 73, 76, 77, 78,
    79, 80, 81, 82, 84, 85,
    86, 87, 88, 89, 90
Civil defense, 112, 184, 213, 269,
    271, 548, 552, 734
    England, 217, 640
    Training, 615
Civil Defense, Office of, 271
CIVIL DISORDERS, NATIONAL
    ADVISORY COMMISSION
    ON (RG 282), 129-130
Civil disturbances, 213

Civil Division, Department of
    Justice, 351, 355, 356
Civil dockets, 74, 78, 79, 82,
    85, 86, 89, 90
Civil law, 75, 318
Civil litigation, 343
Civil Property Custodian,
    Office of the, 194
Civil Relief Act, 572
Civil rights, 73, 117, 339, 745
Civil Rights Act of 1875, 338
Civil Service, Advisory Board of
    the, 568
Civil Service Commission, 64
    97, 122, 153, 364, 371, 499,
    679, 680, 681

CIVIL SERVICE COMMISSION,
    U.S. (RG 146), 568
Civil Service Examiners, Boards
    of, 568
Civil Service Improvement,
    President's Committee on,
    104
Civil Service Retirement Act,
    55, 568
Civil War, 54, 59, 60, 75, 79, 83,
    86, 137, 154, 155, 177, 178,
    180, 208, 220, 232, 233, 234,
    240, 255, 259, 272, 273, 294,
    311, 316, 336, 366, 402, 473,
    474, 501, 525, 572, 573, 574,
    744
    Amnesty and pardons, 137
    Armies, 233, 273-274
    Battlefields, 398, 744
    Claims, 59, 91, 144, 154, 155, 247,
        719, 722
    Land taxes, 60
    Loans, 163
    Military units, 249, 744
    Muster rolls, 311
    Naval operations, 473
    Prisoners and prisons, 253, 254,
        720, 721
    Union, the, 154, 233, 254, 255,
        719
    Vessels, 306, 501, 720
    Veterans, 575
    See also Confederate
        Records, Treasury
        Department Collection of
        (RG 365); Confederate
        Records, War Department
        Collection of (RG 109);
        Confederate States of
        America; Provost Marshal
        General's Bureau (Civil
        War) (RG 110); *and*
        Refugees, Freedmen, and
        Abandoned Lands, Bureau of
Civil War Centennial Commission, 402

CIVIL WAR SPECIAL AGENCIES
    OF THE TREASURY
    DEPARTMENT (RG 366),
    179-180
Civil Works Administration, 98,
    396, 399, 446, 473, 693, 694,
    695, 697, 698, 725
Civil Works Administration,
    Coordinator of, 98
Civil Works Administration, Special
    Advisory Committee on
    Statistical Projects of the, 98
Civilian Awards Board, 212
Civilian Components, Committee
    on, 214
Civilian Conservation Corps, 207, 235,
    370, 371, 396, 399, 400, 402,
    406, 407, 425, 427, 430, 434,
    438, 440, 506, 572, 699
    Camps, 400, 425, 430, 439, 547, 614,
      615
    Indian Division, 385
    Virgin Islands, 725
CIVILIAN CONSERVATION
    CORPS (RG 35), 614-615
Civilian Defense, Office of,
    371, 645
CIVILIAN DEFENSE, OFFICE
    OF (RG 171), 639-640
Civilian Food Reserve Section, 404
Civilian Military Training Camps,
    256
Civilian Production Administration,
    517, 518, 643, 672, 687
Civilian Production Administration
    Priorities Policy Committee, 687
Civilian Public Service Camps, 400
Civilian Supplies, Committee to
    Coordinate the Export of, 665
Claims, 33, 50, 58, 59, 60, 87, 134, 136,
    143, 144, 149, 152, 166, 178,
    180, 193, 194, 208, 213, 223,
    233, 234, 237, 238, 243, 247, 251,
    258, 262, 263, 283, 285, 294, 318,
    327, 336, 338, 340, 366, 372, 373,
    374, 376, 547
    Agents, 264
    Boards, 60, 149, 214, 223, 224, 225,
      239, 243, 247, 261, 318
    Bounty land, 365, 573, 574
    Civil War, 59, 91, 144, 154, 155,
      247, 719, 722
    Commissions, 143-146, 259, 262,
      340, 414, 552, 573
    Estate, 140, 141
    French spoliation, 91, 169, 170,
      338, 352, 483
    Indian, 91, 367, 379, 380, 382,
      383, 384, 552, 574
    Mining, 376, 412, 414, 415, 420
    Pension, 365, 573
    Preemption, 372
    Revolutionary War, 75, 571

    State, 33, 34, 164
    Veracruz, Mexico, 283
    See also Court of Claims, U.S.,
      and Foreign Claims Section
      (War) (RG 213)
Claims Division, Department of
    Justice, 351, 354, 356
Clark, George Rogers,
    Sesquicentennial Commission, 61
Clark, Kenneth, 704
Clarke, Hans, 659
Clarke-McNary Act, 426, 429
Classification Act of 1949, 568
Clausen, Governor, 724
Clay (soil), 409
Clayton Act of 1914, 543
Clemency and Parole Board, 214
Clemency and Parole Board for
    War Criminals, 262
Clergy, 267
Cleveland, Grover, 548, 748
Climate, 299, 333, 431, 436,
    437, 440, 451, 457, 476
Climatology Division, Weather
    Bureau, 477
Clothing, 188, 246, 247, 248,
    272, 308, 309, 458, 490,
    654, 665
Clothing and Hospital Departments,
    Commissioners of Accounts
    for the, 33
Coal, 292, 307, 321, 402, 417, 419,
    579, 590, 593, 594, 595, 688,
    734
    Bituminous, 106, 408, 417-418,
      419, 420, 594, 630, 637,
      644
    See also Fuel
Coal Commission, U.S., 579

COAL COMMISSION, U.S.
    (RG 68), 590-591
Coal Division, Bureau of
    Foreign and Domestic
    Commerce, 407, 408
Coal Economics Division, Bureau
    of Mines, 408
Coal mines, 368, 408, 409
Coal Mines Administrations,
    419, 420
Coalton, W. Va., 595
Coast and Geodetic Survey,
    476, 479, 480, 502

COAST AND GEODETIC SURVEY
    (RG 23), 470-474
Coast artillery, 225, 227, 228,
    272, 275, 276
Coast Artillery, Chief of,
    225, 229
Coast Artillery, Office of the
    Chief of, 226

Coast Artillery Board, 226
Coast Artillery Corps, 225, 272
Coast Artillery School, 226
Coast Artillery Training Center, 226
Coast Artillery War Instruction, 226
Coast Guard, 108, 328, 481, 484,
     502, 613, 677, 692, 741, 746
     Vessels, 58, 524
COAST GUARD, U.S. (RG 26),
     522-525
Coast Guard Academy, 525
Coast Guard Intelligence Division, 524
Coastal defense, 58, 217, 226, 240,
     275, 276, 277, 279
Coastal Information Section, Office
     of the Deputy Chief of Naval
     Operations, 298
Coasts, U.S., 315, 396, 397, 475, 607
Coca, 350
Code of Fair Competition for the
     Petroleum Industry, 415
Code of Regulations for the
     Government of the Navy,
     Board To Prepare a, 295
Coffee, 534, 607
Coins and coinage, 172, 173, 174,
     531, 532
Coke, 419, 593, 594, 595
Cold war activities, 213
Coll y Toste, Cayetano, 726
Collecting, Drilling, and Organizing
     Volunteers Fund, 257, 258
Collective bargaining, 417, 493,
     555, 557, 559, 602, 626
Colleges, 128, 204, 444, 635
     Agricultural, 236, 372, 373,
          433, 434, 446
     Aid programs, 635
     Junior, 506
     Land-grant, 434, 446, 506
     Students, 634
     See also Schools and names of
          institutions
Collet, John C., 665
Collier, John, 379
Collins, J. Lawton, 216
Colombia, 134, 145, 147, 150,
     589, 614
Colonial America, 532
Colonial National Historical
     Park, 400, 402
Colonies, 70, 73
     Danish royal, 724
     North American, 156, 358
     Thirteen Original, 29, 62
Color and Farm Waste Division, 450
Color Laboratory, 450
Colorado, 134, 394, 430, 528
Colorado-Kansas Arkansas River
     Compact Commission, 392
Colorado River, 370, 390, 394
Colorado Territory, 745
Colored Troops Division, 232, 263

Colquitt, Oscar B., 560
Columbia Basin Interagency
     Committee, 421
Columbia Broadcasting System,
     746, 747
Columbia Institution for the
     Deaf, 364, 501
Columbia Law School, 115
Columbia Pictures, Inc., 746, 747
Columbian Exposition, 532
Columbus Memorial Commission, 717
Comanche Indians, 388
Comando Supremo, 735
Combined Administrative
     Liquidating Agency, 192
Combined Chiefs of Staff, 188
     191, 197, 209, 216, 222
Combined Civil Affairs
     Committee, 218, 230, 688
Combined Civil Affairs
     Liquidating Agency, 192
Combined Coal Committee, 688
Combined Command for
     Reconnaissance Activities,
     Far East, 200
Combined Command for
     Reconnaissance Activities,
     Korea, 200
Combined Food Board, 426
Combined Forces Planners, 222
Combined Hides, Skins, and
     Leather Committee, 688
Combined Liquidating Agencies, 192
Combined Production and
     Resources Board, 688
Combined Raw Materials
     Board, 688
Combined Rubber Committee, 688
Combined Shipping Adjustment
     Board, 692
Combined Textile Committee, 688
Combined Tin Committee, 688
Command and General Staff
     School, 197, 219
Command Group, Allied Force
     Headquarters, 193
Commandants
     Marine Corps, 301
     Midshipmen, 322
Commander in Chief, Pacific, 199
Commanding General, Services of
     Supply, 254
Commerce, 31, 83, 91, 179, 180,
     198, 496, 539, 601, 613,
     646, 675, 676, 721
     Censuses of, 468
     Domestic, 60, 464, 486, 539
     Foreign, 415, 445, 464, 478,
          496, 539, 553
     Interstate, 338, 415, 445, 496,
          543, 559, 563, 601
     Virgin Islands, 725

See also Foreign and Domestic
  Commerce, Bureau of;
  Interstate Commerce
  Commission; Reconstruction
  Finance Corporation;
  Tariff Commission, U.S.;
  and Trade
Commerce, Assistant Secretaries of, 486
Commerce, Committee of, 33
Commerce, Department of, 108, 122,
  168, 394, 407, 420, 464, 465,
  469, 470, 474, 476, 479, 480,
  486, 488, 489, 516, 522, 526,
  527, 528, 530, 532, 535, 539,
  543, 581, 591, 595, 602, 607,
  610, 624, 627, 647, 656, 664,
  673, 675, 687
Commerce, Office of the Secretary
  of, 464
Commerce, Secretary of, 108, 464,
  479, 482, 487, 489, 539, 565,
  578, 579, 583
Commerce, Senate Committee on, 604
Commerce and Industry Association
  of New York, 640
Commerce and Labor, Department of,
  345, 394, 464, 465, 470, 474,
  480, 486, 491, 493, 498, 510,
  522, 542
Commerce and Labor, Secretary of, 481
Commerce Clearing House, Inc., 496
COMMERCE COURT, U.S.
  (RG 172), 92
Commercial Affairs, Division of, 136
Commercial Company, U.S.,
  581, 585, 586, 589
Commercial Economy Board, 579
Commissaries, 273
Commissary Department, 34
Commissary General of Military
  Stores, 37
COMMISSARY GENERAL OF
  PRISONERS (RG 249),
  253-254
Commissary General of Purchases,
  248
Commissary General of Purchases,
  Office of the, 246
COMMISSARY GENERAL OF
  SUBSISTENCE, OFFICE
  OF THE (RG 192), 252
Commissioners, U.S., 69, 73, 74, 76,
  77, 78, 79, 80-83, 85, 86-90,
  342, 344
Commissions
  Claims, 143-146, 259, 262, 552
  Interdepartmental, 369
  U.S. boundary, 144
  See also names of commissions
Commissions, international. *See*
  International Conferences,
  Commissions, and Expositions
  (RG 43)

COMMISSIONS ON ORGANIZATION
  OF THE EXECUTIVE
  BRANCH OF THE GOVERNMENT
  (RG 264), 64-65
Committee of Detail, 36, 37
Committees
  Interagency, 369, 391
  See also Interdepartmental and
    Intradepartmental Committees
    (State Department) (RG 353);
    Joint Committees of Congress
    (RG 128); *and names of
    committees*
Committees, Convention of, 32
Committees, international. *See*
  International Conferences,
  Commissions, and Expositions
  (RG 43)
Commodities, 97, 100, 108, 111, 185,
  238, 339, 432, 436, 458, 462,
  486, 570, 586, 647, 648, 650,
  654, 655, 656, 668, 676, 692
  Agricultural, 431, 449, 459, 460,
    461, 488, 626, 647
  Committees, international, 688, 689
  Domestic consumption of, 459
  Foreign consumption of, 459
  Industrial, 488
  Prices, 435, 647, 649, 655, 668
  Procurement, 435, 462, 585
  Rationing, 647, 655
  Scarce, 435, 489, 687, 688
Commodity Credit Corporation,
  426, 624
COMMODITY CREDIT
  CORPORATION (RG 161),
  434-435
Commodity Exchange Act of
  1936, 432
Commodity Exchange Administration,
  432, 459
COMMODITY EXCHANGE
  AUTHORITY (RG 180),
  432
Commodity Stabilization Service,
  435, 436
Common Carriers Bureau, Federal
  Communications Commission,
  536
Common law, 72, 74, 83, 86, 89
Communication Satellite bill, 748
Communications, 146, 147, 186, 187,
  198, 270, 428, 544, 567,
  570, 614, 660, 661, 662
  Air, 255
  Cable, 359, 537, 613
  Censorship, 638
  Electrical, 659
  Foreign, 194, 288, 535, 614, 735
  Interstate, 535
  Networks and stations, 255, 299, 308,
    746, 747
  Systems, 194, 256, 567

Wire and wireless, 307, 535, 536, 613
See also Federal Communications
Commission
Communications Act of 1934, 535
Communications-Electronics, Office
of the Chief of, 254
Communications Satellite Act of
1962, 535
Communism, 747
Communist forces, China and Korea, 196
Communist Party, 298, 735, 736
Community Action Advisory Service,
518
Community Facilities, Bureau of, 704
Community Facilities Administration,
513
Community Facilities Service,
General Services Administration,
513
Community service programs, 696
COMMUNITY WAR SERVICES,
OFFICE OF (RG 215),
640-641
Commutations of sentences, 345, 349
Compagnie Nouvelle du Canal de
Panama, 562
Compagnie Universelle du Canal
Interoceanique, 562
Compensation and Contracts,
Committee on, 600
Compensation Board, Department
of the Navy, 292
Compiled Military Service
Records, 39, 720, 721
Compton, Karl T., 105, 659
Comptroller General of the United
States, 57, 58, 126
Comptroller of the Currency, 160,
161, 538
Comptroller of the Currency, Office
of the, 175
COMPTROLLER OF THE CURRENCY,
OFFICE OF THE (RG 101),
159-161
Computers, 475
Comstock, C. B., 215
Conant, James B., 105, 658
Concentration camps, 328
Axis, 334
German, 663, 702, 729, 730
Concentration of Production,
Committee on, 682
Conciliation, international
conferences on, 146
Conciliation Service, 491, 540, 626
Condemnation cases, 75
Confederate Dead, Office of the
Commissioner for Marking
Graves of, 247
CONFEDERATE RECORDS,
TREASURY DEPARTMENT
COLLECTION OF (RG 365),
721-722

CONFEDERATE RECORDS, WAR
DEPARTMENT COLLECTION
OF (RG 109), 719-721
Confederate Secretary of War,
720-721
Confederate States of America, 54,
168, 247, 273, 296, 719, 720,
721, 722
Armies, 233, 273, 719, 720, 721, 722
Bonds, 722
Courts, 73, 74, 76, 77, 80, 84, 88,
89, 722
Currency, 166, 722
Customs, 170, 722
Fortifications, 233, 255
Loans, 163, 722
Military commands, 720
Navy accounts, 722
Newspapers, 721
Post Office Department, 720
Prisoners of war, 253, 254, 721
Property, 721, 722
Taxes, 722
See also Civil War
Confederate States of America,
Customs Service of the, 168
Confederate War Department, 720
Confederated Bands of the Ute
Indians *v.* The United States, 92
Confederation, U.S., 31, 131
Confederation Congresses, 29, 30, 31,
32, 34, 35, 36, 42, 43
Committees of, 32, 33
President of, 30, 31, 32
Secretary of, 32, 41, 131
Conference, Committees of, 33
Conferences, 31, 148, 256, 404, 457,
503, 623, 663
Inter-American, 146, 392
International, 97, 98, 134, 184, 256,
287, 431, 481, 483, 503, 569,
594, 663, 745, 748
See also International Conferences,
Commissions, and Expositions
(RG 43)

"Confessions of a Nazi Spy" (m.p.), 748
Congested Production Areas,
Committee for, 123

CONGESTED PRODUCTION AREAS,
COMMITTEE FOR (RG 212),
615-616
Congress, Grand Committee of, 33
Congress, U.S., 30, 32, 34, 35, 36, 42,
53, 57, 61, 62, 65, 69, 70, 95,
122, 133, 183, 185, 213, 216,
221, 229, 258, 261, 321, 337,
338, 342, 411, 536, 553, 624
Committees, 221, 329, 612, 619
See also House of Representatives,
U.S.; Joint Committees of
Congress (RG 128); *and* Senate,
U.S.

Congress of Industrial Organizations, 650

Congresses. *See* Continental and Confederation Congresses and the Constitutional Convention (RG 360) *and* International Conferences, Commissions, and Expositions (RG 43)

Congressional Aviation Policy Board, 55

CONGRESSIONAL COMMISSIONS, MINOR (RG 148), 61-62

Congressional Investigations Division, 221

Congressional Joint Resolution 25, 57

Congressmen, 329

Connally "Hot Oil" Act, 415

Connecticut, 34, 35, 53

Conscientious objectors, 564

Conservation, 122, 367, 369, 393, 394, 395, 397, 415, 423, 428, 436, 487, 555, 567, 569, 570, 594, 609, 647, 662, 663, 666, 746

    Education on, 506

    Food, 425, 462, 591, 593, 639

    National Capital, 713

    Utilities, 422

    Wildlife, 370, 399

    See also Civilian Conservation Corps *and* Soil Conservation Service

Conservation in Construction, Committee on, 687

Conservation of Cultural Resources, Committee on, 123

Constitution, U.S., 30, 31, 36, 37, 41, 42, 43, 45, 49, 51, 62, 63, 138, 352, 469, 551, 570, 711

    Amendments, 41, 52

    Ratification of, 32, 41

    Sesquicentennial celebration of the, 748

Constitution Sesquicentennial Commission, U.S., 61, 62, 743

Constitution (U.S.S.), 296, 304

Constitutional Convention, 30, 36, 37, 41, 62

    See also Federal Convention

Construction, 182, 186, 235, 246, 247, 248, 285, 408, 422, 490, 545, 546, 586, 589, 635, 655, 699, 716

    Aircraft, 554

    Contracts, 546, 584

    Defense, 96

    Equipment and materials, 527

    Federal, 408, 498, 545

    Housing, 442, 513, 514, 515, 516, 517, 518, 585, 596, 598, 599, 607, 686

    Industry, 498, 629

    Maritime, 676, 677

    Military, 199, 217, 229, 309

    Projects, 121, 452, 634, 695, 697, 736

    Public, 475

    Runway, 328

    See also Building construction

Construction, Board on, 292

Construction, Bureau of, 545

Construction and Repair, Bureau of, 295, 305, 306, 308, 318, 319

Construction and Repair, Chief of the Bureau of, 307

Construction Division, 210, 243, 246, 332

Construction, Equipment, and Repairs, Bureau of, 295, 305, 306, 307

Construction Industry Stabilization Commission, 706, 707

Construction Organization of the Fleet Corporation, 603, 605

Consular Bureau, Department of State, 131

Consular service, 136, 140, 149

    Posts, 135, 137, 140, 141, 142

    Representatives, 33, 131, 132, 138

Consulate general, 141

Consulates

    Foreign, 138, 723, 733

    U.S., 137, 138, 140, 141

Consuls, 69, 72, 288, 462, 508

    Foreign, 32, 33, 132, 133, 135

    U.S., 35, 131, 132, 133, 138, 140, 141, 164, 431

Consumer and Marketing Service, 460

Consumer Protection and Environmental Health Service, 502

Consumer Protection Division, National Defense Advisory Commission, 647, 649

Consumer Relations Adviser, Office of, 649

Consumers, 436, 488, 493, 649, 650, 651, 652, 656

    Loans, 650

    Organizations, 111, 649

    Products, 507, 653, 654, 655

    Protection, 105

Consumers' Advisory Board, National Recovery Administration, 629

Consumers' Division, 125

Consumers' Research, Inc., 508

Continental Air Defense Command, 200

CONTINENTAL AND CONFEDERATION CONGRESSES AND THE CONSTITUTIONAL CONVENTION (RG 360), 29-37

Continental Army, 38, 163, 241, 258

Continental Army, Commander in
    Chief of the, 154
Continental Army Command, 227, 246
CONTINENTAL COMMANDS,
    U.S. ARMY, 1821-1920
    (RG 393), 273-274
Continental Congresses, 42, 43, 45, 70,
    140, 162, 230, 245, 358, 571
    Presidents of the, 29, 30, 31, 32
    Secretary of the, 29, 32, 45, 131
Contraband Committee, 610
Contract Adjustment, Board
    of, 224, 243
Contract and Commodity Claims
    Committee, 583
Contract Review, Boards of, 223
Contract Settlement, Director of, 641
Contract Settlement, Office of, 664
CONTRACT SETTLEMENT, OFFICE
    OF (RG 246), 641-642
Contract Settlement Act of 1944, 641
Contract Settlement Advisory
    Board, 641, 642
Contractors, 329, 547, 673
Contracts, 32, 58, 59, 91, 136, 154,
    204, 210, 213, 243, 251, 262,
    285, 306, 307, 308, 318, 405,
    432, 496, 498, 522, 546, 565,
    577, 581, 584, 600, 654, 657,
    658, 659, 660, 673
    Aircraft, 319
    American Samoan, 410
    Construction, 546, 584
    Federal, 91, 491, 496, 565, 610,
        628, 643, 702-703
    Labor laws, alien, 345
    Maritime, 676
    Prewar (WW I), 547
    Russian, 577
    War, 261, 292, 340, 356, 641,
        642, 582, 583, 685
    War Department, 223, 224
Contracts and Adjustments,
    Interdepartmental Board of, 243
Control Service War Plans
    Division, 248
Controlled materials plans, 514, 666
Conventions, 31, 36
    Boundary, 143
    Claims, 143
    International, 145, 268, 481
    Postal, 43
    See also Democratic National
        Conventions and Republican
        National Conventions
Convoys, 313, 525, 677
Conway, Granville, 692
Cook, Frederick A., 750
Cooke, Morris L., 106, 110, 440
Coolidge, Calvin, 96, 434, 745,
    747, 748
Coolidge, T. J., 153
Cooper Committee, 187

Cooperation with National Groups
    and Associations,
    Committee on, 121
Cooperativa Azucarera Los Canos, 417
Cooperativa Lafayette, 417
Cooperative Enterprise in Europe,
    Inquiry on, 104
Cooperative Farm Forestry Act
    of 1937, 437
Cooperative Marketing Act of
    1926, 444
Cooperative Research and
    Service Division, 444
Cooperatives, 104, 417, 432, 442, 695
    Agricultural, 443, 444, 608
    Marketing, 608
    Puerto Rican, 416
    Self-help, 695, 698
Cooperatives, President's Commission
    on, 104
Coordination Committee, 369
Coordination of Commercial and
    Cultural Relations Between the
    American Republics, Office
    for, 646
Copenhagen, Denmark, 596
Copolymer, 587
Copper, 409, 584
Copper River Railroad, Alaska, 405
Copra industry, 410
Copyrights, 69, 75, 82, 83, 87, 133,
    339, 351, 355, 543
Corey, Stevenson, 749
Corn, 441, 451, 453, 459
Corn borer, European, 434, 451, 454
Coronado Exposition Commission,
    U.S., 369
Corporation excise tax law, 344
Corporations, 62, 536, 553
    Government, 166, 646
    Interstate, 543
Corporations, Bureau of, 464, 542, 543
Correctional institutions, Federal,
    349, 668, 669
Corregidor, 156
Corsica, 612
Cosmetics, 507, 543
Cost analysis, 204
Cost of living, 55, 340, 344, 560
Cost of Production Division,
    Bureau of Foreign and
    Domestic Commerce, 570
Costa Rica, 145
Cotton, 155, 167, 180, 423, 441,
    451, 456, 722
    Linters, 352
    Stamp program, 459
    Textiles, 630, 684
Cotton-Rubber Exchange
    Agreement, 435
Cotton Stabilization
    Corporation, 534

Cotton States and International
Exposition, 154, 433
Cottonseed, 668
Council of National Defense,
105, 596, 608, 609, 640,
645, 647, 651, 658
Council of National Defense,
Advisory Commission to
the, 425, 578-579, 639,
645, 687
COUNCIL OF NATIONAL
DEFENSE (RG 62), 578-579
Counselor and Chief Special
Agent, Office of the, 136
Counterespionage, German, 732
Counterfeiting, 176, 337, 726
Counterintelligence, 190
County Land Use Planning
Committee, 457
Court of Appeals, 718
See also Emergency Court
of Appeals
Court of Appeals in Cases of
Capture, 70
Court of Claims, U.S., 52, 167, 260,
261, 339, 382
COURT OF CLAIMS, U.S. (RG 123),
90-92
COURT OF CLAIMS SECTION
(JUSTICE) (RG 205),
351-352
Courts, 63, 70, 343, 344, 346-347,
364, 365, 533
Admiralty, 82
Appellate, 69
Clerks, 337, 338, 341, 342
Colonial, 70
Commerce, 92
Confederate, 73, 74, 76, 77,
80, 84, 88, 89, 722
Consular, 135
Federal, 338, 342, 346-347, 353
German, 728, 733
Italian, 193
Maryland, 75
Military, 259
Municipal, 718
New York, 344
North Korean, 736
Orphans', 75
Territorial, 73, 74, 76, 79, 81,
82, 84, 87, 337, 338
Vice admiralty, 82, 87
Virginia County, 75
See also Appeals, United States
Courts of (RG 276); Circuit
courts; Confederate States
of America, courts; District
Courts, U.S.; and Supreme
Court, U.S.
Courts, Administrative Office of
the, U.S., 344

Courts-martial, 95, 191, 214, 232, 234,
235, 255, 258, 259, 260, 275,
284, 286, 290, 294, 300, 317,
322, 336, 524
Courts of inquiry, 233, 258, 259, 294,
317, 318
Crayfish, 395
Creary retirement cases, 260
Creasey, Robert T., 491
Credence, letters of, 32, 46
Credit, 442, 486, 513, 514, 532,
538, 542, 577, 649, 703
Agricultural, 160
Institutions, 533
Public, 152
Retail, 650
To foreign nations, 532
See also Commodity Credit
Corporation; Farm Credit
Administration; and
Reconstruction Finance
Corporation
Credit Mobilier, 338
Credit Policy Adviser, Office
of, 649, 650
Credit unions, 160, 359, 533, 650
Creek Indians, 377, 380, 384, 567
Creek war, 232
Cret, P.P., 104
Creusot works, 304
Crew lists, 169, 346
Crime, Attorney General's
Advisory Committee on, 341
Crime and criminals, 63, 72, 116
177, 267, 268, 341, 348,
349, 354
See also War crimes and
criminals
Crimean War, 336
Criminal cases, 73-90, 343
Criminal Court, U.S., for the
District of Columbia, 75
Criminal dockets, 74, 77, 79, 80,
82, 85, 86, 88, 90
Criminal Identification, Bureau
of, 348
Criminal Identification, National
Bureau of, 348
"Crimping," 481
Critical materials, 544, 580, 584,
666, 687
Stockpiling, 201
Croatia, 736
Croix de Guerre, 288
Crop Estimates, Bureau of,
455, 456
Crop Production and Seed
Loan Office, 533
Crops, 124, 426, 431, 436,
437, 440, 442, 451, 453,
456, 457, 463, 535, 567
Experiments, 451
Foreign, 457

Loans, emergency, 442
Rotation, 437
Cross, Frank C., 675
Crow Indians, 380, 389
Croxton, Fred C., 121
Cuba, 138, 181, 220, 233, 265,
280, 281, 282, 312, 338,
413, 414, 537, 552, 743,
747
Census, 281
Insurrection, *1895*, 340
Postal services in, 360, 361
U.S. troops in, 276, 277, 744
Cuba, Department of, 276, 280
Cuba, Division of, 276, 280
Cuba, Late Military Government
of, 280, 281
Cuba, Military Government of, 413

CUBA, MILITARY GOVERNMENT
OF (RG 140), 280-281
Cuba, Provisional Government
of, 413

CUBA, PROVISIONAL
GOVERNMENT OF
(RG 199), 281-282
Cuban Export Committee,
607, 608
Cuban Pacification, Army of, 276,
277, 282
Culture, Ministry of, Italian, 736
Culture, U.S., 123, 663, 745
Cumberland Road, 238
Cunningham, Glen, 114
Currency, 159, 160, 164, 538
Confederate, 166, 722
Foreign, 126
Fractional, 159
Paper, 157, 175
Redemption of, 158, 161
See also Coins and coinage *and*
Money
Currency, Division of, 162
Currents, 315, 470
Curtiss, Glen H., 328
Custer, George A., 241, 744
Customhouses, 169, 170, 180, 282,
. 483, 568, 745
Customs, 58, 59, 82, 83, 86, 152
175, 339, 353, 413, 570,
606, 610
Collectors, 59, 83, 156, 169,
170, 281, 296, 351, 352,
354, 412, 483, 484, 523
Foreign, 282, 356, 566
Laws, 82, 170, 336, 353, 522, 524
Customs, Bureau of, 481, 483, 484,
522

CUSTOMS, BUREAU OF
(RG 36), 168-172
Customs, Commissioner of,
59, 153, 168, 172, 179
Customs, Division of, 168

Customs, Office of the Commissioner
of, 58, 59
Customs and Insular Affairs,
Division of, 413
Customs Service, 153, 168, 281
Veracruz, 283
Customs Statistics, Bureau of, 486
Cutsinger Elevator Firm, 442
Czar Paul I, 723
Czechoslovakia, 612, 735

D

Daily Newspaper Printing and
Publishing Commission, 633
Dairy Industry, Bureau of, 445
DAIRY INDUSTRY, BUREAU
OF (RG 152), 447
Dairy products, 447, 461, 668
Dairying, Bureau of, 447
Dakota, 134
Dalmatia, 612, 736
Dams, 53, 237, 368, 398, 406, 407,
567, 615, 714
Construction, 400, 428, 439,
541, 697
Dana, Francis W., 35
Daniels, Josephus, 304
Danish West India and Guinea Co., 724
Danish West Indies, 134, 723, 724
Dante Alighieri Society, 355
Danville and New River Railroad
Co., 237
Danzig, 596
D'Aquino, Iva Toguri, 623
Darien route, 562
Dartmouth College, 312
Das Archiv, 734
Data processing, 234
Daughters of the American
Revolution, National
Society of the, 163
Davidson, C. Girard, 367
Davis, Clarence A., 367
Davis, George B., 259
Davis, Jefferson, 172, 743
Davis, John, 80
Davis, John A., 617
Davis, William H., 665
Davis-Bacon Act of 1931, 491
Davis-Holt-Campbell Commission, 60
Dawes, Charles G., 287
Day care, 641
Deaf. *See* Columbia Institution for
the Deaf; Gallaudet College;
and Health, Education, and
Welfare, Department of
Deane, Silas, 33, 166
Dearborn Independent (newspaper), 746
Death records, 141, 574
Death Valley Biological Expedition, 396

Deaths
  Marine Corps, 300
  U.S. citizens abroad, 135
Death's Head Formations, SS, 730
Debtors, 75, 89
Debts
  Due the United States, 352, 353
  Foreign, 166
  National, 33, 164
  Public, 60, 61, 154, 157,
      162-167, 178
de Capriles, Miguel A. *See* Capriles,
    Miguel A. de
de Chaumont, Le Ray. *See* Chaumont,
    Le Ray de
Decimal file, Department of State, 134
Deck courts, 317
Declaration of Independence, 35,
      62, 551
  Signers, 138
Defense, 96, 105, 188, 196, 238, 274,
    403, 422, 425, 436, 440, 442,
    489, 554, 639, 642, 647, 675, 698
  Aerospace, 333
  Aid, 199, 218
  Bonds, 156
  Coastal and harbor, 58, 207, 217,
      226, 238, 240, 274, 275,
      276, 277, 279
  Contracts, 489
  Housing, 513, 514, 520, 539,
      548, 585
  Installations, 308
  Land, 275
  Loans, 270
  Military, 436
  Plants, 565, 688
  Programs, 220, 442, 584, 651
  Puerto Rican, 726
  State and local councils, 578
  Training, 635, 685
  See also Civil defense; Civilian
      Defense, Office of; *and*
      National Defense
Defense, Assistant Secretaries of,
    182, 183, 184, 185, 186, 187
Defense, Department of, 65, 119, 182,
    183, 185, 186, 187, 188, 189,
    201, 202, 207, 212, 216, 220,
    291, 305, 309, 329, 330, 421,
    519, 541, 552, 554, 702
Defense, Office of the Secretary of,
    182, 183, 189, 199, 201,
    202, 203, 212, 329, 331
DEFENSE, OFFICE OF THE
    SECRETARY OF (RG 330),
    182-188
Defense, Secretary of, 119, 182, 183,
    184, 185, 186, 187, 188, 203
Defense Aid Reports, Division of, 624
Defense and Synthetic Liquid Fuels
    Operation, 369
Defense Atomic Support Agency, 182

DEFENSE ATOMIC SUPPORT
    AGENCY (RG 374), 189-191
Defense Communications Board,
    536, 613
Defense Economy Staff East,
    German, 729
DEFENSE ELECTRIC POWER
    ADMINISTRATION (RG 327),
    422
Defense Health and Welfare
    Services, Office of, 640, 641,
    679, 685
Defense Homes Corporation, 520,
    580, 585
Defense Housing, Division of, 519
Defense Housing and Community
    Facilities and Services Act
    of 1951, 514, 520
Defense Housing Coordination,
    Division of, Office for
    Emergency Management, 513
Defense Management Committee, 183
Defense Management Council, 183
Defense Manpower, Management-
    Labor Policy Committee on,
    492
Defense Manpower Administration,
    492
Defense Materials, Division of, 135
Defense Materials Procurement
    Agency, 702
Defense Materials Service,
    551, 552
Defense Mobilization, Office of,
    114, 269, 270, 703, 706
Defense Plant Corporation,
    580, 584
Defense Plants, Office of, 584
Defense Power Administration, 422
Defense Production Act, 703,
    705, 706
Defense Production Administration,
    269, 270, 490
Defense Projects Unit, 96
Defense Research and Engineering,
    Office of the Director of, 186
Defense Supplies, Office of, 584
Defense Supplies Corporation, 580,
    584, 585, 589
Defense Supply Agency, 246
Defense Supply Service—Washington, 213
Defense Test Day, 204
Defense Transportation, Office of,
    612, 645, 692
DEFENSE TRANSPORTATION,
    OFFICE OF (RG 219),
    642-644
Deferment of Federal Employees,
    President's Committee on,
    680, 681
Deferment of Government
    Employees, Review Committee
    on, 679, 680, 681

de Gaulle, Charles. *See* Gaulle,
    Charles de
Degge, James, 34
De la Lande and Fynje, 35
Delaney, Edward, 623
Delano, Frederic A., 123, 713
Delaware Indians, 43, 388
de Lesseps, Ferdinand. *See*
    Lesseps, Ferdinand de
Dellinger, J. Howard, 475
Demobilization, 219
    Industrial, 210
    World War I, 610
Democratic National Committee, 699
Democratic National Conventions
    1952, 551
    1960, 748
    1968, 127
Demography, 493, 567
Demonstrations. *See* Civil Disorders,
    National Advisory Commission on
    (RG 282)
Dempsey, Jack, 89
Dendrology, 430
de Neufville, John. *See* Neufville,
    John de
Denmark, 35, 134, 164, 192, 596,
    612, 723-725
Dental Corps, 250
Dentistry, 302, 383, 685
Department Methods, Committee on,
    97, 452
Dependency Board, 212
Deposit Liquidation Board, 583
Depots
    Army, 241
    British, 164
    Navy, 292, 307, 321
Depression, the, 120, 370, 580
Deputy Chief of Staff, Supreme
    Commander for the Allied
    Powers, 194
Deputy Chief of Staff for Air, 325
Deputy Chief of Staff for
    Personnel, Office of the
    Adjutant General, 231
Deputy Supreme Allied
    Commander, 195
Dermott,_____, 717
Desert Land Act, 373
Desert warfare, 734
Deserters, 257, 273, 290, 347
    Army, 232
    Marine Corps, 300
    Navy, 312, 317
    Puerto Rican, 726
Des Moines River Land
    Claims, 366
Despatch Agency, 135
d'Estaing, Comte, *See* Estaing,
    Comte d'
Detached Squadron, 323
Detail, Committee of, 36, 37

Detail, Office of, 296, 310, 312
Detection devices, 659
Detectives, 257
Detonators, electric, 409
Detroit Tool and Die
    Commission, 633
Deutsche Akademie Muenchen,
    733
Deutsche Arbeiter Partei, 733
Deutsche Wirtschaftsbetriebe
    G.m.b.H., 730
Deutscher Klub of Dallas, 355
Deutsches Haus, 355
Diffraction, 476
Dillon, Douglas, 153
Dimock, Marshall E., 491
Diplomatic Bureau, Department
    of State, 131
Diplomatic service, 140, 143,
    144, 204
    Establishments, 149
    Missions, 132, 137, 176, 569
    Posts, 131, 135, 137, 140, 141
    Representatives, foreign,
        132, 138, 727
    Representatives, U.S., 131,
        132, 146
    See also Foreign Service
Direction finders, 659
Dirigibles, 293, 320, 334, 745
DiSalle, Michael V., 704, 706
Disarmament, conferences on, 146
Disaster Loan Corporation,
    580, 583, 584
Disasters
    Areas, 328, 515
    Dirigible, 55, 256, 334, 530, 748
    Mine, 409
    Natural, 213, 478, 583
    Relief from, 112, 256, 514
    Ship, 169, 315, 523, 524, 525, 726
    Texas City, *1947*, 747
    See also Earthquakes; Floods;
        Hurricanes; Tornados;
        and Typhoons
Disbursement, Division of,
    Treasury Department, 167
Disbursing Clerk, Office of the,
    Department of the
    Treasury, 167, 342
Discount rate, 542
Discrimination, 496, 630, 703
    In housing, 116, 117, 651
    In transportation, 553
    Racial, 616
    Religious, 616
Diseased Animal Transportation
    Act of 1903, 445
Diseases, 203, 233, 383, 502, 503,
    504, 505
    Animals, 445
    Contagious, 282
    Control of, 370, 428, 502, 503

Epidemic, 54, 137, 505, 659
Infant and child, 510
Occupational, 496
Plant, 423, 451, 453, 454, 455
Venereal, 503, 504, 641, 747
"Dispatch from Reuter's" (m.p.), 748
Displaced persons, 193, 194, 198,
    405, 691
Distilleries, 461, 656
Distribution, Office of,
    Agricultural Marketing
    Service, 460, 461
District Court, U.S., of the
    District of Potomac and the
    District of Columbia, 75
District Court for the District
    of Columbia, 75
District courts, U.S., 71, 92, 133,
    338, 339, 352, 480, 718

DISTRICT COURTS OF THE
    UNITED STATES
    (RG 21), 72-90
District of Columbia, 54, 55, 62, 63, 91
    97, 98, 99, 126, 134, 153, 156,
    157, 159, 160, 164, 275, 280,
    304, 316, 343, 352, 365, 398,
    400, 401, 402, 404, 426,
    456, 474, 501, 528, 532, 545,
    548, 567, 581, 588, 599, 669,
    711, 712, 715, 716, 718
Attorney for the, 718
Claims cases, 91
Closed banks, 160
Courts, 75, 76, 216, 415, 718
Monuments and memorials in,
    401, 402, 531, 714, 716, 717
Parked-car survey, 714
Public buildings and grounds,
    237, 238, 402, 531
Slaves in, 61
Soldiers' Home, U.S., 289, 290
See also Capitol, U.S., and
    National Capital Planning
    Commission (RG 328)
District of Columbia, Board of
    Commissioners, 711, 713, 714
District of Columbia, Engineer
    Commissioners of, 712

DISTRICT OF COLUMBIA,
    GOVERNMENT OF THE
    (RG 351), 711-712
District of Columbia Alley
    Dwelling Act of 1934, 712
District of Columbia Council, 711
District of Columbia Credit
    Unions Act of 1932, 160
District of Columbia Police
    Department, 712
District of Columbia Public
    Library, 741
District of Columbia Redevelopment
    Act of 1945, 713

District of Columbia Redevelopment
    Land Agency, 713
District of Columbia Work Projects
    Administration, 402
Disturnell, J., 46
Divorce records, 75, 410, 467
Dixon, Jeremiah, 136
Dockery Act of 1894, 165, 342
Docks, 310, 525, 603
"Document: Deep South," 570
Doenitz, Karl, 735
Dolomite investigations, 391
Domestic Gold and Silver Operations,
    Office of, Bureau of the
    Mint, 173
Domestic Operations Branch,
    Office of War Information, 661
Domestic Wool Section, 609
Dominican Customs Receivership, 413
DOMINICAN CUSTOMS
    RECEIVERSHIP (RG 139),
    282
Dominican Republic, 282, 297, 301,
    414, 743, 746
Dominican Republic, Geological
    Survey of, 393
Dongan, Thomas, 82
Donovan, William J., 341
Dorsey, Herbert G., 750
Douglas, Lewis W., 692
Douglas fir industry, 673
Draft, 119, 257
    Boards, World War I, 265
    Deferments, 212, 679, 680, 681
    See also Selective Service
Dragoons, 271, 272
Drainage, 438, 439, 440, 443, 446,
    447, 448, 449, 535, 581
    Basins, 124, 505
    Camps, 438
    Schedules, 468
    Stations, 671
Drama, 746, 748
Draper, William H., 114
Dredging, 474, 604
Dresdner Bank, 701
Drought, 407, 439
    Cattle program, 459
    Relief, 425, 434, 436, 445,
        534, 695
Drug Abuse Control,
    Bureau of, 350
Drug Abuse Control Amendments
    of 1965, 350
Drugs, 449, 502, 543
    Educational programs, 350
    Importation of, 168
    Traffic, 351
    See also Food and Drug
        Administration
Drugstores, 486
Drury, Newton B., 398, 403
Drydocks, 292, 308, 309, 310, 604, 606

Duffield, Eugene S., 293
Dulles, John Foster, 747
Dumas, Charles W.F., 33, 35
Dumbarton Oaks, 663
Dune control, 439
Dunning, Carroll W., 675
Du Pont Engineering Co., 245
Durkin, Martin P., 491, 492
Dust Bowl, 370, 438
Dust explosions, 409, 450
Duties
    Countervailing, 172
    Tonnage, 169
Dynamic North, The, 750
Dynamite, 409

E

"E" Awards program, 210
Eaker, Ira C., 326
Ear, studies of, 659
Earhart, Amelia, 748
Earth, studies of, 479
Earthquakes, 241, 249, 328, 472,
    527
East Africa, 747
East Base, Antarctica, 750
East Pascagoula, Miss., 289, 290
East River, N.Y., 53
Eastern Defense Command,
    Headquarters, 279
Eastern Department (Army), 273,
    276, 277
Eastern Europe, shipping
    programs in, 693
Eastern European Affairs,
    Division of, 136
Eastern Theater of Operations,
    279
Eastman, Joseph B., 619
Eastman Teaching Films, Inc., 747
Eclipses, 471, 473
Ecology, 376
Economic Adviser, Office of the, 136
Economic Adviser to the National
    Emergency Council, Office of, 98
Economic Affairs, Mission for, 625
Economic Cooperation Act of
    1948, 143
Economic Cooperation
    Administration, 143
Economic Defense Board, 624, 625
Economic Demobilization,
    Committee on, 649
Economic Division, Federal Trade
    Commission, 543
Economic Liaison Committee, 136
Economic Management Office,
    Office of Civil and Defense
    Mobilization, 270
Economic Operations, Board of, 150

Economic Policy and Programs,
    Committee on, 492

ECONOMIC RESEARCH SERVICE
    (RG 354), 444
Economic Security, Committee
    on, 511
Economic Security Controls,
    Division of, 150
Economic Security Policy, Office
    of, 150
Economic Stabilization, Board of, 666
Economic Stabilization, Office
    of, 645, 665
Economic Stabilization Agency,
    517, 705, 706, 707

ECONOMIC STABILIZATION
    AGENCY (RG 296),
    703-704
Economic Stabilization Board, 648
Economic Warfare, Board of, 532,
    586, 587, 623, 624, 625, 645,
    646
Economic Warfare, Office of, 532
Economics, 55, 62, 63, 65, 99, 104-105, 122,
    146, 147, 148, 153, 194, 333, 408,
    479, 486, 493, 559, 570, 586, 651,
    664, 680, 695, 698
    Business, 486
    Conditions, 121, 205, 299, 538,
        543
    Foreign, 65, 108, 126, 138, 184, 185,
        193, 202, 205, 236, 623, 624,
        625, 732, 734, 736
    Programs, 501, 563, 625, 646
    Research and development, 142,
        444, 486, 488, 623
    Trends, 673
    Warfare, 270
    See also Agricultural Economics,
        Bureau of , *and* Foreign
        Economic Administration
Economics, Reich and Prussian
    Ministry of, 728
Economics, Reich Ministry of,
    728, 733, 734
Economics Division, Federal
    Communications
    Commission, 536
Economy and Efficiency,
    Departmental Committee
    on, 367, 369
Economy and Efficiency,
    President's Commission
    on, 96, 97, 153
Ecuador, 138, 143, 145, 147, 433
Edgerton, Glen E., 109
Edgewood Arsenal Experimental
    Grounds, 245
Edison, Thomas A., 746, 748
Edison Company, 747

Education, 103, 108, 112, 122, 139,
184, 371, 441, 444, 506, 569,
570, 634, 636, 657, 662, 745,
746
Adult, 506, 695
Agricultural, 423
Alaskan, 412
Blacks, 506, 695
Citizenship, 346, 347
Civilian Conservation Corps
Camps, 506
Federal assistance to, 505
Foreign, 193, 198, 236, 414,
505, 506, 671
Military, 184, 204, 218, 221
National Park Service, 398
Programs, 189, 501, 646, 695
Refugee, 113
Scientific, 101, 506
Secondary, 506
Teachers, 506
Veterans, 671
Virgin Islands, 724
Vocational, 104, 425, 505, 506, 507,
571, 573, 575, 614, 615, 630,
634, 649, 671, 695
War relocation centers, 691
See also Colleges; Indian Affairs,
Bureau of; Indians, education;
Schools; and Training
Education, Advisory Committee
on, 104
Education, Commissioner of, 104
Education, Department of, 505
Education, Office of, 364, 365,
383, 567, 685
EDUCATION, OFFICE OF
(RG 12), 505-507
Education, Office of the
Commissioner of, 505
Education, White House
Conference on, 507
Education and Labor, Senate
Committee on, 558
Education and Special Training,
Committee on, 218
Education by Radio, Advisory
Committee on, 506
Edwards, John R., 307
Efficiency, Bureau of, 96
Efficiency, Division of, 97
Egg and poultry industry, 463
Egstrom-Holt Co., 605
Egypt, 205, 256, 351
8-hour-day controversy, 560
Eighth Air Force, 328
Einsatzstab Reichsleiter
Rosenberg Headquarters, 198
Eisenhower, Dwight D., 96, 113, 114,
137, 256, 299, 335, 507, 551,
569, 744, 745, 747, 748
Eisenhower, Dwight D., Library, 101
Eisenhower, Milton, 127

Ekern and Meyers Insurance Co., 442
Eklund, Carl R., 749
Elections
Fraud, 344
Laws, 117, 338
Puerto Rican, 726
Supervision of, 83, 89
Surveys, 467
Wartime, 678
See also Inaugural Committees,
National Archives Collection of
(RG 274)
Electoral Missions to Nicaragua,
U.S., 147
Electoral records, 41, 45
Electoral votes, 50, 52, 54
Electors, 45
Electric Home and Farm
Authority, 581, 588
Electric power, 238, 367, 368,
406, 409, 411, 440, 441,
540, 541, 542
Electricity, 393, 422, 424, 440,
441, 475
Generation and distribution
of, 392, 440, 441
Northwest conservation program,
422
Utility companies, 422, 588
Electrification
Puerto Rican, 417
Rural, 695
Electrification Administration,
Rural, 424, 426
ELECTRIFICATION
ADMINISTRATION,
RURAL (RG 221), 440-441
Electromagnetic waves, 659
Electronics, 254, 308, 659
Japanese, 736
Electronics Systems Command, 319
Elihu Thomson, 396
Ellicott, _____, 717
Elliot, G.H., 473
Elliott, Henry W., 394, 397, 548
Ellsworth, Lincoln, 747
El Salvador, 138
Emancipation of Slaves in the District
of Columbia, Board of
Commissioners for the, 61
Embargoes, 82, 169, 170
Embarkation Service, 246, 248
Embassies
Foreign, 132, 138, 733
U.S., 106, 137, 138, 141
Emergency Advisory Committee
for Political Defense, 339
Emergency Appropriation Act, 427
Emergency Conservation Work,
385, 396, 399, 400, 437,
439, 614
Emergency Court of Appeals, 651
Emergency Facilities Committee, 687

Emergency Fleet Corporation, U.S.
    Shipping Board, 601, 604,
    605, 609
Emergency Management, Office for,
    99, 105, 122-123, 354, 513,
    616, 623, 624, 631, 639,
    640, 642, 646, 657, 660, 661,
    665, 678, 679, 687, 689, 692
EMERGENCY MANAGEMENT,
    OFFICE FOR (RG 214),
    644-645
Emergency (Merchant) Fleet
    Corporation, U.S. Shipping
    Board, 603, 605, 606
Emergency Price Control Act
    of 1942, 647
Emergency Procurement Service, 549
Emergency Railroad Transportation
    Act of 1933, 618
Emergency Relief and Construction
    Act of 1932, 155
Emergency Relief Appropriation
    Act of 1935, 416
Emigration, 146, 410, 606
Employees, 292, 496, 497, 561, 620
    Federal, 64, 65, 97, 110, 135,
        184, 568, 680, 681
    Industrial, 684, 689
Employers, 493, 496, 497, 616
Employment, 105, 112, 121, 234,
        235, 407, 457, 458, 491,
        493, 495, 555, 614, 620, 626,
        627, 629, 634, 660, 665,
        684, 694, 696, 697, 698
    Agencies, 120, 499
    Blacks, 617, 618, 651, 694
    Discrimination in, 117, 496, 616,
        651
    Mining, 408
    Part-time, 634
    Prisons, 349
    Puerto Rico, 416
    Refugee, 113
    Stabilization, 122, 123, 672, 680,
        684, 687
    Surveys, 467
    Trends, 122, 683
    See also Children; Civil Service
        Commission; Labor;
        Wage and Hour and
        Public Contracts Divisions
        (RG 155); and Women's
        Bureau (RG 86)
Employment, President's Emergency
    Committee for, 120, 121
Employment of the Handicapped,
    President's Committee on,
    114
Employment of the Physically
    Handicapped, President's
    Committee on, 114
Employment Plans and
    Suggestions, Committee on, 121

Employment Security, Bureau of, 511
EMPLOYMENT SECURITY, BUREAU
    OF (RG 183), 498-500
Employment Service, U.S., 498, 499,
    511, 679, 682, 684, 685, 687
Employment Stabilization Act, 122
Endicott Board, 239
Enemies
    Aliens, 136, 137, 235, 280, 347
    Assets of, 180, 262, 354, 610
    Organizations, 355
    Spies, 328, 525
    Trading with the, 155, 180,
        340, 354
Enemy Prisoner of War Information
    Bureau, 268
Energy conversion, 421
Energy resources, 111, 123
    See also Atomic energy; Coal; Gas;
        and Oil
Enforcement Act of 1870, 338
Engineer Claims Board, 239
Engineer Corps of the Navy, 307
Engineer Department, Confederate,
    720
Engineer Equipment, Board on, 239
Engineer Reproduction Plant, 240
Engineering, 104, 105, 182, 183, 186,
        228, 244, 245, 255, 366, 390,
        406, 417, 428, 430, 452, 554,
        670, 697, 699, 736
    Chemical, 659
    Civil, 447
    Equipment and materials, 238, 307
    Mechanical, 447
    Projects, 695
    Research, 449, 450, 451
    Rural, 448
    Training, 241, 506
    See also Agricultural Chemistry
        and Engineering, Bureau
        of, and Agricultural
        Engineering, Bureau of
Engineering, Bureau of, 305, 306
Engineering, Chief of the Bureau
    of, 307
Engineering Standards, Conference
    on the Unification of, 689
Engineers, 272, 273, 281, 546, 685
    Army, 745
    Forest, 427
    Naval, 307
Engineers, Board of, 239
Engineers, Chief of, 229, 239, 290,
    390, 714
Engineers, Corps of, 179, 207, 213,
        236, 237, 240, 288, 390, 392, 711
    Civil works program, 213, 237, 240
Engineers, Office of the Chief of,
    389, 398
ENGINEERS, OFFICE OF THE
    CHIEF OF (RG 77),
    236-241

Engineers for Rivers and Harbors, Board of, 239, 240
Engines, internal combustion, 409
England, 137, 205, 285, 307, 596, 602, 607, 625, 639, 640, 660, 745, 746
King and Queen of, 636
See also Great Britain
English, teaching of, 569
Engraving and Printing, Bureau of, 160, 164, 166
ENGRAVING AND PRINTING, BUREAU OF (RG 318), 175
Engraving and Printing, Division of, 391
Eniwetok, invasion of, 293
Enrollment, boards of, Provost Marshal General's Bureau, 257
Entente, World War I, 148
Entomologist, Office of the, 453
Entomology, 426, 430, 431, 455
Entomology and Plant Quarantine, Bureau of. 443. 614
ENTOMOLOGY AND PLANT QUARANTINE, BUREAU OF (RG 7), 453-455
Entomology Research Branch, Agricultural Research Service, 453
Environmental Data Service, 479
Environmental Science Services Administration, 476
ENVIRONMENTAL SCIENCE SERVICES ADMINISTRATION (RG 370), 479-480
Environmental Sciences Administration, 470
Epidemics, 54, 137, 286, 503, 505
Equal Opportunity in Housing, President's Committee on, 116, 117
Equal Opportunity in the Armed Forces, President's Committee on, 116
Equality of Treatment and Opportunity in the Armed Services, President's Committee on, 108
Equatorial islands, 404
Equipment
Electrical, 440, 588, 659
Industrial, 270, 629
Maritime, 479
Military, 217, 219, 220, 229, 230, 240, 242, 243, 245, 247, 249, 264, 307, 555
Photographic, 659
Standardization of, 210, 620, 621
Equipment, Bureau of, 295, 305, 307
Equipment and Recruiting, Bureau of, 305, 311, 315, 316
Equipment Board, 212

Equipment Division, Army Air Forces, 324
Equipment Division, Signal Corps, 325
Equity cases, 72-90
Adoptions, 75
Erdman Act, 559, 560
Erie, Pa., 598
Erlanger loan, 722
Ermine, 397
Erosion, 239, 240, 370, 437
Control, 438, 439, 448, 450, 615
Nurseries, 439
Eskimos, 377, 383, 389, 750
Espionage, 659, 732
See also Spies
Espionage Acts, 359
Essential Activities, Interdepartmental Committee on, 682
Essential Activities, List of, 682
Essex Institute, 170
Estaing, Comte d', 34
Estates, 76, 140, 141, 355
Estimates, Division of, 96
Estonia, 729, 735
Ethiopia, 143, 256
Ethnic groups, 747
Ethnology, 148, 523, 552, 566, 567
Eulachon, 395
Europa (U.S.S.), 734
Europe, 104, 137, 139, 195, 205, 236, 276, 328, 737
Historic places in, 566
Occupation of, 220, 729
European Command, 184, 278
European Command Headquarters, 199
European Defense Community, 199
European Migration, Intergovernmental Committee for, 114
European recovery program, 198
See also Marshall Plan
European Squadron, 323
European Theater, U.S. Forces, 278
European Theater of Operations, 197, 205, 262, 326, 611
European Theater of Operations, Headquarters U.S. Army, 278
Evacuation, Joint Committee on, 648
Evans, Waldo, 410
Examiners, Department of Justice, 342
Exchange programs, scientific and cultural, 150
Exclusion
Acts, 346
Alien, 279
Case files, 690
Laws, 345
West coast program, 211, 280, 689-691
Executive agreements, 42

Executive Branch of the Government,
    Commission on Organization
    of the, 109
EXECUTIVE BRANCH OF THE
    GOVERNMENT,
    COMMISSIONS ON
    ORGANIZATION OF THE
    (RG 264), 64-65
Executive clemency, 345
Executive Council, 124
Executive Mansion, 108, 208, 365, 717
    See also White House
Executive Office Building, 401, 402
Executive Office of the President,
    95, 96, 100, 111, 113, 124,
    143, 644
Executive orders, 41, 44, 95, 96,
    155, 549, 600
    No. 10477, 569
    No. 11412, 127
Executive papers, disposition
    of, 55
Executive proclamations, 95
Executive Protective Service, 176
Exequators, 46
Exercise Jigsaw, 200
Exhibitions, international, 146, 147, 241
    See also Expositions
Expeditions, 172, 273, 276, 277, 278,
    295, 302, 314, 317, 366, 370,
    396, 451, 478
    Army, 276
    Mexican Punitive, 233, 255, 256,
        260, 743
    Navy, 241, 316
    Polar, 293, 334, 405, 743, 744,
        745, 747, 749-750
    Rainbow Bridge discovery, 745
Expenditures
    Family, 650
    Federal, 125, 166
Experiment Station Organization,
    Committee on, 446
Experiment Stations, Office of,
    433, 448, 458
EXPERIMENT STATIONS,
    OFFICE OF (RG 164), 446-447
Explorations, 53, 237, 240, 241, 390,
    551, 565, 723
    Archaeological, 567
    See also Expeditions, polar
Explorations and Surveys, Office of,
    233, 238, 366
Explosions, 243, 409, 450
Explosives, 58, 243, 244, 303, 407,
    408, 448, 659, 660
    Mines, 272, 275, 298, 299, 304,
        313, 594
Export Certification Act, 453
Export Control, Administrator
    of, 624, 625
Export-Import Bank Act of
    1945, 532

EXPORT-IMPORT BANK OF THE
    UNITED STATES
    (RG 275), 532-533
Export-Import Bank of
    Washington, 126, 532, 581
Export Licenses, Division of, 610
Exports, 108, 168, 169, 184, 185,
    532, 534, 543, 601, 608,
    610, 611, 623-625, 664,
    733, 735
    Licensing, 624, 625
Exports Administrative Board, 610
Exports Council, 610
Expositions, 61, 147, 153, 154, 209,
    338, 365, 367, 369, 370, 389,
    403, 433, 493, 545
    International, 53, 154, 209, 249,
        291, 365, 395, 426, 433,
        449, 453, 532, 548, 569
    National, 291, 395, 427, 548
    See also International
        Conferences, Commissions,
        and Expositions (RG 43)
Extension Service, 426, 455
    See also Federal Extension
        Service (RG 33)
Extortion, 443
Extradition, 46, 134, 135, 340
    Treaties, 73
"Eyewitness to History" (m.p.), 747

F

Facilities, Bureau of, Post
    Office Department, 361
Facilities and Services,
    Committee on, 202
Factories, powder, 303
Facts and Figures, Office
    of, 660, 661
Factual History, 663
Fahy Committee, 108
Fair competition codes, 555,
    626, 627, 628, 629, 630, 631
Fair Employment Practice,
    Committee on, 645, 679
FAIR EMPLOYMENT PRACTICE,
    COMMITTEE ON (RG 228),
    616-618
Fair Labor Standards Act,
    496, 497
Fairfield, A.P., 692
Fairs
    Agricultural, 370, 433
    World's, 61, 125, 139, 147, 154,
        449, 547, 636
    See also Expositions
Family Security Committee, 641
Family Services, Bureau of, 511
Famine Emergency Committee, 426
Far East, 138, 200, 205, 236, 733
    U.S. Forces in, 197

Far East Command, 194, 195,
    213, 262
  Headquarters, 199
Far Eastern Commission, 147
Farben, I.G., Industries, 198
Farm Cooperative Service, 533
Farm Credit Act of 1933, 533
Farm Credit Administration,
    339, 426, 444, 580, 583
FARM CREDIT ADMINISTRATION
    (RG 103), 533-535
Farm Development Investigations,
    448
Farm Equipment Control, Office
    of, 448
Farm Housing Survey, 458
Farm Management, Office of,
    447, 455
Farm Management and Costs,
    Division of, 456
Farm Management and Farm
    Economics, Office of,
    455, 456
Farm Placement Service,
    499, 684
Farm Population and Rural
    Life, Division of, 456
Farm Security Administration,
    386, 442, 514, 519, 520
Farm Tenancy, President's
    Special Committee on, 456
FARMER COOPERATIVE
    SERVICE (RG 314), 444
Farmers, 416, 423, 434, 435, 436,
    437, 440, 442, 443, 534
FARMERS HOME
    ADMINISTRATION (RG 96),
    442-443
Farmers National Grain
    Corporation, 534
Farms and farming, 99, 156, 356, 396,
    407, 433, 436, 443, 444, 448,
    456, 457, 458, 467, 468, 533,
    534, 535, 570, 593, 608, 662,
    723
  Laborers, migratory, 459
  Machinery, 448, 452, 453, 544
  Management, 442, 456, 457
  Organizations, 111, 434, 440, 649
  Prices, 434
  Products, 430, 431, 434, 435,
    450, 459, 460, 544
  Taxation, 426
  Work by prisoners, 669
  See also Agriculture; Animal
      Industry, Bureau of; and
      Electric Home and Farm
      Authority
Farrand, Max, 37
Fascist Ministry of Popular
    Culture, 137
Fascists, Italian, 737

Fashions, 569, 663
  See also Clothing
Fechet, James R., 326
Fechner, Robert, 614
Federal Advisory Council, 542
Federal agencies. See names of specific
    agencies
Federal aid, 112, 411, 412, 505, 510, 520
Federal-Aid Road Act of 1916, 526
Federal Airways System, 527
Federal Archives, Survey of,
    696, 699
Federal Aviation Act of 1958,
    527, 530
FEDERAL AVIATION
    ADMINISTRATION (RG 237),
    527-528
Federal Aviation Agency, 330,
    527, 530
Federal Aviation Commission, 530
Federal Barge Lines, Inc., 488
Federal Board of Hospitalization,
    96, 98
Federal Bureau of Investigation,
    128, 525, 698, 745
FEDERAL BUREAU OF
    INVESTIGATION (RG 65),
    348-349
Federal Civil Defense
    Administration, 269
Federal Communications
    Commission, 222, 371, 613
FEDERAL COMMUNICATIONS
    COMMISSION (RG 173),
    535-537
Federal Convention, 31
Federal Coordinating Service,
    548, 549
Federal Council of Citizenship
    Training, 346
Federal Credit Unions, Bureau
    of, 511
Federal Crop Insurance
    Corporation, 426
FEDERAL CROP INSURANCE
    CORPORATION (RG 258),
    441-442
Federal Deposit Insurance
    Corporation, 511
FEDERAL DEPOSIT INSURANCE
    CORPORATION (RG 34),
    537-538
Federal Drought Relief
    Committee, 434
Federal Emergency Administration
    of Public Works, 122, 125
    519, 520, 582, 669
Federal Emergency Administrator
    of Public Works, 670
Federal Emergency Relief Act
    of 1933, 695

Federal Emergency Relief
    Administration, 434, 438
    442, 693, 694, 695, 696,
    697, 698, 725
Federal employees, 64, 65, 97,
    110, 135, 184, 568, 680, 681
    Political activities of, 568
Federal Employment Stabilization
    Act of 1931, 123
Federal Employment Stabilization
    Board, 122
Federal Employment Stabilization
    Office, 122, 123
FEDERAL EXTENSION
    SERVICE (RG 33),
    432-434
Federal Facilities Corporation,
    581, 586, 587, 588
Federal Farm Board, 533, 534
Federal Farm Loan Board,
    533, 534
Federal Farm Mortgage
    Corporation, 533, 534
Federal Fire Council, 704, 705
Federal Food and Drugs Act, 508
Federal Food, Drug, and
    Cosmetic Act, 507
Federal Forum Project, 506
FEDERAL FUEL
    DISTRIBUTOR (RG 89),
    579
Federal Government,
    establishment of, 29, 30, 32, 36
Federal Home Loan Bank
    Administration, 596, 598
Federal Home Loan Bank Board,
    513, 538, 597
FEDERAL HOME LOAN
    BANK SYSTEM (RG 195),
    538-539
Federal Horticultural Board,
    453, 454
Federal Housing Administration,
    513, 517, 583, 699
FEDERAL HOUSING
    ADMINISTRATION (RG 31),
    515-516
Federal Inter-Agency Alaskan
    Development Committee, 404
Federal Interagency River Basin
    Committee, 391
FEDERAL INTERAGENCY
    RIVER BASIN
    COMMITTEE (RG 315),
    420-421
Federal Loan Agency, 515, 516,
    532, 538, 581, 583
Federal Maritime Board, 479,
    539, 676
FEDERAL MARITIME
    COMMISSION (RG 358),
    539-540

FEDERAL MEDIATION AND
    CONCILIATION
    SERVICE (RG 280),
    540-541
Federal Narcotics Control
    Board, 350, 351
Federal National Mortgage
    Association, 513, 580,
    581, 583
FEDERAL NATIONAL
    MORTGAGE
    ASSOCIATION (RG 294),
    516-517
Federal National Mortgage
    Association Charter
    Act of 1954, 516
Federal Oil Conservation
    Board, 415, 416
Federal Old-Age Benefits,
    Bureau of, 511
Federal Open Market
    Committee, 542
Federal Pavilion, 1968
    Hemisfair, 147
Federal Power Commission,
    210, 389, 393, 420,
    425, 557
FEDERAL POWER
    COMMISSION
    (RG 138), 541-542
Federal Prison Industries,
    Inc., 349, 350, 669
Federal Project No. 1, 696
Federal Property and
    Administrative Services
    Act of 1949, 544, 548,
    641, 743, 749
Federal Public Housing
    Authority, 520, 585, 704
Federal Radio Commission,
    535, 536
Federal Real Estate Board, 425
Federal Register, 549
Federal Register, Office of
    the, 42, 44, 45
Federal Register Act, 45
Federal Reserve Act of
    1933, 537
Federal Reserve banks, 157,
    158, 162, 542, 580, 608
Federal Reserve Board,
    120, 577
Federal Reserve Building, 542
Federal Reserve notes, 159, 160,
    161, 175, 542
Federal Reserve System, 650
FEDERAL RESERVE
    SYSTEM (RG 82), 542
Federal Savings and Loan
    Associations, 167
Federal Savings and Loan
    Insurance Corporation, 538

Federal Savings and Loan
    System, 538
Federal Security Administration,
    679
Federal Security Administrator,
    501, 511, 640, 658, 679
Federal Security Agency, 465,
    499, 500, 501, 502, 505,
    507, 510, 511, 614, 634,
    640, 679, 685, 686, 694
Federal Seed Act, 462
Federal Shipbuilding and
    Drydock Co., 292
Federal Statistics Board, 98
Federal Supply, Bureau of,
    548, 549

FEDERAL SUPPLY SERVICE
    (GSA) (RG 137),
    548-549
Federal Surplus Commodities
    Corporation, 458, 459
Federal Surplus Relief
    Corporation, 459
Federal Tender Board, 416
Federal Trade Commission,
    578, 593, 647

FEDERAL TRADE
    COMMISSION (RG 122),
    542-544
Federal Traffic Board, 136,
    425, 549
Federal War Agencies
    Committee, 487
Federal Water Power Act
    of 1920, 541
Federal Waterways
    Corporation, 488
Federal Works Administrator,
    Office of the, 669
Federal Works Agency, 123,
    519, 526, 545, 548, 596,
    616, 669, 671, 693, 694,
    698

FEDERAL WORKS AGENCY
    (RG 162), 704-705
Feed, 442, 462, 668
Feed and Food Conservation,
    Office of, 425
Fenian disturbances, 336
Fennemore, J., 394
Ferguson Committee To Review
    Decartelization in
    Germany, 214
Ferry Lake, La., 376
Fertilizer, Committee on, 688
Fertilizers, 451, 452, 567
Fessenden, R.A., 477
Fiala-Ziegler expedition, 750
Fiber, 458
Field army, 227, 274
Field artillery, 225, 228,
    272, 275

Field Artillery, Chief of,
    225, 226
Field Artillery Board, 226
Field Artillery Corps, 272
Field Operations Division, 653
15th Army Group, 193
5th Army, 193
Fifth Auditor, 60
Fifth Pan American
    Commercial Conference, 146
Filibustering, 338, 481
Filled Milk Act, 507
Film Service, 125
Filters, 660
Finance, Bureau of, 361, 362, 553
Finance, Chief of, 229, 290

FINANCE, OFFICE OF THE
    CHIEF OF (ARMY)
    (RG 203), 252-253
Finance, Reich Ministry of, 729
Finance, Superintendent of, 30,
    31, 33, 166
Finance and Accounting, Office
    of the Chief of, 253
Finance Service, War Department,
    252
Financial institutions, 538, 581, 650

FINE ARTS, COMMISSION OF
    (RG 66), 531-532
Finland, 735
    American Relief Administration
        mission to, 596
Finlay, Hugh, 358
Finletter, Thomas K., 107
Finnish Relief Fund, 746
Fir Production Board, 605
Fire and Explosion Risks,
    Committee on, 425
Fire prevention and firefighting,
    269, 370, 388, 399, 409,
    426, 428, 429, 430, 450,
    480, 525, 639, 659, 671,
    704, 705
Firearms, 177, 523
First aid, 302, 409
1st Allied Airborne Army, 192
1st Army, 285
First Assistant Postmaster
    General, Bureau of, 359
First Auditor, Department of the
    Treasury, 59, 61
First Auditor, Office of the,
    Department of the Treasury, 59
First Comptroller, Department of
    the Treasury, 58, 59, 352
First Comptroller, Office of the,
    Department of the Treasury,
    58, 59
First National Bank of Detroit,
    161
First War Powers Act, 354, 664
Fiscal Analysis, Division of, Bureau
    of the Budget, 96

Fiscal and Monetary Advisory
    Board, 99
Fiscal Service of the Treasury
    Department, 157
Fish and fisheries, 65, 145, 168,
    170, 394, 395, 396, 466,
    481, 509, 523, 525, 567,
    604, 723
Fish and Fisheries, Office of
    U.S. Commissioner of, 394
Fish and Wildlife Service, 370,
    399, 525, 566
FISH AND WILDLIFE
    SERVICE (RG 22),
    394-397
Fish Commission, 394, 397, 566
Fish Hawk (SS), 395
Fisheries, Bureau of, 394, 395, 399
Fisheries Commission, 145
Five Civilized Tribes, 367, 370,
    379, 380
Fixed Nitrogen Research
    Laboratory, 452
Flag Office Command, Navy,
    Northwest African
    Waters, 193
Flagg, James Montgomery, 165
Flags, 249, 532
Flaherty, Robert, 436
Flanagan, William E., 674
Flathead Indians, 380, 381
Flax, 441
Fleet
    Allied, 304
    Asiatic, 323
    Atlantic, 308, 323
    Pacific, 323
    United States, 304, 308, 323
    Victory, 677
Fleet Training, Division of, 298
Fleming, Philip B., 705
Fleming, Robert V. 113, 742
Flick, Friedrich, 700
Flood Control, Board of, 239
Flood Control Act of 1944, 411
Flood Rock, N.Y.C., 53
Floods, 247, 249, 271, 328, 392,
    525, 583, 714
    Control of, 237, 241, 407,
        440, 447, 456, 542,
        567, 671
    Victims of, 565, 581
Florida, 134, 156, 233, 247,
    336, 374, 671, 744
    Hurricane disaster of
        1935, 694
Florida-Indian War, 295
Florida Keys, 473
Flour, 508
Flumes, 407
Foch, Ferdinand, 389
Fog, 477, 524
Foley, Edward H., 153, 742

Folsom, Marion B., 153
Fono (American Samoan
    Legislature), 410
Food, 98, 270, 309, 404, 424,
    426, 436, 458, 543, 570,
    592, 593, 647, 654, 661, 665,
    668
    Alaska, 723
    Conservation, 425, 462, 591, 593,
        639
    Germany, 198
    Importation of, 168, 449, 508
    Industries, 460, 629
    Prices, 655
    Supply, 283, 649, 665
Food Administration, 176, 595,
    596, 607, 609, 610
    See also War Food Administration
FOOD ADMINISTRATION,
    U.S. (RG 4), 591-593
Food Administration Grain
    Corporation, 591, 592, 595
Food Administrator, 591, 592,
    593, 595, 596, 607
Food and Agriculture, Interim
    Commission on, 456
Food and Agriculture,
    Reich Ministry for, 730
Food and Agriculture, United
    Nations Conference on, 456
Food and Agriculture
    Organization, 456
Food and Drug Administration,
    350, 454, 502
FOOD AND DRUG
    ADMINISTRATION (RG 88),
    507-510
Food and Drug Inspection,
    Board of, 507, 508, 509
Food and Drugs acts, 353, 434, 449,
    507, 508, 509
Food Commission, 725
Food Control Act, 593
Food Distribution Administration,
    426, 460, 461, 462, 640
Food Distribution Office, 461
Food, Drug, and Insecticide
    Administration, 449, 507,
    508, 509
Food for Peace programs, 143
Food Production Administration, 426
Food Production and Distribution,
    Administration of, 426
Food Purchase Board, 591, 593
Food stamp program, 459
Food Standards Committee, 507
Food Supply and Prices,
    Committee on, 425
Forbes, W. Cameron, 103
Ford, Henry, 746
"Ford Animated Weekly" (m.p.),
    746
"Ford Educational Library" (m.p.), 746

"Ford Educational Weekly" (m.p.), 746
Ford Film Collection, 746
Ford Motion Picture Laboratories, 746
Ford Motor Co., 746
"Ford News" (m.p.), 746
Ford Theater, 54
Forecast Division, Weather Bureau, 478
Foreign Affairs, Committee for, 30, 32
Foreign Affairs, Department of, 30, 32, 35, 131
Foreign Affairs, Secretary for, 30, 32, 35, 131
Foreign Agricultural Relations, Office of, 431
Foreign Agricultural Service, 444
FOREIGN AGRICULTURAL SERVICE (RG 166), 430-431
Foreign aid, 108, 143, 218, 230, 465
Foreign Aid, President's Committee on, 108, 465
Foreign and Domestic Commerce, Bureau of, 126, 407, 408, 465, 570, 610
FOREIGN AND DOMESTIC COMMERCE, BUREAU OF (RG 151), 486-488
Foreign and Domestic Commerce, Office of, 673
FOREIGN ASSETS CONTROL, OFFICE OF (RG 265), 180-181
Foreign Assets Control, Office of, Treasury Department, 355
Foreign Assistance Act of 1961, 142
Foreign Assistance Correlation Committee, 184
Foreign Broadcast Information Branch, 101, 622
Foreign Broadcast Information Service, 622
FOREIGN BROADCAST INTELLIGENCE SERVICE (RG 262), 622-623
Foreign Broadcast Monitoring Service, 622
Foreign Claims, Commission for Adjustment of, 262
FOREIGN CLAIMS SECTION (WAR) (RG 213), 224-225
Foreign Commerce Service, 486
"Foreign Correspondent" (m.p.), 748
Foreign Economic Administration, 106, 532, 585, 586, 587, 645, 646
FOREIGN ECONOMIC ADMINISTRATION (RG 169), 623-626

Foreign Economic Coordination, Office of, 623-624
Foreign Economic Defense Affairs, Office of, 185
Foreign funds, control of, 180, 355
Foreign Information Service, Office of the Coordinator of Information, 662
Foreign Intelligence Branch, 298
Foreign Liquidation Commissioner, Office of, 135
Foreign nationals, 220, 222
Foreign Observer, Office of the, 96
Foreign Operations Administration, 143
Foreign Operations Committee, 666
Foreign Permits Office, 136
Foreign Petroleum Committee, 666
Foreign policy, U.S., 133, 403, 569
Foreign Publications, Interdepartmental Committee for the Acquisition of, 205
FOREIGN RECORDS SEIZED, 1941- , NATIONAL ARCHIVES COLLECTION OF (RG 242), 727-737
Foreign Relief and Rehabilitation Operations, Office of, 623, 625
Foreign Service, 46, 133, 134, 135, 136, 140, 141, 144, 146, 148, 149
Officers, 138
School, 136
See also Diplomatic service
Foreign Service Buildings Commission, 149
Foreign Service Buildings Office, 135
FOREIGN SERVICE POSTS OF THE DEPARTMENT OF STATE (RG 84), 140-142
Forest Homestead Act of 1906, 429
Forest Insect Research Division, Forest Service, 453
Forest Products Laboratory, 429, 430
FOREST SERVICE (RG 95), 426-430
Forest Taxation Inquiry, 430
Forestry, 381, 417, 424, 431, 437, 508, 526, 567, 625, 626, 669
German, 198
Forestry, Bureau of, 426, 427, 429
Forestry, Division of, 374, 426, 427
Forestry Service, 55, 97, 103, 391, 397, 425, 434, 439, 453, 614
Forests, 111, 373, 430, 451, 567
Civilian Conservation Corps camps in, 430

Conservation, 440, 487
Fires, 370, 399, 429
Industries, 486, 625
Lands, 426, 427, 428, 429, 453
Management, 428, 429
National, 65, 119, 370, 373, 393,
    426, 427, 428, 429, 430,
    615, 671
Private, 427
Products, 270, 431, 490, 601
Protection, 235, 399, 429, 439
Rangers, 427
Reserves, 365, 372, 391, 426,
    427, 430
Resources, 427, 428, 429, 487
State, 103, 427, 430
Forfeitures, suits for, 72, 75, 83,
    85, 86
Forge and foundry industry, 684
Forgery, 176
Form standardization, 221
Formal Cases, Bureau of, 553
**FORMER RUSSIAN
    AGENCIES (RG 261),**
    722-723
Formosa, 205
Forrestal, James V., 185, 291,
    292, 293
Fort Defiance Machinery Co., 304
Fort Douglas, 235
Fort Leavenworth, Kans., 259
Fort McPherson, 235
Fort Oglethorpe, 235
Fort Ontario, N.Y., 690, 691
Fort Phil Kearney (or Fetterman)
    massacre, 382
Fort Schuyler, 312
Fort Severn, 321
Fort Shaw Indian School, 387
Fort Story, Va., 409
Fort Totten Agency, 383
Fortas, Abe, 367
Fortifications, 237, 238, 240
    British, 677
    Civil War, 233, 240, 255, 501, 744
    See also Army, posts
Fortifications, Board of Engineers
    for, 239
Forts
    Coastal, 240
    Frontier, 255
    Harbor, 275
    See also names of specific forts
Fountains, 531
4-H Clubs, 434
"Four minute men," 119, 120
Fourney, Stehman, 473
14th Street Bridge, 717
4th Army, 280
Fourth Assistant Postmaster
    General, 361
Fourth Assistant Postmaster
    General, Bureau of, 361

Fourth Auditor, Treasury
    Department, 60, 311
Fourth Auditor, Office of
    the, Treasury
    Department, 60
Fowler, Coronado Walter, 674
Fowler, Henry, 153
Fox farming, 396
Fox Indians, 380
"Fox Movietone News" (m.p.), 663
Foxe Peninsula, 750
France, 43, 143, 163, 166, 178,
    188, 192, 205, 225, 285, 286,
    301, 338, 529, 586, 599,
    600, 602, 612, 663, 735,
    736, 745
    American Forces in, 283,
        284, 285
    Conquest of, 362
    Ministers of, 33, 35
    Treaties with, 164
    World War I, 313, 593, 744
    World War II damage in, 206
France and Great Britain, Joint
        Commissioners for Negotiating
        Treaties With, 33
France (Vichy), 737
Franco-American alliance, 138
Frank, Hans, 700, 734
Frank Lamson-Scribner, 426
Franklin, Benjamin, 31, 33, 35,
    145, 163, 358
Franklin (ship), 677
Franz Joseph Land, 478, 750
Fraud, 338, 340, 342, 359, 698
    Mail, 362
Fredericksburg and Spotsylvania
        County Battlefields
        Memorial Park Commission, 400
Free China, 106
    See also China
Free Delivery System,
        Superintendent of the, 359
Freedman's Savings and Trust
        Company, 160, 161
Freedmen
    Cherokee, 384
    Choctaw, 380
    Government farms for, 156
    Welfare of, 179, 180
    See also Refugees, Freedmen, and
        Abandoned Lands, Bureau of
Freedmen's Branch, 263
Freedmen's Hospital, 364, 502
Freedom Train, 551
Freer Gallery of Art, 566
Freight, 620, 621, 675
    Rates, 601, 603, 606, 612, 676
French, Benjamin B., 715
French, Jesse, 674
French and Indian War, 255
"French Libre Actualities" (m.p.), 663
French West Indies, 33

Frick, H.E., 604
Friedenwald, Herbert, 36
Friedrich Wilhelm III, of
    Prussia, 732
Frigates, 296
Friis, Herman R., 750
Frontiers, sea, 196
Fruit fly, 454, 455
Fruits, 442, 451, 453, 461,
    468
Fuel, 98, 305, 309, 391, 407,
    579, 593, 606, 654
    Oil installations, 607
    Prices, 655
    See also Bituminous coal;
        Coal; Mines, Bureau of;
        Petroleum; *and* Solid
        Fuels Administration for War
Fuel Administration, 609
FUEL ADMINISTRATION,
    U.S. (RG 67),
    593-595
Fuel Administrator, 593, 594
Fuel Distributor. *See* Federal Fuel
    Distributor
Fulton, Robert, 136
Funds, 161
    Blocked, 126
    Commutation, 257
    Federal, 698
    Public, 58, 157, 165, 167
Fungicides, 339
Funston, Frederick, 283
Fur Seal Arbitration of 1895, 145
Fur seals, 145, 464
    Industry, 394, 397, 525, 548
    Killing of Alaskan, 395, 396
Furniture, 178
Furs, 378, 723
Fynje. *See* De la Lande and Fynje

G

Gaceta de Manila, 414
Gallaudet College, 364, 501
Galvin, Michael J., 491
Game, 430, 440, 567
    Birds, 394, 397
    Reservations, 396
    See also Wildlife
Game Commission, Alaska, 396
Gandhi, Mahatma, 748
Gardens, 407, 506, 639, 695
Gardens and Grounds,
    Division of, 450
Garfield, Harry A., 594
Garfield, James A., 76, 744
Garnishment proceedings, 74, 77
Garnsey, Cyrus, Jr., 594
Gas, 319, 368, 409, 540, 541, 588
    Interstate pipelines, 541
    Masks, 408, 606, 660

Natural, 408, 487, 541, 593, 594
    Straw, 450
    Toxic, 266
    Warfare, 266, 302, 408, 639
Gasser Board, 219
Gates, Thomas S., 292
Gaulle, Charles de, 747
Gay, Edwin F., 97
Gaza Strip, 139
Gazetteers, 422
General Accounting Office,
    152, 154, 162, 166,
    180, 183
GENERAL ACCOUNTING
    OFFICE (RG 217),
    57-61
General Agent
    Department of Justice, 341
    Treasury Department, 179, 180
General Counsel, Office of the,
    Department of the
    Treasury, 352
General Courts-Martial
    Division, 232
General Land Office, 156,
    364, 366, 370, 371, 372,
    373, 374, 375
General Land Office,
    Commissioner of the, 366
General Maximum Price
    Regulation of 1942, 648, 655
General Motors Corp., 540
General of the Armies,
    Headquarters, 284
General Officers, Board of, 219
General Post Office, 361
General Recruiting Service, 273
General Services Administration,
    526, 544, 545, 548, 549,
    581, 584, 641, 642, 678,
    702, 704, 705
GENERAL SERVICES
    ADMINISTRATION (RG 269),
    544
General Services, Administrator
    of, 41, 42, 45, 549, 581, 588
General Staff, Allied Operational
    and Occupation
    Headquarters, WW II, 192,
    193, 194
General Staff, Army, 220, 227,
    231, 234, 254, 266, 275
General Staff, War Department,
    218, 220, 223, 225, 229, 236,
    252, 254, 261, 262, 324
"General Staff map collection," 240
General Supply Committee, 154,
    425, 548, 549
Generalbevollmaechtigter fuer die
    Wirtschaft in Serbien, 729
Generalinspektor fuer das
    deutsche Strassenwesen, 730
Geneva award, 164

Geneva Conference, 184
Geneva conventions, 268
Geodesy, 480
Geodesy, Division of, 472
Geodesy and Geophysics,
    International Union of, 393
Geodetic Survey. *See* Coast and
    Geodetic Survey
Geographer of the State
    Department, Office of
    the, 138
Geographer of the United
    States, 34
Geographic Bulletin, 138
Geographic Names, Advisory
    Committee on, 421
Geographic Names, U.S. Board
    on, 421, 422
"Geographic News," 488
Geographic Notes, 138
Geographic Reports, 138
Geographical and Geological
    Survey of the Rocky
    Mountain Region, U.S.,
    389
Geographical Surveys West of the
    One Hundredth Meridian,
    Office of U.S., 238, 389, 566
Geography, 136, 390, 486,
    746, 747
    Historical, 750
    Industrial, 746
    Japanese, 205

GEOGRAPHY, OFFICE OF
    (RG 324), 421
Geologic Names, Committee on,
    391
Geological and Geographical
    Survey of the Territories,
    U.S., 241, 389
Geological Corps, 156
Geological Exploration of the
    Fortieth Parallel, 241, 389
Geological formations, 219,
    394, 440
Geological Survey, 54, 365, 370,
    406, 407, 408, 421
GEOLOGICAL SURVEY
    (RG 57), 389-394
Geology, 390, 391, 472,
    523, 750
Geophysics Division, Coast
    and Geodetic Survey, 472
George VI, 623, 748
George-Deen Act, 506
George Loomis (SS), 370
George S. Blake (U.S.S.), 474
George Washington Bicentennial
    Commission, 61, 62
George Washington Canal, 714
Georgeson, Charles C., 446
Georgetown, D.C., 712, 716

Georgetown mining region,
    Colorado Territory, 745
Georgetown University, 741
Georgia, 36, 343, 394, 722, 747
Georgian Bay, Canada, 241
Gerdes, F.H., 473
German Air Force, 728, 731, 734, 737
German Air Force High Command,
    730, 731, 733
German Air Force Mission in
    Rumania, 731
German Air Force Operations Staff,
    734
German-American Athletic Union
    of North America, 355
German-American Bund, 355, 356
German Armed Forces High
    Command, 728, 730, 731, 733
German Armed Forces Operations
    Staff, 731
German Army, 217, 279, 701, 730,
    732, 734, 736
German Army General Staff, 732
German Army High Command,
    732, 733, 734
German Army Medical Inspector,
    732
"German-Bolshevik Conspiracy,"
    95, 120
German-Bolshevik cooperation,
    137
German Foreign Ministry, 727, 733
German High Command, 189
German Law, Academy for, 733
German Naval Staff, 731
German Navy High Command,
    730, 731, 732, 734, 737
German Plenipotentiary for High
    Frequency Research, 729
German Police, Reich Leader
    SS, Chief of the, 730
German Radio Broadcasting
    Corp., 343
German Railroads Information
    Office, 355, 356
German Roads, General
    Inspector for, 730
German Work in the East,
    Institute for, 733
German Workers' Party, 733
Germany, 137, 144, 198, 205,
    225, 256, 268, 283, 286,
    287, 299, 301, 335, 354,
    356, 362, 612, 671, 700,
    701, 725, 728, 744, 747
    Academies, 728, 731, 733, 734
    Allied military government
        in, 256
    American Zone, 197
    British Zone, 197
    Code of justice, 733
    Decartelization in, 214
    Economics, 205, 732, 734

Festivals and music, 356
Fleet, 304
Military affairs, 138, 214, 279,
    701, 728, 729, 731, 732,
    733, 734, 735, 736, 737
National reconstruction
    program, 728
Occupation by, 205, 729
Occupation of, 138, 150, 283,
    286, 328
Racial policies, 728, 729, 730, 733
Surrender of, 188, 313, 334,
    638, 663, 734, 746, 748
U.S. Commercial Company in,
    586
War damage in, 198, 206, 744
See also Foreign Records Seized,
    1941— , National Archives
    Collection of (RG 242)
Germany, Federal Republic of, 727
Germany, Special Interrogation
    Mission to, 137
Germany, U.S. High Commissioner
    for, 197, 701
Gerry, Elbridge, 37
Gesell, Gerhard A., 116
Gestapo, 729, 730
Gettysburg, Battle of, 249, 402
Gettysburg National Military
    Park Commission, 247
Gettysburg, Pa., 745
Gibraltar, 138, 308
Gibson, John W., 491
Gifford, Walter S., 120, 121
Giles, Benjamin F., 326
Gilhooley, John J., 491
Gillespie Explosion
    Investigation and
    Claims Boards, 243
Gilliss, James M., 316
Girls clubs, 433
Glacier Park, 402
Glaciers, 233
Glass, 409
Glenn, John H., 747
Glenwood, Va., 598
Gliders, 334, 335, 567
Glues, 430
Gneisenau, August Neithardt
    von, 732
Gobierno Politico, 726
Goddard, Robert H., 747
Goebbels, Joseph, 623, 700,
    734, 737
Goering, Hermann, 702,
    731, 737
Goethals, George W., 103, 604
Goethals Memorial Commission,
    103, 104
Gold, 160, 173, 174, 650
    Certificates, 159
Gold Reserve Act of 1934,
    173, 582

Gold Star Mothers' and Widows'
    Pilgrimage to Europe, 248
Goldberg, Arthur J., 491
Golden Fleece, 395
Golden Gate International
    Exposition, 61
"Gone With the Wind" (m.p.), 747
"Good Neighbor" (s.r.), 139
Goode, G. Brown, 394
Gorrell, Edgar S., 284
Gouvion, Jean-Baptiste, 35
Governors Island, N.Y., 235
GOVERNMENT CONTRACT
    COMPLIANCE, COMMITTEE
    ON (RG 325), 702-703
Government contracts. *See*
    Contracts, Federal
Government Contracts,
    President's Committee
    on, 703
Government Employees
    Incentive Awards Act, 568
Government Films, Office of
    the Coordinator of, 125
Government Hospital for the
    Insane, 232, 365
Government Hotels, 599
Government Manual Service,
    U.S., 125
Government National Mortgage
    Association, 517
Government of Occupied Areas,
    School for, 268
Government Organization,
    President's Advisory
    Committee on, 112, 113
Government organization. *See*
    Executive Branch of the
    Government, Commissions on
    Organization of the
Government Printing Office, 52
GOVERNMENT PRINTING
    OFFICE (RG 149), 57
Government Reports, Office of,
    660, 661
GOVERNMENT REPORTS,
    OFFICE OF (RG 44),
    124-126
Government Security, Commission
    on, 62
Government Statistics and
    Information Service,
    Committee on, 98
Government Telegraph
    Offices, 208
Graduation Act, 373
Graham, John S., 153
Grain, 432, 436, 442, 534,
    591, 592, 595
    Elevators, 620
    Products, 462, 668
    Standardization, 461

Grain Corporation, U.S.,
    591, 607

GRAIN CORPORATION, U.S.
    (RG 5), 595-596
Grain Futures Act of 1922, 432
Grain Futures Administration,
    Department of Agriculture,
    432
Grain Stabilization Corporation,
    534
Grampus (schooner), 395
Granary program, ever-normal, 436
Grand, Ferdinand le, 35, 163
Grand Canyon National Park, 409
Grand Committee, Constitutional
    Convention, 36
Grand Coulee Dam, 714
Grand jury, 74, 75, 79, 89, 343, 344
Grand Teton, 394, 402
Granger, Gordon, 744
Granite, 409
Grant, Ulysses S., 208, 215, 744
Grant Civil Service Commission, 568
Grant Memorial Commission, 717
Grants, 668
    Canal and reservoir, 374
    Housing, 519
    Wartime, 704
Grapes, 442
Graphic arts industry, 629
Grasses, 423
    Drought resistant, 451
Grasshopper fungus, 454
Grasslands, national, 427
Graves, Harold N., Jr., 622
Graves Registration Service, 248
Gravity observations, 470, 474
Gravosa, 596
Gray, Gordon, 213
Grazing, 58, 103, 375, 376,
    428, 430
Grazing Service, 371, 375, 376
Great Britain, 35, 70, 139, 143, 144,
    145, 164, 188, 195, 286, 296,
    334, 481, 529, 650, 677, 692, 737
    Prime Minister of, 195, 217, 688
    1782 peace treaty with, 138
    See also England
Great Falls of the Potomac, 392, 395
Great Lakes, 478, 644, 677
"Great Lakes, The" (s.r.), 570
Great Lakes Naval Training
    Station, 313
Great Plains, 437
    Indians of the, 567
Great Smoky Mountains National
    Park, 402, 403
"Great War, The" (m.p.), 746
Great White Fleet, 293
Greater Texas and Pan
    American Exposition, 154
Greco-Bulgar Incident, 747

Greece, 139, 193, 198, 233,
    735, 746
Greenbelt, Md., 514, 520
Greendale, Wis., 514, 520
Greene, Nathanael, 34
Greenfield Village, 746
Greenhills, Ohio, 514
Greenland, 316, 478, 566, 747, 750
Greenleaf, James, 715
"Greentown" housing programs,
    520
Gregory, Francis H., 307
Greifelt, Ulrich, 700
Grew, Joseph C., 136, 689
Greyhound Corp., 540
Grieves, Howard C., 467
Griffith, D.W., 747
Gripsholm (ship), 138, 139
Groener, Wilhelm, 732, 734
Group Control Council,
    U.S., WW II, 197
Grover, Wayne C., 551
Groves, Leslie R., 743
Guadalupe Hidalgo, Treaty
    of, 46
Guam, 292, 361, 404, 447
    Invasion of, 293
Guam Naval Station, 477
Guano islands, 136
Guaranteed Wage Study, 665
Guatemala, 145, 626
Guaynabo cement plant, 417
Guerin, Mark, 259
Guerrilla warfare, 279, 736
Guffey Act of 1935, 417
Gulf of Mexico, 279, 397, 473
Gulf of Mexico-Caribbean
    Sea area, 315
Gulf Stream, 473, 474
Gulick, Luther B., 674
Gunboats, Civil War, 501
Gunderson, Carroll A., 674
Guns and gunnery, 244, 245, 303,
    328, 525
    Allied, 304
    German, 304
    Gunsights, 659
    Specifications, Italian, 734
    See also Firearms *and*
        Ordnance

H

Habeas corpus, 70, 75, 77, 79, 80, 81,
    83, 84, 86, 89
Hackworth, Green H., 137
Hagerman, Herbert J., 387, 743
Hague, Arnold, 391
Hague, The, 138
Haiti, 103, 299, 301, 414
    Geological Survey of, 393

Haiti, President's Commission
for the Study and Review
of Conditions in the Republic
of, 103
Haitian Customs Receivership, 413
Halifax Fisheries Commission, 145
Hall, Charles Francis, 750
Hall of Nobility, Russia, 138
Halleck, H.W., 208, 215
Halley's Comet, 477
Halsey, William F., 747
Hamburg, Germany, 596
Hamburg-American Line—North
German Lloyd, 356
Hamburgh, 715
Hamilton, Alexander, 36
Hamilton, Alexander, Bicentennial
Commission, 62
Hamlin, Charles S., 578
Hancock, John, 32
Hancock Memorial Commission, 717
Hand, Walter C., 517
Handicapped, training and
rehabilitation of the, 114,
466, 501
See also Schools
Hanes, John W., 153
Hanna, Frank A., 674
Hannah, Philip, 491
Hanson, John, 32
Hapsburgs, 747
Harbor Improvements on Lake
Erie, Office of, 238
Harbord, James G., 743
Harbors, 53, 207, 237, 240, 315, 356,
471, 524, 525, 602, 604, 607
Defense of, 207, 217, 238, 275, 279
Improvement of, 239, 241, 256
Naval, 309
Harding, Warren G., 748, 405
Hargrave, Thomas J., 187
Harmon, Millard F., 326
Harmon Foundation, film
collection, 746
Harpers Ferry, 546
Harriman, W. Averell, 625
Harris, John, 296
Harrison, George, 239
Harrison Act of 1914, 350
Harrison Narcotic Act, 339
Harrodsburg, Ky., 289, 290
Hart, Albert Bushnell, 62
Hartley. *See* Taft-Hartley Labor
Management Relations Act
Haruta and Co., Inc., 356
Harvesting, 453
Hassler, Ferdinand Rudolph, 473,
475
"Hasten the Day" (s.r.), 663
Hatch Act of 1887, 446
Hatchery, spawning, 396
Haushofer, Karl, 733
Havana, Captain of the Port of, 281

Havana, Department of, 281
Hawaii, 174, 275, 280, 397, 404,
405, 473, 723, 745, 747
Acquisition of, 276
Industrial codes for, 631
Relief program, *1946*, 514
U.S. Army in, 277
Hawaii, Department of, 276, 277, 279
Hawaiian Defense Command, 200
Hawaiian Homes Commission, 404
Hawkins Taylor Commission, 233
Hawley Board/Committee, 187
Hay, 450, 462
Hayden, Ferdinand V., 390
Hayden Survey, 389, 390, 393,
394, 403
Hayes, Erving P., 121
Hayes, Mrs. Rutherford B., 744
Hayes, Rutherford B., 95, 548, 744
Hazard, Ebenezer, 31
Hazardous Substances Labeling
Act, 507
Heads of state, foreign, 132, 137
Health, 182, 183, 187, 194, 270,
407, 408, 409, 420, 503, 504,
508, 570, 636, 640, 658, 663,
746
Associations, 460, 748
Education programs, 409, 502,
505, 636, 646
Industrial, 495
Maternal, 504, 510
Mental, 412, 745
Services, 302, 502, 503, 548, 567
Standards, labor, 496
Statistics, 502
See also Children;
Indian Affairs, Bureau of;
and Public health
Health, White House Conference
on, *1965*, 504, 505
Health and Medical Committee,
640, 641, 658
Health and Welfare Activities,
Interdepartmental Committee
to Coordinate, 103
Health, Education, and Welfare,
Department of, 350, 420, 502,
505, 507, 510, 511, 552, 615
HEALTH, EDUCATION, AND
WELFARE, DEPARTMENT
OF (RG 235), 501
Health, Education, and Welfare,
Secretary of, 116, 501
Health Needs of the Nation,
President's Commission on
the, 110, 111
Health Services and Mental
Health Administration,
502
Health, Welfare, and Related Defense
Activities, Office of the
Coordinator of, 640

Heeresarchiv, 732
Heeresgruppen, 732
Heinrich Hoffmann Collection, 737
Helgoland, 734
Helicopters, 328, 334, 360
   German, 335
Helium, 58, 319, 328, 407, 408
Helium Production Plant, 319
Helweg-Larsen, Governor, 724
Hemisfair, 147
Hemisphere Communications,
   Interdepartmental Advisory
   Committee on, 613, 614
Hemp, 435, 453
Henderson, Leon, 657, 689
Henry, Joseph, 477
Hess, Rudolf, 733
Hetch Hetchy Dam, 368, 398
Hibben, Paxton, 259
Hickernell, Warren F., 675
Higgins landing craft, 299
High Court, American Samoan, 410
High School Victory Corps, 507
Highway Education Board, 506
Highway Traffic Advisory
   Committee, 526
Highway Transport Department, 643
Highways, 103, 402, 526, 527, 620,
   621, 697, 713, 714, 744
   See also Public Roads, Bureau of
Hildreth, Melvin, 741
Hillculture, 437
Hillers, John K., 394, 745
Hillman, John A., 236
Himmler, Heinrich, 702, 729, 730
Hindenburg, Paul von, 335, 737
Hindenburg disaster, 256, 334,
   530, 748
Hippodrome, N.Y., 356
Hiroshima, 328, 334
   Atomic bomb effects on, 206
Hirsch, Siegfried S., 674
Hirshhorn, Joseph H., Museum
   and Sculpture Garden, 566
Historic sites, 328, 370, 397, 402
   See also Monuments and
     memorials
Historical Records Survey, 696
Historical Section, Department of
   the Navy, 294, 298
Historical Service, National Board
   for, 95
Historical societies, 62, 162, 170,
   696, 727
History and Technology, Museum
   of, 566
Hitchcock, Ethan Allen, 743
Hitchman Coal and Coke Co., 595
Hitler, Adolph, 198, 205, 356, 371,
   623, 689, 729, 730, 731,
   732, 733, 734, 735, 736, 737
   Attempted assassination of,
     702, 734
   1924 trial of, 734

"Hitler Source Book, A," 205
Hitler's Shock Troop, 730
Ho Chi Minh, 747
Hodgdon, Samuel, 37, 38, 296
Hoeflich, George J., 675
Hoffman, William, 253
Hog Island, Pa., 605
Holland, 33, 362, 450
   See also Netherlands, the
Hollander, Jacob H., 743
Holleman, Jerry R., 491
Holmes, George Sanford, 635
Holstein, Friedrich von, 727
Holt Commission. See Davis-Holt-
   Campbell Commission
Home economics, 446, 458
Home Economics, Division of,
   Office of Education, 506
Home Loan Bank Board, 513, 597
Home Owners Loan Act of 1933, 538
Home Owners' Loan Corporation,
   538, 539, 597, 598
Homer (SS), 395
Homes Service, 572, 575
Homestead Act, 373, 429
Homestead Contests Division,
   Bureau of Land
   Management, 374
Homesteads, 375, 429
   Legislation, 412, 429
   Projects, 442, 443
Honduras, 145
Honeybees, 461
Honeybees Importation Act, 453
Honolulu, 607
Hook Commission, 183
Hooker, General, 208
Hoover, Herbert C., 63, 64, 65, 95,
   96, 286, 362, 434, 579,
   593, 744
Hoover, Herbert, Presidential
   Library, 64, 595
Hoover Commission, 64, 109
Hoover Commission Task
   Force, 187
Hoover Institution on War,
   Revolution, and Peace,
   148, 592, 595, 608
Hopkins, Harry, 105
Horticulture, 451, 453, 454, 468
Horton, Robert E., 555
Hospital Corps, 233, 251, 302
Hospitalization, Board of
   Consultants on, 547
Hospitalization, Federal Board
   of, 96, 98
Hospitals, 35, 59, 98, 183, 232,
   263, 364, 365, 466, 501,
   502, 503, 504, 505, 546,
   547, 667
   Cuban, 281
   Military, 168, 169, 203, 233,
     249, 251, 302, 343, 572,
     720, 745

Virgin Islands, 724
"Hot Oil" Act of 1935, 415
Hot Springs, Ark., Reservation,
    Board of Commissioners
    for the, 372
Hough, Charles M., 82
House, Edward M., 148
House Armed Services
    Committee, 182
House of Representatives, U.S., 45,
    49, 50, 103, 154, 180, 329,
    413, 566, 722
    Bills, 51, 52
    Committees, 52, 54, 557, 558,
        604
    Resolutions, 42, 52

HOUSE OF REPRESENTATIVES,
    U.S. (RG 233), 51-53

House Office Annex, 531
Housing, 55, 116, 118, 125, 270, 332,
    371, 385, 404, 458, 467, 475,
    514, 567, 574, 585, 596, 597, 599,
    604, 605, 614, 615, 616, 662,
    665, 704
    Census, 467
    Construction, 442, 513, 514, 515,
        516, 517, 518, 585, 596,
        598, 599, 607, 686
    Cooperative, 104
    Discrimination in, 116, 117, 651
    Family, 186, 329
    Foreign, 416, 417, 597, 599,
        667, 725
    Low-rent, 519, 712, 713
    Management, 442, 458, 519,
        520, 713
    Military and veterans, 515, 517,
        518, 519, 574
    Programs, 371, 517, 518,
        520, 521
    Projects, 138, 424, 514, 515,
        519, 520, 521, 599,
        694, 607
    Refugee, 113
    Registration of, 597, 598
    Research, 513, 514
    Shortage, 585
    Surveys, 458, 597, 713
    The elderly, 515
    War, 513, 515, 519, 520, 609,
        665, 683, 691, 705,
        712
    Washington, D.C., 597, 598, 712-713,
        718
    See also Federal Home Loan Bank
        System (RG 195); Federal
        Housing Administration;
        Federal National Mortgage
        Association; Public Housing
        Administration (RG 196); and
        Rent

Housing acts
    1934, 515, 538
    1937, 519, 712
    1938, 516
    1949, 513
    1954, 513
Housing and Home Finance
    Agency, 513, 514, 515, 516,
    517, 520, 538, 581, 583
Housing and Rent Act of 1947, 517
Housing and Urban Development,
    Department of, 516, 517, 520
HOUSING AND URBAN
    DEVELOPMENT, DEPARTMENT
    OF (RG 207), 513-515
Housing and Urban Development
    Act of 1968, 516
Housing Authority, U.S., 519,
    704, 712
Housing Committee, 597
HOUSING CORPORATION,
    U.S. (RG 3), 596-599
Housing Expediter, Office of
    the, 647
HOUSING EXPEDITER, OFFICE
    OF THE (RG 252), 517-519
Housing Market Analysis, 516
Houston, Tex., 722
Howard, Hubert E., 187
Howard, Oliver Otis, 263, 264
Howard Court of Inquiry, 233
Howard University, 364, 501
Hubbard, Charles J., 750
Hubbard, Maceo W., 617
Hudson Bay Company, 723
Hudson River, 323, 474
Hughes, Charles Evans, 340
Hughes Aircraft Investigation
    Office, 340
Hull, Cordell, 139, 512, 748
HUMAN NUTRITION AND
    HOME ECONOMICS,
    BUREAU OF (RG 176),
    458
Human Rights Year 1968,
    President's Commission
    for the Observance of, 118
Humphrey, George M., 153
Humphreys, A.A., 390
Hungarian Refugee Relief,
    President's Committee
    for, 113
Hungarian revolution of
    1956, 113
Hungary, 113, 144, 198, 612,
    735, 736, 737
Hunt, Edward Eyre, 121
Huntington, Samuel, 32
Hurricanes, 328, 334, 404, 434, 694
Hutchins, Thomas, 34
Hutton, James, 375
Hyde Park, dedication of, 371
Hydraulics, 438, 660

Hydroelectric power, 406, 407, 416,
    541
Hydrographic Inspector, 472
Hydrographic Office, 296,
    305, 476, 537
HYDROGRAPHIC OFFICE
    (RG 37), 313-315
Hydrography, 303, 393, 480, 562, 567
    Surveys, 313, 314, 474, 489
    See also Ordnance and Hydrography,
        Bureau of
Hydrography and Topography,
    Division of, 472
Hydrologic Services, Division of, 478
Hydrology, 392, 421, 437, 438
Hydrology, International
    Association of, 393
Hydroplanes, 293
Hygienic Laboratory, 502, 504, 545
"Hyphenated nationality
    groups," 205

I

"I Can Hear It Now" (s.r.), 748
Ice patrol, 315, 525
Ickes, Harold L., 367, 657, 670
Idaho, 134, 343, 430
Ie Shima, 299
Ihlder, John, 713
Illinois, 34, 134, 409
    See also Chicago
Illinois National Guard, 127
Immigration, 136, 146, 169,
    336, 338, 339, 345, 372,
    502, 506, 570, 606
    Chinese, 168, 346
    To Samoa, 410
Immigration, Office of the
    Commissioner of, 135
Immigration and Nationality
    Act of 1952, 347
Immigration and Naturalization,
    Bureau of, 345, 498
Immigration and Naturalization,
    President's Commission
    on, 111, 112
Immigration and Naturalization
    Service, 113
IMMIGRATION AND
    NATURALIZATION
    SERVICE (RG 85),
    345-348
Immigration Border Patrol, 347
Impeachment, 49, 51, 52
    Articles of, 50
Imperial German Navy, 731
Imperial Russian Government,
    722, 723
Import Milk Act, 507

Imports, 108, 168, 169, 180, 408,
    453, 532, 543, 601, 610,
    623, 624, 664
    Food and drugs, 168, 449, 508
    Illegal, 59
    Japanese, 195
Improvements on the
    Western Rivers,
    Office of, 238
Inaugural balls, 741, 742
Inaugural Ceremonies, Joint
    Committee on, 55
INAUGURAL COMMITTEES,
    NATIONAL ARCHIVES
    COLLECTION OF (RG 274),
    741-742
Inaugurations, Presidential, 55, 127,
    335, 569
Incas, 647
Incendiary devices, 266, 660
    See also Bombs, incendiary
Income Maintenance Programs,
    President's Commission on, 119
Income, 436, 493, 713
    Farm, 99, 435
Indebted Railroads, Office of, 248
Indemnities, 144
    French, 163, 166
    Mexican, 158, 163, 166
    Neopolitan, 166
    Peruvian, 163, 166
    Spanish, 163
    Texan, 163
Independence, Declaration of, 136
Independent Agencies, Staff
    on, 65
"Index of American Design," 696
Indexes and Archives, Bureau of, 135
India, 143, 195, 205, 328, 586
India, National Archives of, 747
India Theater. See China-Burma-
    India Theater
Indian Affairs, Bureau of, 43,
    207, 252, 439, 670
INDIAN AFFAIRS, BUREAU OF
    (RG 75), 377-389
Indian Affairs, Commissioner of,
    364, 377, 378, 379,
    384, 552
Indian Affairs, Office of, 43, 370,
    377, 383, 389, 505
Indian and Swamp Land
    Division, 374
Indian Arts and Crafts Board, 388
INDIAN CLAIMS COMMISSION
    (RG 279), 552
Indian Commissioners, Board of, 387
"Indian Country" (s.r.), 570
Indian Division, Office of the
    Secretary of the Interior, 366
Indian Emergency Conservation
    Work Division, 385

Indian Industrial School at
Genoa, Nebr., 388
Indian Memorial, N.Y., 389
"Indian News" (m.p.), 663
Indian Peace Commission, 367
Indian Reorganization Act of
1934, 380-381, 386
Indian Trade, Office of, 377, 378
Indian Trade, Superintendent of,
378, 389
Indiana, 34, 134
Indians, 34, 35, 44, 59, 119, 220,
255, 342, 344, 366, 367,
368, 370, 375, 380, 440,
502, 552, 566, 567, 743,
744
Agencies, 377, 381, 383, 385,
386, 387, 388, 389
Agriculture, 381, 382, 383, 388
Allotment applications, 374
Census, 380, 389, 468
Claims, 91, 367, 379, 380, 382,
383, 384, 552, 574
Compensation of, 379, 380
Culture, 388, 407, 567
Delegations, 156, 745
Depredations, 91, 352, 378,
381, 382
Dwellings, 273, 566
Economy, 178, 370, 377, 384,
385, 614
Education, 370, 377, 378, 379,
381, 382, 383, 384, 385,
386, 387, 388, 506
Health, 377, 378, 382, 383,
385, 388
In industries, 378, 382, 383, 388
In the Armed Forces, 388
Lands, 91, 344, 372, 375, 376,
377, 379, 380, 381, 383,
384, 388, 389, 393, 439
Languages, 567
Legal rights of, 377, 381
Place names in Maine, 473
Population, 379, 381, 382, 384
Removal, 252, 379, 380, 382
Reservations, 53, 340, 370, 376,
377, 379, 380, 381, 382,
383, 386, 388, 439, 440,
506
Revolt, Alaskan, 723
Sale of liquor to, 344
Scouts, 232, 272
Six Nations of, 34
Superintendencies, 377, 386, 387, 389
Territory, 134, 367, 379
Traders, 338, 381, 384
Treaties, 34, 35, 41, 43, 44, 134,
377, 379, 380, 389
Tribes, 43, 50, 61, 377, 379,
380, 381, 386, 389, 552, 566,
743
Trust Fund, 158, 159

Wars, 60, 232, 240, 255, 373,
389, 573, 574
See also names of specific tribes
Indians at Work, 385
Indochina, 143, 612
Industrial Advisory Board,
National Recovery
Administration, 629
Industrial Advisory Committee, 188
Industrial Analysis, Committee of,
Department of Commerce,
627, 629
Industrial Board, Department of
Commerce, 465
Industrial College of the Armed
Forces, 203, 204
Industrial Commission,
Department of Commerce,
464
Industrial Committee, Natural
Resources Planning Board, 123
Industrial Cooperation, Coordinator
for, 627
Industrial Cooperation, Office of
the Coordinator for, 627
Industrial Cooperation Service, 465
Industrial Division, Bureau of
Prisons, 349, 350
Industrial Economics, Division of,
Department of Commerce, 627
Industrial Emergency Committee, 124
Industrial Farm Products Research
Division, 450
Industrial Housing and Transportation,
Bureau of, Department of
Labor, 596
Industrial Relations, U.S.
Commission on, 492
Industrial Safety, President's
Conference on, 492
Industrial Surveys, Joint Board
on, 596
Industry, 105, 111, 121, 123, 138,
139, 178, 185, 186, 188, 198,
210, 219, 232, 267, 270, 325,
330, 350, 356, 370, 390, 396,
407, 410, 447, 463, 464, 465,
486, 487, 490, 495, 497,
498, 525, 543, 552, 555, 579,
584, 592, 598, 609, 613, 626,
629, 631, 633, 634, 635, 650,
654, 655, 660, 662, 663, 673, 678,
680, 684, 685, 702, 703, 706, 747
Advisory committees, 490, 496,
518, 705
Aid to, 580, 582
Associations, 204, 629, 630, 640,
658, 668
Bomb devastation of, 206
Censuses of, 467
Codes for, 627, 628, 629
Development of, 205, 426, 674
Disputes, 706

Essential, 679, 682
Foreign, 185, 206, 335, 356,
    414, 486, 728, 733, 736
Incentive program, 210
Installations, camouflaged, 639
Locations, 123, 124, 599
Mobilization, 187, 201, 203, 210,
    211, 229, 238, 269, 270,
    422, 687
National dispersion program, 464
Practices, 333, 464, 697
Prison, 669
Problems, 63, 570, 617, 675
Production, 256, 631, 668, 675
Relations, 183, 556, 598, 602,
    617, 630, 656
Research and development,
    107, 122, 205, 426, 499,
    674
Rural, 684, 687
Safety, 492, 493, 495
Schedules of, 468, 469
Surveys, 597, 654
War, 106, 124, 206, 299, 371, 495,
    520, 548, 594, 605, 608,
    672, 673, 683
Women in, 299, 495, 680
See also Indian Affairs,
    Bureau of; Labor;
    Petroleum, industry;
    Plant Industry, Bureau of;
    and War industries

Industry Advisory Committees,
    Office of, 650, 687
Industry Associations
    Committee, 685
Industry Cooperation, Office
    of, 465
Industry Council, 650
Infant care, 510
Infantry, 228, 271, 272, 273,
    274, 285
    German, 732
Infantry, Chief of, 225, 226
Infantry School of Arms, 226
Inflation, 650, 662, 703
Information, Government,
    124, 330, 660
    Clearinghouse for, 124
    Programs, 124, 441, 644,
        645, 646
    Security-classified, 661
    See also Public Information;
        United States Information
        Agency (RG 306); and
        War Information, Office of

Information, Office of the
    Chief of, 221
Information, Office of the
    Coordinator of, 204, 660, 662
Information and Educational
    Exchange, Office of, 139

Information and Educational
    Exchange Act of 1948, 569
Information Bureau, 268
Information Service, U.S.,
    125, 569
Ingraham, William, 211
Injuries, personal, 83
Inland Traffic Service, 248
Inland Transportation
    Service, 246
Inland waterways, 604, 676
INLAND WATERWAYS
    CORPORATION
    (RG 91), 488-489
Inquiry, The, American
    Commission To Negotiate
    Peace, 148
Insect Pest Act, 453
Insecticide Act of 1910, 507
Insecticides, 339, 454, 660
    See also Food, Drug, and
        Insecticide Administration
Insects, 428, 453, 454
Insignia, 531
    Army, 532
Inspection and Survey, Board
    of, 296, 298, 306
Inspection Division, Bureau
    of Indian Bureaus, 384
Inspection for Shore Stations,
    Board of, 299
Inspector General
    Air Force, 331
    Army, 241, 284, 286
    Military Government of
        Cuba, 281
Inspector General, Department of
    the, 215, 230
Inspector General, Office of the
    (Army), 216
INSPECTOR GENERAL, OFFICE
    OF THE (RG 159),
    241-242
Inspectors, military, 273, 301
Institut fuer Deutsche Ostarbeit,
    733
Insular Affairs, Bureau of,
    261, 280, 281, 282, 404
INSULAR AFFAIRS, BUREAU
    OF (RG 350), 413-414
Insular Affairs, Division of, 413
Insular Affairs Section, 261
Insular and Territorial Affairs
    Bureau, 340
Insular possessions, 175, 261,
    340, 413, 414, 446, 471,
    473
Insurance, 62, 129, 496, 534,
    543, 572, 573, 585, 606
    Companies, 155, 355, 442, 580,
        581, 585
    Crop, 426, 441, 442
    Disability, 512, 572

Federal survivors, 510, 512
Germany, 198
Housing, 598
Life, 356, 572, 573, 650
Marine, 83
Maritime, 601, 605, 676
Social, 511
Unemployment, 499
See also Federal Deposit
    Insurance Corporation;
    Reconstruction Finance
    Corporation; *and* War
    Risk Insurance, Bureau
    of
Insurance in Riot-Affected
    Areas, National
    Advisory Panel on, 129
Insurrectionary States, 54
Insurrections, 281, 724
Integration, 747
Intelligence activities, 65, 190, 191, 194,
    195, 197, 200, 205, 206, 217,
    236, 332, 622, 623, 662
Air Force, 325, 327
American Expeditionary Forces,
    284, 286, 288
American Samoan, 410
Coast Guard, 524
German, 198, 730, 731
Japanese, 194
Military, 184, 185, 204, 216, 217,
    218, 219, 229, 300, 301,
    332, 638, 662, 663
See also Central Intelligence Agency
    and Naval Intelligence, Office of
Intelligence Library, 217
Inter-Allied Commission on the
    Repatriation of Prisoners of War,
    287
Inter-Allied operational headquarters, 191
Inter-Allied Petroleum Conference, 594
Inter-Allied Rhineland High Commission,
    286
Inter-Ally Council on War Purchases
    and Finance, 577
Inter-American Advisory Committee
    for Political Defense, 331
Inter-American Affairs, Institute
    of, 143, 646, 647
INTER-AMERICAN AFFAIRS,
    OFFICE OF (RG 229),
    646-647
Inter-American Affairs, Office of
    the Coordinator of, 645, 646
Inter-American Conference at
    Mexico City, 663
Inter-American Highway, 526
Inter-American Transportation,
    Institute of, 646
Inter-Asia Relations Conference, 748
Inter-Regional Traffic Committee
    of the U.S. Railroad
    Administration, 602

Intercontinental Railway
    Commission, 147
Interdepartment Radio Advisory
    Committee, 535, 536, 537
INTERDEPARTMENTAL AND
    INTRADEPARTMENTAL
    COMMITTEES (STATE
    DEPARTMENT) (RG 353),
    149-151
Interdepartmental Committee for
    Coordination of Foreign and
    Domestic Military Purchases,
    624
Interdepartmental Committee on
    Interstate Trade Barriers, 487
Interdepartmental Patent
    Interchange Committee, 149
Interdepartmental Patents Board,
    262
Interdepartmental Social Hygiene
    Board, U.S., 503, 504
Intergovernmental Relations,
    Commission on, 112
Interim Committee, U.S. European
    Command, 199
Interior, Department of the, 37, 38,
    43, 55, 58, 59, 60, 92, 103,
    119, 207, 237, 241, 282, 336,
    337, 338, 364, 365, 367, 368,
    370, 371, 374, 377, 381, 384,
    389, 394, 395, 397, 398, 404,
    407, 409, 411, 412, 413, 415,
    416, 417, 418, 420, 426, 437,
    442, 469, 505, 519, 531, 571,
    573, 637, 689, 690, 691, 714,
    724, 743
Interior, Office of the Secretary of
    the, 384, 415, 669
INTERIOR, OFFICE OF THE
    SECRETARY OF THE
    (RG 48), 364-371
Interior, Reich Ministry of the, 730
Interior, Secretary of the, 265, 269,
    364, 366, 368, 378, 379, 384,
    397, 398, 403, 404, 409, 411,
    412, 414, 415, 416, 418, 419,
    421, 422, 493, 541, 552, 572,
    578, 591, 666, 670, 743
Interior, Zone of, 278
Internal Improvements, Board on,
    238-239
Internal revenue, 55, 60, 154, 344
    Cases, 81, 83, 86, 89, 338
Internal Revenue, Bureau of, 169,
    177, 178, 281, 336
Internal Revenue, Commissioner of,
    177, 350, 351
Internal Revenue Service, 153
INTERNAL REVENUE
    SERVICE (RG 58),
    177-179
Internal Revenue Taxation,
    Joint Committee on, 54

Internal Security and Individual
Rights, President's
Commission on, 110
Internal Security Division, 269
International Activities, Division
of, Office of the Secretary
of the Interior, 369
International Affairs, Assistant
Secretary for, Treasury
Department, 181
International Air-Sea-Rescue
Service, 522
International American Monetary
Commission, 147
International Bank for
Reconstruction and
Development, 663
International Boundary Commission,
241
International Boundary Studies, 138
International Conference on Safety
of Life at Sea, 306
INTERNATIONAL CONFERENCES,
COMMISSIONS, AND
EXPOSITIONS (RG 43),
146-147
International Cooperation
Administration, 113, 143
International Court of Justice
at The Hague, 138
Statute of the, 663
INTERNATIONAL DEVELOPMENT,
AGENCY FOR (RG 286),
142-143
International Development,
President's Task Force on, 119
International Exchange Service, 566
International Exhibition at
Philadelphia, 241
International Finance, Office of,
Treasury Department, 180
International Fur Seal
Convention, 145
International Geophysical Year,
334
International Harvester Co., 540
International Ice Patrol,
523, 524
International Joint Commission
of the United States and
Canada, 392
International Labor Affairs,
Bureau of, 495
INTERNATIONAL MILITARY
AGENCIES (RG 333),
195-196
International Military Tribunal,
262, 699, 700, 701, 702
International Monetary Fund, 663
International Patent Interchange
Committee, 149
International Press Service, 569

International Prosecution
Section, Supreme
Commander for the
Allied Powers, 700
International Rules of Judicial
Procedure, Commission
on, 114, 115
International Sanitary
Commission, 137
International Sanitary
Conference of 1881, 503
International Standards
Commission, 475
International Statistical
Program Office, 468
International Sugar
Committee, 607, 608
International Technical
Consulting Committee on
Radio Communications,
147
International Trade, Office
of, 108
Internees, 235, 268, 347, 405
Austro-Hungarian, 137
Camps, 235, 328
German, 137, 138
Hawaiian, 279
Japanese, 138
Interoceanic Canal Board,
240
INTERSERVICE AGENCIES
(RG 334), 201-204
Interstate commerce, 338, 415, 445,
496, 543, 559, 563, 601
Interstate Commerce Act of
1887, 92
Interstate Commerce
Commission, 92, 476, 487,
527, 530, 535, 559, 579,
580, 582, 600, 637,
643, 655
INTERSTATE COMMERCE
COMMISSION (RG 134),
553
Interstate Commerce Committee,
Senate, 74
Interstate Highway System, 526
Inventions, 217, 219, 242, 243, 261,
262, 303, 304, 306, 318, 326,
469, 470, 658
Investigation, Division of, Public
Works Administration,
670, 671
Investigation, Special Board of, Federal
Trade Commission, 543
INVESTIGATION AND RESEARCH—
TRANSPORTATION, BOARD
OF (RG 198), 612-613
Investigations, Senate Special
Subcommittee on, 213
Investment Advisers Act of 1940, 563
Investment companies, 565

Investment Company Act of 1940, 563
Iowa, 156, 439
Iowa Indians, Confederated, 380
Ireland, R.L., Jr., 106
Iron, 106, 245, 391, 409, 654, 734
Ironclads, 307
Irrigation, 370, 372, 374, 376, 392,
    393, 395, 406, 407, 425, 433, 438,
    439, 440, 446, 447, 448, 449,
    457, 555, 581
  Agricultural, 452
  Foreign, 407
  Indian, 377, 381, 388
  Schedules, 468
  Surveys, 390
Islands, surveys of, 372
  See also Possessions, island, and
    names of islands
Isthmian Canal, 474
Isthmian Canal Commissions, 562
Isthmus of Darien, 241
Italian Armistice Commission
    in France, 137
Italian Expeditionary Force
    in Russia, 736
Italian Foreign Office, 736
Italian Front, 288
Italian Service Unit, 268
Italian Social Republic, 137
Italian War Veterans in the
    United States, Federation of,
    355
Italo-Ethiopian War, 134, 747
Italy, 43, 137, 145, 193, 205,
    256, 285, 286, 299, 313,
    431, 612, 689, 734, 735,
    736, 737
  Air Force, 736
  Army, 734, 736
  Defeat of, 663
  Foreign Minister, 734
  Government, 194, 733, 735, 736
  Liberation of, 663
  War damage in, 139, 198, 206
Izard, Ralph, 33, 35

J

Jack Fork Mountain, 438
Jackson, Andrew, 379
Jackson, Robert H., 699, 700
Jackson, William Henry, 370, 394
Jails, 342, 349
  See also Prisons
James River Bridge, 607
Jamestown Tercentennial
    Exposition, 154, 209,
    365, 433
Jamestown-Williamsburg-
    Yorktown Celebration
    Commission, 402

Japan, 46, 134, 137, 147, 160,
    189, 194, 195, 196, 205, 214,
    219, 220, 229, 256, 268, 293,
    315, 339, 354, 355, 356, 397,
    605, 612, 623, 662, 677, 691,
    733, 735, 736, 737
  Allied Council for, 147
  Allied military government in, 256
  Bombing of, 206, 293, 299, 334
  Customs of, 334- 335
  Defeat of, 206, 663
  Occupation of, 150, 194, 328, 335
  Surrender of, 189, 194, 220, 293,
    334, 700, 748
  Vessels, 525, 736
"Japan in Time of Emergency"
    (m.p.), 702
Japanese-Americans, 689
  Exclusion program, 211, 280,
    689-691
  In the war effort, 256
  Newspapers, 690
  Vital statistics on, 691
Japanese Armed Forces, 736
Japanese Army High
    Command, 736
Japanese beetles, control of, 454
Japanese Embassy, in Germany, 733
Japanese Navy High Command, 736
Japanese peace treaty, 139, 194
Java, 612
Jay, John, 30, 32, 35
Jefferson, Mark, 743
Jefferson, Thomas, 33, 35, 336, 716
Jefferson, Thomas, Bicentennial
    Commission, 61
Jefferson, Thomas, Statue
    Commission, 137
Jefferson Memorial, 401
Jefferson Memorial
    Commission, 402
"Jeffersonian Heritage, The"
    (s.r.), 570
Jensen, Albert, 340
Jensen, Karl E., 635
Jesuit Fathers, 474
Jets, 334, 335
Jewett, Frank B., 659
Jewish Welfare Board, 288
Jews, German persecution of,
    729, 730
Jodl, Alfred, 700
John Marshall, U.S. Commission for
    the Celebration of the Two
    Hundredth Anniversary of
    the Birth of, 402, 403
Johnson, George M., 617
Johnson, Lyndon B., 129, 514, 744
  Inauguration of, 55
Johnson, Mrs. Lyndon B., 744
Johnston, Eric A., 703, 704, 706
Joint Advisory Board on American
    Republics, 201

Joint Air Defense Board, 330
Joint Air Transportation Board, 330
Joint Airborne Troop Board,
    228, 330
Joint Aircraft Committee, 188
Joint Army and Navy Board, 295
Joint Army and Navy Board on
    Aeronautic Cognizance, 202
Joint Army and Navy Board
    on Aeronautics, 202
JOINT ARMY AND NAVY
    BOARDS AND
    COMMITTEES (RG 225),
    200-201
Joint Army and Navy Committee
    on Welfare and Recreation,
    201
Joint Army and Navy Munitions
    Board, 201
Joint Army and Navy Personnel
    Board, 184
Joint Army-Navy Disciplinary
    Control Board, 202
Joint Atomic Information
    Exchange Group, 189
Joint Board of Survey, 261, 340
Joint Board of Survey of the War
    and Justice Departments,
    243
Joint Brazil-United States
    Defense Commission, 196
Joint Brazil-United States
    Military Commission, 196
Joint Chiefs of Staff, 182, 187,
    189, 197, 199, 200, 201,
    204, 209, 216, 222, 297,
    331
JOINT CHIEFS OF STAFF,
    U.S. (RG 218), 188-189
Joint Chiefs of Staff
    Secretariat, 222
JOINT COMMANDS (RG 349),
    199-200
Joint Commission Relative to the
    Preservation of the
    Fisheries in Waters
    Contiguous to Canada and
    the United States, 395
Joint Committee on Projects, 425
Joint Committee on Reserve
    and National Guard
    Policy, 331
JOINT COMMITTEES OF
    CONGRESS (RG 128),
    54-55
Joint Construction Agency, 199
Joint Contract Termination
    Board, 641, 642
Joint Economic Committees, 147
Joint High Commissions, 147
Joint Logistics Committee, 188
Joint Merchant Vessel Board, 299

Joint Military Transportation
    Board, 199
Joint Munitions Allocation
    Committee, 326
Joint New Weapons Committee, 189
Joint Nuclear Accident
    Coordinating Center, 189
Joint Program Information
    Committees, 681
Joint Radiological Safety
    Group, 191
Joint Research and Development
    Board, 189
Joint Secretaries Group, 182
Joint Tactical Air Support
    Board, 330
Joint Treasurers of the United
    Colonies, 30
Joint War Aid Committee, 105
Joint Welfare Board, 200
Jones, Jesse H., 464
Jones, John Paul, 34, 35, 138, 296,
    322
Jones, John Paul, Statue
    Commission, 717
Jones, Lucien, 744
Jordan, Paul H., 674
Joseph, Julius J., 682
Journal of Research of the National
    Bureau of Standards, 475
Journals of the Congresses, 30
"Journey to Jerusalem" (m.p.),
    747
Jucaro and San Fernando Railroad,
    281
Judge Advocate, 194, 233, 258,
    259, 273, 278, 279, 285,
    286
Judge advocate, Military
    Government of Cuba, 281
Judge Advocate General
    Air Force, 290, 331
    Army, 229, 258, 259, 260, 261,
        284, 290
    Navy, 295, 318
JUDGE ADVOCATE GENERAL
    (ARMY), OFFICE OF THE
    (RG 153), 258-263
Judge Advocate General (Navy),
    Office of the, 291
JUDGE ADVOCATE GENERAL
    (NAVY), OFFICE OF THE
    (RG 125), 317-318
Judges, 69, 337, 338, 339, 342,
    343, 345, 348
Judiciary, 70, 338, 339, 353
    Expenses, 337, 338
    Fund, 338
    In American Samoa, 410
Judiciary Act of 1789, 69, 72, 343
Judiciary Act of 1911, 72
Juneau, Alaska, 412
Jungle operations, 299

Junior League baseball program, 748
Jurors, 80, 85, 89
Justice, criminal, 63
Justice, Department of, 60, 63, 92, 135, 161, 176, 180, 218, 260, 261, 317, 343, 344, 345, 348, 349, 350, 351, 352, 354, 355, 356, 357, 362, 364, 573, 609, 654, 718, 722
JUSTICE, DEPARTMENT OF (RG 60), 336-343
Justice, Reich Ministry of, 729
Juvenile delinquency, 63, 510, 640
Juvenile Delinquency and Youth Crime, President's Committee on, 116
Juvenile Delinquency and Youth Offenses Control Act of 1961, 116

K

Kaiser, Henry J., 677
Kaiser, Philip M., 491
Kaiser Wilhelm II, 299
Kaltenbach, Frederick W., 343, 623
Kamikaze attacks, 293
Kansa (Kaw) Indians, 380
Kansas, 134
Kansas-Oklahoma Arkansas River Commission, Compact Committee of the, 393
Kaskaskia, 34
Kaskaskia Indians, Confederated, 380
Kasson, John A., 135
Kaufman, Herbert, 367
Kaufman, Joseph W., 674
Kaw Indians. See Kansa (Kaw) Indians
Kaweah Cooperative Colony, 372
Keechie Indians, 388
Keenan, Joseph B., 700
Keep Commission, 97, 154, 358, 427, 452
Keitel, Wilhelm, 731
Kellogg, Frank B., 135
Kelp, 452
Kendall, David W., 153
Kendall School, 501
Kennedy, John F., 116, 137, 188, 335, 501, 551, 744, 745, 747, 748
   Condolence messages on death of, 569
   Inaugural, 742
   See also President's Commission on the Assassination of President Kennedy (RG 272)

Kennedy, John F., Center for the Performing Arts, 566
Kennedy, Thomas, 106
Kennedy Highway, 744
Kentucky, 34, 289, 290
Keppel, Francis, 507
Kerner, Otto, 129
Kerner Commission, 129
Kerr, Robert S., 657
Kerwin, Hugh L., 491
Kesselring, Albert, 736
Kestnbaum, Meyer, 112
Khrushchev, Nikita, 747
Kickapoo Indians, 380
Kidnappings, 339
Kilmer, Joyce, Reception Center, 113
Kiln drying, 429, 430
King, Clarence, 390
King, Nicholas, 717
King Survey, 389, 390
Kingsley, J. Donald, 107
Kinnaird, Eugene F., 675
Kiowa Indians, 388
Kites, 319
Kmetz, John T., 491
Knapp, Martin A., 560
Knerr, Hugh J., 330
Knox, Frank, 291, 689
Knox, Henry, 34
Kodiak Island, 723
Kootenai River investigations, 392
Korea, 196, 213, 233, 332, 612, 736
   Surrender of Japan in, 189
   U.N. forces in, 736
   U.S. Army Military Government in, 197, 214
   U.S. Forces in, 197, 200, 235, 280, 736
   See also Foreign Assets Control, Office of, and North Korea
Korean Communications Zone, 262
Korean Punitive Expedition, 745
Korean war, 139, 186, 188, 223, 262, 333, 335, 356, 520, 536, 570, 706, 727, 746
   Armistice agreement, 189, 196, 200, 262, 335
Kosciuszko Statue Commission, 717
Krauch, Carl, 700
Kriegsmarine, 731
Krupp, Friedrick, A.G., 702, 734
Ku Klux Klan, 128
Ku Klux Klan Act of 1871, 338
Kuhne, Marie Peary, 749

L

Labor, 97, 98, 108, 109, 118, 194, 209, 210, 230, 268, 285, 308, 347, 416, 439, 459, 460, 464, 481, 488,

493, 495, 496, 498, 540, 556, 570,
591, 602, 604, 605, 609, 610, 615,
617, 618, 619, 632, 633, 639, 643,
645, 650, 672, 679, 680, 681, 682,
683, 684, 702, 703, 706, 720
Agricultural, 455, 456, 459, 684, 687
Camps, migratory, 442, 443
Child, 41, 371, 495, 496, 510, 630
Conditions, 491, 493, 495, 560, 600,
602, 606, 610, 620, 626,
672, 673
Disputes, 338, 417, 498, 540, 555,
556, 557, 560, 580, 600, 605,
626, 627, 631, 632, 633, 693,
706
Foreign, 493, 523, 676, 679, 683,
684, 728, 730, 733
Importation of, 434, 523
Industrial, 462, 518, 596
Laws, 345, 494, 495
Maritime, 626, 676, 693
Markets, 499, 679, 683, 687
Mining, 408
Organizations, 83, 111, 177,
495-496, 498, 620, 650, 668
Railroad, 399, 558, 559, 560, 561,
600, 601, 679, 707
Relations, 55, 213, 367, 558, 591,
619, 620, 650, 652, 672,
673, 680
Shipyard, 604, 676
Unfair practices, 555, 556, 557,
605
Unions, 83, 493, 495, 601, 602,
613, 616, 679, 680
Virgin Islands, 725
World War I, 580
See also Children; Commerce
and Labor, Department of;
and Women
Labor, Assistant Secretaries of, 491
Labor, Bureau of, 285, 493, 594
Labor, Commissioner of, 559
Labor, Department of, 63, 103, 117,
345, 353, 417, 420, 459, 460,
464, 474, 480, 494, 495, 496,
497, 499, 510, 511, 522, 540,
543, 596, 597, 609, 614, 631,
671, 672, 679, 681, 684, 702
LABOR, DEPARTMENT OF
(RG 174), 491-493
Labor, Deputy Under Secretaries
of, 491
Labor, Office of, 459, 460, 650
LABOR, OFFICE OF (WAR FOOD
ADMINISTRATION)
(RG 224), 459-460
Labor, Reich Ministry of, 729
Labor, Secretary of, 98, 115, 116,
491, 492, 493, 496, 497, 540,
578, 580, 672
Labor, Solicitor of the Department
of, 353

Labor, Special Assistants to the
Secretaries of, 491
Labor, Under Secretaries of, 491
Labor Advisory Board, 629
Labor Advisory Service, 518
Labor Consultant, Office of, 686
Labor Division, War Production
Board, 679
Labor Management Relations
Act of 1947, 540, 556
Labor-Management Reporting
and Disclosure Act of
1959, 556
Labor Policy Committee, 650
Labor Relations Adviser, Office
of, 650
Labor Relations, Manning, Training,
and Recruitment, Deputy
Administrator for, 693
Labor Review, Board of, 670
LABOR STANDARDS, BUREAU
OF (RG 100), 495-496
Labor Standards, Division of,
495, 496
Labor Statistics, Bureau of,
491, 697
LABOR STATISTICS, BUREAU
OF (RG 257), 493-494
Labor Supply Committee, 686
Laboratories, naval, 305, 308
Lady Franklin Bay Expedition,
317, 478, 743, 745
Lady Managers, Board of,
World's Columbian
Exposition, 53
Lafayette, Marquis de, 35, 54
Lafayette Building Corporation,
581, 588
La Guardia, Fiorello H., 335,
346, 657
Lahousen, Erwin, 734
Lake Mead Comprehensive
Survey, 392
Lake Michigan, 489
Lake Superior, 245, 370, 397
Lake Survey, U.S., 238, 240
Lamb, John, 33
Lamont, Robert P., 464
Lancaster, Emmer Martin, 464
Land, 60, 65, 118, 123, 155, 156,
219, 232, 243, 245, 260,
262, 263, 300, 314, 338,
344, 364, 366, 372, 373,
374, 428, 430, 431, 436,
442, 443, 456, 457, 518,
546, 547, 552, 567, 715
Abandoned, 263
Acquisition, 352, 353, 424,
546, 713
Arid, 406
Banks, 530, 533, 534, 535,
583
Bounty, 207, 372, 373, 374

Claims, private, 372, 373, 374, 376
Classification, 389, 393, 447
Confiscated, 180, 263, 729
District of Columbia, 546
Forest, 426, 427, 428, 429, 453
Government, 207, 344, 546
Grants, 65, 366, 372, 376, 377
Indian, 91, 344, 372, 375, 376,
  377, 379, 380, 381, 383,
  384, 388, 389, 393, 439
Laws, 65-66, 373, 406
Patents, 65, 373
Public, 33, 58, 65-66, 103, 119,
  152, 178, 336, 341, 368,
  371, 372, 373, 374, 375,
  376, 402
Reclamation of, 365, 366, 368,
  369, 370, 372, 406, 436,
  443, 670
Reform, German, 198, 729
Resources, 65, 112, 123, 375,
  437, 460
Sales, 178, 546
Surveys, 53, 179, 401, 471
Swamp, 372, 374, 375
Tenure, 384
Titles, 336, 337, 341, 438, 546
Utilization, 65, 110, 124, 368,
  369, 373, 393, 421, 430,
  431, 438, 439, 440, 443,
  453, 455, 456, 457, 714
Land Economics, Division of, 456
Land Management, Bureau of,
  375, 376
LAND MANAGEMENT,
  BUREAU OF (RG 49),
  371-377
Land mines, detection of, 659
Landais, Peter, 34
Landing fields, 301, 325, 327, 328,
  362, 698
Landon, Alfred M., 512
Landrum-Griffin Act, 556
Lands and Railroads Division,
  365, 366
Landsberg Prison, 278
Landscaping, 453, 532
Lane, Frederick C., 676
Lane, Jonathan H., 475
Langer, Walter C., 205
Langley Field, Va., 325
Language teaching, 217, 501
Lanham Act, 507, 520, 712
Lansing, Robert, 135
La Paz, Bolivia, U.S. minister
  at, 138
La Puntilla, Presidio of, 726
Larson, Arthur, 491
"Last Rites of the Battleship
  Maine" (m.p.), 328
Latin America, 149, 205, 336,
  339, 585, 589, 624,
  646, 647

Agricultural assistance, 431, 647
Cultures of, 647
Development of, 142
U.S. Commercial Company in, 586
U.S. relations with, 147
Latin American Affairs, Assistant
  Secretary of State for, 136
Latin American Affairs, Division of,
  Department of State, 135
Latitude observations, 316
Latvia, 729, 735
Laurens, Henry, 32, 35
Laurens, John, 35
Laval, Pierre, 623
"La Vie de Ho Chi Minh" (m.p.), 747
Law Commission, Advisory, 281
Law Committee, 613
Law enforcement, 267, 332, 338

**LAW OBSERVANCE AND
  ENFORCEMENT, NATIONAL
  COMMISSION ON (RG 10),**
  63-64

Laws, 41, 42, 72-90, 131, 133, 135,
  267, 336, 348, 484, 496, 550
Admiralty, 69, 72-90, 317,
  318, 722
Affecting status of women, 494
Civil, 75, 318
Conflict-of-interest, 110
Criminal, 63, 75, 343
Customs, 82, 170, 336, 353, 522,
  524
Election, 117, 338
Immigration, 336
Incorporation, 543
International, 137, 317, 734
Labor, 345, 494, 495
Land, 373, 406
Lien, 75
Naturalization, 346
Navigation, 170, 480, 481, 483,
  522, 524, 603
Voting, 678
Lawson, Marjorie M., 617
Lawyers, Advisory Committee on, 104
Lay-Away Project *54*, 213
Lead, 375, 408, 409, 552, 584
League of Nations, 313, 746, 747
Leases, 58, 136, 180, 343, 718
Leather, 270, 490, 654, 688
Leavenworth Penitentiary,
  343, 349
Lee, Arthur, 33, 35
Lee, R.B., Commission, 60
Lee, Richard Henry, 32
Lee, William, 35
Leeb, Wilhelm von, 700
Leffler, Ross L., 367
Legations
  Foreign, 132
  U.S., 141, 142

Legislation, 560
  Nonintercourse, 336
  Pension, 365
  State, 124, 125
Legislative Liaison, Office of the
  Chief of, 221
Legislative Reference, Division
  of, 96
le Grand, Ferdinand. *See* Grand,
  Ferdinand le
Leigh Smith Expedition, 317
Leland, Wilford C., Jr., 617
Lend-lease, 201, 217, 308, 435,
  459, 625, 660, 662, 663
Lend-Lease Act, 326, 624, 676
Lend-Lease Administration, Office
  of, 105, 623, 624
Lending institutions, 65, 515, 532
L'Enfant, Pierre Charles, 715, 717
Lenin, Nikolai, 736
Lesseps, Ferdinand de, 562
Lesseps, Ferdinand de, Monument, 531
Leviathan (SS), 606
Levin, Jacob, 675
Lewis and Clark Centennial
  Exposition, 154, 209, 365
Lexington, Mass., 745
Libel cases, 84
Liberty Loan, 138, 165, 293, 313
Liberty ships, 676
Libraries, 88, 203, 217, 326, 349, 398,
  502, 696, 724, 741, 746
  See also Presidential libraries
Library, Joint Committee on the, 54
Library and Naval War Records,
  Office of, 294
Library of Congress, 30, 32, 36, 54,
  55, 95, 148, 154, 162, 315,
  316, 578, 697, 724, 726, 741
Libya, U.S. assistance to, 143
Licenses, 424, 483
  Fuel, 593
  Marriage, 75
Lieber, Norman, 259
Life insurance. *See* Insurance, life
Life-Saving Appliances, Board of, 523
Lifesaving
  Equipment, 480
  Stations, 374, 522, 523, 524
Lighter-Than-Air Design Branch, 319
Lighters, naval, 310
Lighthouses, 58, 59, 60, 169, 240,
  315, 372, 374, 522, 524, 525,
  726, 745
Lighthouses, Bureau of, 464, 522
Lighthouses, Office of the
  Inspector of, Veracruz, 283
Lightships, 315, 524
Lignite, 408
Limestone, 409
Lincoln, Abraham, 76, 220, 551,
  570, 744
  Assassination of, 259, 712

Lincoln, Benjamin, 34
Lincoln, Charles Henry, 36
Lincoln, Mary Todd, 748
Lincoln Memorial, 531, 717
Lincoln Sesquicentennial Commission,
  62
Lindbergh, Charles A., 256, 334, 362,
  551, 567
Lindsey, Alton A., 749-750
Linguistics, 148, 566
Lippincott, Richard, 34
Liquid Transport Department,
  Office of Defense
  Transportation, 643, 644
Liquidation, Director of, Office
  for Emergency Management,
  99
Liquidation Advisory Committee,
  Office for Emergency
  Management, 99
Liquidation Commission, U.S.,
  225
Liquor, 177, 344, 379, 461, 509,
  523
  Control of, 381, 382
"Lisbon Papers," 736
List, Wilhelm, 700
Literacy, 695
Literature, 570
  Korean, 736
  Russian, 736
Lithuania, 729, 735
Litigation, 260, 338, 352, 356
Little America, Antarctica, 750
Little Rock, Ark., 745
Live-oak lands, 295
Live Stock Drouth Relief,
  Committee on, 445
Liver Diseases, Commission on,
  203
Livestock, 426, 431, 445, 456,
  457, 459, 462, 668
  Loans, 583, 608
Living Conditions of War
  Workers, Commission on,
  596, 597
"Living war memorials," 640
Livingston, Robert R., 30, 32
Load Line Committee, U.S., 482
Loan Policy Board, 583
Loans, 33, 35, 142, 155, 159, 160,
  161, 162, 163, 164, 416,
  422, 434, 435, 440, 441,
  442, 463, 514, 516, 517, 520,
  532, 533, 534, 553, 565, 583,
  608, 650, 668, 704, 722
  Business, 565, 580, 581, 582, 673
  Commissioners of, 162, 163
  Department of the Treasury,
  166
  Foreign, 33, 158, 581
  Home, 513, 519, 538, 539, 596,
  597

Mortgage, 515, 538
Municipal, 597, 598.
National defense, 582
Railroad, 158, 580, 581, 582
Revolutionary War, 163
Self-liquidating, 440
To banks, 155
Loans, Office of, Reconstruction
  Finance Corporation,
  582, 585
Lobbyists, 50
Locke, Edwin A., Jr., 106
Locomotives, 287
Logan Statue Commission, 717
Logbooks, 524
Logging, 325, 328, 379
Logging, Office of the Superintendent
  of, 375
Logistics, 186, 187, 188, 200, 205,
  212, 223, 229, 287, 288, 297,
  333
  German, 287
Logs, vessel, 307, 676
Lokke, Carl L., 36
London, Canada, 241
London, England, 205, 596, 625
  Aerial attack on, 639, 746
London Conference of the Foreign
  Ministers of France, 137
London Mission, 660
London Munitions Assignments
  Board, 195
London Radio Telegraphic
  Conference of 1912, 307
Long Bridge, 715
Longfellow Statue Commission, 717
"Longhorn," military exercise,
  228
"Longines Chronoscope" (m.p.), 747
Longitude observations, 316
Longshoremen, 540, 602
LORAN, 522
Lorentz, Johan, 724
Lorentz, Pare, 443
Lorwin, Lewis, 123
Los Angeles (airship), 313, 320
Lost Pines, 438
Lotteries, 344, 359, 401
  Revolutionary War, 163
  Selective Service, 564
Louis XVI of France, 35
Louisiana, 53, 134, 136, 156, 238,
  336, 376, 394, 402, 489,
  745
Louisiana Purchase, 154, 209
Louisiana Purchase Exposition,
  154, 365, 370, 433, 493
Lower California, 315
Lower Colorado River project, 370
Loyalty Security Board, 183
Lubin, Sigmund, 86
Lubricants, 305
Luchs, George, 165

Luetgebrune, Walter, 733
Luftflotten-Kommandos, 731
Luftgau-Kommandos, 731
Luftwaffe, 217, 279
Lumber, 430, 490, 518, 633,
  654, 674
  Industry, 325, 430, 487
Lumber Division, Bureau of Foreign
  and Domestic Commerce,
  487
Lunar surface, 554
Lüneburg, surrender at, 188
Lusitania, 443
Lutes, Leroy, 187, 217
Lutheran synods, 466
Luxembourg, 192
Lyles, Charles H., 395

                    M

Mabini, Apolinario, 413
MacArthur, Douglas, 220, 700,
  702, 748
MacArthur Histories, 195
McClellan, George B., 208
McClellan Statue Commission,
  717
McClellan (transport), 726
McCord, Robert F., 588
McCrory, S.H., 448
McCully, R.P., 137
McDermott, Albert L., 491
McDonald, Marshall, 394
McGarraghy, Joseph C., 742
McGinnis, Harold A., 326
Machineguns, 245, 285
Machinery, 270, 306, 307, 308,
  490, 654
  Farm, 448, 452, 453, 544
  German, 728
Machinery, General Inspector
  of, 307
McIlvaine, William, 744
McIntyre, H.H., 172
McKay, Douglas, 367
McKay Companies Land Line
  System, 536
McKean, Thomas, 32
McKinley, William, 176, 562
McLaughlin, Charles V., 491
McLean, John, 70
Macmahon, Arthur W., 743
McMillan, Donald, 747
McNamara-O'Hara Service Contract
  Act of 1965, 496
McNarney, Joseph T., 699
McNary-McSweeney Act of
  1928, 427
McNutt, Paul V., 501, 680
Macomber, Irving E., 597
Macon (airship), 320

Macy Board, 605
Madison, James, 31, 54, 336, 715
Madison Square Garden, 356
Madsen, David H., 399
Magazines, naval, 303, 304
Magnesium, 409
Magnetism, 316, 470, 471, 474
Magnuson, Paul, 111
Magoon, Charles E., 281
Mahan, Alfred T., 296
Mahogany, 586
Mahoney, Frank J., 692
Mail, 326, 361, 487, 530, 603
    Contracts, 360, 487, 488, 606
    Equipment, 361, 362
    Naval, 293
    Transportation, 43, 338, 359,
        360, 361, 362
    See also Air Mail, Bureau of,
        and Airmail service
Maine (U.S.S.), 241, 328, 370, 744
Malaria, 505, 659
Mammalogy, 394, 397
Mammoth Cave National Park, 403
"Man Hunt" (m.p.), 747-748
"Man I Married, The" (m.p.), 747
Management Improvement, President's
        Advisory Committee on, 109
Management-Labor Policy
        Committee, 680, 681
Management Research, Division
        of, Office of the
        Secretary of the Interior,
        369
Manchuria, 137, 451, 733
Manchurian Embassy, in
        Germany, 733
Mandamus, writs of, 70
Mandates, 299
Manganese, 414
Manhattan Engineer District,
        189, 239
Manifests, 169, 170
Manila, surrender of, 220
Manila Railroad Co., 413
Manion, Clarence, 112
Mann, John W., 693
Mann-Elkins Act of 1910, 92

Manning tables, 685, 687
Manpower, 118, 183, 190, 219,
        269, 270, 292, 333, 492,
        643, 644, 662, 665, 672,
        673, 680, 681, 683, 684,
        685, 686, 703
    Axis powers, 198, 205, 734
    Training, 499
    Utilization, 184, 679, 685,
        686, 687
    See also War Manpower
        Commission
Manpower, Office of the
        Assistant Secretary for, 499

Manpower and Reserve Forces,
        Assistant Secretary of the
        Army for, 213
Manpower Board, War Department,
        212, 216, 219
Manpower Priorities Committees,
        460, 686
Manpower Utilization, Bureau
        of, 685
Manual for Courts-Martial, 259
Manufactures, Bureau of, 486
Manufacturing, 370, 486, 555, 570
    Censuses of, 467, 468, 469
    Industry, 350, 464, 629
    Schedules of, 467, 468
Manumission, 75
Mapping, 327, 392
    Federal, 551
    Topographic, 389
March Field, Calif., 328
"March of Time, The" (m.p.), 745
Margaret (ship), 677
Marianas Islands, 293, 299
Marine, Agent of the, 30, 31,
        33, 34
Marine, Office of the, 31
Marine, Secretary of, 31
Marine and Dock Industrial
        Relations Division, 602
Marine casualties, 484, 522, 523, 524
Marine Committee, 31, 34, 35
Marine Corps, 291, 313, 323, 410,
        524
    Discharges, 300
    Generals, 301
    Women in, 293
    World War II, 746

MARINE CORPS, U.S. (RG 127),
        300-301
Marine Corps Schools, 185, 188
Marine Hospital Fund, 504
Marine Hospital Service, 502, 503
Marine hospitals, 59, 502, 503,
        504, 505
Marine Inspection and Navigation,
        Bureau of, 168, 169, 464, 522
MARINE INSPECTION AND
        NAVIGATION, BUREAU OF
        (RG 41), 480-485
Marine observations, 397, 476,
        477, 566
Maritime Administration, 519, 676
MARITIME ADMINISTRATION
        (RG 357), 478-479
Maritime Administrator, 479
Maritime affairs, 69, 259, 315, 601,
        602, 605, 626, 676, 693
    International conferences on,
        481, 483
    Jurisdiction, 72, 82-83
    Passenger service, 677
Maritime Canal Co. of Nicaragua, 562

Maritime Commission, U.S., 478,
    603, 642, 672, 692
    See also Federal Maritime
        Commission (RG 358)
MARITIME COMMISSION, U.S.
    (RG 178), 675-678
MARITIME LABOR BOARD
    (RG 157), 626
Maritime Service, 524, 525
Maritime Subsidy Board, 479
Maritime War Emergency Board,
    693
Mark Twain (packet boat), 489
Marketing, 111, 417, 432, 435,
    436, 443, 444, 447, 453,
    457, 460, 461, 462, 487,
    593, 608, 668
    Agreements, 424, 458, 459, 461
    Agricultural, 423, 455
    Wartime restrictions on, 487
Marketing and Transportation
    Research, Division of, 456
Marketing Laws Survey, 487
Marketing Laws Unit, 487
Marketing Services, Office of, 460
Markets
    Foreign, 423, 430, 431, 432
    Labor, 499, 679, 683, 687
    Seaboard, 595
Markets, Office of, 431, 455, 456,
    460
Markets and Crop Estimates, Bureau
    of, 455, 456, 460
Markets and Rural Organization,
    Office of, 460
Marksmanship competitions,
    inter-Allied, 288
Marque, letters of, 34, 136
Marriage records, 75, 141, 264,
    467, 574
Marschner, Francis J., 457
Marshall, George C., 185, 216
Marshall, John, 70
Marshall Islands, 299
Marshall Plan, 139, 143
Marshals, U.S., 69, 71, 336, 337,
    338, 339, 340, 342, 352,
    353, 364, 465
    See also Attorneys and
        Marshals, U.S. (RG 118)
Martin, Glenn L., 328
Martin, Lawrence, 136
Martin-Mitchell controversy,
    260
Maryland, 75, 136, 452, 514,
    520, 714
Mashburn, Lloyd A., 491
Mason, Charles, 136
Mason, John, 166
Massachusetts, 35, 36, 70, 295,
    305, 471, 745
Matanuska Valley, Alaska,
    404, 695

Matanzas, Bay of, 315
Materials, critical, 111, 187,
    269, 667
Materials and Equipment,
    Division of, Office of
    Defense Transportation, 644
Materials and Facilities,
    Office of, 461
Materiel, procurement of, 210, 211
Mathematics, 475, 554, 659
Mather, Stephen T., 403
Matteson, David M., 743
Mattress-Making Project, 695
Maury, Matthew F., 314, 315,
    316, 477, 748
Mauthausen Concentration
    Camp, 700
Maverick, Maury, 673
Maxwell, George H., 406
Maxwell Air Force Base,
    192, 334
May Day celebration, 335
Meade, George G., 208
Meade Memorial Commission, 717
Meat and meatpacking, 425, 445,
    466, 649
Meat Inspection Act of 1891, 445
Meat Inspection Branch,
    Agricultural Research
    Service, 445
Meat Packing Commission, 633
Mechanical Advisory Committee, 619
Mechanized Cavalry Board, 226
Medal for Merit Boards, World
    War II, 95, 96
*Medal of Honor of the United
    States Army, The*, 221
Medals, 173, 174, 523, 531, 532
Mediation, 492, 580
    See also Federal Mediation and
        Conciliation Service (RG 280);
        Maritime Labor Board
        (RG 157); *and* National
        Mediation Board (RG 13)

Mediation, Board of, 559, 560
Mediation and Conciliation,
    U.S. Board of, 559, 560
Medical care, 64, 65, 183, 203,
    206, 251, 326, 502, 504, 508,
    574, 614, 657
    Military, 182, 187, 203, 232,
        256, 273, 720
Medical Care of Dependents of Military
    Personnel, Citizens Advisory
    Committee on, 183
Medical Corps, 250, 685
Medical Purveyor, Office of the, 504
Medical Research, Committee on,
    658, 659
Medical Services Corps, 250
Medicine, 182, 228, 509, 554,
    640, 658

Advertising and labeling,
    508
Foreign, 730, 736
Preventive, 302
Research, 203, 302, 502, 503,
    504, 508, 658, 659
Training, 293
See also Health
Medicine and Sanitation
    Committee, 579
MEDICINE AND SURGERY,
    BUREAU OF (RG 52),
    301-302
Mediterranean Air Transport
    Service Headquarters,
    193
Mediterranean Allied Air
    Forces Headquarters, 193
Mediterranean Allied Photographic
    Reconnaissance Wing, 193
Mediterranean Allied Strategic
    Air Force Headquarters,
    193
Mediterranean Allied Tactical
    Air Force Headquarters,
    193
Mediterranean Fruit Fly
    Board, 454
Mediterranean Sea, 397
Mediterranean Station, 193
Mediterranean Theater of
    Operations, 193, 197,
    205, 262, 326, 611
Meigs, Montgomery C., 366
Melies Company, 747
Melish, John, 46
Melville, Herman, 677
Melville Dollar, 396
Memorial to Women of the Civil
    War Commission, 717
Memorial to Women of the
    World War (I) Commission,
    717
Memorials. See Monuments and
    memorials
Mental health, 412, 745
Merchant fleet, 692
Merchant Fleet Corporation,
    U.S. Shipping Board, 601,
    602, 603
Merchant marine, 478, 479, 484,
    502, 569, 572, 626, 675,
    676, 677, 693
Casualties, 484, 676
History of, 601, 677
Inspection of, 484
Subsidization of, 479, 676
Training, 485, 607
Merchant Marine Academy,
    U.S., 479
Merchant Marine Acts
    1920, 601
    1936, 602, 626, 675

Merchant Marine and Fisheries,
    House Committee on, 604
Merchant Marine Bulletin, The,
    607
Merchant Marine Medal Awards
    Committee, 692
Merchant seamen, 485, 502,
    522, 525
Merchant Shipbuilding Corp., 605
Merchant vessels. See Vessels,
    merchant
Merchant Vessels of the United
    States, List of, 483
Meridian Hill Park, 716
Merrick, Samuel V., 491
Metallurgy, 408, 659
Metals, 111, 174, 270, 391,
    486, 490, 540, 584, 586,
    633
Metals Reserve, Office of, 584
Metals Reserve Company, 580, 584
Meteorological Division,
    Smithsonian Institution, 566
Meteorological Research Office,
    478
Meteorology, 315, 316, 391,
    437, 523, 562, 750
Instruments, 316, 478
Observations, 254, 476, 477
Reporting stations, 255
See also Naval Observatory
    and Weather Bureau
Meteorology of the Arctic, 750
Meters, electric, 409
Metlakahtla Controversy, 383
Metlakahtla Indians, 744
Meuse-Argonne War Memorial,
    530
Mexican Border Inspection
    Act, 453
Mexican Kickapoo, 383
Mexican Punitive Expedition,
    233, 255, 256, 260, 743
Mexican War, 208, 232, 234,
    240, 247, 255, 271, 272,
    290, 525, 573
Veterans of, 373
Mexico, 46, 137, 139, 143, 147,
    156, 158, 163, 166, 219, 220,
    260, 276, 277, 278, 283, 292,
    299, 347, 395, 430, 476, 571,
    684
Treaties with, 164
U.S. Army in, 276, 277
U.S. Railway Mission in,
    646, 647
Mexico, Gulf of, 279, 397, 473
Mexico City, 290, 529, 663
"Miami Report," 127
Michigan, 134, 641
Indians, 380
Micronesian Islands, 589
Microwave radar, 659

"Midnight judges," 84, 86
Midshipmen, U.S. Naval
    Academy, 322
Midway, battle of, 293
Midwest Disaster Loan
    Committee, 582
Midwives, 510
Mifflin, Thomas, 32
Migration, 457
Migratory Bird Treaty Act, 396
Migratory Labor, President's
    Commission on, 109
Milch, Erhard, 700
Miles, Nelson A., 215
Military
    Aeronautics, 211, 324
    Aid, 143, 183, 185, 188
    Attaches, 217, 235, 288, 733
    Brutality, 737
    Campaigns, 240, 249, 288
    Celebrations, 185
    Commissions, 258, 259, 260, 262
    Equipment, 217, 219, 220, 229,
        230, 240, 242, 243, 245,
        247, 249, 264, 307, 555
    Forces, 207, 214, 216, 735
    Foreign development, 184, 279, 734
    Governors, 277, 279
    History, 213, 236, 255
    Installations, 124, 219, 220, 232,
        233, 237, 241, 249, 271,
        274, 280, 284, 299, 734
    Intelligence, 184, 185, 204, 216,
        217, 218, 219, 222, 229,
        298, 300, 301, 332, 638,
        662, 663
    Justice, 213, 221, 258, 259, 317
    Leaders, 138, 188, 206, 328, 525,
        663, 689, 743, 745
    Medical care, 182, 187, 203, 232,
        250, 251, 256, 273, 720
    Occupational classification project,
        184
    Occupational specialties, 228
    Operations, 192, 199, 201, 204,
        213, 216, 217, 219, 220, 233,
        240, 267, 288, 356, 473, 663,
        731, 732, 734, 737
    Organizations, 38, 201, 222, 232,
        414, 637
    Personnel, 33, 34, 95, 221, 327
    Police, 267, 268, 269, 285, 286,
        332
    Posters relating to World War I,
        288
    Prisons, 232, 259, 318
    Procurement, 187, 204, 624
    Prohibited areas, 280
    Real estate, 183, 238
    Reservations, 219, 232, 247,
        249, 260, 262, 372, 373,
        374, 393, 714
    Roads, 376

Security, 185, 734
Service, 37, 39, 207, 257, 265,
    720, 721
Supplies, 211, 216, 217
Training, 107, 184, 185, 188,
    194, 203, 204, 207, 212,
    214, 216, 217, 218, 220,
    221, 222, 227, 228, 230,
    236, 244, 256, 275, 278, 288,
    293, 297, 298, 299, 300, 301,
    312, 313, 320, 321, 327, 328,
    333, 334, 563, 681, 746
Tribunals, 699, 700, 702
See also National Military
    Establishment *and* Schools,
    military
Military Academy, U.S., 207, 219,
    232, 233, 235, 236, 237, 256
MILITARY ACADEMY, U.S.
    (RG 404), 288-289
Military Assistance Advisory
    Group, 184, 204
Military Assistance Program, U.S.,
    President's Committee to
    Study the, 114
Military Asylum, 290
Military Board, Headquarters of
    the Army, 215
Military Board of Allied Supply,
    287
Military Defense Assistance
    Program, 183, 184, 204
Military Geographical Institute
    (Poland), 735
Military Government, School
    of, 268
Military Government for Germany,
    Office of, 197, 198, 699
MILITARY GOVERNMENT OF
    CUBA (RG 140), 280-281
MILITARY GOVERNMENT OF
    VERACRUZ (RG 141),
    283
Military governments, 193, 197, 214,
    221, 236, 267, 268, 279,
    297, 611
    Austria, 197, 198
    Germany, 256, 743
    Italy, 193, 736
    Trieste, 193-194
    Venezia Giulia, 193
Military History, Office of the
    Chief of, 223
Military Information Control
    Committee, 184
Military Intelligence Service,
    197
Military Justice, Bureau of,
    258
Military Justice, Uniform Code
    of, 213, 221, 258
Military Liaison Headquarters,
    193

Military Medical Advisory
    Council, 187
Military Mission to Berlin,
    U.S., 287
Military Mission to Moscow,
    U.S., 204
Military Operations, Office
    of the Deputy Chief of
    Staff for, 222, 254
Military Planning Division,
    Office of the Quartermaster
    General, 249
Military Police Board, 268
Military Railroads, Office of
    U.S., 247
Military Railways, Office of
    the Director General
    of, 238
Military Records, Air Force
    Board for the Correction
    of, 330
Military Roads, Pacific
    Coast, Office of, 238
Military Sea Transportation
    Service, 323
Military Secretary's Office,
    231
Military Storekeeper, Office
    of, 248
Military Stores, Office of
    Superintendent of, 248
Military Telegraph Lines, U.S.,
    255
Militia, 231, 264
    Naval, 312
    State, 264
Militia Affairs, Division of, Office
    of the Secretary of War, 264

Militia Division, Adjutant
    General's Office, 264
Militia Service in Florida, 247
Milk, 436, 447, 461, 462, 507,
    508, 668
    Inspection of, 509
Miller, Dale, 742

Miller, J. Clayton, 464
Miller, Spencer, Jr., 491
Milling industry, 592
Mills, 407, 567
Milwaukee Gas Light Co., 540
Milwaukee Public Museum, 370
Mine laying, 304, 313
Mine planters, 272
Mine Track Bureau, 594
Mine Warfare Section, 298
Minefields, 275
Mineral Contest Division, General
    Land Office, 374
Mineral Imports and Exports,
    Committee on, 408
Mineral Leasing Division,
    Geological Survey, 393

Mineral Resources Division,
    390, 391, 407, 408
Minerals, 119, 270, 367, 369,
    376, 389, 391, 407, 408,
    414, 415, 429, 486, 567,
    586, 625, 626
    Critical, 408, 584
    Deposits, 65, 391, 393
    Industries, 390, 407, 408
    Lands, 243, 245, 374
    Latin American, 647
    Production, 111, 390, 408, 415
    Resources, 65, 98, 124, 338,
        372, 389, 390, 391, 407,
        408, 586
Minerals and Derivatives, Joint
    Information Board on, 408
Minerals and Fuels Division,
    Office of the Secretary of
    the Interior, 369
Mines, Bureau of, 256, 370, 390,
    393, 461
MINES, BUREAU OF (RG 70),
    407-409
Mines and mining, 106, 174, 270,
    288, 370, 372, 376, 391,
    407, 408, 409, 468, 555
    Accidents, 407, 408
    Claims, 370
    Depots, 303, 304
    Disaster, Royalton, Ill., 409
    Health, 407, 408, 409, 420
    Industry, 178, 408, 409, 684
    Locations, 323, 370, 393, 408
    Workers, 174, 417, 594
Minesweeping, 299
Ministers
    Foreign, 32, 131, 132, 146
    U.S., 46, 69, 131, 138, 140,
        141, 164
Ministries Division, Office of the
    Chief of Counsel for War
    Crimes, 701
Minnesota, 134, 156, 344, 489, 745
Minority Group Adviser, 651
Minority groups, 514, 617, 746
    Censuses of, 467
    In the Armed Services, 108
Minority Groups Service, 684
MINT, BUREAU OF THE
    (RG 104), 172-175
Mint, Director of the, 172, 173
Mint, U.S., at Philadelphia, 172,
    173, 745
Mint Service, 173
Missiles, guided, 183, 188, 189,
    332, 334, 659
Mission Indians, 567
"Mission to Moscow" (m.p.),
    747
Missionaries, 423
Missions. See Diplomatic
    Service

Mississippi, 134, 289, 290, 394
Mississippi Choctaw, 380
Mississippi Drainage Basin, 671
Mississippi River, 53, 156, 488, 489
Mississippi Valley, floods in, 247, 249
Mississippi Valley Committee, 669
Missouri, 134, 344
Missouri Basin Interagency Committee, 421
Missouri Basin Survey Commission, 112, 369
Missouri River, 488
Missouri River Basin, 112
Missouri River Commission, 239, 240
Missouri (U.S.S.), 293
Mitchell, James P., 115, 491
Mitchell, William, 259, 260, 334
Mitchell News Bureau, 406
Mixed Claims Commission, 144, 573
Mobile Harbor, 471
Mobilization, 186, 202, 204, 213, 216, 229, 269, 270, 275, 490

  Agricultural, 436
  German, 732, 734
  Industrial, 187, 201, 203, 210, 211, 229, 238, 269, 270, 422, 687
  Italian, 736
  Japanese, 736
  Of scientific personnel, 657
  Wartime, 204, 256, 265, 639, 641, 642, 664, 732
  See also War Mobilization and Reconversion, Office of
Mobilization of Relief Resources, Committee on, 121
Mogensen, Palle, 750
Mohawk Nation Iroquois Confederacy, 389
Mohawk Valley, 34
Moisture conservation, 437, 452
Molasses, 656
Molotov, Vyacheslav M., 335
Moltke, Helmuth Carl Bernhard von, 732
Money, 147, 663
  Counterfeit, 164
  Orders, 361
  Policies, 146, 153, 651, 703
  Public, 165, 352
  See also Currency *and* Mint, Bureau of the (RG 104)
Mongolia, 451

Monitor (U.S.S.), 296
Monitors, 307
Monopolies, 62, 338
Monroe, James, 135
Montana, 134, 430
Montenegro, 736
Montfaucon, France, 530
Montreal Assembly, 118
Monument, Joint Commission on the Dedication of the, 717
Monuments and memorials, 32, 58, 61, 103, 104, 241, 370, 371, 385, 397, 398, 399, 531, 532, 640, 714, 716, 717
  American, in Europe, 529, 530
  Boundary, 144, 145
  District of Columbia, 401, 402, 531, 714, 716, 717
  National, 249, 397, 398, 399, 401, 402
  Preservation of, 193, 611-612
  Public, 402, 548
  War-damaged (WW II), 198
Moon, 333
Mooney, James E., 750
Mooney-Billings case, 64
Morale
  Civilian, 578
  Japanese, 662
  Military, 218
Moran, Edward C., Jr., 491, 676
Morell, Theo, 733
Morgan, John, 34
Mormons, 566

Morris, Robert, 30, 31, 33, 166, 715
Morrison, J. A., 205
Morrissey (SS), 750
Morse, David A., 491
Morse, S.F.B., 358
Mortality
  Infant, 510
  Maternal, 510
  Schedules of, 468, 469
Mortgage and Lien Foreclosure Act, 339

Mortgages, 355, 513, 514, 516, 581, 582, 583, 588
  Chattel, 694
  Federal, 514, 517, 533, 534
  Loans, 515
  Secondary market for, 516, 517, 583
  See also Federal National Mortgage Association
Moscow, 204, 334, 735
Moscow Declaration, 699
Moths, gypsy and browntail, 454
Motion Picture and Television Service, U.S. Information Agency, 569

Motion picture industry, 660, 745, 746, 747
Motion Picture Industry, War Activities Committee of the, 746
Motor Carrier Claims Commission, 644
Motor carriers, 619, 643, 644
"Motor Transport, U.S. Army, 1769 to Date," 223
Motor Transport Corps, 246, 285
Motor Transport Division, 248
Motorboats, safety regulations, 481
Moulton Commission, 183
Mt. Rainier National Park, 362

Mt. Vernon Conference, 31
Mount Vernon Memorial Highway, 402, 527
Mountbatten, Louis, 195
Mounted Service School, 226
"Movietone News" (m.p.), 745
Munich Putsch, 733

Munitions, 137, 195, 201, 270, 326, 555
    Allocation of, 191
    Plants, 689
    Small arms, 215, 244, 245
    See also Ordnance
Munitions Assignments Board, 195

Munitions Assignments Committee, 195, 326
Munitions Boards, 182, 183, 187, 202, 203, 214, 269, 292
Munitions Patent Board, 261
Munitions Standards Board, 579
Munsee Indians, 380
Murder, 127
Murmansk, 286
Murphy Iron Wheel, 303
Murrow, Edward R., 677, 748

Muscle Shoals, 55, 245, 261, 452, 567
Muscle Shoals Grant, 372
Museum, Henry Ford, 746
Museum of Modern Art, 388
Museums, 370, 388, 398, 402, 476, 735, 746
    See also Smithsonian Institution
Music, 636
    Federal Projects, 696, 699
    Foreign, 663
Mussolini, Benito, 623, 736, 737
Muster rolls, 301, 311, 523
Mutual Educational and Cultural Exchange Act of 1961, 569
Mutual Ownership Defense Housing Division, 519
Mutual Security, Director of, 143
Mutual Security Agency, 143
Mutual Security Program, 114, 184

N

Nachtrieb, R.F., 674
Nagasaki, Japan, 328, 677
    Atomic bomb effects on, 206, 334
Nanking, China, 299
Napoleonic wars, 336
Narcotic Division, Bureau of Prohibition, 350, 351
Narcotics, 168, 339
    See also Drugs
NARCOTICS AND DANGEROUS DRUGS, BUREAU OF (RG 170), 350-351
Nathan, Robert R., 665
National Academy of Sciences, 658
NATIONAL ACADEMY OF SCIENCES (RG 189), 554-555
National Adjustment Commission, 602
NATIONAL AERONAUTICS AND SPACE ADMINISTRATION (RG 255), 553-554
National Aeronautics Committee (WW I), 746
National Agricultural Conference, 457
National Agricultural Credit Corporations, 160
National Air and Space Museum, 566
National Airframe Panel, 633
National Airmail Week, 360
National Alien Enemy Relief Committee, 137
National Archeological Museum at Warsaw, 735
National Archives, 141, 149, 282, 719, 726, 727, 741, 747
    Building, 551, 746
National Archives Act of 1934, 743
National Archives and Records Service, 742
NATIONAL ARCHIVES AND RECORDS SERVICE (GSA) (RG 64), 549-551
National Archives Building, Advisory Committee on the, 137, 547
National Archives Collection of Foreign Records Seized, 1941- (RG 242), 727-737
National Archives Council, 551
National Archives Establishment, 549
National Archives Gift Collection, 95, 741
NATIONAL ARCHIVES GIFT COLLECTION (RG 200), 742-749

NATIONAL ARCHIVES GIFT
COLLECTION OF MATERIALS
RELATING TO POLAR
REGIONS (RG 401), 749-751
National Armed Forces Museum
Advisory Board, 566
National Army, 266, 274
National Art Week, 547, 696
National Association of
Broadcasters, 536
National Atlas of the United States,
555
National Banking System, 159
National Banknote Co., 164
National Bankruptcy acts. *See*
Bankruptcy, national acts
National Bituminous Coal
Commission, 420, 637
NATIONAL BITUMINOUS COAL
COMMISSION, 1935-36
(RG 150), 417-418
National Board for the Promotion
of Rifle Practice, 214
National Board of Health, 503
Cuban, 282
National Broadcasting Co., 699, 746
National Bureau of Standards,
514, 551, 554
NATIONAL BUREAU OF
STANDARDS (RG 167),
474-476
National Bureau of Standards Reports,
475
National Cancer Institute, 504
NATIONAL CAPITAL HOUSING
AUTHORITY (RG 302),
712-713
National Capital Park and
Planning Commission, 398
National Capital Park Commission,
713
National Capital Parks, 400, 402
NATIONAL CAPITAL PLANNING
COMMISSION (RG 328),
713-714
National Capital Sesquicentennial
Commission, 61
National Collection of Fine Arts,
566
National Conference of State
Boards of Health of 1884,
503
National Conservation
Commission, 369, 427
National Conservation Congress,
427
National Conservation
Exposition, 427
National Currency Association, 164
National defense, 30, 102, 124,
185, 218, 424, 479, 553, 567,
582, 613, 634, 640, 657
Agencies, 644

Programs, 125, 235, 527, 644
Projects, 547
National Defense, Council of, 120
National Defense, Department of,
216
National Defense Act of 1935,
German, 731
National defense acts
1916, 234
1920, 207, 211, 246, 266
National Defense Advisory
Commission, 105, 371, 644,
648, 672
See also Advisory Commission
to the Council of National
Defense
National Defense Day, *1924*, 748
National Defense Mediation Board,
626, 631, 632
National Defense Power Committee
of the War Department, 210,
369
National Defense Power Staff, 542
National Defense Research
Committee, 223, 658, 659
National Drought Relief
Committee, 425
National Ecuadorian Exposition,
Quito, Ecuador, *1909*,
433
National Education Association,
371
National Educational Television,
468
National Emergency Council,
124, 125, 425, 426
National Enforcement
Commission, 703, 706, 707
National Environmental Satellite
Center, 479
"National Farm Federation News,
The," 649
National Farm Loan Association,
533
National Film Board of Canada,
746
National Forest Reservation
Commission, 427
National Foundation on the
Arts and the Humanities
Act, 496
National 4-H Club Foundation, 747
National Gallery of Art, 566, 567
National Grange, 434
National Guard, 227, 228, 235, 264,
273, 331

NATIONAL GUARD BUREAU
(RG 168), 264-265
National Herbarium, 462
National Historical Publications
Commission, 551

National Home for Disabled
  Volunteer Soldiers,
  241, 242, 571, 572,
  574-575
National Housing Administrator, 585
National Housing Agency, 513,
  515, 517, 518, 520, 538,
  585, 596, 616, 704
National Industrial Recovery Act,
  126, 415, 437, 511, 555,
  626, 669, 725
National Industrial Recovery
  Administration, 588
National Industrial Recovery
  Board, 627
National Institutes of Health,
  502, 504
National Intelligence
  Authority, 101, 222
National Inventors Council, 219
National Irrigation
  Association, 406
National Labor Board, 555,
  556, 557
National Labor-Management
  Panel, 540
National Labor Relations
  Act, 555, 557, 558
National Labor Relations
  Board, 71
  House of Representatives
    Special Committee To
    Investigate the,
    557, 558
NATIONAL LABOR
  RELATIONS BOARD
  (RG 25), 555-558
National Land Defense Board,
  219, 232
National League for Good
  Roads, 526
National Library of Medicine,
  203, 502
National Manpower Priorities
  Committee, 681
NATIONAL MEDIATION
  BOARD (RG 13),
  558-561
National Military
  Establishment, 182, 188, 207,
  212, 216, 219, 231, 268,
  291, 329, 658
National Minerals Advisory
  Council, 369
National Mortgage Association
  of Washington, 516, 583
National Museum, 566, 567
National Negro Health Week,
  1942, 505
National Park Service, 63,
  545, 614, 714
NATIONAL PARK SERVICE
  (RG 79), 397-403

National Parks, Buildings,
  and Reservations, Office
  of, 397
National Parole Conference,
  350
National Plan for American
  Forestry, 430
National Planning Board,
  122, 123, 669
National Portrait Gallery, 566
National Power Policy
  Committee, 369, 669
National Press Club, 551
NATIONAL PRODUCTION
  AUTHORITY (RG 277),
  489-490
National Prohibition Act, 339
National Railroad Adjustment
  Board, 559
National Railway Labor
  Panel, 559, 561
National Reclamation Association,
  406
National Recovery
  Administration, 416, 436,
  493, 627, 669
  Codes, 556
NATIONAL RECOVERY
  ADMINISTRATION (RG 9),
  626-631
National Recovery Review
  Board, 629
National Reemployment Service,
  498, 499
National Research Council,
  302, 395, 508, 554, 555, 658
National Research Information
  Committee, 555
National Resources Board, 122, 123
National Resources Committee,
  122, 396
National Resources Planning
  Board, 99, 669
NATIONAL RESOURCES
  PLANNING BOARD (RG 187),
  122-124
National Roster of Scientific
  and Specialized Personnel, 122,
  679, 684
National Safety Council, 640
National Science Foundation,
  101, 588
National Screw Thread
  Commission, 476
National security, 101, 182, 199,
  202, 267, 578
  Army's role in, 220
National Security Act of 1947,
  101, 188, 201, 207, 212,
  216, 324, 329, 331, 332
National Security Council, 101,
  188, 331

National Security Resources
  Board, 111, 269
National Security Training
  Commission, 184
National Service Bureau, 696
National Shipping Authority,
  479
National Socialist German
  Workers' Party, 733
National Survey of Vocational
  Education and Guidance
  of Negroes, 506
National Telephone
  Commission, 633
National Training School for Boys, 349
National Transportation Safety
  Board, 530
National Trucking Commission, 540
National Tuberculosis Association,
  748
National Voluntary Mortgage
  Credit Extension Committee,
  513, 514
National Wage Stabilization Board,
  498, 631, 632, 633
National War Agencies
  Appropriation Act of
  1846, 616
National War College, 204
National War Labor Board, 495, 498,
  580, 631, 632, 633, 645, 672
NATIONAL WAR LABOR
  BOARD (WORLD WAR I)
  (RG 2), 580
NATIONAL WAR LABOR
  BOARD (WORLD WAR II)
  (RG 202), 631-634
National Weather Records
  Center, 476, 635, 636
National Youth Administration,
  103, 615, 679, 685,
  693-694, 699
NATIONAL YOUTH
  ADMINISTRATION
  (RG 119), 634-636
National Zoological Park,
  566, 567, 714, 716
Nationalsozialistische Deutsche
  Arbeiterpartei, 733
Native Affairs, Office of the
  Secretary of, American
  Samoa, 410
Native American, The, 385
NATO. See North Atlantic
  Treaty Organization
NATO, U.S. Citizens Commission
  on, 137
Natural Gas, Advisory Committee
  on, 594
Natural Gas Act of 1938, 541
Natural History, Museum of, 566
Natural resources, 270, 370,
  479, 614

Foreign, 138, 194, 205, 236
Natural Scientists, Advisory
  Committee on, 104
Naturalization, 74-77, 79-83,
  85-90, 344, 346
  American Samoan, 410
  Laws, 346
  Schools, 346
Naturalization, Bureau of, 345
Nature Notes, 398
Nature study, 746
Nauru Island, 189
Nautical Almanac Office,
  305, 316
Nautical charts, 314, 315, 474
Nautical instruments, 314, 316
Navajo-Hopi Reservation, 439
Navajo Indians, 387, 388, 468
Naval Academy, 295, 311,
  313
  Cruise ships, 322
Naval Academy, Board of
  Visitors of, 312
Naval Academy, Superintendent
  of the, 294, 311-312
NAVAL ACADEMY, U.S.
  (RG 405), 321-322
Naval Academy Division, 312
Naval Advisory Board, 292
Naval Aeronautics, Office of, 318
Naval affairs, 31, 34, 35, 36, 196,
  299, 308, 318, 320, 473,
  563, 601
Naval Air Transport Service, 299
Naval Astronomical Expedition
  to the Southern
  Hemisphere, U.S., 316
Naval Asylum, 295, 310
Naval aviation, 58, 293, 319, 320, 321
Naval Aviation, Office of, 318
Naval bounty cases, 91, 351
Naval Committee, 31
Naval Communication
  Service, 296
Naval Communications,
  Division of, Office of the
  Chief of Naval Operations, 297
Naval Consulting Board, 292, 603
Naval Depot of Charts and
  Instruments, 315
Naval District Affairs Division, Office
  of the Chief of Naval
  Operations, 297
NAVAL DISTRICTS AND
  SHORE ESTABLISHMENTS
  (RG 181), 320-321
Naval Districts Division, Office of
  the Chief of Naval Operations, 299
Naval establishments
  Air stations, 58, 293, 310, 319, 320,
    321
  Bases, 293, 300, 310, 319, 320, 321
  Coal depots, 292, 307, 321

Disciplinary barracks, 318
Dispensaries, 301-302
Radio stations, 307
Shore, 292, 294, 295, 296, 302,
    303, 306, 309, 310, 311,
    313, 319, 477
Stations, 292, 294, 302, 303, 306,
    309, 310, 311, 313, 319,
    320, 321, 477
Stores, 295, 450
Supply depots, 309
Yards, 292, 293, 294, 295, 303,
    305, 308, 309, 310, 312,
    313, 320, 321, 322
Naval Examining Board, 295
Naval Expedition and Survey, 241
Naval Facilities Engineering
    Command, 309
Naval forces, 195, 207, 283, 297,
    298, 323
Naval Forces Operating in
    European Waters, 306, 318
Naval Gun Exercise Manual, 303
Naval Historical Foundation,
    315, 316
Naval History, Office of,
    294, 298
Naval History Division, 727
Naval Home, U.S., 310, 312
Naval Hospital, U.S., 302
Naval Intelligence, Office of,
    293, 294, 295, 296, 298, 692
Naval Medical School, 302
Naval Militia Affairs, Division of,
    312
Naval Observatory, 296, 305, 477
NAVAL OBSERVATORY (RG 78),
    315-317
Naval Observatory, Commission to
    Ascertain the Cost of Removing
    the, 295
Naval Observatory and Hydrographical
    Office, 313, 314, 315
Naval Oceanographic Office, 313
Naval Officer Messenger Mail
    System, 202
Naval Oil Reserve Investigations, 341
NAVAL OPERATING FORCES
    (RG 313), 323
Naval Operations, Chief of, 188,
    291, 297, 305, 323
Naval Operations, Chief of,
    German, 731
Naval Operations, Deputy Chief of
    (Administration), 297
Naval Operations, Deputy Chief
    of (Air), 299
Naval Operations, Deputy Chief of
    (Logistics), 298
Naval Operations, Deputy Chief of
    (Operations), 298
Naval Operations, Office of the
    Chief of, 282, 313, 315, 318

NAVAL OPERATIONS, OFFICE
    OF THE CHIEF OF
    (RG 38), 296-299
Naval ordnance, 304, 376, 624
Naval personnel, 294, 308, 311
    Agents, 294, 295
    Attaches, 298
    Cadets, 312
    Officers, 294, 295, 296, 307,
        310, 311, 312, 322
    Reserves, 321
    Training, 297, 298, 299, 312,
        320, 321
    Women in, 293
Naval Personnel, Bureau of,
    305, 321
NAVAL PERSONNEL, BUREAU
    OF (RG 24), 310-313
Naval Records and Library,
    Office of, 291, 292, 298, 309,
    314
NAVAL RECORDS COLLECTION
    OF THE OFFICE OF NAVAL
    RECORDS AND LIBRARY
    (RG 45), 293-296
Naval Research Personnel Board,
    312
Naval Reserve Midshipmen's
    School, 322
Naval Reserve Supply Corps, 309
Naval School, 321
Naval Ship Systems Command, 305
Naval Stores Act, 507
Naval Stores Research Division, 450
Naval Supply Systems
    Command, 309
Naval Support Force,
    Antarctica, 323
Naval Torpedo Board, 304
Naval Torpedo Boats Board, 304
Naval Training School, 312
Naval vessels, 291, 292, 295, 296,
    298, 300, 302, 306, 307,
    308, 318
Naval War Board, 292, 295
Naval War Claims Board, 318
Naval War Record Office, 294
Naval Weapons, Bureau of, 303, 319
Naval Weather Service Division, 299
Naval Yards and Docks, Bureau of,
    309
Navassa Island Lighthouse Station,
    524
Navigation, 241, 313, 314, 333, 474,
    523, 527
    Air, 327, 554
    Foreign, 729, 736
    Laws, 170, 480, 481, 483, 522,
        524, 603
    Schools, 328
    See also Marine Inspection and
        Navigation, Bureau of, *and*
        Naval Observatory

Navigation, Bureau of, 295, 296, 303, 305, 310, 311, 312, 313, 315, 316, 318, 320, 321, 322, 480, 481, 483

Navigation, Commissioner of, 60, 480, 481, 484

Navigation and Steamboat Inspection, Bureau of, 480, 481, 485

Navy, 108, 113, 191, 204, 255, 256, 257, 292, 297, 300, 307, 308, 309, 312, 316, 317, 321, 419, 503, 522, 527, 593, 659, 660, 692, 737, 746

Applications, appointments, and resignations, 294, 295

Boards, 31, 307, 317

Overseas commands, 196

Powerplants, 309, 310

Veterans, 574

See also Aeronautics, Bureau of (RG 72); Defense, Office of the Secretary of; Joint Commands (RG 349); Judge Advocate General (Navy), Office of the; and Ordnance, Bureau of

Navy, Acting Secretary of, 203

Navy, Assistant Secretary of the, 307, 321

Navy, Department of, 60, 105, 152, 195, 200, 201, 207, 256, 261, 294, 295, 297, 301, 302, 303, 305, 307, 308, 309, 317, 318, 319, 320, 321, 323, 336, 374, 404, 470, 471, 476, 477, 519, 554, 573, 574, 605, 609, 613, 616, 637, 638, 657, 672, 679, 682, 724

Building, 717

Control of Alaska, 412

Control of American Samoa, 409

NAVY, DEPARTMENT OF THE (RG 80), 291-293

Navy, foreign, 293

British, 296, 737

French, 737

German, 730, 731, 732, 734, 737

Italian, 736

Prussian, 731

Navy, Office of the Assistant Secretary of the, 291, 292

Navy, Office of the Secretary of, 291, 292, 294, 296, 297, 305, 310, 317

Navy, Office of the Under Secretary of, 292

Navy, Secretary of the, 119, 200, 269, 291, 294, 295, 296, 297, 300, 304, 305, 307, 309, 311, 316, 317, 318, 321, 322, 323, 364, 409, 571, 578, 593, 678

Navy, Solicitor of the, 317, 318

Navy Air Force, 293

Navy Armament Board, 304

Navy Board for Production Awards, 292

Navy Bureau of Aeronautics, 187

Navy Commissioners, Board of, 291, 292, 294, 295, 305, 307, 308, 315

Navy Department, Auditor for the, 60

Navy Hospital Corps, 302

Navy Hydrographic Office, 474

Navy Manpower Survey Board, 292

Navy Pension Fund, 166, 573

Nazi activities, 699, 701, 702, 728, 730, 732, 737, 747

Leaders, 734, 736

Nazi Party, 729, 730, 733, 734, 737

Nazi Supreme Court, 702

Neapolitan treaty of 1832, 164

Near East, American Relief Administration mission to the, 596

Nebraska, 134, 388, 390

Necessity, Certificates of, 105

Needlework, 631

Nef, Evelyn Stefansson, 750

Negro Affairs, Office of, National Youth Administration, 636

Negro Economics, Division of, Department of Labor, 491

Negro Education, Specialist in, 506

Negroes, King's, 724

"Neighborhood Call" (s.r.), 663

Neill, Charles P., 559

Nelson, Donald M., 106, 657, 688, 689

Nelson, O.L., 216

Nemaha Half-breed Reserve, 380

Netherlands, the, 33, 35, 139, 192, 194, 596, 612, 735

Netherlands Claims Commission, 260

Neufville, John de, 35

Nevada, 103, 134

New Brunswick, N.J., 598

New Deal, 699

New Delhi, India, 205

New England-New York Interagency Committee, 421

New England Research Council on Marketing and Food Supply, 444

New Hampshire Grants, 33, 34

"New Horizons in Science" (s.r.), 570

New Mexico, 134, 404

New Orleans, La., 53, 402, 489

New Orleans Mint, 745

New Orleans Road, 238

New Post Office, Washington, D.C., 362

New Reich Chancellery, 727

"New World of Atomic Energy" (s.r.), 570

New York, U.S. Housing
    Corporation of, 596, 597
New York City, 53
New York Harbor, 343, 471, 561
New York Harbor Line Board, 239
New York Harbor Wage Adjustment
    Board, 602
"New York Hat, The" (m.p.), 747
New York Indians, 380, 384
New York International Airport, 334
New York State, 33, 34, 35, 36, 235,
    344, 356, 598, 640, 690, 691,
    745
New York Times, The, Paris Bureau
    photographic file of, 569
New York World's Fair, 125, 547,
    636
New York World's Fair
    Commission, 61
Newburgh, N.Y., 716
Newlands acts
    1902, 406
    1913, 559
Newman, James R., 665
Newport, R.I., 321
Newport Historical Society, 162
News media, 219, 551, 569, 633,
    638, 646, 746
"News of the Day" (m.p.),
    663, 745
Newsletter of the Women's
    Bureau, 495
Newspaper indexing projects,
    697
Nez Perces Indians, 44
Niagara River, 147
Nicaragua, 137, 145, 562
    Canal surveys, 238
    Guardia Nacional in, 301
    U.S. Electoral Missions to, 147
    U.S. Marines in, 301
Nicaragua Canal Board, 562
Nicaragua Canal Commission,
    562
Nicaragua Ship Canal, 562
Nicaraguan Expeditionary
    Squadron, 323
Nicaro project, 552
Nicholson, John, 715
Nickel, 409, 552
Nickelodeon shows, 747
"Night Train" (m.p.), 748
Nimitz, Chester W., 110
Nisei soldiers, 691
Nitrates, 243, 551
    Plants, 245, 304
Nixon, Richard M., 138, 335
    Inauguration of, 55
Nobility, titles of, 41
Nolen, John, Jr., 713
Nonferrous Metals Commission,
    633
Norfolk, Va., 598
    Ferries, 597, 598

Noriel, Mariano, 413
North Africa, 736
    Military activities in, 236
North African Theater of
    Operations, 193
North Atlantic Fisheries
    Arbitration, 145
North Atlantic Squadron, 323
North Atlantic Treaty
    Affairs, 185
North Atlantic Treaty
    Organization, 143, 184
North Carolina, 36, 344, 397, 471, 745
North Dakota Agricultural
    College, 236
North German Lloyd, 734
North Interior Building, 402
North Korea, 180, 181, 736, 737
    Communist forces of, 196
North Korean Army, 736
North Pacific Exploring Expedition,
    314
North Pacific Surveying
    Expedition, 172
North Pole, 334, 551, 747, 749-751
    See also Polar regions
North Vietnam, 181, 747
Northeast Area Joint
    Committee, 202
Northeast Command, U.S., 200
Northeast Defense Command, 279
Northeast Farm Management
    Research Committee, 444
Northeast Postwar Planning
    Committee, 457
Northeast Production Advisory
    Group, 444
Northeast Regional Committee
    on Production Goals, 457
Northeastern Timber Salvage
    Administration, 427
Northern Brazil Training Group,
    196
Northern Pacific Railroad, 429
Northwest Indian war, 232
Northwest Territory, 134
Northwest Territory
    Celebration Commission,
    61
Northwestern University, Naval
    Reserve Midshipmen's
    School at, 312
Norton Sound, 723
Norway, 192, 612, 735
Nourse, Joseph, 166
Nuclear physics, Germany, 217
Nuclear research, 189
Nunivak (Coast Guard cutter),
    523
Nuremberg, 699, 700, 702
Nuremberg Military Post, 701
Nuremberg Trial, 748
Nurseries, 439

Nurses and nursing, 250, 251, 302, 383, 641, 685
Nursing homes, 515
Nutrition, 446, 458, 462, 640
Nutrition Division, Office of Defense Health and Welfare Services, 640
Nuts, 442, 468

O

Oak Ridge, Tenn., 190
Oaths, loyalty, 33, 482
Oats, 442
Oberbefehlshaber der Kriegsmarine, 731
Oberbefehlshaber der Luftwaffe, 731
Oberbefehlshaber des Heeres, 732
Oberkommando der Kriegsmarine/OKM, 731
Oberkommando der Luftwaffe/OKL, 731
Oberkommando der Wehrmacht/OKW, 730
Oberkommando des Heeres/OKH, 732
Obersalzberg, 198
Observatories, magnetic, 474
    See also Naval Observatory *and* Weather Bureau
Observatory, U.S., 241
OCCUPATION HEADQUARTERS, U.S., WORLD WAR II (RG 260), 197-198
Occupation zones (WW II), 197
Occupational Deferment, Committee on, 681
Occupations, 466, 467, 468, 742
    Classifications, 499
    Critical, 682
Occupied Areas, Office of, 214
Ocean Island, 189
Ocean mail contracts, 359, 487
Ocean-Mail Contracts, Interdepartmental Subcommittee on, 603
Ocean-Mail Contracts, Special Senate Committee Investigating, 603
Oceanography, 313, 314, 315, 477, 478, 479, 480, 522, 747
O'Connell, James T., 491
O'Dell, Charles, 491
Officer-Enlisted Man Relationship Board, 211
Officer Procurement Service, 230
Officers and Fleet, Division of, 312
Official Gazette of Manila, 414

Official Seed Analysts of North America, Association of, 463
Official War Review, World War I, 745
Ogden, Utah Territory, 241
Ohio Joint Stock Land Bank, 534
Ohio-Mississippi Valley, 583
Ohio River, 392, 401
Ohio River Improvement, Office of, 238
Ohio Valley, floods in, 247, 249
Ohlendorf, Otto, 700
Oil, 292, 343, 368, 395, 415, 416, 594, 644, 667
    Industry, 343, 370, 393, 409, 450, 540, 586, 666
    Reserves, 292, 341, 393, 408
    See also Fuel *and* Petroleum
Oil Leasing Organization, 393
Oil Reserves, President's Commission on, 393
Oil shale, 291, 375
Okinawa, invasion of, 293
Oklahoma, 366, 404
Oklahoma Indians, 368
Oklahoma National Guard, 265
"Oklahoma Railroad Bill," 53
Oklahoma Territory, 376
Olcott, Henry S., 257
Old-Age and Survivors Insurance, Bureau of, 511
"Old Georgetown," 531
Old Reich Chancellery, 727, 728
Oltmann, J.G., 473
Olympics, 256, 335, 737
Omaha Indians, 380
Ontario (U.S.S.), 302
Opera, 356, 748
Operation Big Switch, 262
Operation Castle, 191
Operation Crossroads, 190, 304
Operation Frantic, 204
Operation Greenhouse, 191
Operation Ivy, 191
Operation Sandstone, 191
Operation Wigwam, 190
Operation Windstorm, 191
Operational Readiness Division, 298
Opium, 146, 350, 353
Optics, 475, 659
Orange trees, 423
Order of American Knights, 259
Ordnance, 211, 228, 230, 240, 241, 256, 260, 262, 285, 286, 293, 303, 332, 333, 376, 555, 659
    Boards, 243, 304
    Depots, 244, 245
    Foreign, 304, 728, 731, 732
    Proving grounds, 244, 303
    See also Munitions *and* Naval ordnance

Ordnance, Bureau of, 318
ORDNANCE, BUREAU OF
(RG 74), 302-304
Ordnance, Chief of, 229

ORDNANCE, OFFICE OF THE
CHIEF OF (RG 156),
242-245
Ordnance Agency, 245

Ordnance and Fortifications,
Board of, 219
Ordnance and Hydrography,
Bureau of, 295, 302, 313,
314, 315, 316, 321
Ordnance Camp, 245
Ordnance Department, 242,
243, 244
Confederate, 720
Ordnance Department Claims
Board, 243
Ordnance Salvage Board, 243

Ordnance Section, War
Department Claims
Board, 243
Ordnance Training Center, 245
Oregon, 134, 163, 343, 430
Oregon Territory, 138
Ores, 408, 409

Organic Act for the Government
of the Federal District, 75
"Organisation Todt," 728, 734
Organized Reserve Corps, 227, 228

Orinoco-Casiquiare-Negro
waterway survey, 241
Orleans Territory, 134
Ornithology, 394
Orphanages, 466, 510
Ortonville, Minn., 745
Osage Indians, 380
Ostland, 729

Oswald, Lee Harvey, 128
Oswego, N.Y., 691
Ottawa Indians, 380
Otter gear, 604
"Our Own United States"
(m.p.), 747

Outdoor Recreation,
National Conference
on, 102, 103
Outer Continental Shelf,
65, 372
Outposts, Office of
Strategic Services, 205

Overseas Operations Branch,
Office of War
Information, 662
Owen, David Dale, 156

Oxyacetylene torch, 409
Oysters, 396

P

Pace, Frank, 213
Pacific Coast, Board of
Engineers for the, 239
Pacific Development Company,
Inc., 587
Pacific Development
Corporation, 580
Pacific Gas and Electric
Co., 540
Pacific Islands, 314, 405, 566
U.S. Commercial Company
in, 586
Pacific Ocean, 315
Pacific Railroad Act of 1862,
411
Pacific Railway Commission,
U.S., 411, 412
Pacific Southwest Federal
Interagency Technical
Committee, 421
Pacific Wagon Roads Office,
366, 370
Packers and Stockyards
Act, 339, 445
Packers and Stockyards
Administration, 462
Packet boat, 489
Packinghouses, 396, 540
Pago Pago, harbors of, 315
Paine, W.H., 744
Paleobotany, 451
Paley, William S., 111
Palma, T. Estrada, 281
Pan American Affairs and
U.S. Naval Missions,
Division of, 297
Pan American Airline
Service, 362
Pan American Exposition,
154, 433, 493
Panama, 138, 145, 150,
276, 414, 562, 745
U.S. Army in, 277
Panama, Isthmus of, 340
Panama Canal, 103, 166,
207, 213, 256, 413
Construction of, 532,
566, 745
PANAMA CANAL
(RG 185), 562
Panama Canal Company, 562
Panama Canal Department,
276, 277
Panama Canal Zone, 219,
276, 280, 328, 562, 566
Panama Congress, 146
Panama Pacific International
Exposition, 154, 209,
365, 426, 453
Panama Railroad Company, 562
Paper, 654

Papermills, Government, 164
Papers, Useless, Joint
        Committee on
        Disposition of, 54
Paperwork management, 65
Parachutes, 256, 320, 328,
        334
Paraguay, 145
    U.S. assistance to, 143
"Paramount News" (m.p.), 745
Paramount Pictures, Inc.,
        746, 747
Parasites, 454
Paravane, 604
Parcel Post, 361, 362
PARDON ATTORNEY, OFFICE
        OF THE (RG 204),
        344-345
Pardons, 95, 336, 341, 345
    Applications, Federal, 345
    Civil War, 137
    Presidential, 86, 135
Paricutin Volcano, 555, 747
Paris, France, 596
    Expositions, 154, 433, 449, 569
    1934 riots in, 569
    Treaty of, 1898, 725
Paris Naval Board on Claims, 318
Paris Peace Commission, 147
Paris Peace Conference, 97, 98,
        287, 745
Parity payments, 435
Park and Planning Commission.
        See National Capital
        Park and Planning
        Commission

Park Service. See National Park
        Service
Parks, 376, 397, 398, 399, 400,
        453, 483, 547, 716, 717
    District of Columbia, 398, 400,
        402, 713, 714
    European, 714
    Military, 249, 397, 398
    National, 63, 247, 249, 328, 362,
        365, 370, 371, 372, 373,
        391, 393, 397-403, 407,
        409, 434, 526, 545, 566,
        567, 614, 713, 714
    State, 103, 370, 399, 567
    Virgin Islands, 725
Parkways, 214, 241, 262, 397, 399, 713
Parole, 63, 253, 349, 350
    Federal camps, 254
Parrot 100-Pounder Guns
        Board, 304
Pasadena Stadium, 717
Passamaquoddy Tidal Power
        Development, 636
Passenger lists, 136, 168, 169,
        170, 346
Passport Office, 135

Passports, 33, 135, 136, 140,
        141, 377, 725
Pasvolsky, Leo, 136
Patent Office, 364, 365, 423,
        450, 453
    Building, 365
PATENT OFFICE (RG 241),
        469-470
Patents, 63, 83, 91, 147, 149,
        210, 242, 261, 262, 266,
        303, 306, 318, 319, 326,
        340, 351, 365, 372, 373,
        374, 424, 447, 450, 469,
        470, 543, 658, 725, 748
    Foreign, 261, 354
    Laws, 469
    Seized from aliens, WW I, 340
Patents, Commissioner of,
        364, 469
Patents, Superintendent of, 469
Patents and Miscellaneous
        Division, 365
Paterson, William, 36
Pathe Company, 747
"Pathe News" (m.p.), 745
Patrick, Mason M., 326
Patterson, Robert P., 212, 735
Patterson (ship), 473
Paul, M. Rea, 674
Paw Paw Tunnel, 401
Pawnee Indians, 380
Pay Department, Office of the
        Quartermaster General,
        246
Paymaster General, 34, 163
    Navy, 309

PAYMASTER GENERAL, OFFICE
        OF THE (RG 99), 250
Paymasters, 273
    Marine Corps, 300, 301
    Navy, 296
Paymaster's Department, Marine
        Corps, 300
Peace, American Commission
        To Negotiate, 146, 148,
        288, 743
Peace, international conferences
        on, 97, 98, 146, 287, 745
Peaches, 441
Peanuts, 441
Pearl button industry, 396
Pearl culture, 397
Pearl Harbor, 205, 211, 217, 335,
        536, 748
    Navy Yard, 321
Pearl Harbor Attack, Joint
        Committee To
        Investigate the, 54
Peary, Robert E., 315, 748, 749
Peas, 441
Peat, 408, 453
Peck, Gustav, 669

Peek, George N., 126, 127
Pehle, John W., 153
Peirce, Benjamin, 473
Peking, Congress of, 138
Pelagic sealing, 395
Pelican (steamer), 395
Penal institutions, 63, 339, 668
   District of Columbia, 669
   Federal, 336, 342, 349,
      502, 669
   State, 342, 349
   See also Prisons
Penicillin, 659
Penitentiaries, U.S., 343,
   349, 365
Pennsylvania, 33, 34, 35, 136,
   312, 344, 605, 745
   See also Philadelphia, Pa.
Pennsylvania, U.S. Housing
   Corporation of, 596, 597
Pennsylvania Board of
   Public Charities, 347
Pension and Miscellaneous
   Division, 365
Pension Office, 364, 365
   Building, 366, 575
Pensions, 38, 59, 60, 61,
      75, 79, 164, 166, 207, 263,
      365, 467, 511, 571, 572,
      573, 574, 719
Pensions, Bureau of, 571, 572
Pensions, Commissioner of,
      37, 311, 364, 571, 572,
      573, 575
Pentagon, 532, 548
Peonage, 338, 344
People's Commissariat for
   Foreign Trade, 735
Peoria Indians, Confederated,
   380
Perkins, Frances, 491
Perlman, Philip B., 111
Permafrost Expedition.
   See Purdue-Canadian
   Permafrost Expedition
Permanent Commission, Navy
   Department, 295
Permanent International
   Armistice Commission,
   287
Permanent Ordnance Board, 304
Perry, Matthew C., 46, 292
Pershing, John J., 103, 260,
      277, 278, 283, 284,
      287, 335, 743
Pershing's Punitive Expedition,
   277, 278
Persian Gulf, 692
Personnel, Federal. *See*
   Federal employees
Peru, 145, 147, 163, 166,
   457, 589
Peruvian treaty of 1841, 164

Pests, 430, 455
Petain, Henri, 623
Petersburg National Battlefield, 400
Petersburg National Military Park
   Commission, 400
Petrified Forest, 566
Petrograd, Russia, 138
Petrography, 750
Petroleum, 186, 188, 195, 203,
      408, 594, 667
   Industry, 408, 409, 415, 416,
      417, 544, 593, 594,
      643, 666
   Reserves, 291, 292, 389, 586
   See also Oil *and* Fuel
Petroleum Administration
   Board, 370
Petroleum Administration for
   War, 655
**PETROLEUM ADMINISTRATION
   FOR WAR (RG 253),
   666-667**
**PETROLEUM ADMINISTRATIVE
   BOARD (RG 232), 415-416**
Petroleum Board, 666
Petroleum Conservation Division,
   416
Petroleum Coordinator for
   National Defense, Office of
   666
Petroleum Industry War Council,
   666
Petroleum Labor Policy Board,
   415, 416
Petroleum Requirements
   Committee, 666
Petroleum Reserves Corporation,
   580, 586
Petroleum Supply and
   Distribution Committee, 666
Peyote, 382
Pharmaceuticals, 508
Pharmacopoeia Convention,
   U.S., 509
Phenacetine, 509
Philadelphia, Pa., 241, 471, 509,
   566, 598
   Navy Yard, 321
Philadelphia Arsenal, 295, 296
Philadelphia Convention, 36
Philadelphia International
   Centennial Exposition,
   154, 365
Philadelphia Naval Aircraft
   Factory, 320
Philadelphia Sesquicentennial
   International Exposition,
   154
Philippine Affairs, Joint
   Preparatory Committee
   on, 137
Philippine Alien Property
   Administration, 355

Philippine Command, 280
Philippine Commission, 413, 414
Philippine Department, 276, 277
Philippine Exposition Board, 413
Philippine Insurgent Army, 136
Philippine Insurrection, 232, 233,
    255, 744
*Philippine Insurrection Against
    the United States, 1899-1903,
    A History of the,* 413
Philippine Islands, 137, 150, 157,
    158, 162, 174, 189, 197, 205,
    220, 233, 236, 241, 261, 262,
    272, 273, 275, 276, 277, 278,
    279, 354, 360, 361, 404, 413,
    414, 431, 472, 474, 478, 504, 612,
    667, 737, 743, 744, 745, 747
    Legislature, 413
    National Assembly, 413
    U.S. High Commissioner to the,
        404, 405
Philippine Rehabilitation Act of
    1946, 667
**PHILIPPINE WAR DAMAGE
    COMMISSION (RG 268),**
    667
Philippines, Division of the, 276
Photo Review, 663
Photogrammetry, 480
Photogrammetry, American
    Society of, 392
"Photographic Incidents of the
    War," 501
Photography, aerial, 98, 99, 124,
    325, 327, 426
Phthalic anhydride, 449
Physical Fitness, Committee on, 640
Physical Security Equipment
    Agency, 330
Physicians, 383, 685
    See also Surgeon General, Office
        of the
Physics, 452, 475
Physiography, 437
Physiography, Academy of Science
    Commission on (at Cracow),
    735
Piankeshaw Indians, Confederated,
    380
Pickering, Henry G., 38
Pickering, Timothy, 36, 37, 38
Pickett, George E., 744
Pierce, John, 163
Piers, 237
Piez, Charles, 604
Pigeons, homing, 307
Pillsbury, J.E., 473, 474
Pilotage and towage, 83
Pilots, 313, 314, 362, 482
Pinchot, Gifford, 427
Pines, Isle of, 340
Pink bollworm, 454
Pinkerton, Allan, 257

Pipelines, 417, 643, 644, 666, 667
Piracy, 136, 295, 336, 523, 726
Pittman Silver Act, 174
Pittsburgh, Pa., 745
Placement, Bureau of, War
    Manpower Commission, 684
"Plan of Government," 36
Plancors, 587
Planning and Statistics, Central
    Bureau of, 96, 97, 98
Plant Industry, Bureau of, 433,
    439, 448, 449, 450, 451,
    455, 462, 614
Plant Industry, Soils, and
    Agricultural Engineering,
    Bureau of, 437, 449
**PLANT INDUSTRY, SOILS,
    AND AGRICULTURAL
    ENGINEERING, BUREAU
    OF (RG 54),** 450-453
Plant Pest Control Branch,
    Agricultural Research
    Service, 453
Plant Quarantine, Bureau of, 453
Plant Quarantine Act, 453
Plant Quarantine and Control
    Administration, 453
Plantations, 156, 180
Plants, 423, 426, 450, 451,
    452, 453
    Diseases, 339, 423, 443, 451,
        453, 454, 455, 614
    Importation of, 168, 453
    Nurseries, 439
Plateau Station, Antarctica, 750
"Platoon Plan," in public
    schools, 506
Playgrounds, D.C., 713
Plymouth, Mass., 745
Pneumatic tube services, 361
Pocket veto, 42, 95
Pohl, Oswald, 700
Point Barrow, Alaska, 478
Poland, 198, 286, 335, 362, 700,
    702, 733, 735, 736, 744
    American Relief Administration
        mission to, 596
    Typhus epidemic in, 286
Poland, William B., 620
Polar Archives, Center for, 334,
    749-751
Polar regions, 315, 334, 473, 478
    See also Antarctic; Arctic; *and*
        Expeditions, polar
Polaris (U.S.S.), 316, 750
Police, 127, 268, 712
    German, 730
    National academy, 348
    Puerto Rican, 414
Political leaders, 745
    Allied, 663, 689
    Axis, 206, 663, 689, 702, 737
    U.S., 525

Politics, foreign, 132
  German, 701, 728, 730, 732, 734
  Japanese, 736
  Philippine, 414
  Korean, 736
  Russian, 735, 736
Pollak, Walter H., 64
Pollution
  Oil, 395
  Rock Creek studies, 402
  Water, 396, 505
Polygamy, 338
Polymer development, 587, 588
Pomerene, Atlee, 341
Pomology, 450, 451
Pontius, Harry E., 675
Pope, General, 208
Pope, John A., 750
Popes, 136
"Pope's Stone," 717
Popolo d'Italia, 205
Poppy plant, 351
Population, 122, 124, 141, 333,
    426, 431, 458, 467, 468,
    510, 574
  Census schedules, 88, 467,
      468, 469
  Rural, 456, 457
  Statistics, 34, 466, 468
  See also Census *and* Indians,
    Population
Porcupines, 397
Port and Harbor Facilities
    Commission, 602, 607
Portal to Portal Travel Time,
    President's Committee on, 106
Porter, David, 726
Porter, Paul, 657
Porter, Russell W., 750
Ports, 315, 397, 525, 601, 602, 607
  European, 323
  Free, 570
  Great Lakes, 169
  Inland, 169
Portugal, 145, 647, 735
  War trade agreement with, 586
Possessions, island, 282, 391, 403,
    404, 413, 414
  See also Insular possessions *and*
    specific possessions
Post, Wiley, 334, 530
Post Office Appropriation Act
    for fiscal year 1913, 526
Post Office Department, 43, 60,
    152, 453, 487, 745
  British, 358
  Confederate, 720
POST OFFICE DEPARTMENT
    (RG 28), 358-363
Post Office Operations,
    Bureau of, 359
Post offices, 31, 35, 152, 166, 281,
    358, 359, 360, 361, 362

Post roads, improvement of, 526
Post Roads and Post Offices,
    Surveyor of, 358
Post War Planning, Interbureau
    Committee on, 426
Postal Affairs Section, 297
Postal Organization, President's
    Commission on, 118
Postal Saving Funds, 157
Postal Savings System, 157, 159,
    166, 361, 362
Postal service, 55, 118, 353, 358,
    359, 360, 361, 362, 553
  International, 360
  Military, 236, 331, 360
  Puerto Rican, 726
Postal Telegraph System, 536
Postmaster General, 31, 35, 43,
    60, 164, 358, 362, 526, 535
Postmaster General, Office of, 358
Postmasters, 60, 359, 361, 548
Posts, military. *See* Army, installations
    and posts, *and* Military,
    installations
Potash, 356, 391, 452
Potassium nitrate, 391
Potatoes, 441, 453, 454
Potawatomi Indians, 380, 383, 384
Potomac and Shenandoah
    Navigation Lottery, 401
Potomac Company, 401, 402
Potomac Flotilla, 75
Potomac Park, 716
Potomac River, 304, 394
  Floods, 714
  Navigation of, 31, 401
  Waterworks, 238
Poultry, 445, 456, 461, 463
Pound, Ezra, 623
Poverty, 747
Powders and High Explosives,
    Board on, 243
Powell, J.W., 566
Powell Survey, 389, 390, 393,
    394, 745
Power, 147, 328, 369, 370, 389,
    393, 395, 407, 422, 541-542
  Electric, 238, 367, 368, 406,
    409, 411, 440, 441, 540,
    541, 542
  Plants, 309, 310, 385, 406, 407, 422
  Steam, 409
Power, Division of, Office of
    the Secretary of the
    Interior, 368, 669
Prairie dogs, control of, 397
Prairie States Forestry
    Project, 427, 439
Preble, George Henry, 295
Pre-Emption Division, Bureau
    of Land Management, 374
President, Executive Office of
    the, 124, 152

President of the United States, 110, 122,
126, 132, 133, 138, 176, 177, 199,
201, 217, 259, 323, 329, 331, 337,
338, 339, 349, 353, 414, 512, 644,
711
 Appointments and nominations, 95
 Assassinations, 75, 76, 128-129,
176, 259
 Campaign speeches of 1940, 371
 Elections, 50, 52
 Inaugurations, 54, 127, 335, 569,
741, 742
 Messages, 50, 95
 Papers, 549
 Proclamations, 41, 42, 44, 95, 96,
412, 549, 600
 See also names of Presidents
Presidential Advisory Committee on
Water Resources Policy, 369
**PRESIDENTIAL COMMITTEES,
COMMISSIONS, AND
BOARDS (RG 220),**
102-119
Presidential libraries, 64, 95, 101, 102,
549, 550, 595, 748
Presidential Office Space,
President's Advisory
Commission on, 113
Presidential Railroad Commission,
115
President's Agricultural
Conference, 425
President's Air Policy
Commission, 108
President's Commission on Economy
and Efficiency, 96, 97, 153
President's Commission on Oil
Reserves, 393
**PRESIDENT'S COMMISSION ON
THE ASSASSINATION OF
PRESIDENT KENNEDY
(RG 272),** 128-129
President's Committee on
Deferment of Federal
Employees, 680, 681
President's Committee on
Foreign Aid, 108, 465
President's Committee on
Government Contracts, 703
President's Committee on
Wildlife Restoration, 396
President's Conference on Home
Building and Home
Ownership, *1931* , 475
President's Conference on
Industrial Safety, 492
President's Emergency
Committee for
Employment, 120, 121
President's Fuel Distribution
Committee, 579
President's Liaison Committee,
624

President's Materials Policy
Commission, 111, 270,
369
President's Mediation
Commission, 492
President's Reemployment
Agreement, 555, 627, 629
President's Research Committee
on Social Trends, 121
President's Scientific
Research Board, 107
President's Soviet Protocol
Committee, 105
President's Special Committee
on Farm Tenancy, 456
President's Water Resources
Policy Commission, 110
Press, 219, 551, 569, 646, 731
 German, 727
 Voluntary censorship of, 638
Press and Publications Service,
U.S. Information Agency, 569
Press Intelligence, Division of,
Office of Government
Reports, 125
Preston, S. W., 322
Preventive Medicine, Division
of, 302
Pribilof Islands, 395, 396, 397,
548, 723
Price, Xenophon H., 529
Price Adjustment Board, 582
Price Administration, Office of,
176, 371, 404, 418, 419,
462, 517, 518

**PRICE ADMINISTRATION,
OFFICE OF (RG 188),**
647-657
Price Administration and
Civilian Supply, Office
of, 647, 648
Price Administrator, 668
Price Board Management, Office
of, 653
Price Control Act, 650
Price Decontrol Board, 648, 649
**PRICE DECONTROL BOARD
(RG 251),** 668
Price-Fixing Committee, 609

**PRICE STABILIZATION, OFFICE
OF (RG 295),** 705-706
Price Stabilization Division,
National Defense Advisory
Commission, 647, 648
Prices, 98, 204, 340, 435, 436,
493, 579, 596, 650, 651, 652,
653, 654, 655, 656, 668
 Agricultural, 425, 434, 458
 Boards, 212, 214, 581, 582, 653,
654, 656
 Ceilings, 655, 703

Control, 462, 465, 592, 647,
        649, 650, 655, 656, 657,
        665, 668
Decontrol, 649, 651, 655, 703,
        704, 705
Fuel, 593
Regulations, 647, 648, 650, 653,
        654, 655, 656, 705
Schedules, 655
Stabilization and supports, 270,
        435, 462, 463, 465, 647,
        665, 703, 705
PRIME-POTUS, 217
Prince, Frederick H., 620
"Prince plan," 620
Printing, 209, 329, 501
    For Federal Government, 57
    See also Engraving and Printing,
        Bureau of
Printing, Bureau of, 414
Printing, Joint Committee on,
        54, 57
Prinz Sigismund, 311
Prinz Waldemar, 311
PRISON INDUSTRIES
        REORGANIZATION
        ADMINISTRATION
        (RG 209), 668-669
Prisoner of War Division,
        253, 254
Prisoners, 253, 254, 290, 296,
        336, 337, 338, 341, 342,
        343, 344, 349, 669, 721
    British, 166
    Military, 213, 259
    Political, 253, 345
Prisoners, American
        Commissary General
        of, 166, 253-254
Prisoners, Commissioner for
        the Exchange of, Office
        of the, 253, 254
Prisoners, Office of the
        Commissary General
        of, 253
Prisoners' Department, 33
Prisoners of war, 136, 137, 193,
        217, 235, 253, 254, 262,
        267, 268, 278, 284, 287,
        328, 684, 721
    Allied, 663, 728, 731, 732,
        734
    American, 216, 262, 268,
        734, 737
    Axis, 334, 663
    Confederate, 253, 254, 721
    German, 198, 268
    Italian, 193
    Russian, 287
Prisons, 278, 279, 341, 342,
        349, 350, 365, 466, 666,
        669, 720
    American Samoan, 410

German, 702, 729
Superintendent of, 342, 348,
        349, 669
    See also Correctional
        institutions, Federal;
        Military, prisons; Penal
        institutions; and
        Penitentiaries, U.S.
Prisons, Bureau of, 669
PRISONS, BUREAU OF
        (RG 129), 349-350
Pritchard, Benjamin, 743
Private Land Claims
        Division, 374
Privateer Pension Fund, 166
Privateers, 136, 296, 574
Prize cases, 70, 79, 82, 83, 86
Probation, 63, 341
Proclaimed List, Interdepartmental
        Committee on, 150
"Proclaimed List of Certain
        Blocked Nationals," 150
Procurement, 223, 269, 425, 585
Procurement and Assignment,
        Office of, Office of Defense
        Health and Welfare Services, 679
Procurement and Assignment
        Service, Office of Defense
        Health and Welfare
        Services, 640, 685
Procurement and Assignment
        Service, War Manpower
        Commission, 679, 684
Procurement and Cutback
        Determinations, Special
        Assistant on, 664
Procurement Assignment Board, 212
Procurement Committee, U.S., 230
Procurement Division
    Public Buildings Service, 545, 546
    Treasury Department, 548, 549,
        596
Produce Loan Bureau,
        Department of the
        Treasury, 722
Production, Minister of, 688
Production and Marketing
        Administration, 435, 436,
        460, 462, 463
Production Executive
        Committee, 687
Production Management,
        Office of, 616, 647, 672,
        686, 687
Production Readjustment
        Committee, 617
Production Review
        Committee, Office of,
        582
Professional and Service
        Projects, Division of, Work
        Projects Administration, 696
Profiteering, 340

Program Planning and Review Committee, Department of Labor, 492
Program Planning Division, Bureau of Agricultural Economics, 455
Prohibition, 63, 64, 70, 177, 178, 524
Prohibition, Bureau of, 348, 351
Project EVERSHARP, 216
Project for Technical Cooperation with the Bureau of Indian Affairs, 439
Project Redhead, 333
Project Rising Star, 200
Project Vanguard, 554
Projectiles, 659
Promotion, Board for the Examination of Officers for, 295
Propaganda, 138, 139, 194, 204, 339, 622, 660, 661, 662, 746, 748
   Axis, 220
   German, 362, 728
   Italian, 737
   Korean, 736
   Russian, 734, 736
Propellants, 659
Property, 141, 167, 180, 186, 198, 213, 224, 318, 329, 335, 341, 354, 355, 599, 698, 717, 721, 722
   Abandoned and captured, 154, 155, 167, 180, 344
   Alien, 155, 165, 180, 340, 354-356, 645
   Claims, Austrian, 198
   Disposal of, 204, 213, 224, 225
   Federal, surplus, 54, 65, 353, 546, 552
   Management, 539, 544
   U.S., in foreign countries, 181
   See also Federal Property and Administrative Services Act of 1949 and Surplus property
PROPERTY MANAGEMENT AND DISPOSAL SERVICE (GENERAL SERVICES ADMINISTRATION) (RG 291), 551-552
Proposed New Building for the War Department, Board on the, 243
Prosthetic appliances, 575
PROTECTION AND SALVAGE OF ARTISTIC AND HISTORIC MONUMENTS IN WAR AREAS, AMERICAN COMMISSION FOR THE (RG 239), 611-612
Protocol, Office of, 136

Provincetown Harbor, 471
Provisional General Staff, 216
Provisional International Civil Aviation Organization, 211
Provisions and Clothing, Bureau of, 308
Provost court, Veracruz, 283
Provost Marshal General, 208, 256, 257, 267, 268, 283, 284
Provost Marshal General, Office of the, 257, 265
PROVOST MARSHAL GENERAL, OFFICE OF THE, 1941- (RG 389), 267-269
PROVOST MARSHAL GENERAL'S BUREAU (CIVIL WAR) (RG 110), 256-258
Provost marshals, 257, 258, 273, 557, 721
Prussia, 35, 728, 731
"Psychological Analysis of Adolph Hitler, A: His Life and Legend," 205
Psychological warfare. See Warfare, psychological
Psychological Warfare, Office of the Chief of, 223
Psychology, 659
Public Buildings, Commissioner of, 364, 714-715
Public Buildings Administration, 519, 545, 547, 596, 704, 705
Public buildings and grounds, 58, 237, 238, 241, 365, 370, 402, 531, 547, 713, 715
Public Buildings and Grounds, Office of, 95, 402, 531, 741
PUBLIC BUILDINGS AND GROUNDS, OFFICE OF (RG 42), 714-717
Public Buildings and Public Parks of the National Capital, Office of, 63, 402, 545, 714, 716
Public Buildings Service, 598, 714
PUBLIC BUILDINGS SERVICE (RG 121), 545-548
Public Contracts Division, Labor Department, 496, 497
Public debt, 60, 61, 154, 157, 178
PUBLIC DEBT, BUREAU OF THE (RG 53), 162-167
Public Debt, Commissioner of the, 162
Public Debt Accounts and Audit, Division of, 162
Public Debt Service, 162, 165
Public domain, 65, 338, 370, 372, 374, 426
   Administration of, 366, 371, 375

Public Domain, Committee on the
    Conservation and
    Administration of the,
    103, 117
Public funds, 58, 157, 165, 167
Public health, 501, 503, 504,
    570, 647
    Italy, 193
    Japan, 194
    Puerto Rico, 726
Public Health and Marine
    Hospital Service, 502
Public Health Service, 103, 371,
    377, 465, 571
PUBLIC HEALTH SERVICE
    (RG 90), 502-505
Public Housing Administration,
    513, 669
PUBLIC HOUSING
    ADMINISTRATION
    (RG 196), 519-521
Public information, 182, 185
    Army, 221
Public Information, Committee
    on, 95, 609, 746
PUBLIC INFORMATION,
    COMMITTEE ON
    (RG 63), 119-120
PUBLIC LAND LAW REVIEW
    COMMISSION (RG 409),
    65-66
Public Lands and Surveys,
    Senate Committee on, 341
Public Lands Commission, 103
Public Lands Division, 374
Public Moneys, Division of, 165
Public opinion
    Foreign, 132, 569
    Surveys of, 125
Public Printer, 57, 390
Public Relations, Bureau of,
    210, 216
Public Roads, Bureau of,
    399, 447
PUBLIC ROADS, BUREAU
    OF (RG 30), 525-527
Public Roads, Office of,
    447, 526
Public Roads Administration,
    526, 699, 704
Public Roads and Rural
    Engineering, Office of,
    447, 526
Public Roads Inquiry, Office
    of, 526
Public Supplies, Purveyor of, 248
Public utilities, 123, 393, 518,
    541, 579, 608, 619, 629,
    651, 652
Public Utilities, Ministry of
    (Poland), 735
Public Utilities Advisory
    Service, 518

Public Utility Holding
    Company Act of 1935, 563
Public Work Reserve Project, 697
Public works, 120, 121, 123, 194,
    235, 238, 366, 392, 393, 670
    Art project, 546, 547
    National Capital, 713
    Naval, 309, 310
    Puerto Rico, 726
    State, 123
    Wartime, 704, 705
    See also Federal Emergency
        Administration of Public
        Works
Public Works, Bureau of, 712
Public Works, Office of, 238
Public Works, Special Board for, 670
Public Works Administration,
    125, 310, 370, 385,
    396, 440, 704, 725
PUBLIC WORKS
    ADMINISTRATION
    (RG 135), 669-671
Public Works Branch, 548
Publication Office, War
    Records, 233
Pueblo Lands Board, 388, 743
Puerto Rican Hurricane
    Relief Commission,
    404, 434
Puerto Rican Hurricane
    Relief Loan Section, 404
"Puerto Rican Story, The"
    (s.r.), 570
Puerto Rico, 62, 157, 158, 174,
    233, 261, 275, 276, 404,
    405, 413, 414, 416, 468,
    486, 496, 523, 726
    Experiment stations in, 447
    Industrial codes for, 631
    Marriage customs in, 340
    Postal services in, 360
    Public debt, 162
    Territory of, 134
    Towns in, 727
    Transportation in, 643, 644
    U.S. Army in, 277
Puerto Rico, Commonwealth
    of, 726
Puerto Rico, Department
    of, 276-277

PUERTO RICO, SPANISH
    GOVERNORS OF
    (RG 186), 725-727
Puerto Rico, Special
    Industry Committee
    for, 497
Puerto Rico Industry
    Committee, 497
Puerto Rico Reconstruction
    Administration, 405

PUERTO RICO
RECONSTRUCTION
ADMINISTRATION
(RG 323), 416-417
Pulaski Statue Commission,
717
Pullman strike, 559
Punitive Expedition to
Mexico, 276
Purchase, Storage, and
Traffic Division, War
Department, 246
Purchasing Commission for
Russian Relief, 595
Purdue-Canadian Permafrost
Expedition, 750
Pure Food and Drug Act,
353, 434
Putnam, Roger L., 704, 706
Pyle, Ernie, 220, 299
Pyrite, 415
Pyrotechnics, 303

Q

Quapaw Indians, 380
Quarantine, 431, 503, 523
Animal, 445
Plant, 339, 453, 454
Stations, 502, 503, 505
Quarries, 356, 376
Quartermaster Corps, 246,
248, 256
Quartermaster General, 37, 38,
229, 245, 246, 248, 253
Confederate, 720, 721
German, 732, 734
Quartermaster General, Office
of the, 250, 252, 398
QUARTERMASTER GENERAL,
OFFICE OF THE
(RG 92), 245-249
Quartermaster Heraldic Field
Office, 248
Quartermasters, 190, 215, 227,
228, 246, 247, 249, 273,
285, 290, 300
Depots, 247, 248, 249
Quartermaster's Department, 34,
245, 246, 247, 248
Accounts, 59
Confederate, 720
Marine Corps, 301
Quebec Conference, 256
Quinine, 589
Quirnheim, Hermann Ritter
Mertz von, 732

R

Race relations, 230, 269, 617,
651, 652

Racial Relations Adviser, Office
of, 651
Radar, 189, 308, 332, 333, 527,
658, 660, 729
Development of, 334
Radiation, 190, 475
Solar, 477
Radiation Biology Laboratory, 566
Radio, 147, 219, 306, 307, 308, 315,
324, 328, 535, 536, 537, 622,
636, 659
Broadcasts, 118, 139, 156, 335,
343, 491, 521, 525, 535, 537,
613, 622, 623, 638, 639, 640,
655, 656, 663, 677, 683, 691,
747, 748
Facilities, 528, 537
Foreign, 101, 614, 622, 623, 729
Intelligence, 536, 537
Programs, 469, 569, 570, 646,
660, 661, 662
Regulation of, 535
Scripts, 687, 690
Stations, 355, 535, 536, 613
Voluntary censorship of, 638
Radio Division, Department of
Commerce, 535
Radioactivity, 191
Radiodynamic Torpedo Unit, 226
Radiology, 191
Rail Routing Division, Federal
Supply Service, 549
Railroad Accounts, Auditor of, 411
Railroad Administration, U.S., 559,
594, 602, 609
RAILROAD ADMINISTRATION,
U.S. (RG 14), 599-601
Railroad and Airline Wage Board,
703, 707
Railroad Brotherhoods, 650
Railroad Labor Act, 339
Railroad Labor Board, 559, 560
Railroad Lighter Captains
Commission, 561
Railroad Marine Workers
Commission, 561
Railroad Retirement Board, 620
Railroad Wage Commission, 600
Railroad Wages and Working
Conditions, Board of, 600
Railroads, 97, 98, 99, 115, 119, 123,
158, 164, 166, 178, 248, 273,
281, 343, 355, 356, 370, 373,
374, 376, 379, 394, 404, 405,
409, 411, 413, 414, 417, 559,
562, 580, 581, 582, 589, 594,
601, 608, 618, 619, 621, 643,
644, 684, 688, 721, 737
Boards of adjustment, 600, 601
Bonds, 159, 163
Consolidation of, 620
Design, 58
Employment, 560, 561, 601, 620

Equipment, 601, 619, 621
Federal aid to, 411, 412
Federal control of, 599, 601
Financial conditions of, 372,
    560, 582
Industry, 237, 360, 411, 553, 555,
    618, 619, 673
Inter-American, 147
Labor disputes, 558, 559, 560
Land grants, 366, 372, 375, 376
Lines, 621, 644
Loans, 158, 580, 581, 582
Mail-carrying, 360, 362
Marine, 309, 604, 606
Military, 238, 247
Pacific, 158, 163, 164, 233,
    338, 366, 390, 411, 412,
    429, 744
Rights-of-way, 53, 372, 374,
    376, 412
RAILROADS, COMMISSIONER
    OF (RG 193), 411-412
Railroads, Director General of,
    599, 600
Railroads, Office of the
    Commissioner of, 364
Railway Adjustments, Division
    of, 360
Railway Artillery Reserve, 284
Railway Labor Act, 558, 559,
    561, 707
Railway Mail Service, 360, 362
Railway Mission in Mexico,
    U.S., 646-647
Railway Transport Department, 643
Railways. See Railroads
Rainbow Bridge, 745
Rainfall, 438, 448
    Stations, 477
Raisins, 442
Ramirez, Alejandro, 726
Ranches, 533
Randolph, Cary J., 635
Randolph, Edmund, 36
Randolph, Peyton, 29
Rangefinders, 659
Rangeland, 65
    Management of, 428, 430
Ranger (U.S.S.), 296, 315
Ranger VII, 554
Ranger VIII, 554
Rapallo Conference, 286
Rates Appeals Committee, 693
Rationing, 647, 649, 650,
    652, 655, 656
    Boards, 650, 653, 654,
        655, 656
    Discrimination in, 651
    Stamps, 176
Rats, control of, 397
Ravig Engineering Co., 245
Raw materials, 486, 609, 688
    German, 728, 730

Raw Materials Board. See
    Combined Raw Materials
    Board
Ready Reserve (Army), 234
Real estate, 53, 160, 161, 182,
    186, 194, 210, 211, 248,
    260, 309, 318, 333, 355,
    425, 539, 583, 679, 711
    Federal, 544, 546
    See also Housing; Land; and
        Property
"Rebel archives," 719
Rebelion de Lares, 726
Recall, letters of, 46
Receipts and Expenditures,
    Division of, Treasury
    Department, 165
Receivership, 72, 159, 161
Recent Economic Changes,
    Committee on, 121
Reciprocity Commissioner, 135
Reciprocity Information,
    Committee for, 100, 126, 127
Reciprocity Treaties, Interdepartmental
    Advisory Board on, 149, 150
Reciprocity Treaty of 1854, 145
"Recitals" (pardon warrants), 345
Reclamation, Bureau of, 370, 381, 390

RECLAMATION, BUREAU OF
    (RG 115), 406-407
Reclamation, land, 365, 366, 368, 369,
    370, 372, 406, 436, 443, 670
Reclamation Act of 1920, 406
Reclamation Division, General Land
    Office, 374
Reclamation Projects, Office of
    Demonstrations on, 433
Reclamation Service, 406
Reconstruction, Joint Committee
    on, 54
Reconstruction, Southern, 54, 336,
    338
Reconstruction Finance Corporation,
    155, 434, 435, 516, 624, 625,
    647, 673

RECONSTRUCTION FINANCE
    CORPORATION (RG 234),
    580-590
Reconstruction Finance Corporation
    Act of 1932, 155
Reconstruction Finance Corporation
    Liquidation Act, 581
Reconstruction Finance Corporation
    Mortgage Company, 581, 582,
    583, 588
Reconstruction Finance Corporation
    Price Adjustment Board, 581,
    582
Reconversion programs, 584, 664, 665
Reconversion Working Committee, 665
Record and Pension Division, War
    Department, 37, 231

Record and Pension Office, War
        Department, 37, 231, 232, 233,
        234
Recorder's Division, General Land
        Office, 374
Records centers, National Archives
        and Records Service, 549, 550
Records management, 544, 548, 549,
        550
Recreation, 66, 102, 124, 201, 256, 328,
        370, 397, 399, 400, 402, 429,
        430, 440, 525, 548, 615, 636,
        640, 641, 691, 698, 746, 747
    Army, 218
    Foreign, 313
    Indian, 385
Recreational Survey of Federal
        Lands, Joint Committee on, 102
Recruiting, 207, 257
    Army, 231, 234, 235, 255, 273
    Marine Corps, 300, 301
    Navy, 207, 293, 310, 311
    Posters, 233, 241, 249
    Women's Army Corps, 222
Recruiting Division, Adjutant
        General's Office, 232
Red Army, 737
Red Cross, 138, 139, 256, 288, 293,
        313, 328, 534, 663, 686
    International conferences on, 146
    See also American Red Cross
Red Lake Reservation, 381
Reemployment and Recent Changes in
        Industrial Techniques, National
        Research Project on, 697
Referees, Board of, 508, 509
Refineries, 370
Refuge Harbor, Greenland, 478
Refugees, 372
    Arab, 139
    Armenian, 313
    Canadian, 33
    Hungarian, 113, 114
    Jewish, 746
    World War II, 107, 193, 218, 690,
        691, 748
Refugees, Freedmen, and Abandoned
        Lands, Bureau of, 179
REFUGEES, FREEDMEN, AND
    ABANDONED LANDS,
    BUREAU OF (RG 105),
    263-264
Regional Agricultural Credit
        Corporations, 580
Register, Office of the, 33, 162
Registration and Voting
        Participation, President's
        Commission on, 117
Regular Army, 231, 232, 233, 235,
        251, 265, 271, 273, 288
REGULAR ARMY MOBILE
    UNITS, U.S., 1821-1942
    (RG 391), 271-273

Regulation W, 650
Rehabilitation
    Agricultural, 424
    In Virgin Islands, 725
    Rural, 442, 443, 695
    Veterans, 203, 571
    Vocational, 112
Reich Air Ministry, 728, 731, 733
Reich Chancellery, 727
Reich Chancellor, 733
Reich Commissioner for
        Aviation, 728
Reich Commissioner for
        Restoration of Austria
        to Germany, 734
Reich Commissioner for the
        Strengthening of
        Germandom, 729
Reich Defense Council, 734
Reich Economics Office, 728
Reich 4-year plan, 729
Reich Labor Service, 734
Reich Ministry for
        Armaments and War
        Production, 728, 731
Reich Ministry for Food and
        Agriculture, 730
Reich Ministry for Public
        Enlightenment and
        Propaganda, 728
Reich Ministry for the Occupied
        Eastern Territories, 729
Reich Ministry of Economics,
        728, 733, 734
Reich Ministry of Finance, 729
Reich Ministry of Labor, 729
Reich Ministry of the Interior, 730
Reich Navy, 731
Reich Office for Soil
        Exploration, 728
Reich Postal Telegraph Office,
        733
Reich Research Council, 730
Reich War Ministry, 730, 731
Reich Weather Bureau, 730
Reichsamt fuer Wetterdienst,
        730
Reichsarbeitsministerium, 729
Reichsfinanzministerium, 729
Reichsforschumgsrat, 730
Reichsfuehrer SS und Chef der
        deutschen Polizei, 730
Reichsjustizministerium, 729
Reichskommissar fuer die
        Festigung des deutschen
        Volkstums, 729
Reichskommissariat Ostland, 729
Reichsluftfahrtministerium, 728
Reichsmarine, 731
Reichsministerium des
        Innern, 730
Reichsministerium fuer die
        besetzten Ostgebiete, 729

Reichsministerium fuer
    Ernaehrung und,
    Landwirtschaft, 730
Reichsministerium fuer
    Ruestung und
    Kriegsproduktion, 728
Reichsministerium fuer
    Volksaufklaerung und
    Propaganda, 728
Reichswirtschafsministerium, 728
Reims, France, 188
Release Procedures, Attorney
    General's Survey of, 341
Relief, 107, 121, 122
    Drought, 425, 434, 436, 445,
        534, 695
    Emergency, 155, 395, 399, 400,
        416, 424, 425, 514, 582,
        693, 725, 743
    Federal programs, 123, 124,
        694, 696
    Foreign, 416, 456, 459, 595,
        606, 725
    Legislation, 99
    Organizations, 120, 121, 125, 694
    Rural, 694
    Ships, 596
    Stations, 502, 504
    Transient, 695
    See also American Relief
        Administration; Federal
        Emergency Relief
        Administration; Foreign
        Relief and Rehabilitation
        Operations, Office of; and
        United Nations Relief and
        Rehabilitation Administration
Religion, 139, 148
    In Germany, 198
    In Japan, 335
Religious bodies, censuses of,
    467, 468
Religious leaders, 267, 748
Relocation centers, 269, 280,
    689, 690, 691
Remonstrances addressed to
    Confederation Congress,
    32
Renegotiation Act, 582, 664
Renegotiation Branch, Office of
    the Secretary of War, 212
Reno, Marcus A., 262
Renovation of the Executive
    Mansion, Commission
    on the, 108, 109
Rent, 493, 647, 651, 652, 654,
    713
    Advisory boards, 518
    Control, 186, 514, 517, 518, 519,
        597, 617, 649, 650, 703
RENT COMMISSION OF THE
    DISTRICT OF COLUMBIA
    (RG 132), 718

Rent Stabilization, Office of, 517,
    518, 703, 704
Rent Stabilizer, 519
Renting, Requisitions, and Claims
    Services, 225
Reorganization Plan No. 1
    1939, 96, 98, 122, 511, 515,
        526, 532, 704
    1953, 501
    1958, 269
Reorganization Plan No. II of
    1939, 413, 418, 431, 440,
        488, 637
Reorganization Plan No. 2
    1946, 511
    1949, 511
    1962, 101
    1965, 479
Reorganization Plan No. III of
    1940, 157, 162, 165, 527, 530
Reorganization Plan No. 3
    1946, 481
    1947, 513
    1953, 269
    1967, 711
Reorganization Plan No. IV of
    1940, 282, 527, 530
Reorganization Plan No. 5 of
    1949, 568
Reorganization Plan No. 6
    1953, 182
    1961, 538
Reorganization Plan No. 7
    1949, 526
    1953, 143
    1961, 539
Reorganization Plan No. 8 of
    1953, 569
Reorganization Plan No. 21 of
    1950, 478
Reorganization Plan No. 22
    of 1950, 516
Reorganization plans,
    Presidential, 44
Reparation Commission, 147
Repatriation, 138, 139, 268,
    284, 287
Replacement Army, German, 732
Representatives, U.S., 748
Reptiles, 397
Republican National Conventions
    1924, 745
    1960, 748
    1968, 127
Requirements Committee, War
    Production Board, 687
Rescues, 332, 409
    Air Force, 334
    Civilian defense, 639
    Sea, 523, 525, 677

Research, 554, 555, 565, 566,
      613, 619, 657, 659, 733
   Agricultural, 423, 443, 444, 445,
      446, 447, 449, 450, 451,
      453, 455, 458
   Air Force, 326
   Army, 210, 212, 223, 246
   Chemical, 389, 391, 449, 450
   Educational, 503
   Engineering, 449, 450, 451
   Financial, 651
   Forest, 426, 427, 429
   Housing, 513, 514
   Medical, 203, 302, 502, 503,
      504, 508, 658, 659
   Physical, 389, 391, 554
   Physics, 452
   Transportation, 526, 612-613, 619
Research and Development
      Board, 182, 186

Research and Development
      Board/Committee, 189
Research and Development
      Committee, 202
Research and Education
      Division, Federal
      Communications
      Commission, 536
Research and Marketing Act
      of 1946, 443
Research and Records Projects,
      Work Projects
      Administration, 697
Research Laboratories,
      Environmental Science
      Services Administration,
      479
Research Planning Division,
      National Recovery
      Administration, 627
Research Unit on Territorial
      Policy, 404

Reservations, 374, 430
   Indian, 53, 340, 370, 376, 377,
      379, 380, 381, 382, 386,
      388, 439, 440, 506
   Military, 219, 232, 247, 249, 260,
      262, 372, 373, 374, 393,
      714
   National, 397
Reserve and National Guard Policy,
      Joint Committee on, 331
Reserve and ROTC Affairs,
      Office of the Executive
      for, 223
Reserve Officers' Training
      Corps, 222, 224, 226, 227,
      255, 256
Reserve Program Review Board,
      331
Reservoirs, 373, 374, 376, 406,
      407

Resettlement Administration,
      386, 438, 424, 442, 443,
      514, 699
Residence certificates, 346
Resolutions, congressional,
      25, 42, 49, 57
Resources, 65, 66, 99, 183,
      409, 567, 578, 664, 699
   Development of, 122, 567
   Energy, 111, 123
   Forest, 427, 428, 429, 487
   Land, 65, 112, 123, 375,
      437, 460
   Locations, 124
   Mineral, 65, 98, 124, 338,
      372, 389, 390, 391,
      407, 408, 586
   See also Natural resources
Retired Reserve (Army), 234
Retired Securities, Division of,
      Bureau of Public Debt, 162
Retirement
   Federal employees, 55, 97,
      184, 568
   French and Creary cases, 260
Retirement. Committee on, 105
Retirement Policy for Federal
      Personnel Committee on, 184
Retraining and Reemployment
      Administration, 664
RETRAINING AND
      REEMPLOYMENT
      ADMINISTRATION
      (RG 244), 671-672
Retrenchment, Joint Committee
      on, 54
Revenue, 51, 112, 152, 175, 467
   Collectors, 352, 353
   See also Internal revenue
Revenue Act of 1926, 54
Revenue-Cutter Service, 412,
      522, 523, 524
Revenue cutters, 59, 168, 169, 523
Revenue-Marine Division,
      Treasury Department, 523
Review, Board of, Office of
      the Chief of Naval
      Operations, 299
Revision of Style and
      Arrangement,
      Committee on, 37
Revista Alemana, 737
Revolution, American, Joint
      Committee on the
      History of the, 54
Revolutionary War, 35, 37-39,
      43, 59, 136, 140, 162,
      163, 232, 255, 294, 571,
      573, 677
   Claims, 75, 571
   Loans, 163
   Pensions, 79
   Veterans, 373, 571

"Revolutionary War Prize
    Cases," 70, 82
Reyes, Estanislao, 136
Reynolds, James J., 491
Reynolds, Louis C., 674
Rhee, Syngman, 335
Rhode Island Historical
    Society, 162, 170
Ribbentrop, Joachim von,
    623, 737
Rice, 442, 535, 668
Richberg, Donald R., 627
Rickenbacker, Edward V., 334
Rifkind, Simon H., 115
Rifled Guns Board, 304
Rifles, 214, 215, 243, 256,
    272, 304
Rights in Conflict, 127
Rigsarkivet, 724
Ringgold, Cadwalader, 295, 307
RIO, 143
Riots
    Paris, *1934*, 569
    Race, 269
    See also Civil Disorders,
        National Advisory
        Commission on (RG 282)
River and Harbor Improvements,
    Board on, 239
River Clyde, Scotland, 566
Rivers, 31, 53, 114, 119, 147, 156,
    237, 239, 240, 304, 322,
    323, 334, 370, 390, 392,
    393, 394, 397, 401, 407,
    489, 523, 644, 714
    Basins, 111, 369, 437, 478, 488
    Control of, 406, 567
    Improvement of, 237, 238, 239,
        241, 256
    See also Federal Inter-Agency
        River Basin Committee
Rivers and Harbors, Board of
    Engineers for, 239, 240·
Road Inquiry, Office of, 526
Roads, 53, 58, 358, 404, 407, 430,
    567, 736, 737
    Construction, 237, 240,
        397-398, 428, 434, 669
    Philippine, 414
    Puerto Rican, 414
    Virgin Islands, 724, 725
    See also Public Roads, Bureau of,
        and Wagon roads
Roanoke River, N.C., 397
Robert, W.P., Committee
    investigation, 628
Roberts, Edmund, 136
Roberts, Owen J., 341, 611
Robison, Jesse, 674
Rock, George H., 306
Rock, uses of, 391
Rock Creek and Potomac
    Parkway Commission, 716

Rock Creek Park, Board of
    Control of, 716
Rock Creek Park Commission,
    716
Rock Creek Pollution Studies,
    402
Rock Island district (Ill. and
    Iowa), 598
Rockets, 332, 554, 659, 660
    Development of, 334
    German, 335
Rockwell, A.F., 715
Rocky Mountain National
    Park, 398, 409
Rodgers, C.R. Perry, 745
Rodgers, John, 172, 295
Roerich expedition, 451
Rogers, Will, 530, 748
Rohden, Herhudt von, 731
Rolls and Library, Bureau
    of, 136
Rommel, George M., 445
Ronne, Finne, 334
Roon, Albrecht von, 732
Roosa, Isaac P., 135
Roosevelt, Eleanor, 115,
    689, 748
Roosevelt, Franklin D., 99, 104, 106,
    150, 256, 292, 335, 362, 371,
    409, 512, 535, 542, 548, 623,
    636, 663, 677, 688, 744, 745,
    747, 748
    Presidential Library, 550, 748
Roosevelt, Sara Delano, 748
Roosevelt, Theodore, 97, 292, 335,
    403, 744, 745, 748
Root, Elihu, 218
Rope, William F., 746
Roper, Daniel P., 464
Rose, Robert R., Jr., 367
"Rose Garden Papers," 736
Rosenberg, Alfred, 729
Rosenberg, Anna, 183
Rosenberg, Julius J., 692

Ross, Malcolm, 616
ROTC. *See* Reserve Officers'
    Training Corps
Rotterdam, Netherlands, 596
Royall, Kenneth, 213
Rubber, 435, 451, 453, 586, 587,
    654, 688
    Emergency project, 427, 428, 430
    Guayule, 430
    Industry, 105, 106, 490, 587,
        589
    Synthetic, 581, 586, 587, 588,
        666
Rubber, Interagency Policy
    Committee on, 587
Rubber, Policy Committee on, 665
Rubber Development Corporation,
    580, 587, 589

Rubber Producing Facilities
Disposal Act of 1953, 586
Rubber Producing Facilities
Disposal Commission, 581,
587, 588
Rubber Reserve, Office of, 586,
588
Rubber Reserve Company, 580,
586
Rubber Survey, Department of
Agriculture, 452
Rubber Survey Committee,
105, 106
Ruby, Jack, 128
Rumania, 612, 729, 731, 735
American Relief
Administration mission
to, 596
Rural Credit, Joint Committee
on, 55
Rural Electrification
Administration, 424, 426
RURAL ELECTRIFICATION
ADMINISTRATION
(RG 221), 440-441
Rural life, 423, 434, 446,
456, 457, 499
Rural Rehabilitation Division,
442
Russell, John E., 53
Russia, 138, 143, 147, 241, 299,
577, 595, 693, 722, 723,
734, 747
American Military Mission
to, 286
Artworks and books looted
from, 198
Lend-lease assistance to, 105
Political affairs in, 134
World War I, 256, 286, 287
See also South Russia and
Soviet Union
Russian-American Company,
722, 723
Russian Bureau, Inc., 610
Russian Civil War, 219
"Russian News" (m.p.), 663
Russian Orthodox Church, 723
Russian Supply Committee, 723
Russo-Finnish War, 569, 746
Russo-Japanese War, 219
Peace treaty, signing of, 1905,
138
Ryukyu Islands, 189, 198,
214, 293

S

SA (Sturmabteilung), 730
Saar Plebiscite, 569
Sabotage and saboteurs,
328, 659

Sachs, Paul, 611
Sade. See Vic and Sade show
"Safehaven Reports," 262
Safety, 34, 194, 269, 408,
479, 492, 640, 698
Air, 530
At sea, 146, 481, 482, 483
Education programs, 409
Labor, 496, 630
Public, 198, 479
Safety Appliance Acts, 353
"Sailing Directions and
Lists of Harbors," 471
Sailors, black, 263
St. Clair, Arthur, 32
St. Croix, V.I., 723, 724,
725, 745
St. Elizabeth's Hospital,
364, 502
Saint Etienne, Loire,
France, 599
St. George Island, 396
St. John, V.I., 723,
724, 725
St. John's Church, 532
St. Lawrence River, 644
Saint Louis World's Fair,
449
St. Mary's River, 53
St. Paul Island, 396
St. Thomas, Canada, 241
St. Thomas, V.I., 723, 724
St. Thomas Harbor, V.I., 725
Saipan, 293
Saishu Island, 189
Salaries, 177, 559, 561, 631,
632, 633, 706
Army, 243
Professional, 707
See also Wage Adjustment
Board (RG 236), 498
Salary Stabilization Board,
703, 707
Salem Maritime National
Historic Site, 402
Salmon fisheries, Alaskan,
394, 395, 396
Salvage, 82, 83, 249, 272,
305, 443
Salvation Army Congress,
165
Samoa. See American Samoa
and Western Samoa
Samoa (vessel), 410
Samoan High Commission, 147
Sandburg, Carl, 677
Sanders, Jennings B., 36
Sandstone, 409
Sandy Hook Proving
Grounds, 245
San Francisco, Calif., 50, 398,
691, 745
Earthquake, 241, 249, 527

San Francisco, Convent of,
      726
San Francisco, National Park
      Service Field
      Headquarters at, 399
San Francisco Bay, 525
San Francisco Conference, 256
San Francisco Exposition, 403
San Francisco State
      College, 128
San Gabriel River Commission, 369
Sanitation, 137, 146, 183, 251,
      286, 502, 503, 504, 505,
      646, 685, 697, 746
   Veracruz, 283
   Virgin Islands, 724
San Salvador, 138
Santo Domingo, 414
Sardinia, 612
Satellites, 334, 554
Saudi Arabia, 586
Sauk Indians, 380
Saunders, Harold E., 750
Saunders, John E., 675
Saunders, Richardson, 491
Savings, Division of, Bureau
      of the Public Debt, 165
Savings bonds, U.S., 156,
      650, 699
Savings certificates, war, 165
Savings institutions, 538
   See also Banks and banking
Sawyer, Ernest Walker, 367
Scandinavia, 450
Scapa Flow, 304
Scharnhorst, Gerhard Johann
      David von, 732
Schell, S. Duvall, 676
Scheuch, Heinrich, 732
Schlieffen, Alfred von, 732
Schmidding, Wilhelm, 734
Schneider & Co. of France, 304
Scholten, Governor von, 724
School and College Civilian
      Morale Service, 507
School Life, 506
Schoolcraft, Henry R., 388
Schools, 245, 263, 312, 328,
      346, 374, 387, 388, 485,
      506, 548, 635, 695, 714
   Alaskan, 383
   Cuban, 281
   For the handicapped, 466
   German, 728
   Lunch program, 459, 462
   Maritime, 677
   Military, 185, 188, 197, 203, 204,
      207, 217, 218, 219, 226,
      227, 230, 232, 233, 234,
      235, 236, 237, 249, 256,
      266, 268, 288-289, 295,
      302, 311, 312, 313, 321-322,
      328, 525

Philippine, 667
Puerto Rican, 414
Territorial, 370
See also Education; Indians,
      education; Training;
      and individual names
      of institutions
Schoonover, Tedford E., 620
Schutzstaffel/SS, 730
Schwab, Charles M., 604
Schwellenbach, Lewis B., 491
Science, 101, 114, 122, 139, 146, 328,
      371, 426, 443, 446, 455, 473,
      570, 588, 646, 657, 663, 745
   See also National Academy of
      Sciences
Science Advisory Committee,
      President's, 114
Science and Research Division, 325
SCIENCE AND TECHNOLOGY,
      OFFICE OF (RG 359),
      101-102
Science and Technology,
      Office of the Special
      Assistant to the
      President for, 102
Science and Technology,
      Special Assistant to the
      President for, 101
Science Information Exchange,
      566
Scientific Advisory Board,
      Air Force, 331
Scientific and Cultural
      Cooperation,
      Interdepartmental
      Committee on, 150
Scientific Papers, 475
Scientific Research and
      Development, Office of,
      101, 555
SCIENTIFIC RESEARCH AND
      DEVELOPMENT, OFFICE
      OF (RG 227), 657-660
Scientific Research Board, 107
Scotland, 566, 607
Scott, Robert N., 215
Scott, Winfield, 215
Scott (South Pole) Station.
      See Amundsen-Scott
      (South Pole) Station
Scrap collection program,
      695, 698
Screwworm, control of, 454
Scribner, Fred C., Jr., 153
Sculpture, 532, 547, 548, 566
Sea battles, 328
Sea letters, applications for, 33
Sea otter industry, 397
Sea rescues, 523, 525, 677
Sea Service Bureau, 485
Sea Service Section, 480
Sea Training Bureau, 485

Seabees, 309, 310
Seals
  Foreign government, 135
  State and territorial, 135
  U.S., 41, 44, 45, 46, 131, 135
Seals, fur, 195, 394, 395, 396,
  464, 525, 548
Seamen, 79, 82, 83, 84, 132, 133,
  136, 140, 141, 168, 169,
  480, 484, 602, 626, 693
  Foreign, 137
  Merchant, 485, 502, 522, 525
Seamen's Protection Certificates, 484
Seamless Steel Equipment
  Corp., 356
Search warrants, 79
Searles, Richard, 367
Searls, Fred, 692
Seashores, 397
SEATO. See Southeast Asia
  Treaty Organization
Seattle World's Fair, 147
2d Army, 285
Second Assistant Postmaster
  General, 360
Second Assistant Postmaster
  General, Bureau of, 360
Second Auditor, 59, 60
Second Auditor, Office of the, 59
Second Bank of the United
  States, 158, 162, 163
Second Comptroller, 58
Second Comptroller, Office of
  the, 58
Second War Power Act, 664
Secret Correspondence,
  Committee of, 30
Secret Service, 128, 745
SECRET SERVICE, U.S.
  (RG 87), 176-177
Secret Service, U.S., Chief of
  the, 176
Sectional Economic Research
  Project, 695
Securities, 158, 160, 162, 164, 176,
  354, 355, 563, 577, 578
Securities Act of 1933, 563
Securities and Exchange
  Commission, 63, 71
SECURITIES AND EXCHANGE
  COMMISSION (RG 266),
  563
Securities Exchange Act of
  1934, 563
Security, 64, 110, 115, 213, 339,
  560
  International, 143, 182,
    184, 403
  Organizations, British and
    Canadian, 536
  See also National security
Security Advisory Board, 661
Security clearances, 190
Security Force. See Schutzstaffel/SS

Sedimentation, 421, 440
Sedition, 359
"See America First" (m.p.), 747
Seeckt, Hans Friedrich Leopold
  von, 732
Seed Laboratory, 462
Seeds, 423, 434, 450, 451, 462
  Federal laws, 462, 463
Seeds, Division of, 450
Seeger, Lewis, 136
Seismology, 470, 474
Seized records, German. See
  Foreign Records Seized,
  1941- , National Archives
  Collection of (RG 242)
Selective Service, 216, 679
  Appeal boards, 564
  Medical boards, 563-564
Selective Service, Bureau of, 682
Selective Service, National
  Advisory Commission on, 117
Selective Service Act of 1917, 265
Selective Service System, 371, 679,
  680
SELECTIVE SERVICE SYSTEM,
  1940- (RG 147), 563-564
SELECTIVE SERVICE SYSTEM
  (WORLD WAR I)
  (RG 163), 265
Selective Training and Service
  Act of 1940, 563, 681
Selznick International Pictures,
  747
Seminole Indians, 240, 380,
  387, 388
Senate, U.S., 43, 45, 103, 135, 138,
  156, 329, 339, 409, 413,
  566, 711
  Committees of the, 49, 54, 213, 341,
    508, 558, 603, 604
  President of the, 164
  Resolutions, 42
SENATE, U.S. (RG 46), 49-51
Senators, U.S., 748
Sensory devices, 658
Seoul, 196
Sequestration, 74, 77, 89
Serapis (H.M.S.), 296
Serbia, 729
  American Relief
    Administration missions
    to, 596
Serbian Economy, General
  Plenipotentiary for the, 729
Serums, 502
Service academy. See Military
  Academy, U.S.
Service Academy Board, 182
Service Commands, Deputy Chief
  of Staff for, 229
Service Pay, Advisory Committee
  on, 183
Servicemen's Readjustment
  Act, 1944, 582

Services of Supply (Army), 227,
   228, 229, 231, 234, 252,
   258, 264, 266, 267, 274,
   284, 285
Services of Supply, Commanding
   General of the, 228
Services of Supply, Headquarters,
   210
Services of the Rear, 284, 285
"Session laws," 42
Settlement of War Claims Act of
   1928, 340
VII Corps, 280
Severn River Naval Command,
   322
Sewerage systems, 385
Shackleton, Ernest, 747
Shakespearean plays, 748
Shanghai, 139
Sharkey, Jack, 89
Shellac, 508
"Shelterbelt," 427, 430, 439
Shenandoah (dirigible), 293,
   320, 745
Shenandoah National Park,
   403, 409
Shepard, Alan, 551
Sheridan, Philip H., 744
Sheridan Statue Commission,
   717
Sherman, Leroy K., 597
Sherman, Louis, 491
Sherman Statue Commission,
   717
Shiloh National Military
   Park Commission, 247
Ship Defense Installations,
   Coordinator of, 692
Ship Protection Committee, 603
Ship Warrants Act, 693
Shipbuilding, 54, 270, 292, 295,
   299, 305, 306, 307, 308,
   309, 310, 479, 482, 601,
   602, 603, 604, 605, 607,
   675
Shipbuilding, Coordinator of, 307
Shipbuilding Commission,
   633, 672
Shipbuilding Labor Adjustment
   Board, 605
Shipbuilding Stabilization
   Board, 672
SHIPBUILDING STABILIZATION
   COMMITTEE (RG 254),
   672-673
Shippers' Advisory Committee, 620
Shipping, 97, 98, 229, 462, 464,
   479, 484, 487, 539, 553, 605,
   606, 610, 642, 676, 692
   British, 737
   Canadian, 677
   Soviet and East European, 693
   See also War Shipping Administration

Shipping Act of 1916, 601
Shipping Board, U.S., 408, 485, 487,
   609, 675, 676
SHIPPING BOARD, U.S. (RG 32),
   601-607
Shipping Board Bureau, U.S.,
   480, 602, 603, 675
   Advisory Committee, 602
Shipping Board Recruiting
   Service, 481, 485
Shipping Commissioners,
   480, 484
Shipping Control Committee, 605
Shipping Policy and Ocean Mail
   Contracts, Interdepartmental
   Committee on, 487, 488
Ships, 34, 141, 240, 293, 296,
   298, 302, 303, 310, 311, 313,
   315, 320, 321, 340, 355,
   356, 477, 478, 480, 482, 485,
   501, 524, 596, 601, 604, 606,
   607, 609, 619, 675, 677, 692
   British, 70
   Disasters, 169, 315, 523, 524,
      525, 726
   Liberty, 676
   Sale and mortgage abroad, 479
   See also Federal Maritime
      Commission (RG 358);
      Inland Waterways
      Corporation (RG 91);
      Vessels; and names of
      specific ships
SHIPS, BUREAU OF (RG 19),
   305-308
Shipstead-Luce Act, 531
Shipyards, 305, 307, 479, 604,
   607, 635, 676, 684
   Plants, construction of, 605
Shore establishments
   Marine, 301
   Naval, 292, 294, 295, 296,
      302, 303, 306, 309, 310,
      311, 313, 319, 320, 321,
      477
Shore Station Development Board,
   299
Shores, 397
Shrimp fishing, 396
Shulman, Stephen N., 491
Shuttle-bombing. See Operation
   Frantic
Siam, King of, 136
Siberia, 723, 737
   American expedition in, 278
   American Expeditionary
      Forces in, 277
   U.S. Army in, 276
Sicily, 612, 734, 736
   Allied landing in, 205
Siegfried Line, 734
Sign language, Indian, 567
Signal Camp of Instruction, 255

Signal Corps, 59, 254, 255, 256,
    272, 324, 477
Signal Office, 312, 477
Signal Service, 59
Sigsbee, Charles D., 744
Sikorsky, Igor, 334
Silk culture, 454
Sillcox, L.K., 619
Sillimanite, 409
Silver, 409
    Bullion, 173, 174
Silvics, Office of, Forest
    Service, 429
Silviculture, Branch of, Forest
    Service, 428, 430
Simoda (Shimoda), Japan, 46
Sims, William S., 306
Sinking fund, 157, 164
Sino-Japanese conflict, 147,
    299, 747
Sioux Indians, 380, 382, 384,
    388
Siple, Paul A., 749
Sisson, Edgar, 95, 120
"Sisson Documents," 137
Sitka, Alaska, 46, 172, 412, 723
Six Nations of Indians, 34
6-year plans, 698
16th amendment, 177
6th Army Group, 192
Sixth Auditor, 60
Skate (U.S.S.), 551
Skinner, W. W., 450
Skoda Works, 735
Sky radiation measurement,
    477
Slattery, Harry, 440
Slaves and slavery, 61, 75, 83, 86,
    138, 468, 720, 724
    Trade, 170, 336, 337, 365, 523
Slovenia, 736
Slums, 475, 521, 671, 712
    District of Columbia, 714
    Rehabilitation of, 515
Small Arms and Ammunition
    Board, 243
Small Business, Office of, 673, 675
Small Business Act of 1953, 565
Small Business Administration, 581
SMALL BUSINESS
    ADMINISTRATION
    (RG 309), 565
Small Business Division, 673
Small Business Investment
    Act of 1958, 565
Small Defense Plants
    Administration, 565
Smaller War Plants Corporation,
    581
SMALLER WAR PLANTS
    CORPORATION
    (RG 240), 673-675
Smelters, 174, 407, 450

Smith, Erwin F., 426
Smith, George Otis, 591
Smith, Hugh McCormick, 566
Smith, Sumpter, 527
Smith, William S., 33
Smith-Brady Commission, 233
Smith Committee. See National
    Labor Relations Board,
    House of Representatives
    Special Committee to
    Investigate the
Smith-Connally Act. See War
    Labor Disputes Act
Smith-Lever Act of 1914, 458
Smithson, James, 565
Smithsonian Institution, 361, 477,
    554, 741
    Meteorological Division of,
    476
SMITHSONIAN INSTITUTION
    (RG 106), 565-567
Smithsonian Tropical Research
    Institute, 566
Smithsonian Trust Fund, 159
Smokescreens, 639, 660
Smolensk District, Communist
    Party, 735
Smuggling, 168, 282, 523, 603
    Rum, 524, 525
Snuff, 178
Social Hygiene Board. See
    Interdepartmental Social
    Hygiene Board, U.S.
Social Protection Division, Office
    of Community War
    Services, 641
Social Research, Division of,
    Works Projects
    Administration, 697
Social Science Research
    Council, 743
Social Scientists and
    Economists, Advisory
    Committee on,
    104-105
Social security, 371, 511, 662
    Benefits and coverage, 512
    Programs, 501, 698
Social Security Act of
    1935, 498, 510, 511
Social Security
    Administration, 499
SOCIAL SECURITY
    ADMINISTRATION
    (RG 47), 510-512
Social Security Board, 103,
    498, 499, 500, 501,
    510, 511, 640
Social Trends, President's
    Research Committee on, 121
Soil Conservation and
    Domestic Allotment
    Act of 1936, 435

Soil Conservation Service,
    425, 427, 435, 446
    448, 449, 455, 614
SOIL CONSERVATION
    SERVICE (RG 114),
    437-440
SOIL EROSION SERVICE
    (RG 114), 437-440
Soils, 431, 447, 527
    Conservation, 368, 370, 436,
        555, 671
    Erosion, 452, 567
    Investigations, 437, 450, 451,
        452, 453
    Microbiology, 452
    Types, 409, 426, 440, 452, 453
    See also Chemistry and Soils,
        Bureau of, and Plant
        Industry, Soils, and
        Agricultural Engineering,
        Bureau of
Soils, Bureau of, 451, 452
Soils, Division of, 451
Soldiers, 210, 663
    Black, 263
    Disabled, 232, 241, 242, 289, 290,
        571, 572, 574-575
    Discharged, 290
    Nisei, 691
    Volunteer, 232, 234
    See also Troops
SOLDIERS' HOME, U.S.
    (RG 231), 289-290
"Soldiers of Production" (s.r.),
    663
Solicitor, Office of the,
    317, 368, 508
Solicitor and Naval
    Judge-Advocate General,
    317
Solicitor for the U.S. Court
    of Claims, Office of, 351
Solicitor General of the
    United States, 111
SOLICITOR OF THE
    TREASURY (RG 206),
    352-354
Solid Fuels Administration
    for War, 106, 370, 418
SOLID FUELS
    ADMINISTRATION FOR
    WAR (RG 245), 419-420
Solid Fuels Coordinator for
    National Defense, 419
Solid Fuels Coordinator for
    War, 419
Solomon Islands, 293
Solvents, 656
Somervell, Brehon B., 229
Sorghums, 442, 449
South America, 147, 301, 314, 328
    Indian tribal groups, 566
    See also Latin America

South Atlantic Squadron, 75, 323
South Carolina, 36, 394
South Carolina District Court,
    720
South Carolina Interstate West
    Indian Exposition, 154, 433
South Dakota, 430
South Pole, 749-751
South Russia, 137
South Sea Islands, 397
Southeast Area Joint
    Committee, 202
Southeast Asia, 189, 205
Southeast Asia Command, 195
Southeast Asia Treaty
    Organization, 143
Southeastern United States,
    567
Southern Advisory Committee
    on Railroad
    Consolidation, 620
Southern Claims Commission,
    60, 154, 167, 180
Southern Defense Command, 279
Southern Europe, American
    Relief Administration
    mission to, 596
Southern European Task
    Force, Headquarters, 279
Southwest Area Joint
    Committee, 202
Southwest Indians, 370
Southwest Pacific Area, 194,
    195, 315
Southwest Territory, 134

SOUTHWESTERN POWER
    ADMINISTRATION
    (RG 387), 411
Sovereigns, foreign, 132
Soviet Liaison Office, 194
Soviet Purchasing Commission
    at Prague, 735
Soviet Union, 136, 137, 278, 432,
    625, 729, 730, 735, 736, 737
    Army, 734
    Satellites (countries), 736
    Shipping programs in, 693
    See also Russia
Soybeans, 442, 668
Spaatz, Carl A., 326
Space, 479
    Exploration of, 479, 566
    Flight, 747
    Technology, 102, 334
    See also National Aeronautics
        and Space Administration
        (RG 255)
Spain, 33, 35, 46, 143, 145, 163,
    276, 280, 338, 340, 612,
    725, 735
    Claims against, 164, 340
    Colonial government, 523

Spanish-American War, 59, 138, 147, 163, 232, 233, 255, 272, 276, 280, 312, 340, 351, 360, 403, 525, 573, 574, 744
Spanish Civil War, 256, 737
Spanish Navy, 313
Spanish Treaty Claims Commission, 340, 414
Spark plugs, 409
Sparks, Jared, 36
SPARS, 525
Speaker of the House, 52
SPECIAL ADVISER TO THE PRESIDENT ON FOREIGN TRADE, OFFICE OF THE (RG 20), 126-128
Special Advisers on Reclamation, Committee of, 406
Special Agency Service, 168
Special agents
   Civil War, 179, 180
   Department of Justice, 342, 348
   Timber, 375
   Treasury, 353
Special Agents, Division of, 168
Special Investigations, Office of the Director of, 332
Special Services, Bureau of, 125
Special Staffs, War Department, 220
Speech scrambling, study of, 659
Speer, Albert, 728, 734, 737
"Sphinx" project, 227
Spies, 257
   Captured enemy, 328, 525
   See also Espionage
Spitsbergen, 317
Spokane Reservation, 381
Spoliation claims, French, 91, 169, 170, 338, 352, 483
Sponging, 396
Sports, 139, 256, 569, 746, 747
Sprays, fruit and vegetable, 508
Springfield (Hope) Indian School, 387
Spruce Production Corporation, U.S., 325, 328
Spruce Production Division, Army Air Forces, 325
Spy Glass, The, 348
Squadron of Evolution, 323
SS, 701, 730, 733, 734
   Division, Office of the Chief of Counsel for War Crimes, 701
   Officers, 217, 700
   Reich Leader and Chief of the German Police, 730
   Special Employment Troops, 730
   Verfuegungstruppe, 730
   Wirtschafts-Verwaltungshauptamt, 730

Stabilization Act, 177
Stabilization programs
   Agricultural, 435-436
   Economic, 517, 559, 645, 648, 665, 666, 703, 704, 705, 706, 707
   Employment, 122, 672, 680, 684, 687
   Lead-zinc, 552
   Rent, 517, 518, 703, 704
   Shipbuilding industry, 672, 673
   Wage, 270, 459, 460, 465, 497, 498, 561, 631, 632, 633, 673, 703, 706, 707
Stabswache, 730
Stalags, 702
Stalin, Josef, 335
Stamps
   Food, 459
   Postage, 75, 361, 362
   Ration, 176
   Savings, 175
Standard Container Acts, 461
Standard Weights and Measures, Office of, 474, 475
Standards
   Engineering, 689
   Food and drug, 507, 509
   Professional education and college, 506
   See also National Bureau of Standards
Standby Reserve (Army), 234
Standing Liaison Committee, 149
Stanford, Leland, 412
Stanford University, 148, 608
Stanton, Edwin M., 743
Stanton, Robert, Survey, 394
Staphorst, Jacob van, 35
"Star Route," 338, 342
Stars, 316
Stars and Stripes, 278, 284
State, Department of, 29, 32, 36, 37, 38, 41, 42, 43, 44, 46, 60, 105, 113, 126, 128, 141, 142, 143, 144, 146, 148, 149, 150, 164, 169, 176, 184, 197, 204, 205, 282, 296, 336, 340, 345, 371, 431, 435, 445, 469, 486, 530, 610, 611, 613, 624, 625, 646, 661, 662, 700, 722, 723, 727
   Numerical File, 133
STATE, DEPARTMENT OF (RG 59), 131-140
State, Secretary of, 36, 41, 42, 44, 45, 107, 119, 131, 132, 135, 138, 139, 164, 169, 204, 286, 296, 345, 364, 403, 465, 469, 512

State-Army-Navy-Air Force Advisory
    Committee, 213
State-Army-Navy-Air Force
    Coordinating Committee, 202, 213
State-Army-Navy Coordinating
    Committee, 202
State, War, and Navy Building, 717
State, War, and Navy Building, Office
    of the Superintendent of the,
    714, 716
State-War-Navy-Air Force
    Coordinating Committee, 150
State-War-Navy Coordinating
    Committee, 202, 213
State-War-Navy/State-Army-Navy-Air
    Force Coordinating Committee, 222
States, 393, 403, 499, 628
    Assemblies, 34
    Boundaries, 34, 372
    Claims, 33, 34, 164
    Governors, 553
    Guard, 217, 265
    Internal affairs of, 134
    Legislation, 124, 125
    Prisons, 466
    Rebellious, 179, 180, 257
States, Committee of the, 32
States Relations Service, 433,
    446, 458
Statistical Standards, Division
    of, 96, 98
Statistics, 96, 97, 98, 426, 444,
    457, 460, 468
    Census, 465, 466
    Vital, 465, 467, 502, 504, 691
    See also Birth records; Death
        records; Labor Statistics,
        Bureau of; and Marriage
        records
Statistics, Bureau of
    Department of Agriculture,
        431, 455
    Department of Commerce and
        Labor, 486
Statues, 137, 531, 716, 717
    See also Monuments and
        memorials
Status of Women, President's
    Commission on the, 115, 116
Statutes at Large, United States, 42
Steadman Board of Claims, 60
Steam Engineering, Bureau of,
    295, 305, 318, 319
Steam vessels, 82, 119, 136, 180,
    359, 482, 483, 484, 488,
    599, 601, 603, 606, 607, 677
    Inspection, 480, 482, 485
Steamboat Act of 1852, 480
Steamboat-Inspection Service,
    480, 481, 482, 483
Steel, 106, 409, 654
    Industry, 50, 243, 356, 540, 684
    Labor, 630

Steel Commission, 633
Steelman, John R., 107, 665
Stefansson, Vilhjalmur, 750
Stein, Harold, 665
Stephenson, H. K., 660
Sterling, George E., 536
Stern, Carl S., 64
Stevedoring, 606
Stevens, Isaac, expedition, 366
Stevenson, Adlai E., 551, 748
Stevenson, Matilda Cope, 566
Stewart, Duncan VII, 750
Stewart, Ethelbert, 493
Stewart, George Scott, Jr., 744
Stewart, James, and Co., 546
Stills, taxes on, 178
Stilwell, Joseph W., 195, 197
Stimson, A. M., 504
Stimson, Henry L., 135, 239, 414
"Stock driveway files," 375
Stockbridge Indians, 380
Stockholm, Sweden, 205
Stocks, 163, 164
    Confederate, 722
Stockton, Calif., 50
Stone, Livingston, 394
Stone, Roy, 526
Stone, William J., 136
"Stop Silicosis" (m.p.), 496
Stosstrupp Hitler, 730
Strategic Air Command, 333-334
STRATEGIC BOMBING SURVEY,
    U.S. (RG 243), 206
Strategic Services, Office of, 106, 136,
    611, 660
STRATEGIC SERVICES, OFFICE OF
    (RG 226), 204, 205
Stratemeyer, George E., 326
Stratigraphy, 391
Stratosphere, 476
Straub, Charles W., 491
Straus, Michael W., 367
Street layouts, 599 .
Stresemann, Gustav, 727
Strike Commission, U.S., 559
Strikes, 269, 339, 559, 579, 632
    Cannery, 50
    Coal, 1919, 593
    Republic Steel, 50
    See also Labor disputes
Students
    Aid programs, 635, 636, 695
    Foreign, 570
    Graduate, 634
    Work programs, 634, 635
Sturmabteilung, 730
Styer, W. D., 229
Submarine Board, 292
Submarine Boat Corp., 605
Submarine Defense, School of, 226
Submarines, 256, 293, 299, 313, 525, 692
    Bases, 310
    German, 299

Subsidies, 649, 664, 665
  Air carrier, 530
  Housing, 519
  Ship construction, 601
Subsistence Department, 246, 252
Subsistence Homesteads Division,
    Department of Interior, 442
Subsistence programs
  Garden, 695
  Homesteads, 520
Subversive activities, 298, 603
Sudan, U.S. assistance to, 143
Sugamo Prison, 279
Sugar, 172, 449, 462, 591, 607,
    608, 724
  Industry, 414, 450, 451, 466,
      540, 724
  See also Beets, sugar
Sugar Control Extension Act of 1947,
    647
Sugar Distributing Committee, 591,
    592, 593, 607
Sugar Equalization Board, Inc., U.S.,
    591
SUGAR EQUALIZATION BOARD,
    INC., U.S. (RG 6), 607-608
Sugarcane, 442
Sulfur, 409
  Dioxide, 509
Sullivan, John, 34
Sullivan, John L., 153
Sullivan, Paul, 750
Summary of Operations in the World War,
    529
Summit Conference, 184
Superior Blockade Council, 611
Supervising Architect, Office of the,
    153, 545, 546, 548
Supervising Inspectors, Board of, 482, 484
Supervising Tea Examiner, 509
Supervisory Naval Examining Board, 322
Supplies
  Air Force, 329
  Allied, 284, 286, 287, 577
  Army, 38, 39, 213, 221, 223, 230,
      244, 245, 246, 247, 249
  Axis, 205
  Government, 57, 544, 548, 549, 664
  Medical, 251
  Navy, 295, 305, 307
  See also Services of Supply (Army)
SUPPLIES AND ACCOUNTS, BUREAU
    OF (NAVY) (RG 143), 308-309
Supplies Division, Ordnance Department,
    248
Supply Branch, Department of the
    Treasury, 548
Supply Department, Marine Corps,
    300, 301
Supply Division, Office of the Secretary
    of War, 209
Supply Management, Office of the Vice
    Chairman, 188

Supply Management Advisory Council,
    223
Supply Priorities and Allocations Board,
    648, 687
Supreme Allied Commander,
    188-189, 192, 195
Supreme Blockade Committee, 611
Supreme Commander for the Allied
    Powers, 195, 700
  General Headquarters, 194
Supreme Commander of the Armed
    Forces, German, 731
Supreme Court, U.S., 72, 91, 92, 336,
    339, 403, 415, 417, 627, 630,
    690, 699
  Associate Justices, 69
  Bar of the, 71
  Building, 71
  Clerk of the, 69, 70, 71
  Deputy Clerk of the, 69
  Justices, 70, 72, 403, 714, 745
  Librarian of the, 69
  Marshal of the, 69, 71
  Reporter of Decisions of the, 69
  See also Chief Justice, U.S.
Supreme Court of the District of
    Columbia, 75, 261, 415, 718
SUPREME COURT OF THE UNITED
    STATES (RG 267), 69-71
Supreme Economic Council, 611
Supreme Headquarters, Allied
    Powers, Europe, 199
Supreme Headquarters Allied
    Expeditionary Forces, 192, 195
Supreme War Council, 286
Surgeon General, Air Force, 290
Surgeon General (Air Force),
    Office of the, 331
Surgeon General, Army, 575
Surgeon General (Army), Office of
    the, 229, 231, 476, 571
SURGEON GENERAL (ARMY),
    OFFICE OF THE (RG 112),
    250-251
Surgeon General, Public Health
    Service, 502
Surgeons
  Military, 197, 257, 273, 286
  Ship, 302
Surgery. *See* Medicine and Surgery,
    Bureau of (RG 52)
SURPLUS MARKETING
    ADMINISTRATION (RG 124),
    458-459
Surplus property, 674
  Disposal of, 65, 369, 544, 552, 586,
      606, 673, 676
Surplus Property Administration, 678
Surplus Property Board, 664
Surplus War Property Administration, 664
Survey, Board of, Department of
    Justice, 261

Survey, Appraisal, and Sale, Navy, Board
        of, 309
Survey of Current Business, 486
Survey of the Coast, Superintendent
        of the, 470
Surveyor and Custodian of Old
        Records, U.S., 716
Surveyor General of California,
        Office of the, 374
Surveyor General of the Territory
        Northwest of the River
        Ohio, 372, 373
"Surveyor General Scrip," 373
Surveyors general, 371, 372, 373
Surveys, 237, 240, 241, 243, 261,
        340, 372, 375, 390,
        391, 403, 516
    Boundary, 237, 366
    Housing, 458, 597, 713
    Hydrographic, 313, 314, 474,
        489
    Land, 53, 179, 401, 471
    Military, 390
    Pacific Railroad, 744
    Snow, 437, 440, 555
    See also Coast and Geodetic
        Survey *and* Geological Survey
Surveys, Division of, General Land
        Office, 372
Surveys and Maps, Federal Board of,
        96, 98, 99, 392
Survival in the Air Age, 107
Susan E. Peck (ship), 53
Sutlers, 247
Sweden, 205, 735
Swedish Red Cross, 139
Swisher, Charles H., 565
Switzerland, 735
Sydney, Australia, 431
Synoptic Reports and Forecasts,
        Division of, 478
Synthetic Rubber, Office of, 586, 588
Syphilis, 505

T

Tacna-Arica arbitration, 145
Tactical Air Command, 333-334
Taft, Robert A., 657
Taft, William Howard, 96, 256, 281,
        389, 464, 744, 748
Taft Commission, 154, 413, 464, 471
Taft-Hartley Labor Management
        Relations Act, 496, 556, 557, 558
Talisman, 407
Talmage, George, Jr., 692
Tampa (vessel), 524
Tampico, Mexico, 299
Tampico Incident, 283
Tank Car Service Section, Office of
        Defense Transportation, 643

Tank Truck Division, Office of Defense
        Transportation, 643
Tanks, 272, 285
Targets
    Firing, 242
    Practice, 303
Tariff Commission, U.S., 126
TARIFF COMMISSION, U.S.
        (RG 81), 570-571
Tariff Revision Commission, 281
Tariffs, 539, 549, 570, 603, 606,
        628, 676
    International, 185, 570
    Interstate carrier, 553
    See also Customs
Tatham, William, 471
Taussig, F. W., 570
Taverns, 567
Taxes, 60, 65, 99, 111, 153, 166,
        177, 178, 179, 344, 430,
        543, 650, 722
    American Samoan, 410
    Amortization, 230, 422, 490, 565
    Evasion, 55
    German, 729
    Wartime, 60, 177
    See also Revenue
Taxicabs, 643
Taylor, Telford, 699
Taylor, Wayne C., 153
Tea Importation Act, 507, 509
Technical Assistance, Interdepartmental
        Advisory Committee on, 150
Technical Cooperation, Bureau of
        Indian Affairs, 439
Technical Cooperation Administration,
        143
Technologic Branch, Geological
        Survey, 390
Technological Cooperation,
        Interdepartmental Advisory
        Council on, 150
Technological Papers, 475
Technology, 101, 102, 114, 118, 122,
        270, 451, 566
Tehran Conference, 118, 256
Telegraph Committee, 613
Telegraphy, 55, 208, 255, 358, 475,
        536, 537, 540, 613, 614
Telenews, 745
Telephones, 359, 440, 441, 536, 537,
        613, 614, 633, 747
Telescopes. *See* Naval Observatory
Television, 468, 535, 569
Temporary Alaska Claims
        Commission, 117
Temporary Controls, Office of,
        647, 656, 664, 665, 687
TEMPORARY NATIONAL ECONOMIC
        COMMITTEE (RG 144), 62-63
Tennessee, 191, 747
    Centennial Exposition, 154, 433
Tennessee River, 144, 567

-Tennessee Valley Authority, 55, 339, 370, 588
TENNESSEE VALLEY AUTHORITY (RG 142), 567
Terminal Inspection Act, 453
Terracing, 437, 438
Territorial commands, 274
    Overseas, 277, 736
Territorial possessions, U.S., 196, 340, 403, 404
Territorial waters, U.S., 571
Territories, 73, 79, 134, 219, 249, 336, 343, 355, 365, 368, 390, 391, 412, 414, 467, 468, 473
    German-occupied, 729, 730
TERRITORIES, OFFICE OF (RG 126), 403-405
Territories and Island Possessions, Division of, 282, 403, 404, 413
Testing methodology, Bureau of Standards, 475
Testing Ordnance, Board for, 295
Testing Rifled Cannon, Board for, 243
Testing the Experimental Springfield Rifle, Board for, 243
Texas, 154, 163, 505
    Airfields in, 327
    Centennial Exposition, 154
    Confederate eastern district of, 722
    Natural resources, 409
Texas, Republic of, 143, 154
Texas City disaster, 1947, 747
Textile Commission, 633
Textiles, 203, 270, 458, 490, 629, 630, 654, 659, 665, 684, 688
Thailand, U.S. assistance to, 143
Thatcher, Thomas D., 341
Theater, 51, 696, 699
Theaters of operations, 193, 205, 219, 220, 229, 262, 278, 280, 293, 299, 326, 328, 611, 677
THEATERS OF WAR, U.S., WORLD WAR II (RG 332), 196-197
Theatre-on-Film, Inc., 747
Thermonuclear weapons. See Defense Atomic Support Agency
"They Dare Not Love" (m.p.), 748
3d Army, 280, 286
Third Assistant Postmaster General, Bureau of, 361
Third Auditor, 59, 60
Third Auditor of the Treasury, Office of the, 61
Third Reich, 734
Thirteen Original Colonies, 29, 62
38th parallel, 737
"This Is Our Enemy" (s.r.), 663
Thomas, Norman, 748
Thompson, L. R., 504
Thompson-Starrett Co., 589
Thomson, Charles, 29, 32, 33, 41, 45
"Three-Thirds of a Nation" (s.r.), 663

Tides, 470, 473, 514
Tilton, R. L., 279
Timber, 65, 295, 325, 338, 372, 375, 381, 427, 428, 429, 487
    Lands, 381, 426
    Trepasses, 344, 366, 372, 379
    See also Forestry and Forests
Timber and Stone Act, 373
Timber Conservation Board, 487
Timber Culture Act, 373
Time zones, 333, 476, 621
Tin, 408, 581, 588, 688
Tipton, W. H., 402
Tobacco, 177, 441, 451, 453, 461, 468
Tobin, Maurice J., 491, 492
Todt, Fritz, 728
Tokyo, 196, 220, 736
Tokyo Bay, 189
"Tokyo Rose," 623
Toll, Roger W., 398
Tolman, Richard C., 659
Tomatoes, 442
Tomes, Robert, 744
Tongass National Forest, Alaska, 615
Tonnage, 481, 483
Tool and die industry, 673
Topographic Division, Geological Survey, 391
Topographical Bureau, War Department, 237, 238
Topographical Engineers, Bureau of, 233
Topographical Engineers, Corps of, 237, 240
Topographical Engineers Office, 238
Topography, 314, 389, 393, 472
Tornados, damage by, 328
Torpedo Board, 226
Torpedoes, 303, 304, 313
Totem poles, 615
Totenkopf Verbaende, 730
Totten, Joseph G., 237
Towboats, 489
Towns, 407
    Planning, 372, 374, 376, 598, 599
Townships, 376, 407
Towoccaroo Indians, 388
Trachoma, 383, 503
Tractors, 448
Tracy, Daniel, 491
Trade, 33, 83, 108, 142, 150, 179, 180, 181, 194, 377, 378, 389, 465, 486, 487, 543, 601, 621, 626, 631, 656
    Agreements, 100, 126, 134, 185, 611, 663
    Associations, 493, 495, 497, 579, 629, 630, 685
    Centers, world, 431
    Foreign, 100, 126, 137, 185, 299, 431, 444, 467, 486, 532, 539, 543, 570, 605, 611, 677, 736

Reciprocal, 139, 149, 570
Routes, 478, 602, 606, 625,
    676, 677
Unions, 346, 493
See also Commerce, Department of;
    Federal Trade Commission;
    Interstate Commerce Commission;
    Special Adviser to the President
    on Foreign Trade, Office of the
    (RG 20); Tariff Commission,
    U.S.; and War Trade Board
Trade Executive Committee, 100
Trade Expansion Act Advisory
    Committee, 100
Trade Expansion Act of 1962, 100
Trade Information Committee, 100

TRADE NEGOTIATIONS, OFFICE OF
    THE SPECIAL REPRESENTATIVE
    FOR (RG 364), 100
Trade Policy Committee, 491
Trade Staff Committee, 100
Trademarks, 80, 83, 146, 355, 469,
    543, 725
Traders, 432
Trades
    Codes for, 627, 629
    Essential, 682
    See also Vocational education
Trading houses, Government, 377, 378
Trading With the Enemy Act of 1917,
    155, 180, 340, 354
Traffic, 246, 267, 333, 409, 526, 544,
    620, 621, 642
    Interstate, 553
    Military, 186
    See also Federal Traffic Board
Trail Smelter Fumes Investigations, 456
Trails, 397-398, 567
    Nature, 398
    Stock, 375
Training, 189, 441, 499, 617, 635,
    653, 659, 685, 686, 687, 703
    Maritime, 676, 677
    Merchant Marine, 485, 607
    Military, 107, 184, 185, 188, 194,
        203, 204, 207, 212, 214, 216,
        217, 218, 220, 221, 222, 227,
        228, 230, 234, 236, 244, 256,
        275, 278, 279, 288, 293, 298,
        299, 312, 313, 320, 321, 333,
        334, 563, 681
    Professional and technical, 685
    See also Education; Indians,
        education; Schools; and
        Vocational education
Training, Bureau of, 685, 686
Training and Employment Service, U.S.,
    499
Training Camp Activities, Commission
    on, 218
Training Within Industry Service,
    679, 685, 686
Trains. See Railroads

Trans-Mississippi and International
    Exposition, 154, 433
Trans-Mississippi Department, 722
Transit Circle Star Catalogue, 316
Transportation, 43, 105, 123, 124,
    148, 180, 186, 191, 198, 202,
    206, 228, 246, 249, 270, 285,
    287, 288, 323, 330, 333, 338,
    359, 360, 361, 362, 407, 426,
    428, 459, 464, 486, 488, 526,
    527, 530, 553, 579, 589, 592,
    593, 596, 597, 598, 599, 604,
    615, 618, 631, 638, 646, 651,
    652, 655, 659, 661, 663, 679,
    684
    Alaska, 723
    Germany, 728, 732, 734
    Japan, 194
    Philippine, 414
    Puerto Rico, 643
    Rates, 553, 642, 644, 655
    Wartime, 577, 642, 643
    See also Air carriers; Airlines;
        Airplanes; Carriers;
        Defense Transportation,
        Office of; Freight; Highways;
        Railroads; Roads; Shipping;
        and Vessels
Transportation, Bureau of, 360
Transportation, Department of, 481, 522,
    526, 527

TRANSPORTATION, FEDERAL
    COORDINATOR OF (RG 133),
    618-621
Transportation acts
    1920, 488, 559, 599, 600
    1940, 612
    1966, 527, 530
Transportation Division, Advisory
    Commission to the Council of
    National Defense, 642
Transportation Division, Bureau of
    Foreign and Domestic Commerce,
    488
Transportation Service, 248
Travel Bureau, U.S., 399
Treason, 137, 343
Treasurer of the Mint, 173
Treasurer of the United States,
    161, 250, 354

TREASURER OF THE UNITED
    STATES (RG 50), 157-159
Treasury, 59, 60, 61, 160, 161, 165,
    180, 252
Treasury, Agent of the, 352, 354
Treasury, Assistant Secretary of, 153
Treasury, Assistant to the Secretary
    of, 152
Treasury, Board of, 30, 33
Treasury, Committee on the, 30
Treasury, Comptroller of the,
    33, 58, 318, 352

Treasury, Department of the, 30,
38, 57, 58, 60, 63, 96, 99,
103, 105, 159, 162, 164,
165, 166, 167, 168, 170,
172, 173, 175, 176, 177,
180, 181, 263, 296, 342, 345,
353, 355, 356, 362, 371, 390,
394, 412, 470, 471, 474, 480,
483, 486, 487, 502, 522, 523,
545, 546, 547, 548, 571, 572,
573, 577, 581, 596, 599, 608,
610, 613, 641, 642, 668, 699,
721, 722
    Confederate, 720

TREASURY, DEPARTMENT OF THE
(RG 56), 152-157
Treasury, Office of the Register of
the, 57, 61
Treasury, Office of the Secretary
of the, 152, 176, 180
Treasury, Register of the, 60, 162,
163, 164, 371
Treasury, Secretary of the, 60, 107,
152, 153, 155, 161, 162, 163,
164, 165, 168, 172, 173, 174,
175, 176, 178, 179, 180, 345,
352, 353, 354, 364, 371, 372,
395, 411, 471, 480, 481, 482,
509, 523, 545, 547, 571, 577,
581, 585, 588, 599, 600, 608,
641, 703, 722, 744
Treasury, Solicitor of the, 176, 336, 337,
338, 352, 353, 354, 546
Treasury, Under Secretary for Monetary
Affairs, 153
Treasury, Under Secretary of, 152, 153
Treasury Buildings, 158, 176, 545, 546,
745
Treasury Buildings, Office of the
Superintendent of, 153
Treasury Department Special Agencies, 155
Treasury Improvement Committee, 153
Treasury notes, 163, 175, 176
Treaties, 32, 33, 41, 42, 43, 46, 49, 50,
69, 73, 131, 132, 134, 143, 144,
145, 164, 256, 336, 481, 569, 570,
602, 725, 731
    American Samoa, 410
    Berlin, 1899, 409
    Bilateral and multilateral, 134, 143,
184, 185, 536
    Extradition, 73, 134
    Indian, 34, 35, 41, 43, 44, 134, 377,
379, 380, 389
    Panama, 562
    Ratification of, 42, 44, 46, 132
    Reciprocity, 135, 145, 149, 150
    U.S.-Spanish, 340
Trees, 451, 673
    See also Forest Service (RG 95)
Trench mortar, 285
Triangulations, 147, 314

Trieste, Free Territory of, 193,
194, 214
Trimble, South, Jr., 488
Tripartite Claims Commission, 144
Tripartite Working Group, 184
Tripoli, 164
Troops, 184, 229, 250, 256, 264,
273, 276, 277, 283, 744
    Black, 211
    French, 569
    Volunteer, 59, 208
    See also Soldiers
Tropical Deterioration Administrative
Committee, 659
Trucking and trucks, 287, 540, 621, 643
Trucking Commission, 633
True, Alfred Charles, 433, 446
Truesdell, Winfred Porter, 551
Trujillo-Hull Convention, 282
Trullinger, Robert W., 446
Truman, Harry S., 96, 107, 108, 256,
335, 492, 623, 657, 663, 735,
745, 748
    Inaugural, 742
Trumbull, Joint Committee on
Disposal of Paintings by, 54
Trust companies, State, 155, 159, 160,
542, 581, 582, 608
Trust funds, 166
Trust Indenture Act of 1939, 563
Trust Territory of the Pacific
Islands, 404
Trusts, Bureau of, Office of Alien
Property, 355
Trusts, Federal, 517, 543
Tsingtao, China, 255
Tuberculosis, 388, 748
Tucker Act, 71
Tugboats, 643
Tule Lake segregation center, 690
Tungsten, 415
Tunnels, 401, 407, 688
Tunney, Gene, 89
Turkey, 313, 586, 735
    Ambassador to, 136
Turrentine, J. W., 452
12th Army Group, 192
Twenty-Eight Hour Act of
1873, 445
Twenty-Eight Hour Law, 353
21st Army Group, 192
Typhoons, 667
Tyrol, 729
Tyson, George E., 750

U

Ufa-Films, Inc., 356
Ukraine, 729
"Uncle Sam Speaks" (s.r.), 663
"Underground" (m.p.), 748

Unemployment, 99, 121, 122, 493, 499, 512, 697
  Census, 467, 468
  Compensation, 112, 500, 511, 682
  State services, 499
  Youth, 634, 636
Unemployment Compensation, Bureau of, 498, 499-500
Unemployment Insurance Service, 499
UNEMPLOYMENT RELIEF, PRESIDENT'S ORGANIZATION ON (RG 73), 120-121
UNESCO. *See* United Nations Educational, Scientific, and Cultural Organization
Ungava Bay, 750
"Uniform Code of Military Justice," 221
Uniform Code of Military Justice, Committee on a, 213
Union of South Africa, 431
Union of Soviet Socialist Republics. *See* Soviet Union
Union Pacific Railroad, 158, 164
Union Station Plaza, 531
Unions, 346, 497, 557, 620
  Credit, 160, 359, 511, 533, 650
  Labor, 83, 493, 495, 601, 602, 613, 616, 679, 680
United Kingdom, 137, 194, 435, 688
United Maritime Authority Planning Committee, 693
United Mine Workers of America, 106
United Nations, 137, 139, 184, 193, 195, 196, 371, 551, 660, 688
  Charter, 663
  Forces in Korea, 736
  General Assembly, 663
  Organization of, 569
  Security Council, 663
United Nations Command, 196, 268
United Nations Command Military Armistice Commission, 196
United Nations Command Repatriation Group, 196
United Nations Conference on Food and Agriculture, 456
United Nations Conference on International Organization, 663
United Nations Economic and Social Council, Fiscal Commission, 153
United Nations Educational, Scientific, and Cultural Organization, 138, 139, 371, 663
United Nations Relief and Rehabilitation Administration, 371, 663, 688
United Nations Universal Declaration of Human Rights, 118
United Nations War Crimes Commission, 701
"United News" (m.p.), 663
United Seamen's Service, Inc., 693
United Service Organizations, 201
UNITED STATES INFORMATION AGENCY (RG 306), 569-570

United States Lines, 606, 607
United States Pharmacopoeia, 509
United States-Puerto Rico Commission on the Status of Puerto Rico, 62
United States-Venezuela Arbitration Protocol, 138
Universal Agricultural Prize Exhibition, 147
Universal Postal Convention of 1897, 43
Universal Training, President's Advisory Commission on, 107
Universities, 107, 312
  Land-grant, 446
  See also Colleges; Schools; *and names of specific universities*
University of Washington Library, 578
Unknown Soldier, 256
"Untin' Bowler," 750
Urban areas, 124, 393
  Redevelopment, National Capital, 713
  See also Housing and Urban Development, Department of, *and* Towns, planning
Urban Housing, President's Committee on, 118
Urban Company, 747
Urban Renewal Administration, 513
Uruguay, 315
U.S.A., 663
USO. *See* United Service Organizations
U.S.S.R. *See* Union of Soviet Socialist Republics
Utah, 134, 343, 345
Ute Indians, 92, 382, 388
  Commission, 382, 384
Utilities, 194, 206, 270, 309, 440
  Companies, 422, 544, 563, 588
  See also Public utilities
Utilization and Disposal Service, 551

V

Vaccines, 502
Valentine, Alan, 704
Vallejo, Calif., 598
Valley Forge, Pa., 33
Valparaiso, Chile, 299
Valuation Division, Interstate Commerce Commission, 553
Valuation of Commandeered Property, Board on, 318
Vanadium ore, 589
Van Hecke, Maurice T., 109
Van Kleek, Mary, 495
V-E Day, 197, 299, 328, 663
Vegetables, 450, 451, 452, 453, 461
Vegetation, 333, 440, 447
Vehicles
  Amphibious, 659, 660
  Armored, 228, 245, 275, 285

Venereal diseases, 503, 504, 641, 747
Venezia Guilia, 193
Venezuela, 138, 145
Venire facias, writs of, 89
Venus, transits of, 473
Veracruz, Mexico, 260, 276, 283, 299
   U.S. Expeditionary Forces at, 277
Verfuegungstruppe, SS, 730
Vermont, 33, 34
Versailles, Treaty of, 256, 731
Vessel Utilization, Planning, and
   Policies, Office of the Deputy
   Administrator for, 692
Vessels, 35, 38, 60, 137, 140, 141, 169,
   170, 247, 248, 294, 295, 298,
   307, 309, 312, 314, 323, 522, 523,
   525, 535, 602, 604, 605, 606,
   625, 676, 692
   Barges, 310, 488, 489
   Captured, 33, 693
   Chartered, 247, 676
   Civil War, 306, 501, 720
   Coast Guard, 58, 524
   Construction of, 305, 306, 604, 605
   Fishing, 170
   Foreign, 169, 296, 306, 308, 525,
     606, 736
   Health inspection of, 503
   Insurance of, 572, 606
   Merchant, 60, 168, 169, 296, 299,
     311, 316, 479, 481, 482, 483,
     484, 485, 535, 601, 602, 603,
     604, 605, 606, 676, 677, 692,
     744
   Naval, 291, 292, 295, 296, 298, 300,
     302, 306, 307, 308, 318
   Sailing, 677
   War, 291, 292
   See also Ships; Steam vessels; and
     names of specific ships
Veteran Reserve Corps, 257, 258
Veterans, 203, 355, 373, 499, 515, 517,
   571, 572, 651, 652, 665, 673,
   741, 742
   Civil War, 575
   Disabled, 572, 573, 575
   Employment of, 614, 671, 680, 684
   Housing for, 515, 517, 518, 519, 574
   Navy, 574
   Organizations, 652
   Revolutionary War, 373, 571
   Widows of, 574
   World War I, 547, 571, 573
   World War II, 520
   See also Soldiers' Home,
     U.S. (RG 231)
Veterans Administration, 203, 207, 356,
   364, 371, 516, 614, 671
VETERANS ADMINISTRATION
   (RG 15), 571-576
Veterans Affairs, Administrator for,
   572
Veterans' Bureau, 356, 571, 572, 573

Veterans' Emergency Housing Act, 517
Veterans Preference Act of 1944, 568
Veterans' Relations Adviser, Office
   of, 651
Veterinarians, 215, 685
Veterinary Corps, Army, 250
Veterinary Division, 445
Vic and Sade show, 640
Vice President of the United
   States, 50, 52, 138, 566
Vickery, Howard L., 676
Vicksburg National Cemetery, 401
Vicksburg National Military
   Park Commission, 247
Victory, 663
Victory, John F., 554
Victory bonds, 156
Victory Fleet, 677
"Victory Front" (s.r.), 663
Victory gardens, 639
Vietnam combat, 335
   See also North Vietnam
Virgin Islands, 220, 313, 370, 404,
   413, 414, 496, 523, 641, 671,
   724, 745
VIRGIN ISLANDS, GOVERNMENT
   OF THE (RG 55), 723-725
Virgin Islands Company, 404, 725
Virgin Islands Emergency Relief
   Administration, 725
Virginia, 31, 35, 36, 325, 344, 554,
   714, 744
   State Library, 88
Virginia Military District, 373
Virginia Plan, 36
Virus Serum Act of 1913, 445
Visa Office, Department of State, 136
Visitors, Board of, U.S. Military
   Academy, 232
Visitors, Board of, U.S. Naval
   Academy, 322
Vital statistics. See Statistics, vital
V-J Day, 328, 663, 748
Vladivostok, U.S.S.R., 241
V-mail, 236
Vocational education, 507, 614, 615,
   630, 634, 649, 671, 695
Vocational Education, Federal Board for,
   425, 505, 506, 571, 573, 575
Vocational Education, President's
   Committee on, 104
Voice of America, 569, 570
"Voice of Freedom" (s.r.), 663
Volcanic eruptions, 256, 555, 747
Volstead Act, 524
Voltiguers, 272
Volunteer Army, 37, 231, 251
Volunteer Refreshment Saloon, 575
Von Karman, Theodore, 326
Voorhees, Tracy S., 113
Voting, 50, 117, 183, 467
   See also War Ballot Commission,
     U.S. (RG 230)

W

Waco Indians, 388
Wadsworth, Eliot, 121
Waffen-SS, 730, 734
WAGE ADJUSTMENT BOARD
(RG 236), 497-498
WAGE AND HOUR AND PUBLIC
CONTRACTS DIVISIONS
(RG 155), 496-497
Wage and Hour Division, Department
of Labor, 496, 497
WAGE AND SALARY STABILIZATION
BOARDS OF THE ECONOMIC
STABILIZATION AGENCY
(RG 293), 706-707
Wage Board, Air Force, 332
Wage Coordination Board, War
Department, 633
Wage Stabilization Board, 492, 703,
706, 707
Wages, 214, 371, 491, 496, 559, 650,
665, 666, 672, 703, 704
Adjustments, 460, 492, 631, 632,
633, 672
Controls, 465, 703, 706, 707
Minimum, 496, 497
Of women, 494, 680
Railroad, 560, 600, 703, 707
Rates, 491, 493, 495, 496, 498,
560, 632, 672
Stabilization, 270, 459, 460, 465,
497, 498, 561, 631, 632, 633,
673, 703, 706, 707
Wagner Act. See National Labor
Relations Act
Wagner-Peyser Act, 498
Wagon roads, 366, 370, 373, 376
Wainwright, Mayhew, 211
Walker, Robert J., 743
Walker, William, 338
Wallace, George, 127-128
Wallace, Henry A., 99, 748
Wallops Island Station, Va., 554
Walsh Committee, 604
Walsh-Healey Public Contracts
Act of 1936, 496
Walter Reed Hospital, 343, 745
Walters, Theodore A., 367
Wanamaker Exposition, 389
War, 97, 240, 498, 647
Agencies, 99, 222, 612, 645, 664
Boards, 38, 436, 631, 632, 650
Bonds, 299, 650, 662, 663, 746
Claims, 91, 340, 547
Contracts and contractors, 261, 292,
340, 356, 641, 642, 582, 583,
685
Correspondents, 212, 299, 328
Damage, 91, 138, 585, 667
Diaries, 192, 195, 235

Effort, 122, 124, 188, 211, 256, 263,
371, 580, 608, 643, 647, 662,
663, 677, 679, 746
Hemp program, 435
Housing, 513, 515, 519, 520, 609, 665,
683, 691, 705, 712
Journals, foreign, 732, 736
Materials, 287, 293, 548, 673, 677, 730
Materiel, 689
Memorials, 529, 530
Mobilization, 204, 256, 265, 639, 664,
732
Plants, 230, 581, 641, 643, 673-675, 728
Procurement, 687
Programs, 216, 217, 218, 506, 584,
639, 665, 698
Propaganda, 622, 748
Readjustment problems, 204, 664, 665
Savings certificates, 165
Taxes, 60, 177
Workers, 512, 596
See also Prisoners of war
War, Acting Secretary of, 203
War, Assistant Secretary of, 211, 225, 259
War, Board of, 31, 37, 208
War, Office of the Assistant Secretary
of, 211, 224
War, Office of the Secretary of, 252,
253, 264, 377, 413
WAR, OFFICE OF THE SECRETARY
OF (RG 107), 207-212
War, Office of the Under Secretary
of, 210, 211, 228
War, Secretary at, 30, 31, 34, 37
War, Secretary of, 107, 119, 200, 206, 207,
208, 209, 210, 211, 212, 216, 218,
224, 225, 231, 234, 236, 239, 252,
258, 259, 271, 281, 288, 290, 291,
295, 296, 324, 364, 366, 389, 390,
413, 414, 469, 477, 488, 541, 552,
562, 571, 578, 593, 678, 719, 735
Confederate, 720
War, Under Secretary of, 210, 212, 229
War Activities Committee, Motion Picture
Industry, 746
War Activity Liquidation, Office of, 583
War Administration, Committee on, 96
War Agency Liquidation Unit, 690, 691
War and Ordnance, Board of, 30, 34
War and Post-War Adjustment Policies,
Advisory Unit for, 642
War Assets Administration, 586
WAR ASSETS ADMINISTRATION
(RG 270), 678-679
War Assets Corporation, 581, 586, 673, 678
WAR BALLOT COMMISSION, U.S.
(RG 230), 678
War College Board, 218
War Communications, Board of, 536, 537
WAR COMMUNICATIONS, BOARD OF
(RG 259), 613-614
War Contracts Hardship Claims Board, 214
War Credits Board, 253

War Crimes, Office of the Chief of
Counsel for, 699, 700, 701
War crimes and criminals, 198, 211, 262,
278, 279, 699-703, 727, 737
Trials, 194, 256, 262, 702
War Criminal Prison No. 1, 278
War Criminals, Advisory Board on
Clemency for, 701
War Damage Corporation, 581, 585
War Department, 30, 31, 33, 37, 38, 43,
53, 105, 152, 200, 201, 205, 207,
208, 209, 210, 211, 212, 216, 217,
218, 219, 220, 222, 223, 224, 225,
227, 228, 231, 234, 235, 237, 240,
241, 242, 248, 250, 252, 253, 254,
258, 259, 260, 261, 263, 264, 265,
266, 271, 273, 278, 280, 282, 295,
324, 340, 369, 374, 375, 377, 378,
388, 389, 397, 398, 404, 413, 420,
452, 476, 519, 526, 571, 573, 574,
578, 579, 609, 613, 614, 615, 616,
633, 637, 638, 657, 675, 679, 681,
682, 714, 720, 721, 722
Accountant for the, 59
Solicitor of the, 208
War Department Board of Engineers for
Rivers and Harbors, 239, 240, 602
War Department Civil Defense Mission to
England, 217
War Department Claims Board, 225, 243, 261
WAR DEPARTMENT CLAIMS BOARD
(RG 191), 223-224
WAR DEPARTMENT COLLECTION OF
CONFEDERATE RECORDS
(RG 109), 719-721
WAR DEPARTMENT COLLECTION OF
REVOLUTIONARY WAR RECORDS
(RG 93), 37-39
WAR DEPARTMENT GENERAL AND
SPECIAL STAFFS (RG 165),
216-220
War Department General Staff, 218, 220,
223, 225, 229, 236, 252, 254, 261,
262, 324
War Department Manpower Board, 212,
216, 219
War Department Procurement Review
Board, 212, 664
War Department Special Staff, 236,
252, 264
WAR FINANCE CORPORATION
(RG 154), 608
War Finance Corporation Act of 1918, 577
War Food Administration, 404, 426, 435,
459, 461, 624, 655
War History, Departmental, Office of the
Secretary of the Interior, 368
War History Branch, Department of
State, 135
War industries, 106, 124, 206, 371, 520,
548, 594, 605, 608, 672, 673, 683
Women in, 680

War Industries Board, 97, 577, 578, 594,
596, 610
WAR INDUSTRIES BOARD (RG 61),
608-609
War Information, Committee on, 645
War Information, Office of, 106, 124,
125, 139, 204, 640, 645
WAR INFORMATION, OFFICE OF
(RG 208), 660-664
War Information Board, 661
War Insurance Corporation, 585
War Labor Administrator, 580
War Labor Administrator, Advisory
Council to, 609
War Labor Board. See National War Labor
Board
War Labor Disputes Act, 555, 557, 631
War Labor Policies Board, 495
WAR LABOR POLICIES BOARD (RG 1),
609-610
War Manpower Commission, 122, 460,
499, 511, 564, 616, 634, 636,
640, 641, 645
WAR MANPOWER COMMISSION
(RG 211), 679-687
War Materials Board, 448
War Minerals Division, Bureau of Mines,
408
War Minerals Relief Act of 1919, 414
WAR MINERALS RELIEF COMMISSION
(RG 194), 414-415
War Minerals Relief Commissioner, 367
War Mobilization, Office of, 641, 642,
664, 671
War Mobilization and Reconversion,
Director of, 107
War Mobilization and Reconversion,
Office of, 517, 641, 671, 681

WAR MOBILIZATION AND
RECONVERSION, OFFICE OF
(RG 250), 664-666
War Mobilization Committee, 664
War of 1812, 83, 86, 136, 178, 232,
255, 271, 336, 525, 573, 574, 715
Veterans of, 373
War of the Rebellion: A Compilation
of the Official Records of the
Union and Confederate Armies,
720
War Office, 33, 246
"War Pictorial News" (m.p.), 663
War Policies Commission, 210
War Power Acts, 664
War production, 96, 256, 299, 507,
527, 555, 609, 634, 647, 672,
683, 686, 687, 689
German, 728
Japanese, 736
War Production Board, 105, 201, 371,
408, 460, 515, 616, 643, 645,
648, 655, 665, 667, 672, 673,
679, 681, 682, 686

WAR PRODUCTION BOARD (RG 179), 687-689
War Projects Unit, 96
War Property Distribution, Office of, 501
War Records Office, 233
War Refugee Board, 107, 690
War Relocation Authority, 256
WAR RELOCATION AUTHORITY (RG 210), 689-691
War Resources Planning Board, 371
War risk insurance, 235, 260, 285, 357, 693
War Risk Insurance, Bureau of, 155, 356, 571, 572, 573, 575
War Risk Insurance Act of 1917, 356
War Risk Litigation, Bureau of, 573
WAR RISK LITIGATION, BUREAU OF (RG 190), 356-357
War Shipping Administration, 105, 645, 675, 678
WAR SHIPPING ADMINISTRATION (RG 248), 692-693
War Shipping Panel, 633
War Times, 210
War Trade Board, 155, 176, 577, 595, 607
　Building, 611
WAR TRADE BOARD (RG 182), 610-611
War Transactions Board, 261
War Transactions Section, Department of Justice, 340
War Transport, British Ministry of, 692
Ward, Thomas, 215
Wardens, 342
Warehouse Act, U.S., 462
Warehouses, 169, 170
Warfare
　Amphibious, 659, 660, 699
　Antitank, 734
　Chemical, 224, 229, 236, 266, 285, 302, 408, 639, 659
　Guerrilla, 279, 736
　Psychological, 192, 194, 662
　Radiological, 190
Warner Bros. Pictures, Inc., 746, 747
Warrants, 166
　Of arrests, 135
Warrants, Division of, Department of the Treasury, 165
Warrants, Estimates, and Appropriations, Division of, 165
Warren, Earl, 128
Warren, G. K., 262
Warren Commission, 128
Warrior River, 488
Warrior River Terminal Company, 488
Warsaw ghetto, 702
Warships, 296
Wartime Civil Control Administration, 689, 690, 691

Washington, George, 31, 34, 36, 38, 54, 62, 154, 401, 716
Washington, D.C. See District of Columbia
Washington, D.C., Superintendent of, 715
Washington, Treaty of, 1871, 144, 145
Washington Aqueduct, 54, 238, 240-241, 366, 715
Washington Canal Company, 712
Washington City Canal, 239
Washington Conference on the Limitation of Armaments, 211
Washington County, Government of, 712
Washington Dormitories, 599
"Washington Farm Letter," 649
"Washington Interview" (s.r.), 570
Washington Monument, 402, 714, 716, 717
Washington Monument, Joint Commission for the Completion of, 717
Washington National Airport, 527, 548, 670
Washington National Monument Society, 716, 717
Washington Navy Yard, 321
"Washington Parade, The" (m.p.), 747
Washington Policy Group Joint Program Information Committee, 681
Washington Provisional Brigade, 275
Washington Residence Halls, 599
Washington State, 134
　Indians of, 380
Washington Zone Catalogue, 316
Washington zoo, 567
Wasp (U.S.S.), 296
Waste disposal, 452, 621
Waste-Reclamation Service, 465
Watches, 178, 409
Water, 241, 304, 385, 392, 393, 409, 420, 428, 437, 438, 439, 448, 456, 541, 555, 601,
　Carriers, 619, 643
　Pollution, 396, 505
　Resources, 65, 110, 112, 123, 124, 369, 389, 391, 392, 393, 437, 440, 453
　Rights, 58, 369, 406
　Terminals, 488
　Utilization, 392, 393, 406, 420, 457, 502
Water and Power, Assistant Secretary of the Interior for, 422
Water and Power, Division of, 368, 369
Water Resources, Interagency Committee on, 421
"Water Resources Act of 1951," 110

Water Resources Policy Review, 369
Waterfalls, 567
Watershed activities, 428, 437, 567
Watertown, N.Y., 598
Waterway Transport Department,
    643, 644
Waterways, 58, 237, 488-489,
    567, 604, 676
Watson, Robert, 597
"We Fight Back" (s.r.), 663
Wea Indians, Confederated, 380
Weapons, 187, 189, 190, 242, 303,
    319, 334, 659, 660
    Air, 332
    Mechanized, 245
    Nuclear, 189, 190
    See also Ordnance, Bureau of
Weapons Systems Command, 319
Weapons Systems Evaluation
    Group, 186, 187
Weather Bureau, 254, 314, 434, 479,
    480, 554, 566
    See also National Weather Records
        Center
WEATHER BUREAU (RG 27),
    476-478
Weather observations, 239, 315, 327,
    477, 478, 479, 480, 525
Weaver, Robert C., 514
Weaver, William A., 29, 36
Webster, Daniel, 145
Webster, Francis M., 454
Weddell, Kennard, 674
Wedemeyer, Albert C., 197
Week, Committee of the, 32
Weeks Act, 426, 429
Weevils, 454
Wehrkreis, 732
Wehrmacht, 731
Wehrwirtschaftsstab Ost, 729
Weights, standard, 475
Weimar period, 733
Weizsaecker, Ernst von, 700
Welfare
    Army, 201, 212, 214
    Germany, 198
    Japan, 194
    Organizations, 614, 713
    Programs, 103, 119, 359
    Navy, 201
    Virgin Islands, 641, 725
    See also Children and
        Community War Services,
        Office of (RG 215)
Welfare Administration, 511
Well survey, 1910, 452
Wellcome, Henry S., 744
Welles, Sumner, 297, 748
West Coast Aircraft Committee, 633
West Coast Lumber Commission,
    633
West Florida
    Council of, 374

Governor of, 374
    Territory of, 134
West Indian Conference, 404
West Indies, 414, 745
    See also Danish West Indies
        and French West Indies
West Indies Transportation,
    Joint Commission on,
    607, 608
West Point. See Military Academy,
    U.S.
West Virginia Coal and Coke
    Co., 594-595
Western Areal Geology, Section
    of, 391
Western Defense Command, 280
Western Department, 273
Western Log and Lumber
    Administration, 518
Western Military Asylum, 290
Western Samoa, 409
Western Territory, 34
Western Theater of Operations,
    280
Western Union Telegraph
    Co., 536, 540
Westpoint (U.S.S.), 744
Westwall, 734
Whaling operations, 395, 523, 525
Wharton, Francis, 36
Wharves, 53, 237, 603
Wheat, 441, 459, 534, 591, 592, 596
Wheat Director, U.S., 591, 595, 596
Wheeler, George M., 390
Wheeler, Harry A., 121
Wheeler, Hoyt H., 88
Wheeler-Howard Act, 386
Wheeler-Rayburn public utilities
    holding company bill, 541
Wheeler Survey, 389, 390
Wheeling, W. Va., 595
Whiskey, 178, 509
Whiskey Rebellion, 178
"Whiskey Ring," 338
White, Francis, 136
White House, 95, 102, 109, 113, 114,
    401, 532, 553, 581, 699, 716,
    717
    Official functions at, 715
    Police force, 176
    See also Executive Mansion
White House Conference on Child
    Health and Protection, 458
White House Conference on
    Children and Youth, 116
White House Conference on
    Education, 507
White House Conference on Health,
    1965, 504, 505
White House Office, 120
    Building, 716
WHITE HOUSE OFFICE
    (RG 130), 95-96

White Ruthenia, 729
Whitten, Lyman P., 326
Whittlesey, Eliphalet, 263
Whole House, Committee on the, 36
Wichita Indians, 388
Wickard, Claude R., 441
Wickens, Aryness Joy, 491
Wickersham Commission, 63
Wiggins, A. L. M., 153
Wildlife, 103, 397, 398, 400,
    430, 434
    African, 370
    Alaskan, 397
    Control and conservation of,
        394, 396, 399
    Refuges, 65, 373, 394, 396,
        397, 428
    See also Fish and Wildlife
        Service
Wildlife Division, 399
Wildlife Survey, 399
Wiley, Harvey W., 449, 509
Wiley, Henry A., 676
Wilkes Expedition, 314
Wilkes Station, Antarctica, 749
Williams, S. Clay, 627
Willink, Wilhelm and Jan, 35
Willkie, Wendell, 748
Willow Run, Mich., 641
Wills, 76
Wilson, Milburn L., 424
Wilson, P. St. J., 526
Wilson, William B., 491
Wilson, Woodrow, 95, 135, 148,
    255, 256, 286, 287, 313,
    599, 744, 748
Winchester Repeating Arms
    Co., 243
Wind
    Erosion projects, 439
    Movement, 477
"Wing of Expectation," 748
Winnebago Indians, 380
Winnebago Reservation, 380
Winship, Blanton, 259
Winslow, Thacher, 491
Winterfeldt, Hans Karl von, 732
Wirth, Conrad L., 398, 403
Wirtschafts-Verwaltung-
    shauptamt, SS, 730
Wirtz, Willard W., 491
Wisconsin, 156, 344, 514, 520
Witherspoon Statue Commission, 717
Wittenburg Indian School, 387
Wolfbein, Seymour, 491
Wolman, Leo, 629
Woman-In-Industry Service,
    494, 495
Woman Worker, The, 495
Women, 115, 116, 121, 494,
    495, 570, 680, 717
    Employment of, 494, 495,
        510, 680, 694
    Fashions of, 495
    In agriculture, 458, 495
    In defense work, 120, 256, 371,
        569, 578, 579, 662
    In industry, 299, 495, 680
    In military service, 222, 293, 334
    In professions, 495
    Training of, 680, 744
Women's Advisory Committee,
    680, 681
Women's Army Auxiliary
    Corps, 222
Women's Army Corps, 216,
    222, 227

WOMEN'S BUREAU (RG 86),
    494-495
Women's Service Section, 600, 601
Wood, 430, 490
Wood, Leonard, 280, 414
Wood, Robert W., 750
Wood Utilization, National
    Committee on, 487
Woodbury, Coleman, 513
Woodrow Wilson Bridge, 717
Woodruff, Marion T., 673
Woodrum Committee on Compulsory
    Military Training, 220
Woods, Arthur, 120
Woods, Tighe E., 518, 706
Woods, Verda, 62
Woods Committee, 120
Wool, 457, 462, 535, 609
Work, Hubert, 367
Work projects, 400, 635, 694, 695
Work Projects Administration, 125,
    169, 310, 370, 385-386, 391,
    400, 402, 524, 634, 636,
    704, 725
    Districts, 698
    Federal Project No. 1, 696
    National Research Project, 697, 699

WORK PROJECTS ADMINISTRATION
    (RG 69), 693-699
Work Projects Administration,
    Division for Liquidation of
    the, 694
Work Projects Administration
    Emergency Relief Appropriation,
    399, 400
Workers. See Labor
Works Progress Administration,
    53, 125, 241, 425, 487, 550,
    634
    See also Work Projects
        Administration
World Dairy Congress, 1923, 447
World Food Council, 456
World Health Organization, 663
"World in Flames, The" (m.p.), 746
World Trade Intelligence,
    Division of, 150

World War I, 97, 119, 134, 138, 147,
165, 176, 200, 202, 217, 218,
219, 220, 223, 225, 235, 245,
246, 249, 252, 253, 255, 256,
260, 272, 276, 294, 306, 309,
313, 320, 322, 325, 334, 340,
344, 345, 354, 355, 359, 415,
424, 485, 506, 525, 543, 547,
566, 569, 574, 577, 578, 580,
593, 603, 608, 609, 723, 737,
743, 744, 745
Aviation, 328
Battles, 745
Heroes, 748
Memorials, 529, 717
Naturalization of soldiers, 346
Peace conference, 148
Posters, 288, 744
Veterans, 547, 571, 573
Western Front, 288, 529
See also American Expeditionary
Forces (World War I) 1917-23,
(RG 120); and Engineers,
Office of the Chief of
"World War I" (m.p.), 746
World War II, 95, 96, 103, 137, 156, 176,
186, 191, 192, 193, 194, 195, 200,
201, 202, 205, 206, 214, 216, 219,
220, 230, 234, 235, 236, 246, 256,
265, 267, 268, 278, 279, 308, 309,
310, 312, 322, 323, 328, 334, 335,
347, 354, 355, 359, 405, 434, 498,
505, 520, 525, 536, 540, 550, 578,
580, 609, 613, 667, 672, 677, 699,
727, 731, 732, 734, 735, 737, 744,
745, 746, 747, 748
Entry of Soviet Union, 736
Historical program, 466, 492
Japanese campaigns, 736
Liquidation of agencies, 99
Naval activities during, 293, 294, 313
North African campaign, 569
Officer training, 746
Refugees, 107, 193, 218, 690, 691, 748
Research relating to, 555
See also American Commission for
the Protection and Salvage of
Artistic and Historic Monuments
in War Areas (RG 239);
Community War Services,
Office of (RG 215); Defense
Transportation, Office of; Foreign
Broadcast Intelligence Service
(RG 262); Occupation
Headquarters, U.S., World War
II (RG 260); Theaters of
operations; Theaters of War,
U.S., World War II (RG 332);
War Information, Office of;
and War Manpower
Commission
WORLD WAR II WAR CRIMES
RECORDS (RG 238), 699-703

World War II War Crimes Records,
National Archives
Collection of, 727
World's Columbian Exposition, 53,
154, 249, 365, 433, 449, 532
World's fairs. See Fairs, world's
World's Industrial and Cotton
Centennial Exposition, 154
Wormser, Felix E., 367
Wrenshall, John C., 237
Wright, Carroll D., 559
Wright, Kenneth, 748
Wright, Orville, 334
Wright, Ralph, 491
Wright, Wilbur, 334
Wright-Patterson Air Force Base,
332
Writers, 745, 748
Project, Federal, 695, 696, 699
Wyandot Indians, 380
Wyoming, 134

Y

Yachts, 169
Yalta Conference, 256, 663
Yamhill River, 343
YANK, The Army Weekly
magazine, 218
Yankton Indians, 388
Yards and Docks, Bureau of,
295, 318
YARDS AND DOCKS, BUREAU
OF (RG 71), 309-310
Yazoo Land Claims, 144
Yedo, Treaty of, 134
Yellow fever, 282
Epidemic of 1878, 503
Yellow Fever Commission, 503
Yellowstone area, 394
Yellowstone National Park,
391, 398, 402, 409
Yorktown
Battlefield of, 35
Sesquicentennial, 400
Yorktown National Cemetery,
400
Yosemite, Calif., 745
Yosemite National Park, 409
"You Can't Do Business With
Hitler" (s.r.), 663
Young, John J., 744
Young Democrats, 742
Young Men's Christian
Association, 640
Young Republicans, 742
Young Women's Christian
Association, 288
Youth, 116, 122, 640
Employment and training
of, 495, 614

Programs in Germany, 198
  See also National Youth
    Administration
Yugoslavia, 193, 612, 735
Yukon, explorations of, 723
Yukon River area, 523

Zinc, 408, 552, 584
Zion National Park, 402
Zoning, 475
  National Capital, 713
Zoo, District of Columbia.
    See National Zoological
    Park
Zuni Reservation. 383

Z

Zagoskin, Lavrentii A., 723
Ziegler. *See* Fiala-Ziegler
    expedition *and* Baldwin-Ziegler
    expedition

☆ U.S. GOVERNMENT PRINTING OFFICE : 1975 O—594-651

DATE DUE			